# Complete Solutions Manual, Vol

# Calculus: Early Transcendental Functions

**FIFTH EDITION**

**Ron Larson**
The Pennsylvania State University, The Behrend College

**Bruce Edwards**
University of Florida

Prepared by

**Bruce Edwards**
University of Florida

Australia • Brazil • Japan • Korea • Mexico • Singapore • Spain • United Kingdom • United States

For product information and technology assistance, contact us at **Cengage Learning Customer & Sales Support, 1-800-354-9706**

For permission to use material from this text or product, submit all requests online at **www.cengage.com/permissions**
Further permissions questions can be emailed to **permissionrequest@cengage.com**

ISBN-13: 978-0-538-73918-4
ISBN-10: 0-538-73918-5

**Brooks/Cole**
20 Channel Center Street
Boston, MA 02210
USA

Cengage Learning is a leading provider of customized learning solutions with office locations around the globe, including Singapore, the United Kingdom, Australia, Mexico, Brazil, and Japan. Locate your local office at: **www.cengage.com/global**

Cengage Learning products are represented in Canada by Nelson Education, Ltd.

To learn more about Brooks/Cole, visit **www.cengage.com/brookscole**

Purchase any of our products at your local college store or at our preferred online store **www.CengageBrain.com**



Printed in the United States of America
1 2 3 4 5 6 7 13 12 11 10 09

# CONTENTS

# CHAPTER 1
# Preparation for Calculus

# CHAPTER 1
# Preparation for Calculus

## Section 1.1 Graphs and Models

**1.** $y = -\frac{3}{2}x + 3$

$x$-intercept: $(2, 0)$

$y$-intercept: $(0, 3)$

Matches graph (b).

**2.** $y = \sqrt{9 - x^2}$

$x$-intercepts: $(-3, 0), (3, 0)$

$y$-intercept: $(0, 3)$

Matches graph (d).

**3.** $y = 3 - x^2$

$x$-intercepts: $(\sqrt{3}, 0), (-\sqrt{3}, 0)$

$y$-intercept: $(0, 3)$

Matches graph (a).

**4.** $y = x^3 - x$

$x$-intercepts: $(0, 0), (-1, 0), (1, 0)$

$y$-intercept: $(0, 0)$

Matches graph (c).

**5.** $y = \frac{1}{2}x + 2$

| $x$ | $-4$ | $-2$ | 0 | 2 | 4 |
|---|---|---|---|---|---|
| $y$ | 0 | 1 | 2 | 3 | 4 |

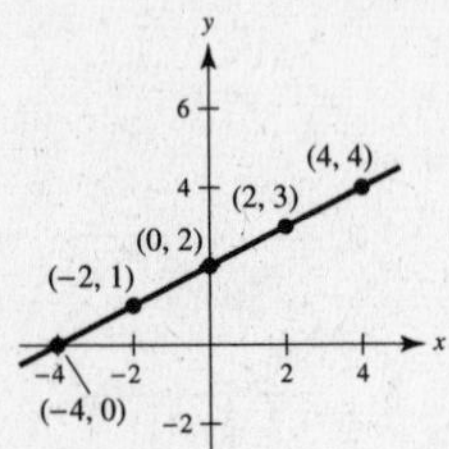


**6.** $y = 5 - 2x$

| $x$ | $-1$ | 0 | 1 | 2 | $\frac{5}{2}$ | 3 | 4 |
|---|---|---|---|---|---|---|---|
| $y$ | 7 | 5 | 3 | 1 | 0 | $-1$ | $-3$ |

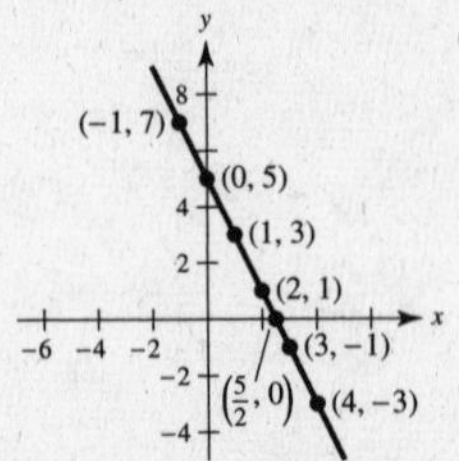


**7.** $y = 4 - x^2$

| $x$ | $-3$ | $-2$ | 0 | 2 | 3 |
|---|---|---|---|---|---|
| $y$ | $-5$ | 0 | 4 | 0 | $-5$ |

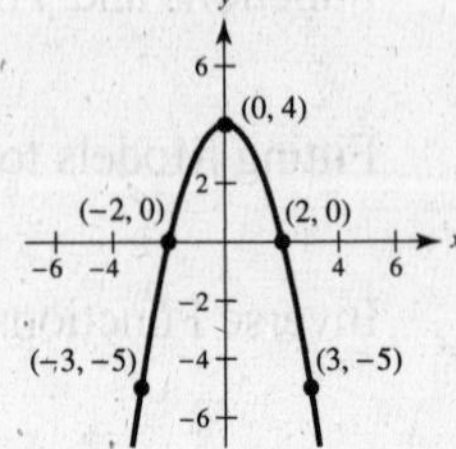


**8.** $y = (x - 3)^2$

| $x$ | 0 | 1 | 2 | 3 | 4 | 5 | 6 |
|---|---|---|---|---|---|---|---|
| $y$ | 9 | 4 | 1 | 0 | 1 | 4 | 9 |

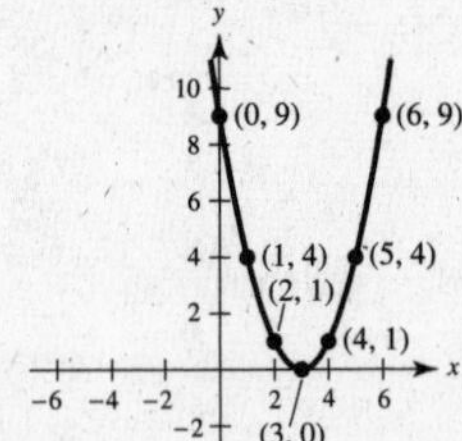


**9.** $y = |x + 2|$

| $x$ | $-5$ | $-4$ | $-3$ | $-2$ | $-1$ | 0 | 1 |
|---|---|---|---|---|---|---|---|
| $y$ | 3 | 2 | 1 | 0 | 1 | 2 | 3 |

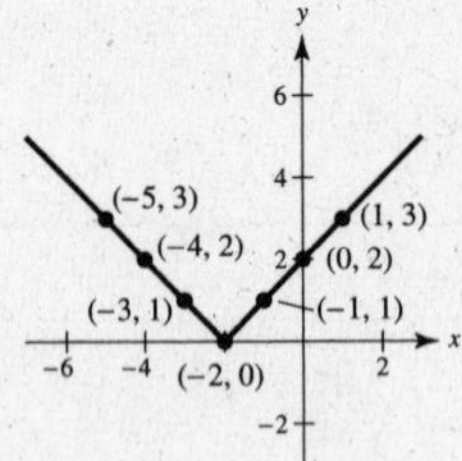

**10.** $y = |x| - 1$

| $x$ | $-3$ | $-2$ | $-1$ | $0$ | $1$ | $2$ | $3$ |
|---|---|---|---|---|---|---|---|
| $y$ | $2$ | $1$ | $0$ | $-1$ | $0$ | $1$ | $2$ |

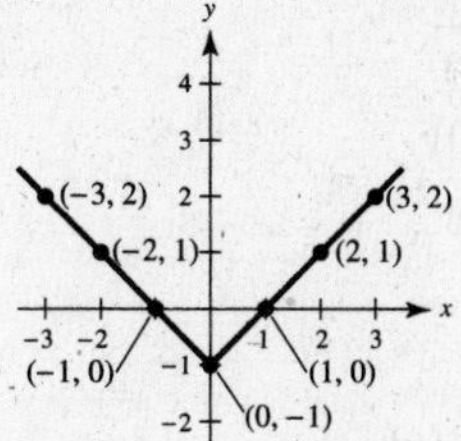


**11.** $y = \sqrt{x} - 6$

| $x$ | $0$ | $1$ | $4$ | $9$ | $16$ |
|---|---|---|---|---|---|
| $y$ | $-6$ | $-5$ | $-4$ | $-3$ | $-2$ |

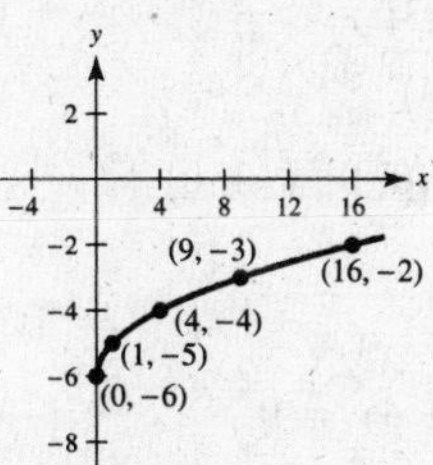


**12.** $y = \sqrt{x + 2}$

| $x$ | $-2$ | $-1$ | $0$ | $2$ | $7$ | $14$ |
|---|---|---|---|---|---|---|
| $y$ | $0$ | $1$ | $\sqrt{2}$ | $2$ | $3$ | $4$ |

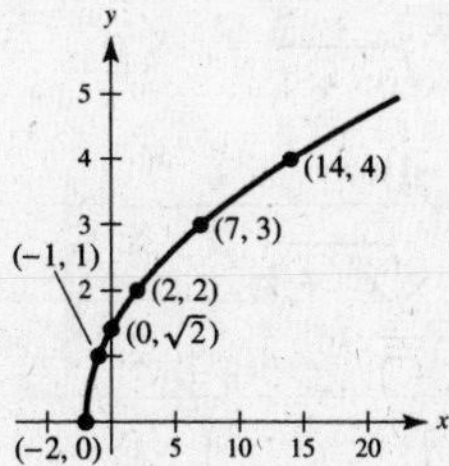


**13.** $y = \dfrac{3}{x}$

| $x$ | $-3$ | $-2$ | $-1$ | $0$ | $1$ | $2$ | $3$ |
|---|---|---|---|---|---|---|---|
| $y$ | $-1$ | $-\frac{3}{2}$ | $-3$ | Undef. | $3$ | $\frac{3}{2}$ | $1$ |

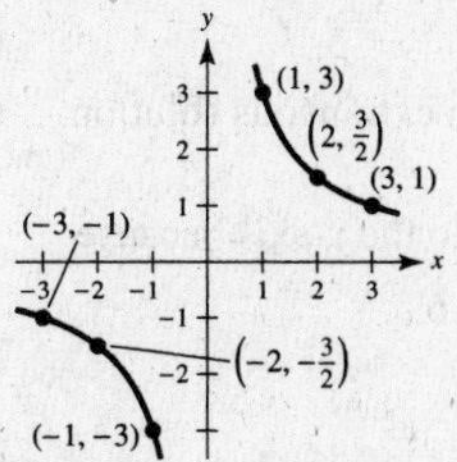


**14.** $y = \dfrac{1}{x + 2}$

| $x$ | $-6$ | $-4$ | $-3$ | $-2$ | $-1$ | $0$ | $2$ |
|---|---|---|---|---|---|---|---|
| $y$ | $-\frac{1}{4}$ | $-\frac{1}{2}$ | $-1$ | Undef. | $1$ | $\frac{1}{2}$ | $\frac{1}{4}$ |

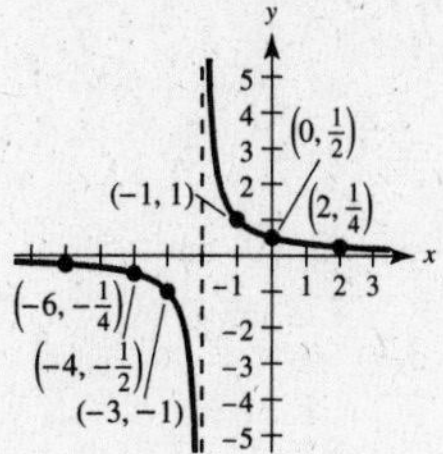


**15.**

Xmin = -5
Xmax = 4
Xscl = 1
Ymin = -5
Ymax = 8
Yscl = 1

Note that $y = -3$ when $x = 0$ and $y = 0$ when $x = -1$.

**16.**

Xmin = -20
Xmax = 30
Xscl = 5
Ymin = -10
Ymax = 40
Yscl = 5

Note that $y = 16$ when $x = 0$ or $16$.

**17.** $y = \sqrt{5 - x}$

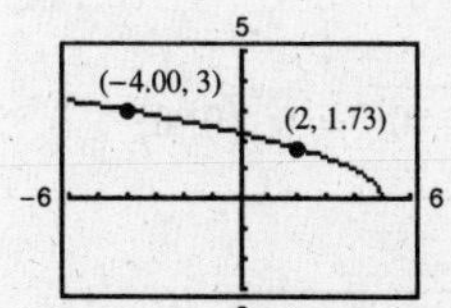


(a) $(2, y) = (2, 1.73)$ $\left(y = \sqrt{5 - 2} = \sqrt{3} \approx 1.73\right)$

(b) $(x, 3) = (-4, 3)$ $\left(3 = \sqrt{5 - (-4)}\right)$

**18.** $y = x^5 - 5x$

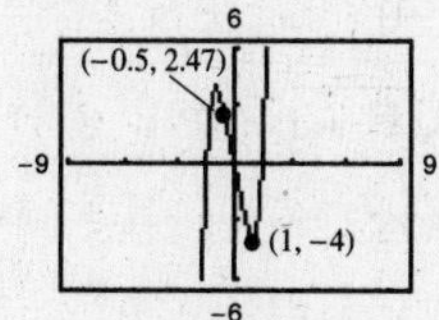


(a) $(-0.5, y) = (-0.5, 2.47)$

(b) $(x, -4) = (-1.65, -4)$ and $(x, -4) = (1, -4)$

**19.** $y = 2x - 5$

$y$-intercept: $y = 2(0) - 5 = -5;\ (0, -5)$

$x$-intercept: $0 = 2x - 5$

$5 = 2x$

$x = \frac{5}{2};\ \left(\frac{5}{2}, 0\right)$

**20.** $y = 4x^2 + 3$

$y$-intercept: $y = 4(0)^2 + 3 = 3;\ (0, 3)$

$x$-intercept: $0 = 4x^2 + 3$

$-3 = 4x^2$

None. $y$ cannot equal 0.

**21.** $y = x^2 + x - 2$

$y$-intercept: $y = 0^2 + 0 - 2$

$y = -2;\ (0, -2)$

$x$-intercepts: $0 = x^2 + x - 2$

$0 = (x + 2)(x - 1)$

$x = -2, 1;\ (-2, 0), (1, 0)$

**22.** $y^2 = x^3 - 4x$

$y$-intercept: $y^2 = 0^3 - 4(0)$

$y = 0;\ (0, 0)$

$x$-intercepts: $0 = x^3 - 4x$

$0 = x(x - 2)(x + 2)$

$x = 0, \pm 2;\ (0, 0), (\pm 2, 0)$

**23.** $y = x\sqrt{16 - x^2}$

$y$-intercept: $y = 0\sqrt{16 - 0^2} = 0;\ (0, 0)$

$x$-intercepts: $0 = x\sqrt{16 - x^2}$

$0 = x\sqrt{(4 - x)(4 + x)}$

$x = 0, 4, -4;\ (0, 0), (4, 0), (-4, 0)$

**24.** $y = (x - 1)\sqrt{x^2 + 1}$

$y$-intercept: $y = (0 - 1)\sqrt{0^2 + 1}$

$y = -1;\ (0, -1)$

$x$-intercept: $0 = (x - 1)\sqrt{x^2 + 1}$

$x = 1;\ (1, 0)$

**25.** $y = \dfrac{2 - \sqrt{x}}{5x}$

$y$-intercept: None. $x$ cannot equal 0.

$x$-intercept: $0 = \dfrac{2 - \sqrt{x}}{5x}$

$0 = 2 - \sqrt{x}$

$x = 4;\ (4, 0)$

**26.** $y = \dfrac{x^2 + 3x}{(3x + 1)^2}$

$y$-intercept: $y = \dfrac{0^2 + 3(0)}{[3(0) + 1]^2}$

$y = 0;\ (0, 0)$

$x$-intercepts: $0 = \dfrac{x^2 + 3x}{(3x + 1)^2}$

$0 = \dfrac{x(x + 3)}{(3x + 1)^2}$

$x = 0, -3;\ (0, 0), (-3, 0)$

**27.** $x^2y - x^2 + 4y = 0$

$y$-intercept: $0^2(y) - 0^2 + 4y = 0$

$y = 0;\ (0, 0)$

$x$-intercept: $x^2(0) - x^2 + 4(0) = 0$

$x = 0;\ (0, 0)$

**28.** $y = 2x - \sqrt{x^2 + 1}$

$y$-intercept: $y = 2(0) - \sqrt{0^2 + 1}$

$y = -1;\ (0, -1)$

$x$-intercept: $0 = 2x - \sqrt{x^2 + 1}$

$2x = \sqrt{x^2 + 1}$

$4x^2 = x^2 + 1$

$3x^2 = 1$

$x^2 = \dfrac{1}{3}$

$x = \pm\dfrac{\sqrt{3}}{3}$

$x = \dfrac{\sqrt{3}}{3};\ \left(\dfrac{\sqrt{3}}{3}, 0\right)$

**Note:** $x = -\sqrt{3}/3$ is an extraneous solution.

**29.** Symmetric with respect to the $y$-axis because $y = (-x)^2 - 6 = x^2 - 6$.

**30.** $y = x^2 - x$

No symmetry with respect to either axis or the origin.

**31.** Symmetric with respect to the $x$-axis because $(-y)^2 = y^2 = x^3 - 8x$.

**32.** Symmetric with respect to the origin because

$$(-y) = (-x)^3 + (-x)$$
$$-y = -x^3 - x$$
$$y = x^3 + x.$$

**33.** Symmetric with respect to the origin because $(-x)(-y) = xy = 4$.

**34.** Symmetric with respect to the $x$-axis because $x(-y)^2 = xy^2 = -10$.

**35.** $y = 4 - \sqrt{x + 3}$

No symmetry with respect to either axis or the origin.

**36.** Symmetric with respect to the origin because

$$(-x)(-y) - \sqrt{4 - (-x)^2} = 0$$
$$xy - \sqrt{4 - x^2} = 0.$$

**37.** Symmetric with respect to the origin because

$$-y = \frac{-x}{(-x)^2 + 1}$$
$$y = \frac{x}{x^2 + 1}.$$

**38.** Symmetric with respect to the $y$-axis because

$$y = \frac{(-x)^2}{(-x)^2 + 1} = \frac{x^2}{x^2 + 1}.$$

**39.** Symmetric with respect to the $y$-axis because

$$y = \left|(-x)^3 + (-x)\right| = \left|-(x^3 + x)\right| = \left|x^3 + x\right|.$$

**40.** Symmetric with respect to the $x$-axis because

$$|-y| - x = 3$$
$$|y| - x = 3.$$

**41.** $y = 2 - 3x$

Intercepts: $(0, 2)$, $\left(\frac{2}{3}, 0\right)$

Symmetry: None

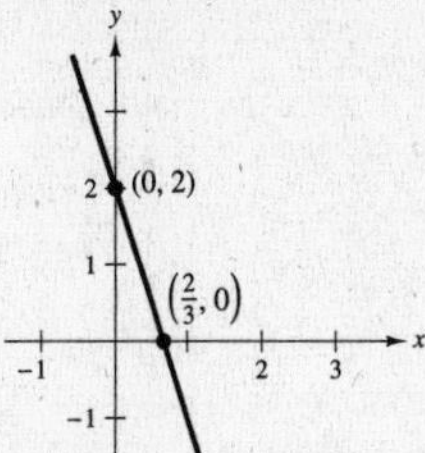

**42.** $y = -\frac{3}{2}x + 6$

Intercepts: $(0, 6)$, $(4, 0)$

Symmetry: None

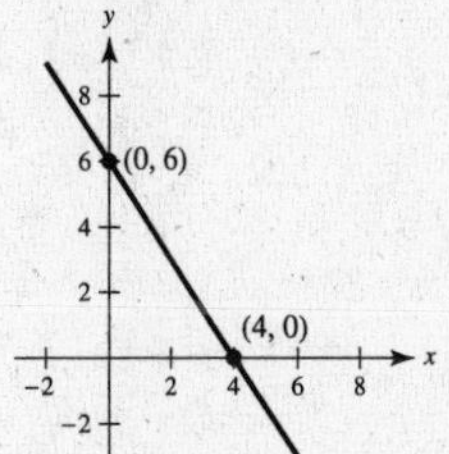

**43.** $y = \frac{1}{2}x - 4$

Intercepts: $(8, 0)$, $(0, -4)$

Symmetry: none

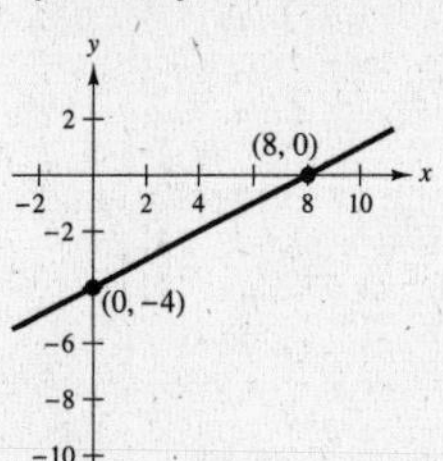

**44.** $y = \frac{2}{3}x + 1$

Intercepts: $(0, 1)$, $\left(-\frac{3}{2}, 0\right)$

Symmetry: none

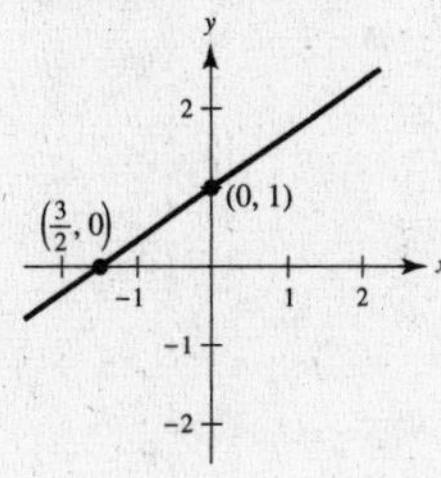

**45.** $y = 9 - x^2$

Intercepts: $(0, 9), (3, 0), (-3, 0)$

Symmetry: $y$-axis

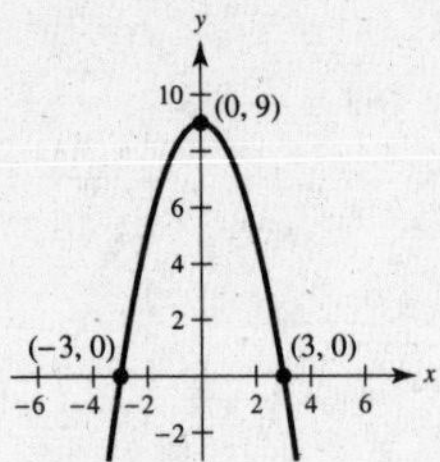


**46.** $y = x^2 + 3$

Intercept: $(0, 3)$

Symmetry: $y$-axis

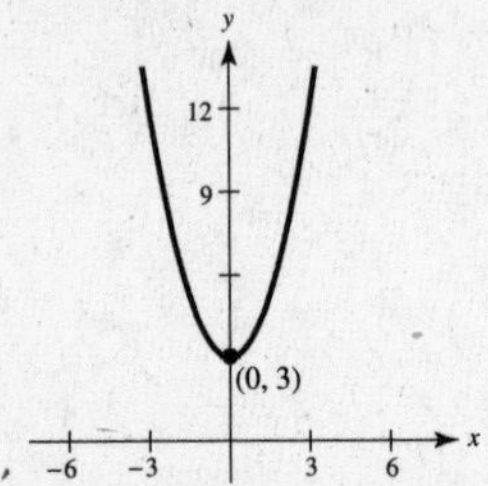


**47.** $y = (x + 3)^2$

Intercepts: $(-3, 0), (0, 9)$

Symmetry: none

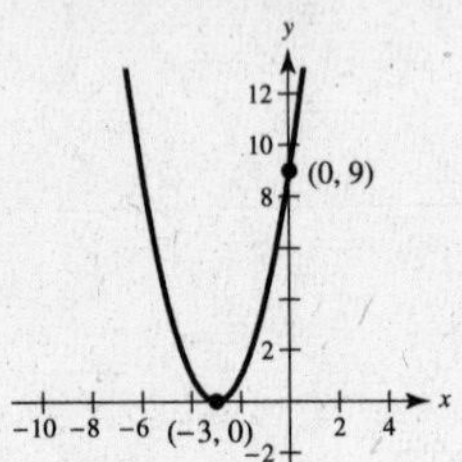


**48.** $y = 2x^2 + x = x(2x + 1)$

Intercepts: $(0, 0), \left(-\frac{1}{2}, 0\right)$

Symmetry: none

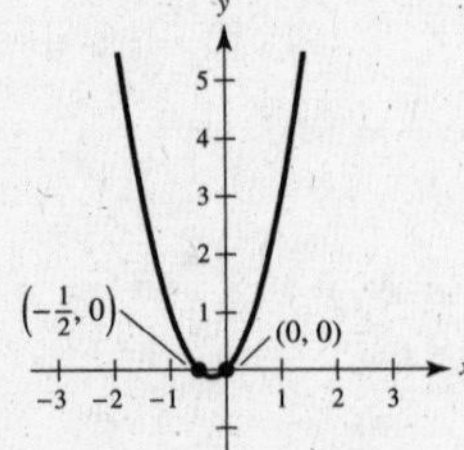


**49.** $y = x^3 + 2$

Intercepts: $\left(-\sqrt[3]{2}, 0\right), (0, 2)$

Symmetry: none

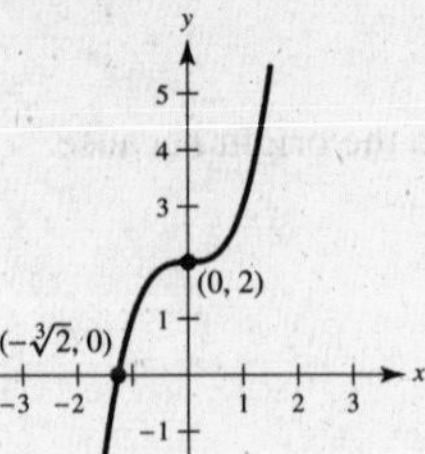


**50.** $y = x^3 - 4x$

Intercepts: $(0, 0), (2, 0), (-2, 0)$

Symmetry: origin

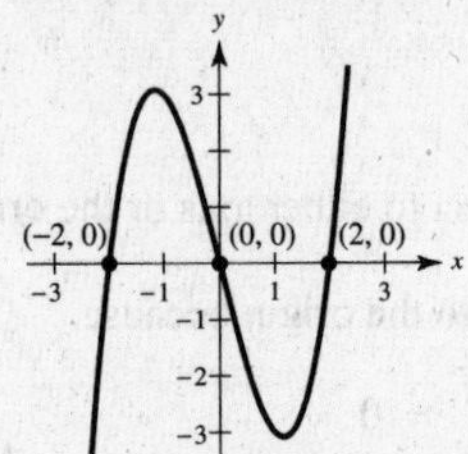


**51.** $y = x\sqrt{x + 5}$

Intercepts: $(0, 0), (-5, 0)$

Symmetry: none

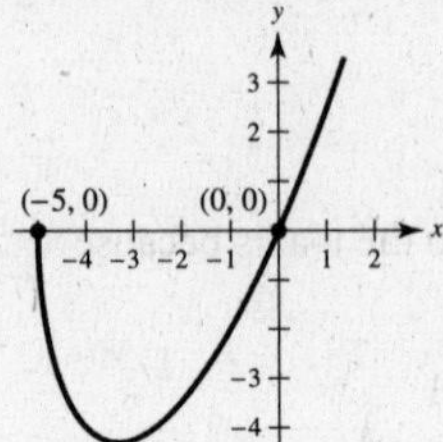


**52.** $y = \sqrt{25 - x^2}$

Intercepts: $(0, 5), (5, 0), (-5, 0)$

Symmetry: $y$-axis

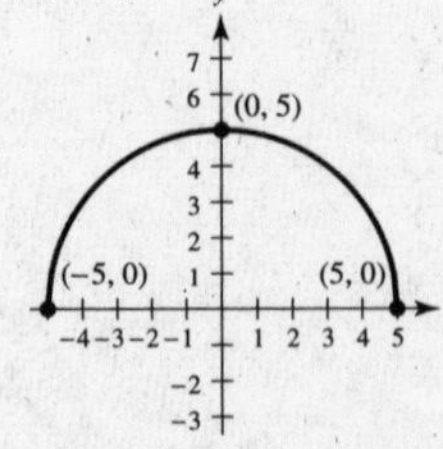

**53.** $x = y^3$

Intercept: $(0, 0)$

Symmetry: origin

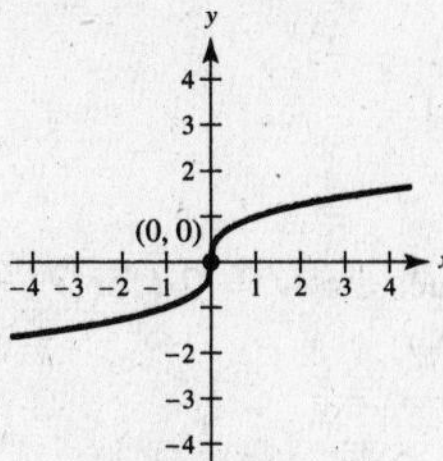

**54.** $x = y^2 - 4$

Intercepts: $(0, 2), (0, -2), (-4, 0)$

Symmetry: $x$-axis

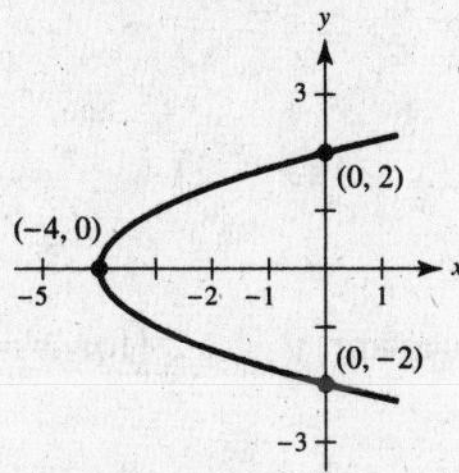

**55.** $y = \dfrac{8}{x}$

Intercepts: none

Symmetry: origin

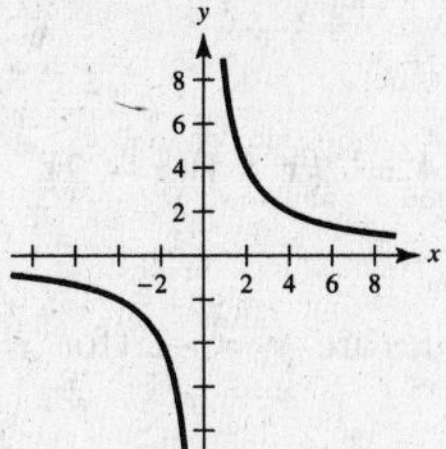

**56.** $y = \dfrac{10}{x^2 + 1}$

Intercept: $(0, 10)$

Symmetry: $y$-axis

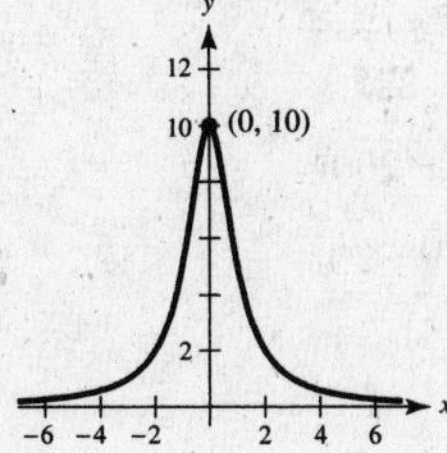

**57.** $y = 6 - |x|$

Intercepts: $(0, 6), (-6, 0), (6, 0)$

Symmetry: $y$-axis

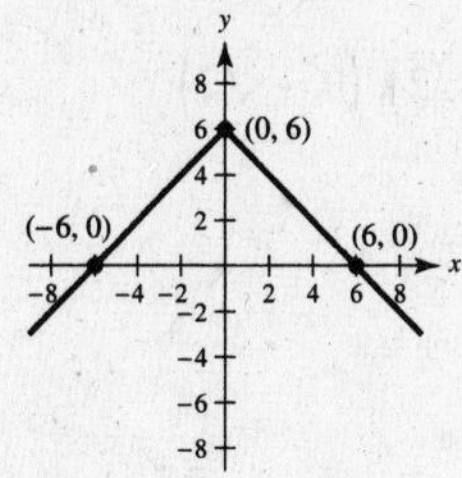

**58.** $y = |6 - x|$

Intercepts: $(0, 6), (6, 0)$

Symmetry: none

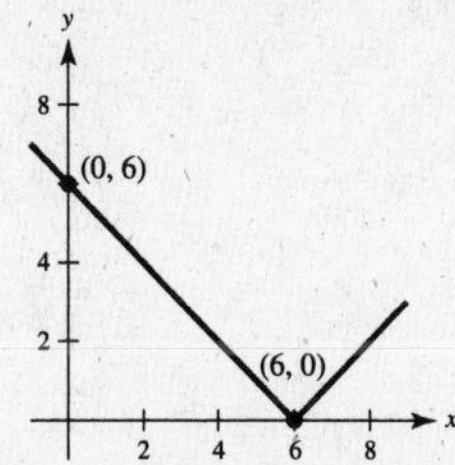

**59.** $y^2 - x = 9$

$$y^2 = x + 9$$

$$y = \pm\sqrt{x + 9}$$

Intercepts: $(0, 3), (0, -3), (-9, 0)$

Symmetry: $x$-axis

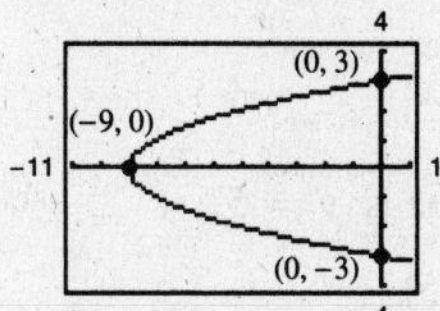

**60.** $x^2 + 4y^2 = 4$

$$4y^2 = 4 - x^2$$

$$y = \pm\frac{\sqrt{4 - x^2}}{2}$$

Intercepts: $(-2, 0), (2, 0), (0, -1), (0, 1)$

Symmetry: origin and both axes

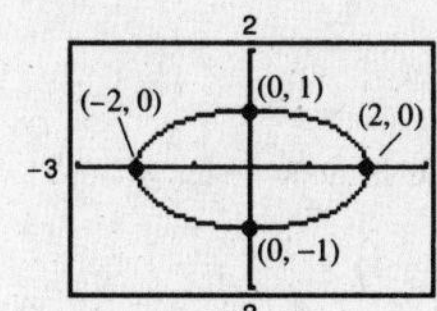

**61.** $x + 3y^2 = 6$

$3y^2 = 6 - x$

$y = \pm\sqrt{\dfrac{6-x}{3}}$

Intercepts: $(6, 0), (0, \sqrt{2}), (0, -\sqrt{2})$

Symmetry: $x$-axis

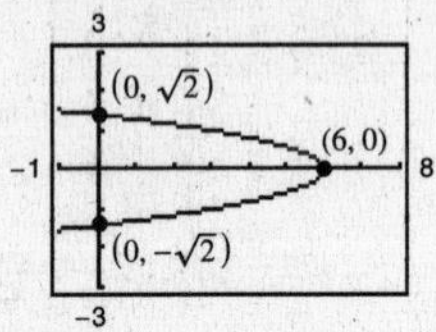


**62.** $3x - 4y^2 = 8$

$4y^2 = 3x - 8$

$y = \pm\sqrt{\tfrac{3}{4}x - 2}$

Intercept: $\left(\tfrac{8}{3}, 0\right)$

Symmetry: $x$-axis

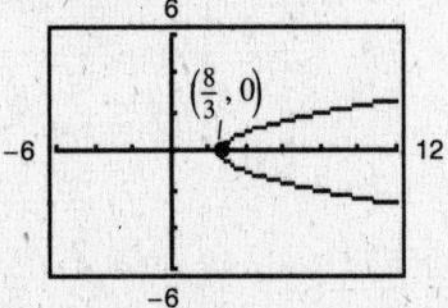


**63.** $x + y = 8 \Rightarrow y = 8 - x$

$4x - y = 7 \Rightarrow y = 4x - 7$

$8 - x = 4x - 7$

$15 = 5x$

$3 = x$

The corresponding $y$-value is $y = 5$.

Point of intersection: (3, 5)

**64.** $3x - 2y = -4 \Rightarrow y = \dfrac{3x+4}{2}$

$4x + 2y = -10 \Rightarrow y = \dfrac{-4x-10}{2}$

$\dfrac{3x+4}{2} = \dfrac{-4x-10}{2}$

$3x + 4 = -4x - 10$

$7x = -14$

$x = -2$

The corresponding $y$-value is $y = -1$.

Point of intersection: $(-2, -1)$

**65.** $x^2 + y = 6 \Rightarrow y = 6 - x^2$

$x + y = 4 \Rightarrow y = 4 - x$

$6 - x^2 = 4 - x$

$0 = x^2 - x - 2$

$0 = (x - 2)(x + 1)$

$x = 2, -1$

The corresponding y-values are $y = 2$ (for $x = 2$) and $y = 5$ (for $x = -1$).

Points of intersection: $(2, 2), (-1, 5)$

**66.** $x = 3 - y^2 \Rightarrow y^2 = 3 - x$

$y = x - 1$

$3 - x = (x - 1)^2$

$3 - x = x^2 - 2x + 1$

$0 = x^2 - x - 2 = (x + 1)(x - 2)$

$x = -1, 2$

The corresponding $y$-values are $y = -2$ (for $x = -1$) and $y = 1$ (for $x = 2$).

Points of intersection: $(-1, -2), (2, 1)$

**67.** $x^2 + y^2 = 5 \Rightarrow y^2 = 5 - x^2$

$x - y = 1 \Rightarrow y = x - 1$

$5 - x^2 = (x - 1)^2$

$5 - x^2 = x^2 - 2x + 1$

$0 = 2x^2 - 2x - 4 = 2(x + 1)(x - 2)$

$x = -1, 2$

The corresponding $y$-values are $y = -2$ (for $x = -1$) and $y = 1$ (for $x = 2$).

Points of intersection: $(-1, -2), (2, 1)$

**68.** $x^2 + y^2 = 25 \Rightarrow y^2 = 25 - x^2$

$-3x + y = 15 \Rightarrow y = 3x + 15$

$25 - x^2 = (3x + 15)^2$

$25 - x^2 = 9x^2 + 90x + 225$

$0 = 10x^2 + 90x + 200$

$0 = x^2 + 9x + 20$

$0 = (x + 5)(x + 4)$

$x = -4, -5$

The corresponding $y$-values are $y = 3$ (for $x = -4$) and $y = 0$ (for $x = -5$).

Points of intersection: $(-4, 3), (-5, 0)$

**69.**
$$y = x^3$$
$$y = x$$
$$x^3 = x$$
$$x^3 - x = 0$$
$$x(x + 1)(x - 1) = 0$$
$$x = 0, -1, 1$$

The corresponding $y$-values are $y = 0$ (for $x = 0$), $y = -1$ (for $x = -1$), and $y = 1$ (for $x = 1$).

Points of intersection: $(0, 0), (-1, -1), (1, 1)$

**70.**
$$y = x^3 - 4x$$
$$y = -(x + 2)$$
$$x^3 - 4x = -(x + 2)$$
$$x^3 - 3x + 2 = 0$$
$$(x - 1)^2(x + 2) = 0$$
$$x = 1, -2$$

The corresponding $y$-values are $y = -3$ (for $x = 1$) and $y = 0$ (for $x = -2$).

Points of intersection: $(1, -3), (-2, 0)$

**71.** $y = x^3 - 2x^2 + x - 1$
$y = -x^2 + 3x - 1$

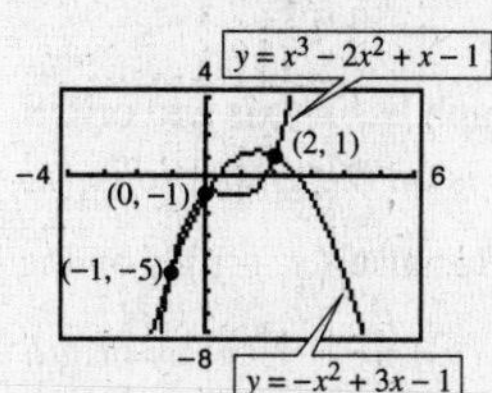


Points of intersection: $(-1, -5), (0, -1), (2, 1)$

Analytically, $x^3 - 2x^2 + x - 1 = -x^2 + 3x - 1$
$$x^3 - x^2 - 2x = 0$$
$$x(x - 2)(x + 1) = 0$$
$$x = -1, 0, 2.$$

**72.** $y = x^4 - 2x^2 + 1$
$y = 1 - x^2$

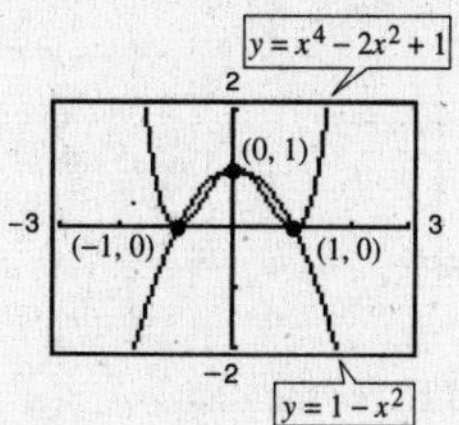


Points of intersection: $(-1, 0), (0, 1), (1, 0)$

Analytically, $1 - x^2 = x^4 - 2x^2 + 1$
$$0 = x^4 - x^2$$
$$0 = x^2(x + 1)(x - 1)$$
$$x = -1, 0, 1.$$

**73.** $y = \sqrt{x + 6}$
$y = \sqrt{-x^2 - 4x}$

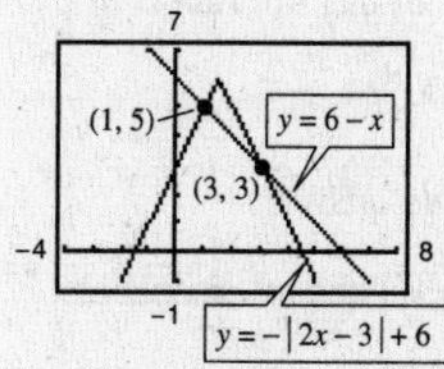


Points of intersection: $(-2, 2), \left(-3, \sqrt{3}\right) \approx (-3, 1.732)$

Analytically, $\sqrt{x + 6} = \sqrt{-x^2 - 4x}$
$$x + 6 = -x^2 - 4x$$
$$x^2 + 5x + 6 = 0$$
$$(x + 3)(x + 2) = 0$$
$$x = -3, -2.$$

**74.** $y = -|2x - 3| + 6$
$y = 6 - x$



Points of intersection: $(3, 3), (1, 5)$

Analytically, $-|2x - 3| + 6 = 6 - x$
$$|2x - 3| = x$$
$$2x - 3 = x \text{ or } 2x - 3 = -x$$
$$x = 3 \text{ or } \quad x = 1.$$

**75.** (a) Using a graphing utility, you obtain

$y = -0.027t^2 + 5.73t + 26.9.$

(b)

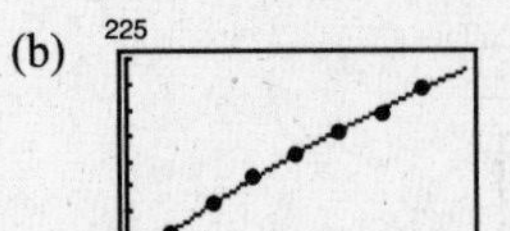

The model is a good fit for the data.

(c) For 2010, $t = 40$ and $y = 212.9$.

**76.** (a) Using a graphing utility, you obtain

$y = 0.77t^2 + 2.1t + 4$

(b)

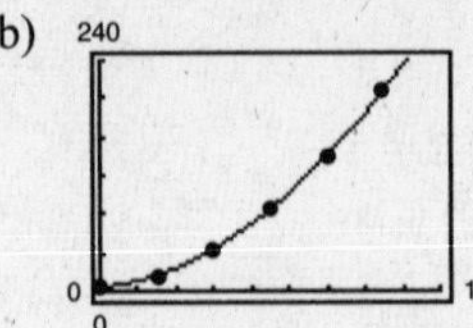

The model is a good fit for the data.

(c) For 2015, $t = 25$ and $y \approx 538$ million subscribers.

**77.**

$$\begin{aligned} C &= R \\ 5.5\sqrt{x} + 10{,}000 &= 3.29x \\ \left(5.5\sqrt{x}\right)^2 &= (3.29x - 10{,}000)^2 \\ 30.25x &= 10.8241x^2 - 65{,}800x + 100{,}000{,}000 \\ 0 &= 10.8241x^2 - 65{,}830.25x + 100{,}000{,}000 \quad \text{Use the Quadratic Formula.} \\ x &\approx 3133 \text{ units} \end{aligned}$$

The other root, $x \approx 2949$, does not satisfy the equation $R = C$.

This problem can also be solved by using a graphing utility and finding the intersection of the graphs of $C$ and $R$.

**78.** $y = \dfrac{10{,}770}{x^2} - 0.37$

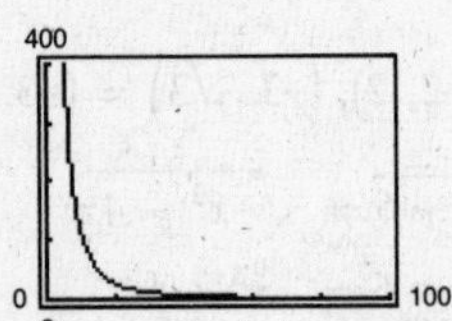

If the diameter is doubled, the resistance is changed by approximately a factor of $\frac{1}{4}$. For instance, $y(20) \approx 26.555$ and $y(40) \approx 6.36125$.

**79.** Answers may vary. *Sample answer*:

$y = (x + 4)(x - 3)(x - 8)$ has intercepts at $x = -4$, $x = 3$, and $x = 8$.

**80.** Answers may vary. *Sample answer*:

$y = \left(x + \frac{3}{2}\right)(x - 4)\left(x - \frac{5}{2}\right)$ has intercepts at $x = -\frac{3}{2}$, $x = 4$, and $x = \frac{5}{2}$.

**81.** (a) If $(x, y)$ is on the graph, then so is $(-x, y)$ by $y$-axis symmetry. Because $(-x, y)$ is on the graph, then so is $(-x, -y)$ by $x$-axis symmetry. So, the graph is symmetric with respect to the origin. The converse is not true. For example, $y = x^3$ has origin symmetry but is not symmetric with respect to either the $x$-axis or the $y$-axis.

(b) Assume that the graph has $x$-axis and origin symmetry. If $(x, y)$ is on the graph, so is $(x, -y)$ by $x$-axis symmetry. Because $(x, -y)$ is on the graph, then so is $(-x, -(-y)) = (-x, y)$ by origin symmetry. Therefore, the graph is symmetric with respect to the $y$-axis. The argument is similar for $y$-axis and origin symmetry.

**82.** (a) v $\left[\text{Because } y = 3(-x)^2 + 3 = 3x^2 + 3\right]$

(b) i $\left[\text{Because } y = 3x^3 - 3x = 3x(x - 1)(x + 1) \text{ has } x\text{-intercepts } (0, 0), (1, 0), (-1, 0)\right]$

(c) None of the equations are symmetric with respect to the $x$-axis.

(d) ii $\left[\text{Because } (-2 + 3)^2 = 1\right]$ and vi $\left[\text{Because } \sqrt{-2 + 3} = 1\right]$

(e) i $\left[\text{Because } 3(-x)^3 - 3(-x) = -3x^3 + 3x = -y\right]$ and iv $\left[\text{Because } \sqrt[3]{-x} = -\sqrt[3]{x} = -y\right]$

(f) i $\left[\text{Because } 3(0)^3 - 3(0) = 0\right]$ and iv $\left[\text{Because } \sqrt[3]{0} = 0\right]$

**83.** False. $x$-axis symmetry means that if $(-4, -5)$ is on the graph, then $(-4, 5)$ is also on the graph. For example, $(4, -5)$ is not on the graph of $x = y^2 - 29$, whereas $(-4, -5)$ is on the graph.

**84.** True. $f(4) = f(-4)$.

**85.** True. The $x$-intercepts are $\left(\dfrac{-b \pm \sqrt{b^2 - 4ac}}{2a}, 0\right)$.

**86.** True. The $x$-intercept is $\left(-\dfrac{b}{2a}, 0\right)$.

**87.**

$$2\sqrt{(x-0)^2 + (y-3)^2} = \sqrt{(x-0)^2 + (y-0)^2}$$
$$4\left[x^2 + (y-3)^2\right] = x^2 + y^2$$
$$4x^2 + 4y^2 - 24y + 36 = x^2 + y^2$$
$$3x^2 + 3y^2 - 24y + 36 = 0$$
$$x^2 + y^2 - 8y + 12 = 0$$
$$x^2 + (y-4)^2 = 4$$

Circle of radius 2 and center (0, 4).

**88.** Distance from the origin $= K \times$ Distance from $(2, 0)$

$$\sqrt{x^2 + y^2} = K\sqrt{(x-2)^2 + y^2},\ K \neq 1$$
$$x^2 + y^2 = K^2(x^2 - 4x + 4 + y^2)$$
$$(1 - K^2)x^2 + (1 - K^2)y^2 + 4K^2x - 4K^2 = 0$$

**Note:** This is the equation of a circle!

## Section 1.2 Linear Models and Rates of Change

**1.** $m = 1$

**2.** $m = 2$

**3.** $m = 0$

**4.** $m = -1$

**5.** $m = -12$

**6.** $m = \frac{40}{3}$

**7.**

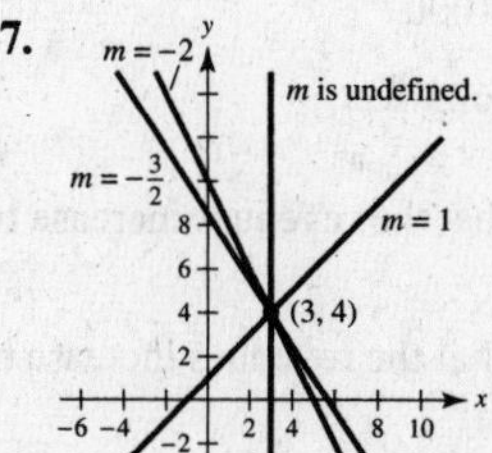


**8.**

**9.** $m = \dfrac{2 - (-4)}{5 - 3} = \dfrac{6}{2} = 3$

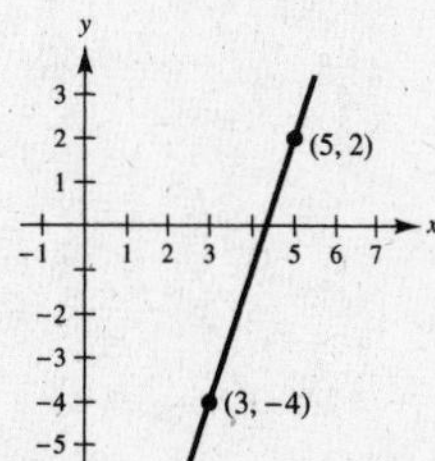

**10.** $m = \dfrac{7 - 1}{-2 - 1} = \dfrac{6}{-3} = -2$

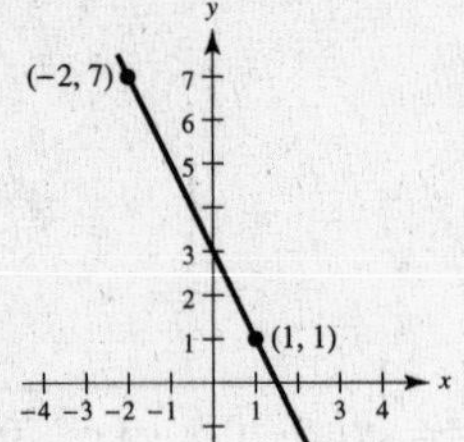


**11.** $m = \dfrac{1 - 6}{4 - 4} = \dfrac{-5}{0}$, undefined.

The line is vertical

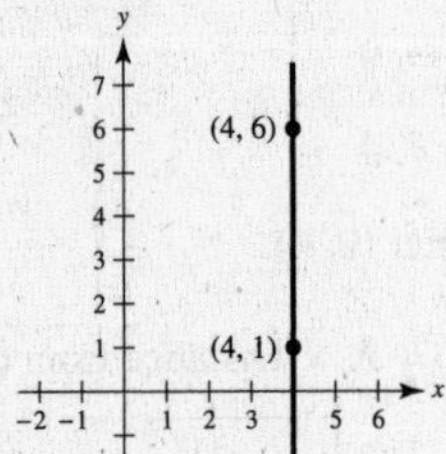


**12.** $m = \dfrac{-5 - (-5)}{5 - 3} = \dfrac{0}{2} = 0$

The line is horizontal

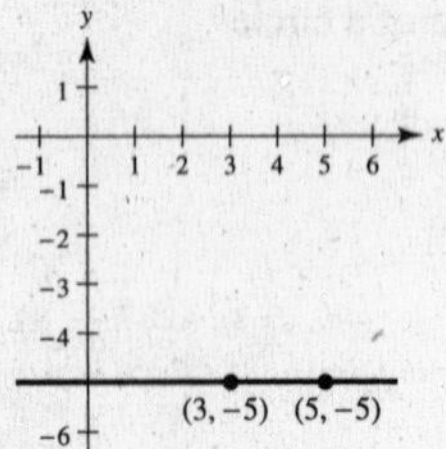


**13.** $m = \dfrac{\dfrac{2}{3} - \dfrac{1}{6}}{-\dfrac{1}{2} - \left(-\dfrac{3}{4}\right)} = \dfrac{\dfrac{1}{2}}{\dfrac{1}{4}} = 2$

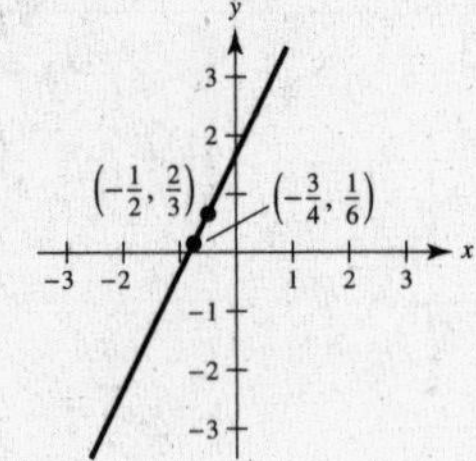

**14.** $m = \dfrac{\left(\dfrac{3}{4}\right) - \left(-\dfrac{1}{4}\right)}{\left(\dfrac{7}{8}\right) - \left(\dfrac{5}{4}\right)} = \dfrac{1}{-\dfrac{3}{8}} = -\dfrac{8}{3}$

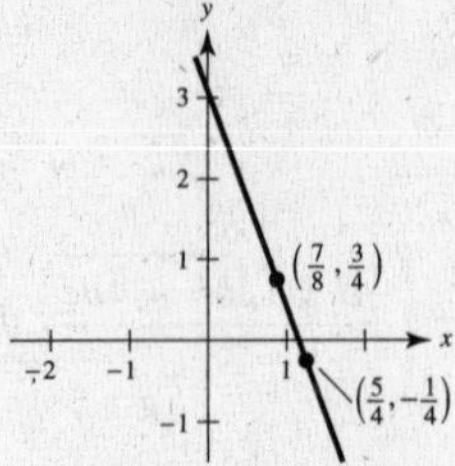

**15.** Because the slope is 0, the line is horizontal and its equation is $y = 2$. So, three additional points are $(0, 2), (1, 2), (5, 2)$.

**16.** Because the slope is undefined, the line is vertical and its equation is $x = -4$. So, three additional points are $(-4, 0), (-4, 1), (-4, 2)$.

**17.** The equation of this line is

$$y - 7 = -3(x - 1)$$
$$y = -3x + 10.$$

So, three additional points are (0, 10), (2, 4), and (3, 1).

**18.** The equation of this line is

$$y + 2 = 2(x + 2)$$
$$y = 2x + 2.$$

So, three additional points are $(-3, -4)$, $(-1, 0)$, and $(0, 2)$.

**19.** (a) Slope $= \dfrac{\Delta y}{\Delta x} = \dfrac{1}{3}$

(b)

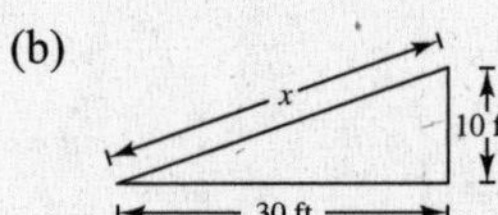


By the Pythagorean Theorem,

$$x^2 = 30^2 + 10^2 = 1000$$
$$x = 10\sqrt{10} \approx 31.623 \text{ feet}.$$

**20.** (a) $m = 800$ indicates that the revenues increase by 800 in one day.

(b) $m = 250$ indicates that the revenues increase by 250 in one day.

(c) $m = 0$ indicates that the revenues do not change from one day to the next.

**21.** (a)

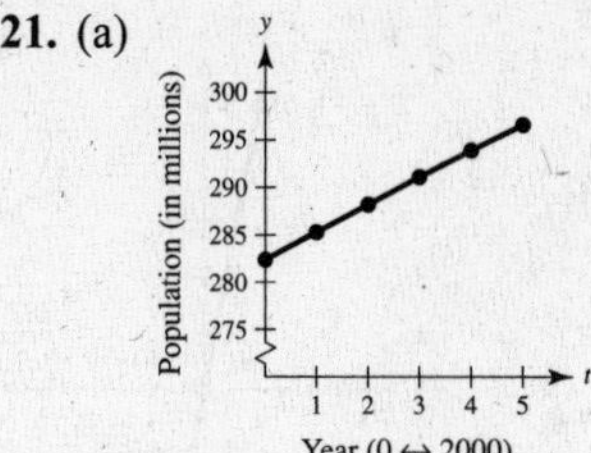


(b) The slopes are:

$$\frac{285.3 - 282.4}{1 - 0} = 2.9$$

$$\frac{288.2 - 285.3}{2 - 1} = 2.9$$

$$\frac{291.1 - 288.2}{3 - 2} = 2.9$$

$$\frac{293.9 - 291.1}{4 - 3} = 2.8$$

$$\frac{296.6 - 293.9}{5 - 4} = 2.7$$

The population increased least rapidly from 2004 to 2005.

**22.** (a)

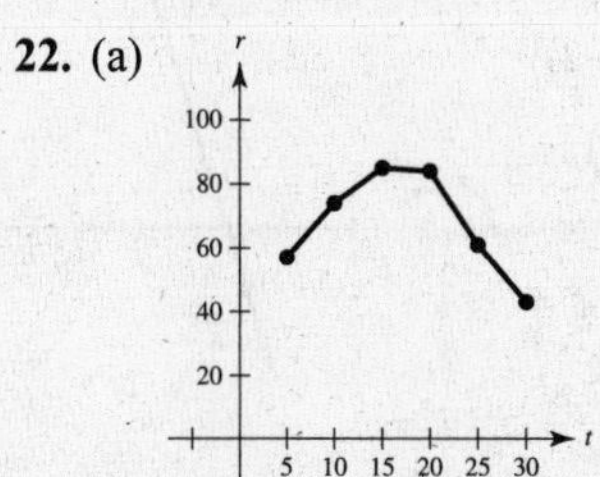

(b) The slopes are:

$$\frac{74 - 57}{10 - 5} = 3.4$$

$$\frac{85 - 74}{15 - 10} = 2.2$$

$$\frac{84 - 85}{20 - 15} = -0.2$$

$$\frac{61 - 84}{25 - 20} = -4.6$$

$$\frac{43 - 61}{30 - 25} = -3.6$$

The rate changed most rapidly between 20 and 25 seconds. The change is $-4.6$ mi/h/sec.

**23.** $y = 4x - 3$

The slope is $m = 4$ and the $y$-intercept is $(0, -3)$.

**24.** $-x + y = 1$

$y = x + 1$

The slope is $m = 1$ and the $y$-intercept is $(0, 1)$.

**25.** $x + 5y = 20$

$y = -\frac{1}{5}x + 4$

The slope is $m = -\frac{1}{5}$ and the $y$-intercept is $(0, 4)$.

**26.** $6x - 5y = 15$

$y = \frac{6}{5}x - 3$

The slope is $m = \frac{6}{5}$ and the $y$-intercept is $(0, -3)$.

**27.** $x = 4$

The line is vertical. So, the slope is undefined and there is no $y$-intercept.

**28.** $y = -1$

The line is horizontal. So, the slope is $m = 0$ and the $y$-intercept is $(0, -1)$.

**29.** $y = \frac{3}{4}x + 3$

$4y = 3x + 12$

$0 = 3x - 4y + 12$

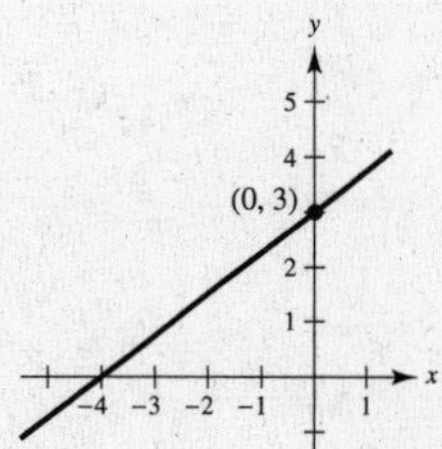


**30.** The slope is undefined so the line is vertical.

$x = -5$

$x + 5 = 0$

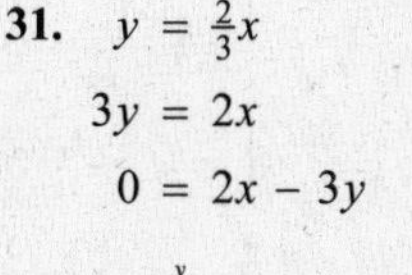


**31.** $y = \frac{2}{3}x$

$3y = 2x$

$0 = 2x - 3y$

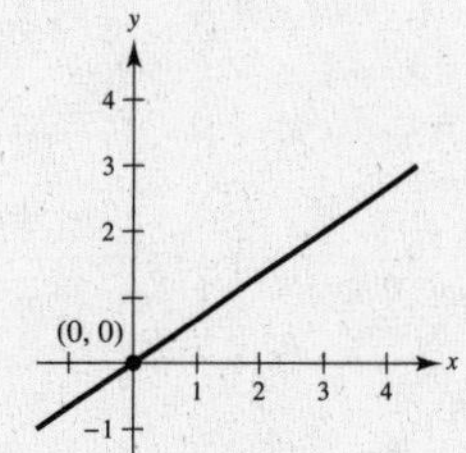

**32.** $y = 4$

$y - 4 = 0$

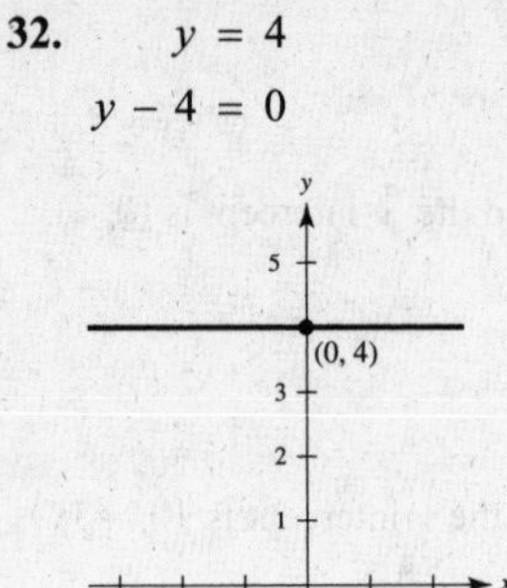


**33.** $y + 2 = 3(x - 3)$

$y + 2 = 3x - 9$

$y = 3x - 11$

$0 = 3x - y - 11$

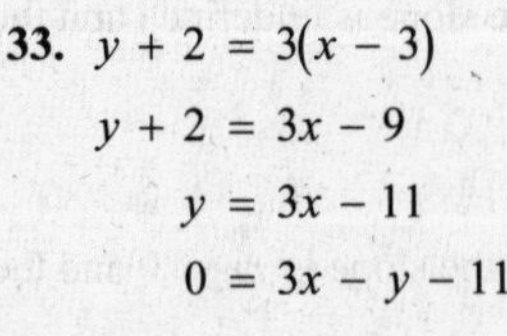

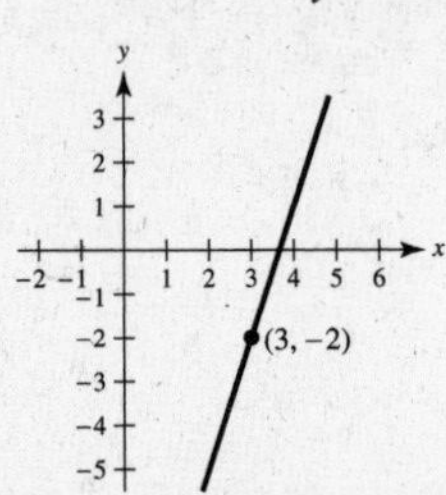


**34.** $y - 4 = -\frac{3}{5}(x + 2)$

$5y - 20 = -3x - 6$

$3x + 5y - 14 = 0$

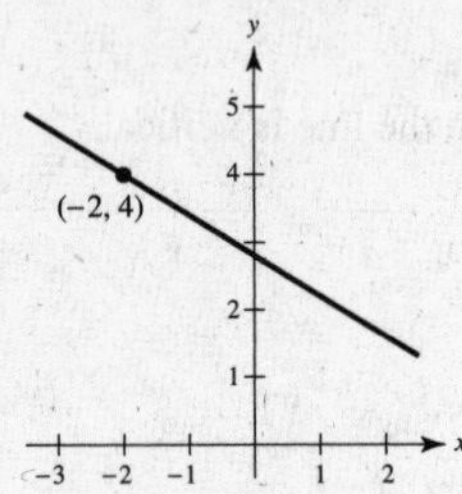


**35.** $m = \dfrac{8 - 0}{4 - 0} = 2$

$y - 0 = 2(x - 0)$

$y = 2x$

$0 = 2x - y$

**36.** $m = \dfrac{5 - 0}{-1 - 0} = -5$

$y - 0 = -5(x - 0)$

$y = -5x$

$5x + y = 0$

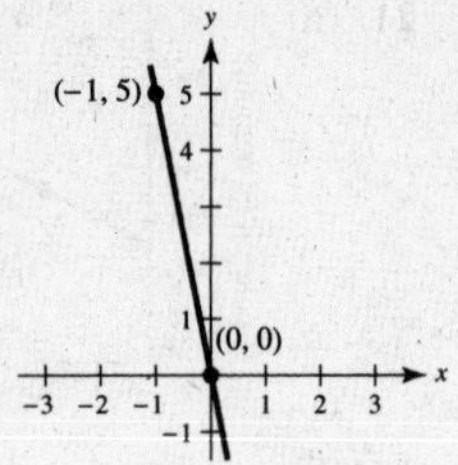


**37.** $m = \dfrac{1 - (-3)}{2 - 0} = 2$

$y - 1 = 2(x - 2)$

$y - 1 = 2x - 4$

$0 = 2x - y - 3$

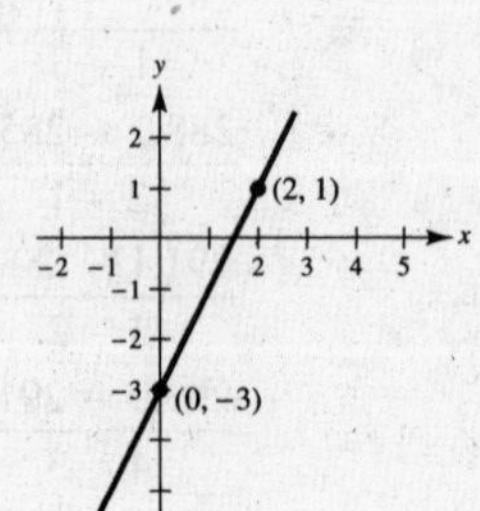


**38.** $m = \dfrac{7 - (-2)}{1 - (-2)} = \dfrac{9}{3} = 3$

$y - (-2) = 3(x - (-2))$

$y + 2 = 3(x + 2)$

$y = 3x + 4$

$0 = 3x - y + 4$

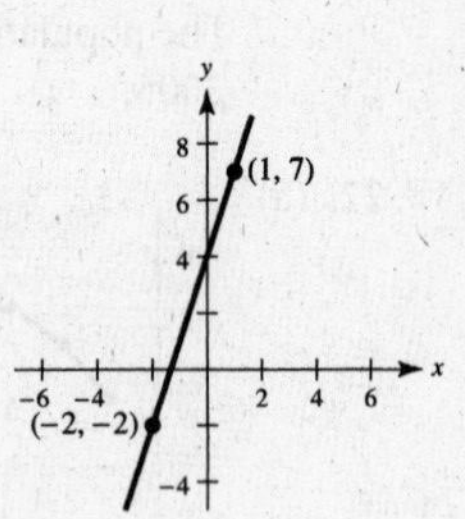


**39.** $m = \dfrac{8 - 0}{2 - 5} = -\dfrac{8}{3}$

$y - 0 = -\frac{8}{3}(x - 5)$

$y = -\frac{8}{3}x + \frac{40}{3}$

$8x + 3y - 40 = 0$

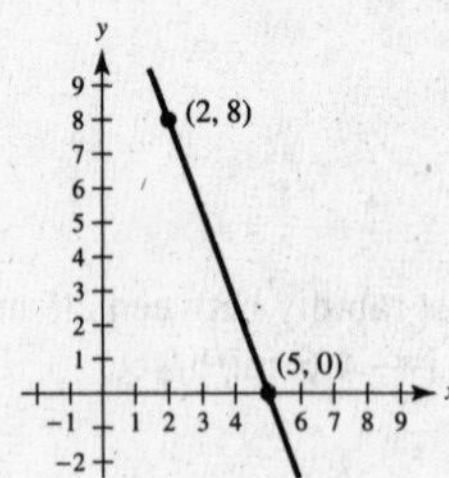

**40.** $m = \dfrac{6-2}{-3-1} = \dfrac{4}{-4} = -1$

$$y - 2 = -1(x - 1)$$
$$y - 2 = -x + 1$$
$$x + y - 3 = 0$$

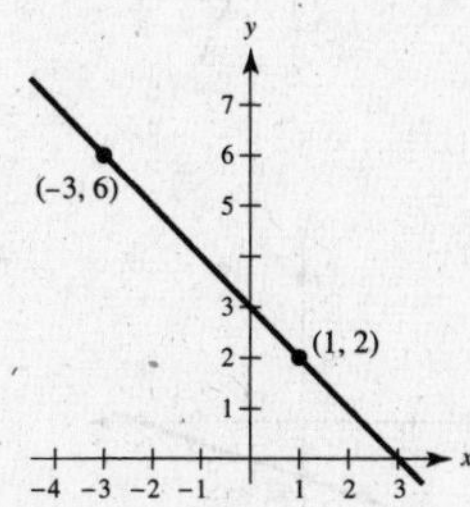


**41.** $m = \dfrac{8-3}{6-6} = \dfrac{5}{0}$, undefined

The line is vertical.

$$x = 6$$
$$x - 6 = 0$$

**42.** $m = \dfrac{-2-(-2)}{3-1} = \dfrac{0}{2} = 0$

The line is horizontal.

$$y = -2$$
$$y + 2 = 0$$

**43.** $m = \dfrac{\frac{7}{2} - \frac{3}{4}}{\frac{1}{2} - 0} = \dfrac{\frac{11}{4}}{\frac{1}{2}} = \dfrac{11}{2}$

$$y - \frac{3}{4} = \frac{11}{2}(x - 0)$$
$$y = \frac{11}{2}x + \frac{3}{4}$$
$$0 = 22x - 4y + 3$$

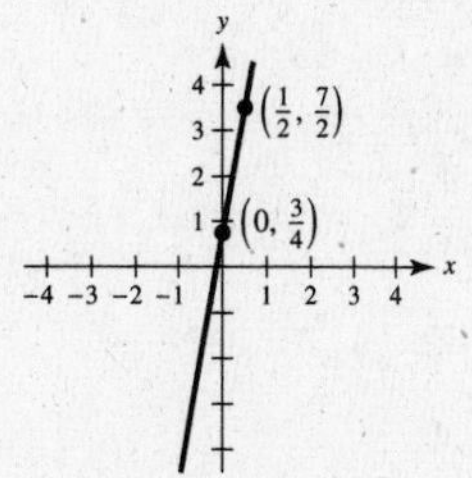


**44.** $m = \dfrac{\frac{3}{4} - \left(-\frac{1}{4}\right)}{\frac{7}{8} - \frac{5}{4}} = \dfrac{1}{-\frac{3}{8}} = -\dfrac{8}{3}$

$$y + \frac{1}{4} = \frac{-8}{3}\left(x - \frac{5}{4}\right)$$
$$12y + 3 = -32x + 40$$
$$32x + 12y - 37 = 0$$

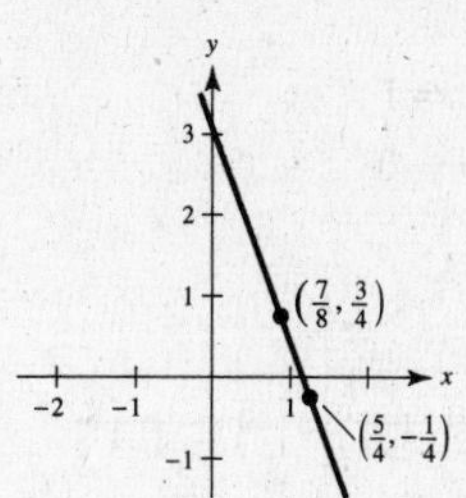


**45.** $x = 3$

$$x - 3 = 0$$

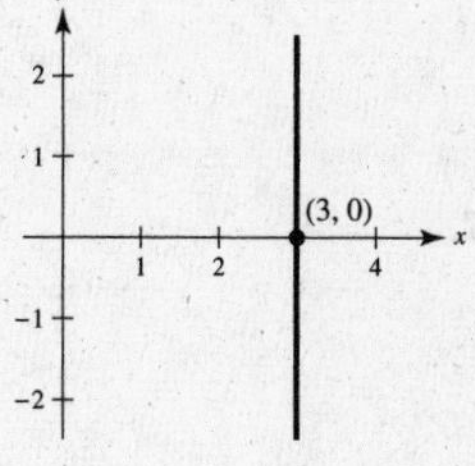


**46.** $m = -\dfrac{b}{a}$

$$y = \frac{-b}{a}x + b$$
$$\frac{b}{a}x + y = b$$
$$\frac{x}{a} + \frac{y}{b} = 1$$

**47.** $\dfrac{x}{2} + \dfrac{y}{3} = 1$

$3x + 2y - 6 = 0$

**48.** $\dfrac{x}{-\frac{2}{3}} + \dfrac{y}{-2} = 1$

$\dfrac{-3x}{2} - \dfrac{y}{2} = 1$

$3x + y = -2$

$3x + y + 2 = 0$

**49.** $\dfrac{x}{a} + \dfrac{y}{a} = 1$

$\dfrac{1}{a} + \dfrac{2}{a} = 1$

$\dfrac{3}{a} = 1$

$a = 3 \Rightarrow x + y = 3$

$x + y - 3 = 0$

**50.** $\dfrac{x}{a} + \dfrac{y}{a} = 1$

$\dfrac{-3}{a} + \dfrac{4}{a} = 1$

$\dfrac{1}{a} = 1$

$a = 1 \Rightarrow x + y = 1$

$x + y - 1 = 0$

**51.** $y = -3$

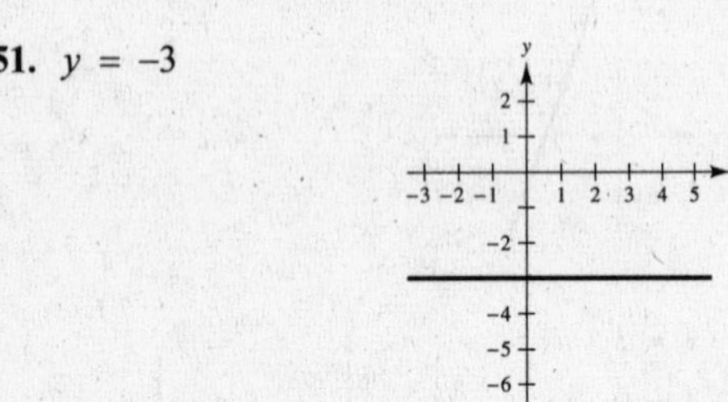

**52.** $x = 4$

**53.** $y = -2x + 1$

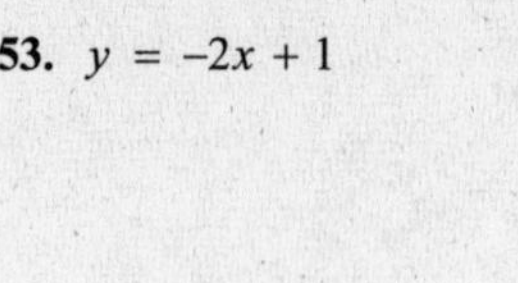

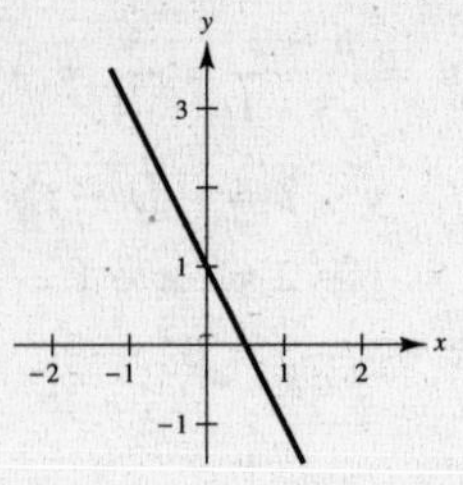

**54.** $y = \frac{1}{3}x - 1$

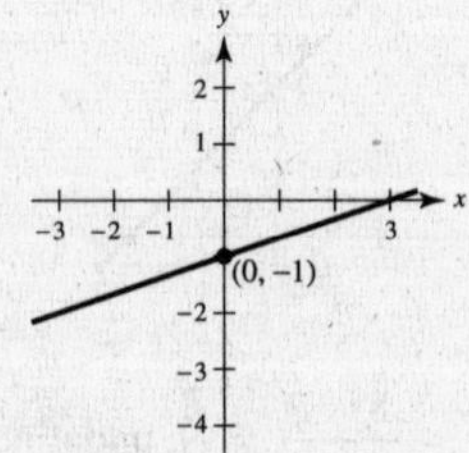


**55.** $y - 2 = \frac{3}{2}(x - 1)$

$y = \frac{3}{2}x + \frac{1}{2}$

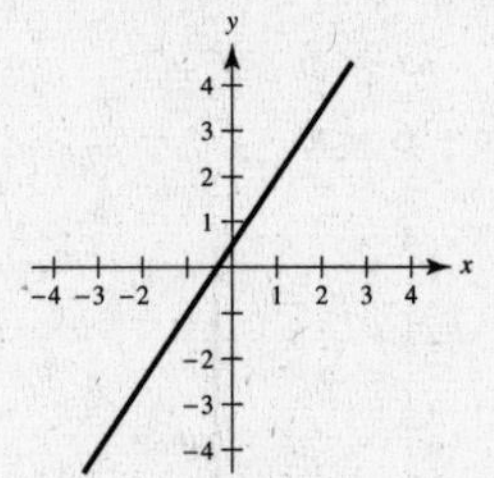

**56.** $y - 1 = 3(x + 4)$

$y = 3x + 13$

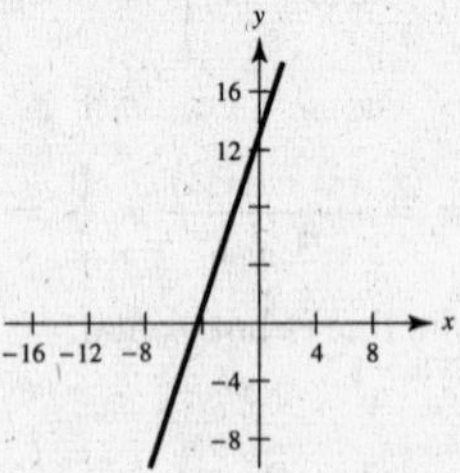

**57.** $2x - y - 3 = 0$

$y = 2x - 3$

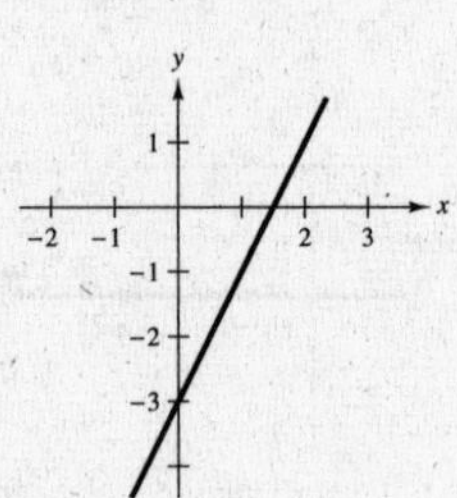

**58.** $x + 2y + 6 = 0$

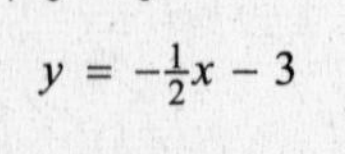

$y = -\frac{1}{2}x - 3$

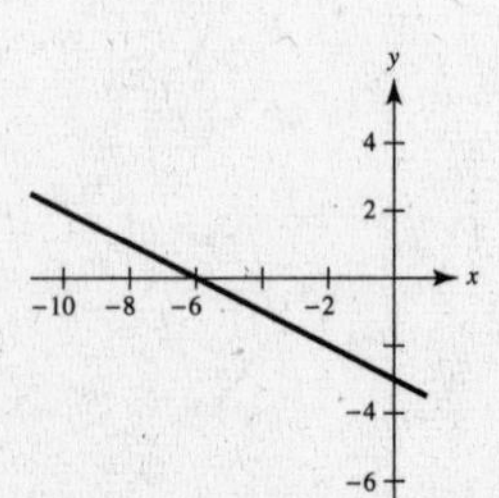

**59.** (a)

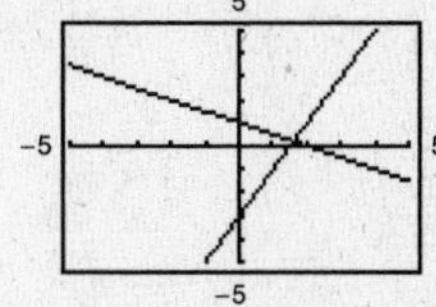

The lines do not appear perpendicular.

(b)

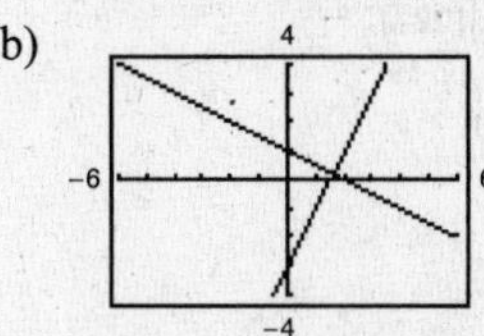

The lines appear perpendicular.

The lines are perpendicular because their slopes 2 and $-\frac{1}{2}$ are negative reciprocals of each other. You must use a square setting in order for perpendicular lines to appear perpendicular. Answers depend on calculator used.

**60.** $ax + by = 4$

(a) The line is parallel to the $x$-axis if $a = 0$ and $b \neq 0$.

(b) The line is parallel to the $y$-axis if $b = 0$ and $a \neq 0$.

(c) Answers will vary. *Sample answer*: $a = -5$ and $b = 8$.

$-5x + 8y = 4$

$y = \frac{1}{8}(5x + 4) = \frac{5}{8}x + \frac{1}{2}$

(d) The slope must be $-\frac{5}{2}$.

Answers will vary. *Sample answer*: $a = 5$ and $b = 2$.

$5x + 2y = 4$

$y = \frac{1}{2}(-5x + 4) = -\frac{5}{2}x + 2$

(e) $a = \frac{5}{2}$ and $b = 3$.

$\frac{5}{2}x + 3y = 4$

$5x + 6y = 8$

**61.** The given line is vertical.

(a) $x = -7$, or $x + 7 = 0$

(b) $y = -2$, or $y + 2 = 0$

**62.** The given line is horizontal.

(a) $y = 0$

(b) $x = -1$, or $x + 1 = 0$

**63.** $4x - 2y = 3$

$y = 2x - \frac{3}{2}$

$m = 2$

(a) $y - 1 = 2(x - 2)$

$y - 1 = 2x - 4$

$0 = 2x - y - 3$

(b) $y - 1 = -\frac{1}{2}(x - 2)$

$2y - 2 = -x + 2$

$x + 2y - 4 = 0$

**64.** $x + y = 7$

$y = -x + 7$

$m = -1$

(a) $y - 2 = -1(x + 3)$

$y - 2 = -x - 3$

$x + y + 1 = 0$

(b) $y - 2 = 1(x + 3)$

$y - 2 = x + 3$

$0 = x - y + 5$

**65.** $5x - 3y = 0$

$y = \frac{5}{3}x$

$m = \frac{5}{3}$

(a) $y - \frac{7}{8} = \frac{5}{3}\left(x - \frac{3}{4}\right)$

$24y - 21 = 40x - 30$

$0 = 40x - 24y - 9$

(b) $y - \frac{7}{8} = -\frac{3}{5}\left(x - \frac{3}{4}\right)$

$40y - 35 = -24x + 18$

$24x + 40y - 53 = 0$

**66.** $3x + 4y = 7$

$4y = -3x + 7$

$y = -\frac{3}{4}x + \frac{7}{4}$

$m = -\frac{3}{4}$

(a) $y - (-5) = -\frac{3}{4}(x - 4)$

$y + 5 = -\frac{3}{4}x + 3$

$4y + 20 = -3x + 12$

$3x + 4y + 8 = 0$

(b) $y - (-5) = \frac{4}{3}(x - 4)$

$y + 5 = \frac{4}{3}x - \frac{16}{3}$

$3y + 15 = 4x - 16$

$0 = 4x - 3y - 31$

**67.** The slope is 250. $V = 1850$ when $t = 8$.

$V = 250(t - 8) + 1850 = 250t - 150$

**68.** The slope is 4.5. $V = 156$ when $t = 8$.

$V = 4.5(t - 8) + 156 = 4.5t + 120$

**69.** The slope is $-1600$. $V = 17{,}200$ when $t = 8$.

$V = -1600(t - 8) + 17{,}200 = -1600t + 30{,}000$

**70.** The slope is $-5600$. $V = 245{,}000$ when $t = 8$.

$V = -5600(t - 8) + 245{,}000 = -5600t + 289{,}800$

**71.** $y = x^2, y = 4x - x^2$

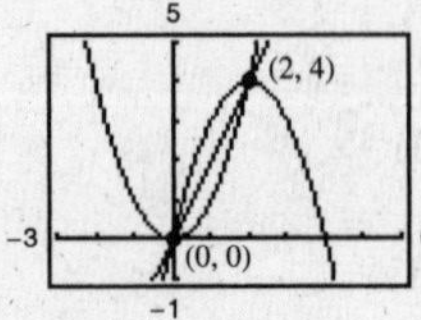


You can use the graphing utility to determine that the points of intersection are (0, 0) and (2, 4). Analytically,

$$\begin{aligned} x^2 &= 4x - x^2 \\ 2x^2 - 4x &= 0 \\ 2x(x - 2) &= 0 \\ x = 0 &\Rightarrow y = 0 \Rightarrow (0, 0) \\ x = 2 &\Rightarrow y = 4 \Rightarrow (2, 4). \end{aligned}$$

The slope of the line joining (0, 0) and (2, 4) is $m = (4 - 0)/(2 - 0) = 2$. So, an equation of the line is

$$\begin{aligned} y - 0 &= 2(x - 0) \\ y &= 2x. \end{aligned}$$

**72.** $y = x^2 - 4x + 3,\ y = -x^2 + 2x + 3$

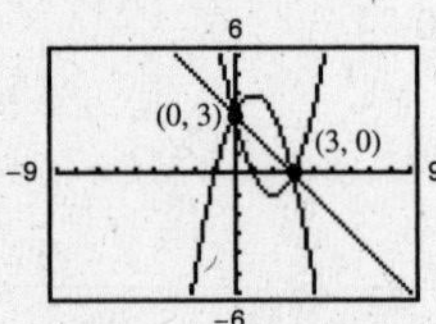


You can use the graphing utility to determine that the points of intersection are (0, 3) and (3, 0). Analytically,

$$\begin{aligned} x^2 - 4x + 3 &= -x^2 + 2x + 3 \\ 2x^2 - 6x &= 0 \\ 2x(x - 3) &= 0 \\ x = 0 &\Rightarrow y = 3 \Rightarrow (0, 3) \\ x = 3 &\Rightarrow y = 0 \Rightarrow (3, 0). \end{aligned}$$

The slope of the line joining (0, 3) and (3, 0) is $m = (0 - 3)/(3 - 0) = -1$. So, an equation of the line is

$$\begin{aligned} y - 3 &= -1(x - 0) \\ y &= -x + 3. \end{aligned}$$

**73.** $m_1 = \dfrac{1 - 0}{-2 - (-1)} = -1$

$m_2 = \dfrac{-2 - 0}{2 - (-1)} = -\dfrac{2}{3}$

$m_1 \neq m_2$

The points are not collinear.

**74.** $m_1 = \dfrac{-6 - 4}{7 - 0} = -\dfrac{10}{7}$

$m_2 = \dfrac{11 - 4}{-5 - 0} = -\dfrac{7}{5}$

$m_1 \neq m_2$

The points are not collinear.

**75.** Equations of perpendicular bisectors:

$$y - \frac{c}{2} = \frac{a - b}{c}\left(x - \frac{a + b}{2}\right)$$

$$y - \frac{c}{2} = \frac{a + b}{-c}\left(x - \frac{b - a}{2}\right)$$

Setting the right-hand sides of the two equations equal and solving for $x$ yields $x = 0$.

Letting $x = 0$ in either equation gives the point of intersection:

$$\left(0, \frac{-a^2 + b^2 + c^2}{2c}\right).$$

This point lies on the third perpendicular bisector, $x = 0$.

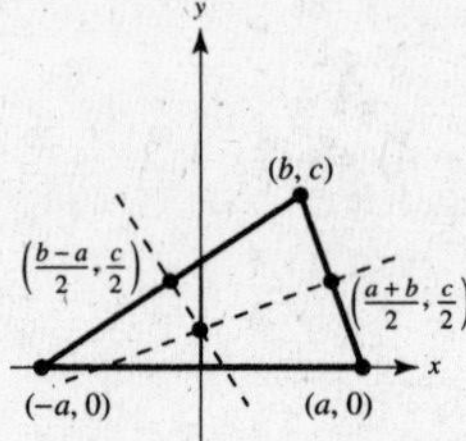


**76.** Equations of medians:

$$y = \frac{c}{b}x$$

$$y = \frac{c}{3a + b}(x + a)$$

$$y = \frac{c}{-3a + b}(x - a)$$

Solving simultaneously, the point of intersection is $\left(\dfrac{b}{3}, \dfrac{c}{3}\right)$.

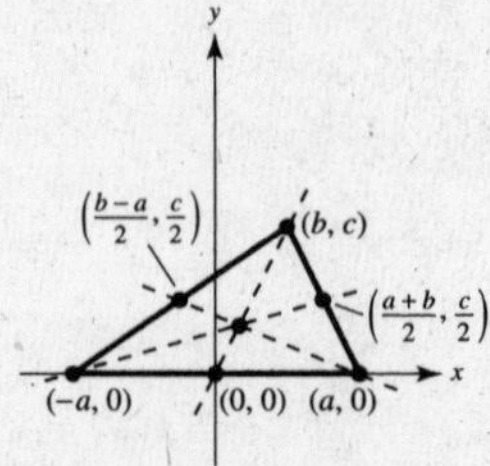

**77.** Equations of altitudes:

$$y = \frac{a - b}{c}(x + a)$$

$$x = b$$

$$y = -\frac{a + b}{c}(x - a)$$

Solving simultaneously, the point of intersection is $\left(b, \dfrac{a^2 - b^2}{c}\right)$.

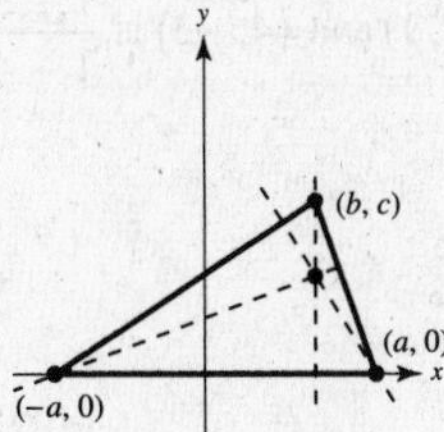


**78.** The slope of the line segment from $\left(\dfrac{b}{3}, \dfrac{c}{3}\right)$ to $\left(b, \dfrac{a^2 - b^2}{c}\right)$ is:

$$m_1 = \frac{\left[(a^2 - b^2)/c\right] - (c/3)}{b - (b/3)}$$

$$= \frac{(3a^2 - 3b^2 - c^2)/(3c)}{(2b)/3} = \frac{3a^2 - 3b^2 - c^2}{2bc}$$

The slope of the line segment from $\left(\dfrac{b}{3}, \dfrac{c}{3}\right)$ to $\left(0, \dfrac{-a^2 + b^2 + c^2}{2c}\right)$ is:

$$m_2 = \frac{\left[(-a^2 + b^2 + c^2)/(2c)\right] - (c/3)}{0 - (b/3)}$$

$$= \frac{(-3a^2 + 3b^2 + 3c^2 - 2c^2)/(6c)}{-b/3} = \frac{3a^2 - 3b^2 - c^2}{2bc}$$

$$m_1 = m_2$$

So, the points are collinear.

**79.** Find the equation of the line through the points (0, 32) and (100, 212).

$$m = \tfrac{180}{100} = \tfrac{9}{5}$$

$$F - 32 = \tfrac{9}{5}(C - 0)$$

$$F = \tfrac{9}{5}C + 32$$

or

$$C = \tfrac{1}{9}(5F - 160)$$

$$5F - 9C - 160 = 0$$

For $F = 72°$, $C \approx 22.2°$.

**80.** $C = 0.48x + 175$

For $x = 137$, $C = 0.48(137) + 175 = \$240.76$.

**81.** (a) $W_1 = 0.75x + 14.50$

$W_2 = 1.30x + 11.20$

(b)

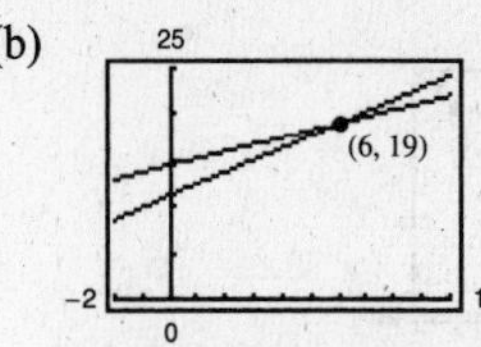


Using a graphing utility, the point of intersection is (6, 19)

Analytically,

$$W_1 = W_2$$

$$0.75x + 14.50 = 1.30x + 11.20$$

$$3.3 = 0.55x$$

$$6 = x$$

$$y = 1.30(6) + 11.20 = 19.$$

(c) When six units are produced, the wage for both options is \$19.00 per hour. Choose option 1 if you think you will produce less than six units per hour, and choose option 2 if you think you will produce more than six.

**82.** (a) Depreciation per year:

$\frac{875}{5} = \$175$

$y = 875 - 175x$

where $0 \le x \le 5$.

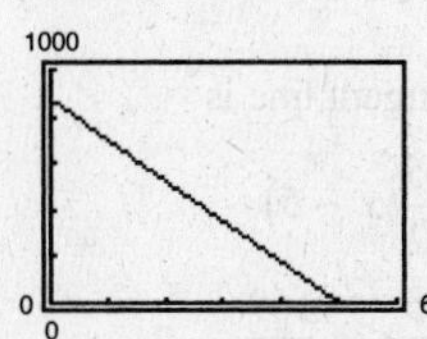


(b) $y = 875 - 175(2) = \$525$

(c) $200 = 875 - 175x$

$175x = 675$

$x \approx 3.86$ years

**83.** (a) Two points are (50, 780) and (47, 825).

The slope is

$$m = \frac{825 - 780}{47 - 50} = \frac{45}{-3} = -15.$$

$$p - 780 = -15(x - 50)$$

$$p = -15x + 750 + 780 = -15x + 1530$$

or

$$x = \frac{1}{15}(1530 - p)$$

(b)

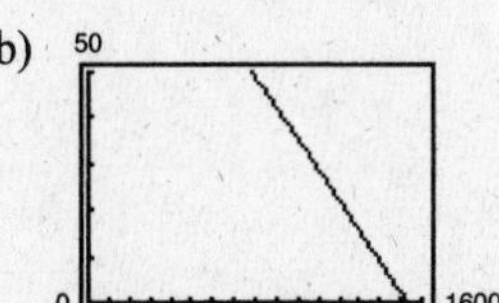


If $p = 855$, then $x = 45$ units.

(c) If $p = 795$, then $x = \dfrac{1}{15}(1530 - 795) = 49$ units.

**84.** (a) $y = 18.91 + 3.97x$

$(x = \text{quiz score}, y = \text{test score})$

(b)

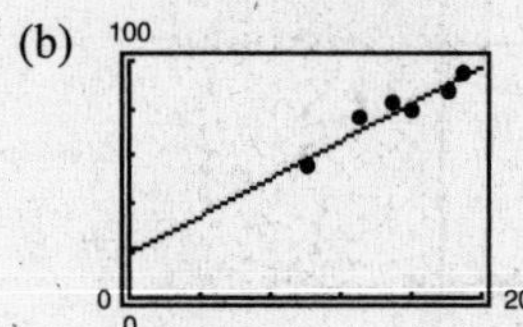


(c) If $x = 17$, $y = 18.91 + 3.97(17) = 86.4$.

(d) The slope shows the average increase in exam score for each unit increase in quiz score.

(e) The points would shift vertically upward 4 units. The new regression line would have a $y$-intercept 4 greater than before: $y = 22.91 + 3.97x$.

**85.** The tangent line is perpendicular to the line joining the point (5, 12) and the center (0, 0).

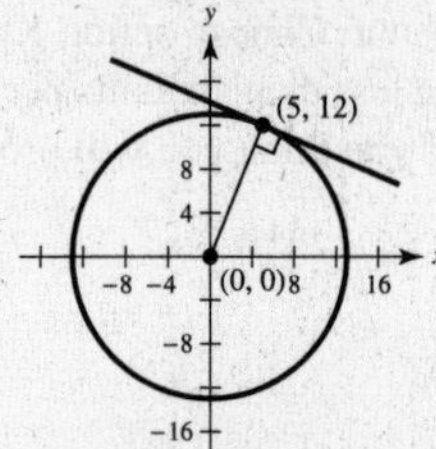


Slope of the line joining (5, 12) and (0, 0) is $\frac{12}{5}$.

The equation of the tangent line is

$$y - 12 = \frac{-5}{12}(x - 5)$$

$$y = \frac{-5}{12}x + \frac{169}{12}$$

$$5x + 12y - 169 = 0.$$

**86.** The tangent line is perpendicular to the line joining the point $(4, -3)$ and the center of the circle, (1, 1).

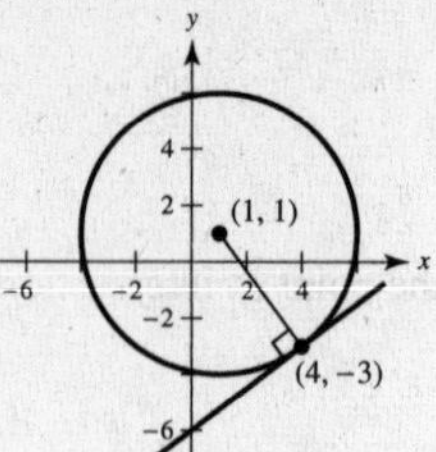


Slope of the line joining (1, 1) and $(4, -3)$ is $\frac{1 + 3}{1 - 4} = \frac{-4}{3}$.

Tangent line:

$$y + 3 = \frac{3}{4}(x - 4)$$

$$y = \frac{3}{4}x - 6$$

$$0 = 3x - 4y - 24$$

**87.** $4x + 3y - 10 = 0 \Rightarrow d = \frac{|4(0) + 3(0) - 10|}{\sqrt{4^2 + 3^2}} = \frac{10}{5} = 2$

**88.** $4x + 3y - 10 = 0 \Rightarrow d = \frac{|4(2) + 3(3) - 10|}{\sqrt{4^2 + 3^2}} = \frac{7}{5}$

**89.** $x - y - 2 = 0 \Rightarrow d = \frac{|1(-2) + (-1)(1) - 2|}{\sqrt{1^2 + 1^2}} = \frac{5}{\sqrt{2}} = \frac{5\sqrt{2}}{2}$

**90.** $x + 1 = 0 \Rightarrow d = \frac{|1(6) + (0)(2) + 1|}{\sqrt{1^2 + 0^2}} = 7$

**91.** A point on the line $x + y = 1$ is (0, 1). The distance from the point (0, 1) to $x + y - 5 = 0$ is

$$d = \frac{|1(0) + 1(1) - 5|}{\sqrt{1^2 + 1^2}} = \frac{|1 - 5|}{\sqrt{2}} = \frac{4}{\sqrt{2}} = 2\sqrt{2}.$$

**92.** A point on the line $3x - 4y = 1$ is $(-1, -1)$. The distance from the point $(-1, -1)$ to $3x - 4y - 10 = 0$ is

$$d = \frac{|3(-1) - 4(-1) - 10|}{\sqrt{3^2 + (-4)^2}} = \frac{|-3 + 4 - 10|}{5} = \frac{9}{5}.$$

**93.** If $A = 0$, then $By + C = 0$ is the horizontal line $y = -C/B$. The distance to $(x_1, y_1)$ is

$$d = \left|y_1 - \left(\frac{-C}{B}\right)\right| = \frac{|By_1 + C|}{|B|} = \frac{|Ax_1 + By_1 + C|}{\sqrt{A^2 + B^2}}.$$

If $B = 0$, then $Ax + C = 0$ is the vertical line $x = -C/A$. The distance to $(x_1, y_1)$ is

$$d = \left|x_1 - \left(\frac{-C}{A}\right)\right| = \frac{|Ax_1 + C|}{|A|} = \frac{|Ax_1 + By_1 + C|}{\sqrt{A^2 + B^2}}.$$

(Note that A and B cannot both be zero.) The slope of the line $Ax + By + C = 0$ is $-A/B$.

The equation of the line through $(x_1, y_1)$ perpendicular to $Ax + By + C = 0$ is:

$$y - y_1 = \frac{B}{A}(x - x_1)$$
$$Ay - Ay_1 = Bx - Bx_1$$
$$Bx_1 - Ay_1 = Bx - Ay$$

The point of intersection of these two lines is:

$$Ax + By = -C \quad \Rightarrow A^2x + ABy = -AC \qquad (1)$$
$$Bx - Ay = Bx_1 - Ay_1 \Rightarrow \underline{B^2x - ABy = B^2x_1 - ABy_1} \qquad (2)$$
$$(A^2 + B^2)x = -AC + B^2x_1 - ABy_1 \quad \text{(By adding equations (1) and (2))}$$
$$x = \frac{-AC + B^2x_1 - ABy_1}{A^2 + B^2}$$

$$Ax + By = -C \quad \Rightarrow ABx + B^2y = -BC \qquad (3)$$
$$Bx - Ay = Bx_1 - Ay_1 \Rightarrow \underline{-ABx + A^2y = -ABx_1 + A^2y_1} \qquad (4)$$
$$(A^2 + B^2)y = -BC - ABx_1 + A^2y_1 \quad \text{(By adding equations (3) and (4))}$$
$$y = \frac{-BC - ABx_1 + A^2y_1}{A^2 + B^2}$$

$$\left(\frac{-AC + B^2x_1 - ABy_1}{A^2 + B^2}, \frac{-BC - ABx_1 + A^2y_1}{A^2 + B^2}\right) \text{ point of intersection}$$

The distance between $(x_1, y_1)$ and this point gives you the distance between $(x_1, y_1)$ and the line $Ax + By + C = 0$.

$$d = \sqrt{\left[\frac{-AC + B^2x_1 - ABy_1}{A^2 + B^2} - x_1\right]^2 + \left[\frac{-BC - ABx_1 + A^2y_1}{A^2 + B^2} - y_1\right]^2}$$

$$= \sqrt{\left[\frac{-AC - ABy_1 - A^2x_1}{A^2 + B^2}\right]^2 + \left[\frac{-BC - ABx_1 - B^2y_1}{A^2 + B^2}\right]^2}$$

$$= \sqrt{\left[\frac{-A(C + By_1 + Ax_1)}{A^2 + B^2}\right]^2 + \left[\frac{-B(C + Ax_1 + By_1)}{A^2 + B^2}\right]^2} = \sqrt{\frac{(A^2 + B^2)(C + Ax_1 + By_1)^2}{(A^2 + B^2)^2}} = \frac{|Ax_1 + By_1 + C|}{\sqrt{A^2 + B^2}}$$

**94.** $y = mx + 4 \Rightarrow mx + (-1)y + 4 = 0$

$$d = \frac{|Ax_1 + By_1 + C|}{\sqrt{A^2 + B^2}} = \frac{|m3 + (-1)(1) + 4|}{\sqrt{m^2 + (-1)^2}} = \frac{|3m + 3|}{\sqrt{m^2 + 1}}$$

The distance is 0 when $m = -1$. In this case, the line $y = -x + 4$ contains the point (3, 1).

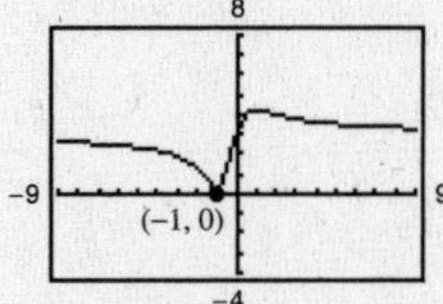

**95.** For simplicity, let the vertices of the rhombus be $(0, 0)$, $(a, 0)$, $(b, c)$, and $(a + b, c)$, as shown in the figure. The slopes of the diagonals are then $m_1 = \dfrac{c}{a + b}$ and $m_2 = \dfrac{c}{b - a}$. Because the sides of the rhombus are equal, $a^2 = b^2 + c^2$, and you have

$$m_1 m_2 = \frac{c}{a + b} \cdot \frac{c}{b - a} = \frac{c^2}{b^2 - a^2} = \frac{c^2}{-c^2} = -1.$$

So, the diagonals are perpendicular.

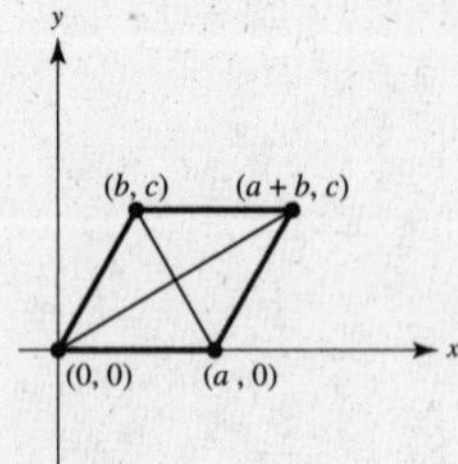


**96.** For simplicity, let the vertices of the quadrilateral be $(0, 0)$, $(a, 0)$, $(b, c)$, and $(d, e)$, as shown in the figure. The midpoints of the sides are

$$\left(\frac{a}{2}, 0\right), \left(\frac{a + b}{2}, \frac{c}{2}\right), \left(\frac{b + d}{2}, \frac{c + e}{2}\right), \text{ and } \left(\frac{d}{2}, \frac{e}{2}\right).$$

The slope of the opposite sides are equal:

$$\frac{\frac{c}{2} - 0}{\frac{a + b}{2} - \frac{a}{2}} = \frac{\frac{c + e}{2} - \frac{e}{2}}{\frac{b + d}{2} - \frac{d}{2}} = \frac{c}{b}$$

$$\frac{0 - \frac{e}{2}}{\frac{a}{2} - \frac{d}{2}} = \frac{\frac{c}{2} - \frac{c + e}{2}}{\frac{a + b}{2} - \frac{b + d}{2}} = -\frac{e}{a - d}$$

So, the figure is a parallelogram.

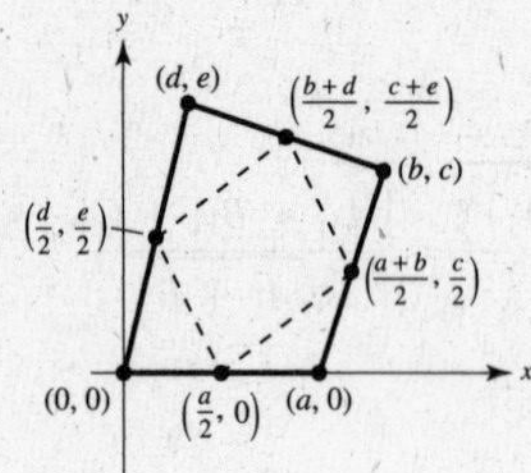


**97.** Consider the figure below in which the four points are collinear. Because the triangles are similar, the result immediately follows.

$$\frac{y_2^* - y_1^*}{x_2^* - x_1^*} = \frac{y_2 - y_1}{x_2 - x_1}$$

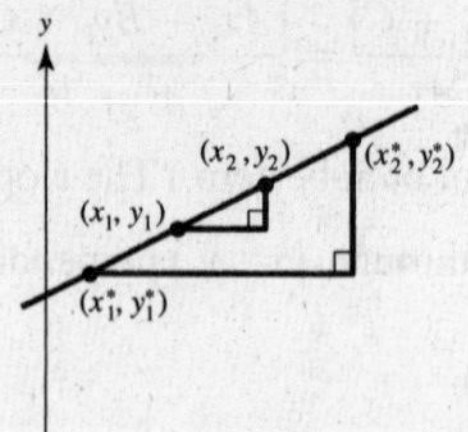


**98.** If $m_1 = -1/m_2$, then $m_1 m_2 = -1$. Let $L_3$ be a line with slope $m_3$ that is perpendicular to $L_1$. Then $m_1 m_3 = -1$. So, $m_2 = m_3 \Rightarrow L_2$ and $L_3$ are parallel. Therefore, $L_2$ and $L_1$ are also perpendicular.

**99.** True.

$$ax + by = c_1 \Rightarrow y = -\frac{a}{b}x + \frac{c_1}{b} \Rightarrow m_1 = -\frac{a}{b}$$

$$bx - ay = c_2 \Rightarrow y = \frac{b}{a}x - \frac{c_2}{a} \Rightarrow m_2 = \frac{b}{a}$$

$$m_2 = -\frac{1}{m_1}$$

**100.** False; if $m_1$ is positive, then $m_2 = -1/m_1$ is negative.

## Section 1.3 Functions and Their Graphs

**1.** (a) Domain of $f$: $-4 \le x \le 4 \Rightarrow [-4, 4]$

Range of $f$: $-3 \le y \le 5 \Rightarrow [-3, 5]$

Domain of $g$: $-3 \le x \le 3 \Rightarrow [-3, 3]$

Range of $g$: $-4 \le y \le 4 \Rightarrow [-4, 4]$

(b) $f(-2) = -1$

$g(3) = -4$

(c) $f(x) = g(x)$ for $x = -1$

(d) $f(x) = 2$ for $x = 1$

(e) $g(x) = 0$ for $x = -1, 1$ and $2$

**2.** (a) Domain of $f$: $-5 \le x \le 5 \Rightarrow [-5, 5]$

Range of $f$: $-4 \le y \le 4 \Rightarrow [-4, 4]$

Domain of $g$: $-4 \le x \le 5 \Rightarrow [-4, 5]$

Range of $g$: $-4 \le y \le 2 \Rightarrow [-4, 2]$

(b) $f(-2) = -2$

$g(3) = 2$

(c) $f(x) = g(x)$ for $x = -2$ and $x = 4$

(d) $f(x) = 2$ for $x = -4, 4$

(e) $g(x) = 0$ for $x = -1$

**3.** (a) $f(0) = 7(0) - 4 = -4$

(b) $f(-3) = 7(-3) - 4 = -25$

(c) $f(b) = 7(b) - 4 = 7b - 4$

(d) $f(x - 1) = 7(x - 1) - 4 = 7x - 11$

**4.** (a) $f(-4) = \sqrt{-4 + 5} = \sqrt{1} = 1$

(b) $f(11) = \sqrt{11 + 5} = \sqrt{16} = 4$

(c) $f(-8) = \sqrt{-8 + 5} = \sqrt{-3}$, undefined

(d) $f(x + \Delta x) = \sqrt{x + \Delta x + 5}$

**5.** (a) $g(0) = 5 - 0^2 = 5$

(b) $g(\sqrt{5}) = 5 - (\sqrt{5})^2 = 5 - 5 = 0$

(c) $g(-2) = 5 - (-2)^2 = 5 - 4 = 1$

(d) $g(t - 1) = 5 - (t - 1)^2 = 5 - (t^2 - 2t + 1)$

$= 4 + 2t - t^2$

**6.** (a) $g(4) = 4^2(4 - 4) = 0$

(b) $g\left(\frac{3}{2}\right) = \left(\frac{3}{2}\right)^2\left(\frac{3}{2} - 4\right) = \frac{9}{4}\left(-\frac{5}{2}\right) = -\frac{45}{8}$

(c) $g(c) = c^2(c - 4) = c^3 - 4c^2$

(d) $g(t + 4) = (t + 4)^2(t + 4 - 4)$

$= (t + 4)^2 t = t^3 + 8t^2 + 16t$

**7.** (a) $f(0) = \cos(2(0)) = \cos 0 = 1$

(b) $f\left(-\frac{\pi}{4}\right) = \cos\left(2\left(-\frac{\pi}{4}\right)\right) = \cos\left(-\frac{\pi}{2}\right) = 0$

(c) $f\left(\frac{\pi}{3}\right) = \cos\left(2\left(\frac{\pi}{3}\right)\right) = \cos\frac{2\pi}{3} = -\frac{1}{2}$

**8.** (a) $f(\pi) = \sin \pi = 0$

(b) $f\left(\frac{5\pi}{4}\right) = \sin\left(\frac{5\pi}{4}\right) = \frac{-\sqrt{2}}{2}$

(c) $f\left(\frac{2\pi}{3}\right) = \sin\left(\frac{2\pi}{3}\right) = \frac{\sqrt{3}}{2}$

**9.** $\dfrac{f(x + \Delta x) - f(x)}{\Delta x} = \dfrac{(x + \Delta x)^3 - x^3}{\Delta x} = \dfrac{x^3 + 3x^2\Delta x + 3x^2(\Delta x)^2 + (\Delta x)^3 - x^3}{\Delta x} = 3x^2 + 3x\Delta x + (\Delta x)^2, \Delta x \ne 0$

**10.** $\dfrac{f(x) - f(1)}{x - 1} = \dfrac{3x - 1 - (3 - 1)}{x - 1} = \dfrac{3(x - 1)}{x - 1} = 3, x \ne 1$

**11.** $\dfrac{f(x) - f(2)}{x - 2} = \dfrac{(1/\sqrt{x - 1} - 1)}{x - 2} = \dfrac{1 - \sqrt{x - 1}}{(x - 2)\sqrt{x - 1}} \cdot \dfrac{\sqrt{x - 1}}{\sqrt{x - 1}} = \dfrac{\sqrt{x - 1} - x + 1}{(x - 2)(x - 1)}, x \ne 2$

**12.** $\dfrac{f(x) - f(1)}{x - 1} = \dfrac{x^3 - x - 0}{x - 1} = \dfrac{x(x + 1)(x - 1)}{x - 1} = x(x + 1), x \ne 1$

**13.** $f(x) = 4x^2$

Domain: $(-\infty, \infty)$

Range: $[0, \infty)$

**14.** $g(x) = x^2 - 5$

Domain: $(-\infty, \infty)$

Range: $[-5, \infty)$

**15.** $g(x) = \sqrt{6x}$

Domain: $6x \geq 0$

$x \geq 0 \Rightarrow [0, \infty)$

Range: $[0, \infty)$

**16.** $h(x) = -\sqrt{x + 3}$

Domain: $x + 3 \geq 0 \Rightarrow [-3, \infty)$

Range: $(-\infty, 0]$

**17.** $f(t) = \sec\dfrac{\pi t}{4}$

$\dfrac{\pi t}{4} \neq \dfrac{(2n + 1)\pi}{2} \Rightarrow t \neq 4n + 2$

Domain: all $t \neq 4n + 2$, $n$ an integer

Range: $(-\infty, -1] \cup [1, \infty)$

**18.** $h(t) = \cot t$

Domain: all $t = n\pi$, $n$ an integer

Range: $(-\infty, \infty)$

**19.** $f(x) = \dfrac{3}{x}$

Domain: all $x \neq 0 \Rightarrow (-\infty, 0) \cup (0, \infty)$

Range: $(-\infty, 0) \cup (0, \infty)$

**20.** $g(x) = \dfrac{2}{x - 1}$

Domain: $(-\infty, 1) \cup (1, \infty)$

Range: $(-\infty, 0) \cup (0, \infty)$

**21.** $f(x) = \sqrt{x} + \sqrt{1 - x}$

$x \geq 0$ and $1 - x \geq 0$

$x \geq 0$ and $x \leq 1$

Domain: $0 \leq x \leq 1 \Rightarrow [0, 1]$

**22.** $f(x) = \sqrt{x^2 - 3x + 2}$

$x^2 - 3x + 2 \geq 0$

$(x - 2)(x - 1) \geq 0$

Domain: $x \geq 2$ or $x \leq 1 \Rightarrow (-\infty, 1] \cup [2, \infty)$

**23.** $g(x) = \dfrac{2}{1 - \cos x}$

$1 - \cos x \neq 0$

$\cos x \neq 1$

Domain: all $x \neq 2n\pi$, $n$ an integer

**24.** $h(x) = \dfrac{1}{\sin x - (1/2)}$

$\sin x - \dfrac{1}{2} \neq 0$

$\sin x \neq \dfrac{1}{2}$

Domain: all $x \neq \dfrac{\pi}{6} + 2n\pi, \dfrac{5\pi}{6} + 2n\pi$, $n$ an integer

**25.** $f(x) = \dfrac{1}{|x + 3|}$

$|x + 3| \neq 0$

$x + 3 \neq 0$

Domain: all $x \neq -3 \Rightarrow (-\infty, -3) \cup (-3, \infty)$

**26.** $g(x) = \dfrac{1}{|x^2 - 4|}$

$|x^2 - 4| \neq 0$

$(x - 2)(x + 2) \neq 0$

Domain: all $x \neq \pm 2 \Rightarrow (-\infty, -2) \cup (-2, 2) \cup (2, \infty)$

**27.** $f(x) = \begin{cases} 2x + 1, & x < 0 \\ 2x + 2, & x \geq 0 \end{cases}$

(a) $f(-1) = 2(-1) + 1 = -1$

(b) $f(0) = 2(0) + 2 = 2$

(c) $f(2) = 2(2) + 2 = 6$

(d) $f(t^2 + 1) = 2(t^2 + 1) + 2 = 2t^2 + 4$

(**Note:** $t^2 + 1 \geq 0$ for all $t$)

Domain: $(-\infty, \infty)$

Range: $(-\infty, 1) \cup [2, \infty)$

**28.** $f(x) = \begin{cases} x^2 + 2, & x \le 1 \\ 2x^2 + 2, & x > 1 \end{cases}$

(a) $f(-2) = (-2)^2 + 2 = 6$

(b) $f(0) = 0^2 + 2 = 2$

(c) $f(1) = 1^2 + 2 = 3$

(d) $f(s^2 + 2) = 2(s^2 + 2)^2 + 2 = 2s^4 + 8s^2 + 10$

(**Note:** $s^2 + 2 > 1$ for all $s$)

Domain: $(-\infty, \infty)$

Range: $[2, \infty)$

**29.** $f(x) = \begin{cases} |x| + 1, & x < 1 \\ -x + 1, & x \ge 1 \end{cases}$

(a) $f(-3) = |-3| + 1 = 4$

(b) $f(1) = -1 + 1 = 0$

(c) $f(3) = -3 + 1 = -2$

(d) $f(b^2 + 1) = -(b^2 + 1) + 1 = -b^2$

Domain: $(-\infty, \infty)$

Range: $(-\infty, 0] \cup [1, \infty)$

**30.** $f(x) = \begin{cases} \sqrt{x + 4}, & x \le 5 \\ (x - 5)^2, & x > 5 \end{cases}$

(a) $f(-3) = \sqrt{-3 + 4} = \sqrt{1} = 1$

(b) $f(0) = \sqrt{0 + 4} = 2$

(c) $f(5) = \sqrt{5 + 4} = 3$

(d) $f(10) = (10 - 5)^2 = 25$

Domain: $[-4, \infty)$

Range: $[0, \infty)$

**31.** $f(x) = 4 - x$

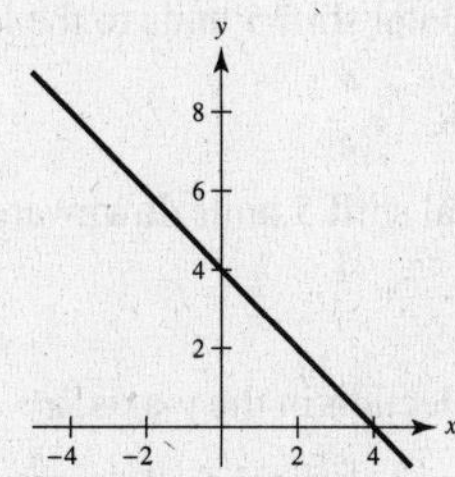

Domain: $(-\infty, \infty)$

Range: $(-\infty, \infty)$

**32.** $g(x) = \dfrac{4}{x}$

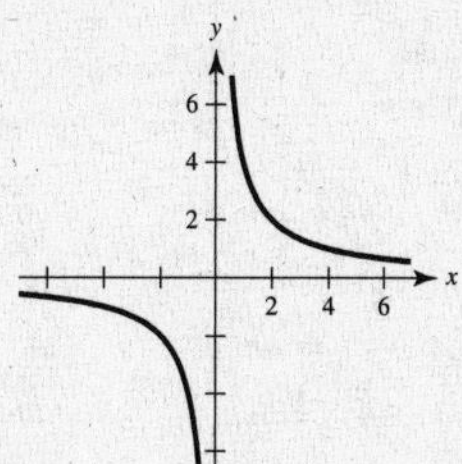

Domain: $(-\infty, 0) \cup (0, \infty)$

Range: $(-\infty, 0) \cup (0, \infty)$

**33.** $h(x) = \sqrt{x - 6}$

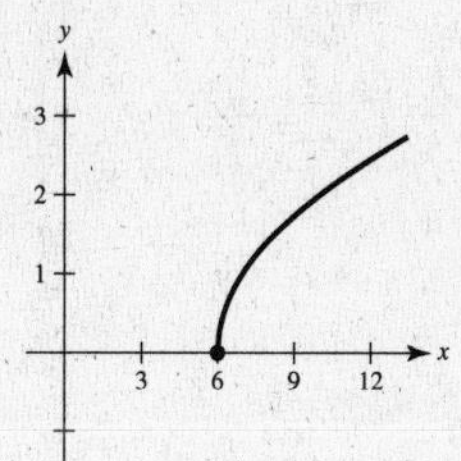

Domain: $x - 6 \ge 0$

$x \ge 6 \Rightarrow [6, \infty)$

Range: $[0, \infty)$

**34.** $f(x) = \frac{1}{4}x^3 + 3$

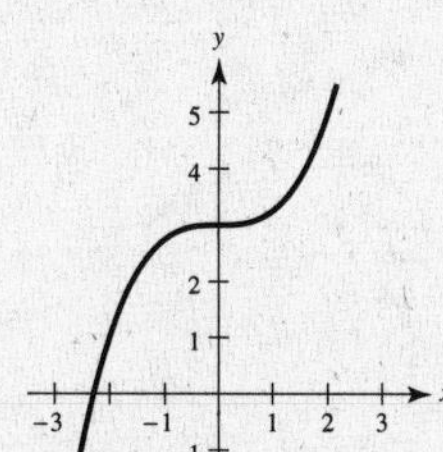

Domain: $(-\infty, \infty)$

Range: $(-\infty, \infty)$

**35.** $f(x) = \sqrt{9 - x^2}$

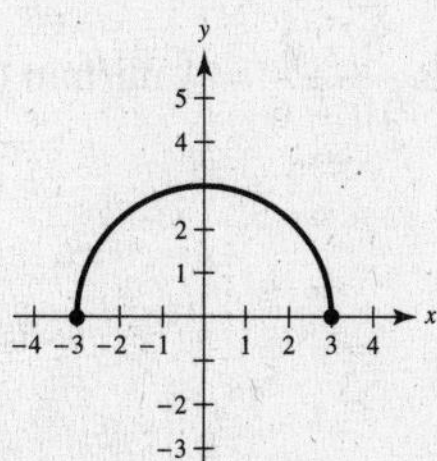

Domain: $[-3, 3]$

Range: $[0, 3]$

**36.** $f(x) = x + \sqrt{4 - x^2}$

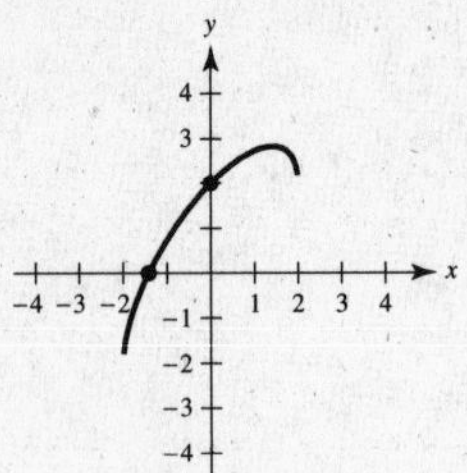

Domain: $[-2, 2]$

Range: $\left[-2, 2\sqrt{2}\right] \approx [-2, 2.83]$

**37.** $g(t) = 3 \sin \pi t$

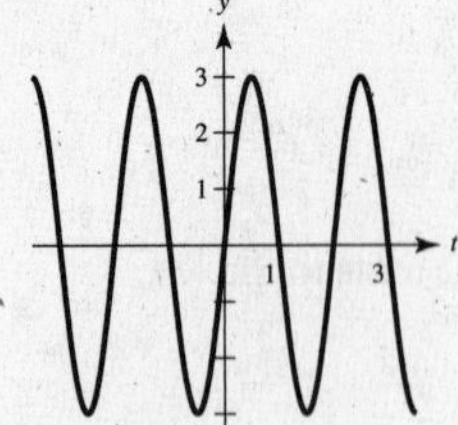

Domain: $(-\infty, \infty)$

Range: $[-3, 3]$

**38.** $h(\theta) = -5 \cos \dfrac{\theta}{2}$

Domain: $(-\infty, \infty)$

Range: $[-5, 5]$

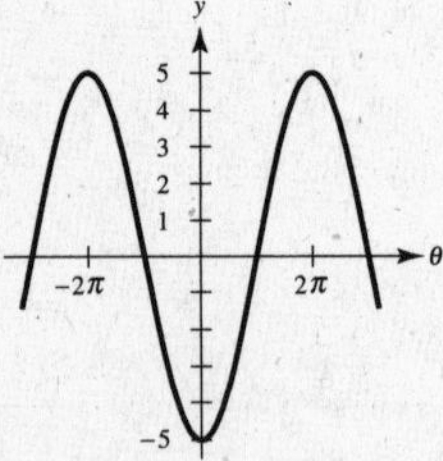

**39.** The student travels $\dfrac{2 - 0}{4 - 0} = \dfrac{1}{2}$ mi/min during the first 4 minutes. The student is stationary for the next 2 minutes. Finally, the student travels $\dfrac{6 - 2}{10 - 6} = 1$ mi/min during the final 4 minutes.

**40.**

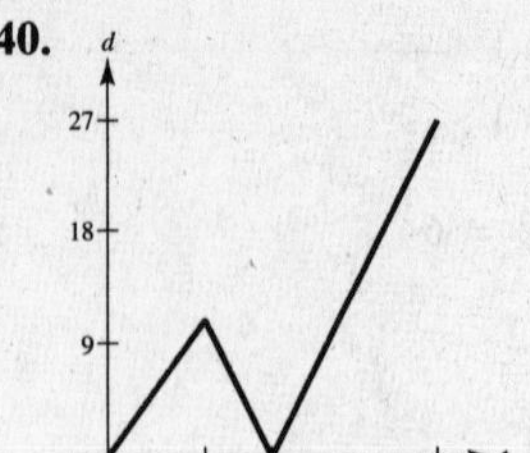

**41.** $x - y^2 = 0 \Rightarrow y = \pm\sqrt{x}$

$y$ is not a function of $x$. Some vertical lines intersect the graph twice.

**42.** $\sqrt{x^2 - 4} - y = 0 \Rightarrow y = \sqrt{x^2 - 4}$

$y$ is a function of $x$. Vertical lines intersect the graph at most once.

**43.** $y$ is a function of $x$. Vertical lines intersect the graph at most once.

**44.** $x^2 + y^2 = 4$

$$y = \pm\sqrt{4 - x^2}$$

$y$ is not a function of $x$. Some vertical lines intersect the graph twice.

**45.** $x^2 + y^2 = 16 \Rightarrow y = \pm\sqrt{16 - x^2}$

$y$ is not a function of $x$ because there are two values of $y$ for some $x$.

**46.** $x^2 + y = 16 \Rightarrow y = 16 - x^2$

$y$ is a function of $x$ because there is one value of $y$ for each $x$.

**47.** $y^2 = x^2 - 1 \Rightarrow y = \pm\sqrt{x^2 - 1}$

$y$ is not a function of $x$ because there are two values of $y$ for some $x$.

**48.** $x^2y - x^2 + 4y = 0 \Rightarrow y = \dfrac{x^2}{x^2 + 4}$

$y$ is a function of $x$ because there is one value of $y$ for each $x$.

**49.** $y = f(x + 5)$ is a horizontal shift 5 units to the left. Matches d.

**50.** $y = f(x) - 5$ is a vertical shift 5 units downward. Matches b.

**51.** $y = -f(-x) - 2$ is a reflection in the $y$-axis, a reflection in the $x$-axis, and a vertical shift downward 2 units. Matches c.

**52.** $y = -f(x - 4)$ is a horizontal shift 4 units to the right, followed by a reflection in the $x$-axis. Matches a.

**53.** $y = f(x + 6) + 2$ is a horizontal shift to the left 6 units, and a vertical shift upward 2 units. Matches e.

**54.** $y = f(x - 1) + 3$ is a horizontal shift to the right 1 unit, and a vertical shift upward 3 units. Matches g.

**55.** (a) The graph is shifted 3 units to the left.

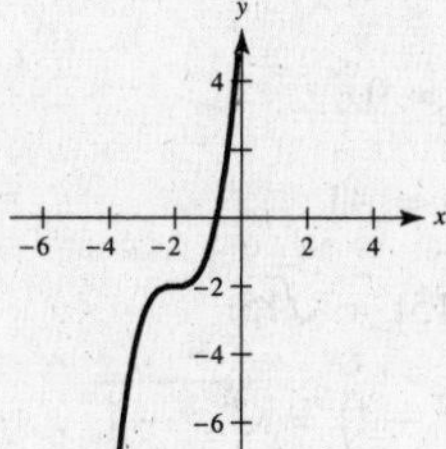

(b) The graph is shifted 1 unit to the right.

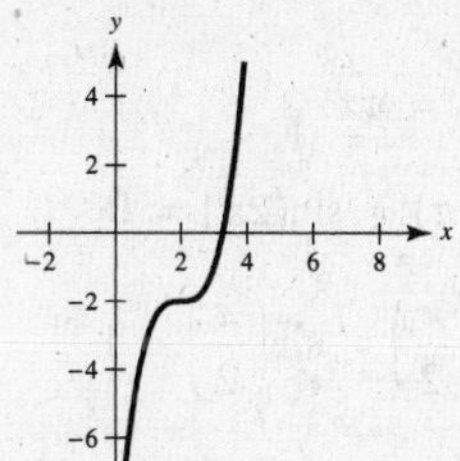

(c) The graph is shifted 2 units upward.

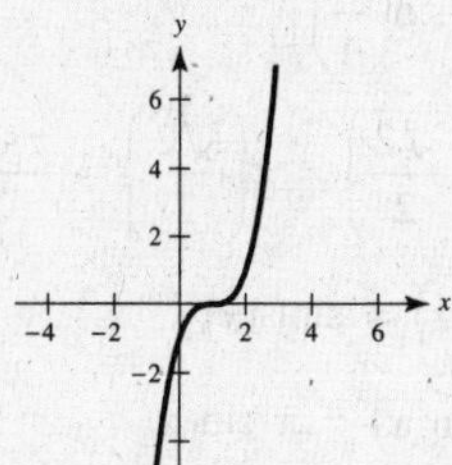

(d) The graph is shifted 4 units downward.

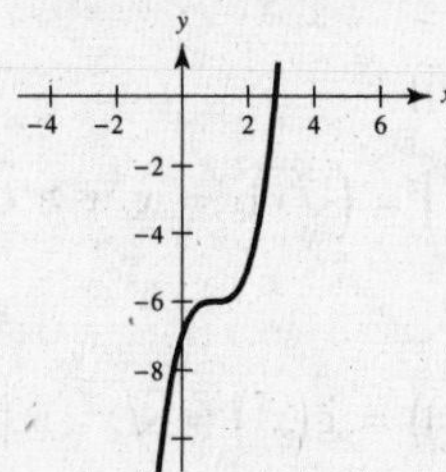

(e) The graph is stretched vertically by a factor of 3.

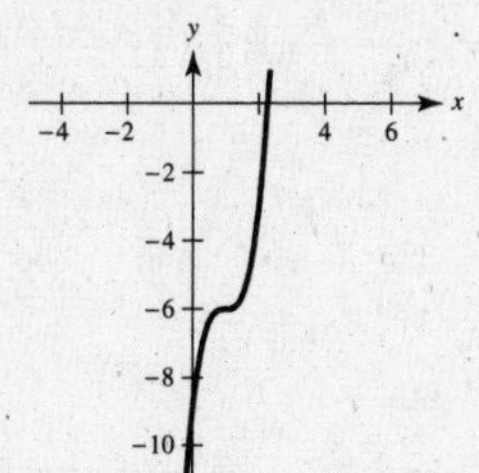

(f) The graph is stretched vertically by a factor of $\frac{1}{4}$.

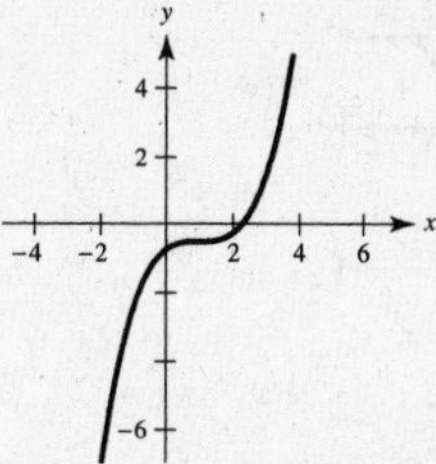

**56.** (a) The graph is shifted 4 units to the right.

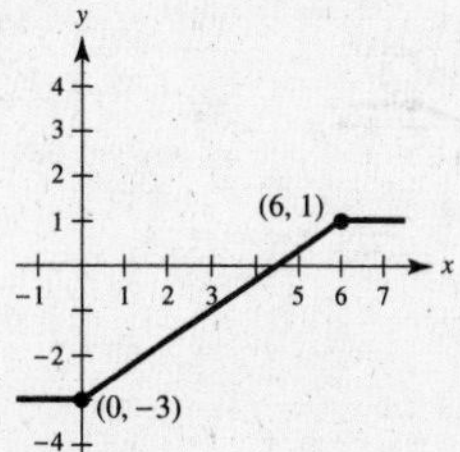


(b) The graph is shifted 2 units to the left.

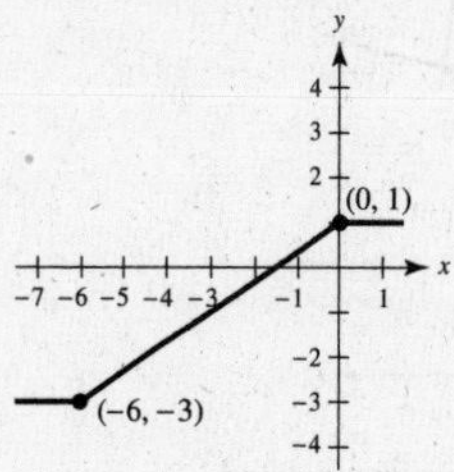


(c) The graph is shifted 4 units upward.

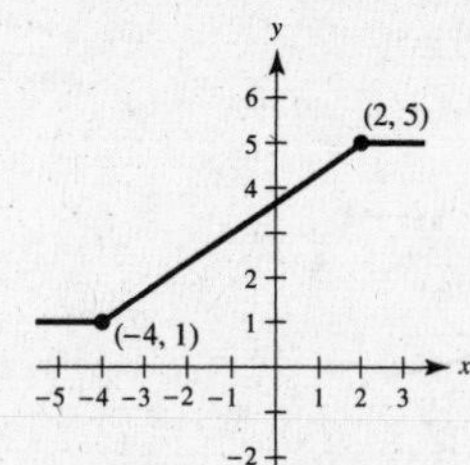


(d) The graph is shifted 1 unit downward.

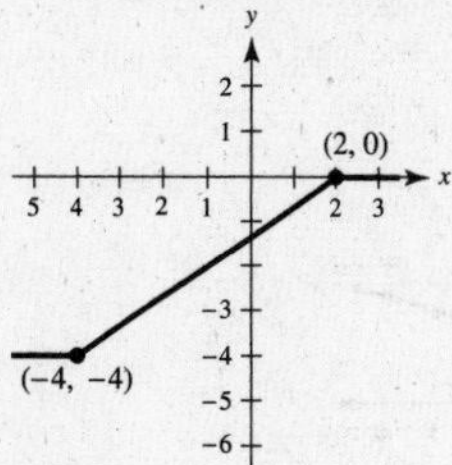

(e) The graph is stretched vertically by a factor of 2.

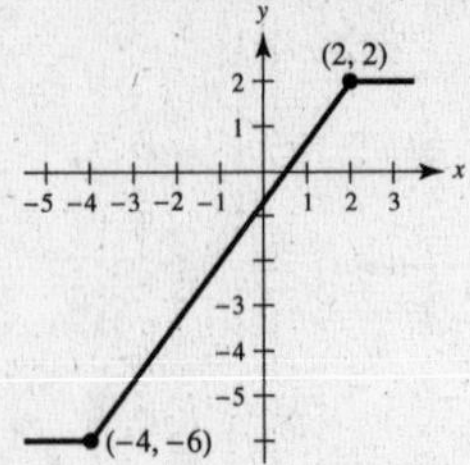


(f) The graph is stretched vertically by a factor of $\frac{1}{2}$.

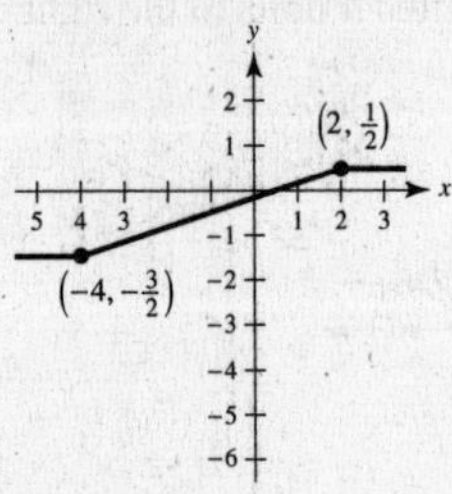


**57.** (a) $y = \sqrt{x} + 2$

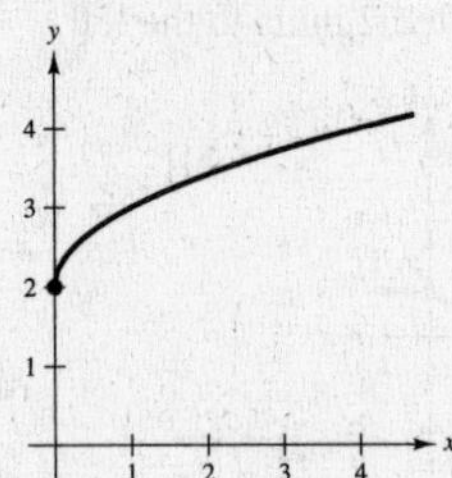

Vertical shift 2 units upward

(b) $y = -\sqrt{x}$

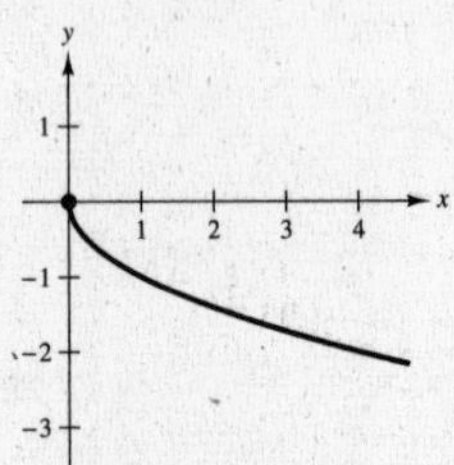

Reflection about the $x$-axis

(c) $y = \sqrt{x-2}$

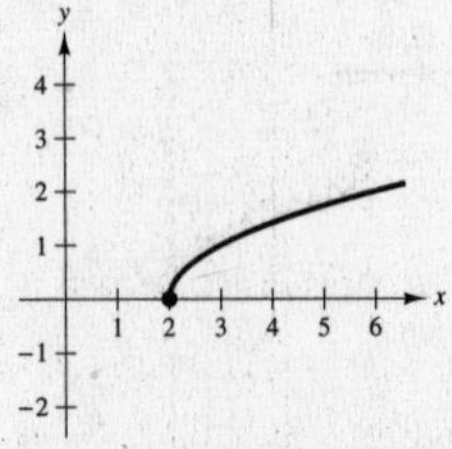

Horizontal shift 2 units to the right

**58.** (a) $h(x) = \sin(x + (\pi/2)) + 1$ is a horizontal shift $\pi/2$ units to the left, followed by a vertical shift 1 unit upwards.

(b) $h(x) = -\sin(x - 1)$ is a horizontal shift 1 unit to the right followed by a reflection about the $x$-axis.

**59.** (a) $f(g(1)) = f(0) = 0$

(b) $g(f(1)) = g(1) = 0$

(c) $g(f(0)) = g(0) = -1$

(d) $f(g(-4)) = f(15) = \sqrt{15}$

(e) $f(g(x)) = f(x^2 - 1) = \sqrt{x^2 - 1}$

(f) $g(f(x)) = g(\sqrt{x}) = (\sqrt{x})^2 - 1 = x - 1,\ (x \geq 0)$

**60.** $f(x) = \sin x,\ g(x) = \pi x$

(a) $f(g(2)) = f(2\pi) = \sin(2\pi) = 0$

(b) $f\left(g\left(\frac{1}{2}\right)\right) = f\left(\frac{\pi}{2}\right) = \sin\left(\frac{\pi}{2}\right) = 1$

(c) $g(f(0)) = g(0) = 0$

(d) $g\left(f\left(\frac{\pi}{4}\right)\right) = g\left(\sin\left(\frac{\pi}{4}\right)\right)$

$= g\left(\frac{\sqrt{2}}{2}\right) = \pi\left(\frac{\sqrt{2}}{2}\right) = \frac{\pi\sqrt{2}}{2}$

(e) $f(g(x)) = f(\pi x) = \sin(\pi x)$

(f) $g(f(x)) = g(\sin x) = \pi \sin x$

**61.** $f(x) = x^2,\ g(x) = \sqrt{x}$

$(f \circ g)(x) = f(g(x))$

$= f(\sqrt{x}) = (\sqrt{x})^2 = x,\ x \geq 0$

Domain: $[0, \infty)$

$(g \circ f)(x) = g(f(x)) = g(x^2) = \sqrt{x^2} = |x|$

Domain: $(-\infty, \infty)$

No. Their domains are different. $(f \circ g) = (g \circ f)$ for $x \geq 0$.

**62.** $f(x) = x^2 - 1,\ g(x) = \cos x$

$(f \circ g)(x) = f(g(x)) = f(\cos x) = \cos^2 x - 1$

Domain: $(-\infty, \infty)$

$(g \circ f)(x) = g(x^2 - 1) = \cos(x^2 - 1)$

Domain: $(-\infty, \infty)$

No, $f \circ g \neq g \circ f$.

**63.** $f(x) = \dfrac{3}{x},\ g(x) = x^2 - 1$

$(f \circ g)(x) = f(g(x)) = f(x^2 - 1) = \dfrac{3}{x^2 - 1}$

Domain: all $x \neq \pm 1 \Rightarrow (-\infty, -1) \cup (-1, 1) \cup (1, \infty)$

$(g \circ f)(x) = g(f(x))$

$= g\left(\dfrac{3}{x}\right) = \left(\dfrac{3}{x}\right)^2 - 1 = \dfrac{9}{x^2} - 1 = \dfrac{9 - x^2}{x^2}$

Domain: all $x \neq 0 \Rightarrow (-\infty, 0) \cup (0, \infty)$

No, $f \circ g \neq g \circ f$.

**64.** $(f \circ g)(x) = f\left(\sqrt{x + 2}\right) = \dfrac{1}{\sqrt{x + 2}}$

Domain: $(-2, \infty)$

$(g \circ f)(x) = g\left(\dfrac{1}{x}\right) = \sqrt{\dfrac{1}{x} + 2} = \sqrt{\dfrac{1 + 2x}{x}}$

You can find the domain of $g \circ f$ by determining the intervals where $(1 + 2x)$ and $x$ are both positive, or both negative.

+ + + − − + + + +
−2 −1 $-\frac{1}{2}$ 0 1 2 $x$

Domain: $\left(-\infty, -\frac{1}{2}\right], (0, \infty)$

**65.** (a) $(f \circ g)(3) = f(g(3)) = f(-1) = 4$

(b) $g(f(2)) = g(1) = -2$

(c) $g(f(5)) = g(-5)$, which is undefined. The graph of $g$ does not exist at $x = -5$.

(d) $(f \circ g)(-3) = f(g(-3)) = f(-2) = 3$

(e) $(g \circ f)(-1) = g(f(-1)) = g(4) = 2$

(f) $f(g(-1)) = f(-4)$, which is undefined. The graph of $f$ does not exist at $x = -4$.

**66.** $(A \circ r)(t) = A(r(t)) = A(0.6t) = \pi(0.6t)^2 = 0.36\pi t^2$

$(A \circ r)(t)$ represents the area of the circle at time $t$.

**67.** $F(x) = \sqrt{2x - 2}$

Let $f(x) = \sqrt{x},\ g(x) = x - 2$, and $h(x) = 2x$.

Then, $(f \circ g \circ h)(x) = f(g(2x)) = f((2x) - 2) = \sqrt{(2x) - 2} = \sqrt{2x - 2} = F(x)$.

[Other answers possible]

**68.** $F(x) = -4\sin(1 - x)$

Let $f(x) = -4x,\ g(x) = \sin x$ and $h(x) = 1 - x$. Then,

$(f \circ g \circ h)(x) = f(g(1 - x)) = f(\sin(1 - x)) = -4\sin(1 - x) = F(x)$.

[Other answers possible]

**69.** $f(-x) = (-x)^2\left(4 - (-x)^2\right) = x^2(4 - x^2) = f(x)$

Even

**70.** $f(-x) = \sqrt[3]{-x} = -\sqrt[3]{x} = -f(x)$

Odd

**71.** $f(-x) = (-x)\cos(-x) = -x\cos x = -f(x)$

Odd

**72.** $f(-x) = \sin^2(-x) = \sin(-x)\sin(-x) = (-\sin x)(-\sin x) = \sin^2 x = f(x)$

Even

**73.** (a) If $f$ is even, then $\left(\frac{3}{2}, 4\right)$ is on the graph.

(b) If $f$ is odd, then $\left(\frac{3}{2}, -4\right)$ is on the graph.

**74.** (a) If $f$ is even, then $(-4, 9)$ is on the graph.

(b) If $f$ is odd, then $(-4, -9)$ is on the graph.

**75.** $f$ is even because the graph is symmetric about the $y$-axis. $g$ is neither even nor odd. $h$ is odd because the graph is symmetric about the origin.

**76.** (a) If $f$ is even, then the graph is symmetric about the $y$-axis.

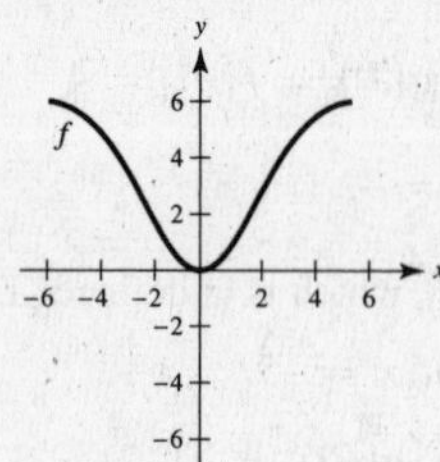

(b) If $f$ is odd, then the graph is symmetric about the origin.

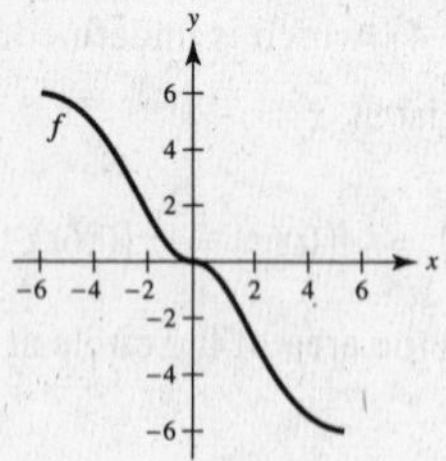

**77.** Slope $= \dfrac{4-(-6)}{-2-0} = \dfrac{10}{-2} = -5$

$$y - 4 = -5(x - (-2))$$
$$y - 4 = -5x - 10$$
$$y = -5x - 6$$

For the line segment, you must restrict the domain.

$f(x) = -5x - 6, -2 \le x \le 0$

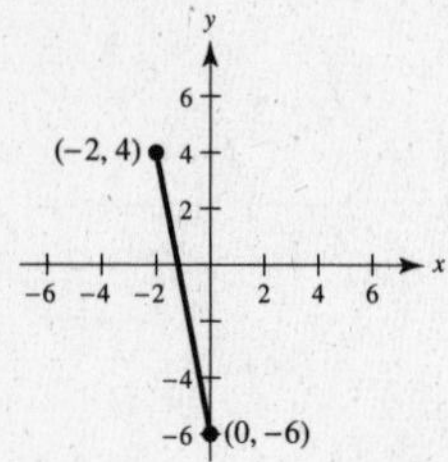


**78.** Slope $= \dfrac{8-1}{5-3} = \dfrac{7}{2}$

$$y - 1 = \frac{7}{2}(x - 3)$$
$$y - 1 = \frac{7}{2}x - \frac{21}{2}$$
$$y = \frac{7}{2}x - \frac{19}{2}$$

For the line segment, you must restrict the domain.

$f(x) = \dfrac{7}{2}x - \dfrac{19}{2}, 3 \le x \le 5$

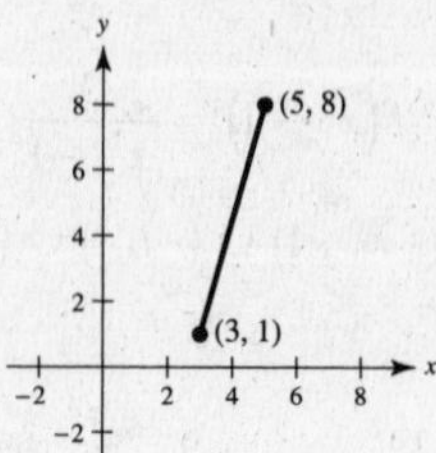


**79.** $x + y^2 = 0$

$$y^2 = -x$$
$$y = -\sqrt{-x}$$
$$f(x) = -\sqrt{-x}, x \le 0$$

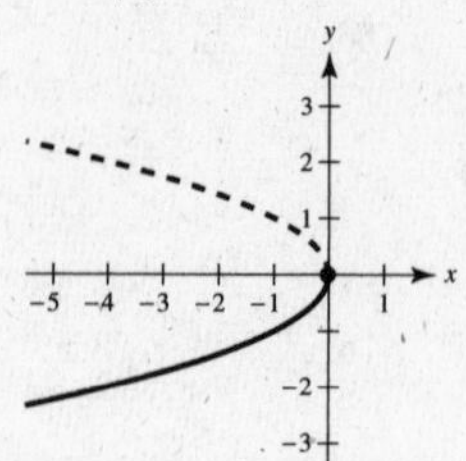

**80.** $x^2 + y^2 = 36$

$$y^2 = 36 - x^2$$
$$y = -\sqrt{36 - x^2}, -6 \le x \le 6$$

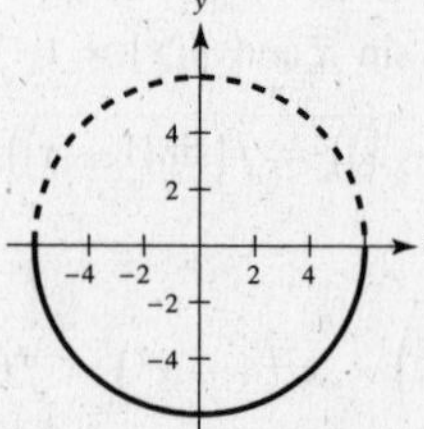

**81.** Answers will vary. *Sample answer*: Speed begins and ends at 0. The speed might be constant in the middle:

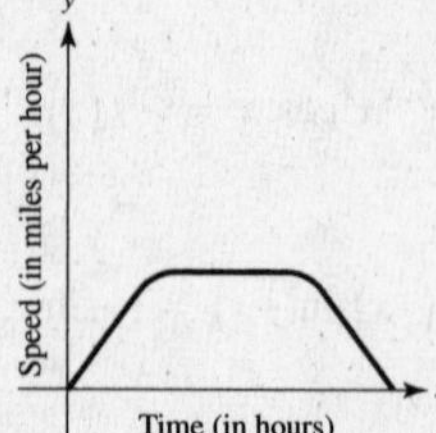

**82.** Answers will vary. *Sample answer*: Height begins a few feet above 0, and ends at 0.

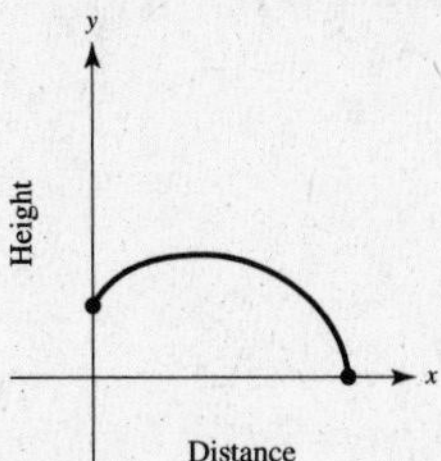


**83.** Answers will vary. *Sample answer*: In general, as the price decreases, the store will sell more.

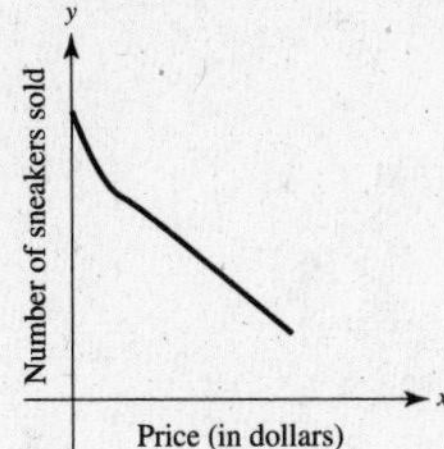


**84.** Answers will vary. *Sample answer*: As time goes on, the value of the car will decrease

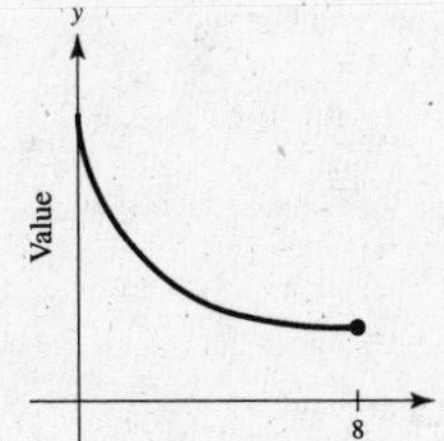


**85.**
$$y = \sqrt{c - x^2}$$
$$y^2 = c - x^2$$
$$x^2 + y^2 = c, \text{ a circle.}$$

For the domain to be $[-5, 5]$, $c = 25$.

**86.** For the domain to be the set of all real numbers, you must require that $x^2 + 3cx + 6 \neq 0$. So, the discriminant must be less than zero:

$$(3c)^2 - 4(6) < 0$$
$$9c^2 < 24$$
$$c^2 < \tfrac{8}{3}$$
$$-\sqrt{\tfrac{8}{3}} < c < \sqrt{\tfrac{8}{3}}$$
$$-\tfrac{2}{3}\sqrt{6} < c < \tfrac{2}{3}\sqrt{6}$$

**87.** (a) $T(4) = 16°\text{C}$, $T(15) \approx 23°\text{C}$

(b) If $H(t) = T(t - 1)$, then the changes in temperature will occur 1 hour later.

(c) If $H(t) = T(t) - 1$, then the overall temperature would be 1 degree lower.

**88.** (a) For each time $t$, there corresponds a depth $d$.

(b) Domain: $0 \leq t \leq 5$

Range: $0 \leq d \leq 30$

(c)

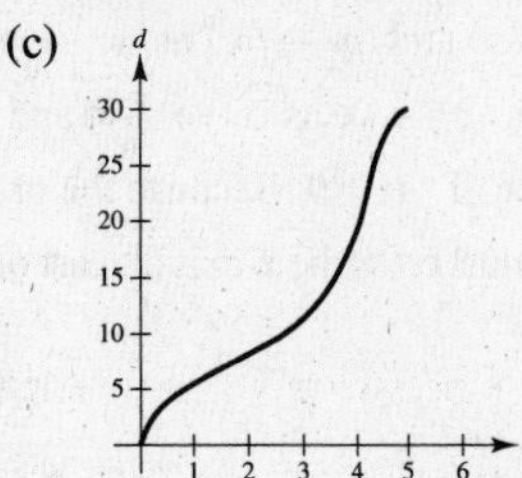


(d) $d(4) \approx 18$. At time 4 seconds, the depth is approximately 18 cm.

**89.** (a)

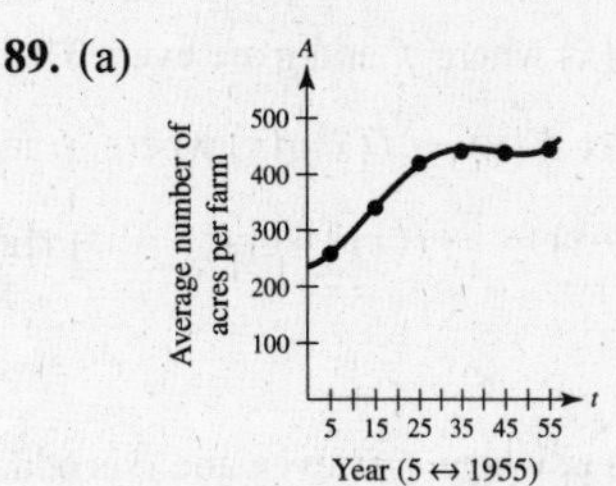


(b) $A(20) \approx 384$ acres/farm

**90.** (a)

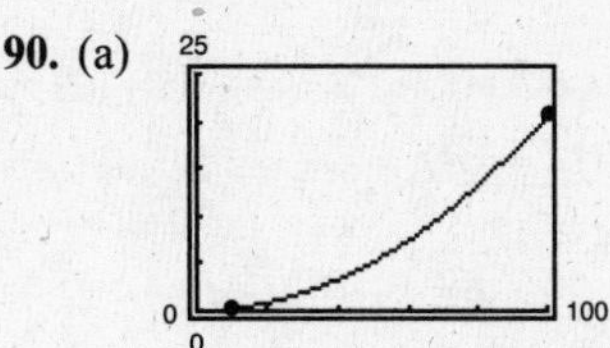


(b) $H\left(\frac{x}{1.6}\right) = 0.002\left(\frac{x}{1.6}\right)^2 + 0.005\left(\frac{x}{1.6}\right) - 0.029$

$= 0.00078125x^2 + 0.003125x - 0.029$

**91.** $f(x) = |x| + |x - 2|$

If $x < 0$, then $f(x) = -x - (x - 2) = -2x + 2$.

If $0 \leq x < 2$, then $f(x) = x - (x - 2) = 2$.

If $x \geq 2$, then $f(x) = x + (x - 2) = 2x - 2$.

So,

$$f(x) = \begin{cases} -2x + 2, & x \leq 0 \\ 2, & 0 < x < 2. \\ 2x - 2, & x \geq 2 \end{cases}$$

**92.** $p_1(x) = x^3 - x + 1$ has one zero. $p_2(x) = x^3 - x$ has three zeros. Every cubic polynomial has at least one zero. Given $p(x) = Ax^3 + Bx^2 + Cx + D$, you have $p \to -\infty$ as $x \to -\infty$ and $p \to \infty$ as $x \to \infty$ if $A > 0$. Furthermore, $p \to \infty$ as $x \to -\infty$ and $p \to -\infty$ as $x \to \infty$ if $A < 0$. Because the graph has no breaks, the graph must cross the $x$-axis at least one time.

**93.** $$\begin{aligned} f(-x) &= a_{2n+1}(-x)^{2n+1} + \cdots + a_3(-x)^3 + a_1(-x) \\ &= -\left[a_{2n+1}x^{2n+1} + \cdots + a_3x^3 + a_1x\right] \\ &= -f(x) \end{aligned}$$

Odd

**94.** $$\begin{aligned} f(-x) &= a_{2n}(-x)^{2n} + a_{2n-2}(-x)^{2n-2} + \cdots + a_2(-x)^2 + a_0 \\ &= a_{2n}x^{2n} + a_{2n-2}x^{2n-2} + \cdots + a_2x^2 + a_0 \\ &= f(x) \end{aligned}$$

Even

**95.** Let $F(x) = f(x)g(x)$ where $f$ and $g$ are even. Then $F(-x) = f(-x)g(-x) = f(x)g(x) = F(x)$.
So, $F(x)$ is even. Let $F(x) = f(x)g(x)$ where $f$ and $g$ are odd. Then
$F(-x) = f(-x)g(-x) = [-f(x)][-g(x)] = f(x)g(x) = F(x)$.
So, $F(x)$ is even.

**96.** Let $F(x) = f(x)g(x)$ where $f$ is even and $g$ is odd. Then
$F(-x) = f(-x)g(-x) = f(x)[-g(x)] = -f(x)g(x) = -F(x)$.
So, $F(x)$ is odd.

**97.** (a) $V = x(24 - 2x)^2$

Domain: $0 < x < 12$

(b)

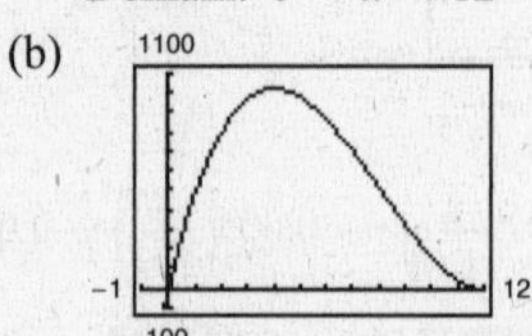


Maximum volume occurs at $x = 4$. So, the dimensions of the box would be $4 \times 16 \times 16$ cm.

(c)

| $x$ | *length and width* | *volume* |
|---|---|---|
| 1 | $24 - 2(1)$ | $1[24 - 2(1)]^2 = 484$ |
| 2 | $24 - 2(2)$ | $2[24 - 2(2)]^2 = 800$ |
| 3 | $24 - 2(3)$ | $3[24 - 2(3)]^2 = 972$ |
| 4 | $24 - 2(4)$ | $4[24 - 2(4)]^2 = 1024$ |
| 5 | $24 - 2(5)$ | $5[24 - 2(5)]^2 = 980$ |
| 6 | $24 - 2(6)$ | $6[24 - 2(6)]^2 = 864$ |

The dimensions of the box that yield a maximum volume appear to be $4 \times 16 \times 16$ cm.

**98.** By equating slopes, $\dfrac{y-2}{0-3} = \dfrac{0-2}{x-3}$

$$y - 2 = \frac{6}{x-3}$$

$$y = \frac{6}{x-3} + 2 = \frac{2x}{x-3},$$

$$L = \sqrt{x^2 + y^2} = \sqrt{x^2 + \left(\frac{2x}{x-3}\right)^2}.$$

**99.** False. If $f(x) = x^2$, then $f(-3) = f(3) = 9$, but $-3 \neq 3$.

**100.** True

**101.** True. The function is even.

**102.** False. If $f(x) = x^2$ then, $f(3x) = (3x)^2 = 9x^2$ and $3f(x) = 3x^2$. So, $3f(x) \neq f(3x)$.

**103.** First consider the portion of $R$ in the first quadrant: $x \geq 0$, $0 \leq y \leq 1$ and $x - y \leq 1$; shown below.

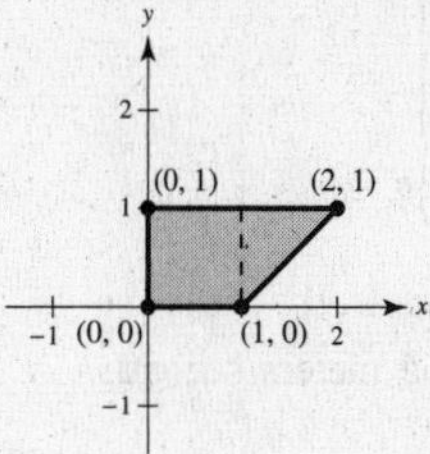


The area of this region is $1 + \frac{1}{2} = \frac{3}{2}$.

By symmetry, you obtain the entire region R:

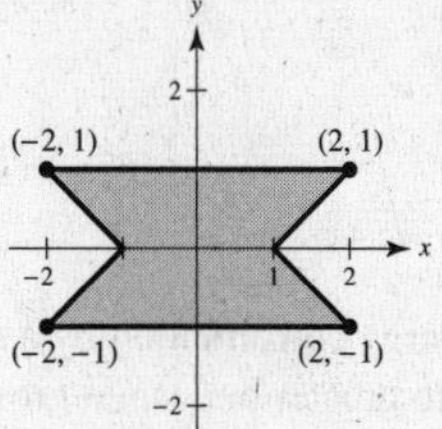


The area of $R$ is $4\left(\frac{3}{2}\right) = 6$.

**104.** Let $g(x) = c$ be constant polynomial.

Then $f(g(x)) = f(c)$ and $g(f(x)) = c$.

So, $f(c) = c$. Because this is true for all real numbers $c$, $f$ is the identity function: $f(x) = x$.

## Section 1.4 Fitting Models to Data

**1.** Trigonometric function

**2.** Quadratic function

**3.** No relationship

**4.** Linear function

**5.** (a), (b)

Yes. The cancer mortality increases linearly with increased exposure to the carcinogenic substance.

(c) If $x = 3$, then $y \approx 136$.

**6.** (a)

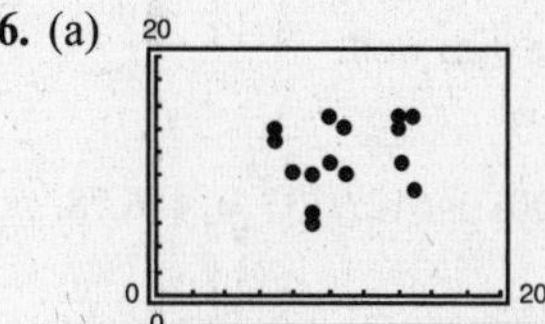


No, the relationship does not appear to be linear.

(b) Quiz scores are dependent on several variables such as study time, class attendance, etc. These variables may change from one quiz to the next.

**7.** (a) $d = 0.066F$

(b)

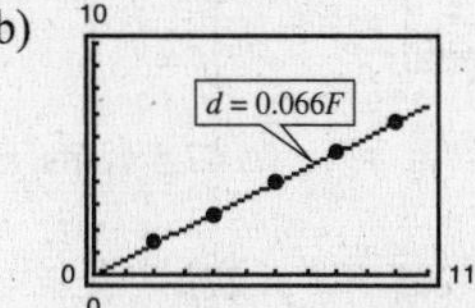


The model fits the data well.

(c) If $F = 55$, then $d \approx 0.066(55) = 3.63$ cm.

**8.** (a) $s = 9.7t + 0.4$

(b)

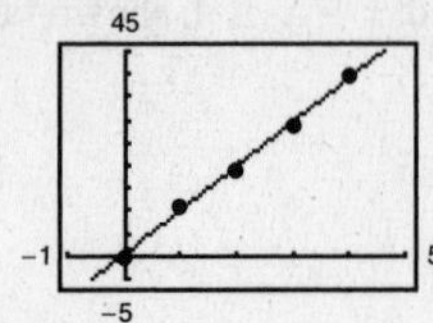

The model fits the data well.

(c) If $t = 2.5$, $s = 24.65$ meters/second.

**9.** (a) Using a graphing utility,

$y = 0.151x + 0.10.$

The correlation coefficient is $r \approx 0.880$.

(b)

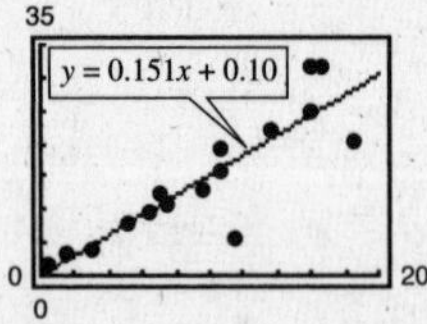


(c) Greater per capita energy consumption by a country tends to correspond to greater per capita gross national product. The four countries that differ most from the linear model are Venezuela, South Korea, Hong Kong, and United Kingdom.

(d) Using a graphing utility,

$y = 0.155x + 0.22$ and $r \approx 0.984$.

**10.** (a) Linear model: $H = -0.3323t + 612.9333$

(b)

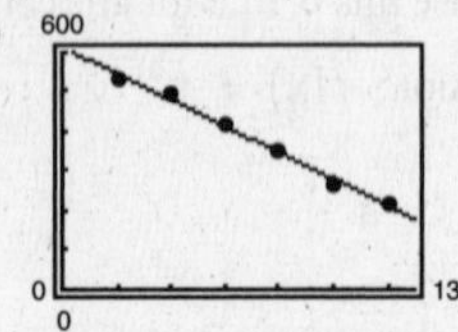

The model fits the data well.

(c) When $t = 500$,

$H = -0.3323(500) + 612.9333 \approx 446.78.$

**11.** (a) $y_1 = 0.04040t^3 - 0.3695t^2 + 1.123t + 5.88$

$y_2 = 0.264t + 3.35$

$y_3 = 0.01439t^3 - 0.1886t^2 + 0.476t + 1.59$

(b)

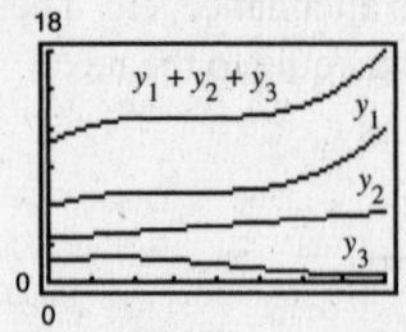

For year 12, $y_1 + y_2 + y_3 \approx 47.5$ cents/mile.

**12.** (a) $S = 180.89x^2 - 205.79x + 272$

(b)

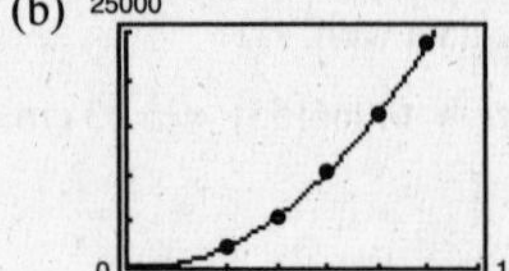

(c) When $x = 2$, $S \approx 583.98$ pounds.

**13.** (a) $t = 0.002s^2 - 0.04s + 1.9$

(b)

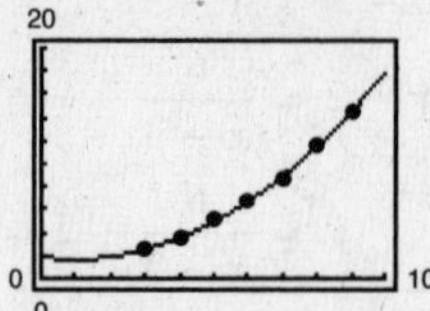

(c) According to the model, the times required to attain speeds of less than 20 miles per hour are all about the same.

(d) Adding (0, 0) to the data produces

$t = 0.002s^2 + 0.02s + 0.1$

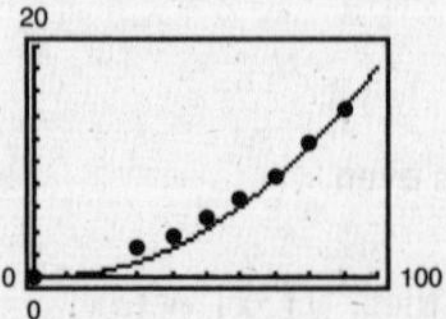

(e) No. From the graph in part (b), you can see that the model from part (a) follows the data more closely than the model from part (d).

**14.** (a) $N_1 = 3.72t + 31.6$

$N_3 = -0.0932t^3 + 1.735t^2 - 3.77t + 35.1$

(b)

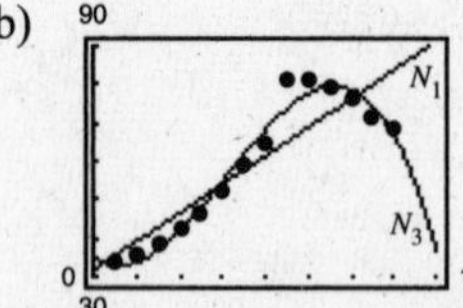

(c) The cubic model is better.

(d) $N_2 = -0.221t^2 + 6.81t + 24.9$

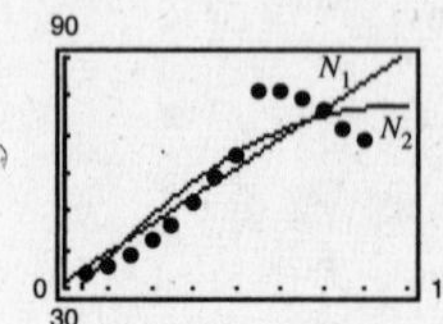

The model does not fit the data well.

(e) For 2007, $t = 17$, and $N_1 \approx 94.8$ million and $N_3 \approx 14.5$ million. Neither seem accurate. The linear model's estimate is too high and the cubic model's estimate is too low.

(f) Answers will vary.

**15.** (a) $y = -1.806x^3 + 14.58x^2 + 16.4x + 10$

(b)

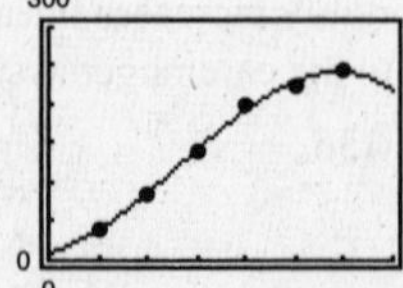

(c) If $x = 4.5$, $y \approx 214$ horsepower.

**16.** (a) $T = 2.9856 \times 10^{-4} p^3 - 0.0641 p^2 + 5.282 p + 143.1$

(b)

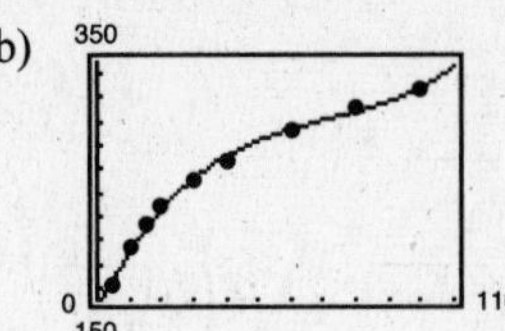


(c) For $T = 300°F$, $p \approx 68.29$ lb/in.$^2$.

(d) The model is based on data up to 100 pounds per square inch.

**17.** (a) Yes, $y$ is a function of $t$. At each time $t$, there is one and only one displacement $y$.

(b) The amplitude is approximately

$(2.35 - 1.65)/2 = 0.35.$

The period is approximately

$2(0.375 - 0.125) = 0.5.$

(c) One model is $y = 0.35 \sin(4\pi t) + 2$.

(d)

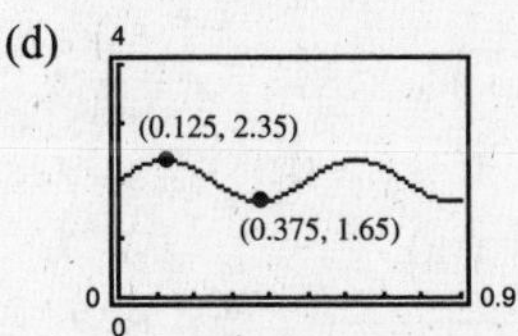


The model appears to fit the data well.

**18.** (a) $S(t) = 56.37 + 25.47 \sin(0.5080t - 2.07)$

(b)

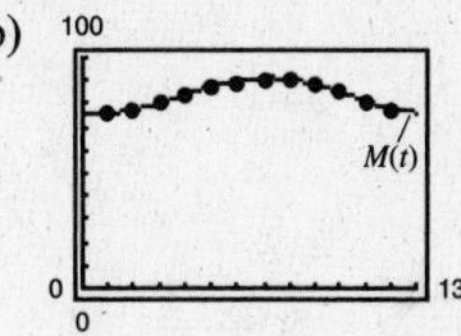


The model is a good fit.

(c)

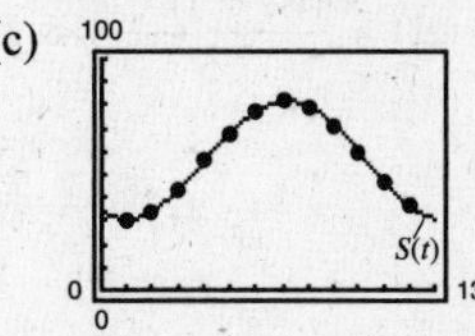


The model is a good fit.

(d) The average is the constant term in each model. 83.70°F for Miami and 56.37°F for Syracuse.

(e) The period for Miami is $2\pi/0.4912 \approx 12.8$. The period for Syracuse is $2\pi/0.5080 \approx 12.4$. In both cases the period is approximately 12, or one year.

(f) Syracuse has greater variability because $25.47 > 7.46$.

**19.** Answers will vary.

**20.** Answers will vary.

**21.** Yes, $A_1 \le A_2$. To see this, consider the two triangles of areas $A_1$ and $A_2$:

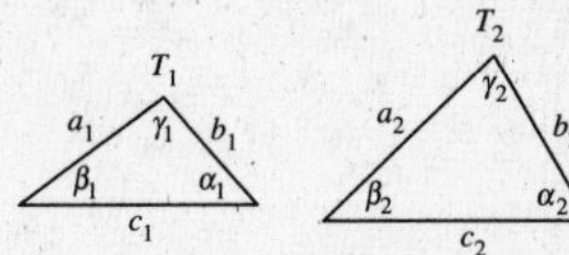


For $i = 1, 2$, the angles satisfy $\alpha i + \beta i + \gamma i = \pi$. At least one of $\alpha_1 \le \alpha_2$, $\beta_1 \le \beta_2$, $\gamma_1 \le \gamma_2$ must hold. Assume $\alpha_1 \le \alpha_2$. Because $\alpha_2 \le \pi/2$ (acute triangle), and the sine function increases on $[0, \pi/2]$, you have

$$A_1 = \tfrac{1}{2} b_1 c_1 \sin \alpha_1 \le \tfrac{1}{2} b_2 c_2 \sin \alpha_1$$
$$\le \tfrac{1}{2} b_2 c_2 \sin \alpha_2 = A_2.$$

## Section 1.5 Inverse Functions

**1.** (a) $f(x) = 5x + 1$

$g(x) = \dfrac{x-1}{5}$

$f(g(x)) = f\left(\dfrac{x-1}{5}\right) = 5\left(\dfrac{x-1}{5}\right) + 1 = x$

$g(f(x)) = g(5x + 1) = \dfrac{(5x+1)-1}{5} = x$

(b)

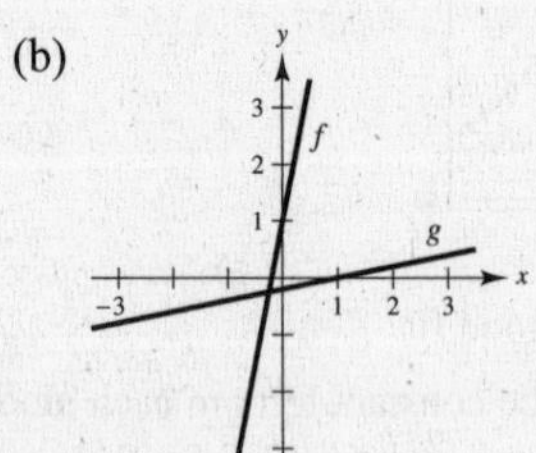


**2.** (a) $f(x) = 3 - 4x$

$g(x) = \dfrac{3-x}{4}$

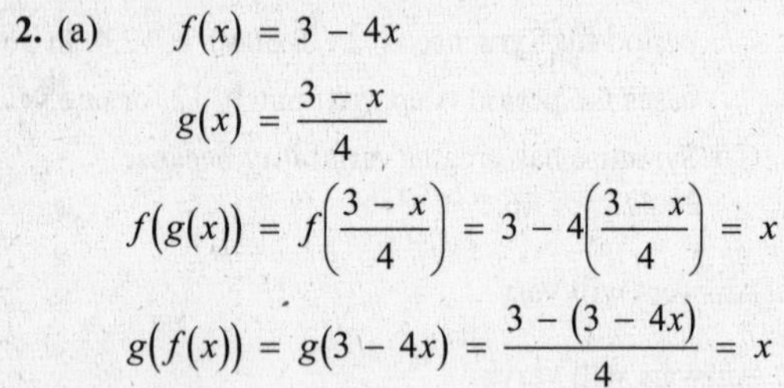

$f(g(x)) = f\left(\dfrac{3-x}{4}\right) = 3 - 4\left(\dfrac{3-x}{4}\right) = x$

$g(f(x)) = g(3 - 4x) = \dfrac{3-(3-4x)}{4} = x$

(b)

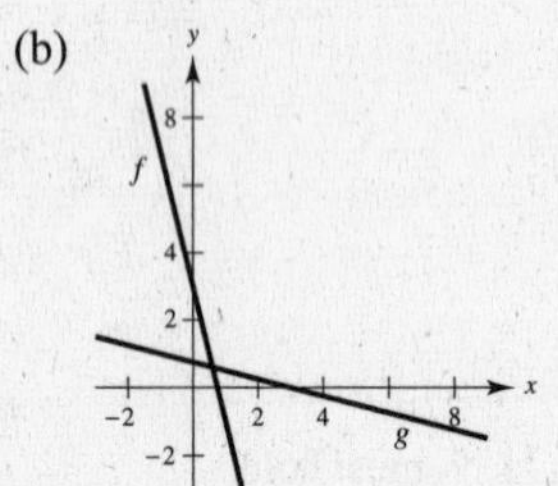


**3.** (a) $f(x) = x^3$

$g(x) = \sqrt[3]{x}$

$f(g(x)) = f\left(\sqrt[3]{x}\right) = \left(\sqrt[3]{x}\right)^3 = x$

$g(f(x)) = g(x^3) = \sqrt[3]{x^3} = x$

(b)

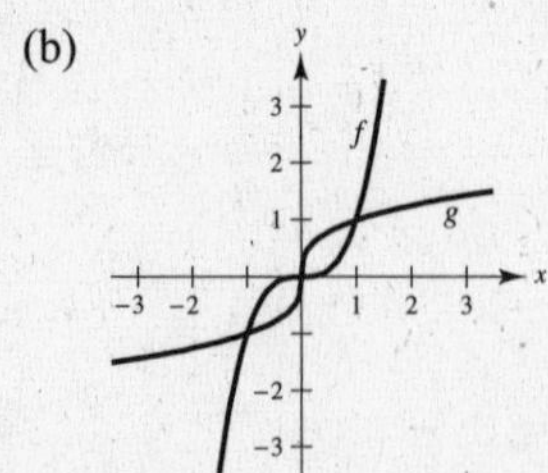


**4.** (a) $f(x) = 1 - x^3$

$g(x) = \sqrt[3]{1-x}$

$f(g(x)) = f\left(\sqrt[3]{1-x}\right) = 1 - \left(\sqrt[3]{1-x}\right)^3$

$= 1 - (1 - x) = x$

$g(f(x)) = g(1 - x^3)$

$= \sqrt[3]{1 - (1 - x^3)} = \sqrt[3]{x^3} = x$

(b)

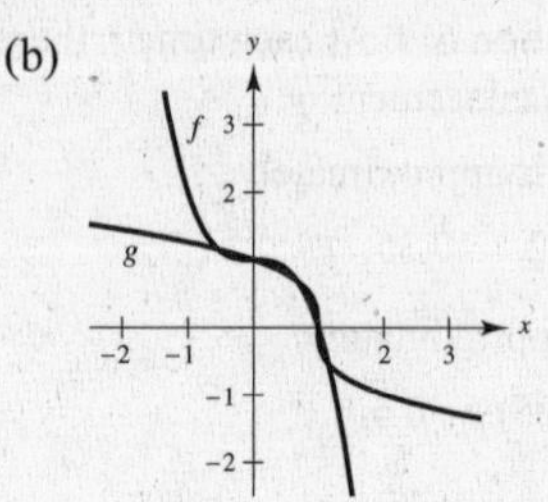


**5.** (a) $f(x) = \sqrt{x-4}$

$g(x) = x^2 + 4, \quad x \geq 0$

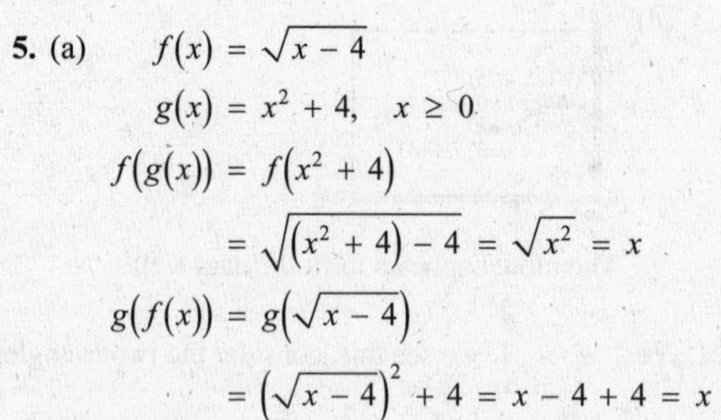

$f(g(x)) = f(x^2 + 4)$

$= \sqrt{(x^2+4)-4} = \sqrt{x^2} = x$

$g(f(x)) = g\left(\sqrt{x-4}\right)$

$= \left(\sqrt{x-4}\right)^2 + 4 = x - 4 + 4 = x$

(b)

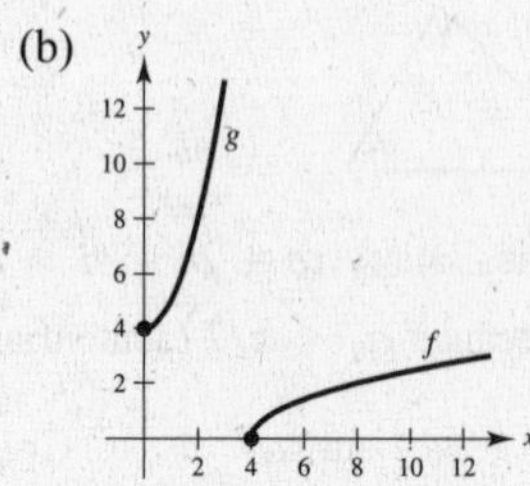


**6.** (a) $f(x) = 16 - x^2, \quad x \geq 0$

$g(x) = \sqrt{16-x}$

$f(g(x)) = f\left(\sqrt{16-x}\right) = 16 - \left(\sqrt{16-x}\right)^2$

$= 16 - (16 - x) = x$

$g(f(x)) = g(16 - x^2) = \sqrt{16 - (16 - x^2)}$

$= \sqrt{x^2} = x$

(b)

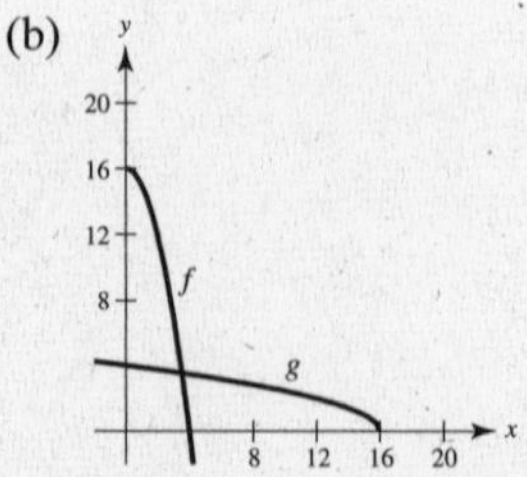

**7.** (a) $f(x) = \dfrac{1}{x}$

$g(x) = \dfrac{1}{x}$

$f(g(x)) = \dfrac{1}{1/x} = x$

$g(f(x)) = \dfrac{1}{1/x} = x$

(b)

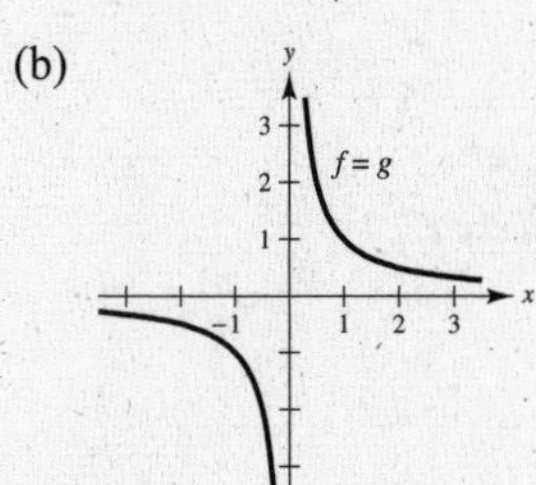


**8.** (a) $f(x) = \dfrac{1}{1+x}, \quad x \ge 0$

$g(x) = \dfrac{1-x}{x}, \quad 0 < x \le 1$

$f(g(x)) = f\left(\dfrac{1-x}{x}\right) = \dfrac{1}{1 + \dfrac{1-x}{x}} = \dfrac{1}{\dfrac{1}{x}} = x$

$g(f(x)) = g\left(\dfrac{1}{1+x}\right) = \dfrac{1 - \dfrac{1}{1+x}}{\dfrac{1}{1+x}} = \dfrac{x}{1+x} \cdot \dfrac{1+x}{1} = x$

(b)

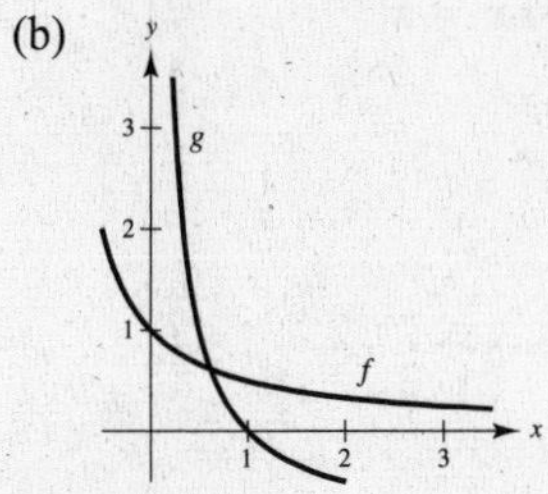


**9.** Matches (c)

**10.** Matches (b)

**11.** Matches (a)

**12.** Matches (d)

**13.** $f(x) = \frac{3}{4}x + 6$

One-to-one; has an inverse

**14.** $f(x) = 5x - 3$

One-to-one; has an inverse

**15.** $f(\theta) = \sin \theta$

Not one-to-one; does not have an inverse

**16.** $f(x) = \dfrac{x^2}{x^2 + 4}$

Not one-to-one; does not have an inverse

**17.** $h(s) = \dfrac{1}{s - 2} - 3$

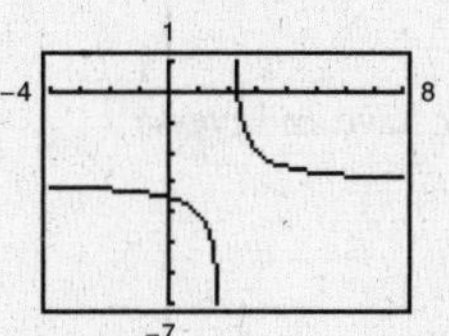

One-to-one; has an inverse

**18.** $f(x) = \dfrac{1}{1 + x^2}$

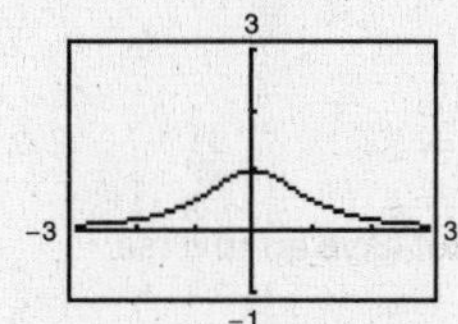

Not one-to-one; does not have an inverse

**19.** $g(t) = \dfrac{1}{\sqrt{t^2 + 1}}$

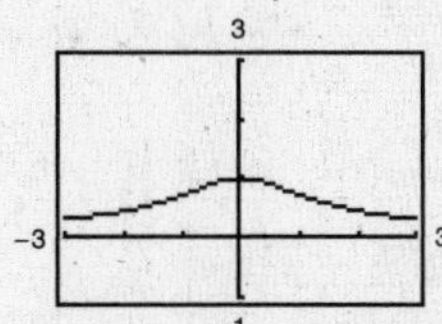

Not one-to-one; does not have an inverse

**20.** $f(x) = 5x\sqrt{x - 1}$

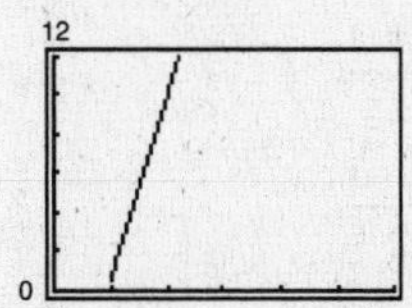

One-to-one; has an inverse

**21.** $g(x) = (x + 5)^3$

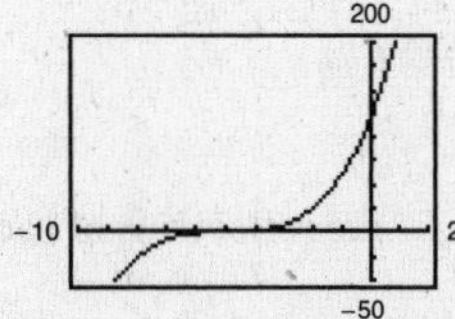

One-to-one; has an inverse

**22.** $h(x) = |x + 4| - |x - 4|$

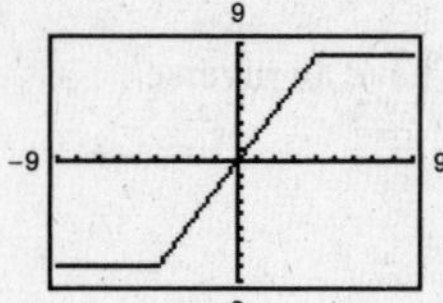


Not one-to-one; does not have an inverse

**23.** $f(x) = (x + a)^3 + b$

One-to-one; has an inverse

**24.** $f(x) = \sin\dfrac{3x}{2}$

Not one-to-one; $f$ does not have an inverse.

**25.** $f(x) = \dfrac{x^4}{4} - 2x^2$

Not one-to-one; $f$ does not have an inverse.

**26.** $f(x) = x^3 - 6x^2 + 12x$

One-to-one; has an inverse

**27.** $f(x) = 2 - x - x^3$

One-to-one; has an inverse

**28.** $f(x) = \sqrt[3]{x + 1}$

One-to-one; has an inverse

**29.** (a) $f(x) = 2x - 3 = y$

$$x = \frac{y + 3}{2}$$

$$y = \frac{x + 3}{2}$$

$$f^{-1}(x) = \frac{x + 3}{2}$$

(b)

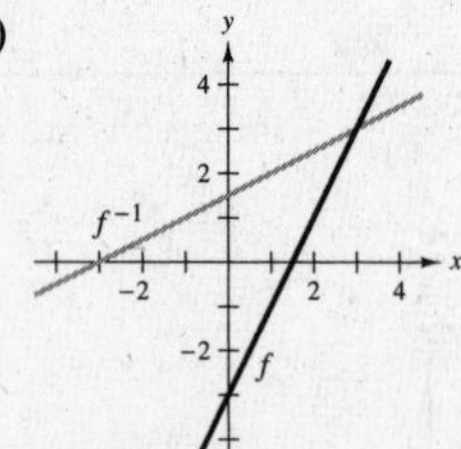


(c) The graphs of $f$ and $f^{-1}$ are reflections of each other in the line $y = x$.

(d) Domain of $f$: all real numbers
Range of $f$: all real numbers
Domain of $f^{-1}$: all real numbers
Range of $f^{-1}$: all real numbers

**30.** (a) $f(x) = 3x = y$

$$x = \frac{y}{3}$$

$$y = \frac{x}{3}$$

$$f^{-1}(x) = \frac{x}{3}$$

(b)

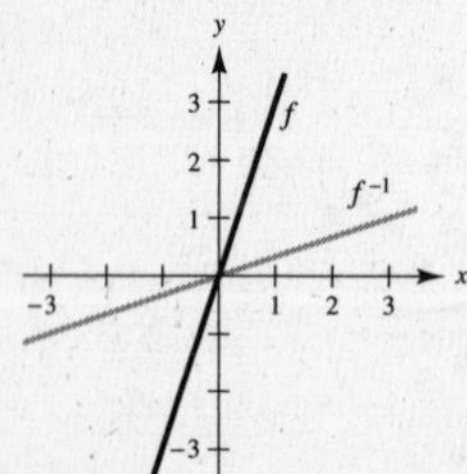


(c) The graphs of $f$ and $f^{-1}$ are reflections of each other in the line $y = x$.

(d) Domain of $f$: all real numbers
Range of $f$: all real numbers
Domain of $f^{-1}$: all real numbers
Range of $f^{-1}$: all real numbers

**31.** (a) $f(x) = x^5 = y$

$$x = \sqrt[5]{y}$$

$$y = \sqrt[5]{x}$$

$$f^{-1}(x) = \sqrt[5]{x} = x^{1/5}$$

(b)

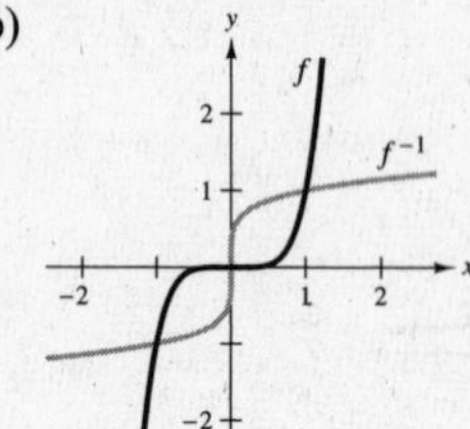


(c) The graphs of $f$ and $f^{-1}$ are reflections of each other in the line $y = x$.

(d) Domain of $f$: all real numbers
Range of $f$: all real numbers
Domain of $f^{-1}$: all real numbers
Range of $f^{-1}$: all real numbers

**32.** (a) $f(x) = x^3 - 1 = y$

$$x = \sqrt[3]{y + 1}$$

$$y = \sqrt[3]{x + 1}$$

$$f^{-1}(x) = \sqrt[3]{x + 1} = (x + 1)^{1/3}$$

(b)

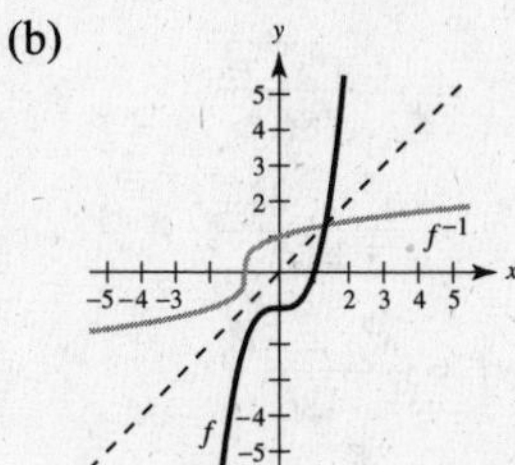


(c) The graphs of $f$ and $f^{-1}$ are reflections of each other in the line $y = x$.

(d) Domain of $f$: all real numbers
Range of $f$: all real numbers
Domain of $f^{-1}$: all real numbers
Range of $f^{-1}$: all real numbers

**33.** (a) $f(x) = \sqrt{x} = y$

$$x = y^2$$

$$y = x^2$$

$$f^{-1}(x) = x^2, \quad x \geq 0$$

(b)

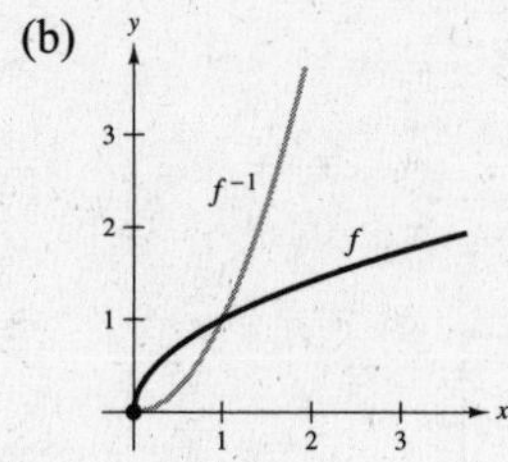


(c) The graphs of $f$ and $f^{-1}$ are reflections of each other in the line $y = x$.

(d) Domain of $f$: $x \geq 0$
Range of $f$: $y \geq 0$
Domain of $f^{-1}$: $x \geq 0$
Range of $f^{-1}$: $y \geq 0$

**34.** (a) $f(x) = x^2 = y, \quad x \geq 0$

$$x = \sqrt{y}$$

$$y = \sqrt{x}$$

$$f^{-1}(x) = \sqrt{x}$$

(b)

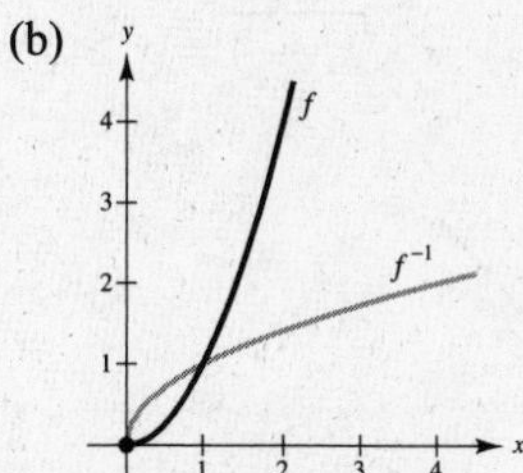


(c) The graphs of $f$ and $f^{-1}$ are reflections of each other in the line $y = x$.

(d) Domain of $f$: $x \geq 0$
Range of $f$: $y \geq 0$
Domain of $f^{-1}$: $x \geq 0$
Range of $f^{-1}$: $y \geq 0$

**35.** (a) $f(x) = \sqrt{4 - x^2} = y, \quad 0 \leq x \leq 2$

$$4 - x^2 = y^2$$

$$x^2 = 4 - y^2$$

$$x = \sqrt{4 - y^2}$$

$$y = \sqrt{4 - x^2}$$

$$f^{-1}(x) = \sqrt{4 - x^2}, \quad 0 \leq x \leq 2$$

(b)

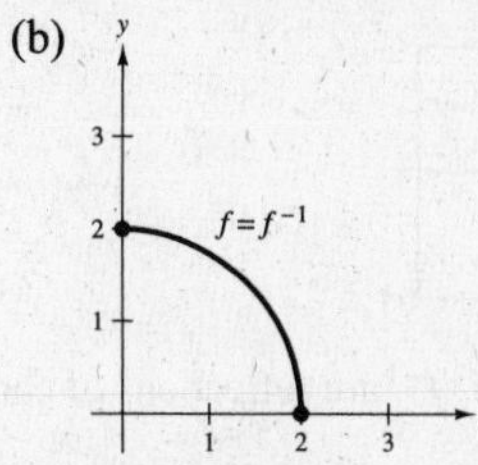


(c) The graphs of $f$ and $f^{-1}$ are reflections of each other in the line $y = x$. In fact, the graphs are identical.

(d) Domain of $f$: $0 \leq x \leq 2$
Range of $f$: $0 \leq y \leq 2$
Domain of $f^{-1}$: $0 \leq x \leq 2$
Range of $f^{-1}$: $0 \leq y \leq 2$

**36.** (a) $f(x) = \sqrt{x^2 - 4} = y, \quad x \geq 2$

$$x^2 = y^2 + 4$$

$$x = \sqrt{y^2 + 4}$$

$$y = \sqrt{x^2 + 4}$$

$$f^{-1}(x) = \sqrt{x^2 + 4}, \quad x \geq 0$$

(b) 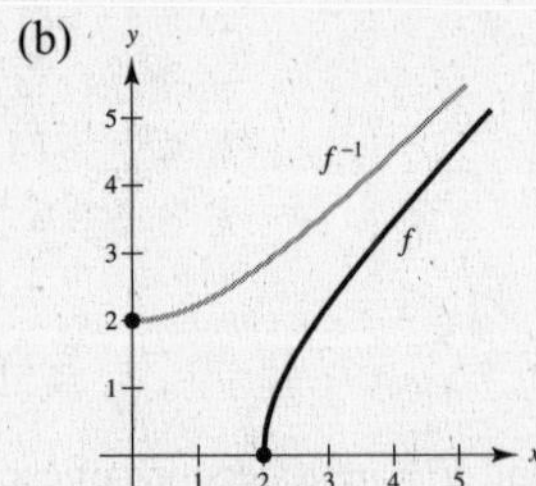


(c) The graphs of $f$ and $f^{-1}$ are reflections of each other in the line $y = x$.

(d) Domain of $f$: $x \geq 2$
Range of $f$: $y \geq 0$
Domain of $f^{-1}$: $x \geq 0$
Range of $f^{-1}$: $y \geq 2$

**37.** (a) $f(x) = \sqrt[3]{x - 1} = y$

$$x - 1 = y^3$$

$$x = y^3 + 1$$

$$y = x^3 + 1$$

$$f^{-1}(x) = x^3 + 1$$

(b) 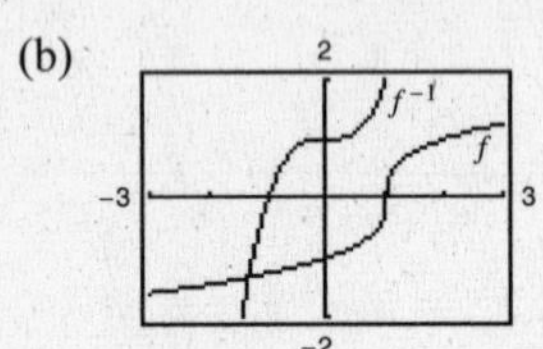


(c) The graphs of $f$ and $f^{-1}$ are reflections of each other in the line $y = x$.

(d) Domain of $f$: all real numbers
Range of $f$: all real numbers
Domain of $f^{-1}$: all real numbers
Range of $f^{-1}$: all real numbers

**38.** (a) $f(x) = 3\sqrt[5]{2x - 1} = y$

$$2x - 1 = \left(\frac{y}{3}\right)^5 = \frac{y^5}{243}$$

$$2x = \frac{y^5 + 243}{243}$$

$$x = \frac{y^5 + 243}{486}$$

$$y = \frac{x^5 + 243}{486}$$

$$f^{-1}(x) = \frac{x^5 + 243}{486}$$

(b) 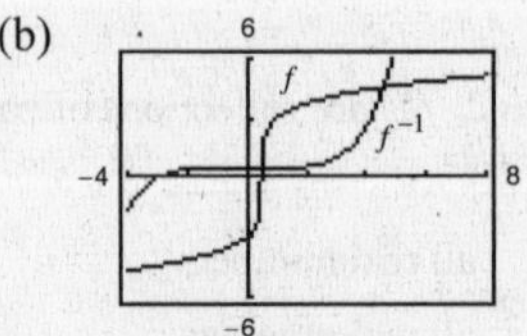


(c) The graphs of $f$ and $f^{-1}$ are reflections of each other in the line $y = x$.

(d) Domain of $f$: all real numbers
Range of $f$: all real numbers
Domain of $f^{-1}$: all real numbers
Range of $f^{-1}$: all real numbers

**39.** (a) $f(x) = x^{2/3} = y, \quad x \geq 0$

$$x = y^{3/2}$$

$$y = x^{3/2}$$

$$f^{-1}(x) = x^{3/2}, \quad x \geq 0$$

(b) 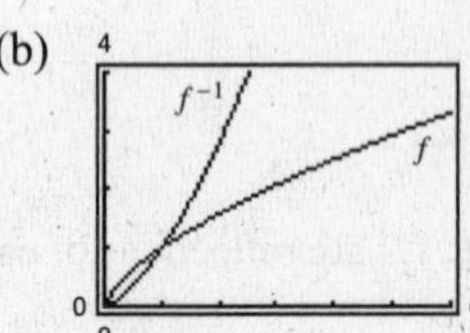


(c) The graphs of $f$ and $f^{-1}$ are reflections of each other in the line $y = x$.

(d) Domain of $f$: $x \geq 0$
Range of $f$: $y \geq 0$
Domain of $f^{-1}$: $x \geq 0$
Range of $f^{-1}$: $y \geq 0$

**40.** (a) $f(x) = x^{3/5} = y$

$$x = y^{5/3}$$
$$y = x^{5/3}$$
$$f^{-1}(x) = x^{5/3}$$

(b)

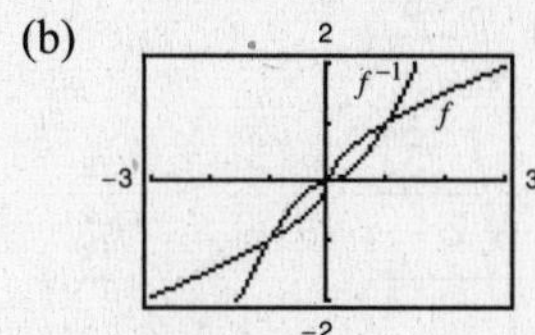


(c) The graphs of $f$ and $f^{-1}$ are reflections of each other in the line $y = x$.

(d) Domain of $f$: all real numbers
Range of $f$: all real numbers
Domain of $f^{-1}$: all real numbers
Range of $f^{-1}$: all real numbers

**41.** (a) $f(x) = \dfrac{x}{\sqrt{x^2 + 7}} = y$

$$x = y\sqrt{x^2 + 7}$$
$$x^2 = y^2(x^2 + 7) = y^2x^2 + 7y^2$$
$$x^2(1 - y^2) = 7y^2$$
$$x = \frac{\sqrt{7}y}{\sqrt{1 - y^2}}$$
$$y = \frac{\sqrt{7}x}{\sqrt{1 - x^2}}$$
$$f^{-1}(x) = \frac{\sqrt{7}x}{\sqrt{1 - x^2}}, \quad -1 < x < 1$$

(b)

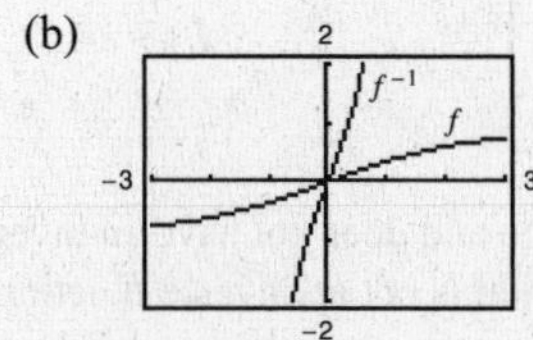


(c) The graphs of $f$ and $f^{-1}$ are reflections of each other in the line $y = x$.

(d) Domain of $f$: all real numbers
Range of $f$: $-1 < y < 1$
Domain of $f^{-1}$: $-1 < x < 1$
Range of $f^{-1}$: all real numbers

**42.** (a) $f(x) = \dfrac{x + 2}{x} = y, \quad x \neq 0$

$$x + 2 = yx$$
$$x(1 - y) = -2$$
$$x = \frac{2}{y - 1}$$
$$y = \frac{2}{x - 1}$$
$$f^{-1}(x) = \frac{2}{x - 1}, \quad x \neq 1$$

(b)

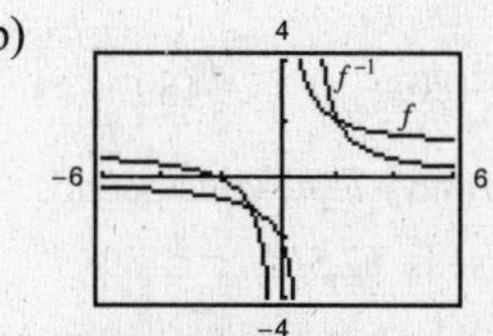


(c) The graphs of $f$ and $f^{-1}$ are reflections of each other in the line $y = x$.

(d) Domain of $f$: all $x \neq 0$
Range of $f$: all $y \neq 1$
Domain of $f^{-1}$: all $x \neq 1$
Range of $f^{-1}$: all $y \neq 0$

**43.**

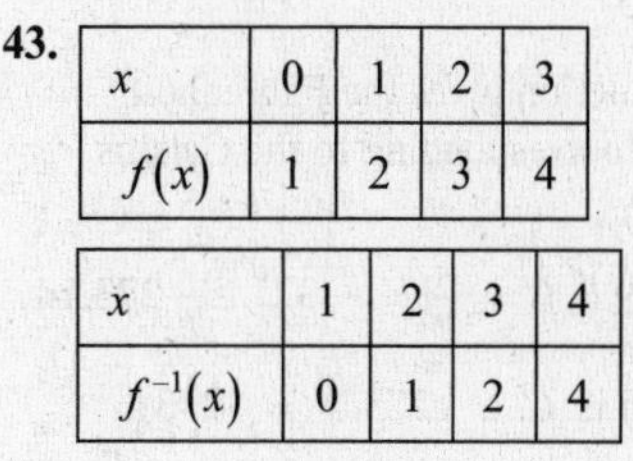

| $x$ | 0 | 1 | 2 | 3 |
|---|---|---|---|---|
| $f(x)$ | 1 | 2 | 3 | 4 |

| $x$ | 1 | 2 | 3 | 4 |
|---|---|---|---|---|
| $f^{-1}(x)$ | 0 | 1 | 2 | 4 |

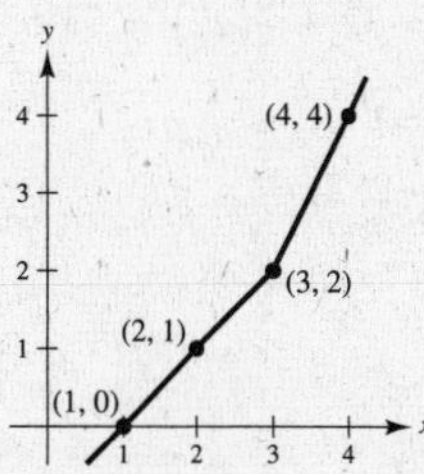


**44.**

| $x$ | 0 | 2 | 6 |
|---|---|---|---|
| $f(x)$ | 4 | 2 | 0 |

| $x$ | 0 | 2 | 4 |
|---|---|---|---|
| $f^{-1}(x)$ | 6 | 2 | 0 |

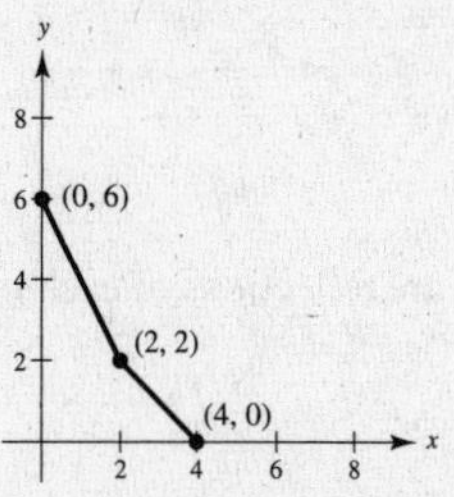

**45.** (a) Let $x$ be the number of pounds of the commodity costing 1.25 per pound. Because there are 50 pounds total, the amount of the second commodity is $50 - x$. The total cost is

$$y = 1.25x + 1.60(50 - x)$$
$$= -0.35x + 80, \quad 0 \le x \le 50.$$

(b) Find the inverse of the original function.

$$y = -0.35x + 80$$
$$0.35x = 80 - y$$
$$x = \tfrac{100}{35}(80 - y)$$

Inverse: $y = \frac{100}{35}(80 - x) = \frac{20}{7}(80 - x)$

$x$ represents cost and $y$ represents pounds.

(c) Domain of inverse is $62.5 \le x \le 80$.

The total cost will be between \$62.50 and \$80.00.

(d) If $x = 73$ in the inverse function, $y = \frac{100}{35}(80 - 73) = \frac{100}{5} = 20$ pounds.

**46.** $C = \frac{5}{9}(F - 32), \quad F \ge -459.6$

(a) $\frac{9}{5}C = F - 32$

$$F = 32 + \tfrac{9}{5}C$$

(b) The inverse function gives the Fahrenheit temperature $F$ corresponding to the Celsius temperature $C$.

(c) For $F \ge -459.6$, $C = \frac{5}{9}(F - 32) \ge -273.1\overline{1}$.

So, the domain is $C \ge -273.\overline{1} = -273\frac{1}{9}$.

(d) If $C = 22°$, then $F = 32 + \frac{9}{5}(22) = 71.6°\text{F}$.

**47.** $f(x) = \dfrac{x}{x^2 - 4} = y$ on $(-2, 2)$

$$x^2y - 4y = x$$
$$x^2y - x - 4y = 0$$

$(a = y, b = -1, c = -4y)$

$$x = \frac{1 \pm \sqrt{1 - 4(y)(-4y)}}{2y} = \frac{1 \pm \sqrt{1 + 16y^2}}{2y}$$

$$y = f^{-1}(x) = \begin{cases} \left(1 - \sqrt{1 + 16x^2}\right)/2x, & \text{if } x \ne 0 \\ 0, & \text{if } x = 0 \end{cases}$$

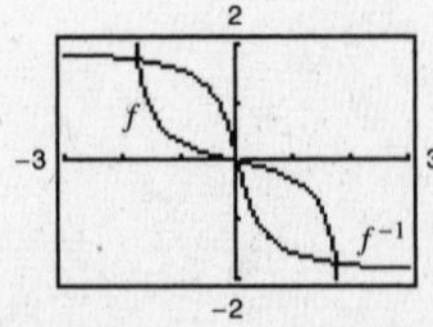


The graphs of $f$ and $f^{-1}$ are reflections of each other in the line $y = x$.

**48.** $f(x) = 2 - \dfrac{3}{x^2} = y$ on $(0, 10)$

$$2x^2 - 3 = x^2y$$
$$x^2(2 - y) = 3$$
$$x = \pm\sqrt{\frac{3}{2 - y}}$$
$$y = \pm\sqrt{\frac{3}{2 - x}}$$
$$f^{-1}(x) = \sqrt{\frac{3}{2 - x}}, \quad x < 2$$

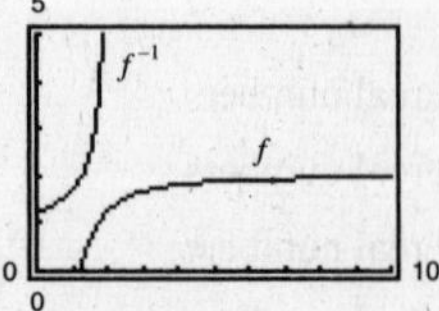


The graphs of $f$ and $f^{-1}$ are reflections of each other in the line $y = x$.

**49.** (a), (b)

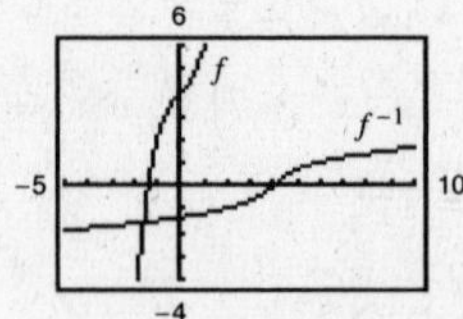


(c) Yes, $f$ is one-to-one and has an inverse. The inverse relation is an inverse function.

**50.** (a), (b)

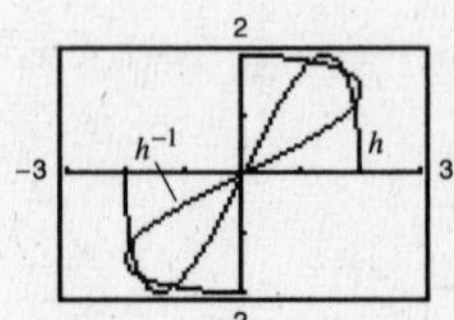


(c) $h$ is not one-to-one and does not have an inverse. The inverse relation is not an inverse function.

**51.** (a), (b)

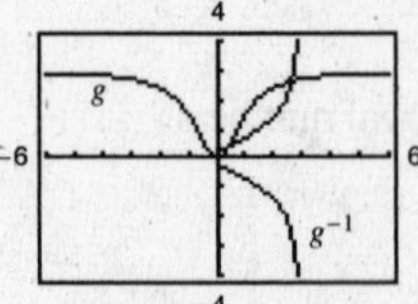


(c) $g$ is not one-to-one and does not have an inverse. The inverse relation is not an inverse function.

**52.** (a), (b)

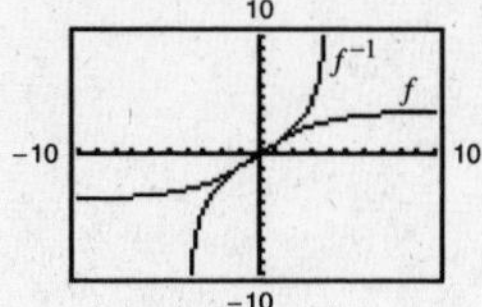


(c) Yes, $f$ is one-to-one and has an inverse. The inverse relation is an inverse function.

**53.** $f(x) = (x - 4)^2$ on $[4, \infty)$

$f$ passes the Horizontal Line Test on $[4, \infty)$, so it is one-to-one.

**54.** $f(x) = |x + 2|$ on $[-2, \infty)$

$f$ passes the Horizontal Line Test on $[-2, \infty)$, so it is one-to-one.

**55.** $f(x) = \dfrac{4}{x^2}$ on $(0, \infty)$

$f$ passes the Horizontal Line Test on $(0, \infty)$, so it is one-to-one.

**56.** $f(x) = \cot x$ on $(0, \pi)$

$f$ passes the Horizontal Line Test on $(0, \pi)$, so it is one-to-one.

**57.** $f(x) = \cos x$ on $[0, \pi]$

$f$ passes the Horizontal Line Test on $[0, \pi]$, so it is one-to-one.

**58.** $f(x) = \sec x$ on $\left[0, \dfrac{\pi}{2}\right)$

$f$ passes the Horizontal Line Test on $[0, \pi/2)$, so it is one-to-one.

**59.** $f(x) = \sqrt{x - 2}$, Domain: $x \ge 2$

$$f'(x) = \frac{1}{2\sqrt{x - 2}} > 0 \text{ for } x > 2$$

$f$ is one-to-one; has an inverse

$$\begin{aligned} \sqrt{x - 2} &= y \\ x - 2 &= y^2 \\ x &= y^2 + 2 \\ y &= x^2 + 2 \\ f^{-1}(x) &= x^2 + 2, \quad x \ge 0 \end{aligned}$$

**60.** $f(x) = -3$

Not one-to-one; does not have an inverse

**61.** 
$$\begin{aligned} f(x) &= |x - 2|, \ x \le 2 \\ &= -(x - 2) \\ &= 2 - x \end{aligned}$$

$f$ is one-to-one; has an inverse

$$\begin{aligned} 2 - x &= y \\ 2 - y &= x \\ f^{-1}(x) &= 2 - x, \quad x \ge 0 \end{aligned}$$

**62.** $f(x) = ax + b$

$f$ is one-to-one; has an inverse

$$\begin{aligned} ax + b &= y \\ x &= \frac{y - b}{a} \\ y &= \frac{x - b}{a} \\ f^{-1}(x) &= \frac{x - b}{a}, \quad a \ne 0 \end{aligned}$$

**63.** $f(x) = (x - 3)^2$ is one-to-one for $x \ge 3$.

$$\begin{aligned} (x - 3)^2 &= y \\ x - 3 &= \sqrt{y} \\ x &= \sqrt{y} + 3 \\ y &= \sqrt{x} + 3 \\ f^{-1}(x) &= \sqrt{x} + 3, \quad x \ge 0 \end{aligned}$$

(Answer is not unique.)

**64.** $f(x) = 16 - x^4$ is one-to-one for $x \ge 0$.

$$\begin{aligned} 16 - x^4 &= y \\ 16 - y &= x^4 \\ \sqrt[4]{16 - y} &= x \\ \sqrt[4]{16 - x} &= y \\ f^{-1}(x) &= \sqrt[4]{16 - x}, \quad x \le 16 \end{aligned}$$

(Answer is not unique.)

**65.** $f(x) = |x + 3|$ is one-to-one for $x \ge -3$.

$$\begin{aligned} x + 3 &= y \\ x &= y - 3 \\ y &= x - 3 \\ f^{-1}(x) &= x - 3, \quad x \ge 0 \end{aligned}$$

(Answer is not unique.)

**66.** $f(x) = |x - 3|$ is one-to-one for $x \geq 3$.

$$x - 3 = y$$
$$x = y + 3$$
$$y = x + 3$$
$$f^{-1}(x) = x + 3, \quad x \geq 0$$

(Answer is not unique.)

**67.** (a) $f(x) = (x + 5)^2$

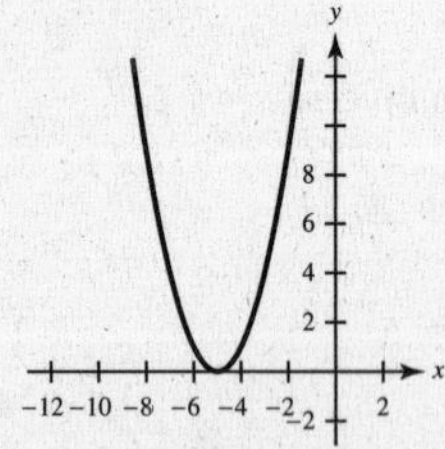

(b) $f$ is one-to-one on $[-5, \infty)$. (Note that $f$ is also one-to-one on $(-\infty, -5]$.)

(c) $f(x) = (x + 5)^2 = y, \quad x \geq -5$

$$x + 5 = \sqrt{y}$$
$$x = \sqrt{y} - 5$$
$$y = \sqrt{x} - 5$$
$$f^{-1}(x) = \sqrt{x} - 5$$

(d) Domain of $f^{-1}$: $x \geq 0$

**68.** (a) $f(x) = (7 - x)^2 = (x - 7)^2$

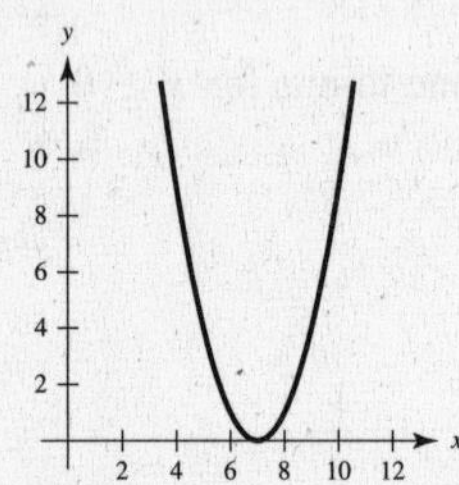

(b) $f$ is one-to-one on $[7, \infty)$. (Note that $f$ is also one-to-one on $(-\infty, 7]$.)

(c) $f(x) = (x - 7)^2 = y, \quad x \geq 7$

$$x - 7 = \sqrt{y}$$
$$x = 7 + \sqrt{y}$$
$$y = 7 + \sqrt{x}$$
$$f^{-1}(x) = 7 + \sqrt{x}$$

(d) Domain of $f^{-1}$: $x \geq 0$

**69.** (a) $f(x) = \sqrt{x^2 - 4x}$

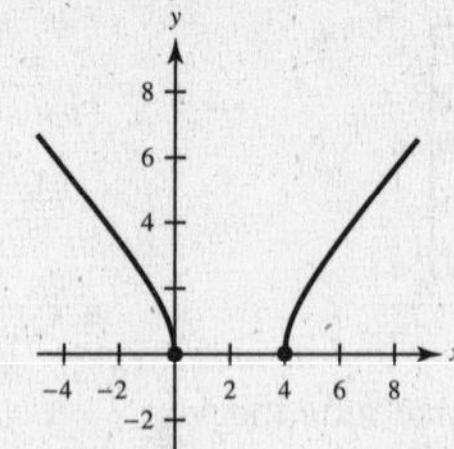

(b) $f$ is one-to-one on $[4, \infty)$. (Note that $f$ is also one-to-one on $(-\infty, 0]$.)

(c) $f(x) = \sqrt{x^2 - 4x} = y, \ x \geq 4$

$$x^2 - 4x = y^2$$
$$x^2 - 4x + 4 = y^2 + 4$$
$$(x - 2)^2 = y^2 + 4$$
$$x - 2 = \sqrt{y^2 + 4}$$
$$x = 2 + \sqrt{y^2 + 4}$$
$$y = 2 + \sqrt{x^2 + 4}$$
$$f^{-1}(x) = 2 + \sqrt{x^2 + 4}$$

(d) Domain of $f^{-1}$: $x \geq 0$

**70.** (a) $f(x) = -\sqrt{25 - x^2}$

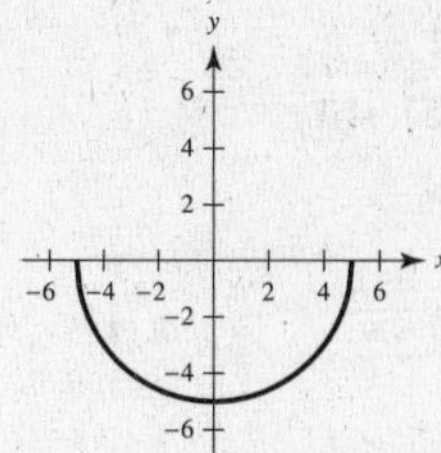

(b) $f$ is one-to-one on $[0, 5]$. (Note that $f$ is also one-to-one on $[-5, 0]$.)

(c) $f(x) = -\sqrt{25 - x^2} = y, \qquad 0 \le x \le 5, -5 \le y \le 0$

$$25 - x^2 = y^2$$
$$x^2 = 25 - y^2$$
$$x = \sqrt{25 - y^2}$$
$$y = \sqrt{25 - x^2}$$
$$f^{-1}(x) = \sqrt{25 - x^2}$$

(d) Domain of $f^{-1}$: $-5 \le x \le 0$

**71.** (a) $f(x) = 3\cos x$

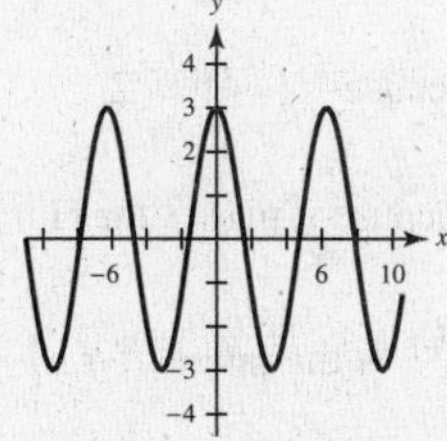

(b) $f$ is one-to-one on $[0, \pi]$. (other answers possible)

(c) $f(x) = 3\cos x = y$

$$\cos x = \frac{y}{3}$$
$$x = \arccos\left(\frac{y}{3}\right)$$
$$y = \arccos\left(\frac{x}{3}\right)$$
$$f^{-1}(x) = \arccos\left(\frac{x}{3}\right)$$

(d) Domain of $f^{-1}$: $-3 \le x \le 3$

**72.** (a) $f(x) = 2\sin x$

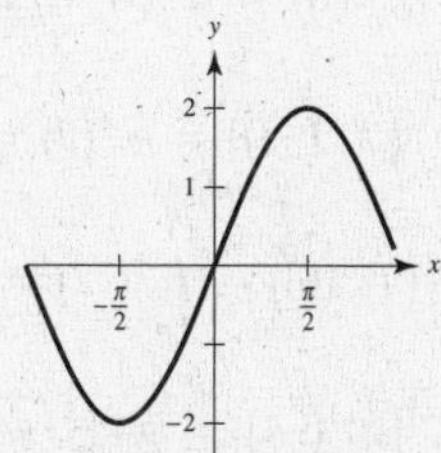

(b) $f$ is one-to-one on $\left[-\frac{\pi}{2}, \frac{\pi}{2}\right]$. (other answers possible)

(c) $f(x) = 2\sin x = y$

$$\sin x = \frac{y}{2}$$
$$x = \arcsin\left(\frac{y}{2}\right)$$
$$y = \arcsin\left(\frac{x}{2}\right)$$
$$f^{-1}(x) = \arcsin\left(\frac{x}{2}\right)$$

(d) Domain of $f^{-1}$: $-2 \le x \le 2$

**73.** $f(x) = x^3 + 2x - 1$

$f(1) = 2 = a \Rightarrow f^{-1}(2) = 1$

**74.** $f(x) = 2x^5 + x^3 + 1$

$f(-1) = -2 = a \Rightarrow f^{-1}(-2) = -1$

**75.** $f(x) = \sin x$

$f\left(\frac{\pi}{6}\right) = \frac{1}{2} = a \Rightarrow f^{-1}\left(\frac{1}{2}\right) = \frac{\pi}{6}$

**76.** $f(x) = \cos 2x$

$f(0) = 1 = a \Rightarrow f^{-1}(1) = 0$

**77.** $f(x) = x^3 - \frac{4}{x}$

$f(2) = 6 = a \Rightarrow f^{-1}(6) = 2$

**78.** $f(x) = \sqrt{x-4}$

$f(8) = 2 = a \Rightarrow f^{-1}(2) = 8$

**In Exercises 79–82, use the following.**

$f(x) = \frac{1}{8}x - 3$ **and** $g(x) = x^3$

$f^{-1}(x) = 8(x+3)$ **and** $g^{-1}(x) = \sqrt[3]{x}$

**79.** $(f^{-1} \circ g^{-1})(1) = f^{-1}(g^{-1}(1)) = f^{-1}(1) = 32$

**80.** $(g^{-1} \circ f^{-1})(-3) = g^{-1}(f^{-1}(-3)) = g^{-1}(0) = 0$

**81.** $(f^{-1} \circ f^{-1})(6) = f^{-1}(f^{-1}(6)) = f^{-1}(72) = 600$

**82.** $(g^{-1} \circ g^{-1})(-4) = g^{-1}(g^{-1}(-4)) = g^{-1}(\sqrt[3]{-4})$

$= \sqrt[3]{\sqrt[3]{-4}} = -\sqrt[9]{4}$

**In Exercises 83–86, use the following.**

$f(x) = x + 4$ **and** $g(x) = 2x - 5$

$f^{-1}(x) = x - 4$ **and** $g^{-1}(x) = \frac{x+5}{2}$

**83.** $(g^{-1} \circ f^{-1})(x) = g^{-1}(f^{-1}(x))$

$= g^{-1}(x-4)$

$= \frac{(x-4)+5}{2}$

$= \frac{x+1}{2}$

**84.** $(f^{-1} \circ g^{-1})(x) = f^{-1}(g^{-1}(x))$

$= f^{-1}\left(\frac{x+5}{2}\right)$

$= \frac{x+5}{2} - 4$

$= \frac{x-3}{2}$

**85.** $(f \circ g)(x) = f(g(x))$

$= f(2x-5)$

$= (2x-5)+4$

$= 2x-1$

So, $(f \circ g)^{-1}(x) = \frac{x+1}{2}$.

**Note:** $(f \circ g)^{-1} = g^{-1} \circ f^{-1}$

**86.** $(g \circ f)(x) = g(f(x))$

$= g(x+4)$

$= 2(x+4) - 5$

$= 2x+3$

So, $(g \circ f)^{-1}(x) = \frac{x-3}{2}$.

**Note:** $(g \circ f)^{-1} = f^{-1} \circ g^{-1}$

**87.** (a) $f$ is one-to-one because it passes the Horizontal Line Test.

(b) The domain of $f^{-1}$ is the range of $f$: $[-2, 2]$.

(c) $f^{-1}(2) = -4$ because $f(-4) = 2$.

**88.** (a) $f$ is one-to-one because it passes the Horizontal Line Test.

(b) The domain of $f^{-1}$ is the range of $f$: $[-3, 3]$.

(c) $f^{-1}(2) \approx 1.73$ because $f(1.73) \approx 2$.

**89.**

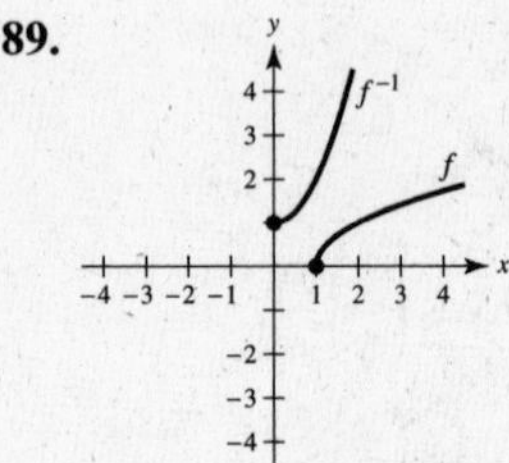


**90.**

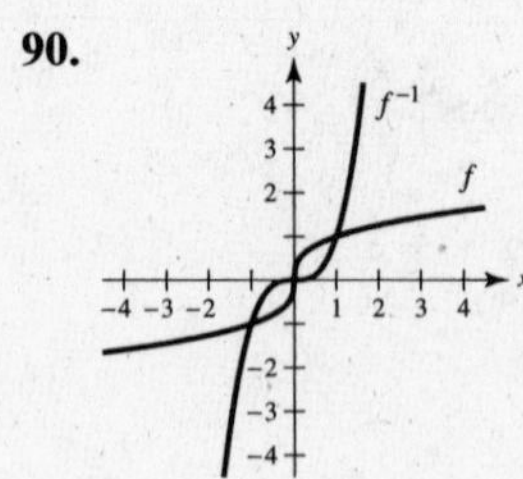

**91.** $y = \arcsin x$

(a)

| $x$ | $-1$ | $-0.8$ | $-0.6$ | $-0.4$ | $-0.2$ | $0$ | $0.2$ | $0.4$ | $0.6$ | $0.8$ | $1$ |
|---|---|---|---|---|---|---|---|---|---|---|---|
| $y$ | $-1.571$ | $-0.927$ | $-0.644$ | $-0.412$ | $-0.201$ | $0$ | $0.201$ | $0.412$ | $0.644$ | $0.927$ | $1.571$ |

(b)

(c)

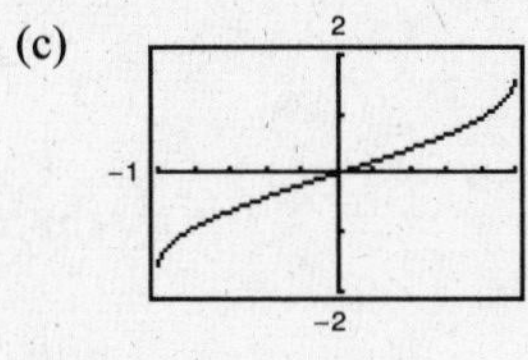


(d) Symmetric about origin: $\arcsin(-x) = -\arcsin x$

Intercept: $(0, 0)$

**92.** $y = \arccos x$

(a)

| $x$ | $-1$ | $-0.8$ | $-0.6$ | $-0.4$ | $-0.2$ | $0$ | $0.2$ | $0.4$ | $0.6$ | $0.8$ | $1$ |
|---|---|---|---|---|---|---|---|---|---|---|---|
| $y$ | $3.142$ | $2.498$ | $2.214$ | $1.982$ | $1.772$ | $1.571$ | $1.369$ | $1.159$ | $0.927$ | $0.644$ | $0$ |

(b)

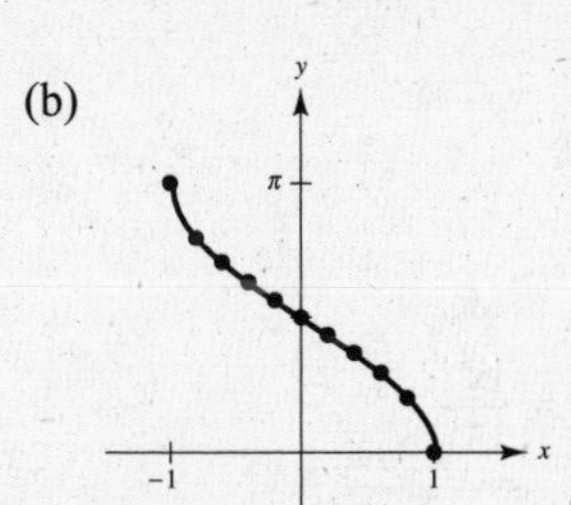


(c)

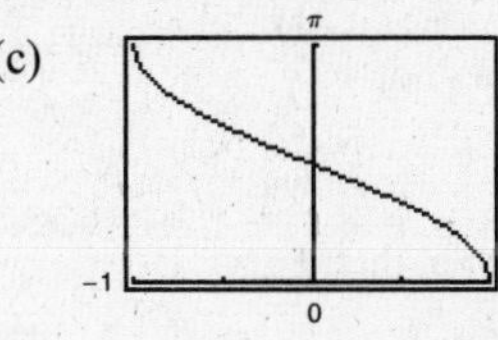


(d) Intercepts: $\left(0, \frac{\pi}{2}\right)$ and $(1, 0)$

**93.** $y = \arccos x$

$\left(-\frac{\sqrt{2}}{2}, \frac{3\pi}{4}\right)$ because $\cos\left(\frac{3\pi}{4}\right) = -\frac{\sqrt{2}}{2}$.

$\left(\frac{1}{2}, \frac{\pi}{3}\right)$ because $\cos\left(\frac{\pi}{4}\right) = \frac{1}{2}$.

$\left(\frac{\sqrt{3}}{2}, \frac{\pi}{6}\right)$ because $\cos\left(\frac{\pi}{6}\right) = \frac{\sqrt{3}}{2}$.

**94.** $y = \arctan x$

$\left(1, \frac{\pi}{4}\right)$ because $\tan\left(\frac{\pi}{4}\right) = 1$.

$\left(-\frac{\sqrt{3}}{3}, -\frac{\pi}{4}\right)$ because $\tan\left(-\frac{\pi}{6}\right) = \frac{-\sqrt{3}}{3}$.

$\left(-\sqrt{3}, -\frac{\pi}{3}\right)$ because $\tan\left(-\frac{\pi}{3}\right) = -\sqrt{3}$.

**95.** $\arcsin \frac{1}{2} = \frac{\pi}{6}$

**96.** $\arcsin 0 = 0$

**97.** $\arccos \frac{1}{2} = \frac{\pi}{3}$

**98.** $\arccos 0 = \frac{\pi}{2}$

**99.** $\arctan \frac{\sqrt{3}}{3} = \frac{\pi}{6}$

**100.** $\operatorname{arccot}\left(-\sqrt{3}\right) = \frac{5\pi}{6}$

**101.** $\operatorname{arccsc}\left(-\sqrt{2}\right) = -\frac{\pi}{4}$

**102.** $\arccos\left(-\frac{\sqrt{3}}{2}\right) = \frac{5\pi}{6}$

**103.** $\arccos(0.8) \approx 2.50$

**104.** $\arcsin(-0.39) \approx -0.40$

**105.** $\operatorname{arcsec}(1.269) = \arccos\left(\frac{1}{1.269}\right) \approx 0.66$

**106.** $\arctan(-3) \approx -1.25$

**107.** Let $y = f(x)$ be one-to-one. Solve for $x$ as a function of $y$. Interchange $x$ and $y$ to get $y = f^{-1}(x)$. Let the domain of $f^{-1}$ be the range of $f$. Verify that $f(f^{-1}(x)) = x$ and $f^{-1}(f(x)) = x$.

Example:

$f(x) = x^3$

$y = x^3$

$x = \sqrt[3]{y}$

$y = \sqrt[3]{x}$

$f^{-1}(x) = \sqrt[3]{x}$

**108.** The graphs of $f$ and $f^{-1}$ are mirror images with respect to the line $y = x$.

**109.** Answers will vary.
Sample answer: $y = x^4 - 2x^3$ on $(-\infty, \infty)$ does not have an inverse.

**110.** The trigonometric functions are not one-to-one. So, their domains must be restricted to define the inverse trigonometric functions.

**111.** If the domains were not restricted, then the trigonometric functions would not be one-to-one and hence would not have inverses.

**112.** You could graph $f(x) = \text{arccot}\,(x)$ as follows.

$$f(x) = \begin{cases} \arctan(1/x) + \pi, & -\infty < x < 0 \\ \pi/2, & x = 0 \\ \arctan(1/x), & 0 < x < \infty \end{cases}$$

**113.** $f(x) = \tan x$

$g(x) = \arctan x$

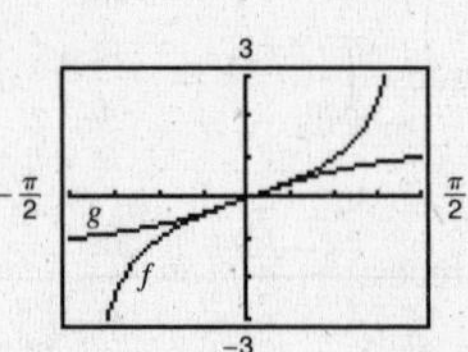


**114.** $f(x) = \sin x, \; -\dfrac{\pi}{2} \le x \le \dfrac{\pi}{2}$

$g(x) = \arcsin x$



**115.** $\cos[\arccos(-0.1)] = -0.1$

**116.** $\arcsin(\sin 3\pi) = \arcsin(0) = 0$

**117.** (a) $\sin\left(\arcsin\dfrac{1}{2}\right) = \sin\left(\dfrac{\pi}{6}\right) = \dfrac{1}{2}$

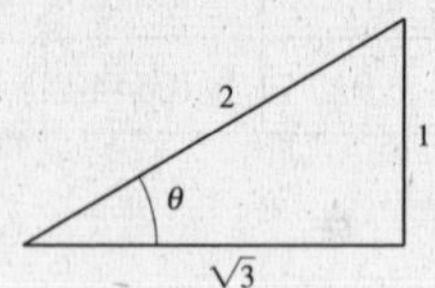


(b) $\cos\left(\arcsin\dfrac{1}{2}\right) = \cos\left(\dfrac{\pi}{6}\right) = \dfrac{\sqrt{3}}{2}$

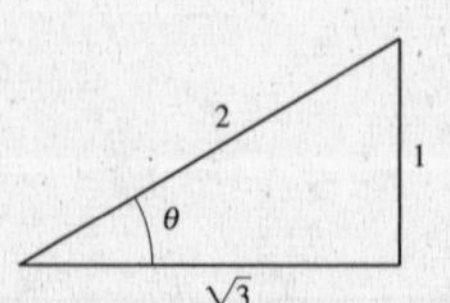


**118.** (a) $\tan\left(\arccos\dfrac{\sqrt{2}}{2}\right) = \tan\left(\dfrac{\pi}{4}\right) = 1$

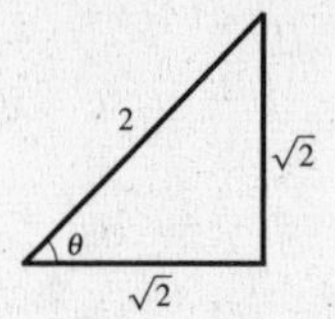


(b) $\cos\left(\arcsin\dfrac{5}{13}\right) = \dfrac{12}{13}$

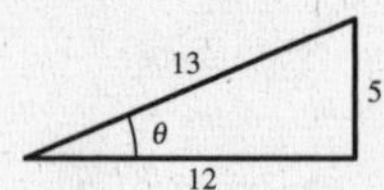


**119.** (a) $\sin\left(\arctan\dfrac{3}{4}\right) = \dfrac{3}{5}$

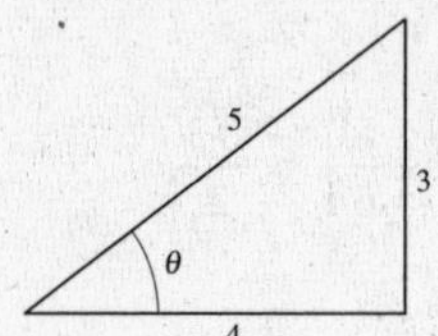


(b) $\sec\left(\arcsin\dfrac{4}{5}\right) = \dfrac{5}{3}$

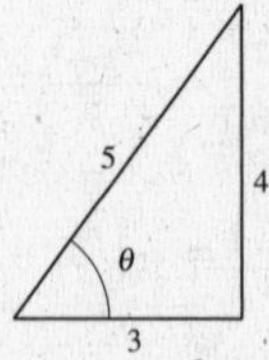

**120.** (a) $\tan(\text{arccot } 2) = \frac{1}{2}$

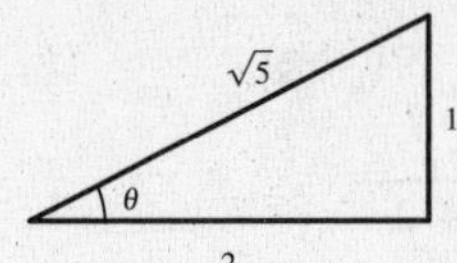


(b) $\cos(\text{arcsec } \sqrt{5}) = \frac{\sqrt{5}}{5}$

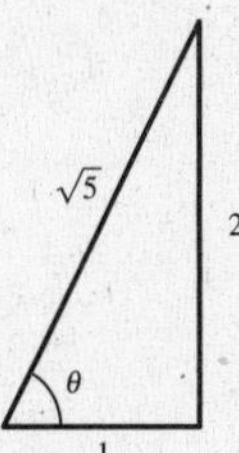


**121.** (a) $\cot\left[\arcsin\left(-\frac{1}{2}\right)\right] = \cot\left(-\frac{\pi}{6}\right) = -\sqrt{3}$

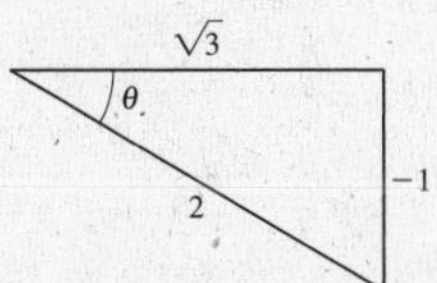


(b) $\csc\left[\arctan\left(-\frac{5}{12}\right)\right] = -\frac{13}{5}$

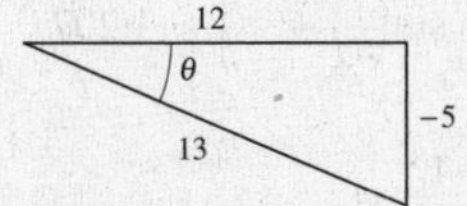


**122.** (a) $\sec\left[\arctan\left(-\frac{3}{5}\right)\right] = \frac{\sqrt{34}}{5}$

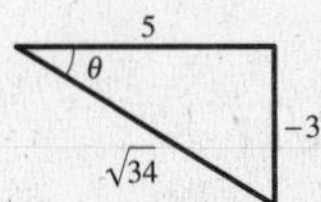


(b) $\tan\left[\arcsin\left(-\frac{5}{6}\right)\right] = -\frac{5\sqrt{11}}{11}$

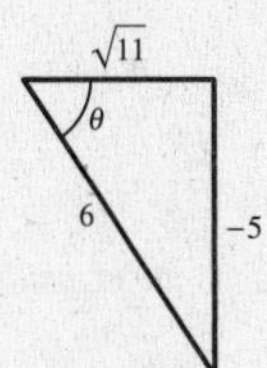


**In Exercises 123–128, use the triangle.**

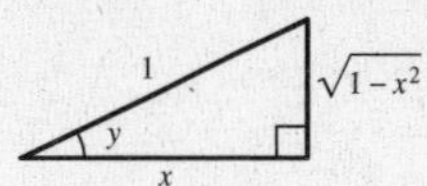


**123.** $y = \arccos x$

$\cos y = x$

**124.** $\sin y = \sqrt{1 - x^2}$

**125.** $\tan y = \frac{\sqrt{1 - x^2}}{x}$

**126.** $\cot y = \frac{x}{\sqrt{1 - x^2}}$

**127.** $\sec y = \frac{1}{x}$

**128.** $\csc y = \frac{1}{\sqrt{1 - x^2}}$

**129.** $y = \tan(\arctan x)$

$\theta = \arctan x$

$y = \tan \theta = x$

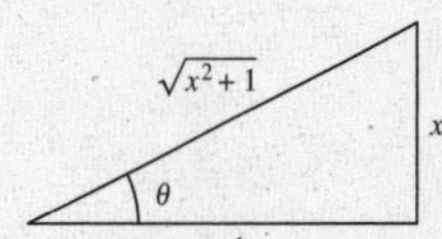


**130.** $y = \sin(\arccos x)$

$\theta = \arccos x$

$y = \sin \theta = \sqrt{1 - x^2}$

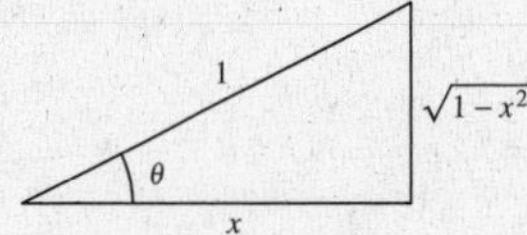


**131.** $y = \cos(\arcsin 2x)$

$\theta = \arcsin 2x$

$y = \cos \theta = \sqrt{1 - 4x^2}$

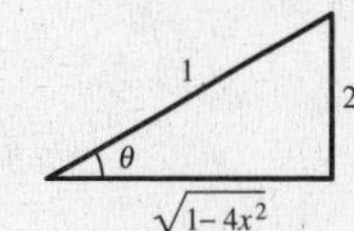

**132.** $\sec(\arctan 4x)$

$\theta = \arctan 4x$

$y = \sec\theta = \sqrt{16x^2 + 1}$

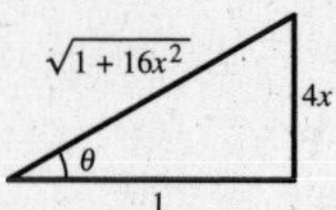


**133.** $y = \sin(\operatorname{arcsec} x)$

$\theta = \operatorname{arcsec} x,\ 0 \le \theta \le \pi,\ \theta \ne \dfrac{\pi}{2}$

$y = \sin\theta = \dfrac{\sqrt{x^2 - 1}}{|x|}$

The absolute value bars on $x$ are necessary because of the restriction $0 \le \theta \le \pi$, $\theta \ne \pi/2$, and $\sin\theta$ for this domain must always be nonnegative.

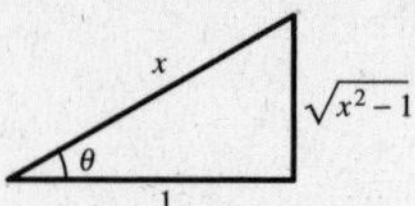


**134.** $y = \cos(\operatorname{arccot} x)$

$\theta = \operatorname{arccot} x$

$y = \cos\theta = \dfrac{x}{\sqrt{x^2 + 1}}$

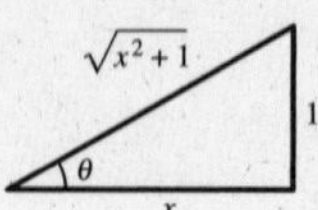


**135.** $y = \tan\left(\operatorname{arcsec}\dfrac{x}{3}\right)$

$\theta = \operatorname{arcsec}\dfrac{x}{3}$

$y = \tan\theta = \dfrac{x^2 - 9}{3}$

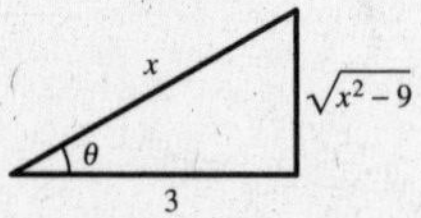


**136.** $y = \sec[\arcsin(x - 1)]$

$\theta = \arcsin(x - 1)$

$y = \sec\theta = \dfrac{1}{\sqrt{2x - x^2}}$

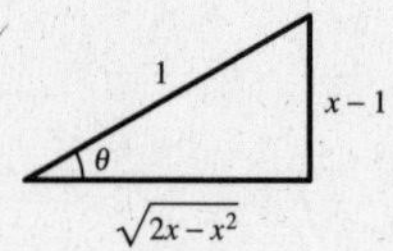


**137.** $y = \csc\left(\arctan\dfrac{x}{\sqrt{2}}\right)$

$\theta = \arctan\dfrac{x}{\sqrt{2}}$

$y = \csc\theta = \dfrac{\sqrt{x^2 + 2}}{x}$

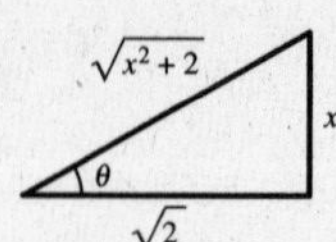


**138.** $y = \cos\left(\arcsin\dfrac{x - h}{r}\right)$

$\theta = \arcsin\dfrac{x - h}{r}$

$y = \cos\theta = \dfrac{\sqrt{r^2 - (x - h)^2}}{r}$

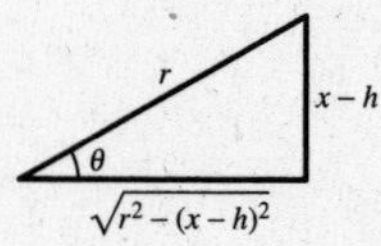


**139.** $\arcsin(3x - \pi) = \frac{1}{2}$

$$3x - \pi = \sin\left(\tfrac{1}{2}\right)$$

$$x = \tfrac{1}{3}\left[\sin\left(\tfrac{1}{2}\right) + \pi\right] \approx 1.207$$

**140.** $\arctan(2x - 5) = -1$

$$2x - 5 = \tan(-1)$$

$$x = \tfrac{1}{2}(5 + \tan(-1)) \approx 1.721$$

**141.** $\arcsin\sqrt{2x} = \arccos\sqrt{x}$

$$\begin{aligned}
\sqrt{2x} &= \sin\left(\arccos\sqrt{x}\right)\\
\sqrt{2x} &= \sqrt{1 - x},\ 0 \le x \le 1\\
2x &= 1 - x\\
3x &= 1\\
x &= \tfrac{1}{3}
\end{aligned}$$

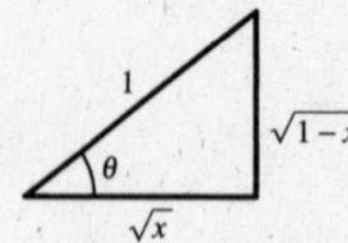

**142.** $\arccos x = \operatorname{arcsec} x$

$$x = \cos(\operatorname{arcsec} x)$$

$$x = \frac{1}{x}$$

$$x^2 = 1$$

$$x = \pm 1$$

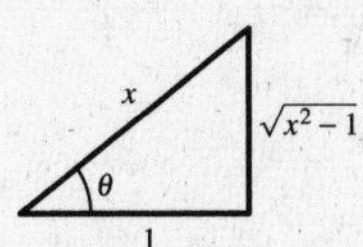


**143.** $y = \arccos x$

$y = \arctan x$

The point of intersection is given by
$f(x) = \arccos x - \arctan x = 0$, $\cos(\arccos x) = \cos(\arctan x)$.

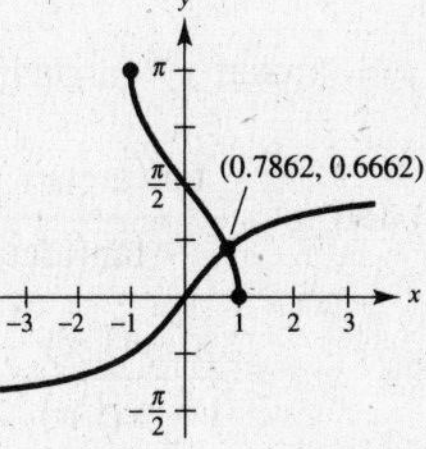


$$x = \frac{1}{\sqrt{1+x^2}}$$

$$x^2(1 + x^2) = 1$$

$$x^4 + x^2 - 1 = 0 \text{ when } x^2 = \frac{-1+\sqrt{5}}{2}.$$

So, $x = \pm\sqrt{\frac{-1+\sqrt{5}}{2}} \approx \pm 0.7862$.

Point of intersection: $(0.7862, 0.6662)$ $[\text{Because } f(-0.7862) = \pi \neq 0.]$

**144.** $y = \arcsin x$

$y = \arccos x$

The point of intersection is given by
$f(x) = \arcsin x - \arccos x = 0$, $\sin(\arcsin x) = \sin(\arccos x)$.

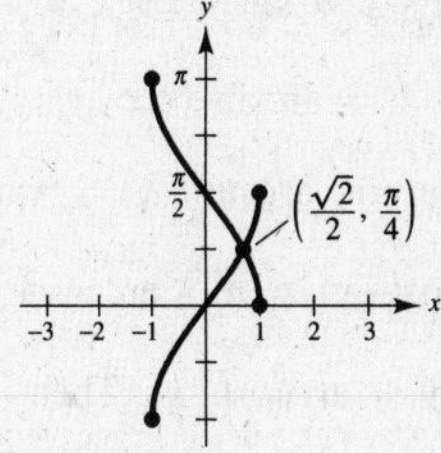


$$x = 1 - x^2$$

$$x^2 = 1 - x^2$$

$$x = \pm\frac{1}{\sqrt{2}} = \pm\frac{\sqrt{2}}{2}$$

Point of intersection: $(\sqrt{2}/2, \pi/4)$ $[\text{Because } f(-\sqrt{2}/2) = -\pi \neq 0.]$

**145.** $\arctan \frac{9}{x} = \arcsin \frac{9}{\sqrt{x^2+81}}$

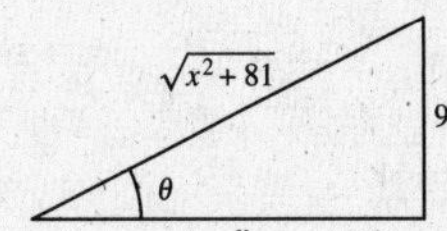


**146.** $\arcsin \frac{\sqrt{36-x^2}}{6} = \arccos \frac{x}{6}$

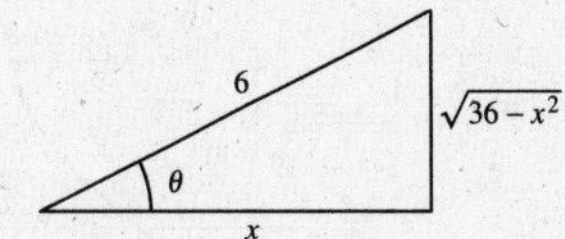

**147.** (a) $\operatorname{arccsc} x = \arcsin \dfrac{1}{x}, |x| \ge 1$

Let $y = \operatorname{arccsc} x$.

Then for $-\dfrac{\pi}{2} \le y < 0$ and $0 < y \le \dfrac{\pi}{2}$,

$\csc y = x \Rightarrow \sin y = \dfrac{1}{x}$.

So, $y = \arcsin\left(\dfrac{1}{x}\right)$. Therefore,

$\operatorname{arccsc} x = \arcsin\left(\dfrac{1}{x}\right)$.

(b) $\arctan x + \arctan\dfrac{1}{x} = \dfrac{\pi}{2}, x > 0$

Let $y = \arctan x + \arctan(1/x)$.

$$\text{Then } \tan y = \frac{\tan(\arctan x) + \tan[\arctan(1/x)]}{1 - \tan(\arctan x)\tan[\arctan(1/x)]}$$

$$= \frac{x + (1/x)}{1 - x(1/x)}$$

$$= \frac{x + (1/x)}{0} \text{ (which is undefined).}$$

So, $y = \pi/2$. Therefore,
$\arctan x + \arctan(1/x) = \pi/2$.

**148.** (a) $\arcsin(-x) = -\arcsin x, |x| \le 1$

Let $y = \arcsin(-x)$.

Then $-x = \sin y \Rightarrow x = -\sin y \Rightarrow x = \sin(-y)$.

So, $-y = \arcsin x \Rightarrow y = -\arcsin x$.

Therefore, $\arcsin(-x) = -\arcsin x$.

(b) $\arccos(-x) = \pi - \arccos x, |x| \le 1$

Let $y = \arccos(-x)$. Then

$-x = \cos y \Rightarrow x = -\cos y \Rightarrow x = \cos(\pi - y)$.

So, $\pi - y = \arccos x \Rightarrow y = \pi - \arccos x$.

Therefore, $\arccos(-x) = \pi - \arccos x$.

**149.** $f(x) = \arcsin(x - 1)$

$x - 1 = \sin y$

$x = 1 + \sin y$

Domain: $[0, 2]$

Range: $[-\pi/2, \pi/2]$

$f(x)$ is the graph of $\arcsin x$ shifted right one unit.

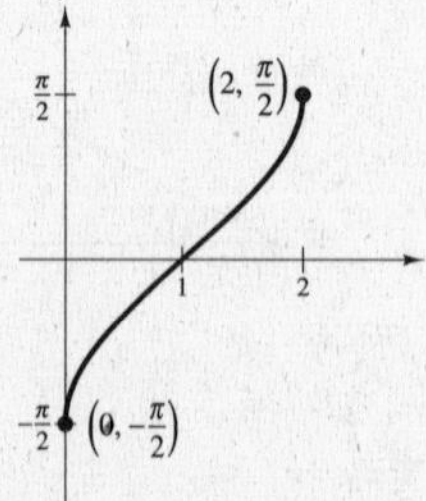


**150.** $f(x) = \arctan x + \dfrac{\pi}{2}$

$x = \tan\left(y - \dfrac{\pi}{2}\right)$

Domain: $(-\infty, \infty)$

Range: $[0, \pi]$

$f(x)$ is the graph of $\arctan x$ shifted $\pi/4$ unit upward.

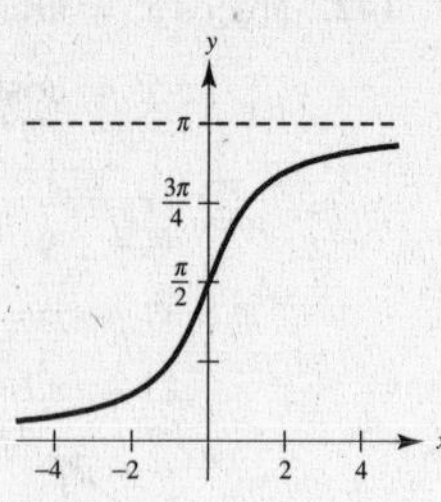


**151.** $f(x) = \operatorname{arcsec} 2x$

$2x = \sec y$

$x = \dfrac{1}{2}\sec y$

Domain: $(-\infty, -1/2], [1/2, \infty)$

Range: $[0, \pi/2), (\pi/2, \pi]$

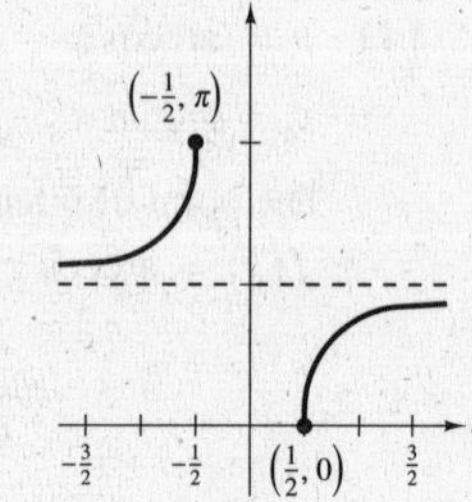


**152.** $f(x) = \arccos\left(\dfrac{x}{4}\right)$

$\dfrac{x}{4} = \cos y$

$x = 4\cos y$

Domain: $[-4, 4]$

Range: $[0, \pi]$

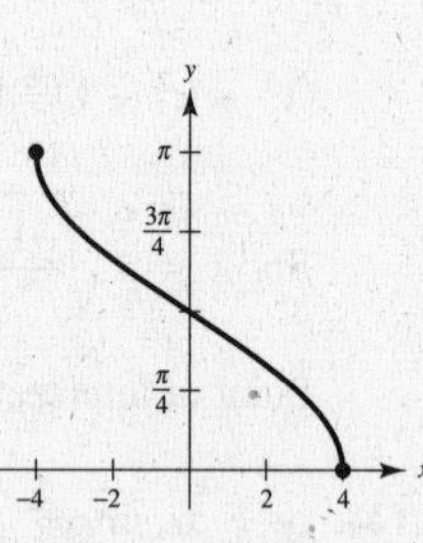


**153.** Because $f(-3) = 8$ and $f$ is one-to-one, you have $f^{-1}(8) = -3$.

**154.** Because $f(0) = 5 + \arccos(0) = 5 + \pi/2$, and $f$ is one-to-one, $f^{-1}(\pi/2 + 5) = 0$.

**155.** Let $f$ and $g$ be one-to-one functions.

Let $(f \circ g)(x) = y$, then $x = (f \circ g)^{-1}(y)$. Also:

$$(f \circ g)(x) = y$$
$$f(g(x)) = y$$
$$g(x) = f^{-1}(y)$$
$$x = g^{-1}(f^{-1}(y))$$
$$x = (g^{-1} \circ f^{-1}(y))$$

So, $(f \circ g)^{-1}(y) = (g^{-1} \circ f^{-1})(y)$ and $(f \circ g)^{-1} = g^{-1} \circ f^{-1}$.

**156.** If $f$ has an inverse, then $f$ and $f^{-1}$ are both one-to-one.

Let $(f^{-1})^{-1}(x) = y$ then $x = f^{-1}(y)$ and $f(x) = y$.

So, $(f^{-1})^{-1} = f$.

**157.** Let $y = \sin^{-1}x$. Then $\sin y = x$ and $\cos(\sin^{-1}x) = \cos(y) = \sqrt{1 - x^2}$, as indicated in the figure.

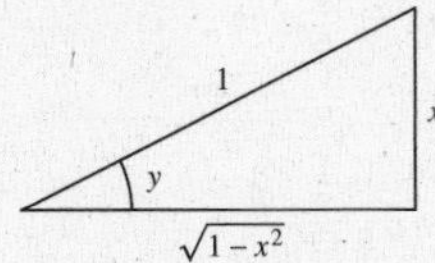


**158.** Suppose $g(x_1) = g(x_2)$. Then

$$\frac{1}{f(x_1)} = \frac{1}{f(x_2)} \Rightarrow f(x_1) = f(x_2).$$

But, $f$ is one-to-one, so $x_1 = x_2$. Therefore, $g$ is one-to-one.

**159.** Suppose $g(x)$ and $h(x)$ are both inverses of $f(x)$. Then the graph of $f(x)$ contains the point $(a, b)$ if and only if the graphs of $g(x)$ and $h(x)$ contain the point $(b, a)$. Because the graphs of $g(x)$ and $h(x)$ are the same, $g(x) = h(x)$. So, the inverse of $f(x)$ is unique.

**160.** If $f$ has an inverse and $f(x_1) = f(x_2)$, then $f^{-1}(f(x_1)) = f^{-1}(f(x_2)) \Rightarrow x_1 = x_2$. So, $f$ is one-to-one. If $f(x)$ is one-to-one, then for every value $b$ in the range, there corresponds exactly one value $a$ in the domain. Define $g(x)$ such that the domain of $g$ equals the range of $f$ and $g(b) = a$. By the reflexive property of inverses, $g = f^{-1}$.

**161.** False. Let $f(x) = x^2$.

**162.** True; if $f$ has a $y$-intercept.

**163.** False

$$\arcsin^2 0 + \arccos^2 0 = 0 + \frac{\pi^2}{2} \neq 1$$

**164.** False

The range of $y = \arcsin x$ is $\left[-\frac{\pi}{2}, \frac{\pi}{2}\right]$.

**165.** True

**166.** False. Let $f(x) = x$ or $g(x) = 1/x$.

**167.** (a) $\operatorname{arccot} x = y$ if and only if $\cot y = x$, $0 < y < \pi$.

For $x > 0$, $\cot y > 0$ and $0 < y < \frac{\pi}{2}$.

So, $\tan y = \frac{1}{x} > 0$ and $y = \arctan\left(\frac{1}{x}\right)$.

For $x = 0$, $\operatorname{arccot}(0) = \frac{\pi}{2}$.

For $x < 0$, $\cot y < 0$ and $\frac{\pi}{2} < y < \pi$.

So, $\tan y = \frac{1}{x} < 0$ and $\arctan\left(\frac{1}{x}\right) < 0$.

Therefore, you need to add $\pi$ to get

$y = \pi + \arctan\left(\frac{1}{x}\right)$.

(b) $y = \operatorname{arcsec} x$ if and only if $\sec y = x$, $|x| \geq 1$, $0 \leq y \leq \pi$, $y \neq \frac{\pi}{2}$.

So, $\cos y = \frac{1}{x}$ and $y = \arccos\left(\frac{1}{x}\right)$.

(c) $y = \operatorname{arccsc} x$ if and only if $\csc y = x$, $|x| \geq 1$, $-\frac{\pi}{2} \leq y \leq \frac{\pi}{2}$, $y \neq 0$.

So, $\sin y = \frac{1}{x}$ and $y = \arcsin\left(\frac{1}{x}\right)$.

**168.** (a) $\operatorname{arccot}(0.5) = \arctan\left(\frac{1}{0.5}\right) = \arctan(2) \approx 1.1071$

(b) $\operatorname{arcsec}(2.7) = \arccos\left(\frac{1}{2.7}\right) \approx 1.1914$

(c) $\operatorname{arccsc}(-3.9) = \arcsin\left(\frac{-1}{3.9}\right) \approx -0.2593$

(d) $\operatorname{arccot}(-0.5) = \pi + \arctan(-2.0) \approx 2.0344$

**169.** $\tan(\arctan x + \arctan y) = \dfrac{\tan(\arctan x + \arctan y)}{1 - \tan(\arctan x)\tan(\arctan y)} = \dfrac{x + y}{1 - xy}, xy \neq 1$

So,

$$\arctan x + \arctan y = \arctan\left(\frac{x + y}{1 - xy}\right), xy \neq 1.$$

Let $x = \dfrac{1}{2}$ and $y = \dfrac{1}{3}$.

$$\arctan\left(\frac{1}{2}\right) + \arctan\left(\frac{1}{3}\right) = \arctan\frac{\frac{1}{2} + \frac{1}{3}}{1 - \left(\frac{1}{2}\cdot\frac{1}{3}\right)} = \arctan\frac{\frac{5}{6}}{1 - \frac{1}{6}} = \arctan\frac{\frac{5}{6}}{\frac{5}{6}} = \arctan 1 = \frac{\pi}{4}$$

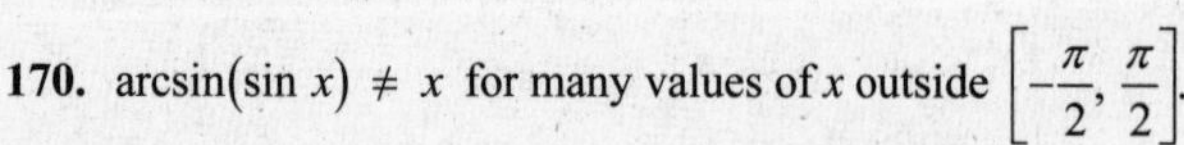

**170.** $\arcsin(\sin x) \neq x$ for many values of $x$ outside $\left[-\dfrac{\pi}{2}, \dfrac{\pi}{2}\right]$.

For example, $\arcsin(\sin 2\pi) = \arcsin(0) = 0 \neq 2\pi$.

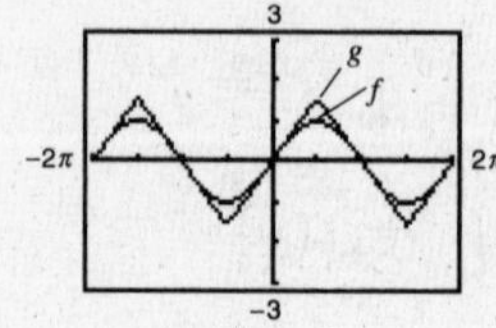


**171.** $y = ax^2 + bx + c$. Interchange $x$ and $y$, and solve for $y$ using the quadratic formula.

$$ay^2 + by + c - x = 0$$

$$y = \frac{-b \pm \sqrt{b^2 - 4a(c - x)}}{2a}$$

Because $x \leq \dfrac{-b}{2a}$, use the negative sign.

$$f^{-1}(x) = \frac{-b - \sqrt{b^2 - 4ac + 4ax}}{2a}$$

**172.** $f$ will be symmetric about the line $y = x$ if $f$ is one-to-one, and equals its inverse. So assume

$$f(x_1) = f(x_2)$$

$$\frac{ax_1 + b}{cx_1 - a} = \frac{ax_2 + b}{cx_2 - a}$$

$$acx_1x_2 - a^2x_1 + bcx_2 - ab = acx_1x_2 + bcx_1 - ab$$

$$(a^2 + bc)x_2 = (a^2 + bc)x_1.$$

So, $x_1 = x_2$ if $a^2 + bc \neq 0$.

To show that $f = f^{-1}$, solve for $x$ as follows:

$$y = \frac{ax + b}{cx - a}$$

$$ycx - ay = ax + b$$

$$(yc - a)x = b + ay$$

$$x = \frac{ay + b}{yc - a}$$

$$f^{-1}(x) = \frac{ax + b}{cx - a} = f(x)$$

So, $f$ is symmetric about the line $y = x$ is and only if $a^2 + bc \neq 0$.

**173.** $f$ is one-to-one if $f(x_1) = f(x_2)$ implies $x_1 = x_2$. So assume

$$\begin{aligned}
f(x_1) &= f(x_2)\\
\frac{ax_1 + b}{cx_1 + d} &= \frac{ax_2 + b}{cx_2 + d}\\
acx_1x_2 + adx_1 + bcx_2 + bd &= acx_1x_2 + adx_2 + bcx_1 + bd\\
adx_1 + bcx_2 &= adx_2 + bcx_1\\
(ad - bc)x_1 &= (ad - bc)x_2.
\end{aligned}$$

So, $x_1 = x_2$ if $ad - bc \neq 0$. To find $f^{-1}$, solve for $x$ as follows.

$$\begin{aligned}
y &= \frac{ax + b}{cx + d}\\
ycx + yd &= ax + b\\
(yc - a)x &= b - yd\\
x &= \frac{b - yd}{yc - a}\\
f^{-1}(x) &= \frac{b - dx}{cx - a}
\end{aligned}$$

**174.** No, $(0, 3\pi/2)$ is not on the graph of $y = \arccos x$.

The domain of $y = \arccos x$ is $[-1, 1]$, and its range is $[0, \pi]$.

So, $\arccos(0) = \pi/2$.

## Section 1.6 Exponential and Logarithmic Functions

**1.** (a) $25^{3/2} = 5^3 = 125$

(b) $81^{1/2} = 9$

(c) $3^{-2} = \frac{1}{3^2} = \frac{1}{9}$

(d) $27^{-1/3} = \frac{1}{27^{1/3}} = \frac{1}{3}$

**2.** (a) $64^{1/3} = 4$

(b) $5^{-4} = \frac{1}{5^4} = \frac{1}{625}$

(c) $\left(\frac{1}{8}\right)^{1/3} = \frac{1}{2}$

(d) $\left(\frac{1}{4}\right)^3 = \frac{1}{64}$

**3.** (a) $(5^2)(5^3) = 5^{2+3} = 5^5 = 3125$

(b) $(5^2)(5^{-3}) = 5^{2-3} = 5^{-1} = \frac{1}{5}$

(c) $\frac{5^3}{25^2} = \frac{5^3}{5^4} = \frac{1}{5}$

(d) $\left(\frac{1}{4}\right)^2 2^6 - \frac{2^6}{2^4} = 2^2 = 4$

**4.** (a) $(2^2)^3 = 2^6 = 64$

(b) $(5^4)^{1/2} = 5^2 = 25$

(c) $\left[(27)^{-1}(27)^{2/3}\right]^3 = \left[27^{-1/3}\right]^3 = 27^{-1} = \frac{1}{27}$

(d) $(25)^{3/2}3^2 = 5^3 3^2 = (125)9 = 1125$

**5.** (a) $e^2(e^4) = e^6$

(b) $(e^3)^4 = e^{12}$

(c) $(e^3)^{-2} = e^{-6} = \frac{1}{e^6}$

(d) $\frac{e^5}{e^3} = e^2$

**6.** (a) $\left(\frac{1}{e}\right)^{-2} = e^2$

(b) $(e^3)^4 = e^{12}$

(c) $e^0 = 1$

(d) $\frac{1}{e^{-3}} = e^3$

**7.** $3^x = 81 \Rightarrow x = 4$

**8.** $4^x = 64 \Rightarrow x = 3$

**9.** $6^{x-2} = 36 \Rightarrow x - 2 = 2 \Rightarrow x = 4$

**10.** $5^{x+1} = 125 \Rightarrow x + 1 = 3 \Rightarrow x = 2$

**11.** $\left(\frac{1}{2}\right)^x = 32 \Rightarrow 2^{-x} = 32 \Rightarrow -x = 5 \Rightarrow x = -5$

**12.** $\left(\frac{1}{4}\right)^x = 16 \Rightarrow 4^{-x} = 16 \Rightarrow -x = 2 \Rightarrow x = -2$

**13.** $\left(\frac{1}{3}\right)^{x-1} = 27 \Rightarrow 3^{1-x} = 27 \Rightarrow 1 - x = 3 \Rightarrow x = -2$

**14.** $\left(\frac{1}{5}\right)^{2x} = 625 \Rightarrow 5^{-2x} = 5^4 \Rightarrow -2x = 4 \Rightarrow x = -2$

**15.** $4^3 = (x+2)^3 \Rightarrow 4 = x + 2 \Rightarrow x = 2$

**16.** $18^2 = (5x-7)^2 \Rightarrow \pm 18 = 5x - 7 \Rightarrow x = 5, -\frac{11}{5}$

**17.** $x^{3/4} = 8 \Rightarrow x = 8^{4/3} = 2^4 = 16$

**18.** $(x+3)^{4/3} = 16 \Rightarrow x + 3 = \pm 16^{3/4}$
$\Rightarrow x + 3 = \pm 8 \Rightarrow x = 5, -11$

**19.** $e^x = 5 \Rightarrow x = \ln 5 \approx 1.609$

**20.** $e^x = 1 = e^0 \Rightarrow x = 0$

**21.** $e^{-2x} = e^5 \Rightarrow -2x = 5 \Rightarrow x = -\frac{5}{2}$

**22.** $e^{3x} = e^{-4} \Rightarrow 3x = -4 \Rightarrow x = -\frac{4}{3}$

**23.** $\left(1 + \frac{1}{1{,}000{,}000}\right)^{1{,}000{,}000} \approx 2.718280469$

$e \approx 2.718281828$

$e > \left(1 + \frac{1}{1{,}000{,}000}\right)^{1{,}000{,}000}$

**24.** $1 + 1 + \frac{1}{2} + \frac{1}{6} + \frac{1}{24} + \frac{1}{120} + \frac{1}{720} + \frac{1}{5040} = 2.71\overline{825396}$

$e \approx 2.718281828$

$e > 1 + 1 + \frac{1}{2} + \frac{1}{6} + \frac{1}{24} + \frac{1}{120} + \frac{1}{720} + \frac{1}{5040}$

**25.** $y = 3^x$

| $x$ | $-2$ | $-1$ | $0$ | $1$ | $2$ |
|---|---|---|---|---|---|
| $y$ | $\frac{1}{9}$ | $\frac{1}{3}$ | $1$ | $3$ | $9$ |

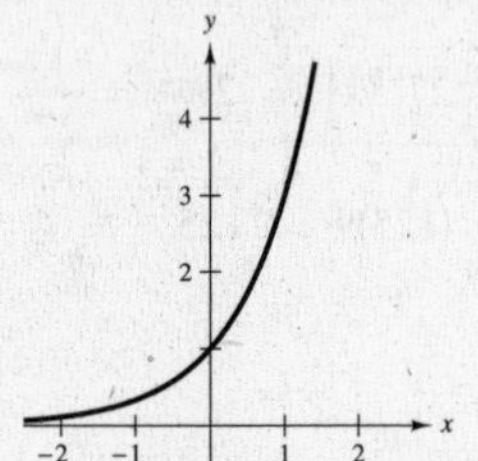

**26.** $y = 3^{x-1}$

| $x$ | $-1$ | $0$ | $1$ | $2$ | $3$ |
|---|---|---|---|---|---|
| $y$ | $\frac{1}{9}$ | $\frac{1}{3}$ | $1$ | $3$ | $9$ |

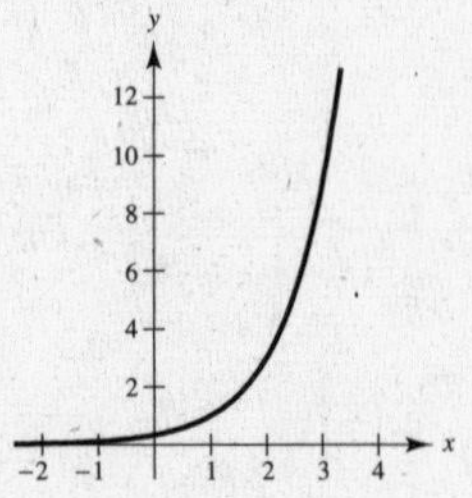

**27.** $y = \left(\frac{1}{3}\right)^x = 3^{-x}$

| $x$ | $-2$ | $-1$ | $0$ | $1$ | $2$ |
|---|---|---|---|---|---|
| $y$ | $9$ | $3$ | $1$ | $\frac{1}{3}$ | $\frac{1}{9}$ |

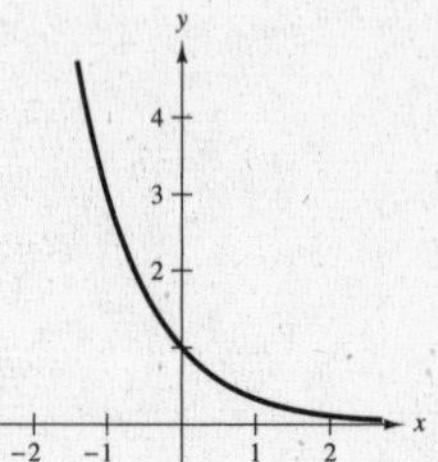

**28.** $y = 2^{-x^2}$

| $x$ | $-2$ | $-1$ | $0$ | $1$ | $2$ | $3$ |
|---|---|---|---|---|---|---|
| $y$ | $\frac{1}{16}$ | $\frac{1}{2}$ | $1$ | $\frac{1}{2}$ | $\frac{1}{16}$ | $0.002$ |

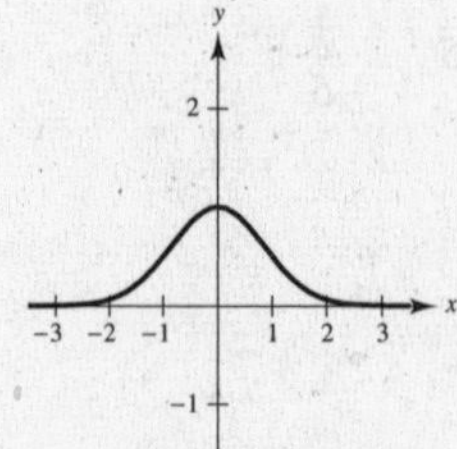

**29.** $f(x) = 3^{-x^2}$

| $x$ | 0 | $\pm 1$ | $\pm 2$ |
|---|---|---|---|
| $y$ | 1 | $\frac{1}{3}$ | 0.0123 |

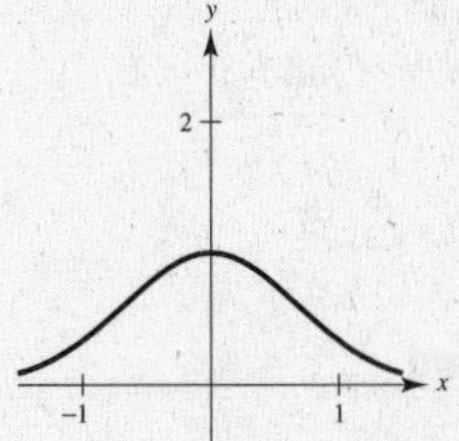

**30.** $f(x) = 3^{|x|}$

| $x$ | 0 | $\pm 1$ | $\pm 2$ |
|---|---|---|---|
| $y$ | 1 | 9 | 9 |

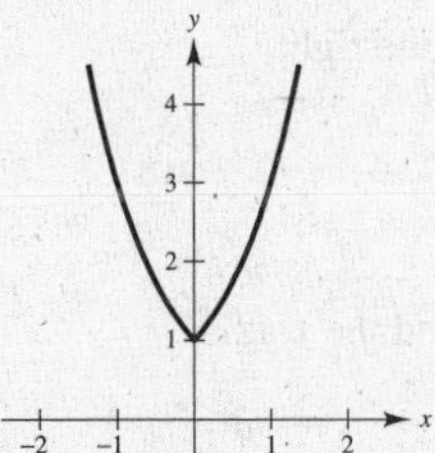

**31.** $h(x) = e^{x-2}$

| $x$ | 0 | 1 | 2 | 3 | 4 |
|---|---|---|---|---|---|
| $y$ | $e^{-2}$ | $e^{-1}$ | 1 | $e$ | $e^2$ |

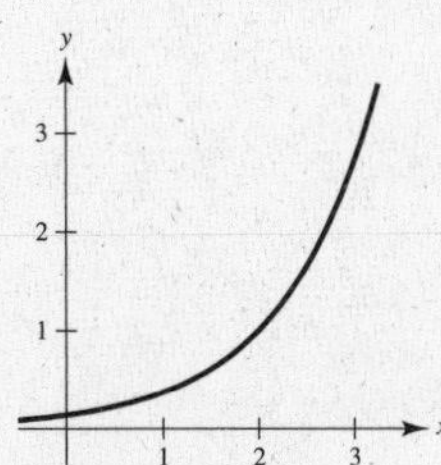

**32.** $g(x) = -e^{x/2}$

| $x$ | $-2$ | 0 | 2 | 4 |
|---|---|---|---|---|
| $y$ | $-\frac{1}{e}$ | $-1$ | $-e$ | $-e^2$ |

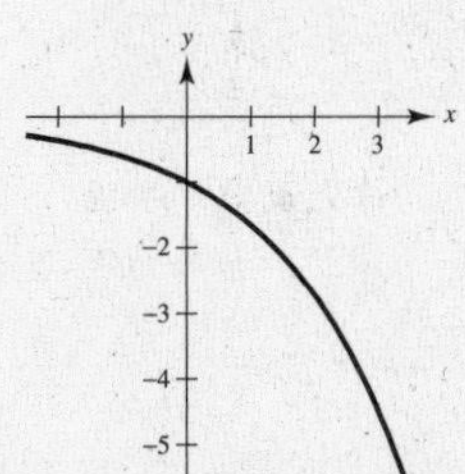

**33.** $y = e^{-x^2}$

Symmetric with respect to the $y$-axis

Horizontal asymptote

$y = 0$

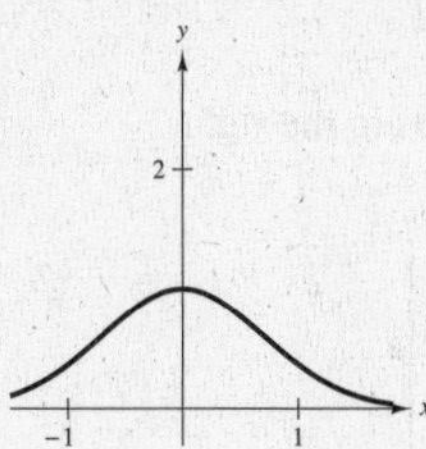

**34.** $y = e^{-x/4}$

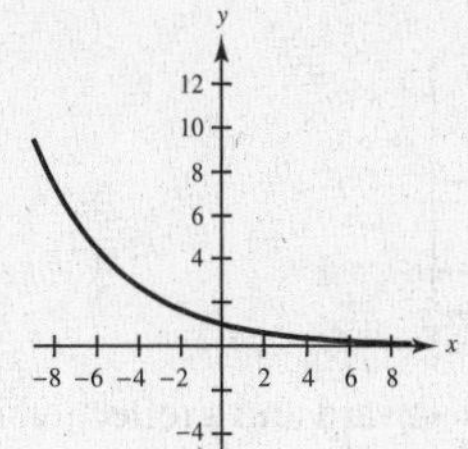

**35.** $f(x) = \dfrac{1}{3 + e^x}$

Because $e^x > 0,\ 3 + e^x > 0.$

Domain: all real numbers

**36.** $f(x) = \dfrac{1}{2 - e^x}$

$2 - e^x = 0 \Rightarrow x = \ln 2$

Domain: all $x \neq \ln 2$

**37.** $f(x) = \sqrt{1 - 4^x}$

$1 - 4^x \geq 0 \Rightarrow 4^x \leq 1 \Rightarrow x \ln 4 \leq \ln 1 = 0$

Domain: $x \leq 0$

**38.** $f(x) = \sqrt{1 + 3^{-x}}$

Because $1 + 3^{-x} > 0$ for all $x$, the domain is all real numbers.

**39.** $f(x) = \sin e^{-x}$

Domain: all real numbers

**40.** $f(x) = \cos e^{-x}$

Domain: all real numbers

**41.** 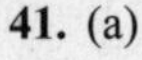 (a)

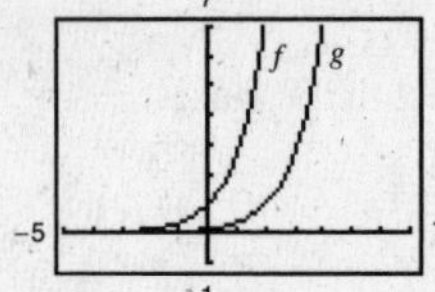


Horizontal shift 2 units to the right.

 (b)

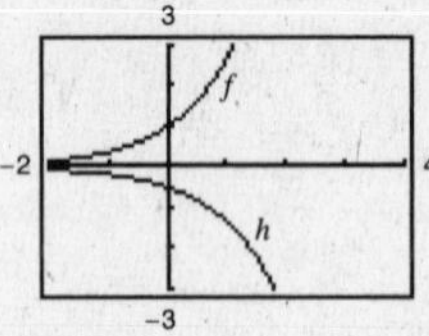


A reflection in the $x$-axis and a vertical shrink.

(c)

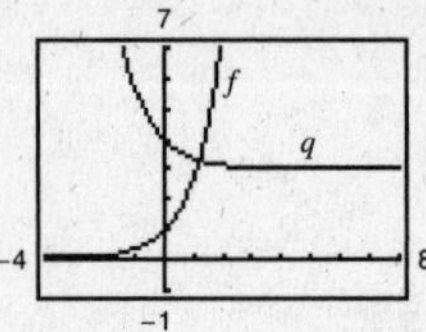


Vertical shift 3 units upward and a reflection in the $y$-axis.

**42.** (a)

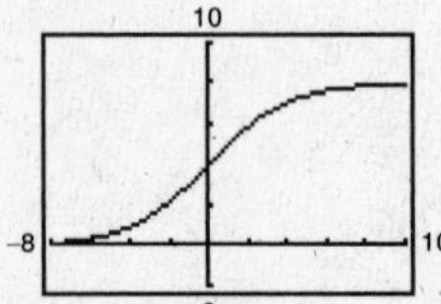


The graph approaches 8 as $x \to \infty$. The graph approaches 0 as $x \to -\infty$.

(b)

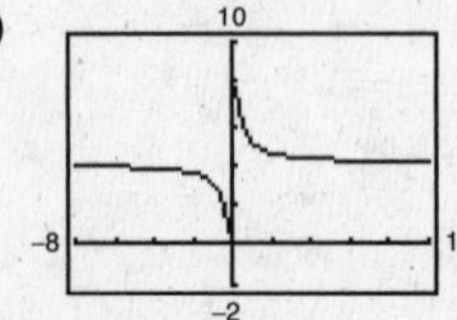


As $x \to \pm\infty$, the graph approaches 4.

**43.** $y = Ce^{ax}$

Horizontal asymptote: $y = 0$

Matches (c)

**44.** $y = Ce^{-ax}$

Horizontal asymptote: $y = 0$

Reflection in the $y$-axis

Matches (d)

**45.** $y = C(1 - e^{-ax})$

Vertical shift $C$ units

Reflection in both the $x$- and $y$-axes

Matches (a)

**46.** $y = \dfrac{C}{1 + e^{-ax}}$

$$\lim_{x\to\infty} \frac{C}{1 + e^{-ax}} = C$$

$$\lim_{x\to-\infty} \frac{C}{1 + e^{-ax}} = 0$$

Horizontal asymptotes: $y = C$ and $y = 0$

Matches (b)

**47.** $f(x) = \ln x + 1$

Vertical shift 1 unit upward

Matches (b)

**48.** $f(x) = -\ln x$

Reflection in the $x$-axis

Matches (d)

**49.** $f(x) = \ln(x - 1)$

Horizontal shift 1 unit to the right

Matches (a)

**50.** $f(x) = -\ln(-x)$

Reflection in the $y$-axis and the $x$-axis

Matches (c)

**51.** $y = Ca^x$

$(0, 2)$: $2 = Ca^0 = C$

$(3, 54)$: $54 = 2a^3$

$27 = a^3$

$3 = a$

$y = 2(3^x)$

**52.** $y = Ca^x$

$(1, 2)$: $2 = Ca$

$(2, 1)$: $1 = Ca^2$

Dividing eliminates $C$: $\dfrac{2}{1} = \dfrac{Ca}{Ca^2} = \dfrac{1}{a}$

So, $a = \dfrac{1}{2}$ and $C = 4$.

$y = 4\left(\dfrac{1}{2}\right)^x = 4(2^{-x})$

**53.** $e^0 = 1$

$\ln 1 = 0$

**54.** $e^{-2} = 0.1353\ldots$

$\ln 0.1353\ldots = -2$

**55.** $\ln 2 = 0.6931\ldots$

$e^{0.6931\ldots} = 2$

**56.** $\ln 0.5 = -0.6931\ldots$

$e^{-0.6931\ldots} = \frac{1}{2}$

**57.** $f(x) = 3 \ln x$

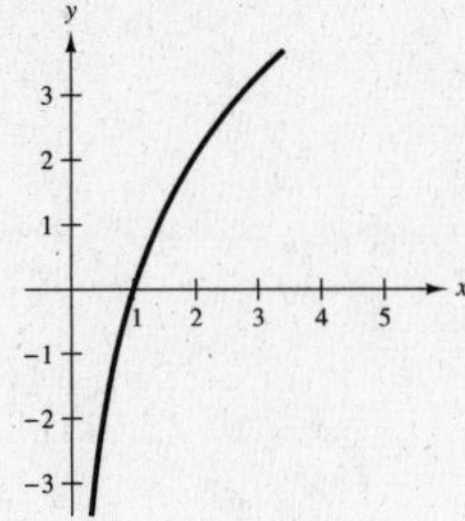

Domain: $x > 0$

**58.** $f(x) = -2 \ln x$

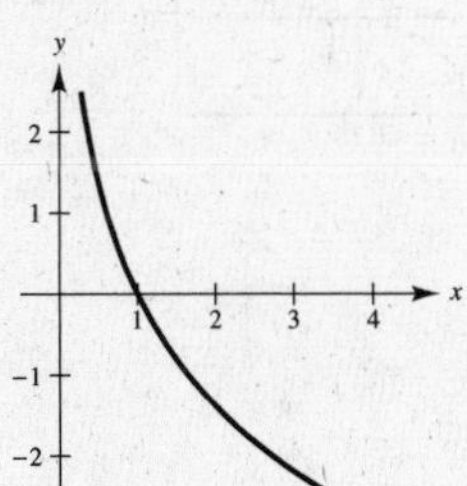

Domain: $x > 0$

**59.** $f(x) = \ln 2x$

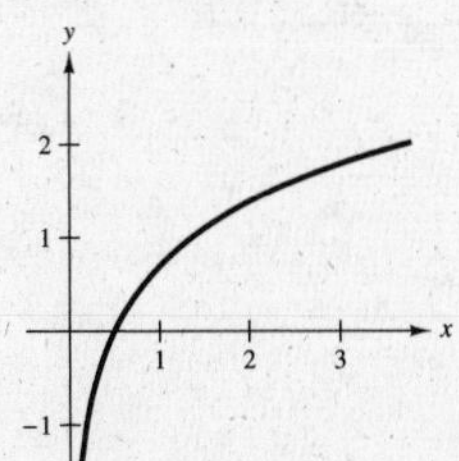

Domain: $x > 0$

**60.** $f(x) = \ln|x|$

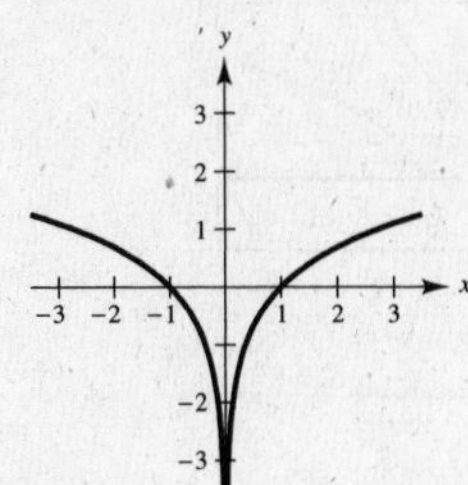

Domain: $x \neq 0$

**61.** $f(x) = \ln(x - 1)$

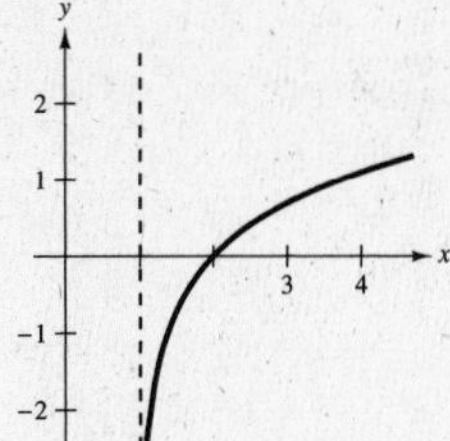

Domain: $x > 1$

**62.** $g(x) = 2 + \ln x$

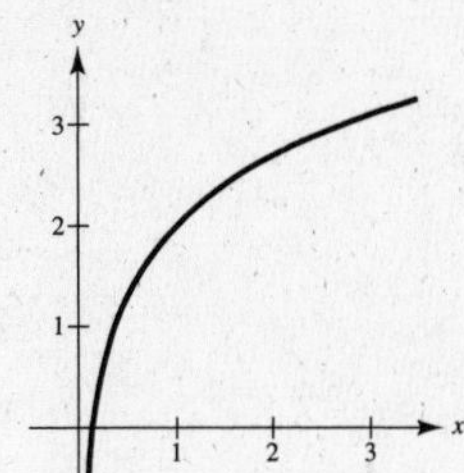

Domain: $x > 0$

**63.** 8 units upward: $e^x + 8$

Reflected in $x$-axis: $-(e^x + 8)$

$y = -(e^x + 8) = -e^x - 8$

**64.** 2 units to the left: $e^{x+2}$

6 units downward: $e^{x+2} - 6$

$y = e^{x+2} - 6$

**65.** 5 units to the right: $\ln(x - 5)$

1 unit downward: $\ln(x - 5) - 1$

$y = \ln(x - 5) - 1$

**66.** 3 units upward: $\ln x + 3$

Reflected in $x$-axis: $\ln(-x) + 3$

$y = \ln(-x) + 3$

**67.** $f(x) = e^{2x}$

$g(x) = \ln\sqrt{x} = \frac{1}{2} \ln x$

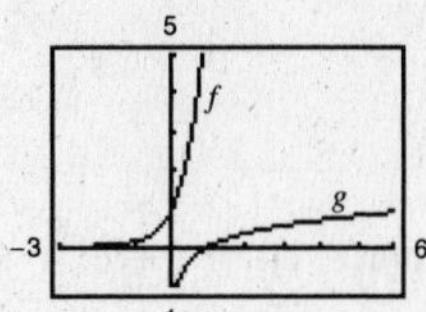

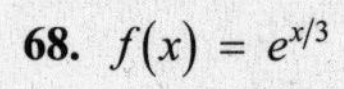

**68.** $f(x) = e^{x/3}$

$g(x) = \ln x^3 = 3 \ln x$

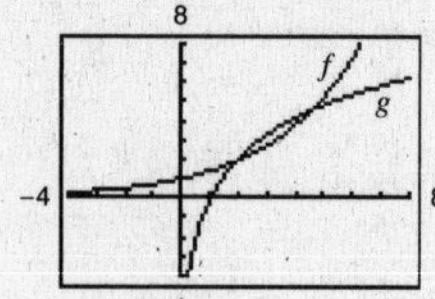


**69.** $f(x) = e^x - 1$

$g(x) = \ln(x + 1)$

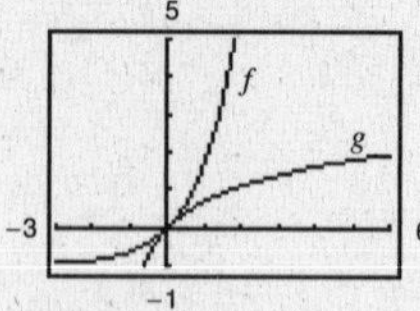


**70.** $f(x) = e^{x-1}$

$g(x) = 1 + \ln x$

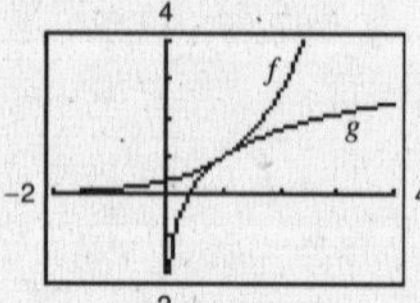


**71.** (a)

$$\begin{aligned} y &= e^{4x-1} \\ \ln y &= 4x - 1 \\ \ln y + 1 &= 4x \\ x &= \tfrac{1}{4}(\ln y + 1) \\ f^{-1}(x) &= \tfrac{1}{4}(\ln x + 1) \end{aligned}$$

(b)

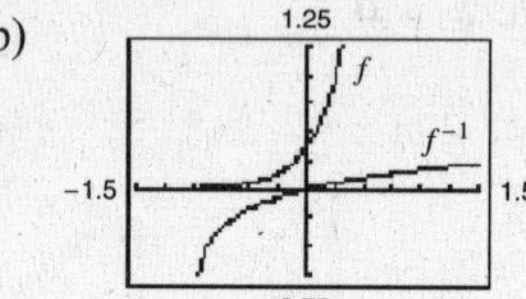


(c) $f^{-1}(f(x)) = f^{-1}(e^{4x-1}) = \frac{1}{4}(\ln e^{4x-1} + 1) = \frac{1}{4}(4x - 1 + 1) = x$

$f(f^{-1}(x)) = f\left(\frac{1}{4}(\ln x + 1)\right) = e^{(\ln x + 1) - 1} = e^{\ln x} = x$

**72.** (a)

$$\begin{aligned} y &= 3e^{-x} \\ \frac{y}{3} &= e^{-x} \\ \ln\frac{y}{3} &= -x \\ x &= -\ln\frac{y}{3} = \ln\frac{3}{y} \\ f^{-1}(x) &= \ln\frac{3}{x} = \ln 3 - \ln x \end{aligned}$$

(b)

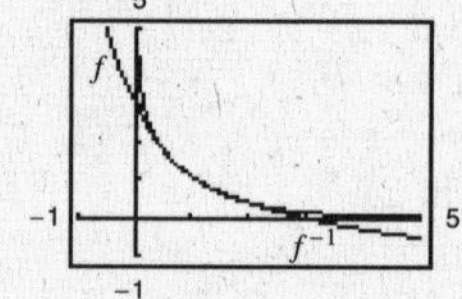


(c) $f^{-1}(f(x)) = f^{-1}(3e^{-x}) = \ln 3 - \ln(3e^{-x}) = \ln 3 - \ln 3 - \ln e^{-x} = x$

$f(f^{-1}(x)) = f\left(\ln\frac{3}{x}\right) = 3e^{-\ln(3/x)} = 3e^{\ln(x/3)} = 3\left(\frac{x}{3}\right) = x$

**73.** (a)

$$\begin{aligned} y &= 2\ln(x - 1) \\ \frac{y}{2} &= \ln(x - 1) \\ e^{y/2} &= x - 1 \\ x &= 1 + e^{y/2} \\ f^{-1}(x) &= 1 + e^{x/2} \end{aligned}$$

(b)

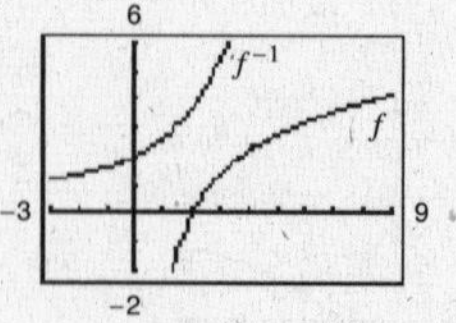


(c) $f^{-1}(f(x)) = f^{-1}(2\ln(x - 1)) = 1 + e^{\ln(x-1)} = 1 + x - 1 = x$

$f(f^{-1}(x)) = f(1 + x^{x/2}) = 2\ln\left[(1 + e^{x/2}) - 1\right] = 2\left(\frac{x}{2}\right) = x$

**74.** (a)

$$\begin{aligned} y &= 3 + \ln(2x) \\ y - 3 &= \ln 2x \\ e^{y-2} &= 2x \\ x &= \tfrac{1}{2}e^{y-3} \\ f^{-1}(x) &= \tfrac{1}{2}e^{x-3} \end{aligned}$$

(b)

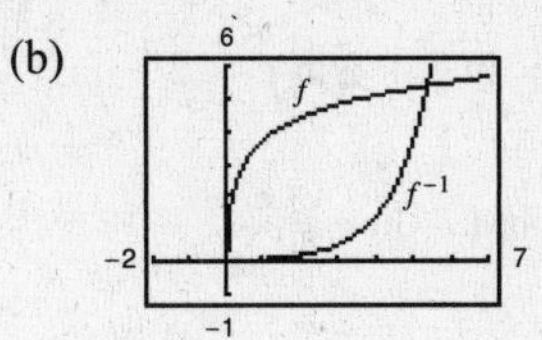


(c)

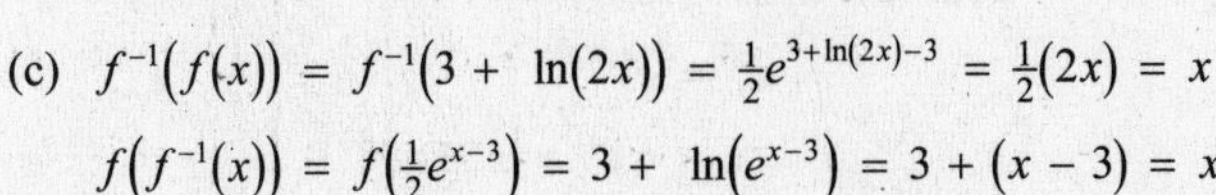
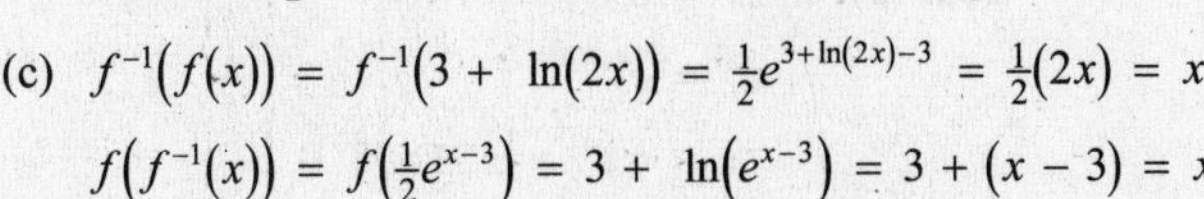

$$f^{-1}(f(x)) = f^{-1}(3 + \ln(2x)) = \tfrac{1}{2}e^{3+\ln(2x)-3} = \tfrac{1}{2}(2x) = x$$

$$f(f^{-1}(x)) = f\left(\tfrac{1}{2}e^{x-3}\right) = 3 + \ln\left(e^{x-3}\right) = 3 + (x - 3) = x$$

**75.** $\ln e^{x^2} = x^2$

**76.** $\ln e^{2x-1} = 2x - 1$

**77.** $e^{\ln(5x+2)} = 5x + 2$

**78.** $e^{\ln\sqrt{x}} = \sqrt{x}$

**79.** $-1 + \ln e^{2x} = -1 + 2x$

**80.** $-8 + e^{\ln x^3} = -8 + x^3$

**81.** (a) $\ln 6 = \ln 2 + \ln 3 \approx 1.7917$

(b) $\ln\frac{2}{3} = \ln 2 - \ln 3 \approx -0.4055$

(c) $\ln 81 = 4 \ln 3 \approx 4.3944$

(d) $\ln\sqrt{3} = \frac{1}{2}\ln 3 \approx 0.5493$

**82.** (a) $\ln 0.25 = \ln\frac{1}{4} = \ln 1 - 2\ln 2 \approx -1.3862$

(b) $\ln 24 = 3\ln 2 + \ln 3 \approx 3.1779$

(c) $\ln\sqrt[3]{12} = \frac{1}{3}(2\ln 2 + \ln 3) \approx 0.8283$

(d) $\ln\frac{1}{72} = \ln 1 - (3\ln 2 + 2\ln 3) \approx -4.2765$

**83.** The domain of the natural logarithmic function is $(0, \infty)$ and the range is $(-\infty, \infty)$. The function is continuous, increasing, and one-to-one, and its graph is concave downward. In addition, if $a$ and $b$ are positive numbers and $n$ is rational, then $\ln(1) = 0$, $\ln(a \cdot b) = \ln a + \ln b$, $\ln(a^n) = n \ln a$, and $\ln(a/b) = \ln a - \ln b$.

**84.** The functions $f(x) = e^x$ and $g(x) = \ln x$ are inverses of each other. So, $\ln e^x = g(f(x)) = x$.

**85.** $f(x) = e^x$. Domain is $(-\infty, \infty)$ and range is $(0, \infty)$. $f$ is continuous, increasing, one-to-one, and concave upwards on its entire domain.

$\lim_{x\to-\infty} e^x = 0$ and $\lim_{x\to\infty} e^x = \infty$

**86.**

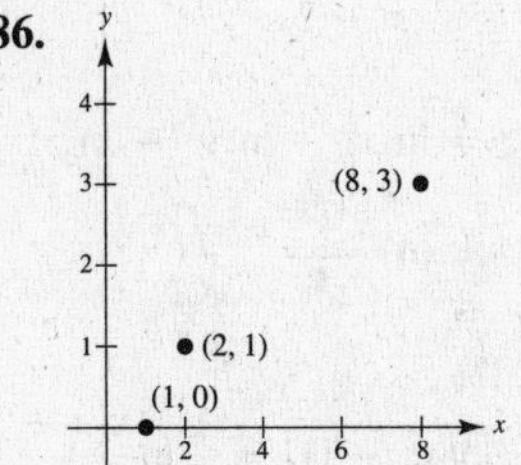


| $x$ | 1 | 2 | 8 |
|---|---|---|---|
| $y$ | 0 | 1 | 3 |

(a) $y$ is an exponential function of $x$: False

(b) $y$ is a logarithmic function of $x$: True; $y = \log_2 x$

(c) $x$ is an exponential function of $y$: True; $2^y = x$

(d) $y$ is a linear function of $x$: False

**87.** $\ln\dfrac{x}{4} = \ln x - \ln 4$

**88.** $\ln\sqrt{x^5} = \ln x^{5/2} = \frac{5}{2}\ln x$

**89.** $\ln\dfrac{xy}{z} = \ln x + \ln y - \ln z$

**90.** $\ln(xyz) = \ln x + \ln y + \ln z$

**91.**

$$\begin{aligned} \ln\left(x\sqrt{x^2 + 5}\right) &= \ln x + \ln\left(x^2 + 5\right)^{1/2} \\ &= \ln x + \tfrac{1}{2}\ln\left(x^2 + 5\right) \end{aligned}$$

**92.** $\ln\sqrt[3]{z + 1} = \ln(z + 1)^{1/3} = \frac{1}{3}\ln(z + 1)$

**93.**

$$\begin{aligned} \ln\sqrt{\frac{x-1}{x}} &= \ln\left(\frac{x-1}{x}\right)^{1/2} = \frac{1}{2}\ln\left(\frac{x-1}{x}\right) \\ &= \frac{1}{2}\left[\ln(x - 1) - \ln x\right] \\ &= \frac{1}{2}\ln(x - 1) - \frac{1}{2}\ln x \end{aligned}$$

**94.**

$$\begin{aligned} \ln z(z - 1)^2 &= \ln z + \ln(z - 1)^2 \\ &= \ln z + 2\ln(z - 1) \end{aligned}$$

**95.** $\ln 3e^2 = \ln 3 + 2\ln e = 2 + \ln 3$

**96.** $\ln \frac{1}{e} = \ln 1 - \ln e = -1$

**97.** $\ln x + \ln 7 = \ln(x \cdot 7) = \ln(7x)$

**98.** $\ln y + \ln x^2 = \ln(yx^2)$

**99.** $\ln(x-2) - \ln(x+2) = \ln \frac{x-2}{x+2}$

**100.** $3\ln x + 2\ln y - 4\ln z = \ln x^3 + \ln y^2 - \ln z^4$

$$= \ln \frac{x^3y^2}{z^4}$$

**101.** $\frac{1}{3}\left[2\ln(x+3) + \ln x - \ln(x^2-1)\right] = \frac{1}{3}\ln\frac{x(x+3)^2}{x^2-1}$

$$= \ln\sqrt[3]{\frac{x(x+3)^2}{x^2-1}}$$

**102.** $2\left[\ln x - \ln(x+1) - \ln(x-1)\right] = 2\ln\frac{x}{(x+1)(x-1)}$

$$= \ln\left(\frac{x}{x^2-1}\right)^2$$

**103.** $2\ln 3 - \frac{1}{2}\ln(x^2+1) = \ln 9 - \ln\sqrt{x^2+1} = \ln\frac{9}{\sqrt{x^2+1}}$

**104.** $\frac{3}{2}\left[\ln(x^2+1) - \ln(x+1) - \ln(x-1)\right] = \frac{3}{2}\ln\frac{x^2+1}{(x+1)(x-1)}$

$$= \ln\sqrt{\left(\frac{x^2+1}{x^2-1}\right)^3}$$

**105.** (a) $e^{\ln x} = 4$

$x = 4$

(b) $\ln e^{2x} = 3$

$2x = 3$

$x = \frac{3}{2}$

**106.** (a) $e^{\ln 2x} = 12$

$2x = 12$

$x = 6$

(b) $\ln e^{-x} = 0$

$-x = 0$

$x = 0$

**107.** (a) $\ln x = 2$

$x = e^2 \approx 7.389$

(b) $e^x = 4$

$x = \ln 4 \approx 1.386$

**108.** (a) $\ln x^2 = 8$

$x^2 = e^8$

$x = \pm e^4 \approx \pm 54.598$

(b) $e^{-2x} = 5$

$-2x = \ln 5$

$x = -\frac{1}{2}\ln 5 \approx -0.805$

**109.** $e^x > 5$

$\ln e^x > \ln 5$

$x > \ln 5$

**110.** $e^{1-x} < 6$

$\ln e^{1-x} < \ln 6$

$1 - x < \ln 6$

$x > 1 - \ln 6$

**111.** $-2 < \ln x < 0$

$e^{-2} < x < e^0 = 1$

$\frac{1}{e^2} < x < 1$

**112.** $1 < \ln x < 100$

$e^1 < x < e^{100}$

$e < x < e^{100}$

**113.**

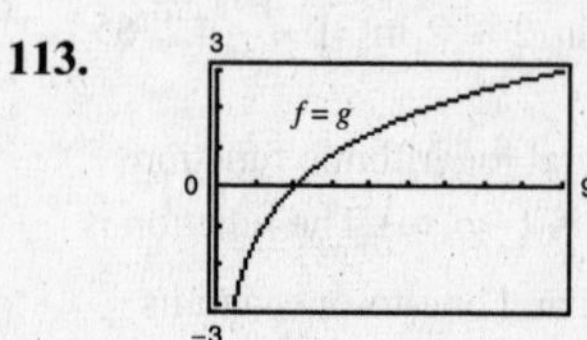


**114.**

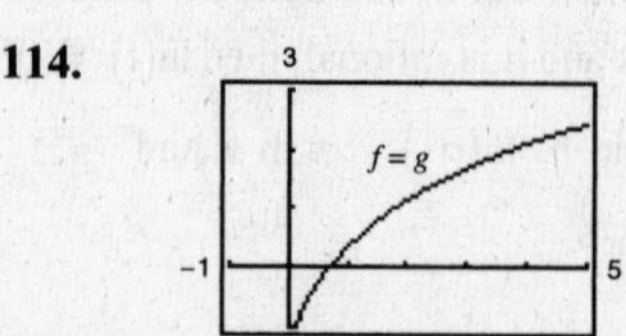


**115.** $\ln x = \ln\left[\left(\frac{x}{y}\right)y\right]$

$= \ln\frac{x}{y} + \ln y \Rightarrow \ln\frac{x}{y} = \ln x - \ln y$

**116.** Let $z = \ln x^y \Rightarrow e^z = x^y \Rightarrow x = e^{z/y}$.

Then $\ln x = z/y \Rightarrow z = \ln x^y = y\ln x$.

**117.** 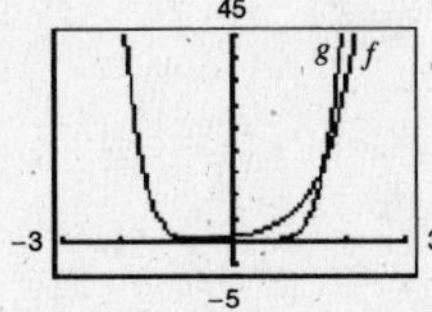


The graphs intersect three times: $(-0.7899, 0.2429)$, $(1.6242, 18.3615)$ and $(6, 46{,}656)$.

The function $f(x) = 6^x$ grows more rapidly.

**118.** 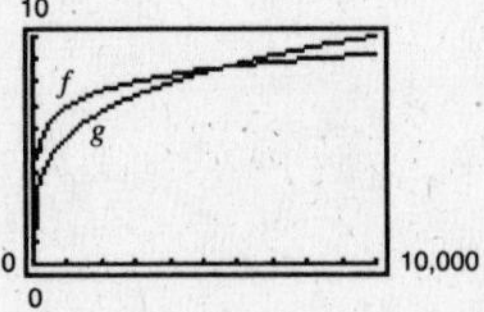


The graphs intersect twice: $(4.1771, 1.4296)$ and $(5503.647, 8.6132)$.

$g(x) = x^{1/4}$ grows more rapidly.

**119.** $f(x) = \ln\left(x + \sqrt{x^2 + 1}\right)$

(a) 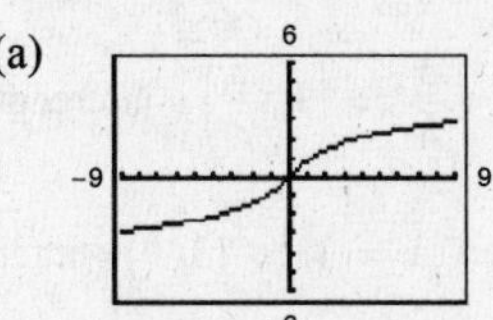


Domain: $-\infty < x < \infty$

(b) $$f(-x) = \ln\left(-x + \sqrt{x^2 + 1}\right)$$
$$= \ln\left[\frac{\left(-x + \sqrt{x^2 + 1}\right)\left(-x - \sqrt{x^2 + 1}\right)}{\left(-x - \sqrt{x^2 + 1}\right)}\right]$$
$$= \ln\left[\frac{\left(x^2 \sqrt{x^2 + 1}\right)}{\left(-x - \sqrt{x^2 + 1}\right)}\right]$$
$$= \ln\left[\frac{1}{\left(x + \sqrt{x^2 + 1}\right)}\right]$$
$$= -\ln\left(x + \sqrt{x^2 + 1}\right) = -f(x)$$

(c) $$y = \ln\left(x + \sqrt{x^2 + 1}\right)$$
$$e^y = x + \sqrt{x^2 + 1}$$
$$\left(e^y - x\right)^2 = x^2 + 1$$
$$2xe^y = e^{2y} - 1$$
$$x = \frac{e^{2y} - 1}{2e^x}$$

**120.** The graphs of $f(x) = \ln x$ and $g(x) = e^x$ are mirror images in the line $y = x$.

## Review Exercises for Chapter 1

**1.** $y = 5x - 8$

$x = 0$: $y = 5(0) - 8 = -8 \Rightarrow (0, -8)$ $y$-intercept

$y = 0$: $0 = 5x - 8 \Rightarrow x = \frac{8}{5} \Rightarrow \left(\frac{8}{5}, 0\right)$ $x$-intercept

**2.** $y = (x - 2)(x - 6)$

$x = 0$: $y = (0 - 2)(0 - 6) = 12 \Rightarrow (0, 12)$ $y$-intercept

$y = 0$: $0 = (x - 2)(x - 6) \Rightarrow x = 2, 6 \Rightarrow (2, 0), (6, 0)$ $x$-intercepts

**3.** $y = \dfrac{x-3}{x-4}$

$x = 0$: $y = \dfrac{0-3}{0-4} = \dfrac{3}{4} \Rightarrow \left(0, \dfrac{3}{4}\right)$ $y$-intercept

$y = 0$: $0 = \dfrac{x-3}{x-4} \Rightarrow x = 3 \Rightarrow (3, 0)$ $x$-intercept.

**4.** $xy = 4$

$x = 0$ and $y = 0$ are both impossible. No intercepts.

**5.** Symmetric with respect to the $y$-axis because

$$(-x)^2 y - (-x)^2 + 4y = 0$$
$$x^2 y - x^2 + 4y = 0.$$

**6.** Symmetric with respect to the $y$-axis because

$$y = (-x)^4 - (-x)^2 + 3$$
$$y = x^4 - x^2 + 3.$$

**7.** $y = -\frac{1}{2}x + \frac{3}{2}$

Slope: $-\frac{1}{2}$

$y$-intercept: $\frac{3}{2}$

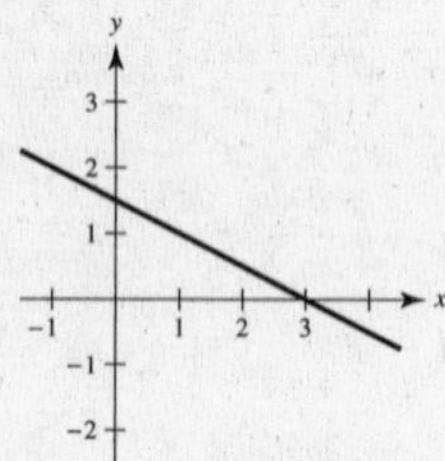

**8.** $6x - 3y = 12$

$$-3y = -6x + 12$$
$$y = 2x - 4$$

Slope: 2

$y$-intercept: $(0, -4)$

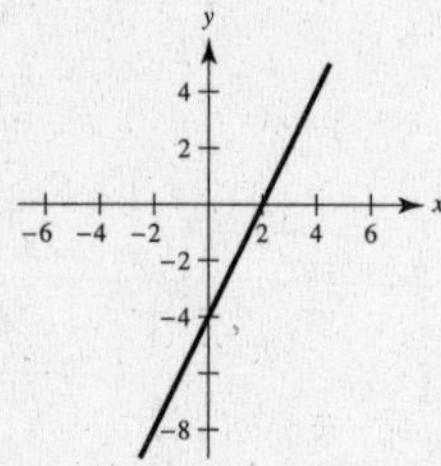

**9.** $-\frac{1}{3}x + \frac{5}{6}y = 1$

$$-\tfrac{2}{5}x + y = \tfrac{6}{5}$$
$$y = \tfrac{2}{5}x + \tfrac{6}{5}$$

Slope: $\frac{2}{5}$

$y$-intercept: $\frac{6}{5}$

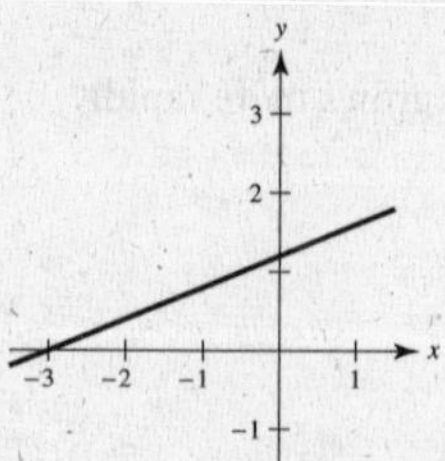

**10.** $0.02x + 0.15y = 0.25$

$$2x + 15y = 25$$
$$y = -\tfrac{2}{15}x + \tfrac{5}{3}$$

Slope: $-\frac{2}{15}$

$y$-intercept: $\left(0, \frac{5}{3}\right)$

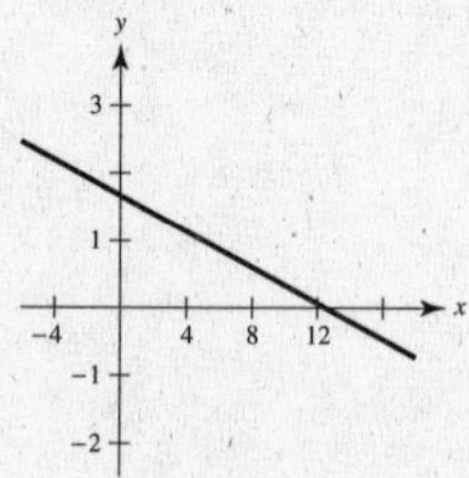

**11.** $y = 9 - 8x - x^2 = -(x - 1)(x + 9)$

$y$-intercept: $(0, 9)$

$x$-intercepts: $(1, 0)$, $(-9, 0)$

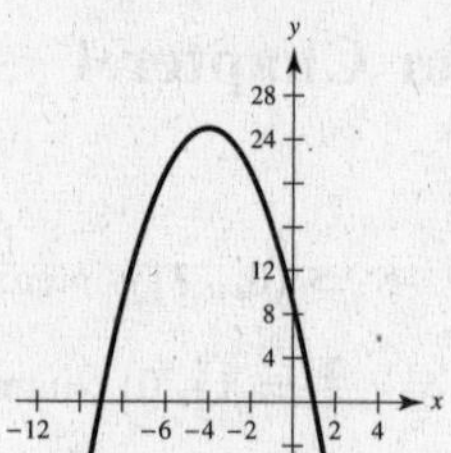

**12.** $y = x(6 - x)$

$y$-intercept: $(0, 0)$

$x$-intercepts: $(0, 0)$, $(6, 0)$

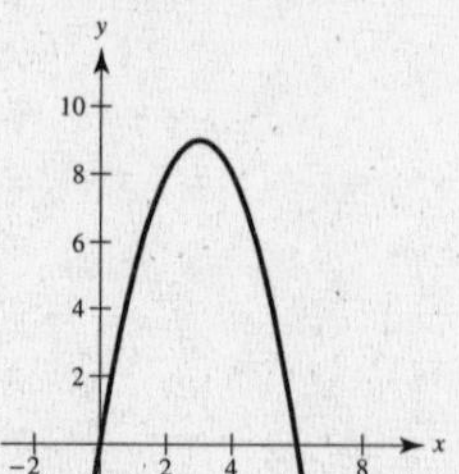

**13.** $y = 2\sqrt{4 - x}$

Domain: $(-\infty, 4]$

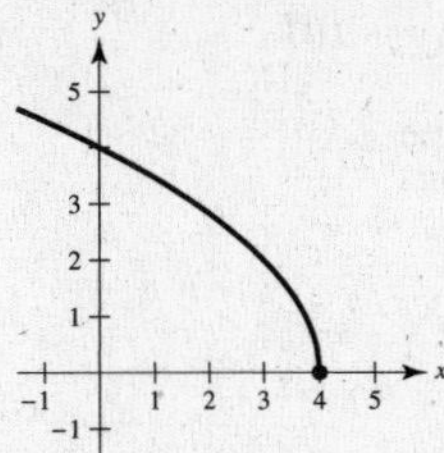

**14.** $y = |x - 4| - 4$

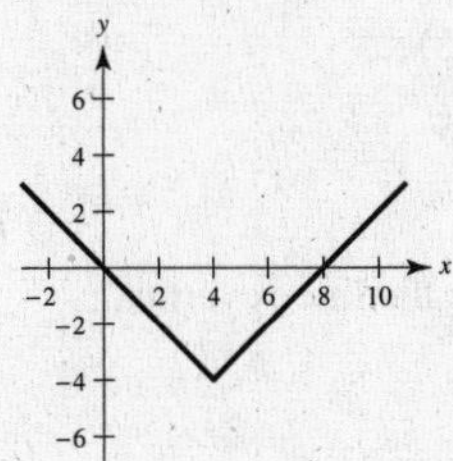

**15.** $5x + 3y = -1 \Rightarrow y = \frac{1}{3}(-5x - 1)$

$x - y = -5 \Rightarrow y = x + 5$

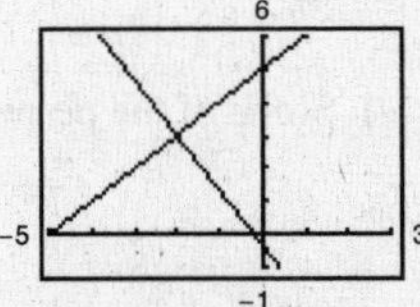

Using a graphing utility, the lines intersect at $(-2, 3)$. Analytically,

$$\begin{aligned} \tfrac{1}{3}(-5x - 1) &= x + 5 \\ -5x - 1 &= 3x + 15 \\ -16 &= 8x \\ -2 &= x. \end{aligned}$$

For $x = -2$, $y = x + 5 = -2 + 5 = 3$.

**16.** $x - y + 1 = 0 \Rightarrow y = x + 1$

$y - x^2 = 7 \Rightarrow y = x^2 + 7$

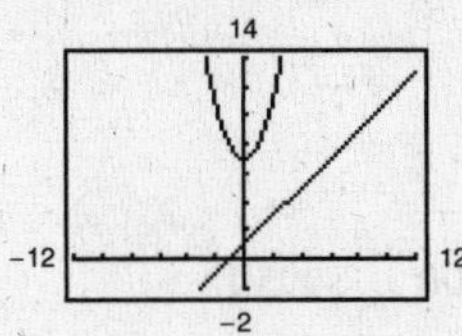

$$\begin{aligned} y &= x + 1 \\ (x + 1) - x^2 &= 7 \\ 0 &= x^2 - x + 6 \end{aligned}$$

No real solution.

No points of intersection.

The graphs of $y = x + 1$ and $y = x^2 + 7$ do not intersect.

**17.**

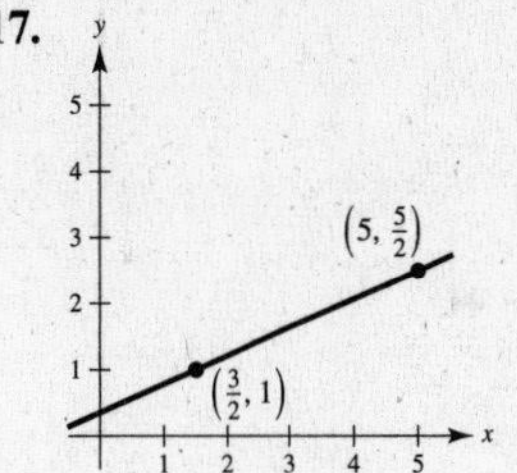

$$\text{Slope} = \frac{\left(\frac{5}{2}\right) - 1}{5 - \left(\frac{3}{2}\right)} = \frac{\frac{3}{2}}{\frac{7}{2}} = \frac{3}{7}$$

**18.** The line is horizontal and has slope 0.

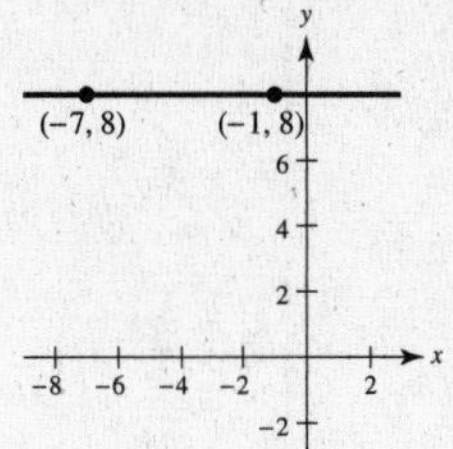

**19.**
$$\begin{aligned} \frac{t - 5}{0 - (-8)} &= \frac{-1 - 5}{2 - (-8)} \\ \frac{t - 5}{8} &= \frac{-6}{10} \\ \frac{t - 5}{8} &= -\frac{3}{5} \\ 5t - 25 &= -24 \\ 5t &= 1 \\ t &= \frac{1}{5} \end{aligned}$$

**20.**
$$\begin{aligned} \frac{3 - (-1)}{-3 - t} &= \frac{3 - 6}{-3 - 8} \\ \frac{4}{-3 - t} &= \frac{-3}{-11} \\ -44 &= 9 + 3t \\ -53 &= 3t \\ t &= -\frac{53}{3} \end{aligned}$$

**21.** $y - (-5) = \frac{7}{4}(x - 3)$

$y + 5 = \frac{7}{4}x - \frac{21}{4}$

$4y + 20 = 7x - 21$

$0 = 7x - 4y - 41$

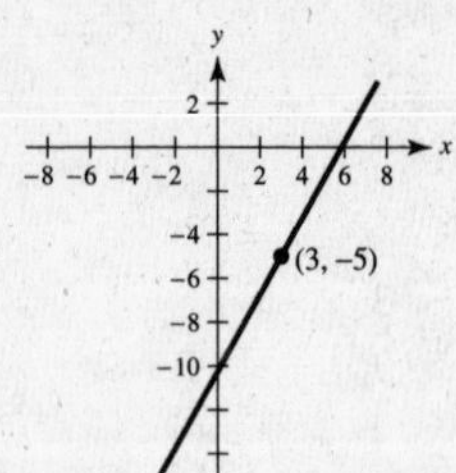

**22.** Because $m$ is undefined the line is vertical.

$x = -8$ or $x + 8 = 0$

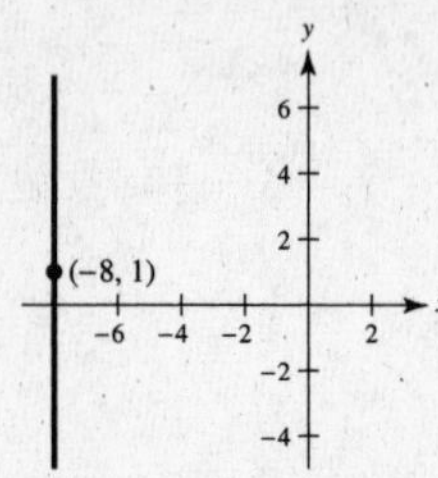

**23.** $y - 0 = -\frac{2}{3}(x - (-3))$

$y = -\frac{2}{3}x - 2$

$2x + 3y + 6 = 0$

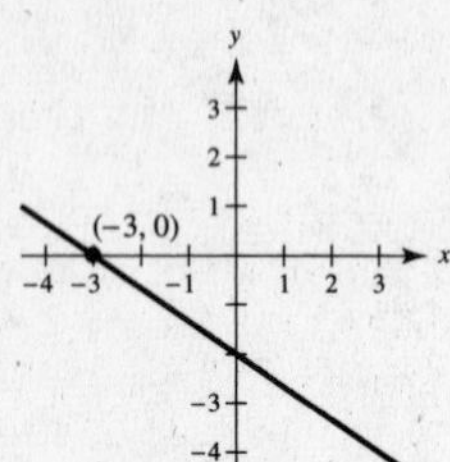

**24.** Because $m = 0$, the line is horizontal.

$y - 4 = 0(x - 5)$

$y = 4$ or $y - 4 = 0$

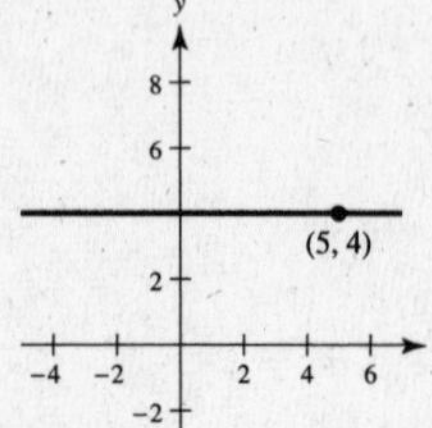

**25.** (a) $y - 5 = \frac{7}{16}(x + 3)$

$16y - 80 = 7x + 21$

$0 = 7x - 16y + 101$

(b) $5x - 3y = 3$ has slope $\frac{5}{3}$.

$y - 5 = \frac{5}{3}(x + 3)$

$3y - 15 = 5x + 15$

$0 = 5x - 3y + 30$

(c) $m = \dfrac{5 - 0}{-3 - 0} = -\dfrac{5}{3}$

$y - 5 = -\frac{5}{3}(x + 3)$

$3y - 15 = -5x - 15$

$5x + 3y = 0$

(d) Slope is undefined so the line is vertical.

$x = -3$

$x + 3 = 0$

**26.** (a) $y - 4 = -\frac{2}{3}(x - 2)$

$3y - 12 = -2x + 4$

$2x + 3y - 16 = 0$

(b) $x + y = 0$ has slope $-1$. Slope of the perpendicular line is 1.

$y - 4 = 1(x - 2)$

$y = x + 2$

$0 = x - y + 2$

(c) $m = \dfrac{4 - 1}{2 - 6} = -\dfrac{3}{4}$

$y - 4 = -\dfrac{3}{4}(x - 2)$

$4y - 16 = -3x + 6$

$3x + 4y - 22 = 0$

(d) Because the line is horizontal the slope is 0.

$y = 4$

$y - 4 = 0$

**27.** The slope is $-850$.

$V = -850t + 12{,}500.$

$V(3) = -850(3) + 12{,}500 = \$9950$

**28.** (a) $C = 9.25t + 13.50t + 36{,}500 = 22.75t + 36{,}500$

(b) $R = 30t$

(c) $30t = 22.75t + 36{,}500$

$7.25t = 36{,}500$

$t \approx 5034.48$ hours to break even

**29.** $x - y^2 = 6$

$y = \pm\sqrt{x - 6}$

Not a function because there are two values of $y$ for some $x$.

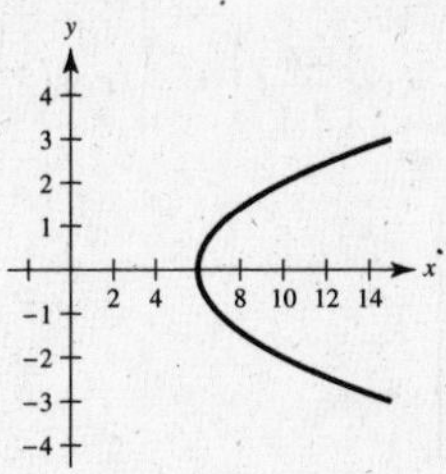

**30.** $x^2 - y = 0$

Function of $x$ because there is one value of $y$ for each $x$.

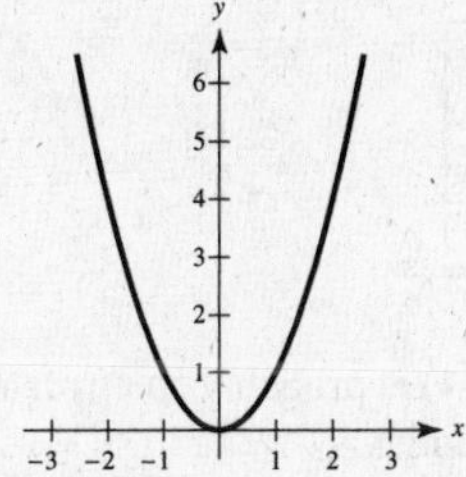

**31.** $y = \dfrac{|x - 2|}{x - 2}$

$y$ is a function of $x$ because there is one value of $y$ for each $x$.

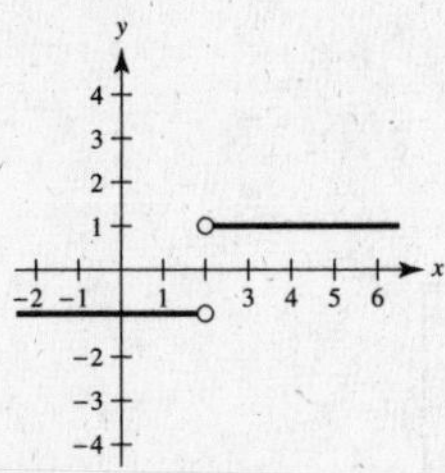

**32.** $x = 9 - y^2$

Not a function of $x$ because there are two values of $y$ for some $x$.

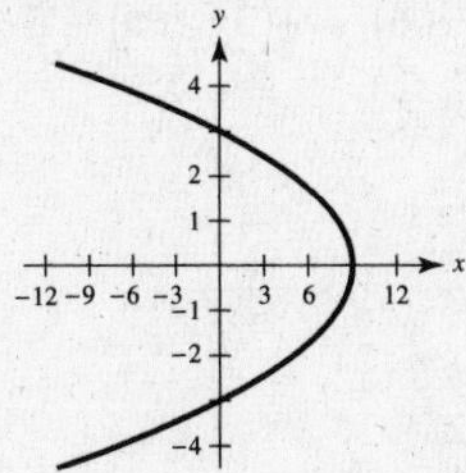

**33.** $f(x) = \dfrac{1}{x}$

(a) $f(0)$ does not exist.

(b) $\dfrac{f(1 + \Delta x) - f(1)}{\Delta x} = \dfrac{\dfrac{1}{1 + \Delta x} - \dfrac{1}{1}}{\Delta x} = \dfrac{1 - 1 - \Delta x}{(1 + \Delta x)\Delta x}$

$= \dfrac{-1}{1 + \Delta x}, \ \Delta x \neq -1, 0$

**34.** $f(x) = \begin{cases} x^2 + 2, & x < 0 \\ |x - 2|, & x \geq 0 \end{cases}$

(a) $f(-4) = (-4)^2 + 2 = 18$ (because $-4 < 0$)

(b) $f(0) = |0 - 2| = 2$

(c) $f(1) = |1 - 2| = 1$

**35.** (a) Domain: $36 - x^2 \geq 0 \Rightarrow -6 \leq x \leq 6$ or $[-6, 6]$

Range: $[0, 6]$

(b) Domain: all $x \neq 5$ or $(-\infty, 5) \cup (5, \infty)$

Range: all $y \neq 0$ or $(-\infty, 0) \cup (0, \infty)$

(c) Domain: all $x$ or $(-\infty, \infty)$

Range: all $y$ or $(-\infty, \infty)$

**36.** $f(x) = 1 - x^2$ and $g(x) = 2x + 1$

(a) $f(x) - g(x) = (1 - x^2) - (2x + 1) = -x^2 - 2x$

(b) $f(x)g(x) = (1 - x^2)(2x + 1) = -2x^3 - x^2 + 2x + 1$

(c) $g(f(x)) = g(1 - x^2) = 2(1 - x^2) + 1 = 3 - 2x^2$

**37.** (a) $f(x) = x^3 + c, c = -2, 0, 2$

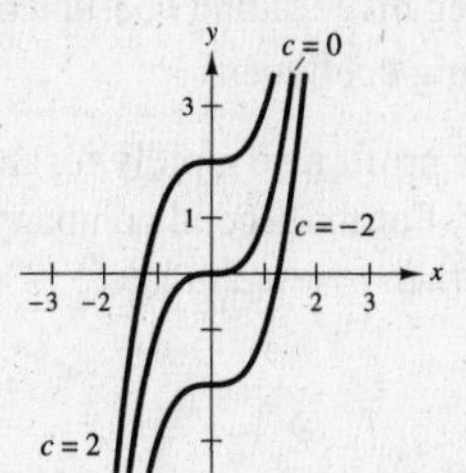


(b) $f(x) = (x - c)^3, c = -2, 0, 2$

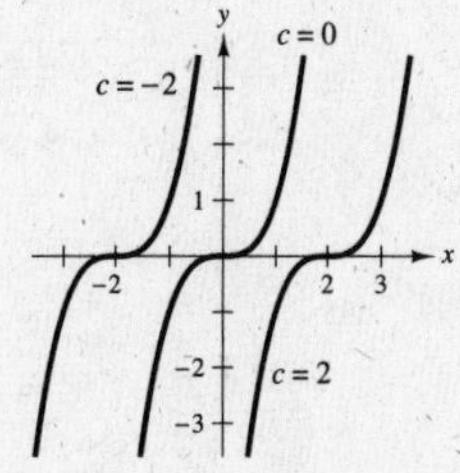

(c) $f(x) = (x - 2)^3 + c,\ c = -2, 0, 2$

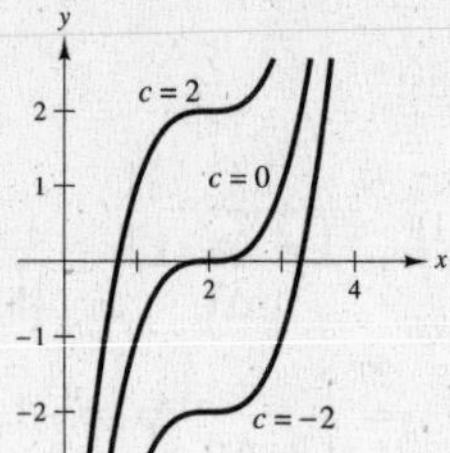


(d) $f(x) = cx^3,\ c = -2, 0, 2$

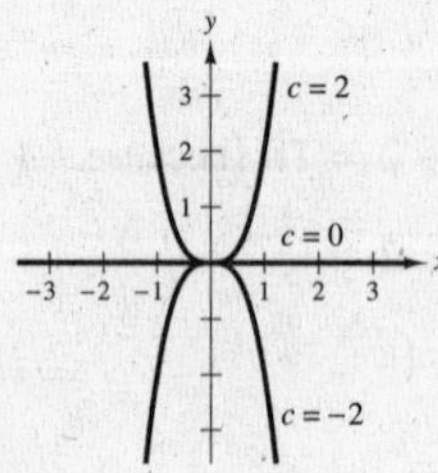


**38.** $f(x) = x^3 - 3x^2$

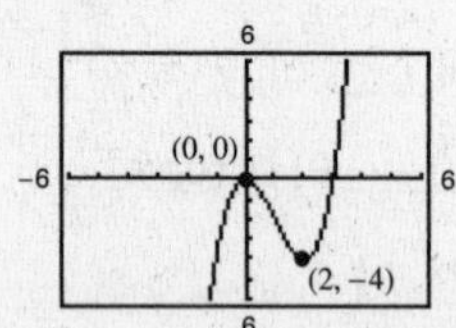


(a) The graph of $g$ is obtained from $f$ by a vertical shift down 1 unit, followed by a reflection in the $x$-axis:

$$g(x) = -[f(x) - 1] = -x^3 + 3x^2 + 1$$

(b) The graph of $g$ is obtained from $f$ by a vertical shift upwards of 1 and a horizontal shift of 2 to the right.

$$g(x) = f(x - 2) + 1 = (x - 2)^3 - 3(x - 2)^2 + 1$$

**39.** (a) 3 (cubic), negative leading coefficient
(b) 4 (quartic), positive leading coefficient
(c) 2 (quadratic), negative leading coefficient
(d) 5, positive leading coefficient

**40.** For company (a) the profit rose rapidly for the first year, and then leveled off. For the second company (b), the profit dropped, and then rose again later.

**41.** (a) Yes, $y$ is a function of $t$. At each time $t$, there is one and only one displacement $y$.

(b) The amplitude is approximately $(0.25 - (-0.25))/2 = 0.25$. The period is approximately 1.1.

(c) One model is $y = \frac{1}{4}\cos\left(\frac{2\pi}{1.1}t\right) \approx \frac{1}{4}\cos(5.7t)$

(d)

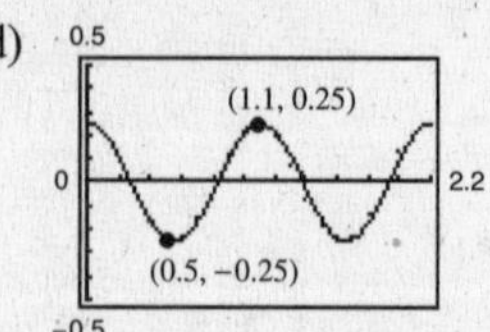


The model appears to fit the data.

**42.** (a) $y = -1.204x + 64.2667$

(b)

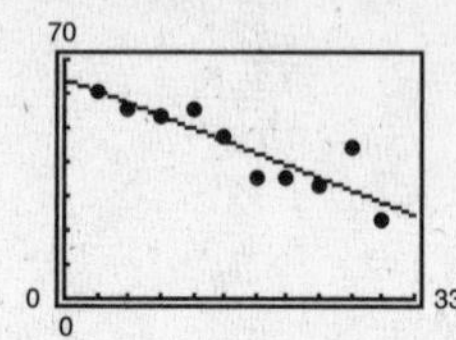

(c) The data point (27, 44) is probably an error. Without this point, the new model is $y = -1.4344x + 66.4387$.

**43.** (a)

$$f(x) = \tfrac{1}{2}x - 3$$
$$y = \tfrac{1}{2}x - 3$$
$$2(y + 3) = x$$
$$2(x + 3) = y$$
$$f^{-1}(x) = 2x + 6$$

(b)

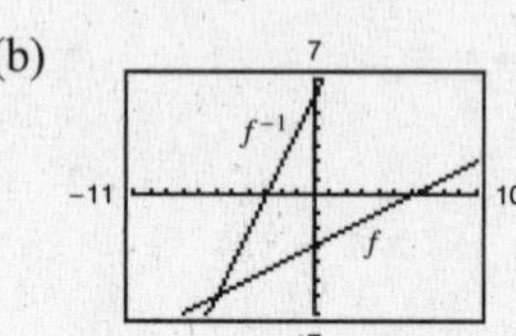


(c) $f^{-1}(f(x)) = f^{-1}\left(\frac{1}{2}x - 3\right) = 2\left(\frac{1}{2}x - 3\right) + 6 = x$

$f(f^{-1}(x)) = f(2x + 6) = \frac{1}{2}(2x + 6) - 3 = x$

**44.** (a)

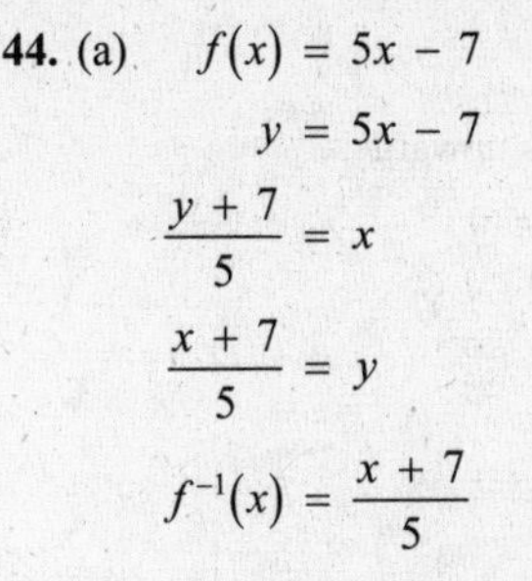

$$f(x) = 5x - 7$$
$$y = 5x - 7$$
$$\frac{y+7}{5} = x$$
$$\frac{x+7}{5} = y$$
$$f^{-1}(x) = \frac{x+7}{5}$$

(b)

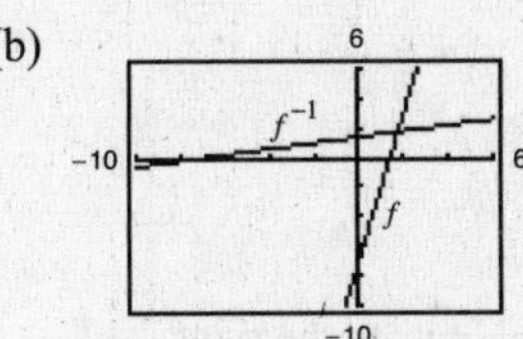

(c) $f^{-1}(f(x)) = f^{-1}(5x - 7) = \dfrac{(5x - 7) + 7}{5} = x$

$f(f^{-1}(x)) = f\left(\dfrac{x+7}{5}\right) = 5\left(\dfrac{x+7}{5}\right) - 7 = x$

**45.** (a)

$$f(x) = \sqrt{x+1}$$
$$y = \sqrt{x+1}$$
$$y^2 - 1 = x$$
$$x^2 - 1 = y$$
$$f^{-1}(x) = x^2 - 1, \quad x \ge 0$$

(b)

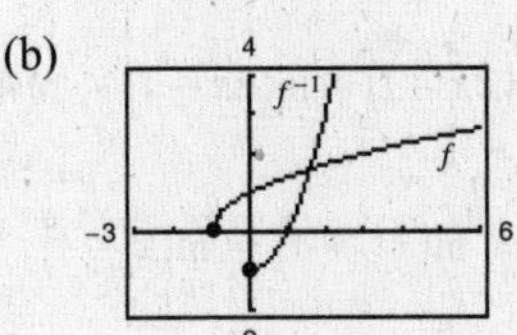

(c) $f^{-1}(f(x)) = f^{-1}(\sqrt{x+1}) = \sqrt{(x^2-1)^2} - 1 = x$

$f(f^{-1}(x)) = f(x^2 - 1) = \sqrt{(x^2 - 1) + 1}$

$= \sqrt{x^2} = x$ for $x \ge 0$

**46.** (a)

$$f(x) = x^3 + 2$$
$$y = x^3 + 2$$
$$\sqrt[3]{y - 2} = x$$
$$\sqrt[3]{x - 2} = y$$
$$f^{-1}(x) = \sqrt[3]{x - 2}$$

(b)

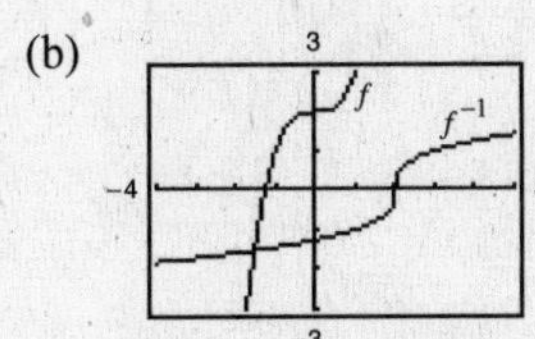

(c) $f^{-1}(f(x)) = f^{-1}(x^3 + 2) = \sqrt[3]{(x^3 + 2) - 2} = x$

$f(f^{-1}(x)) = f(\sqrt[3]{x-2}) = (\sqrt[3]{x-2})^3 + 2 = x$

**47.** (a)

$$f(x) = \sqrt[3]{x+1}$$
$$y = \sqrt[3]{x+1}$$
$$y^3 - 1 = x$$
$$x^3 - 1 = y$$
$$f^{-1}(x) = x^3 - 1$$

(b)

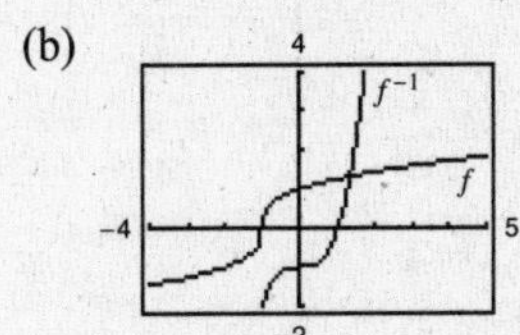

(c) $f^{-1}(f(x)) = f^{-1}(\sqrt[3]{x+1})$

$= (\sqrt[3]{x+1})^3 - 1 = x$

$f(f^{-1}(x)) = f(x^3 - 1) = \sqrt[3]{(x^3 - 1) + 1} = x$

**48.** (a)

$$f(x) = x^2 - 5, \quad x \ge 0$$
$$y = x^2 - 5$$
$$\sqrt{y+5} = x$$
$$\sqrt{x+5} = y$$
$$f^{-1}(x) = \sqrt{x+5}$$

(b)

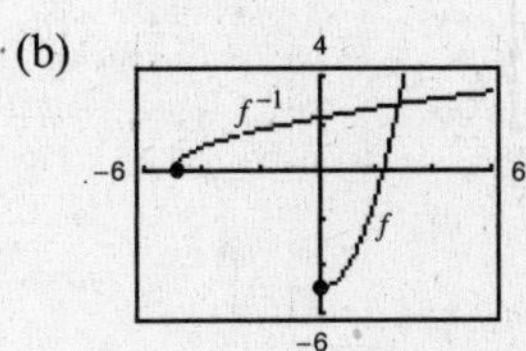

(c) $f^{-1}(f(x)) = f^{-1}(x^2 - 5)$

$= \sqrt{(x^2 - 5) + 5} = x$ for $x \ge 0$.

$f(f^{-1}(x)) = f(\sqrt{x+5}) = (\sqrt{x+5})^2 - 5 = x$

**49.** $f(x) = 2 \arctan(x + 3)$

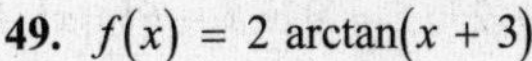

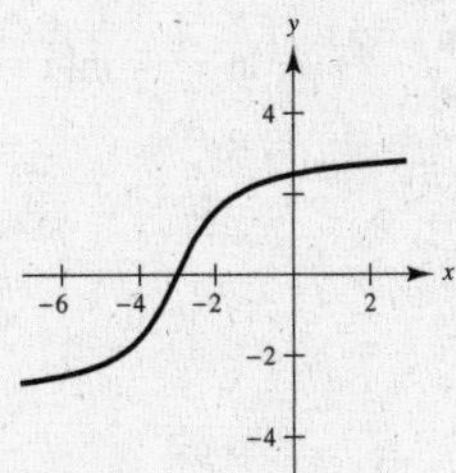

**50.** $h(x) = -3 \arcsin(2x)$

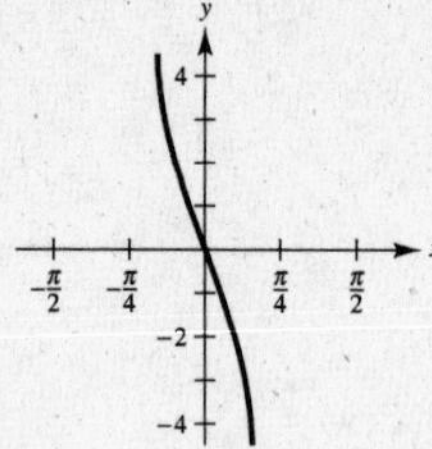


**51.** Let $\theta = \arcsin \frac{1}{2}$.

$\sin \theta = \frac{1}{2}$

$\sin\left(\arcsin\frac{1}{2}\right) = \sin \theta = \frac{1}{2}$

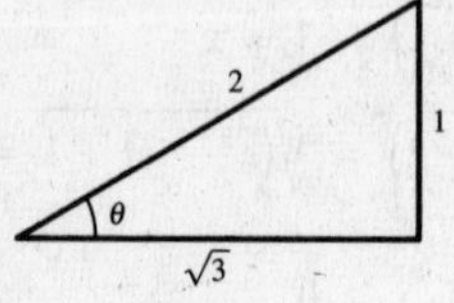


**52.** Let $\theta = \operatorname{arccot} 2$.

$\cot \theta = 2$

$\tan(\operatorname{arccot}) = \tan \theta = \frac{1}{2}$

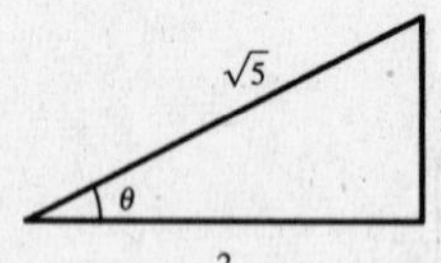


**53.** $f(x) = \ln x + 3$

Vertical shift three units upward

Vertical asymptote: $x = 0$

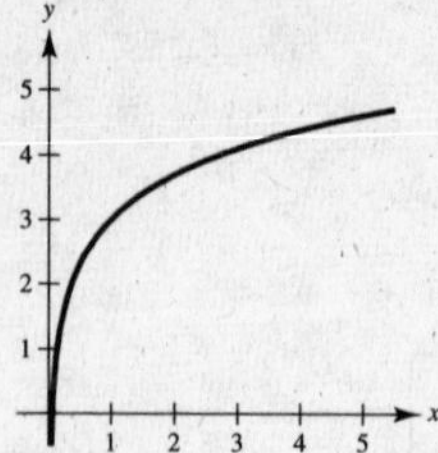


**54.** $f(x) = \ln(x - 3)$

Horizontal shift three units to the right

Vertical asymptote: $x = 3$

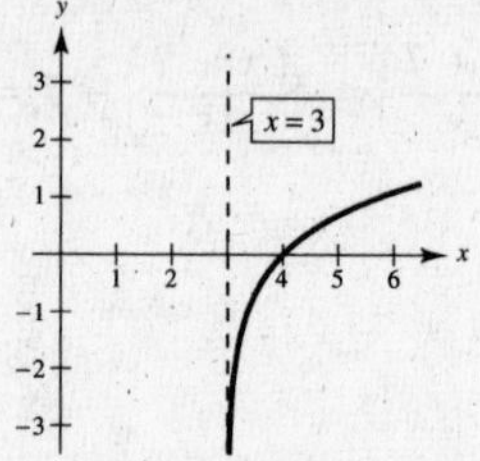


**55.** $$\ln \sqrt[5]{\frac{4x^2 - 1}{4x^2 + 1}} = \frac{1}{5} \ln \frac{(2x - 1)(2x + 1)}{4x^2 + 1}$$
$$= \frac{1}{5}\left[\ln(2x - 1) + \ln(2x + 1) - \ln\left(4x^2 + 1\right)\right]$$

**56.** $\ln\left[\left(x^2 + 1\right)(x - 1)\right] = \ln\left(x^2 + 1\right) + \ln(x - 1)$

**57.** $$\ln 3 + \frac{1}{3}\ln\left(4 - x^2\right) - \ln x = \ln 3 + \ln \sqrt[3]{4 - x^2} - \ln x$$
$$= \ln\left(\frac{3\sqrt[3]{4 - x^2}}{x}\right)$$

**58.** $$3\left[\ln x - 2\ln\left(x^2 + 1\right)\right] + 2\ln 5 = 3\ln x - 6\ln\left(x^2 + 1\right) + \ln 5^2$$
$$= \ln x^3 - \ln\left(x^2 + 1\right)^6 + \ln 25 = \ln\left[\frac{25x^3}{\left(x^2 + 1\right)^6}\right]$$

**59.** $$\ln\sqrt{x + 1} = 2$$
$$\sqrt{x + 1} = e^2$$
$$x + 1 = e^4$$
$$x = e^4 - 1 \approx 53.598$$

**60.** $\ln x + \ln(x - 3) = 0$

$\ln x(x - 3) = 0$

$x(x - 3) = e^0$

$x^2 - 3x - 1 = 0$

$x = \dfrac{3 \pm \sqrt{13}}{2}$

$x = \dfrac{3 + \sqrt{13}}{2}$ only because $\dfrac{3 - \sqrt{13}}{2} < 0.$

**61.** (a) $f(x) = \ln \sqrt{x}$

$y = \ln \sqrt{x}$

$e^y = \sqrt{x}$

$e^{2y} = x$

$e^{2x} = y$

$f^{-1}(x) = e^{2x}$

(b)

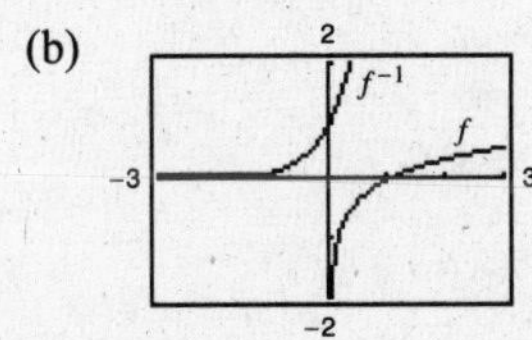


(c) $f^{-1}(f(x)) = f^{-1}(\ln \sqrt{x}) = e^{2 \ln \sqrt{x}} = e^{\ln x} = x$

$f(f^{-1}(x)) = f(e^{2x}) = \ln \sqrt{e^{2x}} = \ln e^x = x$

**62.** (a) $f(x) = e^{1-x}$

$y = e^{1-x}$

$\ln y = 1 - x$

$x = 1 - \ln y$

$y = 1 - \ln x$

$f^{-1}(x) = 1 - \ln x$

(b)

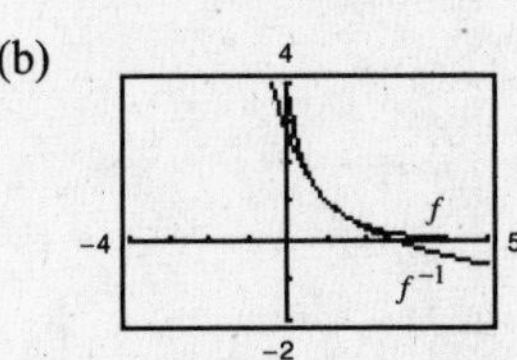


(c) $f^{-1}(f(x)) = f^{-1}(e^{1-x}) = 1 - \ln(e^{1-x})$

$= 1 - (1 - x) = x$

$f(f^{-1}(x)) = f(1 - \ln x) = e^{1-(1-\ln x)} = e^{\ln x} = x$

**63.** $f = e^{-x/2}$

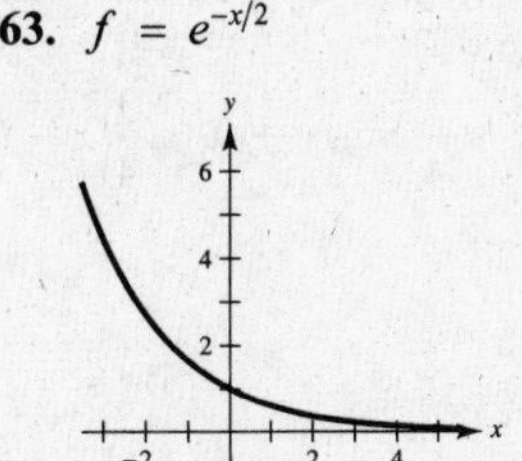


**64.** $f = 4e^{-x^2}$

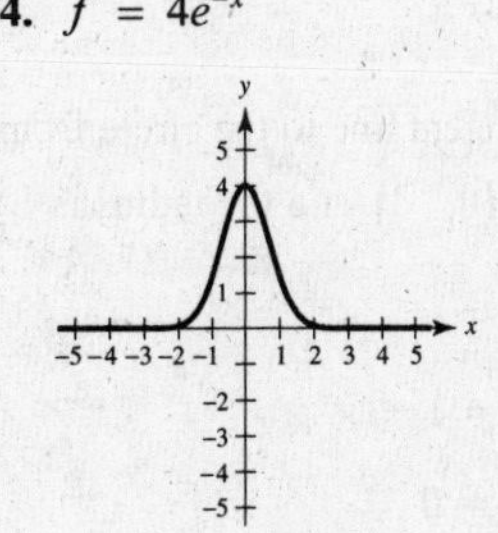


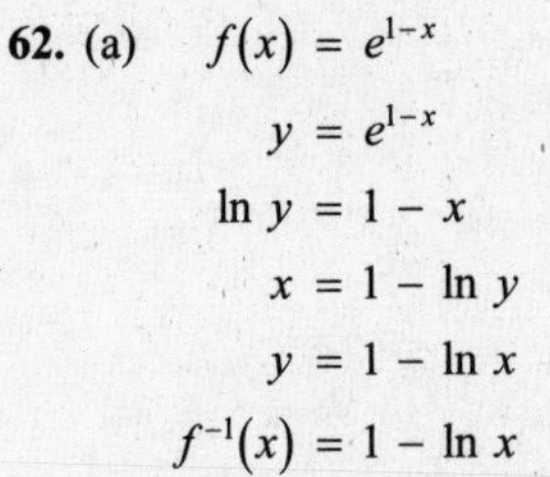

## Problem Solving for Chapter 1

**1.** (a)
$$x^2 - 6x + y^2 - 8y = 0$$
$$(x^2 - 6x + 9) + (y^2 - 8y + 16) = 9 + 16$$
$$(x - 3)^2 + (y - 4)^2 = 25$$

Center: (3, 4); Radius: 5

(b) Slope of line from (0, 0) to (3, 4) is $\frac{4}{3}$. Slope of tangent line is $-\frac{3}{4}$. So, $y - 0 = -\frac{3}{4}(x - 0) \Rightarrow y = -\frac{3}{4}x$ Tangent line

(c) Slope of line from (6, 0) to (3, 4) is $\frac{4 - 0}{3 - 6} = -\frac{4}{3}$.

Slope of tangent line is $\frac{3}{4}$. So, $y - 0 = \frac{3}{4}(x - 6) \Rightarrow y = \frac{3}{4}x - \frac{9}{2}$ Tangent line

(d) $-\frac{3}{4}x = \frac{3}{4}x - \frac{9}{2}$

$\frac{3}{2}x = \frac{9}{2}$

$x = 3$

Intersection: $\left(3, -\frac{9}{4}\right)$

**2.** Let $y = mx + 1$ be a tangent line to the circle from the point (0, 1). Because the center of the circle is at $(0, -1)$ and the radius is 1 you have the following.

$$x^2 + (y + 1)^2 = 1$$
$$x^2 + (mx + 1 + 1)^2 = 1$$
$$(m^2 + 1)x^2 + 4mx + 3 = 0$$

Setting the discriminant $b^2 - 4ac$ equal to zero,

$$16m^2 - 4(m^2 + 1)(3) = 0$$
$$16m^2 - 12m^2 = 12$$
$$4m^2 = 12$$
$$m = \pm\sqrt{3}$$

Tangent lines: $y = \sqrt{3}x + 1$ and $y = -\sqrt{3}x + 1$.

**3.** $H(x) = \begin{cases} 1, & x \geq 0 \\ 0, & x < 0 \end{cases}$

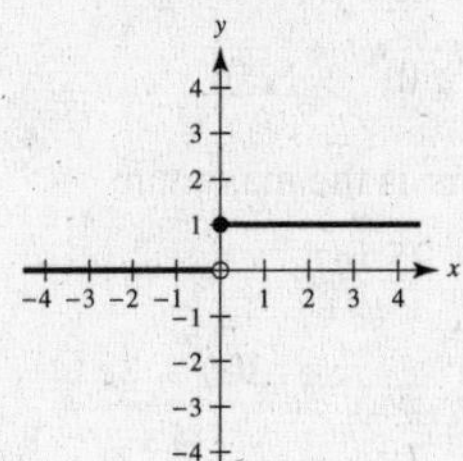

(a) $H(x) - 2 = \begin{cases} -1, & x \geq 0 \\ -2, & x < 0 \end{cases}$

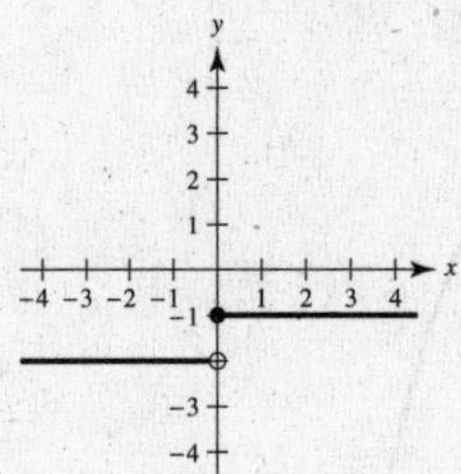

(b) $H(x - 2) = \begin{cases} 1, & x \geq 2 \\ 0, & x < 2 \end{cases}$

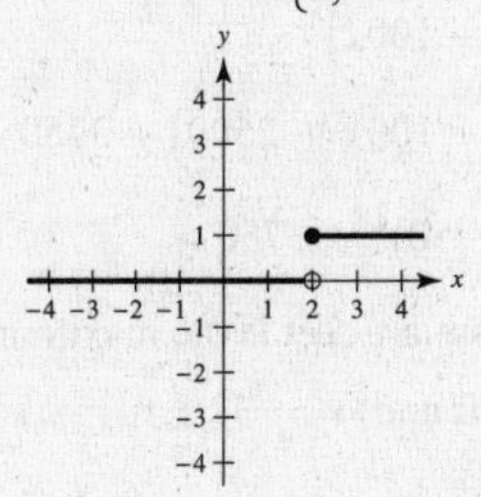

(c) $-H(x) = \begin{cases} -1, & x \geq 0 \\ 0, & x < 0 \end{cases}$

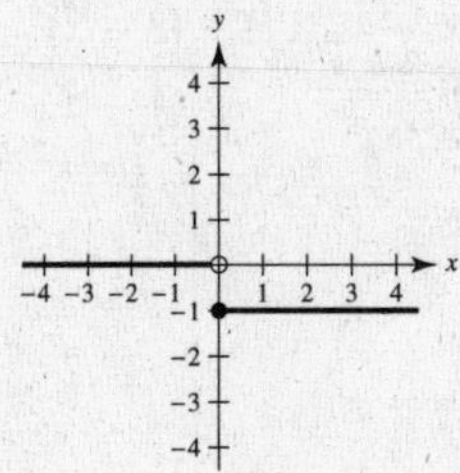

(d) $H(-x) = \begin{cases} 1, & x \leq 0 \\ 0, & x > 0 \end{cases}$

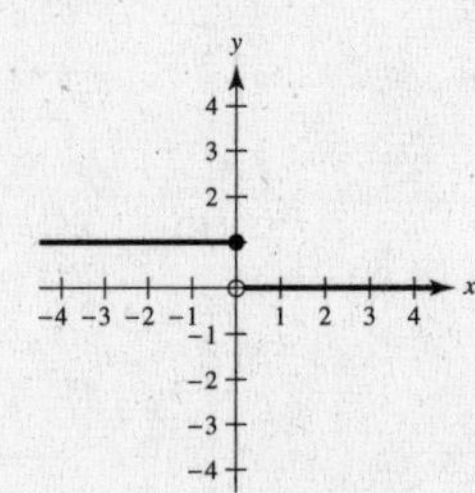

(e) $\frac{1}{2}H(x) = \begin{cases} \frac{1}{2}, & x \geq 0 \\ 0, & x < 0 \end{cases}$

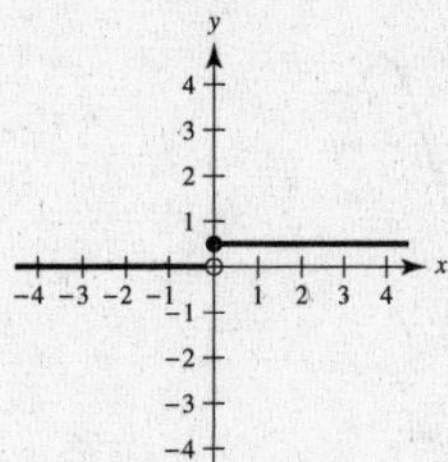

(f) $-H(x - 2) + 2 = \begin{cases} 1, & x \geq 2 \\ 2, & x < 2 \end{cases}$

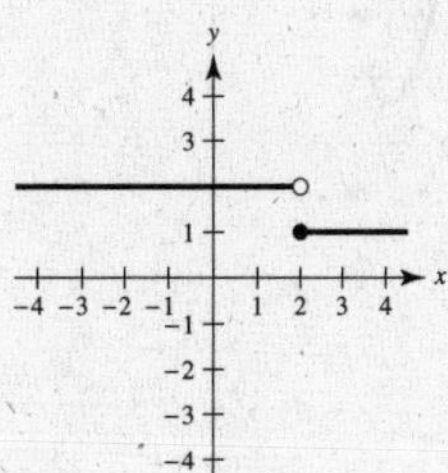

**4.** (a) $f(x + 1)$

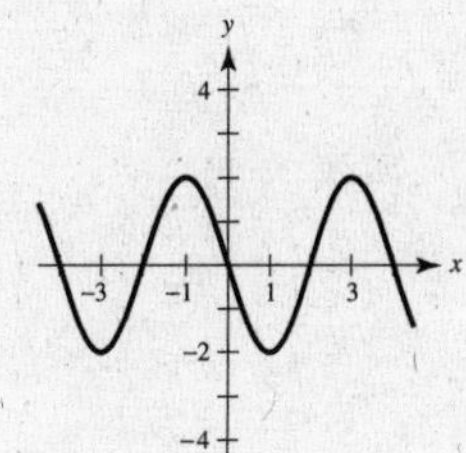

(b) $f(x) + 1$

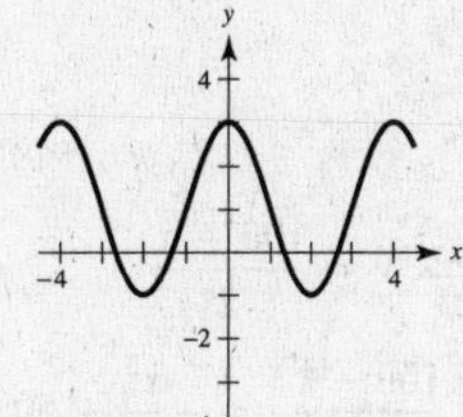

(c) $2f(x)$

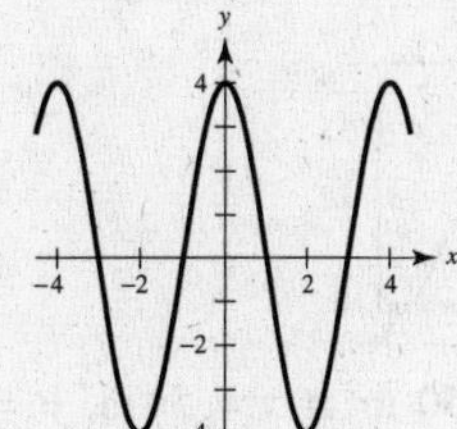

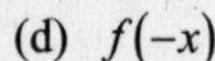

(d) $f(-x)$

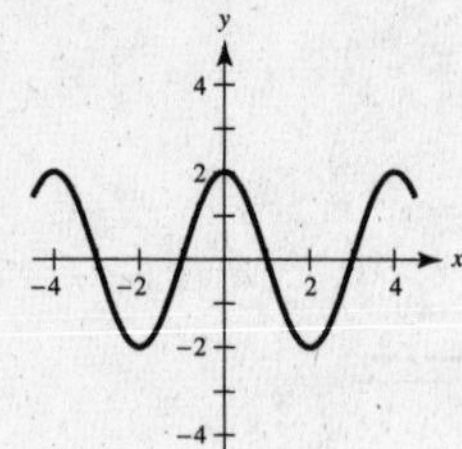


(e) $-f(x)$

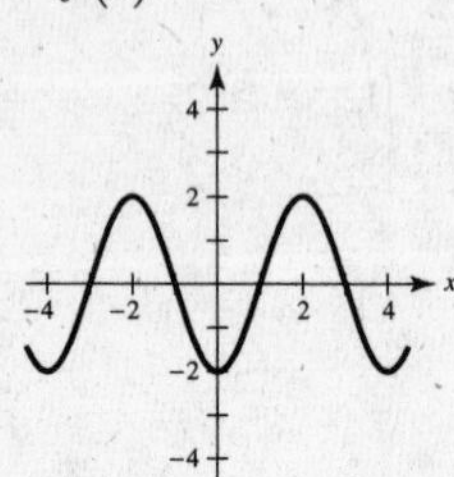


(f) $|f(x)|$

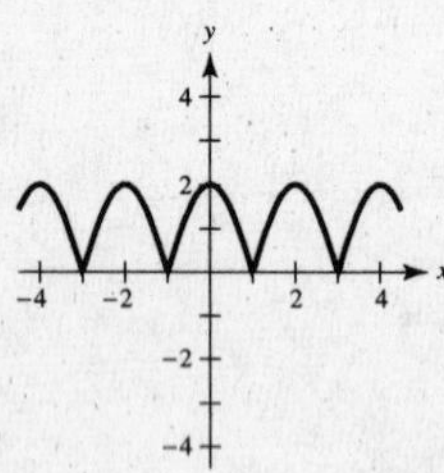


(g) $f(|x|)$

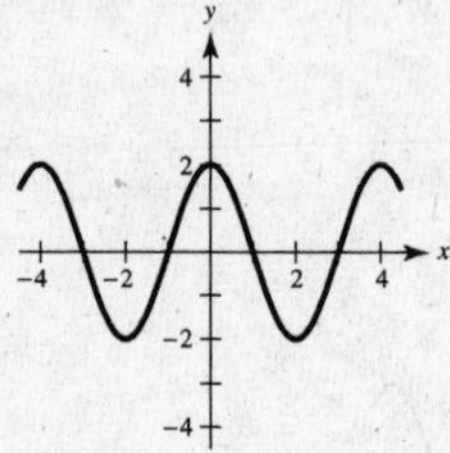


**5.** (a) $x + 2y = 100 \Rightarrow y = \dfrac{100 - x}{2}$

$$A(x) = xy = x\left(\frac{100 - x}{2}\right) = -\frac{x^2}{2} + 50x$$

Domain: $0 < x < 100$ or $(0, 100)$

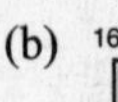

(b)

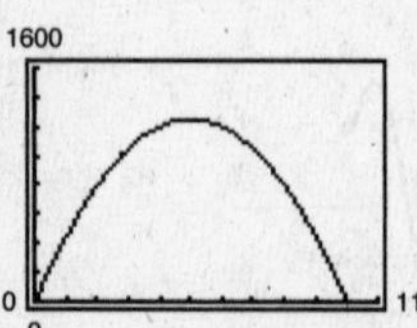


Maximum of 1250 $\text{m}^2$ at $x = 50$ m, $y = 25$ m.

(c) $A(x) = -\frac{1}{2}(x^2 - 100x)$

$$= -\tfrac{1}{2}(x^2 - 100x + 2500) + 1250$$

$$= -\tfrac{1}{2}(x - 50)^2 + 1250$$

$A(50) = 1250$ $\text{m}^2$ is the maximum.

$x = 50$ m, $y = 25$ m

**6.** (a) $4y + 3x = 300 \Rightarrow y = \dfrac{300 - 3x}{4}$

$$A(x) = x(2y) = x\left(\frac{300 - 3x}{2}\right) = \frac{-3x^2 + 300x}{2}$$

Domain: $0 < x < 100$

(b)

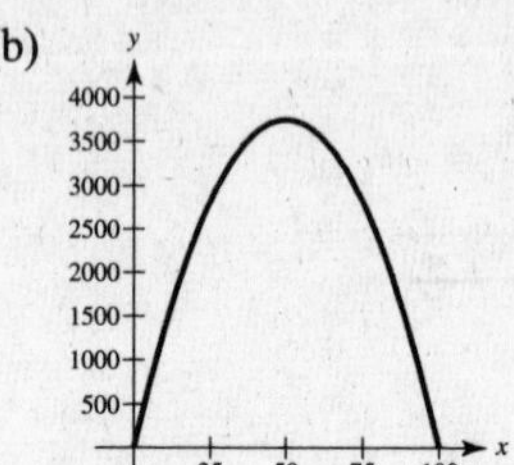


Maximum of 3750 $\text{ft}^2$ at $x = 50$ ft, $y = 37.5$ ft.

(c) $A(x) = -\frac{3}{2}(x^2 - 100x)$

$$= -\tfrac{3}{2}(x^2 - 100x + 2500) + 3750$$

$$= -\tfrac{3}{2}(x - 50)^2 + 3750$$

$A(50) = 3750$ square feet is the maximum area, where $x = 50$ ft and $y = 37.5$ ft.

**7.** The length of the trip in the water is $\sqrt{2^2 + x^2}$, and the length of the trip over land is $\sqrt{1 + (3 - x)^2}$. So, the total time is $T = \dfrac{\sqrt{4 + x^2}}{2} + \dfrac{\sqrt{1 + (3 - x)^2}}{4}$ hours.

**8.** $f(x) = e^x = e^{-x}$

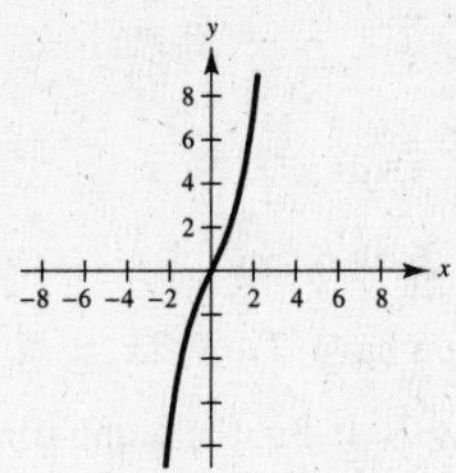


$$y = e^x - e^{-x}$$

$$ye^x = e^{2x} - 1$$

$$\left(e^x\right)^2 - ye^x - 1 = 0 \qquad \left(\text{Quadratic in } e^x\right)$$

$$e^x = \frac{y \pm \sqrt{y^2 + 4}}{2}$$

$$e^x = \frac{x + \sqrt{y^2 + 4}}{2} \qquad \text{(Use positive solution.)}$$

$$e^y = \frac{x + \sqrt{x^2 + 4}}{2}$$

$$f^{-1}(x) = y = \ln\left[\frac{x + \sqrt{x^2 + 4}}{2}\right] \qquad \text{Inverse}$$

**9.** (a) Slope $= \dfrac{9 - 4}{3 - 2} = 5$. Slope of tangent line is less than 5.

(b) Slope $= \dfrac{4 - 1}{2 - 1} = 3$. Slope of tangent line is greater than 3.

(c) Slope $= \dfrac{4.41 - 4}{2.1 - 2} = 4.1$. Slope of tangent line is less than 4.1.

(d) Slope $= \dfrac{f(2 + h) - f(2)}{(2 + h) - 2}$

$$= \frac{(2 + h)^2 - 4}{h}$$

$$= \frac{4h + h^2}{h}$$

$$= 4 + h, \; h \neq 0$$

(e) Letting $h$ get closer and closer to 0, the slope approaches 4. So, the slope at (2, 4) is 4.

**10.**

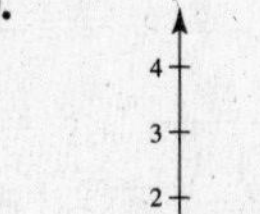

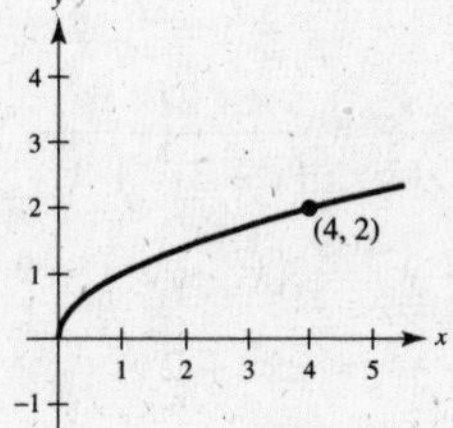


(a) Slope $= \dfrac{3 - 2}{9 - 4} = \dfrac{1}{5}$. Slope of tangent line is greater than $\dfrac{1}{5}$.

(b) Slope $= \dfrac{2 - 1}{4 - 1} = \dfrac{1}{3}$. Slope of tangent line is less than $\dfrac{1}{3}$.

(c) Slope $= \dfrac{2.1 - 2}{4.41 - 4} = \dfrac{10}{41}$. Slope of tangent line is greater than $\dfrac{10}{41}$.

(d) Slope $= \dfrac{f(4 + h) - f(4)}{(4 + h) - 4} = \dfrac{\sqrt{4 + h} - 2}{h}$

(e) $$\frac{\sqrt{4+h}-2}{h} = \frac{\sqrt{4+h}-2}{h} \cdot \frac{\sqrt{4+h}+2}{\sqrt{4+h}+2}$$

$$= \frac{(4+h)-4}{h\left(\sqrt{4+h}+2\right)}$$

$$= \frac{1}{\sqrt{4+h}+2}, \; h \neq 0$$

As $h$ gets closer to 0, the slope gets closer to $\frac{1}{4}$. The slope is $\frac{1}{4}$ at the point (4, 2).

**11.** Using the definition of absolute value, you can rewrite the equation.

$$y + |y| = x + |x|$$

$$\begin{cases} 2y, & y > 0 \\ 0, & y \le 0 \end{cases} = \begin{cases} 2x, & x > 0 \\ 0, & x \le 0 \end{cases}.$$

For $x > 0$ and $y > 0$, you have $2y = 2x \Rightarrow y = x$.

For any $x \le 0$, y is any $y \le 0$. So, the graph of $y + |y| = x + |x|$ is as follows.

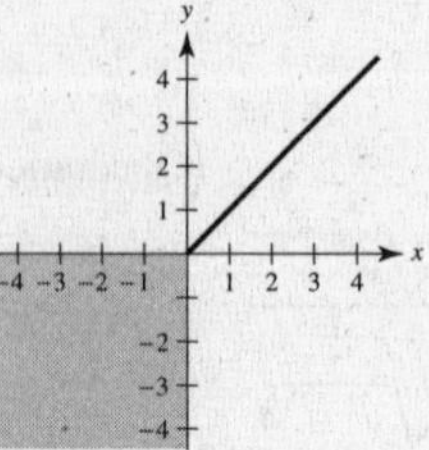

**12.** (a) $$\frac{I}{x^2} = \frac{2I}{(x-3)^2}$$

$$x^2 - 6x + 9 = 2x^2$$

$$x^2 + 6x - 9 = 0$$

$$x = \frac{-6 \pm \sqrt{36+36}}{2} = -3 \pm \sqrt{18} \approx 1.2426, -7.2426$$

(b) $$\frac{I}{x^2+y^2} = \frac{2I}{(x-3)^2+y^2}$$

$$(x-3)^2 + y^2 = 2\left(x^2+y^2\right)$$

$$x^2 - 6x + 9 + y^2 = 2x^2 + 2y^2$$

$$x^2 + y^2 + 6x - 9 = 0$$

$$(x+3)^2 + y^2 = 18$$

Circle of radius $\sqrt{18}$ and center $(-3, 0)$.

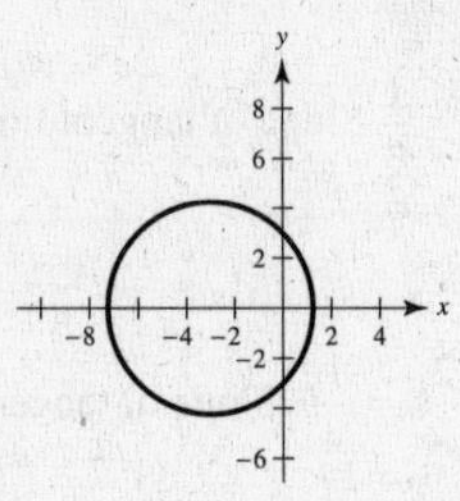

**13.** (a) $\dfrac{I}{x^2 + y^2} = \dfrac{kI}{(x-4)^2 + y^2}$

$(x-4)^2 + y^2 = k(x^2 + y^2)$

$(k-1)x^2 + 8x + (k-1)y^2 = 16$

If $k = 1$, then $x = 2$ is a vertical line. Assume $k \neq 1$.

$$x^2 + \frac{8x}{k-1} + y^2 = \frac{16}{k-1}$$

$$x^2 + \frac{8x}{k-1} + \frac{16}{(k-1)^2} + y^2 = \frac{16}{k-1} + \frac{16}{(k-1)^2}$$

$$\left(x + \frac{4}{k-1}\right)^2 + y^2 = \frac{16k}{(k-1)^2}, \text{ Circle}$$

(b) If $k = 3$, $(x+2)^2 + y^2 = 12$.

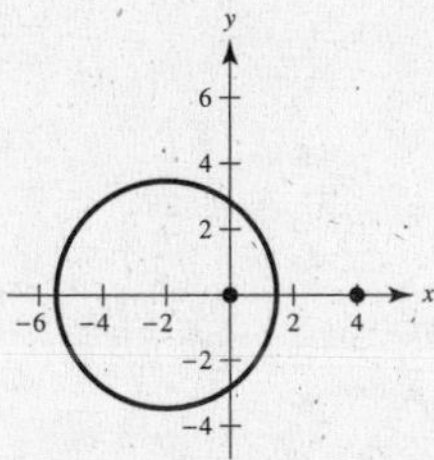

(c) As $k$ becomes very large, $\dfrac{4}{k-1} \to 0$ and $\dfrac{16k}{(k-1)^2} \to 0$.

The center of the circle gets closer to (0, 0), and its radius approaches 0.

**14.**

$$d_1 d_2 = 1$$

$$\left[(x+1)^2 + y^2\right]\left[(x-1)^2 + y^2\right] = 1$$

$$(x+1)^2(x-1)^2 + y^2\left[(x+1)^2 + (x-1)^2\right] + y^4 = 1$$

$$\left(x^2 - 1\right)^2 + y^2\left[2x^2 + 2\right] + y^4 = 1$$

$$x^4 - 2x^2 + 1 + 2x^2y^2 + 2y^2 + y^4 = 1$$

$$\left(x^4 + 2x^2y^2 + y^4\right) - 2x^2 + 2y^2 = 0$$

$$\left(x^2 + y^2\right)^2 = 2\left(x^2 - y^2\right)$$

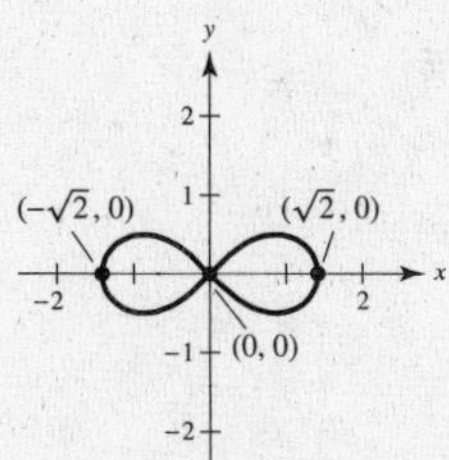


Let $y = 0$. Then $x^4 = 2x^2 \Rightarrow x = 0$ or $x^2 = 2$.

So, $(0, 0)$, $\left(\sqrt{2}, 0\right)$ and $\left(-\sqrt{2}, 0\right)$ are on the curve.

**15.** $f(x) = y = \dfrac{1}{1 - x}$

(a) Domain: all $x \neq 1$ or $(-\infty, 1) \cup (1, \infty)$

Range: all $y \neq 0$ or $(-\infty, 0) \cup (0, \infty)$

(b) $f(f(x)) = f\left(\dfrac{1}{1 - x}\right) = \dfrac{1}{1 - \left(\dfrac{1}{1 - x}\right)} = \dfrac{1}{\dfrac{1 - x - 1}{1 - x}} = \dfrac{1 - x}{-x} = \dfrac{x - 1}{x}$

Domain: all $x \neq 0, 1$ or $(-\infty, 0) \cup (0, 1) \cup (1, \infty)$

(c) $f(f(f(x))) = f\left(\dfrac{x - 1}{x}\right) = \dfrac{1}{1 - \left(\dfrac{x - 1}{x}\right)} = \dfrac{1}{\dfrac{1}{x}} = x$

Domain: all $x \neq 0, 1$ or $(-\infty, 0) \cup (0, 1) \cup (1, \infty)$

(d) The graph is not a line. It has holes at (0, 0) and (1, 1).

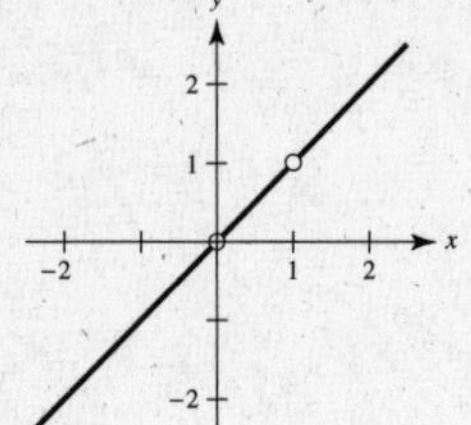

# CHAPTER 2
# Limits and Their Properties

# CHAPTER 2
# Limits and Their Properties

## Section 2.1 A Preview of Calculus

**1.** Precalculus: $(20 \text{ ft/sec})(15 \text{ sec}) = 300 \text{ ft}$

**2.** Calculus required: Velocity is not constant.
Distance $\approx (20 \text{ ft/sec})(15 \text{ sec}) = 300 \text{ ft}$

**3.** Calculus required: Slope of the tangent line at $x = 2$ is the rate of change, and equals about 0.16.

**4.** Precalculus: rate of change = slope = 0.08

**5.** (a) Precalculus: Area $= \frac{1}{2}bh = \frac{1}{2}(5)(4) = 10$ sq. units

(b) Calculus required: Area $= bh$
$$\approx 2(2.5)$$
$$= 5 \text{ sq. units}$$

**6.** $f(x) = \sqrt{x}$

(a)

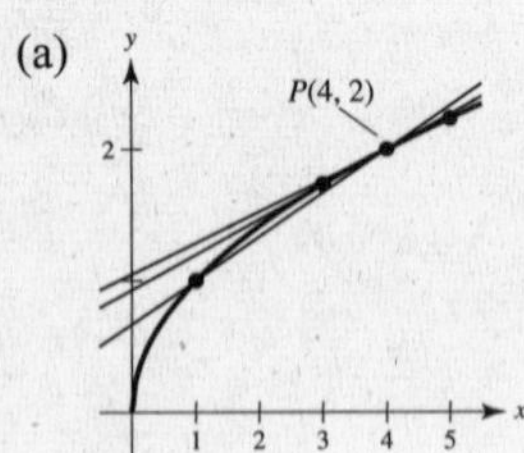


(b) slope $= m = \dfrac{\sqrt{x} - 2}{x - 4}$

$$= \frac{\sqrt{x} - 2}{(\sqrt{x} + 2)(\sqrt{x} - 2)}$$

$$= \frac{1}{\sqrt{x} + 2}, x \neq 4$$

$x = 1, m = \dfrac{1}{\sqrt{1} + 2} = \dfrac{1}{3}$

$x = 3, m = \dfrac{1}{\sqrt{3} + 2} \approx 0.2679$

$x = 5, m = \dfrac{1}{\sqrt{5} + 2} \approx 0.2361$

(c) At $P(4, 2)$ the slope is $\dfrac{1}{\sqrt{4} + 2} = \dfrac{1}{4} = 0.25.$

You can improve your approximation of the slope at $x = 4$ by considering $x$-values very close to 4.

**7.** $f(x) = 6x - x^2$

(a)

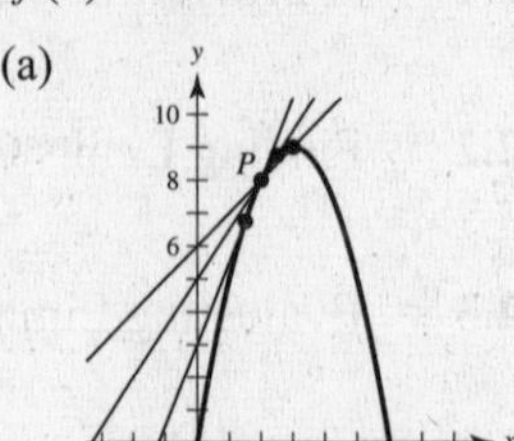


(b) slope $= m = \dfrac{(6x - x^2) - 8}{x - 2} = \dfrac{(x - 2)(4 - x)}{x - 2}$

$$= (4 - x), x \neq 2$$

For $x = 3, m = 4 - 3 = 1$

For $x = 2.5, m = 4 - 2.5 = 1.5 = \dfrac{3}{2}$

For $x = 1.5, m = 4 - 1.5 = 2.5 = \dfrac{5}{2}$

(c) At $P(2, 8)$, the slope is 2. You can improve your approximation by considering values of $x$ close to 2.

**8.** (a) For the figure on the left, each rectangle has width $\dfrac{\pi}{4}$.

$$\text{Area} \approx \frac{\pi}{4}\left[\sin\frac{\pi}{4} + \sin\frac{\pi}{2} + \sin\frac{3\pi}{4} + \sin\pi\right]$$
$$= \frac{\pi}{4}\left[\frac{\sqrt{2}}{2} + 1 + \frac{\sqrt{2}}{2}\right]$$
$$= \frac{\sqrt{2}+1}{4}\pi \approx 1.8961$$

For the figure on the right, each rectangle has width $\dfrac{\pi}{6}$.

$$\text{Area} \approx \frac{\pi}{6}\left[\sin\frac{\pi}{6} + \sin\frac{\pi}{3} + \sin\frac{\pi}{2} + \sin\frac{2\pi}{3} + \sin\frac{5\pi}{6} + \sin\pi\right]$$
$$= \frac{\pi}{6}\left[\frac{1}{2} + \frac{\sqrt{3}}{2} + 1 + \frac{\sqrt{3}}{2} + \frac{1}{2}\right]$$
$$= \frac{\sqrt{3}+2}{6}\pi \approx 1.9541$$

(b) You could obtain a more accurate approximation by using more rectangles. You will learn later that the exact area is 2.

**9.** (a) $\text{Area} \approx 5 + \frac{5}{2} + \frac{5}{3} + \frac{5}{4} \approx 10.417$

$\text{Area} \approx \frac{1}{2}\left(5 + \frac{5}{1.5} + \frac{5}{2} + \frac{5}{2.5} + \frac{5}{3} + \frac{5}{3.5} + \frac{5}{4} + \frac{5}{4.5}\right) \approx 9.145$

(b) You could improve the approximation by using more rectangles.

**10.** Answers will vary. *Sample answer*:

The instantaneous rate of change of an automobile's position is the velocity of the automobile, and can be determined by the speedometer.

**11.** (a) $D_1 = \sqrt{(5-1)^2 + (1-5)^2} = \sqrt{16+16} \approx 5.66$

(b) $D_2 = \sqrt{1 + \left(\frac{5}{2}\right)^2} + \sqrt{1 + \left(\frac{5}{2} - \frac{5}{3}\right)^2} + \sqrt{1 + \left(\frac{5}{3} - \frac{5}{4}\right)^2} + \sqrt{1 + \left(\frac{5}{4} - 1\right)^2}$

$\approx 2.693 + 1.302 + 1.083 + 1.031 \approx 6.11$

(c) Increase the number of line segments.

## Section 2.2 Finding Limits Graphically and Numerically

**1.**

| $x$ | 3.9 | 3.99 | 3.999 | 4.001 | 4.01 | 4.1 |
|---|---|---|---|---|---|---|
| $f(x)$ | 0.2041 | 0.2004 | 0.2000 | 0.2000 | 0.1996 | 0.1961 |

$\displaystyle\lim_{x\to 4}\frac{x-4}{x^2-3x-4} \approx 0.2000$ $\left(\text{Actual limit is } \dfrac{1}{5}.\right)$

**2.**

| $x$ | 1.9 | 1.99 | 1.999 | 2.001 | 2.01 | 2.1 |
|---|---|---|---|---|---|---|
| $f(x)$ | 0.2564 | 0.2506 | 0.2501 | 0.2499 | 0.2494 | 0.2439 |

$\displaystyle\lim_{x\to 2}\frac{x-2}{x^2-4} \approx 0.2500$ $\left(\text{Actual limit is } \dfrac{1}{4}.\right)$

**3.**

| $x$ | 2.9 | 2.99 | 2.999 | 3.001 | 3.01 | 3.1 |
|---|---|---|---|---|---|---|
| $f(x)$ | –0.0641 | –0.0627 | –0.0625 | –0.0625 | –0.0623 | –0.0610 |

$$\lim_{x\to 3} \frac{[1/(x+1)] - (1/4)}{x-3} \approx -0.0625 \qquad \left(\text{Actual limit is } -\frac{1}{16}.\right)$$

**4.**

| $x$ | –5.1 | –5.01 | –5.001 | –4.999 | –4.99 | –4.9 |
|---|---|---|---|---|---|---|
| $f(x)$ | –0.1662 | –0.1666 | –0.1667 | –0.1667 | –0.1667 | –0.1671 |

$$\lim_{x\to -5} \frac{\sqrt{4-x} - 3}{x+5} \approx -0.1667 \qquad \left(\text{Actual limit is } -\frac{1}{6}.\right)$$

**5.**

| $x$ | –0.1 | –0.01 | –0.001 | 0.001 | 0.01 | 0.1 |
|---|---|---|---|---|---|---|
| $f(x)$ | 0.9983 | 0.99998 | 1.0000 | 1.0000 | 0.99998 | 0.9983 |

$$\lim_{x\to 0} \frac{\sin x}{x} \approx 1.0000 \qquad (\text{Actual limit is } 1.)\ (\text{Make sure you use radian mode.})$$

**6.**

| $x$ | –0.1 | –0.01 | –0.001 | 0.001 | 0.01 | 0.1 |
|---|---|---|---|---|---|---|
| $f(x)$ | 0.0500 | 0.0050 | 0.0005 | –0.0005 | –0.0050 | –0.0500 |

$$\lim_{x\to 0} \frac{\cos x - 1}{x} \approx 0.0000 \qquad (\text{Actual limit is } 0.)\ (\text{Make sure you use radian mode.})$$

**7.**

| $x$ | –0.1 | –0.01 | –0.001 | 0.001 | 0.01 | 0.1 |
|---|---|---|---|---|---|---|
| $f(x)$ | 0.9516 | 0.9950 | 0.9995 | 1.0005 | 1.0050 | 1.0517 |

$$\lim_{x\to 0} \frac{e^x - 1}{x} \approx 1.0000 \qquad (\text{Actual limit is } 1.)$$

**8.**

| $x$ | –0.1 | –0.01 | –0.001 | 0.001 | 0.01 | 0.1 |
|---|---|---|---|---|---|---|
| $f(x)$ | 3.99982 | 4 | 4 | 0 | 0 | 0.00018 |

$$\lim_{x\to 0} \frac{4}{1 + e^{1/x}} \text{ does not exist.}$$

**9.**

| $x$ | –0.1 | –0.01 | –0.001 | 0.001 | 0.01 | 0.1 |
|---|---|---|---|---|---|---|
| $f(x)$ | 1.0536 | 1.0050 | 1.0005 | 0.9995 | 0.9950 | 0.9531 |

$$\lim_{x\to 0} \frac{\ln(x+1)}{x} \approx 1.0000 \qquad (\text{Actual limit is } 1.)$$

**10.**

| $x$ | 1.9 | 1.99 | 1.999 | 2.001 | 2.01 | 2.1 |
|---|---|---|---|---|---|---|
| $f(x)$ | 0.5129 | 0.5013 | 0.5001 | 0.4999 | 0.4988 | 0.4879 |

$$\lim_{x\to 2} \frac{\ln x - \ln 2}{x-2} \approx 0.5000 \qquad \left(\text{Actual limit is } \frac{1}{2}.\right)$$

**11.**

| $x$ | 0.9 | 0.99 | 0.999 | 1.001 | 1.01 | 1.1 |
|---|---|---|---|---|---|---|
| $f(x)$ | 0.2564 | 0.2506 | 0.2501 | 0.2499 | 0.2494 | 0.2439 |

$\lim_{x\to 1} \frac{x-2}{x^2+x-6} \approx 0.2500$ $\left(\text{Actual limit is } \frac{1}{4}.\right)$

**12.**

| $x$ | −3.1 | −3.01 | −3.001 | −2.999 | −2.99 | −2.9 |
|---|---|---|---|---|---|---|
| $f(x)$ | 1.1111 | 1.0101 | 1.0010 | 0.9990 | 0.9901 | 0.9091 |

$\lim_{x\to -3} \frac{x+3}{x^2+7x+12} \approx 1.0000$ (Actual limit is 1.)

**13.**

| $x$ | 0.9 | 0.99 | 0.999 | 1.001 | 1.01 | 1.1 |
|---|---|---|---|---|---|---|
| $f(x)$ | 0.7340 | 0.6733 | 0.6673 | 0.6660 | 0.6600 | 0.6015 |

$\lim_{x\to 1} \frac{x^4-1}{x^6-1} \approx 0.6666$ $\left(\text{Actual limit is } \frac{2}{3}.\right)$

**14.**

| $x$ | −2.1 | −2.01 | −2.001 | −1.999 | −1.99 | −1.9 |
|---|---|---|---|---|---|---|
| $f(x)$ | 12.6100 | 12.0601 | 12.0060 | 11.9940 | 11.9401 | 11.4100 |

$\lim_{x\to -2} \frac{x^3+8}{x+2} \approx 12.0000$ (Actual limit is 12.)

**15.**

| $x$ | −0.1 | −0.01 | −0.001 | 0.001 | 0.01 | 0.1 |
|---|---|---|---|---|---|---|
| $f(x)$ | 1.9867 | 1.9999 | 2.0000 | 2.0000 | 1.9999 | 1.9867 |

$\lim_{x\to 0} \frac{\sin 2x}{x} \approx 2.0000$ (Actual limit is 2.) (Make sure you use radian mode.)

**16.**

| $x$ | −0.1 | −0.01 | −0.001 | 0.001 | 0.01 | 0.1 |
|---|---|---|---|---|---|---|
| $f(x)$ | 0.4950 | 0.5000 | 0.5000 | 0.5000 | 0.5000 | 0.4950 |

$\lim_{x\to 0} \frac{\tan x}{\tan 2x} \approx 0.5000$ $\left(\text{Actual limit is } \frac{1}{2}.\right)$

**17.** $\lim_{x\to 3}(4-x) = 1$

**18.** $\lim_{x\to 1}(x^2+3) = 4$

**19.** $\lim_{x\to 2} \frac{|x-2|}{x-2}$ does not exist.

For values of $x$ to the left of 2, $\frac{|x-2|}{(x-2)} = -1$, whereas

for values of $x$ to the right of 2, $\frac{|x-2|}{(x-2)} = 1$.

**20.** $\lim_{x\to 1} f(x) = \lim_{x\to 1}(x^2+3) = 4$

**21.** $\lim_{x\to 1} \sin \pi x = 0$

**22.** $\lim_{x\to 5} \frac{2}{x-5}$ does not exist because the function increases and decreases without bound as $x$ approaches 5.

**23.** $\lim_{x\to 1} \sqrt[3]{x} \ln|x-2| = 0$

**24.** $\lim_{x\to 0} \frac{4}{2+e^{1/x}}$ does not exist. The function approaches 2 from the left side of 0 by it approaches 0 from the left side of 0.

**25.** $\lim_{x\to 0} \cos(1/x)$ does not exist because the function oscillates between −1 and 1 as $x$ approaches 0.

**26.** $\lim_{x \to \pi/2} \tan x$ does not exist because the function increases without bound as $x$ approaches $\frac{\pi}{2}$ from the left and decreases without bound as $x$ approaches $\frac{\pi}{2}$ from the right.

**27.** (a) $f(1)$ exists. The black dot at $(1, 2)$ indicates that $f(1) = 2$.

(b) $\lim_{x \to 1} f(x)$ does not exist. As x approaches 1 from the left, $f(x)$ approaches 3.5, whereas as $x$ approaches 1 from the right, $f(x)$ approaches 1.

(c) $f(4)$ does not exist. The hollow circle at $(4, 2)$ indicates that $f$ is not defined at 4.

(d) $\lim_{x \to 4} f(x)$ exists. As $x$ approaches 4, $f(x)$ approaches 2: $\lim_{x \to 4} f(x) = 2$.

**28.** (a) $f(-2)$ does not exist. The vertical dotted line indicates that $f$ is not defined at $-2$.

(b) $\lim_{x \to -2} f(x)$ does not exist. As $x$ approaches $-2$, the values of $f(x)$ do not approach a specific number.

(c) $f(0)$ exists. The black dot at $(0, 4)$ indicates that $f(0) = 4$.

(d) $\lim_{x \to 0} f(x)$ does not exist. As $x$ approaches 0 from the left, $f(x)$ approaches $\frac{1}{2}$, whereas as $x$ approaches 0 from the right, $f(x)$ approaches 4.

(e) $f(2)$ does not exist. The hollow circle at $\left(2, \frac{1}{2}\right)$ indicates that $f(2)$ is not defined.

(f) $\lim_{x \to 2} f(x)$ exists. As $x$ approaches 2, $f(x)$ approaches $\frac{1}{2}$: $\lim_{x \to 2} f(x) = \frac{1}{2}$.

(g) $f(4)$ exists. The black dot at $(4, 2)$ indicates that $f(4) = 2$.

(h) $\lim_{x \to 4} f(x)$ does not exist. As $x$ approaches 4, the values of $f(x)$ do not approach a specific number.

**29.** $\lim_{x \to c} f(x)$ exists for all $c \neq -3$.

**30.** $\lim_{x \to c} f(x)$ exists for all $c \neq -2, 0$.

**31.**

$\lim_{x \to c} f(x)$ exists for all $c \neq 4$.

**32.**

$\lim_{x \to c} f(x)$ exists for all $c \neq \pi$.

**33.** One possible answer is:

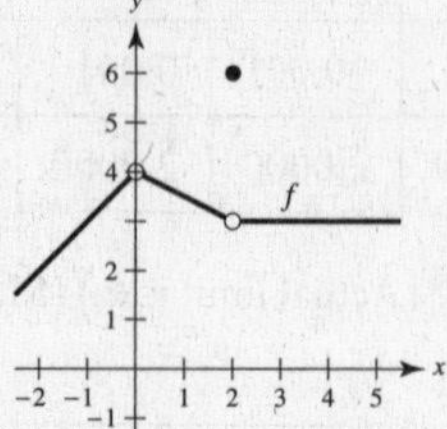

**34.** One possible answer is:

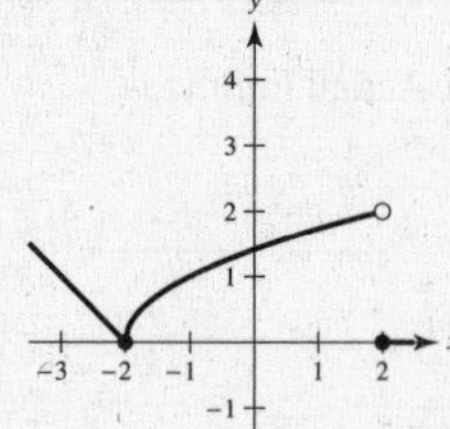

**35.** 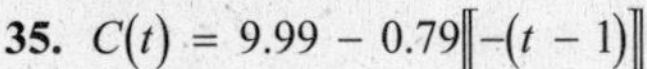 $C(t) = 9.99 - 0.79[\![-(t - 1)]\!]$

(a) 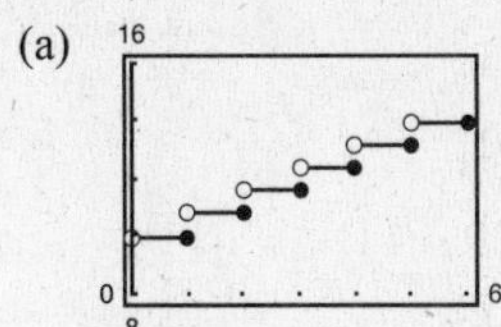


(b)

| $t$ | 3 | 3.3 | 3.4 | 3.5 | 3.6 | 3.7 | 4 |
|---|---|---|---|---|---|---|---|
| $C$ | 11.57 | 12.36 | 12.36 | 12.36 | 12.36 | 12.36 | 12.36 |

$\lim_{t \to 3.5} C(t) = 12.36$

(c)

| $t$ | 2 | 2.5 | 2.9 | 3 | 3.1 | 3.5 | 4 |
|---|---|---|---|---|---|---|---|
| $C$ | 10.78 | 11.57 | 11.57 | 11.57 | 12.36 | 12.36 | 12.36 |

$\lim_{t \to 3} C(t)$ does not exist because the values of $C$ approach different values as $t$ approaches 3 from both sides.

**36.** $C(t) = 5.79 - 0.99[\![-(t - 1)]\!]$

(a) 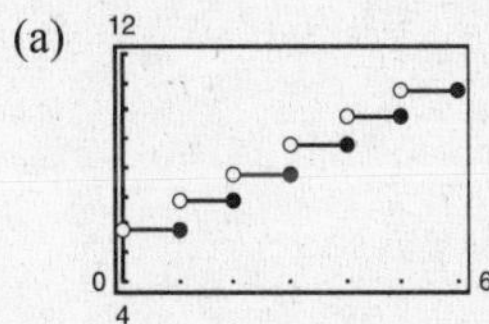


(b)

| $t$ | 3 | 3.3 | 3.4 | 3.5 | 3.6 | 3.7 | 4 |
|---|---|---|---|---|---|---|---|
| $C$ | 7.77 | 8.76 | 8.76 | 8.76 | 8.76 | 8.76 | 8.76 |

$\lim_{t \to 3.5} C(t) = 8.76$

(c)

| $t$ | 2 | 2.5 | 2.9 | 3 | 3.1 | 3.5 | 4 |
|---|---|---|---|---|---|---|---|
| $C$ | 6.78 | 7.77 | 7.77 | 7.77 | 8.76 | 8.76 | 8.76 |

$\lim_{t \to 3} C(t)$ does not exist because the values of $C$ approach different values as $t$ approaches 3 from both sides.

**37.** You need $|f(x) - 3| = |(x + 1) - 3| = |x - 2| < 0.4$. So, take $\delta = 0.4$. If $0 < |x - 2| < 0.4$, then $|x - 2| = |(x + 1) - 3| = |f(x) - 3| < 0.4$, as desired.

**38.** You need $|f(x) - 1| = \left|\frac{1}{x - 1} - 1\right| = \left|\frac{2 - x}{x - 1}\right| < 0.01$. Let $\delta = \frac{1}{101}$. If $0 < |x - 2| < \frac{1}{101}$, then

$$-\frac{1}{101} < x - 2 < \frac{1}{101} \Rightarrow 1 - \frac{1}{101} < x - 1 < 1 + \frac{1}{101}$$

$$\Rightarrow \frac{100}{101} < x - 1 < \frac{102}{101}$$

$$\Rightarrow |x - 1| > \frac{100}{101}$$

and you have

$$|f(x) - 1| = \left|\frac{1}{x - 1} - 1\right| = \left|\frac{2 - x}{x - 1}\right| < \frac{1/101}{100/101} = \frac{1}{100} = 0.01.$$

**39.** You need to find $\delta$ such that $0 < |x - 1| < \delta$ implies $|f(x) - 1| = \left|\frac{1}{x} - 1\right| < 0.1$. That is,

$$-0.1 < \frac{1}{x} - 1 < 0.1$$
$$1 - 0.1 < \frac{1}{x} < 1 + 0.1$$
$$\frac{9}{10} < \frac{1}{x} < \frac{11}{10}$$
$$\frac{10}{9} > x > \frac{10}{11}$$
$$\frac{10}{9} - 1 > x - 1 > \frac{10}{11} - 1$$
$$\frac{1}{9} > x - 1 > -\frac{1}{11}.$$

So take $\delta = \frac{1}{11}$. Then $0 < |x - 1| < \delta$ implies

$$-\frac{1}{11} < x - 1 < \frac{1}{11}$$
$$-\frac{1}{11} < x - 1 < \frac{1}{9}.$$

Using the first series of equivalent inequalities, you obtain

$$|f(x) - 1| = \left|\frac{1}{x} - 1\right| < 0.1.$$

**40.** You need to find $\delta$ such that $0 < |x - 2| < \delta$ implies $|f(x) - 3| = |x^2 - 1 - 3| = |x^2 - 4| < 0.2$. That is,

$$-0.2 < x^2 - 4 < 0.2$$
$$4 - 0.2 < x^2 < 4 + 0.2$$
$$3.8 < x^2 < 4.2$$
$$\sqrt{3.8} < x < \sqrt{4.2}$$
$$\sqrt{3.8} - 2 < x - 2 < \sqrt{4.2} - 2.$$

So take $\delta = \sqrt{4.2} - 2 \approx 0.0494$.

Then $0 < |x - 2| < \delta$ implies

$$-\left(\sqrt{4.2} - 2\right) < x - 2 < \sqrt{4.2} - 2$$
$$\sqrt{3.8} - 2 < x - 2 < \sqrt{4.2} - 2.$$

Using the first series of equivalent inequalities, you obtain

$$|f(x) - 3| = |x^2 - 4| < 0.2.$$

**41.** $\lim_{x \to 2}(3x + 2) = 8 = L$

$$|(3x + 2) - 8| < 0.01$$
$$|3x - 6| < 0.01$$
$$3|x - 2| < 0.01$$
$$0 < |x - 2| < \frac{0.01}{3} \approx 0.0033 = \delta$$

So, if $0 < |x - 2| < \delta = \frac{0.01}{3}$, you have

$$3|x - 2| < 0.01$$
$$|3x - 6| < 0.01$$
$$|(3x + 2) - 8| < 0.01$$
$$|f(x) - L| < 0.01.$$

**42.** $\lim_{x \to 4}\left(4 - \frac{x}{2}\right) = 2 = L$

$$\left|\left(4 - \frac{x}{2}\right) - 2\right| < 0.01$$
$$\left|2 - \frac{x}{2}\right| < 0.01$$
$$\left|-\frac{1}{2}(x - 4)\right| < 0.01$$
$$0 < |x - 4| < 0.02 = \delta$$

So, if $0 < |x - 4| < \delta = 0.02$, you have

$$\left|-\frac{1}{2}(x - 4)\right| < 0.01$$
$$\left|2 - \frac{x}{2}\right| < 0.01$$
$$\left|\left(4 - \frac{x}{2}\right) - 2\right| < 0.01$$
$$|f(x) - L| < 0.01.$$

**43.** $\lim_{x\to 2}(x^2 - 3) = 1 = L$

$$\left|(x^2 - 3) - 1\right| < 0.01$$
$$\left|x^2 - 4\right| < 0.01$$
$$\left|(x + 2)(x - 2)\right| < 0.01$$
$$\left|x + 2\right|\left|x - 2\right| < 0.01$$
$$\left|x - 2\right| < \frac{0.01}{\left|x + 2\right|}$$

If you assume $1 < x < 3$, then $\delta = 0.01/5 = 0.002$.

So, if $0 < \left|x - 2\right| < \delta = 0.002$, you have

$$\left|x - 2\right| < 0.002 = \frac{1}{5}(0.01) < \frac{1}{\left|x + 2\right|}(0.01)$$
$$\left|x + 2\right|\left|x - 2\right| < 0.01$$
$$\left|x^2 - 4\right| < 0.01$$
$$\left|(x^2 - 3) - 1\right| < 0.01$$
$$\left|f(x) - L\right| < 0.01.$$

**44.** $\lim_{x\to 5}(x^2 + 4) = 29 = L$

$$\left|(x^2 + 4) - 29\right| < 0.01$$
$$\left|x^2 - 25\right| < 0.01$$
$$\left|(x + 5)(x - 5)\right| < 0.01$$
$$\left|x - 5\right| < \frac{0.01}{\left|x + 5\right|}$$

If you assume $4 < x < 6$, then $\delta = 0.01/11 \approx 0.0009$.

So, if $0 < \left|x - 5\right| < \delta = \frac{0.01}{11}$, you have

$$\left|x - 5\right| < \frac{0.01}{11} < \frac{1}{\left|x + 5\right|}(0.01)$$
$$\left|x - 5\right|\left|x + 5\right| < 0.01$$
$$\left|x^2 - 25\right| < 0.01$$
$$\left|(x^2 + 4) - 29\right| < 0.01$$
$$\left|f(x) - L\right| < 0.01.$$

**45.** $\lim_{x\to 2}(x + 3) = 5$

Given $\varepsilon > 0$:

$$\left|(x + 3) - 5\right| < \varepsilon$$
$$\left|x - 2\right| < \varepsilon$$

So, let $\delta = \varepsilon$.

So, if $0 < \left|x - 2\right| < \delta = \varepsilon$, you have

$$\left|x - 2\right| < \varepsilon$$
$$\left|(x + 3) - 5\right| < \varepsilon$$
$$\left|f(x) - L\right| < \varepsilon.$$

**46.** $\lim_{x\to -3}(2x + 5) = -1$

Given $\varepsilon > 0$:

$$\left|(2x + 5) - (-1)\right| < \varepsilon$$
$$\left|2x + 6\right| < \varepsilon$$
$$2\left|x + 3\right| < \varepsilon$$
$$\left|x + 3\right| < \frac{\varepsilon}{2}$$

So, let $\delta = \varepsilon/2$.

So, if $0 < \left|x + 3\right| < \delta = \frac{\varepsilon}{2}$, you have

$$\left|x + 3\right| < \frac{\varepsilon}{2}$$
$$\left|2x + 6\right| < \varepsilon$$
$$\left|(2x + 5) - (-1)\right| < \varepsilon$$
$$\left|f(x) - L\right| < \varepsilon.$$

**47.** $\lim_{x\to -4}\left(\frac{1}{2}x - 1\right) = \frac{1}{2}(-4) - 1 = -3$

Given $\varepsilon > 0$:

$$\left|\left(\tfrac{1}{2}x - 1\right) - (-3)\right| < \varepsilon$$
$$\left|\tfrac{1}{2}x + 2\right| < \varepsilon$$
$$\tfrac{1}{2}\left|x - (-4)\right| < \varepsilon$$
$$\left|x - (-4)\right| < 2\varepsilon$$

So, let $\delta = 2\varepsilon$.

So, if $0 < \left|x - (-4)\right| < \delta = 2\varepsilon$, you have

$$\left|x - (-4)\right| < 2\varepsilon$$
$$\left|\tfrac{1}{2}x + 2\right| < \varepsilon$$
$$\left|\left(\tfrac{1}{2}x - 1\right) + 3\right| < \varepsilon$$
$$\left|f(x) - L\right| < \varepsilon.$$

**48.** $\lim_{x\to 1}\left(\frac{2}{3}x + 9\right) = \frac{2}{3}(1) + 9 = \frac{29}{3}$

Given $\varepsilon > 0$:

$$\left|\left(\frac{2}{3}x + 9\right) - \frac{29}{3}\right| < \varepsilon$$
$$\left|\frac{2}{3}x - \frac{2}{3}\right| < \varepsilon$$
$$\frac{2}{3}|x - 1| < \varepsilon$$
$$|x - 1| < \frac{3}{2}\varepsilon$$

So, let $\delta = (3/2)\varepsilon$.

So, if $0 < |x - 1| < \delta = \frac{3}{2}\varepsilon$, you have

$$|x - 1| < \frac{3}{2}\varepsilon$$
$$\left|\frac{2}{3}x - \frac{2}{3}\right| < \varepsilon$$
$$\left|\left(\frac{2}{3}x + 9\right) - \frac{29}{3}\right| < \varepsilon$$
$$|f(x) - L| < \varepsilon.$$

**49.** $\lim_{x\to 6} 3 = 3$

Given $\varepsilon > 0$:

$$|3 - 3| < \varepsilon$$
$$0 < \varepsilon$$

So, any $\delta > 0$ will work.

So, for any $\delta > 0$, you have

$$|3 - 3| < \varepsilon$$
$$|f(x) - L| < \varepsilon.$$

**50.** $\lim_{x\to 2} (-1) = -1$

Given $\varepsilon > 0$: $|-1 - (-1)| < \varepsilon$

$$0 < \varepsilon$$

So, any $\delta > 0$ will work.

So, for any $\delta > 0$, you have

$$|(-1) - (-1)| < \varepsilon$$
$$|f(x) - L| < \varepsilon.$$

**51.** $\lim_{x\to 0} \sqrt[3]{x} = 0$

Given $\varepsilon > 0$: $\left|\sqrt[3]{x} - 0\right| < \varepsilon$

$$\left|\sqrt[3]{x}\right| < \varepsilon$$
$$|x| < \varepsilon^3$$

So, let $\delta = \varepsilon^3$.

So, for $0 < |x - 0| < \delta = \varepsilon^3$, you have

$$|x| < \varepsilon^3$$
$$\left|\sqrt[3]{x}\right| < \varepsilon$$
$$\left|\sqrt[3]{x} - 0\right| < \varepsilon$$
$$|f(x) - L| < \varepsilon.$$

**52.** $\lim_{x\to 4} \sqrt{x} = \sqrt{4} = 2$

Given $\varepsilon > 0$: $\left|\sqrt{x} - 2\right| < \varepsilon$

$$\left|\sqrt{x} - 2\right|\left|\sqrt{x} + 2\right| < \varepsilon\left|\sqrt{x} + 2\right|$$
$$|x - 4| < \varepsilon\left|\sqrt{x} + 2\right|$$

Assuming $1 < x < 9$, you can choose $\delta = 3\varepsilon$. Then,

$$0 < |x - 4| < \delta = 3\varepsilon \Rightarrow |x - 4| < \varepsilon\left|\sqrt{x} + 2\right|$$
$$\Rightarrow \left|\sqrt{x} - 2\right| < \varepsilon.$$

**53.** $\lim_{x\to -2} |x - 2| = |(-2) - 2| = 4$

Given $\varepsilon > 0$:

$$\big||x - 2| - 4\big| < \varepsilon$$
$$|-(x - 2) - 4| < \varepsilon \quad (x - 2 < 0)$$
$$|-x - 2| = |x + 2| = |x - (-2)| < \varepsilon$$

So, let $\delta = \varepsilon$.

So, for $0 < |x - (-2)| < \delta = \varepsilon$, you have

$$|x + 2| < \varepsilon$$
$$|-(x + 2)| < \varepsilon$$
$$|-(x - 2) - 4| < \varepsilon$$
$$\big||x - 2| - 4\big| < \varepsilon \quad (\text{because } x - 2 < 0)$$
$$|f(x) - L| < \varepsilon.$$

**54.** $\lim_{x \to 3} |x - 3| = 0$

Given $\varepsilon > 0$:

$$||x - 3| - 0| < \varepsilon$$
$$|x - 3| < \varepsilon$$

So, let $\delta = \varepsilon$.

So, for $0 < |x - 3| < \delta = \varepsilon$, you have

$$|x - 3| < \varepsilon$$
$$||x - 3| - 0| < \varepsilon$$
$$|f(x) - L| < \varepsilon.$$

**55.** $\lim_{x \to 1} (x^2 + 1) = 2$

Given $\varepsilon > 0$:

$$|(x^2 + 1) - 2| < \varepsilon$$
$$|x^2 - 1| < \varepsilon$$
$$|(x + 1)(x - 1)| < \varepsilon$$
$$|x - 1| < \frac{\varepsilon}{|x + 1|}$$

If you assume $0 < x < 2$, then $\delta = \varepsilon/3$.

So, for $0 < |x - 1| < \delta = \dfrac{\varepsilon}{3}$, you have

$$|x - 1| < \frac{1}{3}\varepsilon < \frac{1}{|x + 1|}\varepsilon$$
$$|x^2 - 1| < \varepsilon$$
$$|(x^2 + 1) - 2| < \varepsilon$$
$$|f(x) - 2| < \varepsilon.$$

**56.** $\lim_{x \to -3} (x^2 + 3x) = 0$

Given $\varepsilon > 0$:

$$|(x^2 + 3x) - 0| < \varepsilon$$
$$|x(x + 3)| < \varepsilon$$
$$|x + 3| < \frac{\varepsilon}{|x|}$$

If you assume $-4 < x < -2$, then $\delta = \varepsilon/4$.

So, for $0 < |x - (-3)| < \delta = \dfrac{\varepsilon}{4}$, you have

$$|x + 3| < \frac{1}{4}\varepsilon < \frac{1}{|x|}\varepsilon$$
$$|x(x + 3)| < \varepsilon$$
$$|x^2 + 3x - 0| < \varepsilon$$
$$|f(x) - L| < \varepsilon.$$

**57.** $\lim_{x \to \pi} f(x) = \lim_{x \to \pi} 4 = 4$

**58.** $\lim_{x \to \pi} f(x) = \lim_{x \to \pi} x = \pi$

**59.** $f(x) = \dfrac{\sqrt{x + 5} - 3}{x - 4}$

$\lim_{x \to 4} f(x) = \dfrac{1}{6}$

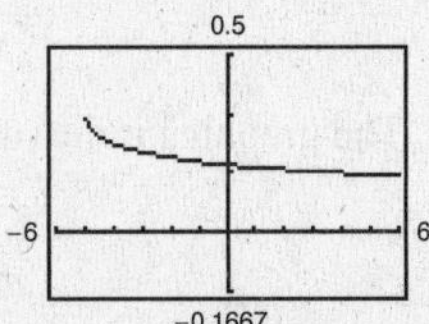


The domain is $[-5, 4) \cup (4, \infty)$. The graphing utility does not show the hole at $\left(4, \dfrac{1}{6}\right)$.

**60.** $f(x) = \dfrac{x - 3}{x^2 - 4x + 3}$

$\lim_{x \to 3} f(x) = \dfrac{1}{2}$

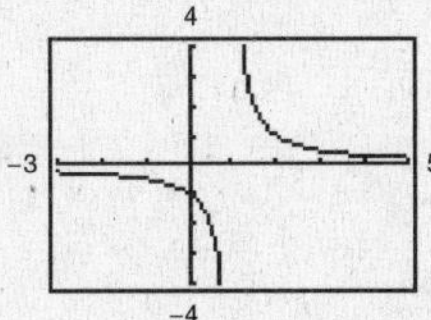


The domain is all $x \neq 1, 3$. The graphing utility does not show the hole at $\left(3, \dfrac{1}{2}\right)$.

**61.** $f(x) = \dfrac{x - 9}{\sqrt{x} - 3}$

$\lim_{x \to 9} f(x) = 6$

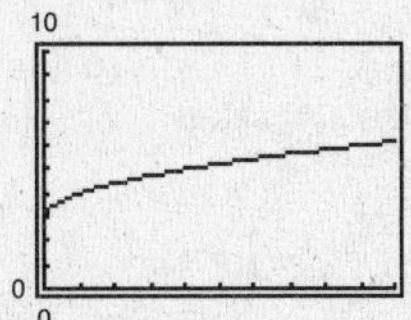


The domain is all $x \geq 0$ except $x = 9$. The graphing utility does not show the hole at $(9, 6)$.

**62.** $f(x) = \dfrac{e^{x/2} - 1}{x}$

$\lim_{x \to 0} f(x) = \dfrac{1}{2}$

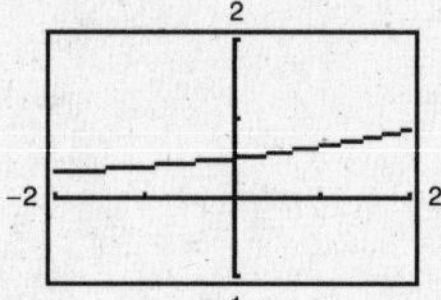


The domain is all $x \neq 0$. The graphing utility does not show the hole at $\left(0, \dfrac{1}{2}\right)$.

**63.** $\lim_{x \to 8} f(x) = 25$ means that the values of $f$ approach 25 as $x$ gets closer and closer to 8.

**64.** In the definition of $\lim_{x \to c} f(x)$, $f$ must be defined on both sides of $c$, but does not have to be defined at $c$ itself. The value of $f$ at $c$ has no bearing on the limit as $x$ approaches $c$.

**65.** (i) The values of $f$ approach different numbers as $x$ approaches $c$ from different sides of $c$:

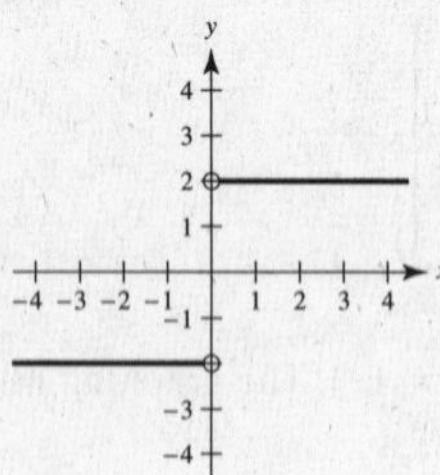

(ii) The values of $f$ increase or decrease without bound as $x$ approaches $c$:

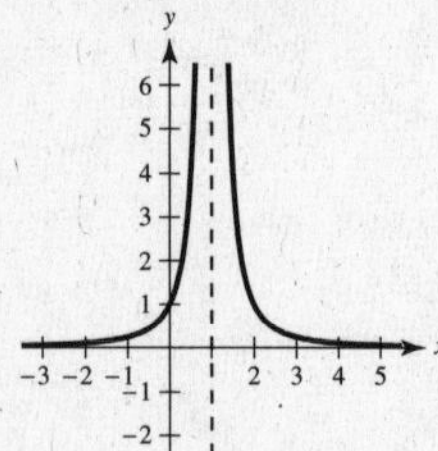

(iii) The values of $f$ oscillate between two fixed numbers as $x$ approaches $c$:

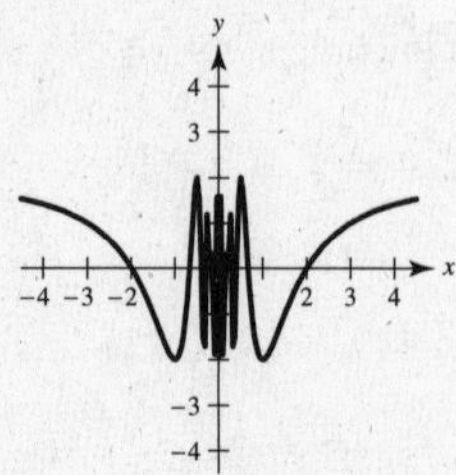

**66.** (a) No. The fact that $f(2) = 4$ has no bearing on the existence of the limit of $f(x)$ as $x$ approaches 2.

(b) No. The fact that $\lim_{x \to 2} f(x) = 4$ has no bearing on the value of $f$ at 2.

**67.** (a) $C = 2\pi r$

$r = \dfrac{C}{2\pi} = \dfrac{6}{2\pi} = \dfrac{3}{\pi} \approx 0.9549$ cm

(b) When $C = 5.5: r = \dfrac{5.5}{2\pi} \approx 0.87535$ cm

When $C = 6.5: r = \dfrac{6.5}{2\pi} \approx 1.03451$ cm

So, $0.87535 < r < 1.03451$.

(c) $\lim_{x \to 3/\pi} (2\pi r) = 6;\ \varepsilon = 0.5;\ \delta \approx 0.0796$

**68.** $V = \dfrac{4}{3}\pi r^3, V = 2.48$

(a) $2.48 = \dfrac{4}{3}\pi r^3$

$r^3 = \dfrac{1.86}{\pi}$

$r \approx 0.8397$ in.

(b) $2.45 \leq V \leq 2.51$

$2.45 \leq \dfrac{4}{3}\pi r^3 \leq 2.51$

$0.5849 \leq r^3 \leq 0.5992$

$0.8363 \leq r \leq 0.8431$

(c) For $\varepsilon = 2.51 - 2.48 = 0.03$, $\delta \approx 0.003$.

**69.** $f(x) = (1 + x)^{1/x}$

$\lim_{x \to 0} (1 + x)^{1/x} = e \approx 2.71828$

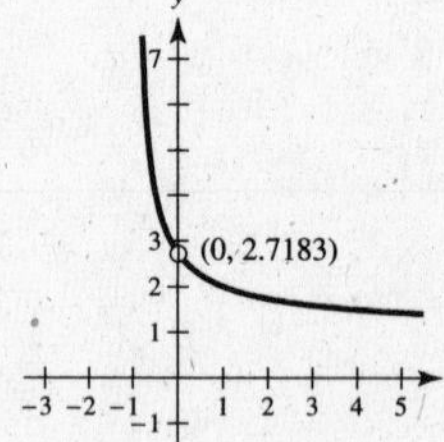


| $x$ | $f(x)$ |
|---|---|
| −0.1 | 2.867972 |
| −0.01 | 2.731999 |
| −0.001 | 2.719642 |
| −0.0001 | 2.718418 |
| −0.00001 | 2.718295 |
| −0.000001 | 2.718283 |

| $x$ | $f(x)$ |
|---|---|
| 0.1 | 2.593742 |
| 0.01 | 2.704814 |
| 0.001 | 2.716942 |
| 0.0001 | 2.718146 |
| 0.00001 | 2.718268 |
| 0.000001 | 2.718280 |

**70.** $f(x) = \dfrac{|x + 1| - |x - 1|}{x}$

| $x$ | $-1$ | $-0.5$ | $-0.1$ | $0$ | $0.1$ | $0.5$ | $1.0$ |
|---|---|---|---|---|---|---|---|
| $f(x)$ | 2 | 2 | 2 | Undef. | 2 | 2 | 2 |

$\lim\limits_{x \to 0} f(x) = 2$

Note that for $-1 < x < 1, x \neq 0$,

$f(x) = \dfrac{(x + 1) + (x - 1)}{x} = 2.$

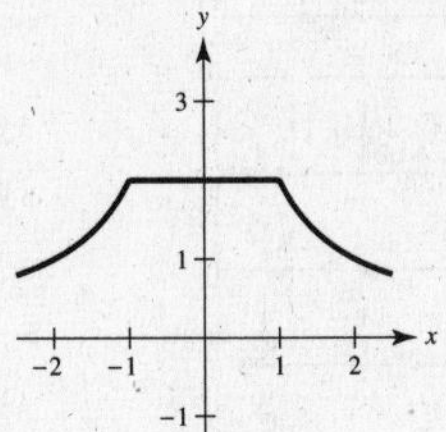


**71.**

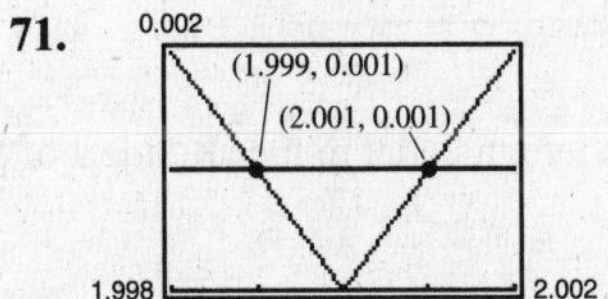


Using the zoom and trace feature, $\delta = 0.001$. So, $(2 - \delta, 2 + \delta) = (1.999, 2.001)$.

**Note:** $\dfrac{x^2 - 4}{x - 2} = x + 2$ for $x \neq 2$.

**72.**

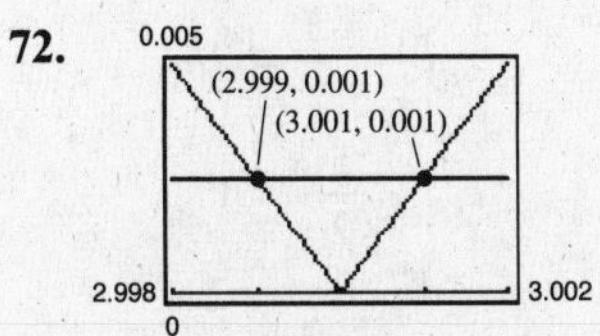


From the graph, $\delta = 0.001$. So, $(3 - \delta, 3 + \delta) = (2.999, 3.001)$.

**Note:** $\dfrac{x^2 - 3x}{x - 3} = x$ for $x \neq 3$.

**73.** False. The existence or nonexistence of $f(x)$ at $x = c$ has no bearing on the existence of the limit of $f(x)$ as $x \to c$.

**74.** True

**75.** False. Let

$$f(x) = \begin{cases} x - 4, & x \neq 2 \\ 0, & x = 2 \end{cases}$$

$f(2) = 0$

$\lim\limits_{x \to 2} f(x) = \lim\limits_{x \to 2}(x - 4) = 2 \neq 0$

**76.** False. Let

$$f(x) = \begin{cases} x - 4, & x \neq 2 \\ 0, & x = 2 \end{cases}$$

$\lim\limits_{x \to 2} f(x) = \lim\limits_{x \to 2}(x - 4) = 2$ and $f(2) = 0 \neq 2$

**77.** $f(x) = \sqrt{x}$

$\lim\limits_{x \to 0.25} \sqrt{x} = 0.5$ is true.

As $x$ approaches $0.25 = \frac{1}{4}$ from either side, $f(x) = \sqrt{x}$ approaches $\frac{1}{2} = 0.5$.

**78.** $f(x) = \sqrt{x}$

$\lim\limits_{x \to 0} \sqrt{x} = 0$ is false.

$f(x) = \sqrt{x}$ is not defined on an open interval containing 0 because the domain of $f$ is $x \geq 0$.

**79.** Using a graphing utility, you see that

$\lim\limits_{x \to 0} \dfrac{\sin x}{x} = 1$

$\lim\limits_{x \to 0} \dfrac{\sin 2x}{x} = 2$, etc.

So, $\lim\limits_{x \to 0} \dfrac{\sin nx}{x} = n$.

**80.** Using a graphing utility, you see that

$\lim\limits_{x \to 0} \dfrac{\tan x}{x} = 1$

$\lim\limits_{x \to 0} \dfrac{\tan 2x}{x} = 2$, etc.

So, $\lim\limits_{x \to 0} \dfrac{\tan(nx)}{x} = n$.

**81.** If $\lim\limits_{x \to c} f(x) = L_1$ and $\lim\limits_{x \to c} f(x) = L_2$, then for every $\varepsilon > 0$, there exists $\delta_1 > 0$ and $\delta_2 > 0$ such that $|x - c| < \delta_1 \Rightarrow |f(x) - L_1| < \varepsilon$ and $|x - c| < \delta_2 \Rightarrow |f(x) - L_2| < \varepsilon$. Let $\delta$ equal the smaller of $\delta_1$ and $\delta_2$. Then for $|x - c| < \delta$, you have $|L_1 - L_2| = |L_1 - f(x) + f(x) - L_2| \leq |L_1 - f(x)| + |f(x) - L_2| < \varepsilon + \varepsilon$. So, $|L_1 - L_2| < 2\varepsilon$. Because $\varepsilon > 0$ is arbitrary, it follows that $L_1 = L_2$.

**82.** $f(x) = mx + b, m \neq 0$. Let $\varepsilon > 0$ be given. Take

$\delta = \dfrac{\varepsilon}{|m|}$.

If $0 < |x - c| < \delta = \dfrac{\varepsilon}{|m|}$, then

$$|m||x - c| < \varepsilon$$
$$|mx - mc| < \varepsilon$$
$$|(mx + b) - (mc + b)| < \varepsilon$$

which shows that $\lim_{x\to c} (mx + b) = mc + b$.

**83.** $\lim_{x\to c}[f(x) - L] = 0$ means that for every $\varepsilon > 0$ there exists $\delta > 0$ such that if

$0 < |x - c| < \delta$,

then

$|(f(x) - L) - 0| < \varepsilon$.

This means the same as $|f(x) - L| < \varepsilon$ when

$0 < |x - c| < \delta$.

So, $\lim_{x\to c} f(x) = L$.

**84.** (a) $$(3x+1)(3x-1)x^2 + 0.01 = (9x^2 - 1)x^2 + \frac{1}{100}$$
$$= 9x^4 - x^2 + \frac{1}{100}$$
$$= \frac{1}{100}(10x^2 - 1)(90x^2 - 1)$$

So, $(3x + 1)(3x - 1)x^2 + 0.01 > 0$ if

$10x^2 - 1 < 0$ and $90x^2 - 1 < 0$.

Let $(a, b) = \left(-\dfrac{1}{\sqrt{90}}, \dfrac{1}{\sqrt{90}}\right)$.

For all $x \neq 0$ in $(a, b)$, the graph is positive.

You can verify this with a graphing utility.

(b) You are given $\lim_{x\to c} g(x) = L > 0$. Let

$\varepsilon = \dfrac{1}{2}L$. There exists $\delta > 0$ such that

$0 < |x - c| < \delta$ implies that

$|g(x) - L| < \varepsilon = \dfrac{L}{2}$. That is,

$$-\frac{L}{2} < g(x) - L < \frac{L}{2}$$
$$\frac{L}{2} < g(x) < \frac{3L}{2}$$

For $x$ in the interval $(c - \delta, c + \delta)$, $x \neq c$, you

have $g(x) > \dfrac{L}{2} > 0$, as desired.

**85.** Answers will vary.

**86.** $\lim_{x\to 4} \dfrac{x^2 - x - 12}{x - 4} = 7$

| $n$ | $4 + [0.1]^n$ | $f(4 + [0.1]^n)$ |
|---|---|---|
| 1 | 4.1 | 7.1 |
| 2 | 4.01 | 7.01 |
| 3 | 4.001 | 7.001 |
| 4 | 4.0001 | 7.0001 |

| $n$ | $4 - [0.1]^n$ | $f(4 - [0.1]^n)$ |
|---|---|---|
| 1 | 3.9 | 6.9 |
| 2 | 3.99 | 6.99 |
| 3 | 3.999 | 6.999 |
| 4 | 3.9999 | 6.9999 |

**87.** The radius $OP$ has a length equal to the altitude $z$ of the triangle plus $\dfrac{h}{2}$. So, $z = 1 - \dfrac{h}{2}$.

Area triangle $= \dfrac{1}{2}b\left(1 - \dfrac{h}{2}\right)$

Area rectangle $= bh$

Because these are equal, $\dfrac{1}{2}b\left(1 - \dfrac{h}{2}\right) = bh$

$$1 - \frac{h}{2} = 2h$$
$$\frac{5}{2}h = 1$$
$$h = \frac{2}{5}.$$

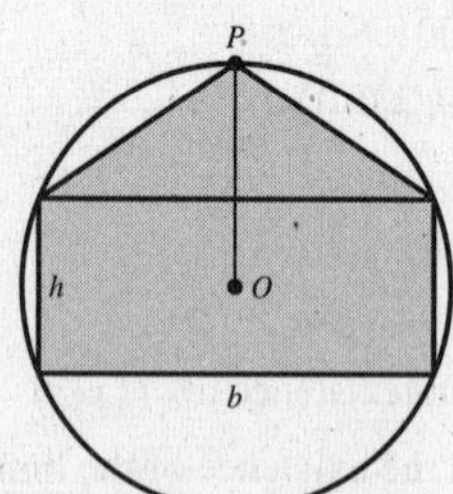

**88.** Consider a cross section of the cone, where $EF$ is a diagonal of the inscribed cube. $AD = 3$, $BC = 2$. Let $x$ be the length of a side of the cube. Then $EF = x\sqrt{2}$.

By similar triangles,

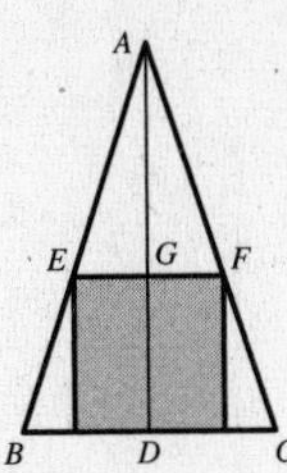


$$\frac{EF}{BC} = \frac{AG}{AD}$$

$$\frac{x\sqrt{2}}{2} = \frac{3-x}{3}.$$

Solving for $x$, $\quad 3\sqrt{2}x = 6 - 2x$

$$\left(3\sqrt{2} + 2\right)x = 6$$

$$x = \frac{6}{3\sqrt{2} + 2} = \frac{9\sqrt{2} - 6}{7} \approx 0.96.$$

## Section 2.3 Evaluating Limits Analytically

**1.**

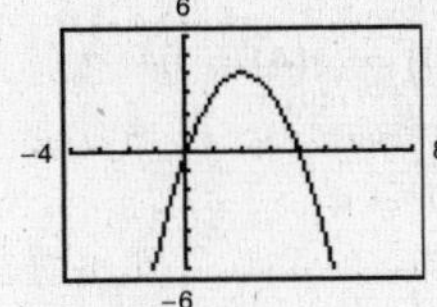


$h(x) = -x^2 + 4x$

(a) $\lim_{x\to 4} h(x) = 0$

(b) $\lim_{x\to -1} h(x) = -5$

**2.**

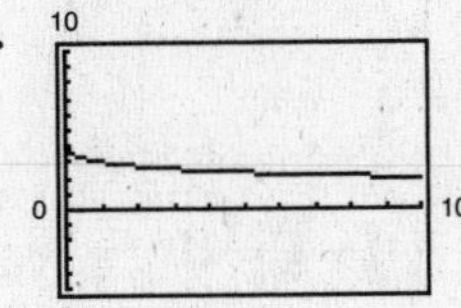


$$g(x) = \frac{12\left(\sqrt{x} - 3\right)}{x - 9}$$

(a) $\lim_{x\to 4} g(x) = 2.4$

(b) $\lim_{x\to 0} g(x) = 4$

**3.**

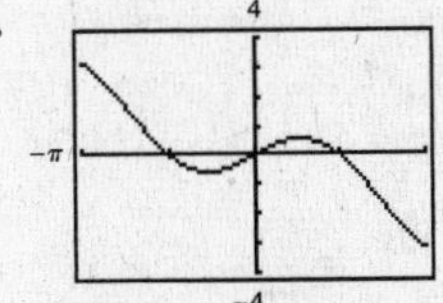


$f(x) = x\cos x$

(a) $\lim_{x\to 0} f(x) = 0$

(b) $\lim_{x\to \pi/3} f(x) \approx 0.524$

$\left(= \dfrac{\pi}{6}\right)$

**4.**

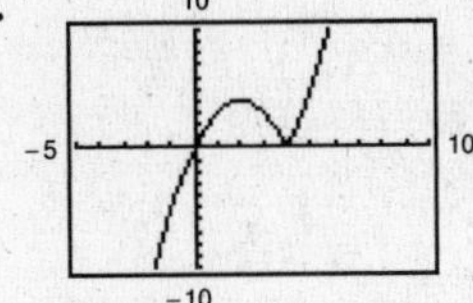


$f(t) = t|t - 4|$

(a) $\lim_{t\to 4} f(t) = 0$

(b) $\lim_{t\to -1} f(t) = -5$

**5.** $\lim_{x\to 2} x^3 = 2^3 = 8$

**6.** $\lim_{x\to -2} x^4 = (-2)^4 = 16$

**7.** $\lim_{x\to 0} (2x - 1) = 2(0) - 1 = -1$

**8.** $\lim_{x\to -3} (3x + 2) = 3(-3) + 2 = -7$

**9.** $\lim_{x\to -3} \left(2x^2 + 4x + 1\right) = 2(-3)^2 + 4(-3) + 1$
$= 18 - 12 + 1 = 7$

**10.** $\lim_{x\to 1} \left(3x^3 - 4x^2 + 3\right) = 3(1)^3 - 4(1)^2 + 3 = 2$

**11.** $\lim_{x\to 3} \sqrt{x + 1} = \sqrt{3 + 1} = 2$

**12.** $\lim_{x\to 4} \sqrt[3]{x + 4} = \sqrt[3]{4 + 4} = 2$

**13.** $\lim_{x\to 2} \dfrac{1}{x} = \dfrac{1}{2}$

**14.** $\lim_{x\to -3} \dfrac{2}{x + 2} = \dfrac{2}{-3 + 2} = -2$

**15.** $\lim_{x\to 1} \dfrac{x}{x^2 + 4} = \dfrac{1}{1^2 + 4} = \dfrac{1}{5}$

16. $\lim_{x\to 1} \frac{2x-3}{x+5} = \frac{2(1)-3}{1+5} = \frac{-1}{6}$

17. $\lim_{x\to 7} \frac{3x}{\sqrt{x+2}} = \frac{3(7)}{\sqrt{7+2}} = \frac{21}{3} = 7$

18. $\lim_{x\to 2} \frac{\sqrt{x+2}}{x-4} = \frac{\sqrt{2+2}}{2-4} = \frac{2}{-2} = -1$

19. $\lim_{x\to\pi/2} \sin x = \sin\frac{\pi}{2} = 1$

20. $\lim_{x\to\pi} \tan x = \tan \pi = 0$

21. $\lim_{x\to 1} \cos\frac{\pi x}{3} = \cos\frac{\pi}{3} = \frac{1}{2}$

22. $\lim_{x\to 2} \sin\frac{\pi x}{2} = \sin\frac{\pi(2)}{2} = 0$

23. $\lim_{x\to 0} \sec 2x = \sec 0 = 1$

24. $\lim_{x\to\pi} \cos 3x = \cos 3\pi = -1$

25. $\lim_{x\to 5\pi/6} \sin x = \sin\frac{5\pi}{6} = \frac{1}{2}$

26. $\lim_{x\to 5\pi/3} \cos x = \cos\frac{5\pi}{3} = \frac{1}{2}$

27. $\lim_{x\to 3} \tan\left(\frac{\pi x}{4}\right) = \tan\frac{3\pi}{4} = -1$

28. $\lim_{x\to 7} \sec\left(\frac{\pi x}{6}\right) = \sec\frac{7\pi}{6} = \frac{-2\sqrt{3}}{3}$

29. $\lim_{x\to 0} e^x \cos 2x = e^0 \cos 0 = 1$

30. $\lim_{x\to 0} e^{-x} \sin \pi x = e^0 \sin 0 = 0$

31. $\lim_{x\to 1} \left(\ln 3x + e^x\right) = \ln 3 + e$

32. $\lim_{x\to 1} \ln\left(\frac{x}{e^x}\right) = \ln\left(\frac{1}{e}\right) = \ln e^{-1} = -1$

33. (a) $\lim_{x\to 1} f(x) = 5 - 1 = 4$

(b) $\lim_{x\to 4} g(x) = 4^3 = 64$

(c) $\lim_{x\to 1} g(f(x)) = g(f(1)) = g(4) = 64$

34. (a) $\lim_{x\to -3} f(x) = (-3) + 7 = 4$

(b) $\lim_{x\to 4} g(x) = 4^2 = 16$

(c) $\lim_{x\to -3} g(f(x)) = g(4) = 16$

35. (a) $\lim_{x\to 1} f(x) = 4 - 1 = 3$

(b) $\lim_{x\to 3} g(x) = \sqrt{3+1} = 2$

(c) $\lim_{x\to 1} g(f(x)) = g(3) = 2$

36. (a) $\lim_{x\to 4} f(x) = 2(4^2) - 3(4) + 1 = 21$

(b) $\lim_{x\to 21} g(x) = \sqrt[3]{21+6} = 3$

(c) $\lim_{x\to 4} g(f(x)) = g(21) = 3$

37. (a) $\lim_{x\to c}[5g(x)] = 5\lim_{x\to c} g(x) = 5(2) = 10$

(b) $\lim_{x\to c}[f(x) + g(x)] = \lim_{x\to c} f(x) + \lim_{x\to c} g(x) = 3 + 2 = 5$

(c) $\lim_{x\to c}[f(x)g(x)] = \left[\lim_{x\to c} f(x)\right]\left[\lim_{x\to c} g(x)\right] = (3)(2) = 6$

(d) $\lim_{x\to c}\frac{f(x)}{g(x)} = \frac{\lim_{x\to c} f(x)}{\lim_{x\to c} g(x)} = \frac{3}{2}$

38. (a) $\lim_{x\to c}[4f(x)] = 4\lim_{x\to c} f(x) = 4\left(\frac{3}{2}\right) = 6$

(b) $\lim_{x\to c}[f(x) + g(x)] = \lim_{x\to c} f(x) + \lim_{x\to c} g(x) = \frac{3}{2} + \frac{1}{2} = 2$

(c) $\lim_{x\to c}[f(x)g(x)] = \left[\lim_{x\to c} f(x)\right]\left[\lim_{x\to c} g(x)\right] = \left(\frac{3}{2}\right)\left(\frac{1}{2}\right) = \frac{3}{4}$

(d) $\lim_{x\to c}\frac{f(x)}{g(x)} = \frac{\lim_{x\to c} f(x)}{\lim_{x\to c} g(x)} = \frac{3/2}{1/2} = 3$

**39.** (a) $\lim_{x\to c}[f(x)]^3 = \left[\lim_{x\to c} f(x)\right]^3 = (4)^3 = 64$

(b) $\lim_{x\to c}\sqrt{f(x)} = \sqrt{\lim_{x\to c} f(x)} = \sqrt{4} = 2$

(c) $\lim_{x\to c}[3f(x)] = 3\lim_{x\to c} f(x) = 3(4) = 12$

(d) $\lim_{x\to c}[f(x)]^{3/2} = \left[\lim_{x\to c} f(x)\right]^{3/2} = (4)^{3/2} = 8$

**40.** (a) $\lim_{x\to c}\sqrt[3]{f(x)} = \sqrt[3]{\lim_{x\to c} f(x)} = \sqrt[3]{27} = 3$

(b) $\lim_{x\to c}\frac{f(x)}{18} = \frac{\lim_{x\to c} f(x)}{\lim_{x\to c} 18} = \frac{27}{18} = \frac{3}{2}$

(c) $\lim_{x\to c}[f(x)]^2 = \left[\lim_{x\to c} f(x)\right]^2 = (27)^2 = 729$

(d) $\lim_{x\to c}[f(x)]^{2/3} = \left[\lim_{x\to c} f(x)\right]^{2/3} = (27)^{2/3} = 9$

**41.** $f(x) = x - 1$ and $g(x) = \dfrac{x^2 - x}{x}$ agree except at $x = 0$.

(a) $\lim_{x\to 0} g(x) = \lim_{x\to 0} f(x) = 0 - 1 = -1$

(b) $\lim_{x\to -1} g(x) = \lim_{x\to -1} f(x) = -1 - 1 = -2$

**42.** $f(x) = -x + 3$ and $h(x) = \dfrac{-x^2 + 3x}{x}$ agree except at $x = 0$.

(a) $\lim_{x\to 2} h(x) = \lim_{x\to 2} f(x) = -2 + 3 = 1$

(b) $\lim_{x\to 0} h(x) = \lim_{x\to 0} f(x) = -0 + 3 = 3$

**43.** $f(x) = x(x + 1)$ and $g(x) = \dfrac{x^3 - x}{x - 1}$ agree except at $x = 1$.

(a) $\lim_{x\to 1} g(x) = \lim_{x\to 1} f(x) = 2$

(b) $\lim_{x\to -1} g(x) = \lim_{x\to -1} f(x) = 0$

**44.** $g(x) = \dfrac{1}{x - 1}$ and $f(x) = \dfrac{x}{x^2 - x}$ agree except at $x = 0$.

(a) $\lim_{x\to 1} f(x)$ does not exist.

(b) $\lim_{x\to 0} f(x) = -1$

**45.** $f(x) = \dfrac{x^2 - 1}{x + 1}$ and $g(x) = x - 1$ agree except at $x = -1$.

$\lim_{x\to -1} f(x) = \lim_{x\to -1} g(x) = -2$

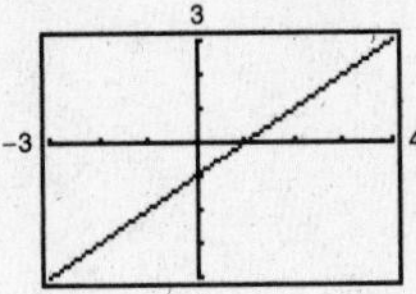


**46.** $f(x) = \dfrac{2x^2 - x - 3}{x + 1}$ and $g(x) = 2x - 3$ agree except at $x = -1$.

$\lim_{x\to -1} f(x) = \lim_{x\to -1} g(x) = -5$

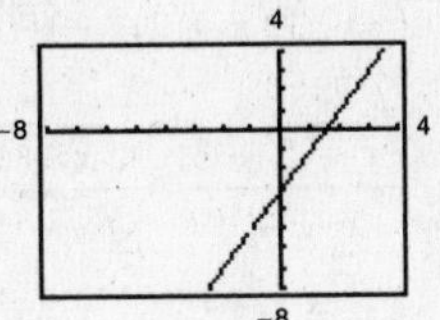


**47.** $f(x) = \dfrac{x^3 - 8}{x - 2}$ and $g(x) = x^2 + 2x + 4$ agree except at $x = 2$.

$\lim_{x\to 2} f(x) = \lim_{x\to 2} g(x) = 12$

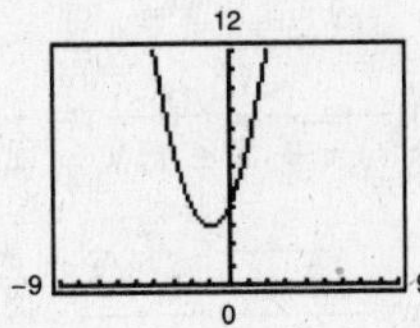


**48.** $f(x) = \dfrac{x^3 + 1}{x + 1}$ and $g(x) = x^2 - x + 1$ agree except at $x = -1$.

$\lim_{x\to -1} f(x) = \lim_{x\to -1} g(x) = 3$

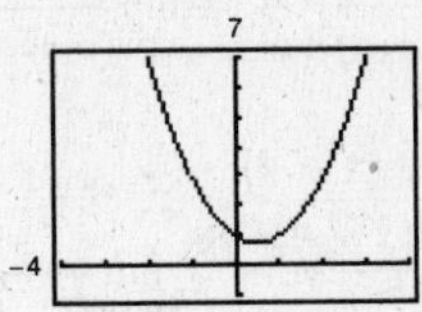


**49.** $f(x) = \dfrac{(x + 4)\ln(x + 6)}{x^2 - 16}$ and $g(x) = \dfrac{\ln(x + 6)}{x - 4}$ agree except at $x = -4$.

$\lim_{x\to -4} f(x) = \lim_{x\to -4} g(x) = \dfrac{\ln 2}{-8} \approx -0.0866$

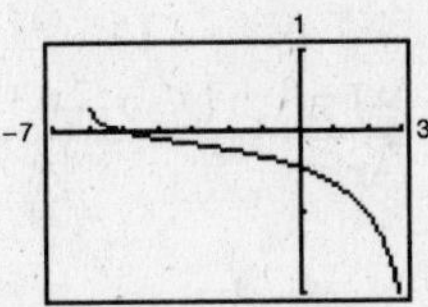

**50.** $f(x) = \dfrac{e^{2x} - 1}{e^x - 1}$ and $g(x) = e^x + 1$ agree except at $x = 0$.

$\lim\limits_{x\to 0} f(x) = \lim\limits_{x\to 0} g(x) = e^0 + 1 = 2$

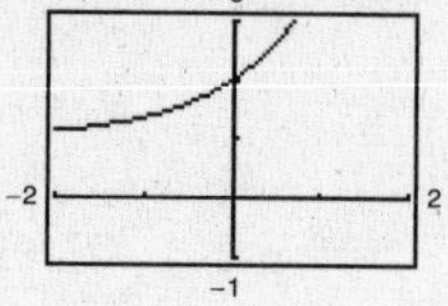

**51.** $\lim\limits_{x\to 0}\dfrac{x}{x^2 - x} = \lim\limits_{x\to 0}\dfrac{x}{x(x - 1)} = \lim\limits_{x\to 0}\dfrac{1}{x - 1} = -1$

**52.** $\lim\limits_{x\to 0}\dfrac{3x}{x^2 + 2x} = \lim\limits_{x\to 0}\dfrac{3x}{x(x + 2)} = \lim\limits_{x\to 0}\dfrac{3}{x + 2} = \dfrac{3}{2}$

**53.** $\lim\limits_{x\to 4}\dfrac{x - 4}{x^2 - 16} = \lim\limits_{x\to 4}\dfrac{x - 4}{(x + 4)(x - 4)} = \lim\limits_{x\to 4}\dfrac{1}{x + 4} = \dfrac{1}{8}$

**54.** $\lim\limits_{x\to 3}\dfrac{3 - x}{x^2 - 9} = \lim\limits_{x\to 3}\dfrac{3 - x}{(x - 3)(x + 3)} = \lim\limits_{x\to 3}\dfrac{-1}{x + 3} = -\dfrac{1}{6}$

**55.** $\lim\limits_{x\to -3}\dfrac{x^2 + x - 6}{x^2 - 9} = \lim\limits_{x\to -3}\dfrac{(x + 3)(x - 2)}{(x + 3)(x - 3)} = \lim\limits_{x\to -3}\dfrac{x - 2}{x - 3} = \dfrac{-5}{-6} = \dfrac{5}{6}$

**56.** $\lim\limits_{x\to 3}\dfrac{x^2 - x - 6}{x^2 - 5x + 6} = \lim\limits_{x\to 3}\dfrac{(x - 3)(x + 2)}{(x - 3)(x - 2)} = \lim\limits_{x\to 3}\dfrac{x + 2}{x - 2} = \dfrac{5}{1} = 5$

**57.** $\lim\limits_{x\to 4}\dfrac{\sqrt{x + 5} - 3}{x - 4} = \lim\limits_{x\to 4}\dfrac{\sqrt{x + 5} - 3}{x - 4}\cdot\dfrac{\sqrt{x + 5} + 3}{\sqrt{x + 5} + 3} = \lim\limits_{x\to 4}\dfrac{(x + 5) - 9}{(x - 4)\left(\sqrt{x + 5} + 3\right)} = \lim\limits_{x\to 4}\dfrac{1}{\sqrt{x + 5} + 3} = \dfrac{1}{\sqrt{9} + 3} = \dfrac{1}{6}$

**58.** $\lim\limits_{x\to 3}\dfrac{\sqrt{x + 1} - 2}{x - 3} = \lim\limits_{x\to 3}\dfrac{\sqrt{x + 1} - 2}{x - 3}\cdot\dfrac{\sqrt{x + 1} + 2}{\sqrt{x + 1} + 2} = \lim\limits_{x\to 3}\dfrac{x - 3}{(x - 3)\left[\sqrt{x + 1} + 2\right]} = \lim\limits_{x\to 3}\dfrac{1}{\sqrt{x + 1} + 2} = \dfrac{1}{4}$

**59.** $\lim\limits_{x\to 0}\dfrac{\sqrt{x + 5} - \sqrt{5}}{x} = \lim\limits_{x\to 0}\dfrac{\sqrt{x + 5} - \sqrt{5}}{x}\cdot\dfrac{\sqrt{x + 5} + \sqrt{5}}{\sqrt{x + 5} + \sqrt{5}} = \lim\limits_{x\to 0}\dfrac{(x + 5) - 5}{x\left(\sqrt{x + 5} + \sqrt{5}\right)}$

$= \lim\limits_{x\to 0}\dfrac{1}{\sqrt{x + 5} + \sqrt{5}} = \dfrac{1}{2\sqrt{5}} = \dfrac{\sqrt{5}}{10}$

**60.** $\lim\limits_{x\to 0}\dfrac{\sqrt{3 + x} - \sqrt{3}}{x} = \lim\limits_{x\to 0}\dfrac{\sqrt{3 + x} - \sqrt{3}}{x}\cdot\dfrac{\sqrt{3 + x} + \sqrt{3}}{\sqrt{3 + x} + \sqrt{3}} = \lim\limits_{x\to 0}\dfrac{(3 + x) - 3}{\left(\sqrt{3 + x} + \sqrt{3}\right)x}$

$= \lim\limits_{x\to 0}\dfrac{1}{\sqrt{3 + x} + \sqrt{3}} = \dfrac{1}{3\sqrt{3}} = \dfrac{\sqrt{3}}{9}$

**61.** $\lim\limits_{x\to 0}\dfrac{\dfrac{1}{3 + x} - \dfrac{1}{3}}{x} = \lim\limits_{x\to 0}\dfrac{3 - (3 + x)}{(3 + x)3(x)} = \lim\limits_{x\to 0}\dfrac{-x}{(3 + x)(3)(x)} = \lim\limits_{x\to 0}\dfrac{-1}{(3 + x)3} = -\dfrac{1}{9}$

**62.** $\lim\limits_{x\to 0}\dfrac{\dfrac{1}{x + 4} - \dfrac{1}{4}}{x} = \lim\limits_{x\to 0}\dfrac{\dfrac{4 - (x + 4)}{4(x + 4)}}{x} = \lim\limits_{x\to 0}\dfrac{-1}{4(x + 4)} = -\dfrac{1}{16}$

**63.** $\lim\limits_{\Delta x\to 0}\dfrac{2(x + \Delta x) - 2x}{\Delta x} = \lim\limits_{\Delta x\to 0}\dfrac{2x + 2\Delta x - 2x}{\Delta x} = \lim\limits_{\Delta x\to 0} 2 = 2$

**64.** $\lim\limits_{\Delta x\to 0}\dfrac{(x + \Delta x)^2 - x^2}{\Delta x} = \lim\limits_{\Delta x\to 0}\dfrac{x^2 + 2x\Delta x + (\Delta x)^2 - x^2}{\Delta x} = \lim\limits_{\Delta x\to 0}\dfrac{\Delta x(2x + \Delta x)}{\Delta x} = \lim\limits_{\Delta x\to 0}(2x + \Delta x) = 2x$

**65.** $\lim\limits_{\Delta x\to 0}\dfrac{(x + \Delta x)^2 - 2(x + \Delta x) + 1 - (x^2 - 2x + 1)}{\Delta x} = \lim\limits_{\Delta x\to 0}\dfrac{x^2 + 2x\Delta x + (\Delta x)^2 - 2x - 2\Delta x + 1 - x^2 + 2x - 1}{\Delta x}$

$= \lim\limits_{\Delta x\to 0}(2x + \Delta x - 2) = 2x - 2$

**66.** $\lim_{\Delta x \to 0} \frac{(x + \Delta x)^3 - x^3}{\Delta x} = \lim_{\Delta x \to 0} \frac{x^3 + 3x^2\Delta x + 3x(\Delta x)^2 + (\Delta x)^3 - x^3}{\Delta x} = \lim_{\Delta x \to 0} \frac{\Delta x\left(3x^2 + 3x\Delta x + (\Delta x)^2\right)}{\Delta x}$

$= \lim_{\Delta x \to 0} \left(3x^2 + 3x\Delta x + (\Delta x)^2\right) = 3x^2$

**67.** $\lim_{x \to 0} \frac{\sin x}{5x} = \lim_{x \to 0} \left[\left(\frac{\sin x}{x}\right)\left(\frac{1}{5}\right)\right] = (1)\left(\frac{1}{5}\right) = \frac{1}{5}$

**68.** $\lim_{x \to 0} \frac{5(1 - \cos x)}{x} = \lim_{x \to 0} \left[5\left(\frac{1 - \cos x}{x}\right)\right] = (5)(0) = 0$

**69.** $\lim_{x \to 0} \frac{\sin x(1 - \cos x)}{x^2} = \lim_{x \to 0} \left[\frac{\sin x}{x} \cdot \frac{1 - \cos x}{x}\right]$

$= (1)(0) = 0$

**70.** $\lim_{\theta \to 0} \frac{\cos \theta \tan \theta}{\theta} = \lim_{\theta \to 0} \frac{\sin \theta}{\theta} = 1$

**71.** $\lim_{x \to 0} \frac{\sin^2 x}{x} = \lim_{x \to 0} \left[\frac{\sin x}{x} \sin x\right] = (1) \sin 0 = 0$

**72.** $\lim_{x \to 0} \frac{2 \tan^2 x}{x} = \lim_{x \to 0} \frac{2 \sin^2 x}{x \cos^2 x} = 2 \lim_{x \to 0} \left[\frac{\sin x}{x} \cdot \frac{\sin x}{\cos^2 x}\right]$

$= 2(1)(0) = 0$

**73.** $\lim_{h \to 0} \frac{(1 - \cos h)^2}{h} = \lim_{h \to 0} \left[\frac{1 - \cos h}{h}(1 - \cos h)\right]$

$= (0)(0) = 0$

**74.** $\lim_{\phi \to \pi} \phi \sec \phi = \pi(-1) = -\pi$

**75.** $\lim_{x \to \pi/2} \frac{\cos x}{\cot x} = \lim_{x \to \pi/2} \sin x = 1$

**76.** $\lim_{x \to \pi/4} \frac{1 - \tan x}{\sin x - \cos x} = \lim_{x \to \pi/4} \frac{\cos x - \sin x}{\sin x \cos x - \cos^2 x}$

$= \lim_{x \to \pi/4} \frac{-(\sin x - \cos x)}{\cos x(\sin x - \cos x)}$

$= \lim_{x \to \pi/4} \frac{-1}{\cos x} = \lim_{x \to \pi/4} (-\sec x)$

$= -\sqrt{2}$

**77.** $\lim_{x \to 0} \frac{1 - e^{-x}}{e^x - 1} = \lim_{x \to 0} \frac{1 - e^{-x}}{e^x - 1} \cdot \frac{e^{-x}}{e^{-x}} = \lim_{x \to 0} \frac{(1 - e^{-x})e^{-x}}{1 - e^{-x}}$

$= \lim_{x \to 0} e^{-x} = 1$

**78.** $\lim_{x \to 0} \frac{4(e^{2x} - 1)}{e^x - 1} = \lim_{x \to 0} \frac{4(e^x - 1)(e^x + 1)}{e^x - 1}$

$= \lim_{x \to 0} 4(e^x + 1) = 4(2) = 8$

**79.** $\lim_{t \to 0} \frac{\sin 3t}{2t} = \lim_{t \to 0} \left(\frac{\sin 3t}{3t}\right)\left(\frac{3}{2}\right) = (1)\left(\frac{3}{2}\right) = \frac{3}{2}$

**80.** $\lim_{x \to 0} \frac{\sin 2x}{\sin 3x} = \lim_{x \to 0} \left[2\left(\frac{\sin 2x}{2x}\right)\left(\frac{1}{3}\right)\left(\frac{3x}{\sin 3x}\right)\right]$

$= 2(1)\left(\frac{1}{3}\right)(1) = \frac{2}{3}$

**81.** $f(x) = \frac{\sqrt{x + 2} - \sqrt{2}}{x}$

| $x$ | −0.1 | −0.01 | −0.001 | 0 | 0.001 | 0.01 | 0.1 |
|---|---|---|---|---|---|---|---|
| $f(x)$ | 0.358 | 0.354 | 0.354 | ? | 0.354 | 0.353 | 0.349 |

It appears that the limit is 0.354.

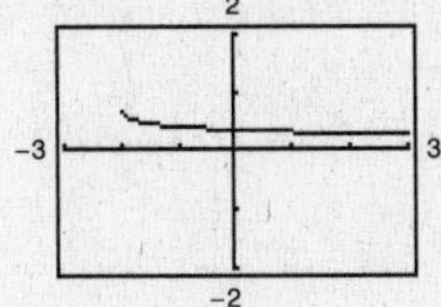


The graph has a hole at $x = 0$.

Analytically, $\lim_{x \to 0} \frac{\sqrt{x + 2} - \sqrt{2}}{x} = \lim_{x \to 0} \frac{\sqrt{x + 2} - \sqrt{2}}{x} \cdot \frac{\sqrt{x + 2} + \sqrt{2}}{\sqrt{x + 2} + \sqrt{2}}$

$= \lim_{x \to 0} \frac{(x + 2) - 2}{x\left(\sqrt{x + 2} + \sqrt{2}\right)} = \lim_{x \to 0} \frac{1}{\sqrt{x + 2} + \sqrt{2}} = \frac{1}{2\sqrt{2}} = \frac{\sqrt{2}}{4} \approx 0.354.$

**82.** $f(x) = \dfrac{4 - \sqrt{x}}{x - 16}$

| $x$ | 15.9 | 15.99 | 15.999 | 16 | 16.001 | 16.01 | 16.1 |
|---|---|---|---|---|---|---|---|
| $f(x)$ | –0.1252 | –0.125 | –0.125 | ? | –0.125 | –0.125 | –0.1248 |

It appears that the limit is –0.125.

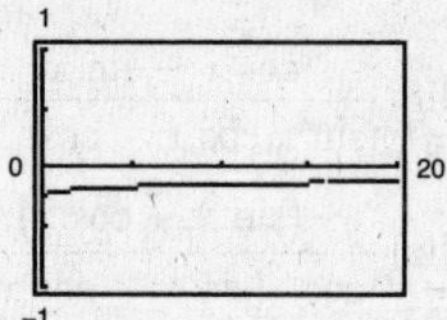


The graph has a hole at $x = 16$.

Analytically, $\lim_{x\to16} \dfrac{4 - \sqrt{x}}{x - 16} = \lim_{x\to16} \dfrac{(4 - \sqrt{x})}{(\sqrt{x} + 4)(\sqrt{x} - 4)} = \lim_{x\to16} \dfrac{-1}{\sqrt{x} + 4} = -\dfrac{1}{8}$.

**83.** $f(x) = \dfrac{\dfrac{1}{2 + x} - \dfrac{1}{2}}{x}$

| $x$ | –0.1 | –0.01 | –0.001 | 0 | 0.001 | 0.01 | 0.1 |
|---|---|---|---|---|---|---|---|
| $f(x)$ | –0.263 | –0.251 | –0.250 | ? | –0.250 | –0.249 | –0.238 |

It appears that the limit is –0.250.

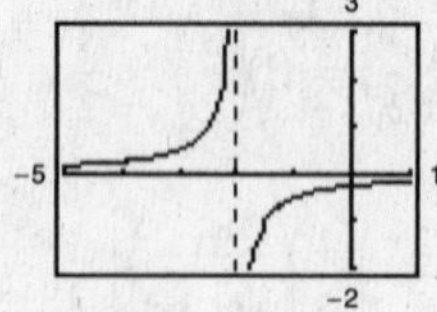


The graph has a hole at $x = 0$.

Analytically, $\lim_{x\to0} \dfrac{\dfrac{1}{2 + x} - \dfrac{1}{2}}{x} = \lim_{x\to0} \dfrac{2 - (2 + x)}{2(2 + x)} \cdot \dfrac{1}{x} = \lim_{x\to0} \dfrac{-x}{2(2 + x)} \cdot \dfrac{1}{x} = \lim_{x\to0} \dfrac{-1}{2(2 + x)} = -\dfrac{1}{4}$.

**84.** $f(x) = \dfrac{x^5 - 32}{x - 2}$

| $x$ | 1.9 | 1.99 | 1.999 | 1.9999 | 2.0 | 2.0001 | 2.001 | 2.01 | 2.1 |
|---|---|---|---|---|---|---|---|---|---|
| $f(x)$ | 72.39 | 79.20 | 79.92 | 79.99 | ? | 80.01 | 80.08 | 80.80 | 88.41 |

It appears that the limit is 80.

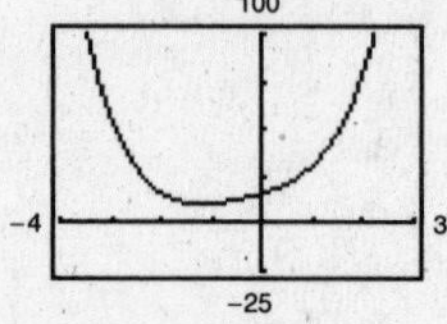


The graph has a hole at $x = 2$.

Analytically, $\lim_{x\to2} \dfrac{x^5 - 32}{x - 2} = \lim_{x\to2} \dfrac{(x - 2)(x^4 + 2x^3 + 4x^2 + 8x + 16)}{x - 2} = \lim_{x\to2}(x^4 + 2x^3 + 4x^2 + 8x + 16) = 80$.

(*Hint:* Use long division to factor $x^5 - 32$.)

**85.** $f(t) = \dfrac{\sin 3t}{t}$

| $t$ | −0.1 | −0.01 | −0.001 | 0 | 0.001 | 0.01 | 0.1 |
|---|---|---|---|---|---|---|---|
| $f(t)$ | 2.96 | 2.9996 | 3 | ? | 3 | 2.9996 | 2.96 |

It appears that the limit is 3.

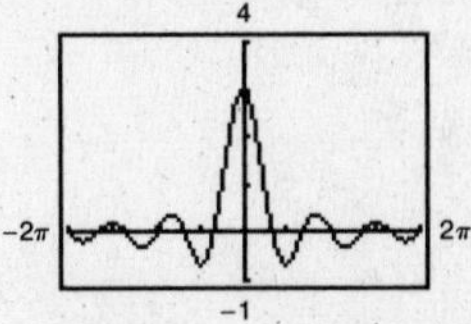


The graph has a hole at $t = 0$.

Analytically, $\lim\limits_{t\to 0}\dfrac{\sin 3t}{t} = \lim\limits_{t\to 0} 3\left(\dfrac{\sin 3t}{3t}\right) = 3(1) = 3.$

**86.** $f(x) = \dfrac{\cos x - 1}{2x^2}$

| $x$ | −1 | −0.1 | −0.01 | 0.01 | 0.1 | 1 |
|---|---|---|---|---|---|---|
| $f(x)$ | −0.2298 | −0.2498 | −0.25 | −0.25 | −0.2498 | −0.2298 |

It appears that the limit is −0.25.

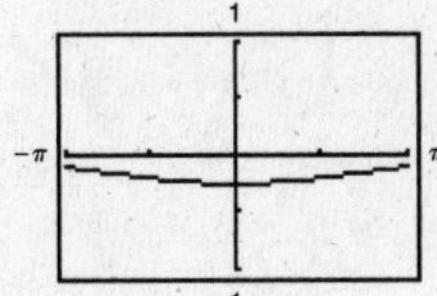


The graph has a hole at $x = 0$.

$$\begin{aligned}\frac{\cos x - 1}{2x^2}\cdot\frac{\cos x + 1}{\cos x + 1} &= \frac{\cos^2 x - 1}{2x^2(\cos x + 1)}\\ &= \frac{-\sin^2 x}{2x^2(\cos x + 1)}\\ &= \frac{\sin^2 x}{x^2}\cdot\frac{-1}{2(\cos x + 1)}\end{aligned}$$

Analytically, $\lim\limits_{x\to 0}\left[\dfrac{\sin^2 x}{x^2}\cdot\dfrac{-1}{2(\cos x + 1)}\right] = 1\left(\dfrac{-1}{4}\right) = -\dfrac{1}{4} = -0.25.$

**87.** $f(x) = \dfrac{\sin x^2}{x}$

| $x$ | –0.1 | –0.01 | –0.001 | 0 | 0.001 | 0.01 | 0.1 |
|---|---|---|---|---|---|---|---|
| $f(x)$ | –0.099998 | –0.01 | –0.001 | ? | 0.001 | 0.01 | 0.099998 |

It appears that the limit is 0.

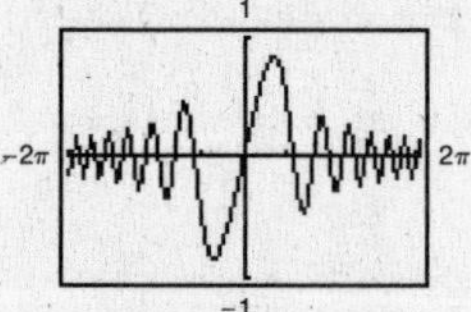


The graph has a hole at $x = 0$.

Analytically, $\lim\limits_{x\to 0}\dfrac{\sin x^2}{x} = \lim\limits_{x\to 0} x\left(\dfrac{\sin x^2}{x}\right) = 0(1) = 0.$

**88.** $f(x) = \dfrac{\sin x}{\sqrt[3]{x}}$

| $x$ | –0.1 | –0.01 | –0.001 | 0 | 0.001 | 0.01 | 0.1 |
|---|---|---|---|---|---|---|---|
| $f(x)$ | 0.215 | 0.0464 | 0.01 | ? | 0.01 | 0.0464 | 0.215 |

It appears that the limit is 0.

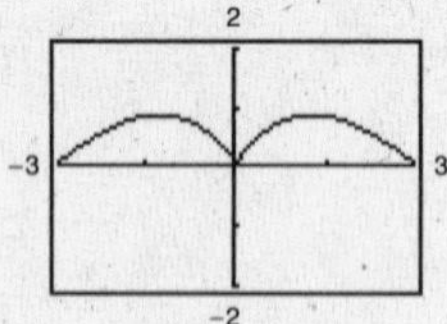


The graph has a hole at $x = 0$.

Analytically, $\lim\limits_{x\to 0}\dfrac{\sin x}{\sqrt[3]{x}} = \lim\limits_{x\to 0}\sqrt[3]{x^2}\left(\dfrac{\sin x}{x}\right) = (0)(1) = 0.$

**89.** $f(x) = \dfrac{\ln x}{x - 1}$

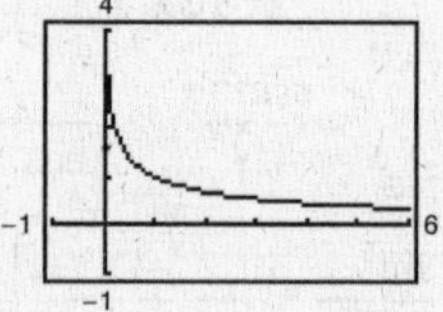


| $x$ | 0.5 | 0.9 | 0.99 | 1.01 | 1.1 | 1.5 |
|---|---|---|---|---|---|---|
| $f(x)$ | 1.3863 | 1.0536 | 1.0050 | 0.9950 | 0.9531 | 0.8109 |

It appears that the limit is 1.

Analytically, $\lim\limits_{x\to 1}\dfrac{\ln x}{x - 1} = 1.$

**90.** $f(x) = \dfrac{e^{3x} - 8}{e^{2x} - 4}$

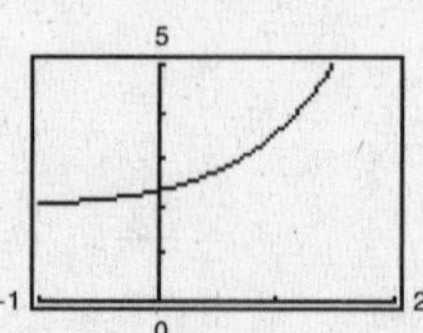


| $x$ | 0.5 | 0.6 | 0.69 | 0.70 | 0.8 | 0.9 |
|---|---|---|---|---|---|---|
| $f(x)$ | 2.7450 | 2.8687 | 2.9953 | 3.0103 | 3.1722 | 3.3565 |

It appears that the limit is 3.

Analytically, $\lim\limits_{x\to \ln 2}\dfrac{e^{3x} - 8}{e^{2x} - 4} = \lim\limits_{x\to \ln 2}\dfrac{(e^x - 2)(e^{2x} + 2e^x + 4)}{(e^x - 2)(e^x + 2)} = \lim\limits_{x\to \ln 2}\dfrac{e^{2x} + 2e^x + 4}{e^x + 2} = \dfrac{4 + 4 + 4}{2 + 2} = 3.$

**91.** $\displaystyle\lim_{\Delta x\to 0}\frac{f(x+\Delta x)-f(x)}{\Delta x} = \lim_{\Delta x\to 0}\frac{3(x+\Delta x)-2-(3x-2)}{\Delta x} = \lim_{\Delta x\to 0}\frac{3x+30x-2-3x+2}{\Delta x} = \lim_{\Delta x\to 0}\frac{3\Delta x}{\Delta x} = 3$

**92.** $\displaystyle\lim_{\Delta x\to 0}\frac{f(x+\Delta x)-f(x)}{\Delta x} = \lim_{\Delta x\to 0}\frac{\sqrt{x+\Delta x}-\sqrt{x}}{\Delta x} = \lim_{\Delta x\to 0}\frac{\sqrt{x+\Delta x}-\sqrt{x}}{\Delta x}\cdot\frac{\sqrt{x+\Delta x}+\sqrt{x}}{\sqrt{x+\Delta x}+\sqrt{x}}$

$\displaystyle = \lim_{\Delta x\to 0}\frac{x+\Delta x-x}{\Delta x\left(\sqrt{x+\Delta x}+\sqrt{x}\right)} = \lim_{\Delta x\to 0}\frac{1}{\sqrt{x+\Delta x}+\sqrt{x}} = \frac{1}{2\sqrt{x}}$

**93.** $\displaystyle\lim_{\Delta x\to 0}\frac{f(x+\Delta x)-f(x)}{\Delta x} = \lim_{\Delta x\to 0}\frac{\frac{1}{x+\Delta x+3}-\frac{1}{x+3}}{\Delta x} = \lim_{\Delta x\to 0}\frac{x+3-(x+\Delta x+3)}{(x+\Delta x+3)(x+3)}\cdot\frac{1}{\Delta x}$

$\displaystyle = \lim_{\Delta x\to 0}\frac{-\Delta x}{(x+\Delta x+3)(x+3)\Delta x} = \lim_{\Delta x\to 0}\frac{-1}{(x+\Delta x+3)(x+3)} = \frac{-1}{(x+3)^2}$

**94.** $\displaystyle\lim_{\Delta x\to 0}\frac{f(x+\Delta x)-f(x)}{\Delta x} = \lim_{\Delta x\to 0}\frac{(x+\Delta x)^2-4(x+\Delta x)-(x^2-4x)}{\Delta x} = \lim_{\Delta x\to 0}\frac{x^2+2x\Delta x+\Delta x^2-4x-4\Delta x-x^2+4x}{\Delta x}$

$\displaystyle = \lim_{\Delta x\to 0}\frac{\Delta x(2x+\Delta x-4)}{\Delta x} = \lim_{\Delta x\to 0}(2x+\Delta x-4) = 2x-4$

**95.** $\displaystyle\lim_{x\to 0}(4-x^2) \le \lim_{x\to 0}f(x) \le \lim_{x\to 0}(4+x^2)$

$\displaystyle 4 \le \lim_{x\to 0}f(x) \le 4$

So, $\displaystyle\lim_{x\to 0}f(x) = 4$.

**96.** $\displaystyle\lim_{x\to a}\left[b-|x-a|\right] \le \lim_{x\to a}f(x) \le \lim_{x\to a}\left[b+|x-a|\right]$

$\displaystyle b \le \lim_{x\to a}f(x) \le b$

So, $\displaystyle\lim_{x\to a}f(x) = b$.

**97.** $f(x) = x\cos x$

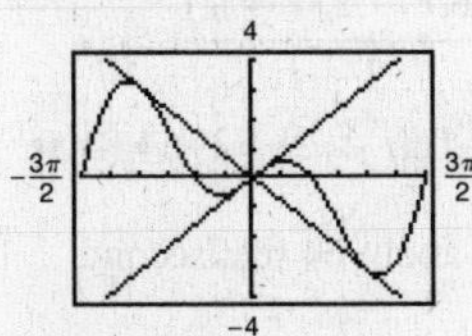


$\displaystyle\lim_{x\to 0}(x\cos x) = 0$

**98.** $f(x) = |x\sin x|$

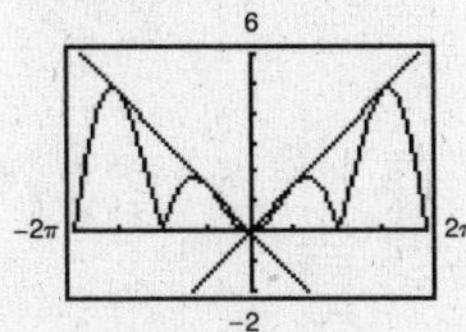


$\displaystyle\lim_{x\to 0}|x\sin x| = 0$

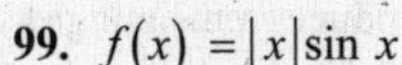

**99.** $f(x) = |x|\sin x$

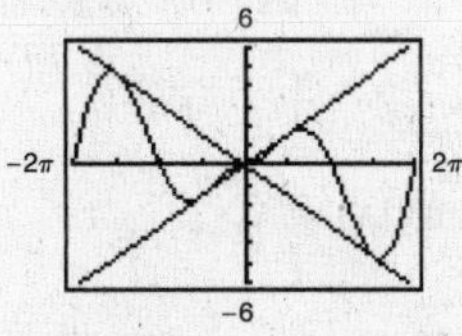


$\displaystyle\lim_{x\to 0}|x|\sin x = 0$

**100.** $f(x) = |x|\cos x$

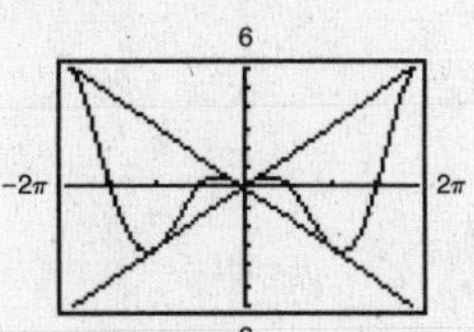


$\displaystyle\lim_{x\to 0}|x|\cos x = 0$

**101.** $f(x) = x\sin\frac{1}{x}$

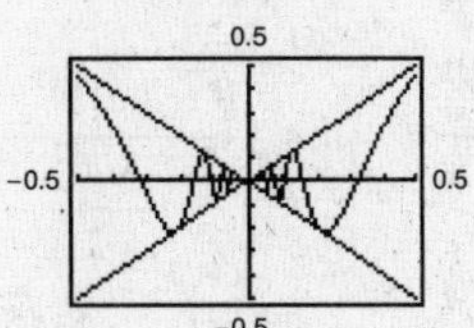


$\displaystyle\lim_{x\to 0}\left(x\sin\frac{1}{x}\right) = 0$

**102.** $h(x) = x\cos\dfrac{1}{x}$

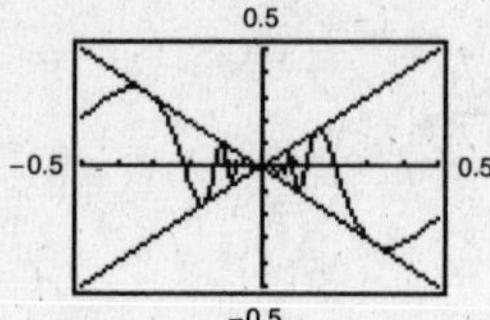


$$\lim_{x\to 0}\left(x\cos\frac{1}{x}\right) = 0$$

**103.** You say that two functions $f$ and $g$ agree at all but one point (on an open interval) if $f(x) = g(x)$ for all $x$ in the interval except for $x = c$, where $c$ is in the interval.

**104.** $f(x) = \dfrac{x^2 - 1}{x - 1}$ and $g(x) = x + 1$ agree at all points except $x = 1$.

**105.** An indeterminant form is obtained when evaluating a limit using direct substitution produces a meaningless fractional expression such as $0/0$. That is,

$$\lim_{x\to c}\frac{f(x)}{g(x)}$$

for which $\lim_{x\to c} f(x) = \lim_{x\to c} g(x) = 0$.

**106.** If a function $f$ is squeezed between two functions $h$ and $g$, $h(x) \le f(x) \le g(x)$, and $h$ and $g$ have the same limit $L$ as $x \to c$, then $\lim_{x\to c} f(x)$ exists and equals $L$.

**107.** $f(x) = x$, $g(x) = \sin x$, $h(x) = \dfrac{\sin x}{x}$

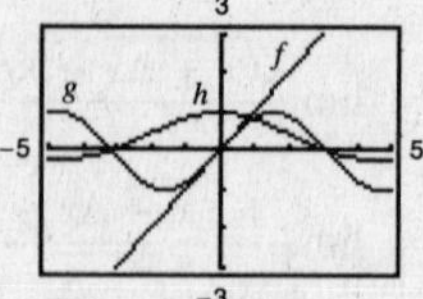


When the $x$-values are "close to" 0 the magnitude of $f$ is approximately equal to the magnitude of $g$. So, $|g|/|f| \approx 1$ when $x$ is "close to" 0.

**108.** $f(x) = x$, $g(x) = \sin^2 x$, $h(x) = \dfrac{\sin^2 x}{x}$

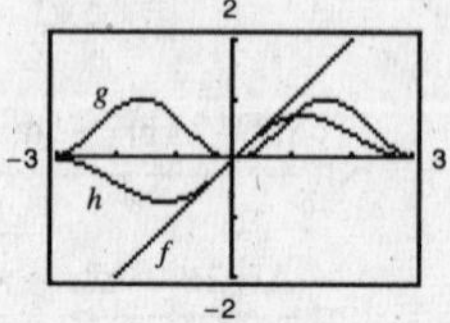


When the $x$-values are "close to" 0 the magnitude of $g$ is "smaller" than the magnitude of $f$ and the magnitude of $g$ is approaching zero "faster" than the magnitude of $f$. So, $|g|/|f| \approx 0$ when $x$ is "close to" 0.

**109.** $s(t) = -16t^2 + 500$

$$\begin{aligned}\lim_{t\to 2}\frac{s(2) - s(t)}{2 - t} &= \lim_{t\to 2}\frac{-16(2)^2 + 500 - \left(-16t^2 + 500\right)}{2 - t}\\ &= \lim_{t\to 2}\frac{436 + 16t^2 - 500}{2 - t}\\ &= \lim_{t\to 2}\frac{16\left(t^2 - 4\right)}{2 - t}\\ &= \lim_{t\to 2}\frac{16(t - 2)(t + 2)}{2 - t}\\ &= \lim_{t\to 2} -16(t + 2) = -64 \text{ ft/sec}\end{aligned}$$

The wrench is falling at about 64 feet/second.

**110.** $s(t) = -16t^2 + 500 = 0$ when $t = \sqrt{\dfrac{500}{16}} = \dfrac{5\sqrt{5}}{2}$ sec. The velocity at time $a = \dfrac{5\sqrt{5}}{2}$ is

$$\begin{aligned}\lim_{t\to\left(\frac{5\sqrt{5}}{2}\right)}\frac{s\left(\frac{5\sqrt{5}}{2}\right) - s(t)}{\frac{5\sqrt{5}}{2} - t} &= \lim_{t\to\left(\frac{5\sqrt{5}}{2}\right)}\frac{0 - \left(-16t^2 + 500\right)}{\frac{5\sqrt{5}}{2} - t} = \lim_{t\to\left(\frac{5\sqrt{5}}{2}\right)}\frac{16\left(t^2 - \frac{125}{4}\right)}{\frac{5\sqrt{5}}{2} - t}\\ &= \lim_{t\to\left(\frac{5\sqrt{5}}{2}\right)}\frac{16\left(t + \frac{5\sqrt{5}}{2}\right)\left(t - \frac{5\sqrt{5}}{2}\right)}{\frac{5\sqrt{5}}{2} - t} = \lim_{t\to\frac{5\sqrt{5}}{2}}\left[-16\left(t + \frac{5\sqrt{5}}{2}\right)\right]\\ &= -80\sqrt{5} \text{ ft/sec} \approx -178.9 \text{ ft/sec.}\end{aligned}$$

The velocity of the wrench when it hits the ground is about 178.9 ft/sec.

**111.** $s(t) = -4.9t^2 + 200$

$$\lim_{t\to3}\frac{s(3)-s(t)}{3-t} = \lim_{t\to3}\frac{-4.9(3)^2+200-\left(-4.9t^2+200\right)}{3-t}$$
$$= \lim_{t\to3}\frac{4.9\left(t^2-9\right)}{3-t}$$
$$= \lim_{t\to3}\frac{4.9(t-3)(t+3)}{3-t}$$
$$= \lim_{t\to3}\left[-4.9(t+3)\right]$$
$$= -29.4 \text{ m/sec}$$

The object is falling about 29.4 m/sec.

**112.** $-4.9t^2 + 200 = 0$ when $t = \sqrt{\dfrac{200}{4.9}} = \dfrac{20\sqrt{5}}{7}$ sec. The velocity at time $a = \dfrac{20\sqrt{5}}{7}$ is

$$\lim_{t\to a}\frac{s(a)-s(t)}{a-t} = \lim_{t\to a}\frac{0-\left[-4.9t^2+200\right]}{a-t}$$
$$= \lim_{t\to a}\frac{4.9(t+a)(t-a)}{a-t}$$
$$= \lim_{t\to\frac{20\sqrt{5}}{7}}\left[-4.9\left(t+\frac{20\sqrt{5}}{7}\right)\right] = -28\sqrt{5} \text{ m/sec}$$
$$\approx -62.6 \text{ m/sec.}$$

The velocity of the object when it hits the ground is about 62.6 m/sec.

**113.** Let $f(x) = 1/x$ and $g(x) = -1/x$. $\lim_{x\to0} f(x)$ and $\lim_{x\to0} g(x)$ do not exist. However,

$$\lim_{x\to0}\left[f(x)+g(x)\right] = \lim_{x\to0}\left[\frac{1}{x}+\left(-\frac{1}{x}\right)\right] = \lim_{x\to0}[0] = 0$$

and therefore does exist.

**114.** Suppose, on the contrary, that $\lim_{x\to c} g(x)$ exists. Then, because $\lim_{x\to c} f(x)$ exists, so would $\lim_{x\to c}\left[f(x)+g(x)\right]$, which is a contradiction. So, $\lim_{x\to c} g(x)$ does not exist.

**115.** Given $f(x) = b$, show that for every $\varepsilon > 0$ there exists a $\delta > 0$ such that $\left|f(x) - b\right| < \varepsilon$ whenever $\left|x - c\right| < \delta$. Because $\left|f(x) - b\right| = \left|b - b\right| = 0 < \varepsilon$ for every $\varepsilon > 0$, any value of $\delta > 0$ will work.

**116.** Given $f(x) = x^n$, $n$ is a positive integer, then

$$\lim_{x\to c} x^n = \lim_{x\to c}\left(xx^{n-1}\right)$$
$$= \left[\lim_{x\to c} x\right]\left[\lim_{x\to c} x^{n-1}\right] = c\left[\lim_{x\to c}\left(xx^{n-2}\right)\right]$$
$$= c\left[\lim_{x\to c} x\right]\left[\lim_{x\to c} x^{n-2}\right] = c(c)\lim_{x\to c}\left(xx^{n-3}\right)$$
$$= \cdots = c^n.$$

**117.** If $b = 0$, the property is true because both sides are equal to 0. If $b \neq 0$, let $\varepsilon > 0$ be given. Because $\lim_{x\to c} f(x) = L$, there exists $\delta > 0$ such that $\left|f(x) - L\right| < \varepsilon/|b|$ whenever $0 < \left|x - c\right| < \delta$. So, whenever $0 < \left|x - c\right| < \delta$, we have

$$|b|\left|f(x) - L\right| < \varepsilon \quad\text{or}\quad \left|bf(x) - bL\right| < \varepsilon$$

which implies that $\lim_{x\to c}\left[bf(x)\right] = bL$.

**118.** Given $\lim_{x\to c} f(x) = 0$:

For every $\varepsilon > 0$, there exists $\delta > 0$ such that $\left|f(x) - 0\right| < \varepsilon$ whenever $0 < \left|x - c\right| < \delta$.

Now $\left|f(x) - 0\right| = \left|f(x)\right| = \left|\left|f(x)\right| - 0\right| < \varepsilon$ for $\left|x - c\right| < \delta$. So, $\lim_{x\to c}\left|f(x)\right| = 0$.

**119.**
$$-M\left|f(x)\right| \le f(x)g(x) \le M\left|f(x)\right|$$
$$\lim_{x\to c}\left(-M\left|f(x)\right|\right) \le \lim_{x\to c} f(x)g(x) \le \lim_{x\to c}\left(M\left|f(x)\right|\right)$$
$$-M(0) \le \lim_{x\to c} f(x)g(x) \le M(0)$$
$$0 \le \lim_{x\to c} f(x)g(x) \le 0$$

So, $\lim_{x\to c} f(x)g(x) = 0$.

**120.** (a) If $\lim_{x\to c}|f(x)| = 0$, then $\lim_{x\to c}\left[-|f(x)|\right] = 0$.

$$-|f(x)| \le f(x) \le |f(x)|$$

$$\lim_{x\to c}\left[-|f(x)|\right] \le \lim_{x\to c} f(x) \le \lim_{x\to c}|f(x)|$$

$$0 \le \lim_{x\to c} f(x) \le 0$$

So, $\lim_{x\to c} f(x) = 0$.

(b) Given $\lim_{x\to c} f(x) = L$:

For every $\varepsilon > 0$, there exists $\delta > 0$ such that $|f(x) - L| < \varepsilon$ whenever $0 < |x - c| < \delta$. Because $\left||f(x)| - |L|\right| \le |f(x) - L| < \varepsilon$ for $|x - c| < \delta$, then $\lim_{x\to c}|f(x)| = |L|$.

**121.** Let

$$f(x) = \begin{cases} 4, & \text{if } x \ge 0 \\ -4, & \text{if } x < 0 \end{cases}$$

$\lim_{x\to 0}|f(x)| = \lim_{x\to 0} 4 = 4.$

$\lim_{x\to 0} f(x)$ does not exist because for $x < 0$, $f(x) = -4$ and for $x \ge 0$, $f(x) = 4$.

**122.** $\lim_{x\to 2^-} f(x) = \lim_{x\to 2^+} f(x) = \lim_{x\to 2} f(x) = 3$

The value of $f$ at $x = 2$ is irrelevant.

**123.** False. The limit does not exist because the function approaches 1 from the right side of 0 and approaches −1 from the left side of 0.

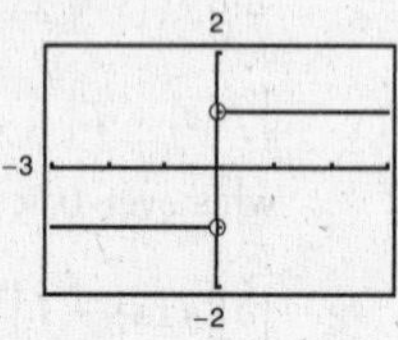


**124.** False. $\lim_{x\to\pi}\frac{\sin x}{x} = \frac{0}{\pi} = 0$

**125.** True

**126.** False. Let

$$f(x) = \begin{cases} x & x \ne 1 \\ 3 & x = 1 \end{cases}, \quad c = 1.$$

Then $\lim_{x\to 1} f(x) = 1$ but $f(1) \ne 1$.

**127.** False. The limit does not exist because $f(x)$ approaches 3 from the left side of 2 and approaches 0 from the right side of 2.

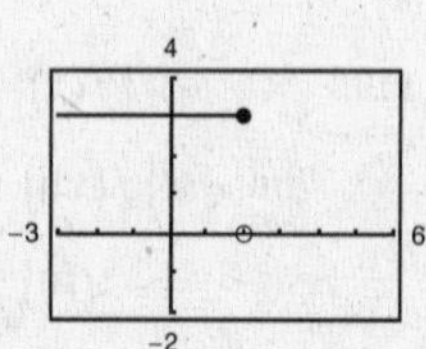


**128.** False. Let

$f(x) = \frac{1}{2}x^2$ and $g(x) = x^2$.

Then $f(x) < g(x)$ for all $x \ne 0$. But

$\lim_{x\to 0} f(x) = \lim_{x\to 0} g(x) = 0.$

**129.**
$$\lim_{x\to 0}\frac{1 - \cos x}{x} = \lim_{x\to 0}\frac{1 - \cos x}{x}\cdot\frac{1 + \cos x}{1 + \cos x}$$
$$= \lim_{x\to 0}\frac{1 - \cos^2 x}{x(1 + \cos x)} = \lim_{x\to 0}\frac{\sin^2 x}{x(1 + \cos x)}$$
$$= \lim_{x\to 0}\frac{\sin x}{x}\cdot\frac{\sin x}{1 + \cos x}$$
$$= \left[\lim_{x\to 0}\frac{\sin x}{x}\right]\left[\lim_{x\to 0}\frac{\sin x}{1 + \cos x}\right]$$
$$= (1)(0) = 0$$

**130.**
$$f(x) = \begin{cases} 0, & \text{if } x \text{ is rational} \\ 1, & \text{if } x \text{ is irrational} \end{cases}$$

$$g(x) = \begin{cases} 0, & \text{if } x \text{ is rational} \\ x, & \text{if } x \text{ is irrational} \end{cases}$$

$\lim_{x\to 0} f(x)$ does not exist.

No matter how "close to" 0 $x$ is, there are still an infinite number of rational and irrational numbers so that $\lim_{x\to 0} f(x)$ does not exist.

$\lim_{x\to 0} g(x) = 0$

When $x$ is "close to" 0, both parts of the function are "close to" 0.

**131.** $f(x) = \frac{\sec x - 1}{x^2}$

(a) The domain of $f$ is all $x \ne 0, \pi/2 + n\pi$.

(b)

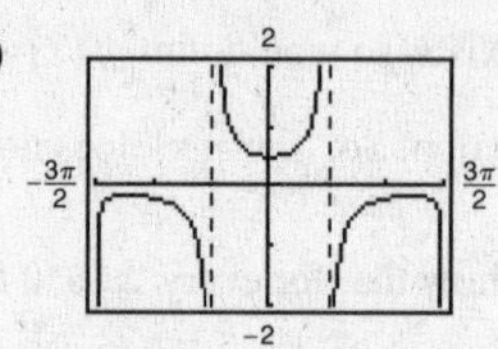


The domain is not obvious. The hole at $x = 0$ is not apparent.

(c) $\lim_{x\to 0} f(x) = \frac{1}{2}$

(d)
$$\frac{\sec x - 1}{x^2} = \frac{\sec x - 1}{x^2}\cdot\frac{\sec x + 1}{\sec x + 1} = \frac{\sec^2 x - 1}{x^2(\sec x + 1)}$$
$$= \frac{\tan^2 x}{x^2(\sec x + 1)} = \frac{1}{\cos^2 x}\left(\frac{\sin^2 x}{x^2}\right)\frac{1}{\sec x + 1}$$

So,
$$\lim_{x\to 0}\frac{\sec x - 1}{x^2} = \lim_{x\to 0}\frac{1}{\cos^2 x}\left(\frac{\sin^2 x}{x^2}\right)\frac{1}{\sec x + 1}$$
$$= 1(1)\left(\frac{1}{2}\right) = \frac{1}{2}.$$

**132.** (a) $\lim_{x\to0}\frac{1-\cos x}{x^2} = \lim_{x\to0}\frac{1-\cos x}{x^2}\cdot\frac{1+\cos x}{1+\cos x}$

$= \lim_{x\to0}\frac{1-\cos^2 x}{x^2(1+\cos x)}$

$= \lim_{x\to0}\frac{\sin^2 x}{x^2}\cdot\frac{1}{1+\cos x}$

$= (1)\left(\frac{1}{2}\right) = \frac{1}{2}$

(b) From part (a),

$\frac{1-\cos x}{x^2} \approx \frac{1}{2} \Rightarrow 1-\cos x \approx \frac{1}{2}x^2 \Rightarrow \cos x \approx 1-\frac{1}{2}x^2$ for $x \approx 0$.

(c) $\cos(0.1) \approx 1 - \frac{1}{2}(0.1)^2 = 0.995$

(d) $\cos(0.1) \approx 0.9950$, which agrees with part (c).

**133.** The graphing utility was set in degree mode, instead of *radian* mode.

## Section 2.4 Continuity and One-Sided Limits

**1.** (a) $\lim_{x\to4^+} f(x) = 3$

(b) $\lim_{x\to4^-} f(x) = 3$

(c) $\lim_{x\to4} f(x) = 3$

The function is continuous at $x = 4$ and is continuous on $(-\infty, \infty)$.

**2.** (a) $\lim_{x\to-2^+} f(x) = -2$

(b) $\lim_{x\to-2^-} f(x) = -2$

(c) $\lim_{x\to-2} f(x) = -2$

The function is continuous at $x = -2$.

**3.** (a) $\lim_{x\to3^+} f(x) = 0$

(b) $\lim_{x\to3^-} f(x) = 0$

(c) $\lim_{x\to3} f(x) = 0$

The function is NOT continuous at $x = 3$.

**4.** (a) $\lim_{x\to-3^+} f(x) = 3$

(b) $\lim_{x\to-3^-} f(x) = 3$

(c) $\lim_{x\to-3} f(x) = 3$

The function is NOT continuous at $x = -3$.

**5.** (a) $\lim_{x\to2^+} f(x) = -3$

(b) $\lim_{x\to2^-} f(x) = 3$

(c) $\lim_{x\to2} f(x)$ does not exist.

The function is NOT continuous at $x = 2$.

**6.** (a) $\lim_{x\to-1^+} f(x) = 0$

(b) $\lim_{x\to-1^-} f(x) = 2$

(c) $\lim_{x\to-1} f(x)$ does not exist.

The function is NOT continuous at $x = -1$.

**7.** $\lim_{x\to8^+}\frac{1}{x+8} = \frac{1}{8+8} = \frac{1}{16}$

**8.** $\lim_{x\to5^-}-\frac{3}{x+5} = -\frac{3}{5+5} = -\frac{3}{10}$

**9.** $\lim_{x\to5^+}\frac{x-5}{x^2-25} = \lim_{x\to5^+}\frac{1}{x+5} = \frac{1}{10}$

**10.** $\lim_{x\to2^+}\frac{2-x}{x^2-4} = \lim_{x\to2^+}-\frac{1}{x+2} = -\frac{1}{4}$

**11.** $\lim_{x\to-3^-}\frac{x}{\sqrt{x^2-9}}$ does not exist because

$\frac{x}{\sqrt{x^2-9}}$ decreases without bound as $x \to -3^-$.

**12.** $\displaystyle\lim_{x\to 9^-}\frac{\sqrt{x}-3}{x-9} = \lim_{x\to 9^-}\frac{\sqrt{x}-3}{x-9}\cdot\frac{\sqrt{x}+3}{\sqrt{x}+3}$

$\displaystyle = \lim_{x\to 9^-}\frac{x-9}{(x-9)(\sqrt{x}+3)}$

$\displaystyle = \lim_{x\to 9^-}\frac{1}{\sqrt{x}+3} = \frac{1}{6}$

**13.** $\displaystyle\lim_{x\to 0^-}\frac{|x|}{x} = \lim_{x\to 0^-}\frac{-x}{x} = -1$

**14.** $\displaystyle\lim_{x\to 10^+}\frac{|x-10|}{x-10} = \lim_{x\to 10^+}\frac{x-10}{x-10} = 1$

**15.** $\displaystyle\lim_{\Delta x\to 0^-}\frac{\frac{1}{x+\Delta x}-\frac{1}{x}}{\Delta x} = \lim_{\Delta x\to 0^-}\frac{x-(x+\Delta x)}{x(x+\Delta x)}\cdot\frac{1}{\Delta x} = \lim_{\Delta x\to 0^-}\frac{-\Delta x}{x(x+\Delta x)}\cdot\frac{1}{\Delta x}$

$\displaystyle = \lim_{\Delta x\to 0^-}\frac{-1}{x(x+\Delta x)}$

$\displaystyle = \frac{-1}{x(x+0)} = -\frac{1}{x^2}$

**16.** $\displaystyle\lim_{\Delta x\to 0^+}\frac{(x+\Delta x)^2+(x+\Delta x)-(x^2+x)}{\Delta x} = \lim_{\Delta x\to 0^+}\frac{x^2+2x(\Delta x)+(\Delta x)^2+x+\Delta x-x^2-x}{\Delta x}$

$\displaystyle = \lim_{\Delta x\to 0^+}\frac{2x(\Delta x)+(\Delta x)^2+\Delta x}{\Delta x}$

$\displaystyle = \lim_{\Delta x\to 0^+}(2x+\Delta x+1)$

$= 2x+0+1 = 2x+1$

**17.** $\displaystyle\lim_{x\to 3^-} f(x) = \lim_{x\to 3^-}\frac{x+2}{2} = \frac{5}{2}$

**18.** $\displaystyle\lim_{x\to 2^+} f(x) = \lim_{x\to 2^+}(-x^2+4x-2) = 2$

$\displaystyle\lim_{x\to 2^-} f(x) = \lim_{x\to 2^-}(x^2-4x+6) = 2$

$\displaystyle\lim_{x\to 2} f(x) = 2$

**19.** $\displaystyle\lim_{x\to 1^+} f(x) = \lim_{x\to 1^+}(x+1) = 2$

$\displaystyle\lim_{x\to 1^-} f(x) = \lim_{x\to 1^-}(x^3+1) = 2$

$\displaystyle\lim_{x\to 1} f(x) = 2$

**20.** $\displaystyle\lim_{x\to 1^+} f(x) = \lim_{x\to 1^+}(1-x) = 0$

**21.** $\displaystyle\lim_{x\to\pi}\cot x$ does not exist because

$\displaystyle\lim_{x\to\pi^+}\cot x$ and $\displaystyle\lim_{x\to\pi^-}\cot x$ do not exist.

**22.** $\displaystyle\lim_{x\to\pi/2}\sec x$ does not exist because

$\displaystyle\lim_{x\to(\pi/2)^+}\sec x$ and $\displaystyle\lim_{x\to(\pi/2)^-}\sec x$ do not exist.

**23.** $\displaystyle\lim_{x\to 4^-}(5[\![x]\!]-7) = 5(3)-7 = 8$

$([\![x]\!] = 3 \text{ for } 3 \le x < 4)$

**24.** $\displaystyle\lim_{x\to 3^+}(3x-[\![x]\!]) = 3(3)-3 = 6$

**25.** $\displaystyle\lim_{x\to 3}(2-[\![-x]\!])$ does not exist because

$\displaystyle\lim_{x\to 3^-}(2-[\![-x]\!]) = 2-(-3) = 5$

and

$\displaystyle\lim_{x\to 3^+}(2-[\![-x]\!]) = 2-(-4) = 6.$

**26.** $\displaystyle\lim_{x\to 1}\left(1-\left[\!\!\left[-\frac{x}{2}\right]\!\!\right]\right) = 1-(-1) = 2$

**27.** $\displaystyle\lim_{x\to 3^+}\ln(x-3) = \ln 0$

does not exist.

**28.** $\displaystyle\lim_{x\to 6^-}\ln(6-x) = \ln 0$

does not exist.

**29.** $\displaystyle\lim_{x\to 2^-}\ln\left[x^2(3-x)\right] = \ln\left[4(1)\right] = \ln 4$

**30.** $\displaystyle\lim_{x\to 5^+}\ln\frac{x}{\sqrt{x-4}} = \ln\frac{5}{1} = \ln 5$

**31.** $\displaystyle f(x) = \frac{1}{x^2-4}$

has discontinuities at $x = -2$ and $x = 2$ because $f(-2)$ and $f(2)$ are not defined.

**32.** $f(x) = \dfrac{x^2 - 1}{x + 1}$ has a discontinuity at $x = -1$ because $f(-1)$ is not defined.

**33.** $f(x) = \dfrac{[\![x]\!]}{2} + x$ has discontinuities at each integer $k$ because $\lim_{x\to k^-} f(x) \neq \lim_{x\to k^+} f(x)$.

**34.** $f(x) = \begin{cases} x, & x < 1 \\ 2, & x = 1 \\ 2x - 1, & x > 1 \end{cases}$ has a discontinuity at $x = 1$ because $f(1) = 2 \neq \lim_{x\to 1} f(x) = 1$.

**35.** $g(x) = \sqrt{49 - x^2}$ is continuous on $[-7, 7]$.

**36.** $f(t) = 2 - \sqrt{9 - t^2}$ is continuous on $[-2, 2]$.

**37.** $\lim_{x\to 0^-} f(x) = 3 = \lim_{x\to 0^+} f(x)$. $f$ is continuous on $[-1, 4]$.

**38.** $g(2)$ is not defined. $g$ is continuous on $[-1, 2)$.

**39.** $f(x) = \dfrac{6}{x}$ has a nonremovable discontinuity at $x = 0$.

**40.** $f(x) = \dfrac{3}{x - 2}$ has a nonremovable discontinuity at $x = 2$.

**41.** $f(x) = x^2 - 9$ is continuous for all real $x$.

**42.** $f(x) = x^2 - 2x + 1$ is continuous for all real $x$.

**43.** $f(x) = \dfrac{1}{4 - x^2} = \dfrac{1}{(2 - x)(2 + x)}$ has nonremovable discontinuities at $x = \pm 2$ because $\lim_{x\to 2} f(x)$ and $\lim_{x\to -2} f(x)$ do not exist.

**44.** $f(x) = \dfrac{1}{x^2 + 1}$ is continuous for all real $x$.

**45.** $f(x) = 3x - \cos x$ is continuous for all real $x$.

**46.** $f(x) = \cos\dfrac{\pi x}{4}$ is continuous for all real $x$.

**47.** $f(x) = \dfrac{x}{x^2 - x}$ is not continuous at $x = 0, 1$. Because $\dfrac{x}{x^2 - x} = \dfrac{1}{x - 1}$ for $x \neq 0$, $x = 0$ is a removable discontinuity, whereas $x = 1$ is a nonremovable discontinuity.

**48.** $f(x) = \dfrac{x}{x^2 - 1}$ has nonremovable discontinuities at $x = 1$ and $x = -1$ because $\lim_{x\to 1} f(x)$ and $\lim_{x\to -1} f(x)$ do not exist.

**49.** $f(x) = \dfrac{x}{x^2 + 1}$ is continuous for all real $x$.

**50.** $f(x) = \dfrac{x - 3}{x^2 - 9}$ has a nonremovable discontinuity at $x = -3$ because $\lim_{x\to -3} f(x)$ does not exist, and has a removable discontinuity at $x = 3$ because

$$\lim_{x\to 3} f(x) = \lim_{x\to 3} \frac{1}{x + 3} = \frac{1}{6}.$$

**51.** $f(x) = \dfrac{x + 2}{(x + 2)(x - 5)}$ has a nonremovable discontinuity at $x = 5$ because $\lim_{x\to 5} f(x)$ does not exist, and has a removable discontinuity at $x = -2$ because

$$\lim_{x\to -2} f(x) = \lim_{x\to -2} \frac{1}{x - 5} = -\frac{1}{7}.$$

**52.** $f(x) = \dfrac{x - 1}{(x + 2)(x - 1)}$ has a nonremovable discontinuity at $x = -2$ because $\lim_{x\to -2} f(x)$ does not exist, and has a removable discontinuity at $x = 1$ because

$$\lim_{x\to 1} f(x) = \lim_{x\to 1} \frac{1}{x + 2} = \frac{1}{3}.$$

**53.** $f(x) = \dfrac{|x + 2|}{x + 2}$ has a nonremovable discontinuity at $x = -2$ because $\lim_{x\to -2} f(x)$ does not exist.

**54.** $f(x) = \dfrac{|x - 3|}{x - 3}$ has a nonremovable discontinuity at $x = 3$ because $\lim_{x\to 3} f(x)$ does not exist.

**55.** $f(x) = \begin{cases} x, & x \le 1 \\ x^2, & x > 1 \end{cases}$

has a **possible** discontinuity at $x = 1$.

1. $f(1) = 1$
2. $\left.\begin{aligned} \lim_{x\to1^-} f(x) &= \lim_{x\to1^-} x = 1 \\ \lim_{x\to1^+} f(x) &= \lim_{x\to1^+} x^2 = 1 \end{aligned}\right\} \lim_{x\to1} f(x) = 1$
3. $f(1) = \lim_{x\to1} f(x)$

$f$ is continuous at $x = 1$, so, $f$ is continuous for all real $x$.

**56.** $f(x) = \begin{cases} -2x + 3, & x < 1 \\ x^2, & x \ge 1 \end{cases}$

has a **possible** discontinuity at $x = 1$.

1. $f(1) = 1^2 = 1$
2. $\left.\begin{aligned} \lim_{x\to1^-} f(x) &= \lim_{x\to1^-} (-2x + 3) = 1 \\ \lim_{x\to1^+} f(x) &= \lim_{x\to1^+} x^2 = 1 \end{aligned}\right\} \lim_{x\to1} f(x) = 1$
3. $f(1) = \lim_{x\to1} f(x)$

$f$ is continuous at $x = 1$, so, $f$ is continuous for all real $x$.

**57.** $f(x) = \begin{cases} \dfrac{x}{2} + 1, & x \le 2 \\ 3 - x, & x > 2 \end{cases}$

has a **possible** discontinuity at $x = 2$.

1. $f(2) = \dfrac{2}{2} + 1 = 2$
2. $\left.\begin{aligned} \lim_{x\to2^-} f(x) &= \lim_{x\to2^-} \left(\frac{x}{2} + 1\right) = 2 \\ \lim_{x\to2^+} f(x) &= \lim_{x\to2^+} (3 - x) = 1 \end{aligned}\right\} \lim_{x\to2} f(x)$ does not exist.

So, $f$ has a nonremovable discontinuity at $x = 2$.

**58.** $f(x) = \begin{cases} -2x, & x \le 2 \\ x^2 - 4x + 1, & x > 2 \end{cases}$

has a **possible** discontinuity at $x = 2$.

1. $f(2) = -2(2) = -4$
2. $\left.\begin{aligned} \lim_{x\to2^-} f(x) &= \lim_{x\to2^-} (-2x) = -4 \\ \lim_{x\to2^+} f(x) &= \lim_{x\to2^+} (x^2 - 4x + 1) = -3 \end{aligned}\right\} \lim_{x\to2} f(x)$ does not exist.

So, $f$ has a nonremovable discontinuity at $x = 2$.

**59.** $f(x) = \begin{cases} \tan\dfrac{\pi x}{4}, & |x| < 1 \\ x, & |x| \ge 1 \end{cases}$

$= \begin{cases} \tan\dfrac{\pi x}{4}, & -1 < x < 1 \\ x, & x \le -1 \text{ or } x \ge 1 \end{cases}$

has **possible** discontinuities at $x = -1, x = 1$.

1. $f(-1) = -1$ $\qquad f(1) = 1$
2. $\lim_{x\to-1} f(x) = -1$ $\qquad \lim_{x\to1} f(x) = 1$
3. $f(-1) = \lim_{x\to-1} f(x)$ $\qquad f(1) = \lim_{x\to1} f(x)$

$f$ is continuous at $x = \pm1$, so, $f$ is continuous for all real $x$.

**60.** $f(x) = \begin{cases} \csc\dfrac{\pi x}{6}, & |x - 3| \le 2 \\ 2, & |x - 3| > 2 \end{cases}$

$= \begin{cases} \csc\dfrac{\pi x}{6}, & 1 \le x \le 5 \\ 2, & x < 1 \text{ or } x > 5 \end{cases}$

has **possible** discontinuities at $x = 1, x = 5$.

1. $f(1) = \csc\dfrac{\pi}{6} = 2$ $\qquad f(5) = \csc\dfrac{5\pi}{6} = 2$
2. $\lim_{x\to1} f(x) = 2$ $\qquad \lim_{x\to5} f(x) = 2$
3. $f(1) = \lim_{x\to1} f(x)$ $\qquad f(5) = \lim_{x\to5} f(x)$

$f$ is continuous at $x = 1$ and $x = 5$, so, $f$ is continuous for all real $x$.

**61.** $f(x) = \begin{cases} \ln(x+1), & x \ge 0 \\ 1 - x^2, & x < 0 \end{cases}$

has a **possible** discontinuity at $x = 0$.

1. $f(0) = \ln(0 + 1) = \ln 1 = 0$

2. $\left.\begin{aligned} \lim_{x\to 0^-} f(x) &= 1 - 0 = 1 \\ \lim_{x\to 0^+} f(x) &= 0 \end{aligned}\right\} \lim_{x\to 0} f(x)$ does not exist.

So, $f$ has a nonremovable discontinuity at $x = 0$.

**62.** $f(x) = \begin{cases} 10 - 3e^{5-x}, & x > 5 \\ 10 - \frac{3}{5}x, & x \le 5 \end{cases}$

has a **possible** discontinuity at $x = 5$.

1. $f(5) = 7$

2. $\left.\begin{aligned} \lim_{x\to 5^+} f(x) &= 10 - 3e^{5-5} = 7 \\ \lim_{x\to 5^-} f(x) &= 10 - \tfrac{3}{5}(5) = 7 \end{aligned}\right\} \lim_{x\to 5} f(x) = 7$

3. $f(5) = \lim_{x\to 5} f(x)$

   $f$ is continuous at $x = 5$, so, $f$ is continuous for all real $x$.

**63.** $f(x) = \csc 2x$ has nonremovable discontinuities at integer multiples of $\pi/2$.

**64.** $f(x) = \tan\dfrac{\pi x}{4}$ has nonremovable discontinuities at each $4k + 2$, $k$ is an integer.

**65.** $f(x) = [\![x - 8]\!]$ has nonremovable discontinuities at each integer $k$.

**66.** $f(x) = 5 - [\![x]\!]$ has nonremovable discontinuities at each integer $k$.

**67.** $\lim_{x\to 0^+} f(x) = 0$

$\lim_{x\to 0^-} f(x) = 0$

$f$ is not continuous at $x = -2$.

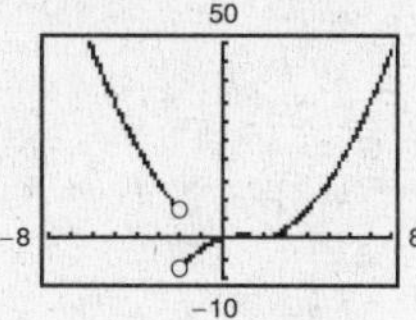


**68.** $\lim_{x\to 0^+} f(x) = 0$

$\lim_{x\to 0^-} f(x) = 0$

$f$ is not continuous at $x = -4$.

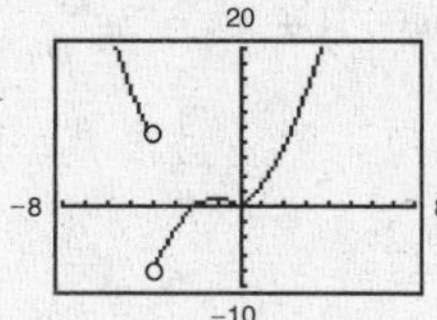


**69.** $f(1) = 3$

Find $a$ so that $\lim_{x\to 1^-} (ax - 4) = 3$

$$a(1) - 4 = 3$$
$$a = 7.$$

**70.** $f(1) = 3$

Find $a$ so that $\lim_{x\to 1^+} (ax + 5) = 3$

$$a(1) + 5 = 3$$
$$a = -2.$$

**71.** $f(2) = 8$

Find $a$ so that $\lim_{x\to 2^+} ax^2 = 8 \Rightarrow a = \frac{8}{2^2} = 2.$

**72.** $\lim_{x\to 0^-} g(x) = \lim_{x\to 0^-} \dfrac{4 \sin x}{x} = 4$

$\lim_{x\to 0^+} g(x) = \lim_{x\to 0^+} (a - 2x) = a$

Let $a = 4$.

**73.** Find $a$ and $b$ such that $\lim_{x\to -1^+} (ax + b) = -a + b = 2$ and $\lim_{x\to 3^-} (ax + b) = 3a + b = -2$.

$$\begin{aligned} a - b &= -2 \\ (+)3a + b &= -2 \\ \hline 4a \quad &= -4 \\ a &= -1 \\ b &= 2 + (-1) = 1 \end{aligned}$$

$$f(x) = \begin{cases} 2, & x \le -1 \\ -x + 1, & -1 < x < 3 \\ -2, & x \ge 3 \end{cases}$$

**74.** $\lim_{x \to a} g(x) = \lim_{x \to a} \frac{x^2 - a^2}{x - a}$

$= \lim_{x \to a}(x + a) = 2a$

Find $a$ such that $2a = 8 \Rightarrow a = 4$.

**75.** $f(1) = \arctan(1 - 1) + 2 = 2$

Find $a$ such that $\lim_{x \to 1^-} \left(ae^{x-1} + 3\right) = 2$

$$\begin{aligned} ae^{1-1} + 3 &= 2 \\ a + 3 &= 2 \\ a &= -1. \end{aligned}$$

**76.** $f(4) = 2e^{4a} - 2$

Find $a$ such that $\lim_{x \to 4^+} \ln(x - 3) + x^2 = 2e^{4a} - 2$

$$\begin{aligned} \ln(4 - 3) + 4^2 &= 2e^{4a} - 2 \\ 16 &= 2e^{4a} - 2 \\ 9 &= e^{4a} \\ \ln 9 &= 4a \\ a &= \frac{\ln 9}{4} = \frac{\ln 3^2}{4} = \frac{\ln 3}{2}. \end{aligned}$$

**77.** $f(g(x)) = (x - 1)^2$

Continuous for all real $x$

**78.** $f(g(x)) = \frac{1}{\sqrt{x - 1}}$

Nonremovable discontinuity at $x = 1$. Continuous for all $x > 1$.

**79.** $f(g(x)) = \frac{1}{(x^2 + 5) - 6} = \frac{1}{x^2 - 1}$

Nonremovable discontinuities at $x = \pm 1$

**80.** $f(g(x)) = \sin x^2$

Continuous for all real $x$

**81.** $y = [\![x]\!] - x$

Nonremovable discontinuity at each integer

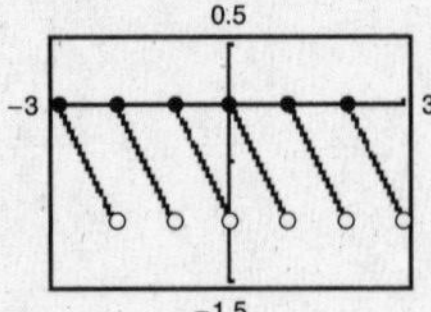


**82.** $h(x) = \frac{1}{(x + 1)(x - 2)}$

Nonremovable discontinuities at $x = -1$ and $x = 2$.

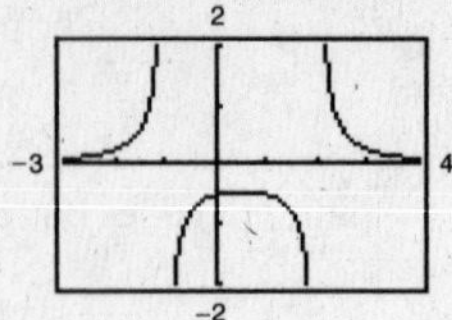


**83.** $g(x) = \begin{cases} x^2 - 3x, & x > 4 \\ 2x - 5, & x \le 4 \end{cases}$

Nonremovable discontinuity at $x = 4$.

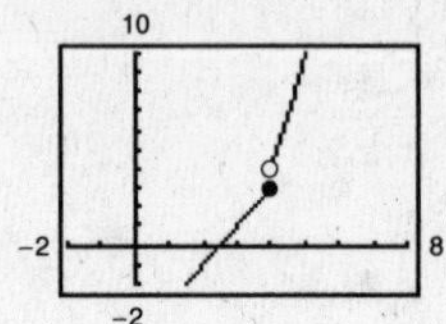


**84.** $f(x) = \begin{cases} \frac{\cos x - 1}{x}, & x < 0 \\ 5x, & x \ge 0 \end{cases}$

$f(0) = 5(0) = 0$

$\lim_{x \to 0^-} f(x) = \lim_{x \to 0^-} \frac{(\cos x - 1)}{x} = 0$

$\lim_{x \to 0^+} f(x) = \lim_{x \to 0^+} (5x) = 0$

So, $\lim_{x \to 0} f(x) = 0 = f(0)$ and $f$ is continuous on the entire real line.

($x = 0$ was the only possible discontinuity.)

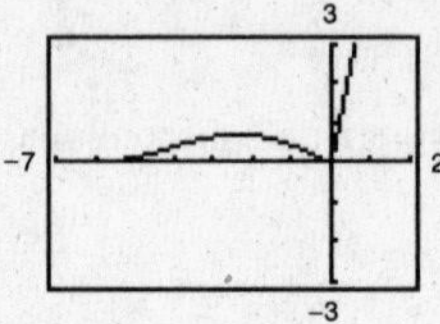


**85.** $f(x) = \frac{x}{x^2 + x + 2}$

Continuous on $(-\infty, \infty)$

**86.** $f(x) = x\sqrt{x + 3}$

Continuous on $[-3, \infty)$

**87.** $f(x) = \sec\frac{\pi x}{4}$

Continuous on:

$\ldots, (-6, -2), (-2, 2), (2, 6), (6, 10), \ldots$

**88.** $f(x) = \dfrac{x+1}{\sqrt{x}}$

Continuous on $(0, \infty)$

**89.** $f(x) = \dfrac{\sin x}{x}$

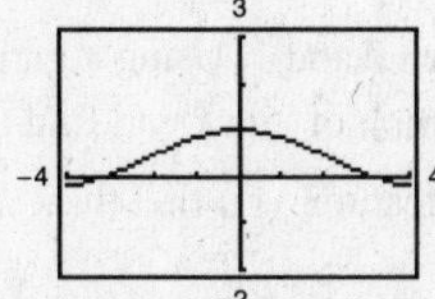


The graph **appears** to be continuous on the interval $[-4, 4]$. Because $f(0)$ is not defined, you know that $f$ has a discontinuity at $x = 0$. This discontinuity is removable so it does not show up on the graph.

**90.** $f(x) = \dfrac{x^3 - 8}{x - 2}$

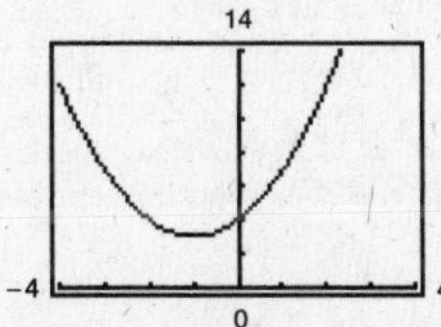


The graph **appears** to be continuous on the interval $[-4, 4]$. Because $f(2)$ is not defined, you know that $f$ has a discontinuity at $x = 2$. This discontinuity is removable so it does not show up on the graph.

**91.** 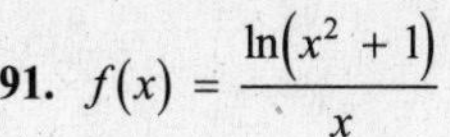 $f(x) = \dfrac{\ln(x^2 + 1)}{x}$

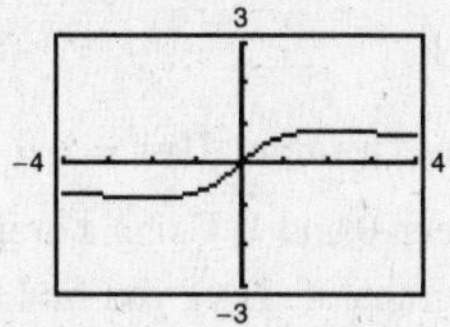


The graph **appears** to be continuous on the interval $[-4, 4]$. Because $f(0)$ is not defined, you know that $f$ has a discontinuity at $x = 0$. This discontinuity is removable so it does not show up on the graph.

**92.** $f(x) = \dfrac{-e^{-x} + 1}{e^x - 1}$

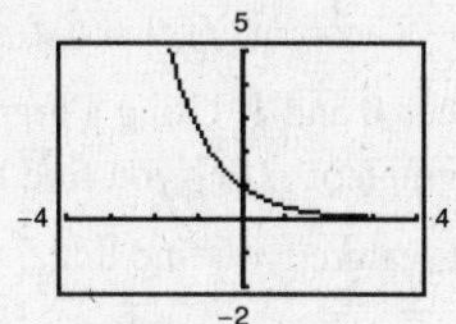


The graph **appears** to be continuous on the interval $[-4, 4]$. Because $f(0)$ is not defined, you know that $f$ has a discontinuity at $x = 0$. This discontinuity is removable so it does not show up on the graph.

**93.** $f(x) = \frac{1}{12}x^4 - x^3 + 4$ is continuous on the interval $[1, 2]$. $f(1) = \frac{37}{12}$ and $f(2) = -\frac{8}{3}$. By the Intermediate Value Theorem, there exists a number $c$ in $[1, 2]$ such that $f(c) = 0$.

**94.** $f(x) = x^3 + 5x - 3$ is continuous on the interval $[0, 1]$. $f(0) = -3$ and $f(1) = 3$. By the Intermediate Value Theorem, there exists a number $c$ in $[0, 1]$ such that $f(c) = 0$.

**95.** $h$ is continuous on the interval $\left[0, \dfrac{\pi}{2}\right]$. $h(0) = -2 < 0$ and $h\left(\dfrac{\pi}{2}\right) \approx 0.91 > 0$. By the Intermediate Value Theorem, there exists a number $c$ in $\left[0, \dfrac{\pi}{2}\right]$ such that $h(c) = 0$.

**96.** $g$ is continuous on the interval $[0, 1]$. $g(0) \approx -2.77 < 0$ and $g(1) \approx 1.61 > 0$. By the Intermediate Value Theorem, there exists a number $c$ in $[0, 1]$ such that $g(c) = 0$.

**97.** $f(x) = x^3 + x - 1$

$f(x)$ is continuous on $[0, 1]$.

$f(0) = -1$ and $f(1) = 1$

By the Intermediate Value Theorem, $f(c) = 0$ for at least one value of $c$ between 0 and 1. Using a graphing utility to zoom in on the graph of $f(x)$, you find that $x \approx 0.68$. Using the root feature, you find that $x \approx 0.6823$.

**98.** $f(x) = x^3 + 3x - 3$

$f(x)$ is continuous on $[0, 1]$.

$f(0) = -3$ and $f(1) = 1$

By the Intermediate Value Theorem, $f(c) = 0$ for at least one value of $c$ between 0 and 1. Using a graphing utility to zoom in on the graph of $f(x)$, you find that $x \approx 0.82$. Using the root feature, you find that $x \approx 0.8177$.

**99.** $g(t) = 2\cos t - 3t$

$g$ is continuous on $[0, 1]$.

$g(0) = 2 > 0$ and $g(1) \approx -1.9 < 0$.

By the Intermediate Value Theorem, $g(c) = 0$ for at least one value of $c$ between 0 and 1. Using a graphing utility to zoom in on the graph of $g(t)$, you find that $t \approx 0.56$. Using the root feature, you find that $t \approx 0.5636$.

**100.** $h(\theta) = 1 + \theta - 3\tan\theta$

$h$ is continuous on $[0, 1]$.

$h(0) = 1 > 0$ and $h(1) \approx -2.67 < 0$.

By the Intermediate Value Theorem, $h(c) = 0$ for at least one value of $c$ between 0 and 1. Using a graphing utility to zoom in on the graph of $h(\theta)$, you find that $\theta \approx 0.45$. Using the root feature, you find that $\theta \approx 0.4503$.

**101.** $f(x) = x + e^x - 3$

$f$ is continuous on $[0, 1]$.

$f(0) = e^0 - 3 = -2 < 0$ and

$f(1) = 1 + e - 3 = e - 2 > 0$.

By the Intermediate Value Theorem, $f(c) = 0$ for at least one value of $c$ between 0 and 1. Using a graphing utility to zoom in on the graph of $f(x)$, you find that $x \approx 0.79$. Using the root feature, you find that $x \approx 0.7921$.

**102.** $g(x) = 5\ln(x + 1) - 2$

$g$ is continuous on $[0, 1]$.

$g(0) = 5\ln(0 + 1) - 2 = -2$ and

$g(1) = 5\ln(2) - 2 > 0$.

By the Intermediate Value Theorem, $g(c) = 0$ for at least one value of $c$ between 0 and 1. Using a graphing utility to zoom in on the graph of $g(x)$, you find that $x \approx 0.49$. Using the root feature, you find that $x \approx 0.4918$.

**103.** $f(x) = x^2 + x - 1$

$f$ is continuous on $[0, 5]$.

$f(0) = -1$ and $f(5) = 29$

$$-1 < 11 < 29$$

The Intermediate Value Theorem applies.

$$x^2 + x - 1 = 11$$
$$x^2 + x - 12 = 0$$
$$(x + 4)(x - 3) = 0$$
$$x = -4 \text{ or } x = 3$$

$c = 3$ ($x = -4$ is not in the interval.)

So, $f(3) = 11$.

**104.** $f(x) = x^2 - 6x + 8$

$f$ is continuous on $[0, 3]$.

$f(0) = 8$ and $f(3) = -1$

$$-1 < 0 < 8$$

The Intermediate Value Theorem applies.

$$x^2 - 6x + 8 = 0$$
$$(x - 2)(x - 4) = 0$$
$$x = 2 \text{ or } x = 4$$

$c = 2$ ($x = 4$ is not in the interval.)

So, $f(2) = 0$.

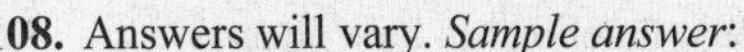

**105.** $f(x) = x^3 - x^2 + x - 2$

$f$ is continuous on $[0, 3]$.

$f(0) = -2$ and $f(3) = 19$

$-2 < 4 < 19$

The Intermediate Value Theorem applies.

$$x^3 - x^2 + x - 2 = 4$$
$$x^3 - x^2 + x - 6 = 0$$
$$(x - 2)(x^2 + x + 3) = 0$$
$$x = 2$$

$(x^2 + x + 3$ has no real solution.$)$

$c = 2$

So, $f(2) = 4$.

**106.** $f(x) = \dfrac{x^2 + x}{x - 1}$

$f$ is continuous on $\left[\dfrac{5}{2}, 4\right]$. The nonremovable discontinuity, $x = 1$, lies outside the interval.

$f\left(\dfrac{5}{2}\right) = \dfrac{35}{6}$ and $f(4) = \dfrac{20}{3}$

$\dfrac{35}{6} < 6 < \dfrac{20}{3}$

The Intermediate Value Theorem applies.

$$\frac{x^2 + x}{x - 1} = 6$$
$$x^2 + x = 6x - 6$$
$$x^2 - 5x + 6 = 0$$
$$(x - 2)(x - 3) = 0$$
$$x = 2 \text{ or } x = 3$$

$c = 3$ ($x = 2$ is not in the interval.)

So, $f(3) = 6$.

**107.** (a) The limit does not exist at $x = c$.
(b) The function is not defined at $x = c$.
(c) The limit exists at $x = c$, but it is not equal to the value of the function at $x = c$.
(d) The limit does not exist at $x = c$.

**108.** Answers will vary. *Sample answer*:

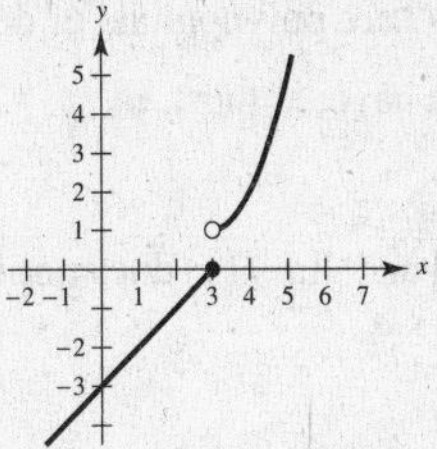

The function is not continuous at $x = 3$ because $\lim\limits_{x\to3^+} f(x) = 1 \neq 0 = \lim\limits_{x\to3^-} f(x)$.

**109.** If $f$ and $g$ are continuous for all real $x$, then so is $f + g$ (Theorem 2.11, part 2). However, $f/g$ might not be continuous if $g(x) = 0$. For example, let $f(x) = x$ and $g(x) = x^2 - 1$. Then $f$ and $g$ are continuous for all real $x$, but $f/g$ is not continuous at $x = \pm1$.

**110.** A discontinuity at $c$ is removable if the function $f$ can be made continuous at $c$ by appropriately defining (or redefining) $f(c)$. Otherwise, the discontinuity is nonremovable.

(a) $f(x) = \dfrac{|x - 4|}{x - 4}$

(b) $f(x) = \dfrac{\sin(x + 4)}{x + 4}$

(c) $f(x) = \begin{cases} 1, & x \geq 4 \\ 0, & -4 < x < 4 \\ 1, & x = -4 \\ 0, & x < -4 \end{cases}$

$x = 4$ is nonremovable, $x = -4$ is removable

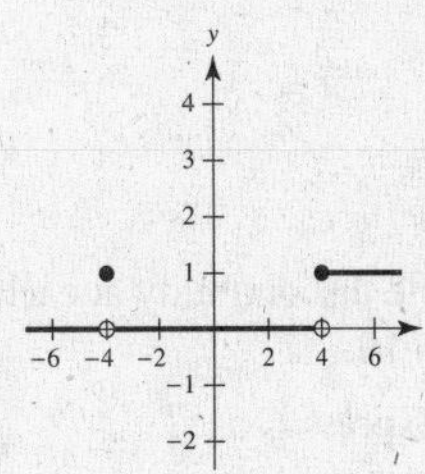

**111.** True

1. $f(c) = L$ is defined.
2. $\lim\limits_{x\to c} f(x) = L$ exists.
3. $f(c) = \lim\limits_{x\to c} f(x)$

All of the conditions for continuity are met.

**112.** True. If $f(x) = g(x)$, $x \neq c$, then $\lim\limits_{x\to c} f(x) = \lim\limits_{x\to c} g(x)$ (if they exist) and at least one of these limits then does not equal the corresponding function value at $x = c$.

**113.** False. A rational function can be written as $P(x)/Q(x)$ where $P$ and $Q$ are polynomials of degree $m$ and $n$, respectively. It can have, at most, $n$ discontinuities.

**114.** False. $f(1)$ is not defined and $\lim_{x\to 1} f(x)$ does not exist.

**115.** $\lim_{t\to 4^-} f(t) \approx 28$

$\lim_{t\to 4^+} f(t) \approx 56$

At the end of day 3, the amount of chlorine in the pool has decreased to about 28 oz. At the beginning of day 4, more chlorine was added, and the amount is now about 56 oz.

**116.** The functions agree for integer values of $x$:

$$\left.\begin{aligned} g(x) &= 3 - [\![-x]\!] = 3 - (-x) = 3 + x \\ f(x) &= 3 + [\![x]\!] = 3 + x \end{aligned}\right\} \text{for } x \text{ an integer}$$

However, for non-integer values of $x$, the functions differ by 1.

$$f(x) = 3 + [\![x]\!] = g(x) - 1 = 2 - [\![-x]\!]$$

For example,

$$f\left(\tfrac{1}{2}\right) = 3 + 0 = 3,\ g\left(\tfrac{1}{2}\right) = 3 - (-1) = 4.$$

**117.** $$C(t) = \begin{cases} 0.40, & 0 < t \le 10 \\ 0.40 + 0.05[\![t - 9]\!], & t > 10,\ t \text{ not an integer} \\ 0.40 + 0.05(t - 10), & t > 10,\ t \text{ an integer} \end{cases}$$

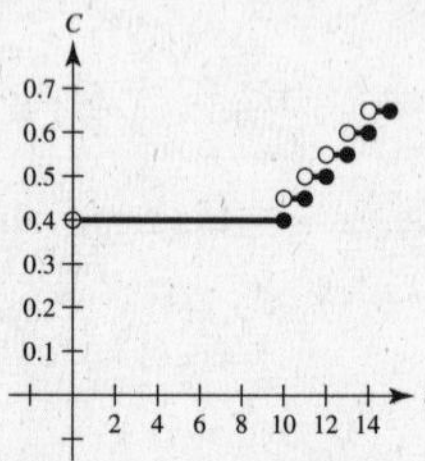


There is a nonremovable discontinuity at each integer greater than or equal to 10.

Note: You could also express $C$ as

$$C(t) = \begin{cases} 0.40, & 0 < t \le 10 \\ 0.40 - 0.05[\![10 - t]\!], & t > 10 \end{cases}.$$

**118.** $N(t) = 25\left(2\left[\!\left[\dfrac{t+2}{2}\right]\!\right] - t\right)$

| $t$ | 0 | 1 | 1.8 | 2 | 3 | 3.8 |
|---|---|---|---|---|---|---|
| $N(t)$ | 50 | 25 | 5 | 50 | 25 | 5 |

Discontinuous at every positive even integer. The company replenishes its inventory every two months.

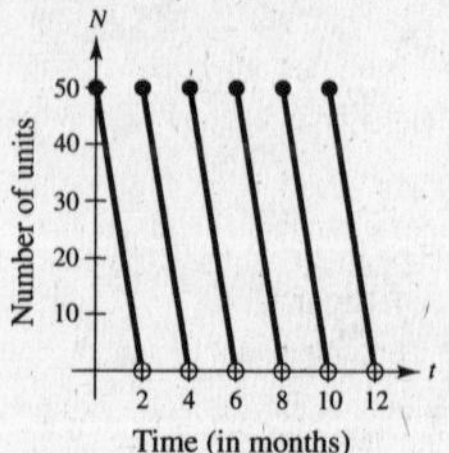


**119.** Let $s(t)$ be the position function for the run up to the campsite. $s(0) = 0$ ($t = 0$ corresponds to 8:00 A.M., $s(20) = k$ (distance to campsite)). Let $r(t)$ be the position function for the run back down the mountain: $r(0) = k, r(10) = 0$. Let $f(t) = s(t) - r(t)$.

When $t = 0$ (8:00 A.M.),

$f(0) = s(0) - r(0) = 0 - k < 0.$

When $t = 10$ (8:10 A.M.), $f(10) = s(10) - r(10) > 0.$

Because $f(0) < 0$ and $f(10) > 0$, then there must be a value $t$ in the interval $[0, 10]$ such that $f(t) = 0$. If $f(t) = 0$, then $s(t) - r(t) = 0$, which gives us $s(t) = r(t)$. So, at some time $t$, where $0 \le t \le 10$, the position functions for the run up and the run down are equal.

**120.** Let $V = \dfrac{4}{3}\pi r^3$ be the volume of a sphere with radius $r$.

$V$ is continuous on $[5, 8]$. $V(5) = \dfrac{500\pi}{3} \approx 523.6$ and

$V(8) = \dfrac{2048\pi}{3} \approx 2144.7.$ Because

$523.6 < 1500 < 2144.7$, the Intermediate Value Theorem guarantees that there is at least one value $r$ between 5 and 8 such that $V(r) = 1500$. (In fact, $r \approx 7.1012$.)

**121.** Suppose there exists $x_1$ in $[a, b]$ such that $f(x_1) > 0$ and there exists $x_2$ in $[a, b]$ such that $f(x_2) < 0$. Then by the Intermediate Value Theorem, $f(x)$ must equal zero for some value of $x$ in $[x_1, x_2]$ (or $[x_2, x_1]$ if $x_2 < x_1$). So, $f$ would have a zero in $[a, b]$, which is a contradiction. Therefore, $f(x) > 0$ for all $x$ in $[a, b]$ or $f(x) < 0$ for all $x$ in $[a, b]$.

**122.** Let $c$ be any real number. Then $\lim_{x\to c} f(x)$ does not exist because there are both rational and irrational numbers arbitrarily close to $c$. So, $f$ is not continuous at $c$.

**123.** If $x = 0$, then $f(0) = 0$ and $\lim_{x\to 0} f(x) = 0$. So, $f$ is continuous at $x = 0$.

If $x \neq 0$, then $\lim_{t\to x} f(t) = 0$ for $x$ rational, whereas $\lim_{t\to x} f(t) = \lim_{t\to x} kt = kx \neq 0$ for $x$ irrational. So, $f$ is not continuous for all $x \neq 0$.

**124.** 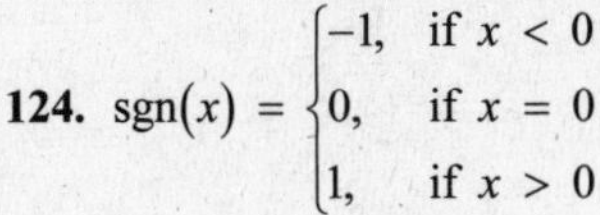

$$\operatorname{sgn}(x) = \begin{cases} -1, & \text{if } x < 0 \\ 0, & \text{if } x = 0 \\ 1, & \text{if } x > 0 \end{cases}$$

(a) $\lim_{x\to 0^-} \operatorname{sgn}(x) = -1$

(b) $\lim_{x\to 0^+} \operatorname{sgn}(x) = 1$

(c) $\lim_{x\to 0} \operatorname{sgn}(x)$ does not exist.

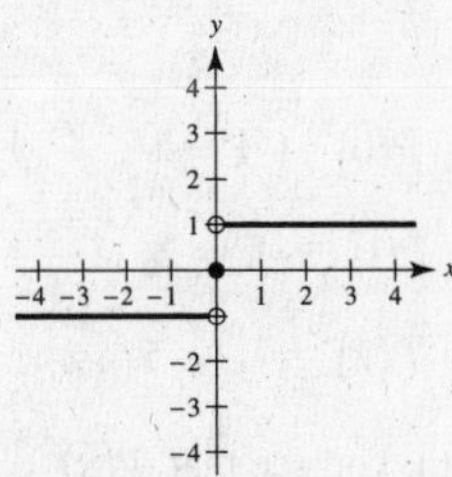


**125.** (a)

s
t
60
50
40
30
20
10
5 10 15 20 25 30

(b) There appears to be a limiting speed and a possible cause is air resistance.

**126.** (a) $f(x) = \begin{cases} 0, & 0 \le x < b \\ b, & b < x \le 2b \end{cases}$

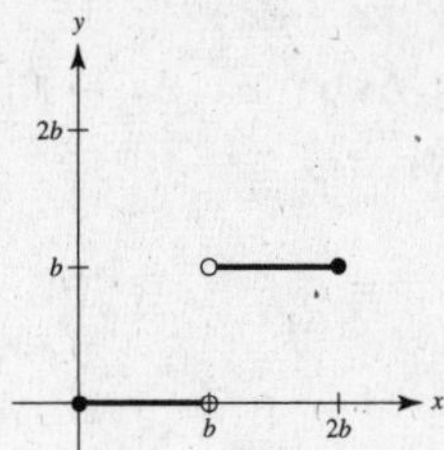


NOT continuous at $x = b$

(b) $g(x) = \begin{cases} \dfrac{x}{2}, & 0 \le x \le b \\ b - \dfrac{x}{2}, & b < x \le 2b \end{cases}$

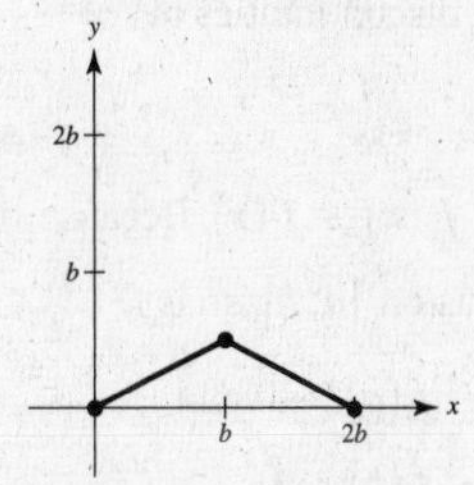


Continuous on $[0, 2b]$

**127.** $f(x) = \begin{cases} 1 - x^2, & x \le c \\ x, & x > c \end{cases}$

$f$ is continuous for $x < c$ and for $x > c$. At $x = c$, you need $1 - c^2 = c$. Solving $c^2 + c - 1 = 0$, you obtain

$$c = \frac{-1 \pm \sqrt{1 + 4}}{2} = \frac{-1 \pm \sqrt{5}}{2}.$$

**128.** Let $y$ be a real number. If $y = 0$, then $x = 0$. If $y > 0$, then let $0 < x_0 < \pi/2$ such that $M = \tan x_0 > y$ (this is possible because the tangent function increases without bound on $[0, \pi/2)$). By the Intermediate Value Theorem, $f(x) = \tan x$ is continuous on $[0, x_0]$ and $0 < y < M$, which implies that there exists $x$ between 0 and $x_0$ such that $\tan x = y$. The argument is similar if $y < 0$.

**129.** $f(x) = \dfrac{\sqrt{x + c^2} - c}{x}, c > 0$

Domain: $x + c^2 \ge 0 \Rightarrow x \ge -c^2$ and $x \neq 0, [-c^2, 0) \cup (0, \infty)$

$$\lim_{x\to 0} \frac{\sqrt{x + c^2} - c}{x} = \lim_{x\to 0} \frac{\sqrt{x + c^2} - c}{x} \cdot \frac{\sqrt{x + c^2} + c}{\sqrt{x + c^2} + c} = \lim_{x\to 0} \frac{(x + c^2) - c^2}{x\left[\sqrt{x + c^2} + c\right]} = \lim_{x\to 0} \frac{1}{\sqrt{x + c^2} + c} = \frac{1}{2c}$$

Define $f(0) = 1/(2c)$ to make $f$ continuous at $x = 0$.

**130.** 1. $f(c)$ is defined.

2. $\lim_{x\to c} f(x) = \lim_{\Delta x\to 0} f(c + \Delta x) = f(c)$ exists.

[Let $x = c + \Delta x$. As $x \to c$, $\Delta x \to 0$]

3. $\lim_{x\to c} f(x) = f(c)$.

So, $f$ is continuous at $x = c$.

**131.** $h(x) = x[\![x]\!]$

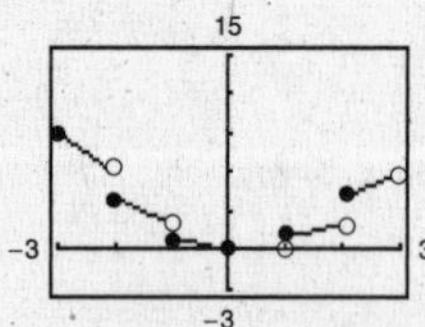


$h$ has nonremovable discontinuities at $x = \pm1, \pm2, \pm3, \ldots$.

**132.** (a) Define $f(x) = f_2(x) - f_1(x)$. Because $f_1$ and $f_2$ are continuous on $[a, b]$, so is $f$.

$f(a) = f_2(a) - f_1(a) > 0$ and

$f(b) = f_2(b) - f_1(b) < 0$

By the Intermediate Value Theorem, there exists $c$ in $[a, b]$ such that $f(c) = 0$.

$f(c) = f_2(c) - f_1(c) = 0 \Rightarrow f_1(c) = f_2(c)$

(b) Let $f_1(x) = x$ and $f_2(x) = \cos x$, continuous on $[0, \pi/2]$, $f_1(0) < f_2(0)$ and $f_1(\pi/2) > f_2(\pi/2)$.

So by part (a), there exists $c$ in $[0, \pi/2]$ such that $c = \cos(c)$.

Using a graphing utility, $c \approx 0.739$.

**133.** $f(x) = \dfrac{4}{1 + 2^{4/x}}$

(a) Domain: all $x \neq 0$

(b)

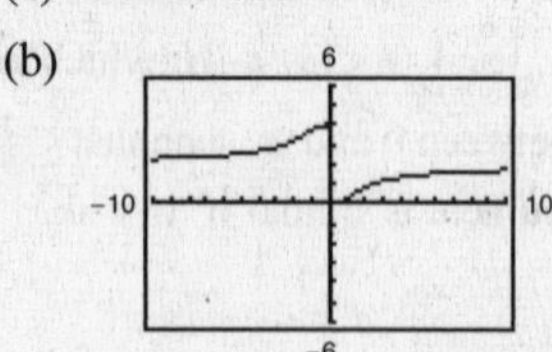


(c) $\lim_{x\to 0^-} f(x) = 4$, $\lim_{x\to 0^+} f(x) = 0$

(d) For $x$ near 0 and negative, $\dfrac{4}{1 + 2^{4/x}} \approx \dfrac{4}{1 + 0} \approx 4$.

For $x$ near 0 and positive, $\dfrac{4}{1 + 2^{4/x}} \approx 0$.

**134.** The statement is true.

If $y \geq 0$ and $y \leq 1$, then $y(y - 1) \leq 0 \leq x^2$, as desired. So assume $y > 1$. There are now two cases.

Case 1: If $x \leq y - \frac{1}{2}$, then $2x + 1 \leq 2y$ and

$$\begin{aligned} y(y - 1) &= y(y + 1) - 2y \\ &\leq (x + 1)^2 - 2y \\ &= x^2 + 2x + 1 - 2y \\ &\leq x^2 + 2y - 2y \\ &= x^2. \end{aligned}$$

Case 2: If $x \geq y - \frac{1}{2}$

$$\begin{aligned} x^2 &\geq \left(y - \tfrac{1}{2}\right)^2 \\ &= y^2 - y + \tfrac{1}{4} \\ &> y^2 - y \\ &= y(y - 1). \end{aligned}$$

In both cases, $y(y - 1) \leq x^2$.

**135.** $P(1) = P(0^2 + 1) = P(0)^2 + 1 = 1$

$P(2) = P(1^2 + 1) = P(1)^2 + 1 = 2$

$P(5) = P(2^2 + 1) = P(2)^2 + 1 = 5$

Continuing this pattern, you see that $P(x) = x$ for infinitely many values of $x$. So, the finite degree polynomial must be constant: $P(x) = x$ for all $x$.

## Section 2.5 Infinite Limits

**1.** $f(x) = \frac{1}{x - 4}$

As $x$ approaches 4 from the left, $x - 4$ is a small negative number. So,

$$\lim_{x\to 4^-} f(x) = -\infty.$$

As $x$ approaches 4 from the right, $x - 4$ is a small positive number. So,

$$\lim_{x\to 4^+} f(x) = \infty.$$

**2.** $f(x) = \frac{-1}{x - 4}$

As $x$ approaches 4 from the left, $x - 4$ is a small negative number. So,

$$\lim_{x\to 4^-} f(x) = \infty.$$

As $x$ approaches 4 from the right, $x - 4$ is a small positive number. So,

$$\lim_{x\to 4^+} f(x) = -\infty.$$

**3.** $f(x) = \frac{1}{(x - 4)^2}$

As $x$ approaches 4 from the left or right, $(x - 4)^2$ is a small positive number. So,

$$\lim_{x\to 4^+} f(x) = \lim_{x\to 4^-} f(x) = \infty.$$

**4.** $f(x) = \frac{-1}{(x - 4)^2}$

As $x$ approaches 4 from the left or right, $(x - 4)^2$ is a small positive number. So,

$$\lim_{x\to 4^-} f(x) = \lim_{x\to 4^+} f(x) = -\infty.$$

**5.** $\lim_{x\to -2^+} 2\left|\frac{x}{x^2 - 4}\right| = \infty$

$\lim_{x\to -2^-} 2\left|\frac{x}{x^2 - 4}\right| = \infty$

**6.** $\lim_{x\to -2^+} \frac{-1}{x + 2} = -\infty$

$\lim_{x\to -2^-} \frac{1}{x + 2} = \infty$

**7.** $\lim_{x\to -2^+} \tan\frac{\pi x}{4} = -\infty$

$\lim_{x\to -2^-} \tan\frac{\pi x}{4} = \infty$

**8.** $\lim_{x\to -2^+} \sec\frac{\pi x}{4} = \infty$

$\lim_{x\to -2^-} \sec\frac{\pi x}{4} = -\infty$

**9.** $f(x) = \frac{1}{x^2 - 9}$

| $x$ | −3.5 | −3.1 | −3.01 | −3.001 | −2.999 | −2.99 | −2.9 | −2.5 |
|---|---|---|---|---|---|---|---|---|
| $f(x)$ | 0.308 | 1.639 | 16.64 | 166.6 | −166.7 | −16.69 | −1.695 | −0.364 |

$\lim_{x\to -3^-} f(x) = \infty$

$\lim_{x\to -3^+} f(x) = -\infty$

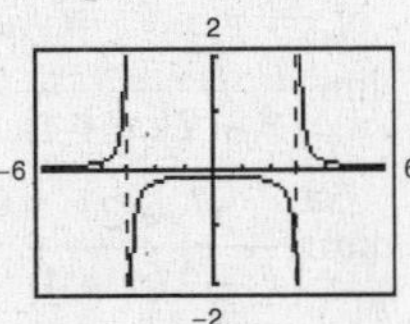


**10.** $f(x) = \frac{x}{x^2 - 9}$

| $x$ | −3.5 | −3.1 | −3.01 | −3.001 | −2.999 | −2.99 | −2.9 | −2.5 |
|---|---|---|---|---|---|---|---|---|
| $f(x)$ | −1.077 | −5.082 | −50.08 | −500.1 | 499.9 | 49.92 | 4.915 | 0.9091 |

$\lim_{x\to -3^-} f(x) = -\infty$

$\lim_{x\to -3^+} f(x) = \infty$

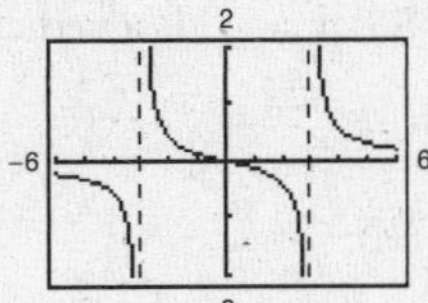

**11.** $f(x) = \dfrac{x^2}{x^2 - 9}$

| $x$ | −3.5 | −3.1 | −3.01 | −3.001 | −2.999 | −2.99 | −2.9 | −2.5 |
|---|---|---|---|---|---|---|---|---|
| $f(x)$ | 3.769 | 15.75 | 150.8 | 1501 | −1499 | −149.3 | −14.25 | −2.273 |

$\lim_{x \to -3^-} f(x) = \infty$

$\lim_{x \to -3^+} f(x) = -\infty$

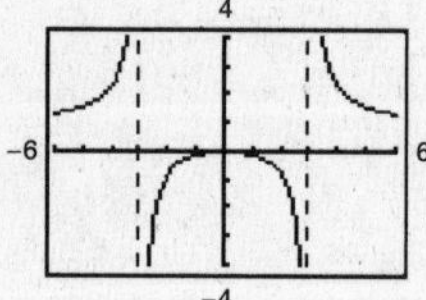

**12.** $f(x) = \sec\dfrac{\pi x}{6}$

| $x$ | −3.5 | −3.1 | −3.01 | −3.001 | −2.999 | −2.99 | −2.9 | −2.5 |
|---|---|---|---|---|---|---|---|---|
| $f(x)$ | −3.864 | −19.11 | −191.0 | −1910 | 1910 | 191.0 | 19.11 | 3.864 |

$\lim_{x \to -3^-} f(x) = -\infty$

$\lim_{x \to -3^+} f(x) = \infty$

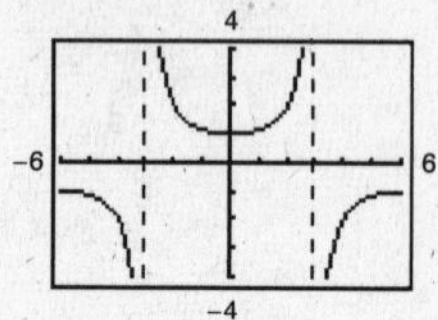

**13.** $\lim_{x \to 0^+} \dfrac{1}{x^2} = \infty = \lim_{x \to 0^-} \dfrac{1}{x^2}$

So, $x = 0$ is a vertical asymptote.

**14.** $\lim_{x \to 2^+} \dfrac{4}{(x - 2)^3} = \infty$

$\lim_{x \to 2^-} \dfrac{4}{(x - 2)^3} = -\infty$

So, $x = 2$ is a vertical asymptote.

**15.** $\lim_{x \to -2^-} \dfrac{x^2}{x^2 - 4} = \infty$ and $\lim_{x \to -2^+} \dfrac{x^2}{x^2 - 4} = -\infty$

So, $x = -2$ is a vertical asymptote.

$\lim_{x \to 2^-} \dfrac{x^2}{x^2 - 4} = -\infty$ and $\lim_{x \to 2^+} \dfrac{x^2}{x^2 - 4} = \infty$

So, $x = 2$ is a vertical asymptote.

**16.** No vertical asymptote because the denominator is never zero.

**17.** No vertical asymptote because the denominator is never zero.

**18.** $\lim_{s \to -5^-} h(s) = -\infty$ and $\lim_{s \to -5^+} h(s) = \infty$.

So, $s = -5$ is a vertical asymptote.

$\lim_{s \to 5^-} h(s) = -\infty$ and $\lim_{s \to 5^+} h(s) = \infty$.

So, $s = 5$ is a vertical asymptote.

**19.** $\lim_{x \to 2^+} \dfrac{x^2 - 2}{(x - 2)(x + 1)} = \infty$

$\lim_{x \to 2^-} \dfrac{x^2 - 2}{(x - 2)(x + 1)} = -\infty$

So, $x = 2$ is a vertical asymptote.

$\lim_{x \to -1^+} \dfrac{x^2 - 2}{(x - 2)(x + 1)} = \infty$

$\lim_{x \to -1^-} \dfrac{x^2 - 2}{(x - 2)(x + 1)} = -\infty$

So, $x = -1$ is a vertical asymptote.

**20.** $\lim_{x\to 0^-} \dfrac{2+x}{x^2(1-x)} = \infty = \lim_{x\to 0^+} \dfrac{2+x}{x^2(1-x)}$

So, $x = 0$ is a vertical asymptote.

$\lim_{x\to 1^-} \dfrac{2+x}{x^2(1-x)} = \infty$

$\lim_{x\to 1^+} \dfrac{2+x}{x^2(1-x)} = -\infty$

So, $x = 1$ is a vertical asymptote.

**21.** $\lim_{t\to 0^+}\left(1 - \dfrac{4}{t^2}\right) = -\infty = \lim_{t\to 0^-}\left(1 - \dfrac{4}{t^2}\right)$

So, $t = 0$ is a vertical asymptote.

**22.** $g(x) = \dfrac{(1/2)x^3 - x^2 - 4x}{3x^2 - 6x - 24} = \dfrac{1}{6}\dfrac{x(x^2 - 2x - 8)}{x^2 - 2x - 8}$

$= \dfrac{1}{6}x, \quad x \neq -2, 4$

No vertical asymptote. The graph has holes at $x = -2$ and $x = 4$.

**23.** $f(x) = \dfrac{3}{x^2 + x - 2} = \dfrac{3}{(x+2)(x-1)}$

Vertical asymptotes at $x = -2$ and $x = 1$.

**24.** $f(x) = \dfrac{3x^2 - 12x + 9}{-x^4 + 3x^3 + x - 3}$

$= \dfrac{3(x^2 - 4x + 3)}{-x^3(x-3) + (x-3)}$

$= \dfrac{3(x-3)(x-1)}{-(x-3)(x^3-1)}$

$= \dfrac{3(x-3)(x-1)}{-(x-3)(x-1)(x^2+x+1)}$

$= \dfrac{-3}{x^2 + x + 1}, \quad x \neq 1, 3$

No vertical asymptote. The graph has holes at $x = 1$ and $x = 3$.

**25.** $f(x) = \dfrac{x^3 + 1}{x + 1} = \dfrac{(x+1)(x^2 - x + 1)}{x + 1}$

No vertical asymptote because

$\lim_{x\to -1} f(x) = \lim_{x\to -1}(x^2 - x + 1) = 3.$

The graph has a hole at $x = -1$.

**26.** $h(x) = \dfrac{x^2 - 4}{x^3 - 2x^2 + x - 2} = \dfrac{(x+2)(x-2)}{(x-2)(x^2+1)}$

No vertical asymptote because

$\lim_{x\to 2} h(x) = \lim_{x\to 2}\dfrac{x+2}{x^2+1} = \dfrac{4}{5}.$

The graph has a hole at $x = 2$.

**27.** $f(x) = \dfrac{e^{-2x}}{x - 1}$

$x = 1$ is a vertical asymptote.

**28.** $g(x) = xe^{-2x}$

No vertical asymptote.

**29.** $h(t) = \dfrac{\ln(t^2 + 1)}{t + 2}$

$t = -2$ is a vertical asymptote.

**30.** $f(z) = \ln(z^2 - 4) = \ln(z - 2) + \ln(z + 2)$

$z = \pm 2$ are vertical asymptotes.

**31.** $f(x) = \dfrac{1}{e^x - 1}$

$x = 0$ is a vertical asymptote.

**32.** $f(x) = \ln(x + 3)$

$x = -3$ is a vertical asymptote.

**33.** $f(x) = \tan \pi x = \dfrac{\sin \pi x}{\cos \pi x}$ has vertical asymptotes at

$x = \dfrac{2n+1}{2}$, $n$ any integer.

**34.** $f(x) = \sec \pi x = \dfrac{1}{\cos \pi x}$ has vertical asymptotes at

$x = \dfrac{2n+1}{2}$, $n$ any integer.

**35.** $s(t) = \dfrac{t}{\sin t}$ has vertical asymptotes at $t = n\pi$, $n$ a nonzero integer. There is no vertical asymptote at $t = 0$ because

$\lim_{t\to 0}\dfrac{t}{\sin t} = 1.$

**36.** $g(\theta) = \dfrac{\tan\theta}{\theta} = \dfrac{\sin\theta}{\theta\cos\theta}$ has vertical asymptotes at

$\theta = \dfrac{(2n+1)\pi}{2} = \dfrac{\pi}{2} + n\pi$, $n$ any interger.

There is no vertical asymptote at $\theta = 0$ because

$\lim\limits_{\theta\to 0}\dfrac{\tan\theta}{\theta} = 1.$

**37.** $\lim\limits_{x\to -1}\dfrac{x^2-1}{x+1} = \lim\limits_{x\to -1}(x-1) = -2$

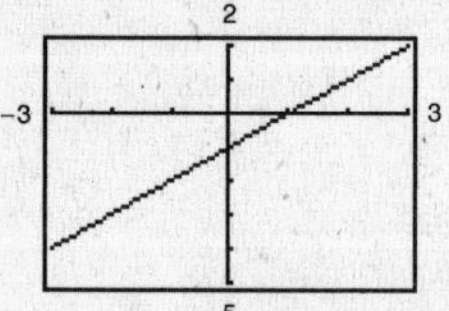

Removable discontinuity at $x = -1$

**38.** $\lim\limits_{x\to -1}\dfrac{x^2-6x-7}{x+1} = \lim\limits_{x\to -1}(x-7) = -8$

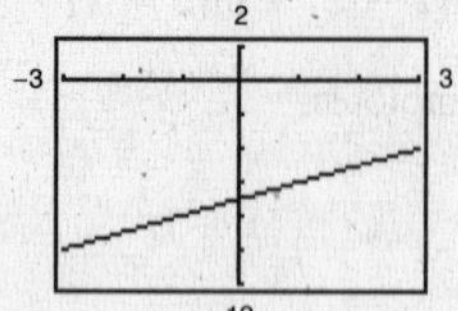

Removable discontinuity at $x = -1$

**39.** $\lim\limits_{x\to -1^+}\dfrac{x^2+1}{x+1} = \infty$

$\lim\limits_{x\to -1^-}\dfrac{x^2+1}{x+1} = -\infty$

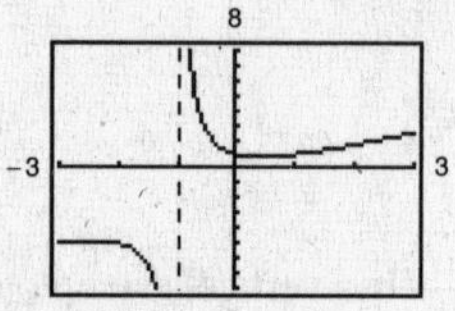

Vertical asymptote at $x = -1$

**40.** $\lim\limits_{x\to -1}\dfrac{\sin(x+1)}{x+1} = 1$

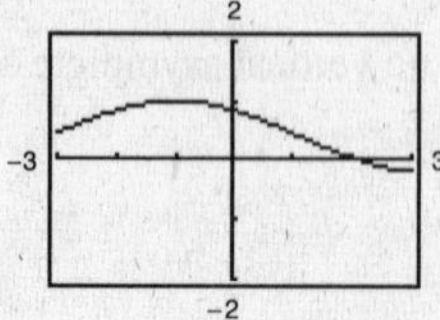

Removable discontinuity at $x = -1$

**41.** $f(x) = \dfrac{e^{2(x+1)}-1}{e^{x+1}-1}$

$= \dfrac{(e^{x+1}-1)(e^{x+1}+1)}{e^{x+1}-1} = e^{x+1}, \quad x \neq -1$

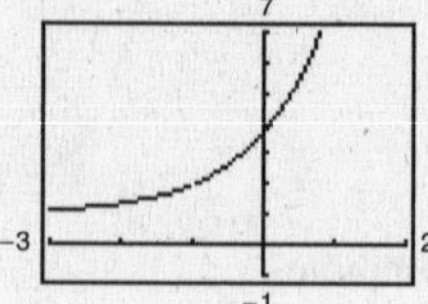

Removable discontinuity at $x = -1$

**42.** $f(x) = \dfrac{\ln(x^2+1)}{x+1}$

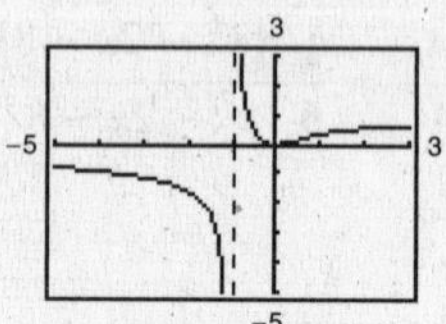

Vertical asymptote at $x = -1$

**43.** $\lim\limits_{x\to -1^+}\dfrac{1}{x+1} = \infty$

**44.** $\lim\limits_{x\to 1^-}\dfrac{-1}{(x-1)^2} = -\infty$

**45.** $\lim\limits_{x\to 2^+}\dfrac{x}{x-2} = \infty$

**46.** $\lim\limits_{x\to 1^+}\dfrac{x(2+x)}{1-x} = -\infty$

**47.** $\lim\limits_{x\to 1^+}\dfrac{x^2}{(x-1)^2} = \infty$

**48.** $\lim\limits_{x\to 4^-}\dfrac{x^2}{x^2+16} = \dfrac{1}{2}$

**49.** $\lim\limits_{x\to -3^-}\dfrac{x+3}{(x^2+x-6)} = \lim\limits_{x\to -3^-}\dfrac{x+3}{(x+3)(x-2)}$

$= \lim\limits_{x\to -3^-}\dfrac{1}{x-2} = -\dfrac{1}{5}$

**50.** $\lim\limits_{x\to -(1/2)^+}\dfrac{6x^2+x-1}{4x^2-4x-3} = \lim\limits_{x\to -(1/2)^+}\dfrac{(3x-1)(2x+1)}{(2x-3)(2x+1)}$

$= \lim\limits_{x\to -(1/2)^+}\dfrac{3x-1}{2x-3} = \dfrac{5}{8}$

**51.** $\lim\limits_{x\to 1}\dfrac{x-1}{(x^2+1)(x-1)} = \lim\limits_{x\to 1}\dfrac{1}{x^2+1} = \dfrac{1}{2}$

**52.** $\lim_{x\to 3} \dfrac{x-2}{x^2} = \dfrac{1}{9}$

**53.** $\lim_{x\to 0^-} \left(1 + \dfrac{1}{x}\right) = -\infty$

**54.** $\lim_{x\to 0^-} \left(x^2 - \dfrac{2}{x}\right) = \infty$

**55.** $\lim_{x\to 0^+} \dfrac{2}{\sin x} = \infty$

**56.** $\lim_{x\to(\pi/2)^+} \dfrac{-2}{\cos x} = \infty$

**57.** $\lim_{x\to 8^-} \dfrac{e^x}{(x-8)^3} = -\infty$

**58.** $\lim_{x\to 4^+} \ln(x^2 - 16) = -\infty$

**59.** $\lim_{x\to(\pi/2)^-} \ln|\cos x| = \ln\left|\cos\dfrac{\pi}{2}\right| = \ln 0 = -\infty$

**60.** $\lim_{x\to 0^+} e^{-0.5x} \sin x = 1(0) = 0$

**61.** $\lim_{x\to(1/2)^-} x\sec(\pi x) = \infty$ and $\lim_{x\to(1/2)^+} x\sec(\pi x) = -\infty$.

So, $\lim_{x\to(1/2)} x\sec(\pi x)$ does not exist.

**62.** $\lim_{x\to(1/2)^-} x^2 \tan \pi x = \infty$ and $\lim_{x\to(1/2)^+} x^2 \tan \pi x = -\infty$.

So, $\lim_{x\to(1/2)} x^2 \tan \pi x$ does not exist.

**63.** $f(x) = \dfrac{x^2 + x + 1}{x^3 - 1} = \dfrac{x^2 + x + 1}{(x-1)(x^2 + x + 1)}$

$\lim_{x\to 1^+} f(x) = \lim_{x\to 1^+} \dfrac{1}{x-1} = \infty$

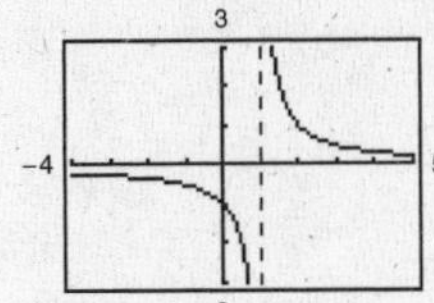


**64.** $f(x) = \dfrac{x^3 - 1}{x^2 + x + 1} = \dfrac{(x-1)(x^2 + x + 1)}{x^2 + x + 1}$

$\lim_{x\to 1^-} f(x) = \lim_{x\to 1^-} (x - 1) = 0$

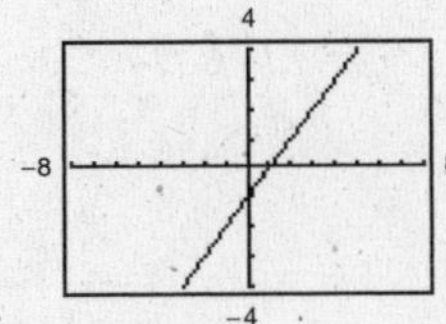


**65.** $f(x) = \dfrac{1}{x^2 - 25}$

$\lim_{x\to 5^-} f(x) = -\infty$

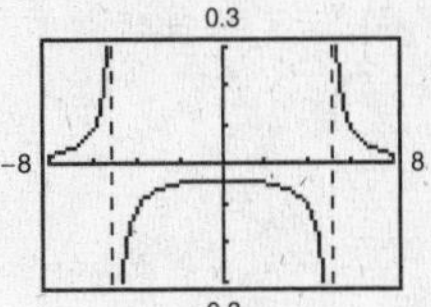


**66.** $f(x) = \sec\dfrac{\pi x}{8}$

$\lim_{x\to 4^+} f(x) = -\infty$

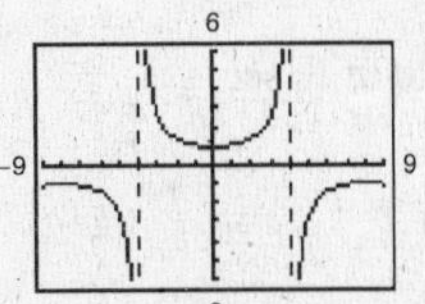


**67.** A limit in which $f(x)$ increases or decreases without bound as $x$ approaches $c$ is called an infinite limit. $\infty$ is not a number. Rather, the symbol

$\lim_{x\to c} f(x) = \infty$

says how the limit fails to exist.

**68.** The line $x = c$ is a vertical asymptote if the graph of $f$ approaches $\pm\infty$ as $x$ approaches $c$.

**69.** One answer is

$f(x) = \dfrac{x-3}{(x-6)(x+2)} = \dfrac{x-3}{x^2 - 4x - 12}$.

**70.** No. For example, $f(x) = \dfrac{1}{x^2 + 1}$ has no vertical asymptote.

**71.**

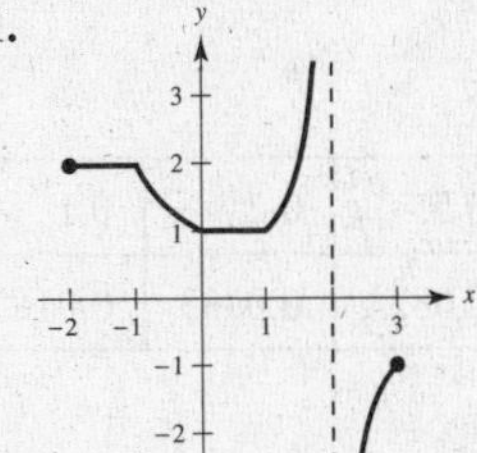


**72.** No, it is not true. Consider $p(x) = x^2 - 1$. The function

$f(x) = \dfrac{x^2 - 1}{x - 1} = \dfrac{p(x)}{x - 1}$

has a hole at $(1, 2)$, not a vertical asymptote.

**73.** $m = \dfrac{m_0}{\sqrt{1 - (v^2/c^2)}}$

$$\lim_{v \to c^-} m = \lim_{v \to c^-} \frac{m_0}{\sqrt{1 - (v^2/c^2)}} = \infty$$

**74.** $P = \dfrac{k}{V}$

$$\lim_{V \to 0^+} \frac{k}{V} = k(\infty) = \infty$$

(In this case you know that $k > 0$.)

**75.** (a) $r = 50\pi \sec^2 \dfrac{\pi}{6} = \dfrac{200\pi}{3}$ ft/sec

(b) $r = 50\pi \sec^2 \dfrac{\pi}{3} = 200\pi$ ft/sec

(c) $\displaystyle\lim_{\theta \to (\pi/2)^-} \left[50\pi \sec^2 \theta\right] = \infty$

**76.** (a) $r = \dfrac{2(7)}{\sqrt{625 - 49}} = \dfrac{7}{12}$ ft/sec

(b) $r = \dfrac{2(15)}{\sqrt{625 - 225}} = \dfrac{3}{2}$ ft/sec

(c) $\displaystyle\lim_{x \to 25^-} \frac{2x}{\sqrt{625 - x^2}} = \infty$

**77.** (a) Average speed $= \dfrac{\text{Total distance}}{\text{Total time}}$

$$50 = \frac{2d}{(d/x) + (d/y)}$$

$$50 = \frac{2xy}{y + x}$$

$$50y + 50x = 2xy$$

$$50x = 2xy - 50y$$

$$50x = 2y(x - 25)$$

$$\frac{25x}{x - 25} = y$$

Domain: $x > 25$

(b)

| $x$ | 30 | 40 | 50 | 60 |
|---|---|---|---|---|
| $y$ | 150 | 66.667 | 50 | 42.857 |

(c) $\displaystyle\lim_{x \to 25^+} \frac{25x}{\sqrt{x - 25}} = \infty$

As $x$ gets close to 25 mi/h, $y$ becomes larger and larger.

**78.** (a)

| $x$ | 1 | 0.5 | 0.2 | 0.1 | 0.01 | 0.001 | 0.0001 |
|---|---|---|---|---|---|---|---|
| $f(x)$ | 0.1585 | 0.0411 | 0.0067 | 0.0017 | $\approx 0$ | $\approx 0$ | $\approx 0$ |

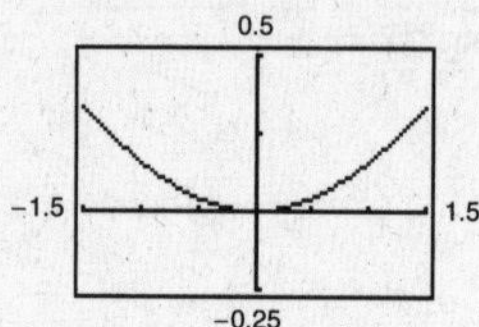


$$\lim_{x \to 0^+} \frac{x - \sin x}{x} = 0$$

(b)

| $x$ | 1 | 0.5 | 0.2 | 0.1 | 0.01 | 0.001 | 0.0001 |
|---|---|---|---|---|---|---|---|
| $f(x)$ | 0.1585 | 0.0823 | 0.0333 | 0.0167 | 0.0017 | $\approx 0$ | $\approx 0$ |

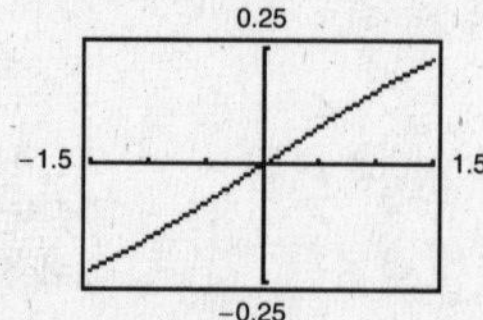


$$\lim_{x \to 0^+} \frac{x - \sin x}{x^2} = 0$$

(c)

| $x$ | 1 | 0.5 | 0.2 | 0.1 | 0.01 | 0.001 | 0.0001 |
|---|---|---|---|---|---|---|---|
| $f(x)$ | 0.1585 | 0.1646 | 0.1663 | 0.1666 | 0.1667 | 0.1667 | 0.1667 |

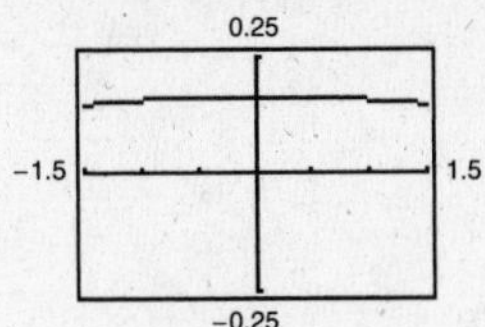


$$\lim_{x\to 0^+} \frac{x - \sin x}{x^3} = 0.1667 \ (= 1/6)$$

(d)

| $x$ | 1 | 0.5 | 0.2 | 0.1 | 0.01 | 0.001 | 0.0001 |
|---|---|---|---|---|---|---|---|
| $f(x)$ | 0.1585 | 0.3292 | 0.8317 | 1.6658 | 16.67 | 166.7 | 1667.0 |

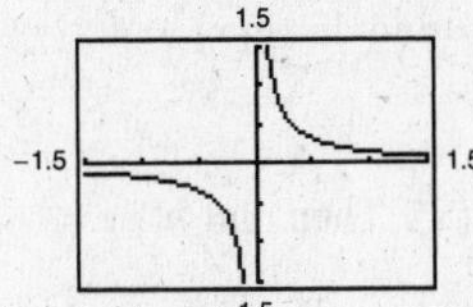


$$\lim_{x\to 0^+} \frac{x - \sin x}{x^4} = \infty$$

For $n > 3$, $\lim_{x\to 0^+} \dfrac{x - \sin x}{x^n} = \infty$.

**79.** (a) $A = \dfrac{1}{2}bh - \dfrac{1}{2}r^2\theta = \dfrac{1}{2}(10)(10 \tan \theta) - \dfrac{1}{2}(10)^2\theta = 50 \tan \theta - 50\theta$

Domain: $\left(0, \dfrac{\pi}{2}\right)$

(b)

| $\theta$ | 0.3 | 0.6 | 0.9 | 1.2 | 1.5 |
|---|---|---|---|---|---|
| $f(\theta)$ | 0.47 | 4.21 | 18.0 | 68.6 | 630.1 |

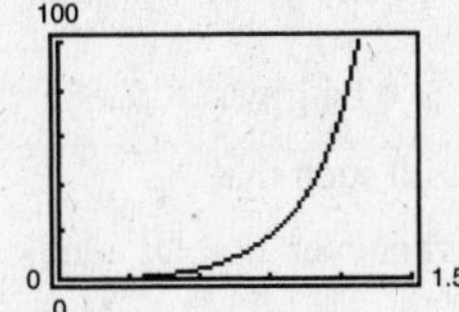


(c) $\lim_{\theta\to \pi/2^-} A = \infty$

**80.** (a) Because the circumference of the motor is half that of the saw arbor, the saw makes $1700/2 = 850$ revolutions per minute.

(b) The direction of rotation is reversed.

(c) $2(20 \cot \phi) + 2(10 \cot \phi)$: straight sections. The angle subtended in each circle is $2\pi - \left(2\left(\dfrac{\pi}{2} - \phi\right)\right) = \pi + 2\phi$.

So, the length of the belt around the pulleys is $20(\pi + 2\phi) + 10(\pi + 2\phi) = 30(\pi + 2\phi)$.

Total length $= 60 \cot \phi + 30(\pi + 2\phi)$

Domain: $\left(0, \dfrac{\pi}{2}\right)$

(d)

| $\phi$ | 0.3 | 0.6 | 0.9 | 1.2 | 1.5 |
|---|---|---|---|---|---|
| $L$ | 306.2 | 217.9 | 195.9 | 189.6 | 188.5 |

(e)

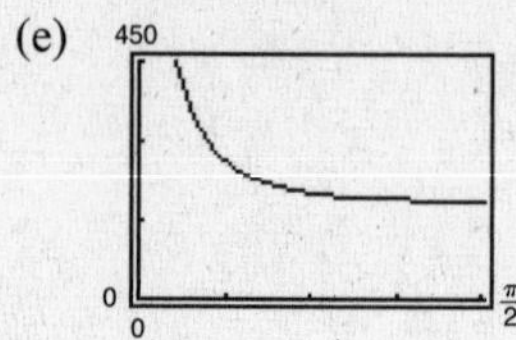


(f) $\lim_{\phi\to(\pi/2)^-} L = 60\pi \approx 188.5$

(All the belts are around pulleys.)

(g) $\lim_{\phi\to 0^+} L = \infty$

**81.** False. For instance, let

$$f(x) = \frac{x^2 - 1}{x - 1} \text{ or}$$

$$g(x) = \frac{x}{x^2 + 1}.$$

**82.** True

**83.** False. The graphs of $y = \tan x$, $y = \cot x$, $y = \sec x$ and $y = \csc x$ have vertical asymptotes.

**84.** False. Let

$$f(x) = \begin{cases} \frac{1}{x}, & x \neq 0 \\ 3, & x = 0. \end{cases}$$

The graph of $f$ has a vertical asymptote at $x = 0$, but $f(0) = 3$.

**85.** Let $f(x) = \frac{1}{x^2}$ and $g(x) = \frac{1}{x^4}$, and $c = 0$.

$$\lim_{x\to 0}\frac{1}{x^2} = \infty \text{ and } \lim_{x\to 0}\frac{1}{x^4} = \infty, \text{ but}$$

$$\lim_{x\to 0}\left(\frac{1}{x^2} - \frac{1}{x^4}\right) = \lim_{x\to 0}\left(\frac{x^2 - 1}{x^4}\right) = -\infty \neq 0.$$

**86.** Given $\lim_{x\to c} f(x) = \infty$ and $\lim_{x\to c} g(x) = L$:

(1) Difference:

Let $h(x) = -g(x)$. Then $\lim_{x\to c} h(x) = -L$, and

$$\lim_{x\to c}\left[f(x) - g(x)\right] = \lim_{x\to c}\left[f(x) + h(x)\right]$$
$$= \infty, \text{ by the Sum Property.}$$

(2) Product:

If $L > 0$, then for $\varepsilon = L/2 > 0$ there exists $\delta_1 > 0$ such that $|g(x) - L| < L/2$ whenever $0 < |x - c| < \delta_1$. So, $L/2 < g(x) < 3L/2$. Because $\lim_{x\to c} f(x) = \infty$ then for $M > 0$, there exists $\delta_2 > 0$ such that $f(x) > M(2/L)$ whenever $|x - c| < \delta_2$. Let $\delta$ be the smaller of $\delta_1$ and $\delta_2$. Then for $0 < |x - c| < \delta$, you have $f(x)g(x) > M(2/L)(L/2) = M$. So $\lim_{x\to c} f(x)g(x) = \infty$. The proof is similar for $L < 0$.

(3) Quotient: Let $\varepsilon > 0$ be given.

There exists $\delta_1 > 0$ such that $f(x) > 3L/2\varepsilon$ whenever $0 < |x - c| < \delta_1$ and there exists $\delta_2 > 0$ such that $|g(x) - L| < L/2$ whenever $0 < |x - c| < \delta_2$. This inequality gives us $L/2 < g(x) < 3L/2$. Let $\delta$ be the smaller of $\delta_1$ and $\delta_2$. Then for $0 < |x - c| < \delta$, you have

$$\left|\frac{g(x)}{f(x)}\right| < \frac{3L/2}{3L/2\varepsilon} = \varepsilon.$$

So, $\lim_{x\to c}\frac{g(x)}{f(x)} = 0$.

**87.** Given $\lim_{x\to c} f(x) = \infty$, let $g(x) = 1$. Then

$\lim_{x\to c}\frac{g(x)}{f(x)} = 0$ by Theorem 2.15.

**88.** Given $\lim_{x\to c}\frac{1}{f(x)} = 0$. Suppose $\lim_{x\to c} f(x)$ exists and equals $L$.

Then, $\lim_{x\to c}\frac{1}{f(x)} = \frac{\lim_{x\to c} 1}{\lim_{x\to c} f(x)} = \frac{1}{L} = 0.$

This is not possible. So, $\lim_{x\to c} f(x)$ does not exist.

**89.** $f(x) = \frac{1}{x-3}$ is defined for all $x > 3$. Let $M > 0$ be given. You need $\delta > 0$ such that

$f(x) = \frac{1}{x-3} > M$ whenever $3 < x < 3 + \delta$.

Equivalently, $x - 3 < \frac{1}{M}$ whenever

$|x - 3| < \delta, x > 3$.

So take $\delta = \frac{1}{M}$. Then for $x > 3$ and

$|x - 3| < \delta, \frac{1}{x-3} > \frac{1}{8} = M$ and so $f(x) > M$.

**90.** $f(x) = \frac{1}{x-5}$ is defined for all $x < 5$. Let $N < 0$ be given. You need $\delta > 0$ such that $f(x) = \frac{1}{x-5} < N$ whenever $5 - \delta < x < 5$. Equivalently, $x - 5 > \frac{1}{N}$ whenever $|x - 5| < \delta, x < 5$. Equivalently, $\frac{1}{|x-5|} < -\frac{1}{N}$ whenever $|x - 5| < \delta, x < 5$. So take $\delta = -\frac{1}{N}$. Note that $\delta > 0$ because $N < 0$. For $|x - 5| < \delta$ and $x < 5, \frac{1}{|x-5|} > \frac{1}{\delta} = -N$, and $\frac{1}{x-5} = -\frac{1}{|x-5|} < N$.

## Review Exercises for Chapter 2

**1.** Calculus required. Using a graphing utility, you can estimate the length to be 8.3. Or, the length is slightly longer than the distance between the two points, approximately 8.25.

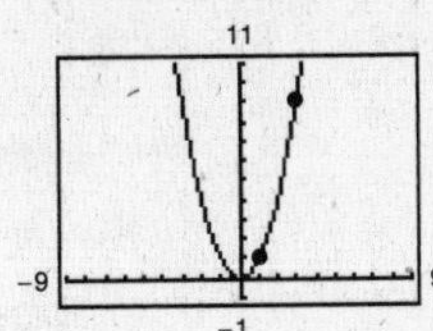


**2.** Precalculus. $L = \sqrt{(9-1)^2 + (3-1)^2} \approx 8.25$

**3.** $f(x) = \dfrac{\frac{4}{x+2} - 2}{x}$

| $x$ | $-0.1$ | $-0.01$ | $-0.001$ | $0.001$ | $0.01$ | $0.1$ |
|---|---|---|---|---|---|---|
| $f(x)$ | $-1.0526$ | $-1.0050$ | $-1.0005$ | $-0.9995$ | $-0.9950$ | $-0.9524$ |

$\lim_{x\to 0} f(x) \approx -1.0$

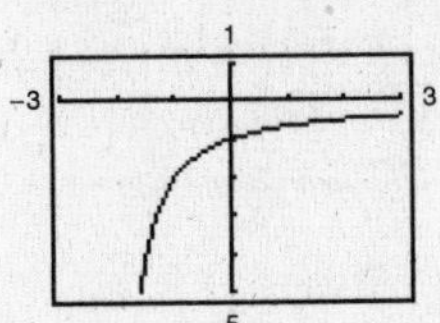

**4.**

| $x$ | –0.1 | –0.01 | –0.001 | 0.001 | 0.01 | 0.1 |
|---|---|---|---|---|---|---|
| $f(x)$ | 1.432 | 1.416 | 1.414 | 1.414 | 1.413 | 1.397 |

$\lim_{x\to 0} f(x) \approx 1.414$

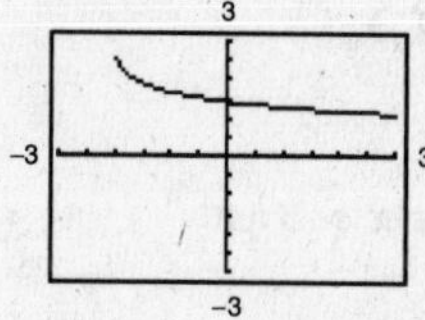

**5.**

| $x$ | –0.1 | –0.01 | –0.001 | 0.001 | 0.01 | 0.1 |
|---|---|---|---|---|---|---|
| $f(x)$ | 0.8867 | 0.0988 | 0.0100 | –0.0100 | –0.1013 | –1.1394 |

$\lim_{x\to 0} f(x) = 0$

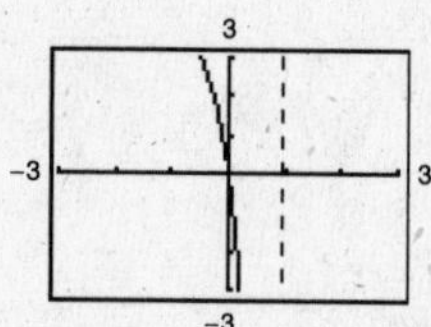

**6.**

| $x$ | –0.1 | –0.01 | –0.001 | 0.001 | 0.01 | 0.1 |
|---|---|---|---|---|---|---|
| $f(x)$ | 0.202 | 0.2 | 0.2 | 0.2 | 0.2 | 0.198 |

$\lim_{x\to 0} f(x) \approx 0.2$

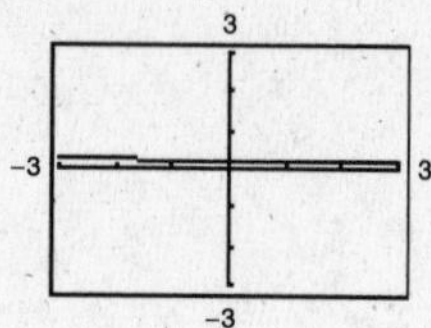

**7.** $h(x) = \dfrac{4x - x^2}{x} = \dfrac{x(4 - x)}{x} = 4 - x, x \neq 0$

(a) $\lim_{x\to 0} h(x) = 4 - 0 = 4$

(b) $\lim_{x\to -1} h(x) = 4 - (-1) = 5$

**8.** $g(x) = \dfrac{-2x}{x - 3}$

(a) $\lim_{x\to 3} g(x)$ does not exist.

(b) $\lim_{x\to 0} g(x) = \dfrac{-2(0)}{0 - 3} = 0$

**9.** $f(t) = \dfrac{\ln(t + 2)}{t}$

(a) $\lim_{t\to 0} f(t)$ does not exist.

(b) $\lim_{t\to -1} f(t) = 0$

**10.** $g(x) = e^{-x/2} \sin \pi x$

(a) $\lim_{x\to 0} g(x) = 0$

(b) $\lim_{x\to 2} g(x) = 0$

**11.** $\lim_{x\to 1}(x + 4) = 1 + 4 = 5$

Let $\varepsilon > 0$ be given. Choose $\delta = \varepsilon$. Then for $0 < |x - 1| < \delta = \varepsilon$, you have

$$|x - 1| < \varepsilon$$
$$|(x + 4) - 5| < \varepsilon$$
$$|f(x) - L| < \varepsilon.$$

**12.** $\lim_{x\to 9}\sqrt{x} = \sqrt{9} = 3$

Let $\varepsilon > 0$ be given. You need

$$\left|\sqrt{x} - 3\right| < \varepsilon \Rightarrow \left|\sqrt{x} + 3\right|\left|\sqrt{x} - 3\right| < \varepsilon\left|\sqrt{x} + 3\right| \Rightarrow |x - 9| < \varepsilon\left|\sqrt{x} + 3\right|.$$

Assuming $4 < x < 16$, you can choose $\delta = 5\varepsilon$.

So, for $0 < |x - 9| < \delta = 5\varepsilon$, you have

$$|x - 9| < 5\varepsilon < \left|\sqrt{x} + 3\right|\varepsilon$$
$$\left|\sqrt{x} - 3\right| < \varepsilon$$
$$|f(x) - L| < \varepsilon.$$

**13.** $\lim_{x\to 2}(1 - x^2) = 1 - 2^2 = -3$

Let $\varepsilon > 0$ be given. You need

$$\left|1 - x^2 - (-3)\right| < \varepsilon \Rightarrow \left|x^2 - 4\right| = |x - 2||x + 2| < \varepsilon \Rightarrow |x - 2| < \frac{1}{|x + 2|}\varepsilon.$$

Assuming $1 < x < 3$, you can choose $\delta = \dfrac{\varepsilon}{5}$.

So, for $0 < |x - 2| < \delta = \dfrac{\varepsilon}{5}$, you have

$$|x - 2| < \frac{\varepsilon}{5} < \frac{\varepsilon}{|x + 2|}$$
$$|x - 2||x + 2| < \varepsilon$$
$$\left|x^2 - 4\right| < \varepsilon$$
$$\left|4 - x^2\right| < \varepsilon$$
$$\left|(1 - x^2) - (-3)\right| < \varepsilon$$
$$|f(x) - L| < \varepsilon.$$

**14.** $\lim_{x\to 5} 9 = 9$. Let $\varepsilon > 0$ be given. $\delta$ can be any positive number. So, for $0 < |x - 5| < \delta$, you have

$$|9 - 9| < \varepsilon$$
$$|f(x) - L| < \varepsilon.$$

**15.** $\lim_{x\to 6}(x - 2)^2 = (6 - 2)^2 = 16$

**16.** $\lim_{x\to 7}(10 - x)^4 = (10 - 7)^4 = 3^4 = 81$

**17.** $\lim_{t\to 4}\sqrt{t + 2} = \sqrt{4 + 2} = \sqrt{6} \approx 2.45$

**18.** $\lim_{y\to 4} 3|y - 1| = 3|4 - 1| = 9$

**19.** $\lim_{t\to -2}\dfrac{t + 2}{t^2 - 4} = \lim_{t\to -2}\dfrac{1}{t - 2} = -\dfrac{1}{4}$

**20.** $\lim_{t\to 3}\dfrac{t^2 - 9}{t - 3} = \lim_{t\to 3}(t + 3) = 6$

**21.** $\lim_{x\to4}\frac{\sqrt{x-3}-1}{x-4} = \lim_{x\to4}\frac{\sqrt{x-3}-1}{x-4}\cdot\frac{\sqrt{x-3}+1}{\sqrt{x-3}+1} = \lim_{x\to4}\frac{(x-3)-1}{(x-4)\left(\sqrt{x-3}+1\right)} = \lim_{x\to4}\frac{1}{\sqrt{x-3}+1} = \frac{1}{2}$

**22.** $\lim_{x\to0}\frac{\sqrt{4+x}-2}{x} = \lim_{x\to0}\frac{\sqrt{4+x}-2}{x}\cdot\frac{\sqrt{4+x}+2}{\sqrt{4+x}+2} = \lim_{x\to0}\frac{1}{\sqrt{4+x}+2} = \frac{1}{4}$

**23.** $\lim_{x\to0}\frac{\left[1/(x+1)\right]-1}{x} = \lim_{x\to0}\frac{1-(x+1)}{x(x+1)} = \lim_{x\to0}\frac{-1}{x+1} = -1$

**24.** $\lim_{s\to0}\frac{\left(1/\sqrt{1+s}\right)-1}{s} = \lim_{s\to0}\left[\frac{\left(1/\sqrt{1+s}\right)-1}{s}\cdot\frac{\left(1/\sqrt{1+s}\right)+1}{\left(1/\sqrt{1+s}\right)+1}\right]$

$= \lim_{s\to0}\frac{\left[1/(1+s)\right]-1}{s\left[\left(1/\sqrt{1+s}\right)+1\right]} = \lim_{s\to0}\frac{-1}{(1+s)\left[\left(1/\sqrt{1+s}\right)+1\right]} = -\frac{1}{2}$

**25.** $\lim_{x\to-5}\frac{x^3+125}{x+5} = \lim_{x\to-5}\frac{(x+5)(x^2-5x+25)}{x+5}$

$= \lim_{x\to-5}\left(x^2-5x+25\right) = 75$

**26.** $\lim_{x\to-2}\frac{x^2-4}{x^3+8} = \lim_{x\to-2}\frac{(x+2)(x-2)}{(x+2)(x^2-2x+4)}$

$= \lim_{x\to-2}\frac{x-2}{x^2-2x+4} = -\frac{4}{12} = -\frac{1}{3}$

**27.** $\lim_{x\to0}\frac{1-\cos x}{\sin x} = \lim_{x\to0}\left(\frac{x}{\sin x}\right)\left(\frac{1-\cos x}{x}\right) = (1)(0) = 0$

**28.** $\lim_{x\to(\pi/4)}\frac{4x}{\tan x} = \frac{4(\pi/4)}{1} = \pi$

**29.** $\lim_{x\to1} e^{x-1}\sin\frac{\pi x}{2} = e^0\sin\frac{\pi}{2} = 1$

**30.** $\lim_{x\to2}\frac{\ln(x-1)^2}{\ln(x-1)} = \lim_{x\to2}\frac{2\ln(x-1)}{\ln(x-1)} = \lim_{x\to2} 2 = 2$

**31.** $\lim_{\Delta x\to0}\frac{\sin\left[(\pi/6)+\Delta x\right]-(1/2)}{\Delta x} = \lim_{\Delta x\to0}\frac{\sin(\pi/6)\cos\Delta x+\cos(\pi/6)\sin\Delta x-(1/2)}{\Delta x}$

$= \lim_{\Delta x\to0}\frac{1}{2}\cdot\frac{(\cos\Delta x-1)}{\Delta x} + \lim_{\Delta x\to0}\frac{\sqrt{3}}{2}\cdot\frac{\sin\Delta x}{\Delta x}$

$= 0 + \frac{\sqrt{3}}{2}(1)$

$= \frac{\sqrt{3}}{2}$

**32.** $\lim_{\Delta x\to0}\frac{\cos(\pi+\Delta x)+1}{\Delta x} = \lim_{\Delta x\to0}\frac{\cos\pi\cos\Delta x-\sin\pi\sin\Delta x+1}{\Delta x}$

$= \lim_{\Delta x\to0}\left[-\frac{(\cos\Delta x-1)}{\Delta x}\right] - \lim_{\Delta x\to0}\left[\sin\pi\frac{\sin\Delta x}{\Delta x}\right]$

$= -0-(0)(1)$

$= 0$

**33.** $\lim_{x\to c}\left[f(x)\cdot g(x)\right] = \left(-\frac{3}{4}\right)\left(\frac{2}{3}\right) = -\frac{1}{2}$

**34.** $\lim_{x\to c}\frac{f(x)}{g(x)} = \frac{\lim_{x\to c}f(x)}{\lim_{x\to c}g(x)} = \frac{-3/4}{2/3} = -\frac{9}{8}$

**35.** $\lim_{x\to c}\left[f(x)+2g(x)\right] = -\frac{3}{4}+2\left(\frac{2}{3}\right) = \frac{7}{12}$

**36.** $\lim_{x\to c}\left[f(x)\right]^2 = \left[\lim_{x\to c}f(x)\right]^2 = \left(-\frac{3}{4}\right)^2 = \frac{9}{16}$

**37.** $f(x) = \dfrac{\sqrt{2x+1} - \sqrt{3}}{x - 1}$

(a)

| $x$ | 1.1 | 1.01 | 1.001 | 1.0001 |
|---|---|---|---|---|
| $f(x)$ | 0.5680 | 0.5764 | 0.5773 | 0.5773 |

$\lim_{x \to 1^+} \dfrac{\sqrt{2x+1} - \sqrt{3}}{x - 1} \approx 0.577$ $\left(\text{Actual limit is } \sqrt{3}/3.\right)$

(b)

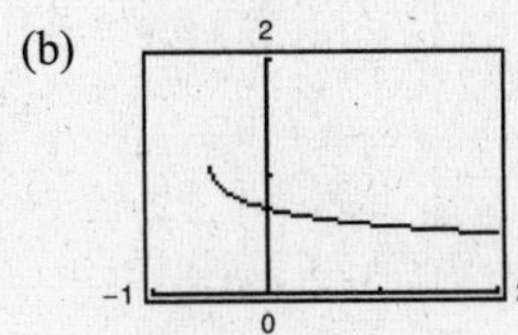


The graph has a hole at $x = 1$.

$\lim_{x \to 1^+} f(x) \approx 0.5774.$

(c)
$$\lim_{x \to 1^+} \frac{\sqrt{2x+1} - \sqrt{3}}{x - 1} = \lim_{x \to 1^+} \frac{\sqrt{2x+1} - \sqrt{3}}{x - 1} \cdot \frac{\sqrt{2x+1} + \sqrt{3}}{\sqrt{2x+1} + \sqrt{3}}$$
$$= \lim_{x \to 1^+} \frac{(2x+1) - 3}{(x-1)\left(\sqrt{2x+1} + \sqrt{3}\right)}$$
$$= \lim_{x \to 1^+} \frac{2}{\sqrt{2x+1} + \sqrt{3}}$$
$$= \frac{2}{2\sqrt{3}} = \frac{1}{\sqrt{3}} = \frac{\sqrt{3}}{3}$$

**38.** $f(x) = \dfrac{1 - \sqrt[3]{x}}{x - 1}$

(a)

| $x$ | 1.1 | 1.01 | 1.001 | 1.0001 |
|---|---|---|---|---|
| $f(x)$ | −0.3228 | −0.3322 | −0.3332 | −0.3333 |

$\lim_{x \to 1^+} \dfrac{1 - \sqrt[3]{x}}{x - 1} \approx -0.333$ $\left(\text{Actual limit is } -\dfrac{1}{3}.\right)$

(b)

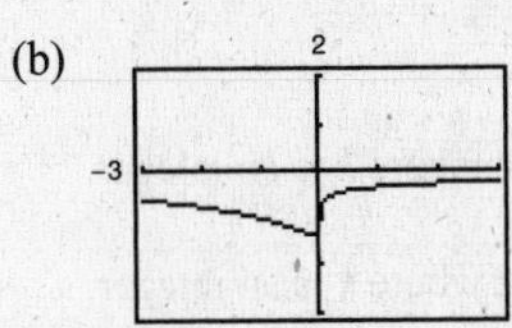


The graph has a hole at $x = 1$.

$\lim_{x \to 1^+} f(x) \approx 0.333.$

(c)
$$\lim_{x \to 1^+} \frac{1 - \sqrt[3]{x}}{x - 1} = \lim_{x \to 1^+} \frac{1 - \sqrt[3]{x}}{x - 1} \cdot \frac{1 + \sqrt[3]{x} + \left(\sqrt[3]{x}\right)^2}{1 + \sqrt[3]{x} + \left(\sqrt[3]{x}\right)^2}$$
$$= \lim_{x \to 1^+} \frac{1 - x}{(x-1)\left[1 + \sqrt[3]{x} + \left(\sqrt[3]{x}\right)^2\right]}$$
$$= \lim_{x \to 1^+} \frac{-1}{1 + \sqrt[3]{x} + \left(\sqrt[3]{x}\right)^2} = -\frac{1}{3}$$

**39.** $v = \lim_{t\to 4}\dfrac{s(4) - s(t)}{4 - t}$

$= \lim_{t\to 4}\dfrac{\left[-4.9(16) + 250\right] - \left[-4.9t^2 + 250\right]}{4 - t}$

$= \lim_{t\to 4}\dfrac{4.9\left(t^2 - 16\right)}{4 - t}$

$= \lim_{t\to 4}\dfrac{4.9(t - 4)(t + 4)}{4 - t}$

$= \lim_{t\to 4}\left[-4.9(t + 4)\right] = -39.2$ m/sec

The object is falling at about 39.2 m/sec.

**40.** $-4.9t^2 + 250 = 0 \Rightarrow t = \dfrac{50}{7}$ sec

When $a = \dfrac{50}{7}$, the velocity is

$\lim_{t\to a}\dfrac{s(a) - s(t)}{a - t} = \lim_{t\to a}\dfrac{\left[-4.9a^2 + 250\right] - \left[-4.9t^2 + 250\right]}{a - t}$

$= \lim_{t\to a}\dfrac{4.9\left(t^2 - a^2\right)}{a - t}$

$= \lim_{t\to a}\dfrac{4.9(t - a)(t + a)}{a - t}$

$= \lim_{t\to a}\left[-4.9(t + a)\right]$

$= -4.9(2a) \qquad \left(a = \dfrac{50}{7}\right)$

$= -70$ m/sec.

The velocity of the object when it hits the ground is about 70 m/sec.

**41.** $\lim_{x\to 3^-}\dfrac{|x - 3|}{x - 3} = \lim_{x\to 3^-}\dfrac{-(x - 3)}{x - 3} = -1$

**42.** $\lim_{x\to 4}[\![x - 1]\!]$ does not exist. There is a break in the graph at $x = 4$.

**43.** $\lim_{x\to 2} f(x) = 0$

**44.** $\lim_{x\to 1^+} g(x) = 1 + 1 = 2$

**45.** $\lim_{t\to 1} h(t)$ does not exist because $\lim_{t\to 1^-} h(t) = 1 + 1 = 2$ and $\lim_{t\to 1^+} h(t) = \frac{1}{2}(1 + 1) = 1$.

**46.** $\lim_{s\to -2} f(s) = 2$

**47.** $f(x) = -3x^2 + 7$

Continuous on $(-\infty, \infty)$

**48.** $f(x) = x^2 - \dfrac{2}{x}$

Continuous on $(-\infty, 0) \cup (0, \infty)$

**49.** $f(x) = [\![x + 3]\!]$

$\lim_{x\to k^+}[\![x + 3]\!] = k + 3$ where $k$ is an integer.

$\lim_{x\to k^-}[\![x + 3]\!] = k + 2$ where $k$ is an integer.

Nonremovable discontinuity at each integer $k$

Continuous on $(k, k + 1)$ for all integers $k$

**50.** $f(x) = \dfrac{3x^2 - x - 2}{x - 1} = \dfrac{(3x + 2)(x - 1)}{x - 1}$

Continuous on $(-\infty, 1) \cup (1, \infty)$

**51.** $f(x) = \dfrac{3x^2 - x - 2}{x - 1} = \dfrac{(3x + 2)(x - 1)}{x - 1}$

$\lim_{x\to 1} f(x) = \lim_{x\to 1}(3x + 2) = 5$

Removable discontinuity at $x = 1$

Continuous on $(-\infty, 1) \cup (1, \infty)$

**52.** $f(x) = \begin{cases} 5 - x, & x \le 2 \\ 2x - 3, & x > 2 \end{cases}$

$\lim_{x\to 2^-} (5 - x) = 3$

$\lim_{x\to 2^+} (2x - 3) = 1$

Nonremovable discontinuity at $x = 2$

Continuous on $(-\infty, 2) \cup (2, \infty)$

**53.** $f(x) = \dfrac{1}{(x-2)^2}$

$\lim_{x\to 2} \dfrac{1}{(x-2)^2} = \infty$

Nonremovable discontinuity at $x = 2$

Continuous on $(-\infty, 2) \cup (2, \infty)$

**54.** $f(x) = \sqrt{\dfrac{x+1}{x}} = \sqrt{1 + \dfrac{1}{x}}$

$\lim_{x\to 0^+} \sqrt{1 + \dfrac{1}{x}} = \infty$

Domain: $(-\infty, -1], (0, \infty)$

Nonremovable discontinuity at $x = 0$

Continuous on $(-\infty, -1] \cup (0, \infty)$

**55.** $f(x) = \dfrac{3}{x+1}$

$\lim_{x\to 1^-} f(x) = -\infty$

$\lim_{x\to 1^+} f(x) = \infty$

Nonremovable discontinuity at $x = -1$

Continuous on $(-\infty, -1) \cup (-1, \infty)$

**56.** $f(x) = \dfrac{x+1}{2x+2}$

$\lim_{x\to -1} \dfrac{x+1}{2(x+1)} = \dfrac{1}{2}$

Removable discontinuity at $x = -1$

Continuous on $(-\infty, -1) \cup (-1, \infty)$

**57.** $f(x) = \csc\dfrac{\pi x}{2}$

Nonremovable discontinuities at each even integer.

Continuous on $(2k, 2k + 2)$ for all integers $k$.

**58.** $f(x) = \tan 2x$

Nonremovable discontinuities when

$x = \dfrac{(2n+1)\pi}{4}$

Continuous on

$\left(\dfrac{(2n-1)\pi}{4}, \dfrac{(2n+1)\pi}{4}\right)$

for all integers $n$.

**59.** $g(x) = 2e^{[\![x]\!]/4}$ is continuous on all intervals $(n, n + 1)$, where $n$ is an integer. $g$ has nonremovable discontinuities at each $n$.

**60.** $h(x) = -2 \ln|5 - x|$

Because $|5 - x| > 0$ except for $x = 5$, $h$ is continuous on $(-\infty, 5) \cup (5, \infty)$.

**61.** $f(2) = 5$

Find $c$ so that $\lim_{x\to 2^+} (cx + 6) = 5$.

$$c(2) + 6 = 5$$
$$2c = -1$$
$$c = -\frac{1}{2}$$

**62.** $\lim_{x\to 1^+} (x + 1) = 2$

$\lim_{x\to 3^-} (x + 1) = 4$

Find $b$ and $c$ so that $\lim_{x\to 1^-} (x^2 + bx + c) = 2$ and $\lim_{x\to 3^+} (x^2 + bx + c) = 4$.

Consequently you get $1 + b + c = 2$ and $9 + 3b + c = 4$.

Solving simultaneously, $b = -3$ and $c = 4$.

**63.** $f$ is continuous on $[1, 2]$. $f(1) = -1 < 0$ and $f(2) = 13 > 0$. So by the Intermediate Value Theorem, there is at least one value $c$ in $(1, 2)$ such that $2c^3 - 3 = 0$.

**64.** $C(x) = 12.80 + 2.50[\![-[\![-x]\!] - 1]\!], \quad x > 0$

$= 12.80 - 2.50[\![[\![-x]\!] + 1]\!], \quad x > 0$

Nonremovable discontinuity at each integer 1, 2, 3,...

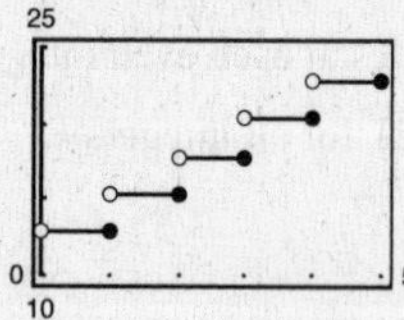


**65.** $A = 5000(1.06)^{[\![2t]\!]}$

Nonremovable discontinuity every 6 months

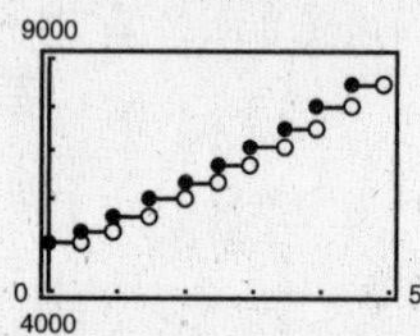


**66.** $f(x) = \sqrt{(x-1)x}$

(a) Domain: $(-\infty, 0] \cup [1, \infty)$

(b) $\lim_{x\to 0^-} f(x) = 0$

(c) $\lim_{x\to 1^+} f(x) = 0$

**67.** $g(x) = 1 + \frac{2}{x}$

Vertical asymptote at $x = 0$

**68.** $h(x) = \frac{4x}{4 - x^2}$

Vertical asymptotes at $x = 2$ and $x = -2$

**69.** $f(x) = \frac{8}{(x-10)^2}$

Vertical asymptote at $x = 10$

**70.** $f(x) = \csc \pi x$

Vertical asymptotes at every integer $k$

**71.** $g(x) = \ln(25 - x^2)$

Vertical asymptotes at $x = 5$ and $x = -5$

**72.** $f(x) = 7e^{-3/x}$

Vertical asymptote at $x = 0$

**73.** $\lim_{x\to -2^-} \frac{2x^2 + x + 1}{x + 2} = -\infty$

**74.** $\lim_{x\to (1/2)^+} \frac{x}{2x - 1} = \infty$

**75.** $\lim_{x\to -1^+} \frac{x+1}{x^3+1} = \lim_{x\to -1^+} \frac{1}{x^2 - x + 1} = \frac{1}{3}$

**76.** $\lim_{x\to -1^-} \frac{x+1}{x^4 - 1} = \lim_{x\to -1^-} \frac{1}{(x^2+1)(x-1)} = -\frac{1}{4}$

**77.** $\lim_{x\to 1^-} \frac{x^2 + 2x + 1}{x - 1} = -\infty$

**78.** $\lim_{x\to -1^+} \frac{x^2 - 2x + 1}{x + 1} = \infty$

**79.** $\lim_{x\to 0^+} \frac{\sin 4x}{5x} = \lim_{x\to 0^+} \left[\frac{4}{5}\left(\frac{\sin 4x}{4x}\right)\right] = \frac{4}{5}$

**80.** $\lim_{x\to 0^+} \frac{\sec x}{x} = \infty$

**81.** $\lim_{x\to 0^+} \frac{\csc 2x}{x} = \lim_{x\to 0^+} \frac{1}{x \sin 2x} = \infty$

**82.** $\lim_{x\to 0^-} \frac{\cos^2 x}{x} = -\infty$

**83.** $\lim_{x\to 0^+} \ln(\sin x) = -\infty$

**84.** $\lim_{x\to 0^-} 12e^{-2/x} = \infty$

**85.** $f(x) = \dfrac{\tan 2x}{x}$

(a)

| $x$ | –0.1 | –0.01 | –0.001 | 0.001 | 0.01 | 0.1 |
|---|---|---|---|---|---|---|
| $f(x)$ | 2.0271 | 2.0003 | 2.0000 | 2.0000 | 2.0003 | 2.0271 |

$\lim_{x\to 0} \dfrac{\tan 2x}{x} = 2$

(b) Yes, define $f(x) = \begin{cases} \dfrac{\tan 2x}{x}, & x \neq 0 \\ 2, & x = 0 \end{cases}$.

Now $f(x)$ is continuous at $x = 0$.

## Problem Solving for Chapter 2

**1.** (a) Perimeter $\Delta PAO = \sqrt{x^2 + (y-1)^2} + \sqrt{x^2 + y^2} + 1$

$= \sqrt{x^2 + (x^2 - 1)^2} + \sqrt{x^2 + x^4} + 1$

Perimeter $\Delta PBO = \sqrt{(x-1)^2 + y^2} + \sqrt{x^2 + y^2} + 1$

$= \sqrt{(x-1)^2 + x^4} + \sqrt{x^2 + x^4} + 1$

(b) $r(x) = \dfrac{\sqrt{x^2 + (x^2-1)^2} + \sqrt{x^2 + x^4} + 1}{\sqrt{(x-1)^2 + x^4} + \sqrt{x^2 + x^4} + 1}$

| $x$ | 4 | 2 | 1 | 0.1 | 0.01 |
|---|---|---|---|---|---|
| Perimeter $\Delta PAO$ | 33.02 | 9.08 | 3.41 | 2.10 | 2.01 |
| Perimeter $\Delta PBO$ | 33.77 | 9.60 | 3.41 | 2.00 | 2.00 |
| $r(x)$ | 0.98 | 0.95 | 1 | 1.05 | 1.005 |

(c) $\lim_{x\to 0^+} r(x) = \dfrac{1 + 0 + 1}{1 + 0 + 1} = \dfrac{2}{2} = 1$

**2.** (a) Area $\Delta PAO = \dfrac{1}{2}bh = \dfrac{1}{2}(1)(x) = \dfrac{x}{2}$

Area $\Delta PBO = \dfrac{1}{2}bh = \dfrac{1}{2}(1)(y) = \dfrac{y}{2} = \dfrac{x^2}{2}$

(b) $a(x) = \dfrac{\text{Area } \Delta PBO}{\text{Area } \Delta PAO} = \dfrac{x^2/2}{x/2} = x$

| $x$ | 4 | 2 | 1 | 0.1 | 0.01 |
|---|---|---|---|---|---|
| Area $\Delta PAO$ | 2 | 1 | 1/2 | 1/20 | 1/200 |
| Area $\Delta PBO$ | 8 | 2 | 1/2 | 1/200 | 1/20,000 |
| $a(x)$ | 4 | 2 | 1 | 1/10 | 1/100 |

(c) $\lim_{x\to 0^+} a(x) = \lim_{x\to 0^+} x = 0$

**3.** (a) There are 6 triangles, each with a central angle of $60° = \pi/3$. So,

$$\text{Area hexagon} = 6\left[\frac{1}{2}bh\right] = 6\left[\frac{1}{2}(1)\sin\frac{\pi}{3}\right] = \frac{3\sqrt{3}}{2} \approx 2.598.$$

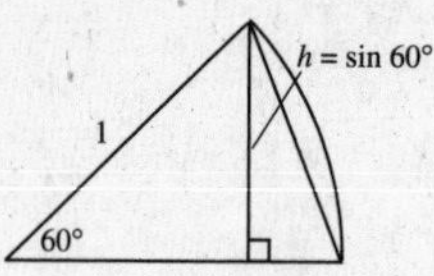


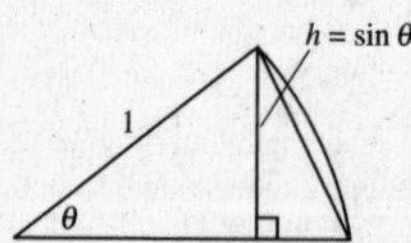


$$\text{Error} = \text{Area (Circle)} - \text{Area (Hexagon)} = \pi - \frac{3\sqrt{3}}{2} \approx 0.5435$$

(b) There are $n$ triangles, each with central angle of $\theta = 2\pi/n$. So,

$$A_n = n\left[\frac{1}{2}bh\right] = n\left[\frac{1}{2}(1)\sin\frac{2\pi}{n}\right] = \frac{n\sin(2\pi/n)}{2}.$$

(c)

| $n$ | 6 | 12 | 24 | 48 | 96 |
|---|---|---|---|---|---|
| $A_n$ | 2.598 | 3 | 3.106 | 3.133 | 3.139 |

(d) As $n$ gets larger and larger, $2\pi/n$ approaches 0. Letting $x = 2\pi/n$, $A_n = \dfrac{\sin(2\pi/n)}{2/n} = \dfrac{\sin(2\pi/n)}{(2\pi/n)}\pi = \dfrac{\sin x}{x}\pi$

which approaches $(1)\pi = \pi$.

**4.** (a) Slope $= \frac{4}{3}$

(b) Slope of tangent line is $-\frac{3}{4}$.

$$y - 4 = -\frac{3}{4}(x - 3)$$
$$y = -\frac{3}{4}x + \frac{25}{4}$$

(c) $Q = (x, y) = \left(x, \sqrt{25 - x^2}\right)$

$$m_x = \frac{\sqrt{25 - x^2} - 4}{x - 3}$$

(d)
$$\lim_{x\to3} m_x = \lim_{x\to3}\frac{\sqrt{25 - x^2} - 4}{x - 3}\cdot\frac{\sqrt{25 - x^2} + 4}{\sqrt{25 - x^2} + 4}$$
$$= \lim_{x\to3}\frac{(25 - x^2) - 16}{(x - 3)\left(\sqrt{25 - x^2} + 4\right)}$$
$$= \lim_{x\to3}\frac{(3 - x)(3 + x)}{(x - 3)\left(\sqrt{25 - x^2} + 4\right)}$$
$$= \lim_{x\to3}\frac{-(3 + x)}{\sqrt{25 - x^2} + 4} = \frac{-6}{4 + 4} = -\frac{3}{4}$$

This is the slope of the tangent line at $P$.

**5.** (a) Slope $= -\frac{12}{5}$

(b) Slope of tangent line is $\frac{5}{12}$.

$$y + 12 = \frac{5}{12}(x - 5)$$
$$y = \frac{5}{12}x - \frac{169}{12},$$

(c) $Q = (x, y) = \left(x, -\sqrt{169 - x^2}\right)$

$$m_x = \frac{-\sqrt{169 - x^2} + 12}{x - 5}$$

(d)
$$\lim_{x\to5} m_x = \lim_{x\to5}\frac{12 - \sqrt{169 - x^2}}{x - 5}\cdot\frac{12 + \sqrt{169 - x^2}}{12 + \sqrt{169 - x^2}}$$
$$= \lim_{x\to5}\frac{144 - (169 - x^2)}{(x - 5)\left(12 + \sqrt{169 - x^2}\right)}$$
$$= \lim_{x\to5}\frac{x^2 - 25}{(x - 5)\left(12 + \sqrt{169 - x^2}\right)}$$
$$= \lim_{x\to5}\frac{(x + 5)}{12 + \sqrt{169 - x^2}} = \frac{10}{12 + 12} = \frac{5}{12}$$

This is the same slope as part (b).

**6.** $\dfrac{\sqrt{a+bx}-\sqrt{3}}{x} = \dfrac{\sqrt{a+bx}-\sqrt{3}}{x} \cdot \dfrac{\sqrt{a+bx}+\sqrt{3}}{\sqrt{a+bx}+\sqrt{3}}$

$= \dfrac{(a+bx)-3}{x\left(\sqrt{a+bx}+\sqrt{3}\right)}.$

Letting $a = 3$ simplifies the numerator.

So,

$$\lim_{x\to 0}\frac{\sqrt{3+bx}-\sqrt{3}}{x} = \lim_{x\to 0}\frac{bx}{x\left(\sqrt{3+bx}+\sqrt{3}\right)}$$

$$= \lim_{x\to 0}\frac{b}{\sqrt{3+bx}+\sqrt{3}}$$

Setting $\dfrac{b}{\sqrt{3}+\sqrt{3}} = \sqrt{3}$, you obtain $b = 6$. So, $a = 3$ and $b = 6$.

**7.** (a) $3 + x^{1/3} \ge 0$

$x^{1/3} \ge -3$

$x \ge -27$

Domain: $x \ge -27, x \ne 1$ or $[-27, 1) \cup (1, \infty)$

(b)

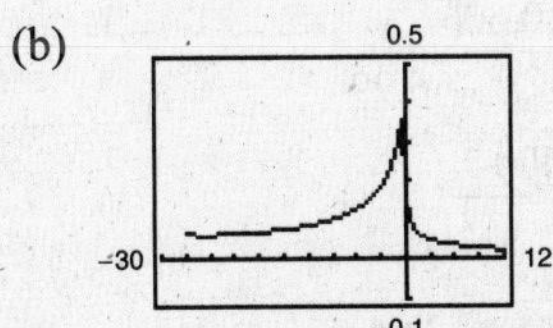


(c) $\displaystyle\lim_{x\to -27^+} f(x) = \frac{\sqrt{3+(-27)^{1/3}}-2}{-27-1} = \frac{-2}{-28} = \frac{1}{14} \approx 0.0714$

(d) $\displaystyle\lim_{x\to 1} f(x) = \lim_{x\to 1}\frac{\sqrt{3+x^{1/3}}-2}{x-1}\cdot\frac{\sqrt{3+x^{1/3}}+2}{\sqrt{3+x^{1/3}}+2}$

$$= \lim_{x\to 1}\frac{3+x^{1/3}-4}{(x-1)\left(\sqrt{3+x^{1/3}}+2\right)}$$

$$= \lim_{x\to 1}\frac{x^{1/3}-1}{\left(x^{1/3}-1\right)\left(x^{2/3}+x^{1/3}+1\right)\left(\sqrt{3+x^{1/3}}+2\right)}$$

$$= \lim_{x\to 1}\frac{1}{\left(x^{2/3}+x^{1/3}+1\right)\left(\sqrt{3+x^{1/3}}+2\right)}$$

$$= \frac{1}{(1+1+1)(2+2)} = \frac{1}{12}$$

**8.** $\displaystyle\lim_{x\to 0^-} f(x) = \lim_{x\to 0^-}\left(a^2-2\right) = a^2 - 2$

$\displaystyle\lim_{x\to 0^+} f(x) = \lim_{x\to 0^+}\frac{ax}{\tan x} = a\left(\text{because } \lim_{x\to 0}\frac{\tan x}{x} = 1\right)$

So,

$a^2 - 2 = a$

$a^2 - a - 2 = 0$

$(a-2)(a+1) = 0$

$a = -1, 2.$

**9.** (a) $\displaystyle\lim_{x\to 2} f(x) = 3$: $g_1, g_4$

(b) $f$ continuous at 2: $g_1$

(c) $\displaystyle\lim_{x\to 2^-} f(x) = 3$: $g_1, g_3, g_4$

**10.**

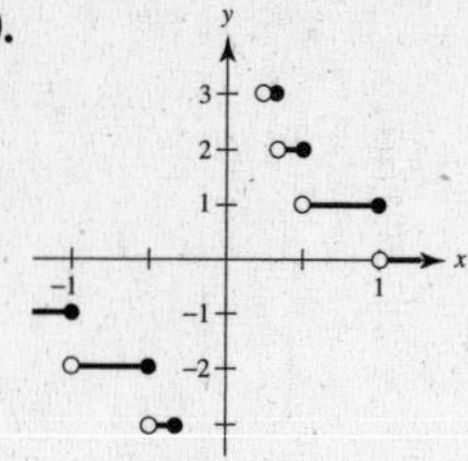

(a) $f\left(\frac{1}{4}\right) = [\![4]\!] = 4$

$f(3) = \left[\!\left[\frac{1}{3}\right]\!\right] = 0$

$f(1) = [\![1]\!] = 1$

(b) $\lim_{x\to 1^-} f(x) = 1$

$\lim_{x\to 1^+} f(x) = 0$

$\lim_{x\to 0^-} f(x) = -\infty$

$\lim_{x\to 0^+} f(x) = \infty$

(c) $f$ is continuous for all real numbers except

$x = 0, \pm 1, \pm\frac{1}{2}, \pm\frac{1}{3}, \ldots$

**11.**

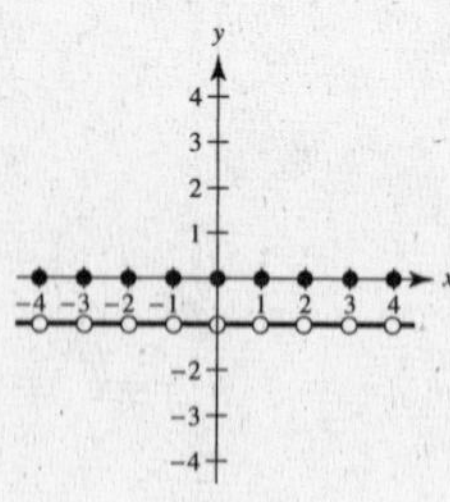

(a) $f(1) = [\![1]\!] + [\![-1]\!] = 1 + (-1) = 0$

$f(0) = 0$

$f\left(\frac{1}{2}\right) = 0 + (-1) = -1$

$f(-2.7) = -3 + 2 = -1$

(b) $\lim_{x\to 1^-} f(x) = -1$

$\lim_{x\to 1^+} f(x) = -1$

$\lim_{x\to 1/2} f(x) = -1$

(c) $f$ is continuous for all real numbers except

$x = 0, \pm 1, \pm 2, \pm 3, \ldots$

**12.** (a)

$$v^2 = \frac{192{,}000}{r} + v_0^2 - 48$$

$$\frac{192{,}000}{r} = v^2 - v_0^2 + 48$$

$$r = \frac{192{,}000}{v^2 - v_0^2 + 48}$$

$$\lim_{v\to 0} r = \frac{192{,}000}{48 - v_0^2}$$

Let $v_0 = \sqrt{48} = 4\sqrt{3}$ mi/sec.

(b)

$$v^2 = \frac{1920}{r} + v_0^2 - 2.17$$

$$\frac{1920}{r} = v^2 - v_0^2 + 2.17$$

$$r = \frac{1920}{v^2 - v_0^2 + 2.17}$$

$$\lim_{v\to 0} r = \frac{1920}{2.17 - v_0^2}$$

Let $v_0 = \sqrt{2.17}$ mi/sec $(\approx 1.47 \text{ mi/sec})$.

(c)

$$r = \frac{10{,}600}{v^2 - v_0^2 + 6.99}$$

$$\lim_{v\to 0} r = \frac{10{,}600}{6.99 - v_0^2}$$

Let $v_0 = \sqrt{6.99} \approx 2.64$ mi/sec.

Because this is smaller than the escape velocity for Earth, the mass is less.

**13.** (a)

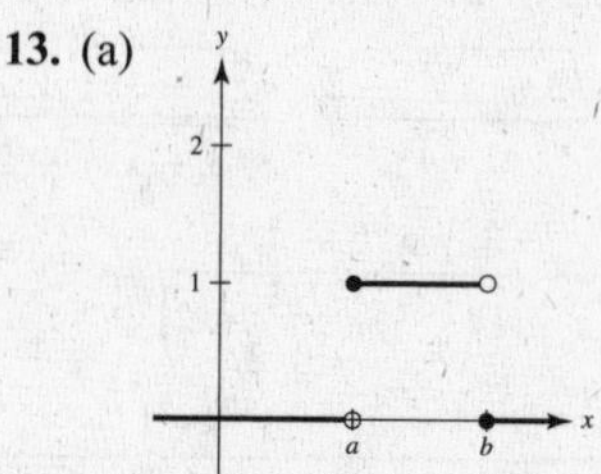

(b) (i) $\lim_{x\to a^+} P_{a,b}(x) = 1$

(ii) $\lim_{x\to a^-} P_{a,b}(x) = 0$

(iii) $\lim_{x\to b^+} P_{a,b}(x) = 0$

(iv) $\lim_{x\to b^-} P_{a,b}(x) = 1$

(c) $P_{a,b}$ is continuous for all positive real numbers except $x = a, b$.

(d) The area under the graph of $U$, and above the $x$-axis, is 1.

**14.** Let $a \neq 0$ and let $\varepsilon > 0$ be given. There exists $\delta_1 > 0$ such that if $0 < |x - 0| < \delta_1$ then $|f(x) - L| < \varepsilon$. Let $\delta = \delta_1/|a|$. Then for $0 < |x - 0| < \delta = \delta_1/|a|$, you have

$$|x| < \frac{\delta_1}{|a|}$$

$$|ax| < \delta_1$$

$$|f(ax) - L| < \varepsilon.$$

As a counterexample, let

$$a = 0 \text{ and } f(x) = \begin{cases} 1, & x \neq 0 \\ 2, & x = 0 \end{cases}.$$

Then $\lim_{x \to 0} f(x) = 1 = L$, but

$$\lim_{x \to 0} f(ax) = \lim_{x \to 0} f(0) = \lim_{x \to 0} 2 = 2.$$

# CHAPTER 3
# Differentiation

# CHAPTER 3
# Differentiation

## Section 3.1 The Derivative and the Tangent Line Problem

**1.** (a) At $(x_1, y_1)$, slope $= 0$.

At $(x_2, y_2)$, slope $= \frac{5}{2}$.

(b) At $(x_1, y_1)$, slope $= -\frac{5}{2}$.

At $(x_2, y_2)$, slope $= 2$.

**2.** (a) At $(x_1, y_1)$, slope $= \frac{2}{3}$.

At $(x_2, y_2)$, slope $= -\frac{2}{5}$.

(b) At $(x_1, y_1)$, slope $= \frac{5}{4}$.

At $(x_2, y_2)$, slope $= \frac{5}{4}$.

**3.** (a), (b)

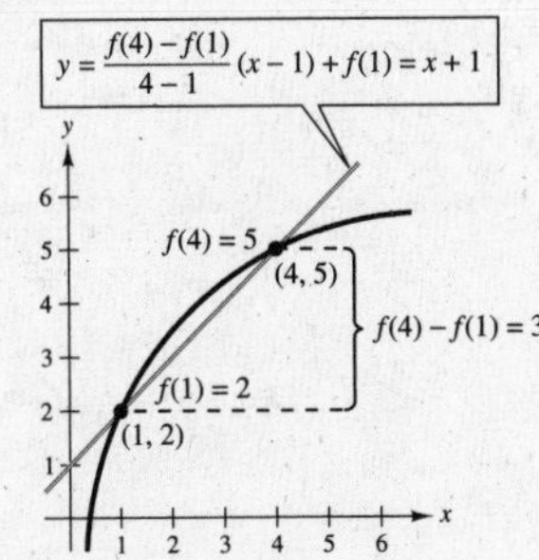


(c) $$y = \frac{f(4) - f(1)}{4 - 1}(x - 1) + f(1)$$
$$= \frac{3}{3}(x - 1) + 2$$
$$= 1(x - 1) + 2$$
$$= x + 1$$

**4.** (a) $$\frac{f(4) - f(1)}{4 - 1} = \frac{5 - 2}{3} = 1$$
$$\frac{f(4) - f(3)}{4 - 3} \approx \frac{5 - 4.75}{1} = 0.25$$

So, $\dfrac{f(4) - f(1)}{4 - 1} > \dfrac{f(4) - f(3)}{4 - 3}$.

(b) The slope of the tangent line at $(1, 2)$ equals $f'(1)$. This slope is steeper than the slope of the line through $(1, 2)$ and $(4, 5)$. So,

$$\frac{f(4) - f(1)}{4 - 1} < f'(1).$$

**5.** $f(x) = 3 - 5x$ is a line. Slope $= -5$

**6.** $g(x) = \frac{3}{2}x + 1$ is a line. Slope $= \frac{3}{2}$

**7.** Slope at $(2, -5)$
$$= \lim_{\Delta x \to 0} \frac{g(2 + \Delta x) - g(2)}{\Delta x}$$
$$= \lim_{\Delta x \to 0} \frac{(2 + \Delta x)^2 - 9 - (-5)}{\Delta x}$$
$$= \lim_{\Delta x \to 0} \frac{4 + 4(\Delta x) + (\Delta x)^2 - 4}{\Delta x}$$
$$= \lim_{\Delta x \to 0} (4 + \Delta x) = 4$$

**8.** Slope at $(1, 5)$
$$= \lim_{\Delta x \to 0} \frac{g(1 + \Delta x) - g(1)}{\Delta x}$$
$$= \lim_{\Delta x \to 0} \frac{6 - (1 + \Delta x)^2 - 5}{\Delta x}$$
$$= \lim_{\Delta x \to 0} \frac{6 - 1 - 2(\Delta x) - (\Delta x)^2 - 5}{\Delta x}$$
$$= \lim_{\Delta x \to 0} (-2 - \Delta x) = -2$$

**9.** Slope at $(0, 0)$
$$= \lim_{\Delta t \to 0} \frac{f(0 + \Delta t) - f(0)}{\Delta t}$$
$$= \lim_{\Delta t \to 0} \frac{3(\Delta t) - (\Delta t)^2 - 0}{\Delta t}$$
$$= \lim_{\Delta t \to 0} (3 - \Delta t) = 3$$

**10.** Slope at $(-2, 7)$
$$= \lim_{\Delta t \to 0} \frac{h(-2 + \Delta t) - h(-2)}{\Delta t}$$
$$= \lim_{\Delta t \to 0} \frac{(-2 + \Delta t)^2 + 3 - 7}{\Delta t}$$
$$= \lim_{\Delta t \to 0} \frac{4 - 4(\Delta t) + (\Delta t)^2 - 4}{\Delta t}$$
$$= \lim_{\Delta t \to 0} (-4 + \Delta t) = -4$$

**11.** $f(x) = 7$

$$f'(x) = \lim_{\Delta x \to 0} \frac{f(x + \Delta x) - f(x)}{\Delta x}$$
$$= \lim_{\Delta x \to 0} \frac{7 - 7}{\Delta x}$$
$$= \lim_{\Delta x \to 0} 0 = 0$$

**12.** $g(x) = -3$

$$g'(x) = \lim_{\Delta x \to 0} \frac{g(x + \Delta x) - g(x)}{\Delta x} = \lim_{\Delta x \to 0} \frac{-3 - (-3)}{\Delta x} = \lim_{\Delta x \to 0} \frac{0}{\Delta x} = 0$$

**13.** $f(x) = -5x$

$$f'(x) = \lim_{\Delta x \to 0} \frac{f(x + \Delta x) - f(x)}{\Delta x} = \lim_{\Delta x \to 0} \frac{-5(x + \Delta x) - (-5x)}{\Delta x} = \lim_{\Delta x \to 0} -5 = -5$$

**14.** $f(x) = 3x + 2$

$$f'(x) = \lim_{\Delta x \to 0} \frac{f(x + \Delta x) - f(x)}{\Delta x} = \lim_{\Delta x \to 0} \frac{[3(x + \Delta x) + 2] - [3x + 2]}{\Delta x} = \lim_{\Delta x \to 0} \frac{3\Delta x}{\Delta x} = \lim_{\Delta x \to 0} 3 = 3$$

**15.** $h(s) = 3 + \frac{2}{3}s$

$$h'(s) = \lim_{\Delta s \to 0} \frac{h(s + \Delta s) - h(s)}{\Delta s} = \lim_{\Delta s \to 0} \frac{3 + \frac{2}{3}(s + \Delta s) - \left(3 + \frac{2}{3}s\right)}{\Delta s} = \lim_{\Delta s \to 0} \frac{\frac{2}{3}\Delta s}{\Delta s} = \frac{2}{3}$$

**16.** $f(x) = 8 - \frac{1}{5}x$

$$f'(x) = \lim_{\Delta x \to 0} \frac{f(x + \Delta x) - f(x)}{\Delta x} = \lim_{\Delta x \to 0} \frac{8 - \frac{1}{5}(x + \Delta x) - \left(8 - \frac{1}{5}x\right)}{\Delta x} = \lim_{\Delta x \to 0} \frac{-\frac{1}{5}(\Delta x)}{\Delta x} = \lim_{\Delta x \to 0}\left(-\frac{1}{5}\right) = -\frac{1}{5}$$

**17.** $f(x) = x^2 + x - 3$

$$\begin{aligned} f'(x) &= \lim_{\Delta x \to 0} \frac{f(x + \Delta x) - f(x)}{\Delta x} \\ &= \lim_{\Delta x \to 0} \frac{(x + \Delta x)^2 + (x + \Delta x) - 3 - (x^2 + x - 3)}{\Delta x} \\ &= \lim_{\Delta x \to 0} \frac{x^2 + 2x(\Delta x) + (\Delta x)^2 + x + \Delta x - 3 - x^2 - x + 3}{\Delta x} \\ &= \lim_{\Delta x \to 0} \frac{2x(\Delta x) + (\Delta x)^2 + \Delta x}{\Delta x} \\ &= \lim_{\Delta x \to 0} (2x + \Delta x + 1) = 2x + 1 \end{aligned}$$

**18.** $f(x) = 2 - x^2$

$$\begin{aligned} f'(x) &= \lim_{\Delta x \to 0} \frac{f(x + \Delta x) - f(x)}{\Delta x} \\ &= \lim_{\Delta x \to 0} \frac{2 - (x + \Delta x)^2 - (2 - x^2)}{\Delta x} \\ &= \lim_{\Delta x \to 0} \frac{2 - x^2 - 2x(\Delta x) - (\Delta x)^2 - 2 + x^2}{\Delta x} \\ &= \lim_{\Delta x \to 0} \frac{-2x(\Delta x) - (\Delta x)^2}{\Delta x} \\ &= \lim_{\Delta x \to 0} [-2x - \Delta x] = -2x \end{aligned}$$

**19.** $f(x) = x^3 - 12x$

$$f'(x) = \lim_{\Delta x \to 0} \frac{f(x + \Delta x) - f(x)}{\Delta x}$$

$$= \lim_{\Delta x \to 0} \frac{\left[(x + \Delta x)^3 - 12(x + \Delta x)\right] - \left[x^3 - 12x\right]}{\Delta x}$$

$$= \lim_{\Delta x \to 0} \frac{x^3 + 3x^2\Delta x + 3x(\Delta x)^2 + (\Delta x)^3 - 12x - 12\,\Delta x - x^3 + 12x}{\Delta x}$$

$$= \lim_{\Delta x \to 0} \frac{3x^2\Delta x + 3x(\Delta x)^2 + (\Delta x)^3 - 12\,\Delta x}{\Delta x}$$

$$= \lim_{\Delta x \to 0}\left(3x^2 + 3x\,\Delta x + (\Delta x)^2 - 12\right) = 3x^2 - 12$$

**20.** $f(x) = x^3 + x^2$

$$f'(x) = \lim_{\Delta x \to 0} \frac{f(x + \Delta x) - f(x)}{\Delta x}$$

$$= \lim_{\Delta x \to 0} \frac{\left[(x + \Delta x)^3 + (x + \Delta x)^2\right] - \left[x^3 + x^2\right]}{\Delta x}$$

$$= \lim_{\Delta x \to 0} \frac{x^3 + 3x^2\Delta x + 3x(\Delta x)^2 + (\Delta x)^3 + x^2 + 2x\,\Delta x + (\Delta x)^2 - x^3 - x^2}{\Delta x}$$

$$= \lim_{\Delta x \to 0} \frac{3x^2\,\Delta x + 3x(\Delta x)^2 + (\Delta x)^3 + 2x\,\Delta x + (\Delta x)^2}{\Delta x}$$

$$= \lim_{\Delta x \to 0}\left(3x^2 + 3x\,\Delta x + (\Delta x)^2 + 2x + (\Delta x)\right) = 3x^2 + 2x$$

**21.** $f(x) = \dfrac{1}{x - 1}$

$$f'(x) = \lim_{\Delta x \to 0} \frac{f(x + \Delta x) - f(x)}{\Delta x}$$

$$= \lim_{\Delta x \to 0} \frac{\dfrac{1}{x + \Delta x - 1} - \dfrac{1}{x - 1}}{\Delta x}$$

$$= \lim_{\Delta x \to 0} \frac{(x - 1) - (x + \Delta x - 1)}{\Delta x(x + \Delta x - 1)(x - 1)}$$

$$= \lim_{\Delta x \to 0} \frac{-\Delta x}{\Delta x(x + \Delta x - 1)(x - 1)}$$

$$= \lim_{\Delta x \to 0} \frac{-1}{(x + \Delta x - 1)(x - 1)}$$

$$= -\frac{1}{(x - 1)^2}$$

**22.** $f(x) = \dfrac{1}{x^2}$

$$f'(x) = \lim_{\Delta x \to 0} \frac{f(x + \Delta x) - f(x)}{\Delta x}$$

$$= \lim_{\Delta x \to 0} \frac{\dfrac{1}{(x + \Delta x)^2} - \dfrac{1}{x^2}}{\Delta x}$$

$$= \lim_{\Delta x \to 0} \frac{x^2 - (x + \Delta x)^2}{\Delta x(x + \Delta x)^2 x^2}$$

$$= \lim_{\Delta x \to 0} \frac{-2x\,\Delta x - (\Delta x)^2}{\Delta x(x + \Delta x)^2 x^2}$$

$$= \lim_{\Delta x \to 0} \frac{-2x - \Delta x}{(x + \Delta x)^2 x^2}$$

$$= \frac{-2x}{x^4}$$

$$= -\frac{2}{x^3}$$

**23.** $f(x) = \sqrt{x+4}$

$$f'(x) = \lim_{\Delta x \to 0} \frac{f(x+\Delta x) - f(x)}{\Delta x}$$

$$= \lim_{\Delta x \to 0} \frac{\sqrt{x+\Delta x+4} - \sqrt{x+4}}{\Delta x} \cdot \left(\frac{\sqrt{x+\Delta x+4} + \sqrt{x+4}}{\sqrt{x+\Delta x+4} + \sqrt{x+4}}\right)$$

$$= \lim_{\Delta x \to 0} \frac{(x+\Delta x+4) - (x+4)}{\Delta x\left[\sqrt{x+\Delta x+4} + \sqrt{x+4}\right]}$$

$$= \lim_{\Delta x \to 0} \frac{1}{\sqrt{x+\Delta x+4} + \sqrt{x+4}} = \frac{1}{\sqrt{x+4} + \sqrt{x+4}} = \frac{1}{2\sqrt{x+4}}$$

**24.** $f(x) = \dfrac{4}{\sqrt{x}}$

$$f'(x) = \lim_{\Delta x \to 0} \frac{f(x+\Delta x) - f(x)}{\Delta x}$$

$$= \lim_{\Delta x \to 0} \frac{\dfrac{4}{\sqrt{x+\Delta x}} - \dfrac{4}{\sqrt{x}}}{\Delta x}$$

$$= \lim_{\Delta x \to 0} \frac{4\sqrt{x} - 4\sqrt{x+\Delta x}}{\Delta x\sqrt{x}\sqrt{x+\Delta x}} \cdot \left(\frac{\sqrt{x} + \sqrt{x+\Delta x}}{\sqrt{x} + \sqrt{x+\Delta x}}\right)$$

$$= \lim_{\Delta x \to 0} \frac{4x - 4(x+\Delta x)}{\Delta x\sqrt{x}\sqrt{x+\Delta x}\left(\sqrt{x} + \sqrt{x+\Delta x}\right)}$$

$$= \lim_{\Delta x \to 0} \frac{-4}{\sqrt{x}\sqrt{x+\Delta x}\left(\sqrt{x} + \sqrt{x+\Delta x}\right)}$$

$$= \frac{-4}{\sqrt{x}\sqrt{x}\left(\sqrt{x} + \sqrt{x}\right)} = \frac{-2}{x\sqrt{x}}$$

**25.** (a) $f(x) = x^2 + 3$

$$f'(x) = \lim_{\Delta x \to 0} \frac{f(x+\Delta x) - f(x)}{\Delta x}$$

$$= \lim_{\Delta x \to 0} \frac{\left[(x+\Delta x)^2 + 3\right] - \left[x^2 + 3\right]}{\Delta x}$$

$$= \lim_{\Delta x \to 0} \frac{2x\,\Delta x + (\Delta x)^2}{\Delta x}$$

$$= \lim_{\Delta x \to 0} (2x + \Delta x) = 2x$$

At $(1, 4)$, the slope of the tangent line is $m = 2(1) = 2$. The equation of the tangent line is

$$y - 4 = 2(x - 1)$$
$$y - 4 = 2x - 2$$
$$y = 2x + 2.$$

(b)

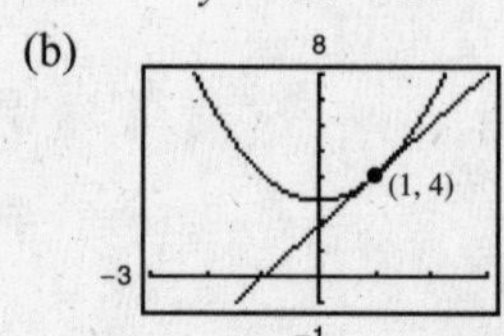


(c) Graphing utility confirms $\dfrac{dy}{dx} = 2$ at $(1, 4)$.

**26.** (a) $f(x) = x^2 + 3x + 4$

$$f'(x) = \lim_{\Delta x \to 0} \frac{f(x + \Delta x) - f(x)}{\Delta x}$$

$$= \lim_{\Delta x \to 0} \frac{(x + \Delta x)^2 + 3(x + \Delta x) + 4 - (x^2 + 3x + 4)}{\Delta x}$$

$$= \lim_{\Delta x \to 0} \frac{x^2 + 2x(\Delta x) + (\Delta x)^2 + 3x + 3\Delta x + 4 - x^2 - 3x - 4}{\Delta x}$$

$$= \lim_{\Delta x \to 0} \frac{2x(\Delta x) + (\Delta x)^2 + 3\Delta x}{\Delta x}$$

$$= \lim_{\Delta x \to 0} (2x + \Delta x + 3) = 2x + 3$$

At $(-2, 2)$, the slope of the tangent line is $m = 2(-2) + 3 = -1$. The equation of the tangent line is

$$y - 2 = -1(x + 2)$$

$$y = -x$$

(b)

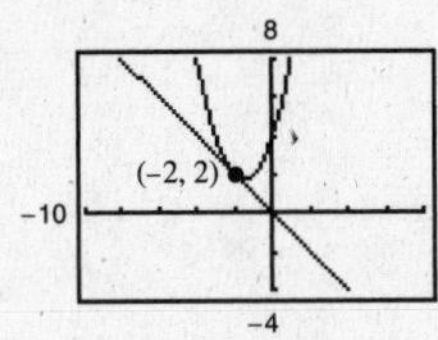


(c) Graphing utility confirms $\frac{dy}{dx} = -1$ at $(-2, 2)$.

**27.** (a) $f(x) = x^3$

$$f'(x) = \lim_{\Delta x \to 0} \frac{f(x + \Delta x) - f(x)}{\Delta x}$$

$$= \lim_{\Delta x \to 0} \frac{(x + \Delta x)^3 - x^3}{\Delta x}$$

$$= \lim_{\Delta x \to 0} \frac{3x^2\Delta x + 3x(\Delta x)^2 + (\Delta x)^3}{\Delta x}$$

$$= \lim_{\Delta x \to 0} \left(3x^2 + 3x\,\Delta x + (\Delta x)^2\right) = 3x^2$$

At $(2, 8)$, the slope of the tangent is $m = 3(2)^2 = 12$. The equation of the tangent line is

$$y - 8 = 12(x - 2)$$

$$y = 12x - 16.$$

(b)

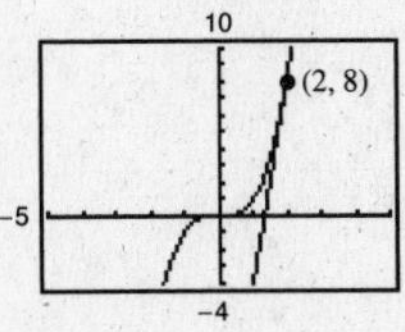


(c) Graphing utility confirms $\frac{dy}{dx} = 12$ at $(2, 8)$.

**28.** (a) $f(x) = x^3 + 1$

$$f'(x) = \lim_{\Delta x \to 0} \frac{f(x + \Delta x) - f(x)}{\Delta x}$$

$$= \lim_{\Delta x \to 0} \frac{\left[(x + \Delta x)^3 + 1\right] - (x^3 + 1)}{\Delta x}$$

$$= \lim_{\Delta x \to 0} \frac{x^3 + 3x^2(\Delta x) + 3x(\Delta x)^2 + (\Delta x)^3 + 1 - x^3 - 1}{\Delta x}$$

$$= \lim_{\Delta x \to 0}\left[3x^2 + 3x(\Delta x) + (\Delta x)^2\right] = 3x^2$$

At $(1, 2)$, the slope of the tangent line is $m = 3(1)^2 = 3$. The equation of the tangent line is

$y - 2 = 3(x - 1)$

$y = 3x - 1.$

(b)

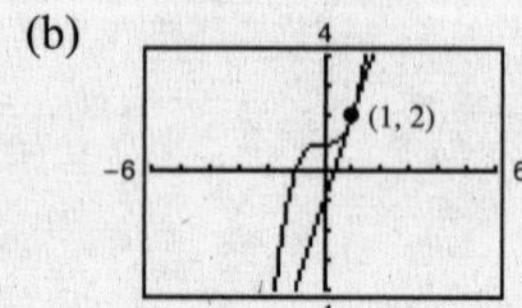


(c) Graphing utility confirms $\frac{dy}{dx} = 3$ at $(1, 2)$.

**29.** (a) $f(x) = \sqrt{x}$

$$f'(x) = \lim_{\Delta x \to 0} \frac{f(x + \Delta x) - f(x)}{\Delta x}$$

$$= \lim_{\Delta x \to 0} \frac{\sqrt{x + \Delta x} - \sqrt{x}}{\Delta x} \cdot \frac{\sqrt{x + \Delta x} + \sqrt{x}}{\sqrt{x + \Delta x} + \sqrt{x}}$$

$$= \lim_{\Delta x \to 0} \frac{(x + \Delta x) - x}{\Delta x\left(\sqrt{x + \Delta x} + \sqrt{x}\right)}$$

$$= \lim_{\Delta x \to 0} \frac{1}{\sqrt{x + \Delta x} + \sqrt{x}} = \frac{1}{2\sqrt{x}}$$

At $(1, 1)$, the slope of the tangent line is $m = \frac{1}{2\sqrt{1}} = \frac{1}{2}$.

The equation of the tangent line is

$y - 1 = \frac{1}{2}(x - 1)$

$y = \frac{1}{2}x + \frac{1}{2}.$

(b)

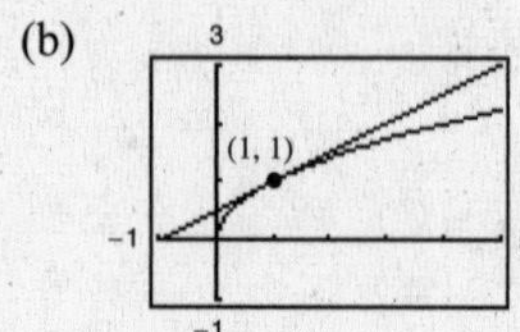


(c) Graphing utility confirms $\frac{dy}{dx} = \frac{1}{2}$ at $(1, 1)$.

**30.** (a) $f(x) = \sqrt{x-1}$

$$f'(x) = \lim_{\Delta x \to 0} \frac{f(x+\Delta x) - f(x)}{\Delta x}$$

$$= \lim_{\Delta x \to 0} \frac{\sqrt{x+\Delta x-1} - \sqrt{x-1}}{\Delta x} \cdot \left(\frac{\sqrt{x+\Delta x-1} + \sqrt{x-1}}{\sqrt{x+\Delta x-1} + \sqrt{x-1}}\right)$$

$$= \lim_{\Delta x \to 0} \frac{(x+\Delta x-1) - (x-1)}{\Delta x\left(\sqrt{x+\Delta x-1} + \sqrt{x-1}\right)}$$

$$= \lim_{\Delta x \to 0} \frac{1}{\sqrt{x+\Delta x-1} + \sqrt{x-1}} = \frac{1}{2\sqrt{x-1}}$$

At $(5, 2)$, the slope of the tangent line is $m = \dfrac{1}{2\sqrt{5-1}} = \dfrac{1}{4}$.

The equation of the tangent line is

$$y - 2 = \frac{1}{4}(x-5)$$

$$y = \frac{1}{4}x + \frac{3}{4}.$$

(b)

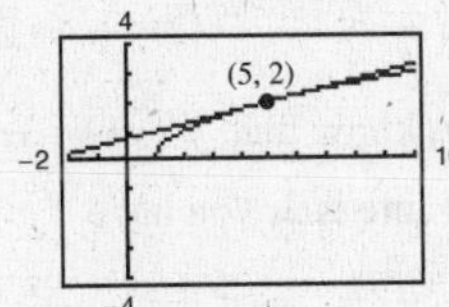


(c) Graphing utility confirms $\dfrac{dy}{dx} = \dfrac{1}{4}$ at $(5, 2)$.

**31.** (a) $f(x) = x + \dfrac{4}{x}$

$$f'(x) = \lim_{\Delta x \to 0} \frac{f(x+\Delta x) - f(x)}{\Delta x}$$

$$= \lim_{\Delta x \to 0} \frac{(x+\Delta x) + \dfrac{4}{x+\Delta x} - \left(x + \dfrac{4}{x}\right)}{\Delta x}$$

$$= \lim_{\Delta x \to 0} \frac{x(x+\Delta x)(x+\Delta x) + 4x - x^2(x+\Delta x) - 4(x+\Delta x)}{x(\Delta x)(x+\Delta x)}$$

$$= \lim_{\Delta x \to 0} \frac{x^3 + 2x^2(\Delta x) + x(\Delta x)^2 - x^3 - x^2(\Delta x) - 4(\Delta x)}{x(\Delta x)(x+\Delta x)}$$

$$= \lim_{\Delta x \to 0} \frac{x^2(\Delta x) + x(\Delta x)^2 - 4(\Delta x)}{x(\Delta x)(x+\Delta x)}$$

$$= \lim_{\Delta x \to 0} \frac{x^2 + x(\Delta x) - 4}{x(x+\Delta x)}$$

$$= \frac{x^2 - 4}{x^2} = 1 - \frac{4}{x^2}$$

At $(4, 5)$, the slope of the tangent line is $m = 1 - \dfrac{4}{16} = \dfrac{3}{4}$.

The equation of the tangent line is

$$y - 5 = \frac{3}{4}(x-4)$$

$$y = \frac{3}{4}x + 2.$$

(b)

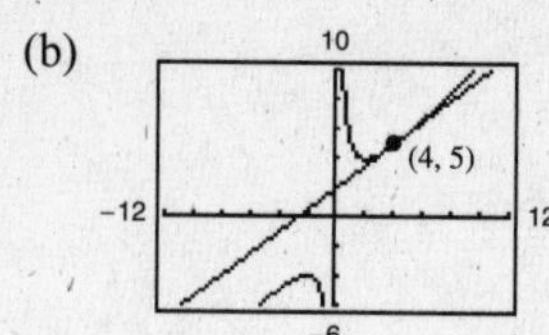


(c) Graphing utility confirms $\frac{dy}{dx} = \frac{3}{4}$ at $(4, 5)$.

**32.** (a) $f(x) = \dfrac{1}{x+1}$

$$f'(x) = \lim_{\Delta x \to 0} \frac{f(x + \Delta x) - f(x)}{\Delta x}$$

$$= \lim_{\Delta x \to 0} \frac{\dfrac{1}{x + \Delta x + 1} - \dfrac{1}{x + 1}}{\Delta x}$$

$$= \lim_{\Delta x \to 0} \frac{(x + 1) - (x + \Delta x + 1)}{\Delta x(x + \Delta x + 1)(x + 1)}$$

$$= \lim_{\Delta x \to 0} -\frac{1}{(x + \Delta x + 1)(x + 1)}$$

$$= -\frac{1}{(x + 1)^2}$$

At $(0, 1)$, the slope of the tangent line is

$$m = \frac{-1}{(0 + 1)^2} = -1.$$

The equation of the tangent line is $y = -x + 1$.

(b)

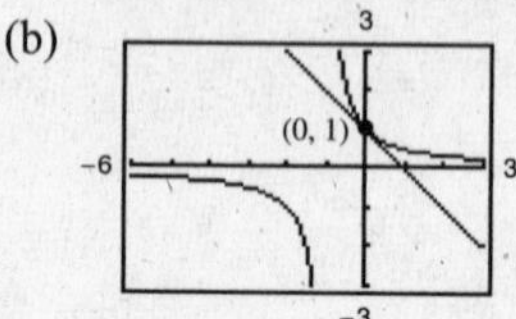


(c) Graphing utility confirms $\frac{dy}{dx} = -1$ at $(0, 1)$.

**33.** Using the limit definition of derivative, $f'(x) = 2x$. Because the slope of the given line is 2, you have

$$2x = 2$$
$$x = 1$$

So, at the point $(1, 1)$, the tangent line is parallel to $2x - y + 1 = 0$. The equation of this line is

$$y - 1 = 2(x - 1)$$
$$y = 2x - 1.$$

**34.** Using the limit definition of derivative, $f'(x) = 4x$. Because the slope of the given line is $-4$, you have

$$4x = -4$$
$$x = -1.$$

So, at the point $(-1, 2)$, the tangent line is parallel to $4x + y + 3 = 0$. The equation of this line is

$$y - 2 = -4(x + 1)$$
$$y = -4x - 2.$$

**35.** From Exercise 27 you know that $f'(x) = 3x^2$. Because the slope of the given line is 3, you have

$$3x^2 = 3$$
$$x = \pm 1.$$

So, at the points $(1, 1)$ and $(-1, -1)$, the tangent lines are parallel to $3x - y + 1 = 0$. These lines have equations

$$y - 1 = 3(x - 1) \text{ and } y + 1 = 3(x + 1)$$
$$y = 3x - 2 \qquad y = 3x + 2.$$

**36.** Using the limit definition of derivative, $f'(x) = 3x^2$. Because the slope of the given line is 3, you have

$$3x^2 = 3$$
$$x^2 = 1 \Rightarrow x = \pm 1.$$

So, at the points $(1, 3)$ and $(-1, 1)$, the tangent lines are parallel to $3x - y - 4 = 0$. These lines have equations

$$y - 3 = 3(x - 1) \text{ and } y - 1 = 3(x + 1)$$
$$y = 3x \qquad y = 3x + 4.$$

**37.** Using the limit definition of derivative,

$$f'(x) = \frac{-1}{2x\sqrt{x}}.$$

Because the slope of the given line is $-\frac{1}{2}$, you have

$$-\frac{1}{2x\sqrt{x}} = -\frac{1}{2}$$
$$x = 1.$$

So, at the point $(1, 1)$, the tangent line is parallel to $x + 2y - 6 = 0$. The equation of this line is

$$y - 1 = -\frac{1}{2}(x - 1)$$
$$y - 1 = -\frac{1}{2}x + \frac{1}{2}$$
$$y = -\frac{1}{2}x + \frac{3}{2}.$$

**38.** Using the limit definition of derivative,

$$f'(x) = \frac{-1}{2(x-1)^{3/2}}.$$

Because the slope of the given line is $-\frac{1}{2}$, you have

$$\frac{-1}{2(x-1)^{3/2}} = -\frac{1}{2}$$
$$1 = (x-1)^{3/2}$$
$$1 = x - 1 \Rightarrow x = 2.$$

So, at the point $(2, 1)$, the tangent line is parallel to $x + 2y + 7 = 0$. The equation of the tangent line is

$$y - 1 = -\frac{1}{2}(x - 2)$$
$$y = -\frac{1}{2}x + 2.$$

**39.** $f(x) = x \Rightarrow f'(x) = 1$ Matches (b).

**40.** $f(x) = x^2 \Rightarrow f'(x) = 2x$ Matches (d).

**41.** $f(x) = \sqrt{x} \Rightarrow f'(x) = \frac{1}{2\sqrt{x}}$ Matches (a).

(decreasing slope as $x \to \infty$)

**42.** $f'$ does not exist at $x = 0$. Matches (c).

**43.** $g(4) = 5$ because the tangent line passes through $(4, 5)$.

$$g'(4) = \frac{5-0}{4-7} = -\frac{5}{3}$$

**44.** $h(-1) = 4$ because the tangent line passes through $(-1, 4)$.

$$h'(-1) = \frac{6-4}{3-(-1)} = \frac{2}{4} = \frac{1}{2}$$

**45.** The slope of the graph of $f$ is 1 for all $x$-values.

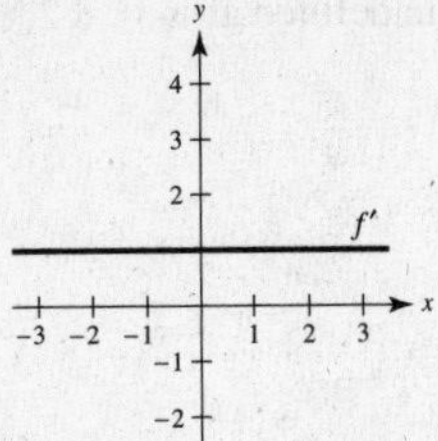


**46.** The slope of the graph of $f$ is 0 for all $x$-values.

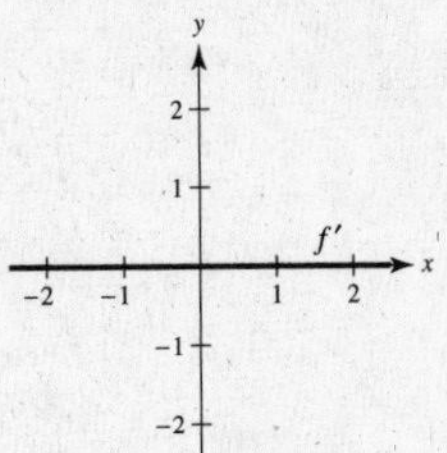


**47.** The slope of the graph of $f$ is negative for $x < 4$, positive for $x > 4$, and 0 at $x = 4$.

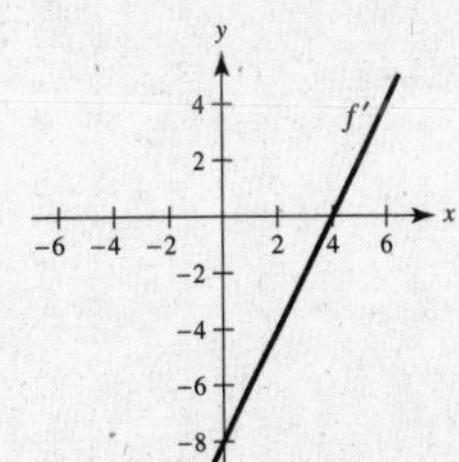


**48.** The slope of the graph of $f$ is $-1$ for $x < 4$, 1 for $x > 4$, and undefined at $x = 4$.

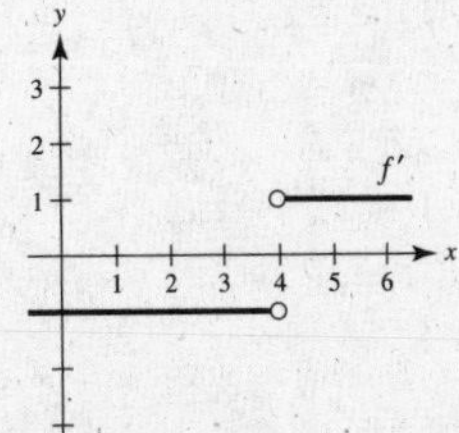


**49.** The slope of the graph of $f$ is negative for $x < 0$ and positive for $x > 0$. The slope is undefined at $x = 0$.

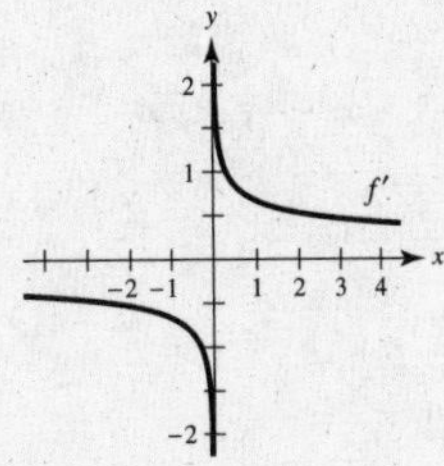

**50.** The slope is positive for $-2 < x < 0$ and negative for $0 < x < 2$. The slope is undefined at $x = \pm 2$, and 0 at $x = 0$.

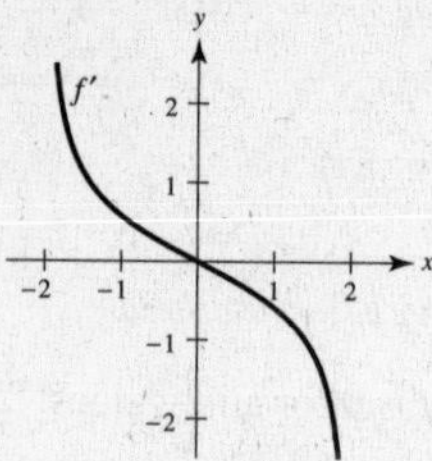

**51.** Answers will vary.

*Sample answer:* $y = -x$

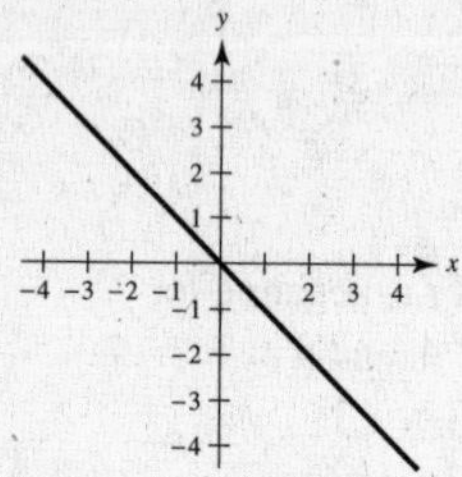

**52.** Answers will vary.

*Sample answer:* $y = x$

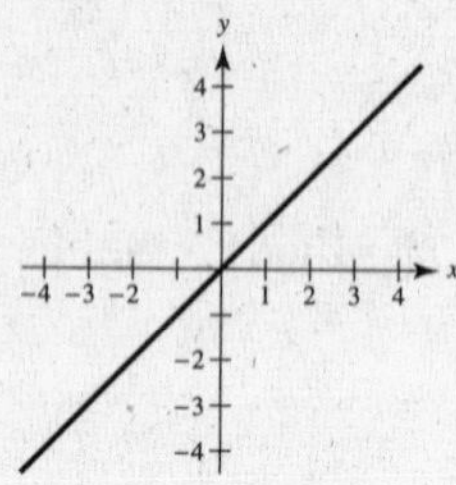

**53.** $f(x) = 5 - 3x$ and $c = 1$

**54.** $f(x) = x^3$ and $c = -2$

**55.** $f(x) = -x^2$ and $c = 6$

**56.** $f(x) = 2\sqrt{x}$ and $c = 9$

**57.** $f(0) = 2$ and $f'(x) = -3, -\infty < x < \infty$

$f(x) = -3x + 2$

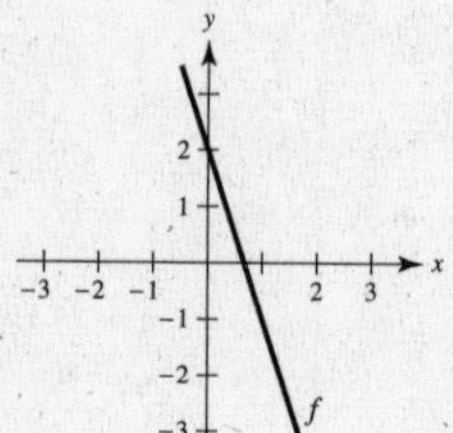

**58.** $f(0) = 4, f'(0) = 0; f'(x) < 0$ for $x < 0, f'(x) > 0$ for $x > 0$

Answers will vary. *Sample answer:* $f(x) = x^2 + 4$

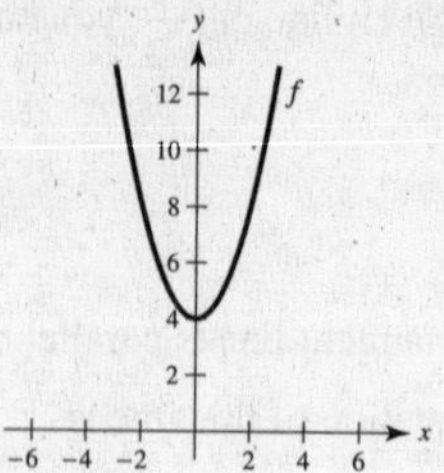

**59.** $f(0) = 0; f'(0) = 0; f'(x) > 0$ if $x \neq 0$

Answers will vary. *Sample answer:* $f(x) = x^3$

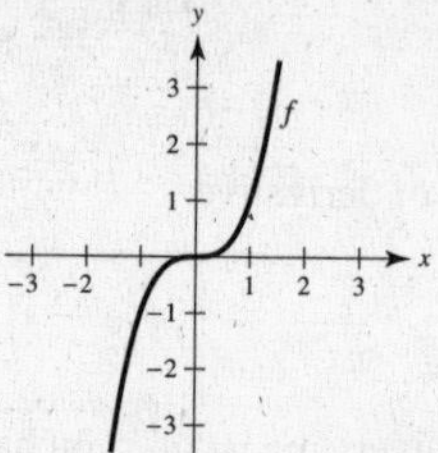

**60.** (a) If $f'(c) = 3$ and $f$ is odd, then $f'(-c) = f'(c) = 3$.

(b) If $f'(c) = 3$ and $f$ is even, then $f'(-c) = -f'(c) = -3$.

**61.** Let $(x_0, y_0)$ be a point of tangency on the graph of $f$. By the limit definition for the derivative, $f'(x) = 4 - 2x$. The slope of the line through $(2, 5)$ and $(x_0, y_0)$ equals the derivative of $f$ at $x_0$:

$$\frac{5 - y_0}{2 - x_0} = 4 - 2x_0$$

$$5 - y_0 = (2 - x_0)(4 - 2x_0)$$

$$5 - (4x_0 - x_0^2) = 8 - 8x_0 + 2x_0^2$$

$$0 = x_0^2 - 4x_0 + 3$$

$$0 = (x_0 - 1)(x_0 - 3) \Rightarrow x_0 = 1, 3$$

So, the points of tangency are $(1, 3)$ and $(3, 3)$, and the corresponding slopes are 2 and $-2$. The equations of the tangent lines are:

$y - 5 = 2(x - 2)$ $\quad$ $y - 5 = -2(x - 2)$

$y = 2x + 1$ $\quad$ $y = -2x + 9$

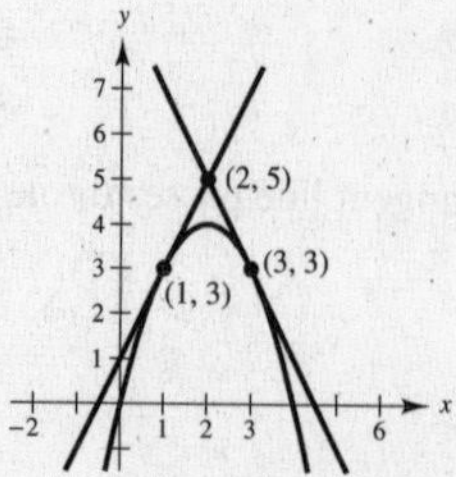

**62.** Let $(x_0, y_0)$ be a point of tangency on the graph of $f$. By the limit definition for the derivative, $f'(x) = 2x$. The slope of the line through $(1, -3)$ and $(x_0, y_0)$ equals the derivative of $f$ at $x_0$:

$$\frac{-3 - y_0}{1 - x_0} = 2x_0$$
$$-3 - y_0 = (1 - x_0)2x_0$$
$$-3 - x_0^2 = 2x_0 - 2x_0^2$$
$$x_0^2 - 2x_0 - 3 = 0$$
$$(x_0 - 3)(x_0 + 1) = 0 \Rightarrow x_0 = 3, -1$$

So, the points of tangency are $(3, 9)$ and $(-1, 1)$, and the corresponding slopes are 6 and –2. The equations of the tangent lines are:

$y + 3 = 6(x - 1)$ $\quad$ $y + 3 = -2(x - 1)$

$y = 6x - 9$ $\quad$ $y = -2x - 1$

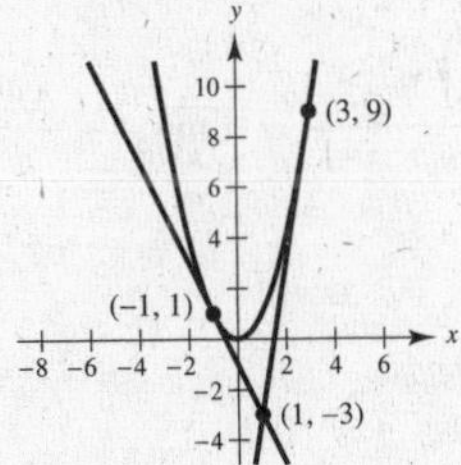


**63.** (a) $f(x) = x^2$

$$f'(x) = \lim_{\Delta x \to 0} \frac{f(x + \Delta x) - f(x)}{\Delta x}$$
$$= \lim_{\Delta x \to 0} \frac{(x + \Delta x)^2 - x^2}{\Delta x}$$
$$= \lim_{\Delta x \to 0} \frac{x^2 + 2x(\Delta x) + (\Delta x)^2 - x^2}{\Delta x}$$
$$= \lim_{\Delta x \to 0} \frac{\Delta x(2x + \Delta x)}{\Delta x}$$
$$= \lim_{\Delta x \to 0} (2x + \Delta x) = 2x$$

At $x = -1$, $f'(-1) = -2$ and the tangent line is

$y - 1 = -2(x + 1)$ or $y = -2x - 1$.

At $x = 0$, $f'(0) = 0$ and the tangent line is $y = 0$.

At $x = 1$, $f'(1) = 2$ and the tangent line is

$y = 2x - 1$.

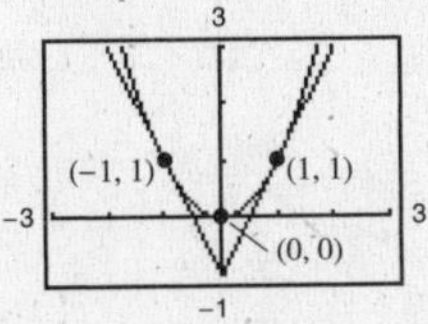


For this function, the slopes of the tangent lines are always distinct for different values of $x$.

(b) $$g'(x) = \lim_{\Delta x \to 0} \frac{g(x + \Delta x) - g(x)}{\Delta x}$$
$$= \lim_{\Delta x \to 0} \frac{(x + \Delta x)^3 - x^3}{\Delta x}$$
$$= \lim_{\Delta x \to 0} \frac{x^3 + 3x^2(\Delta x) + 3x(\Delta x)^2 + (\Delta x)^3 - x^3}{\Delta x}$$
$$= \lim_{\Delta x \to 0} \frac{\Delta x\left(3x^2 + 3x(\Delta x) + (\Delta x)^2\right)}{\Delta x}$$
$$= \lim_{\Delta x \to 0} \left(3x^2 + 3x(\Delta x) + (\Delta x)^2\right) = 3x^2$$

At $x = -1$, $g'(-1) = 3$ and the tangent line is

$y + 1 = 3(x + 1)$ or $y = 3x + 2$.

At $x = 0$, $g'(0) = 0$ and the tangent line is $y = 0$.

At $x = 1$, $g'(1) = 3$ and the tangent line is

$y - 1 = 3(x - 1)$ or $y = 3x - 2$.

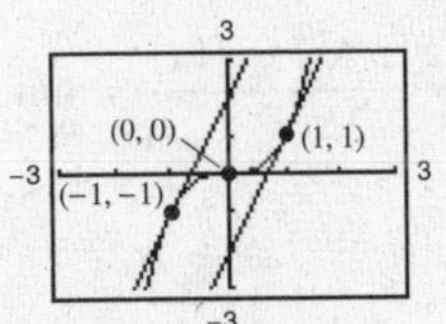


For this function, the slopes of the tangent lines are sometimes the same.

**64.** (a) $g'(0) = -3$

(b) $g'(3) = 0$

(c) Because $g'(1) = -\frac{8}{3}$, $g$ is decreasing (falling) at $x = 1$.

(d) Because $g'(-4) = \frac{7}{3}$, $g$ is increasing (rising) at $x = -4$.

(e) Because $g'(4)$ and $g'(6)$ are both positive, $g(6)$ is greater than $g(4)$, and $g(6) - g(4) > 0$.

(f) No, it is not possible. All you can say is that $g$ is decreasing (falling) at $x = 2$.

**65.** $f(x) = \frac{1}{2}x^2$

(a)

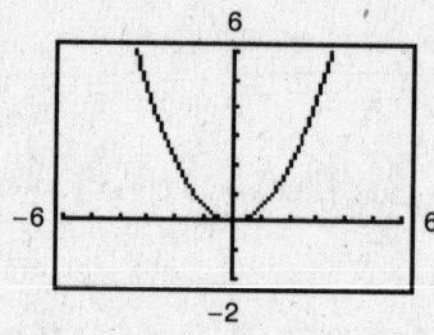

$f'(0) = 0, f'(1/2) = 1/2, f'(1) = 1, f'(2) = 2$

(b) By symmetry: $f'(-1/2) = -1/2, f'(-1) = -1, f'(-2) = -2$

(c)

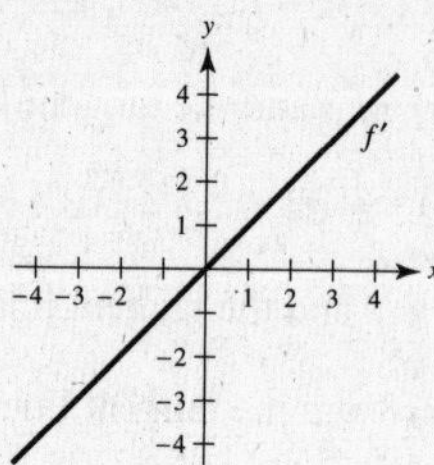

(d) $f'(x) = \lim_{\Delta x \to 0} \frac{f(x + \Delta x) - f(x)}{\Delta x} = \lim_{\Delta x \to 0} \frac{\frac{1}{2}(x + \Delta x)^2 - \frac{1}{2}x^2}{\Delta x} = \lim_{\Delta x \to 0} \frac{\frac{1}{2}\left(x^2 + 2x(\Delta x) + (\Delta x)^2\right) - \frac{1}{2}x^2}{\Delta x} = \lim_{\Delta x \to 0}\left(x + \frac{\Delta x}{2}\right) = x$

**66.** $f(x) = \frac{1}{3}x^3$

(a)

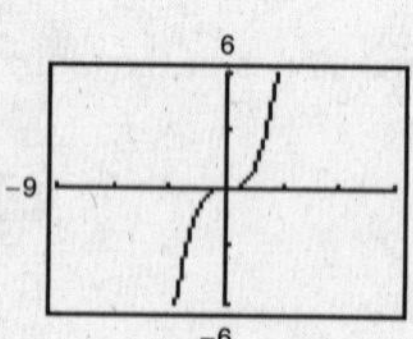

$f'(0) = 0, f'(1/2) = 1/4, f'(1) = 1, f'(2) = 4, f'(3) = 9$

(b) By symmetry: $f'(-1/2) = 1/4, f'(-1) = 1, f'(-2) = 4, f'(-3) = 9$

(c)

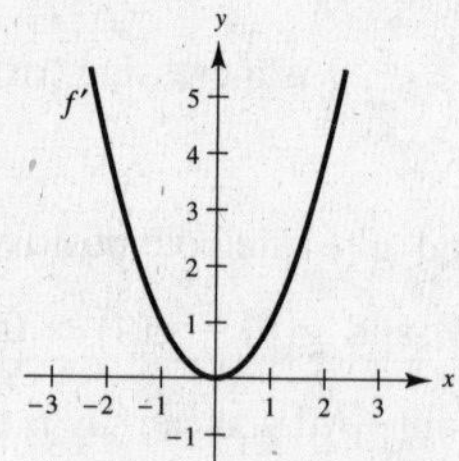

(d)
$$\begin{aligned} f'(x) &= \lim_{\Delta x \to 0} \frac{f(x + \Delta x) - f(x)}{\Delta x} \\ &= \lim_{\Delta x \to 0} \frac{\frac{1}{3}(x + \Delta x)^3 - \frac{1}{3}x^3}{\Delta x} \\ &= \lim_{\Delta x \to 0} \frac{\frac{1}{3}\left(x^3 + 3x^2(\Delta x) + 3x(\Delta x)^2 + (\Delta x)^3\right) - \frac{1}{3}x^3}{\Delta x} \\ &= \lim_{\Delta x \to 0}\left[x^2 + x(\Delta x) + \frac{1}{3}(\Delta x)^2\right] = x^2 \end{aligned}$$

**67.** $g(x) = \dfrac{f(x + 0.01) - f(x)}{0.01}$

$= \left[2(x + 0.01) - (x + 0.01)^2 - 2x + x^2\right]100$

$= 2 - 2x - 0.01$

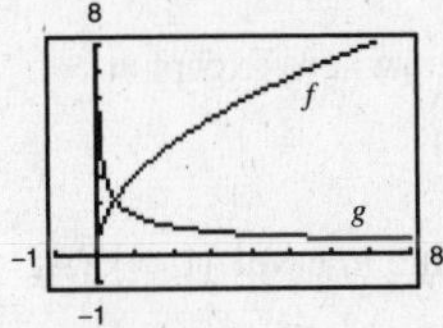


The graph of $g(x)$ is approximately the graph of $f'(x) = 2 - 2x$.

**68.** $g(x) = \dfrac{f(x + 0.01) - f(x)}{0.01}$

$= \left(3\sqrt{x + 0.01} - 3\sqrt{x}\right)100$

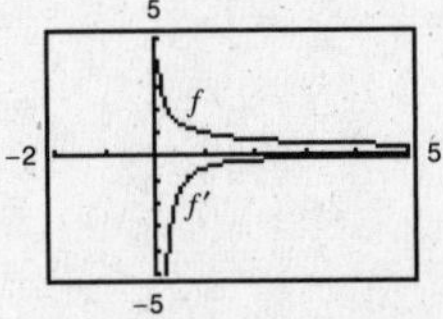


The graph of $g(x)$ is approximately the graph of $f'(x) = \dfrac{3}{2\sqrt{x}}$.

**69.** $f(2) = 2(4 - 2) = 4,\ f(2.1) = 2.1(4 - 2.1) = 3.99$

$f'(2) \approx \dfrac{3.99 - 4}{2.1 - 2} = -0.1 \quad \left[\text{Exact: } f'(2) = 0\right]$

**70.** $f(2) = \dfrac{1}{4}(2^3) = 2,\ f(2.1) = 2.31525$

$f'(2) \approx \dfrac{2.31525 - 2}{2.1 - 2} = 3.1525 \quad \left[\text{Exact: } f'(2) = 3\right]$

**71.** $f(x) = \dfrac{1}{\sqrt{x}}$ and $f'(x) = \dfrac{-1}{2x^{3/2}}$.

As $x \to \infty$, $f$ is nearly horizontal and so $f' \approx 0$.

**72.** $f(x) = \dfrac{x^3}{4} - 3x$ and $f'(x) = \dfrac{3}{4}x^2 - 3$

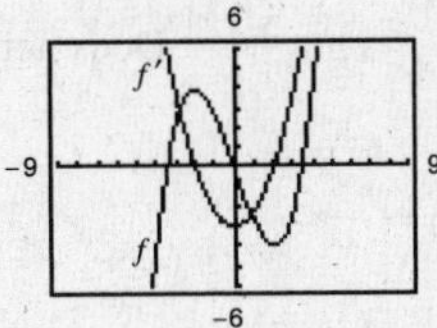


When $f$ is increasing, $f' > 0$.

When $f$ is decreasing, $f' < 0$.

**73.** $f(x) = x^2 - 5,\ c = 3$

$$\begin{aligned} f'(3) &= \lim_{x\to3} \frac{f(x) - f(3)}{x - 3} \\ &= \lim_{x\to3} \frac{x^2 - 5 - (9 - 5)}{x - 3} \\ &= \lim_{x\to3} \frac{(x - 3)(x + 3)}{x - 3} \\ &= \lim_{x\to3}(x + 3) = 6 \end{aligned}$$

**74.** $g(x) = x(x - 1) = x^2 - x,\ c = 1$

$$\begin{aligned} g'(1) &= \lim_{x\to1} \frac{g(x) - g(1)}{x - 1} \\ &= \lim_{x\to1} \frac{x^2 - x - 0}{x - 1} \\ &= \lim_{x\to1} \frac{x(x - 1)}{x - 1} = \lim_{x\to1} x = 1 \end{aligned}$$

**75.** $f(x) = x^3 + 2x^2 + 1,\ c = -2$

$$\begin{aligned} f'(-2) &= \lim_{x\to-2} \frac{f(x) - f(-2)}{x + 2} \\ &= \lim_{x\to-2} \frac{\left(x^3 + 2x^2 + 1\right) - 1}{x + 2} \\ &= \lim_{x\to-2} \frac{x^2(x + 2)}{x + 2} = \lim_{x\to-2} x^2 = 4 \end{aligned}$$

**76.** $f(x) = x^3 + 6x,\ c = 2$

$$\begin{aligned} f'(2) &= \lim_{x\to2} \frac{f(x) - f(2)}{x - 2} \\ &= \lim_{x\to2} \frac{\left(x^3 + 6x\right) - 20}{x - 2} \\ &= \lim_{x\to2} \frac{(x - 2)\left(x^2 + 2x + 10\right)}{x - 2} \\ &= \lim_{x\to2}\left(x^2 + 2x + 10\right) = 18 \end{aligned}$$

**77.** $g(x) = \sqrt{|x|}, c = 0$

$$g'(0) = \lim_{x\to 0}\frac{g(x) - g(0)}{x - 0} = \lim_{x\to 0}\frac{\sqrt{|x|}}{x}.$$ Does not exist.

As $x \to 0^-$, $\dfrac{\sqrt{|x|}}{x} = \dfrac{-1}{\sqrt{|x|}} \to -\infty$.

As $x \to 0^+$, $\dfrac{\sqrt{|x|}}{x} = \dfrac{1}{\sqrt{x}} \to \infty$.

So, $g(x)$ is not differentiable at $x = 0$.

**78.** $f(x) = \dfrac{2}{x}, c = 5$

$$\begin{aligned}f'(5) &= \lim_{x\to 5}\frac{f(x) - f(5)}{x - 5}\\ &= \lim_{x\to 5}\frac{\frac{2}{x} - \frac{2}{5}}{x - 5}\\ &= \lim_{x\to 5}\frac{2(5 - x)}{5x(x - 5)}\\ &= \lim_{x\to 5} -\frac{2}{5x} = -\frac{2}{25}\end{aligned}$$

**79.** $f(x) = (x - 6)^{2/3}, c = 6$

$$\begin{aligned}f'(6) &= \lim_{x\to 6}\frac{f(x) - f(6)}{x - 6}\\ &= \lim_{x\to 6}\frac{(x - 6)^{2/3} - 0}{x - 6} = \lim_{x\to 6}\frac{1}{(x - 6)^{1/3}}.\end{aligned}$$

Does not exist.

So, $f(x)$ is not differentiable at $x = 6$.

**80.** $g(x) = (x + 3)^{1/3}, c = -3$

$$\begin{aligned}g'(-3) &= \lim_{x\to -3}\frac{g(x) - g(-3)}{x - (-3)}\\ &= \lim_{x\to -3}\frac{(x + 3)^{1/3} - 0}{x + 3} = \lim_{x\to -3}\frac{1}{(x + 3)^{2/3}}.\end{aligned}$$

Does not exist.

So, $g(x)$ is not differentiable at $x = -3$.

**81.** $h(x) = |x + 7|, c = -7$

$$\begin{aligned}h'(-7) &= \lim_{x\to -7}\frac{h(x) - h(-7)}{x - (-7)}\\ &= \lim_{x\to -7}\frac{|x + 7| - 0}{x + 7} = \lim_{x\to -7}\frac{|x + 7|}{x + 7}.\end{aligned}$$

Does not exist.

So, $h(x)$ is not differentiable at $x = -7$.

**82.** $f(x) = |x - 6|, c = 6$

$$\begin{aligned}f'(6) &= \lim_{x\to 6}\frac{f(x) - f(6)}{x - 6}\\ &= \lim_{x\to 6}\frac{|x - 6| - 0}{x - 6} = \lim_{x\to 6}\frac{|x - 6|}{x - 6}.\end{aligned}$$

Does not exist.

So, $f(x)$ is not differentiable at $x = 6$.

**83.** $f(x)$ is differentiable everywhere except at $x = 3$. (Discontinuity)

**84.** $f(x)$ is differentiable everywhere except at $x = \pm 3$. (Sharp turns in the graph)

**85.** $f(x)$ is differentiable everywhere except at $x = -4$. (Sharp turn in the graph)

**86.** $f(x)$ is differentiable everywhere except at $x = \pm 2$. (Discontinuities)

**87.** $f(x)$ is differentiable on the interval $(1, \infty)$. (At $x = 1$ the tangent line is vertical.)

**88.** $f(x)$ is differentiable everywhere except at $x = 0$. (Discontinuity)

**89.** $f(x) = |x - 5|$ is differentiable everywhere except at $x = -5$. There is a sharp corner at $x = 5$.

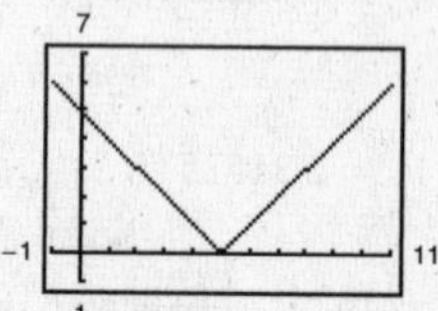


**90.** $f(x) = \dfrac{4x}{x - 3}$ is differentiable everywhere except at $x = 3$. $f$ is not defined at $x = 3$. (Vertical asymptote)

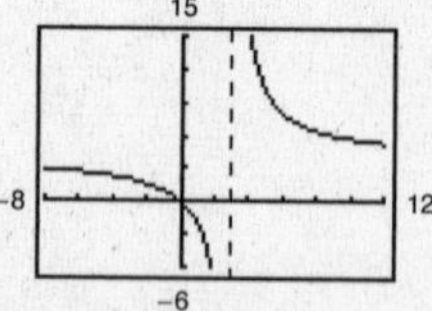


**91.** $f(x) = x^{2/5}$ is differentiable for all $x \neq 0$. There is a sharp corner at $x = 0$.

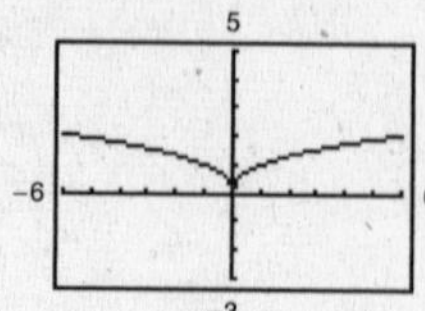

**92.** $f$ is differentiable for all $x \neq 1$.

$f$ is not continuous at $x = 1$.

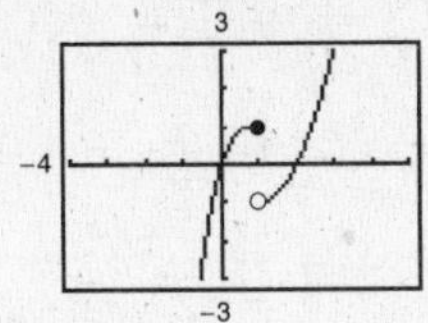


**93.** $f(x) = |x - 1|$

The derivative from the left is

$$\lim_{x \to 1^-} \frac{f(x) - f(1)}{x - 1} = \lim_{x \to 1^-} \frac{|x - 1| - 0}{x - 1} = -1.$$

The derivative from the right is

$$\lim_{x \to 1^+} \frac{f(x) - f(1)}{x - 1} = \lim_{x \to 1^+} \frac{|x - 1| - 0}{x - 1} = 1.$$

The one-sided limits are not equal. So, $f$ is not differentiable at $x = 1$.

**94.** $f(x) = \sqrt{1 - x^2}$

The derivative from the left does not exist because

$$\lim_{x \to 1^-} \frac{f(x) - f(1)}{x - 1} = \lim_{x \to 1^-} \frac{\sqrt{1 - x^2} - 0}{x - 1}$$

$$= \lim_{x \to 1^-} \frac{\sqrt{1 - x^2}}{x - 1} \cdot \frac{\sqrt{1 - x^2}}{\sqrt{1 - x^2}}$$

$$= \lim_{x \to 1^-} -\frac{1 + x}{\sqrt{1 - x^2}} = -\infty.$$

(Vertical tangent)

The limit from the right does not exist because $f$ is undefined for $x > 1$. So, $f$ is not differentiable at $x = 1$.

**95.** $f(x) = \begin{cases} (x - 1)^3, & x \leq 1 \\ (x - 1)^2, & x > 1 \end{cases}$

The derivative from the left is

$$\lim_{x \to 1^-} \frac{f(x) - f(1)}{x - 1} = \lim_{x \to 1^-} \frac{(x - 1)^3 - 0}{x - 1}$$

$$= \lim_{x \to 1^-} (x - 1)^2 = 0.$$

The derivative from the right is

$$\lim_{x \to 1^+} \frac{f(x) - f(1)}{x - 1} = \lim_{x \to 1^+} \frac{(x - 1)^2 - 0}{x - 1}$$

$$= \lim_{x \to 1^+} (x - 1) = 0.$$

The one-sided limits are equal. So, $f$ is differentiable at $x = 1$. $\left(f'(1) = 0\right)$

**96.** $f(x) = \begin{cases} x, & x \leq 1 \\ x^2, & x > 1 \end{cases}$

The derivative from the left is

$$\lim_{x \to 1^-} \frac{f(x) - f(1)}{x - 1} = \lim_{x \to 1^-} \frac{x - 1}{x - 1} = \lim_{x \to 1^-} 1 = 1.$$

The derivative from the right is

$$\lim_{x \to 1^+} = \frac{f(x) - f(1)}{x - 1} = \lim_{x \to 1^+} \frac{x^2 - 1}{x - 1} = \lim_{x \to 1^+} (x + 1) = 2.$$

The one-sided limits are not equal. So, $f$ is not differentiable at $x = 1$.

**97.** Note that $f$ is continuous at $x = 2$.

$f(x) = \begin{cases} x^2 + 1, & x \leq 2 \\ 4x - 3, & x > 2 \end{cases}$

The derivative from the left is

$$\lim_{x \to 2^-} \frac{f(x) - f(2)}{x - 2} = \lim_{x \to 2^-} \frac{(x^2 + 1) - 5}{x - 2}$$

$$= \lim_{x \to 2^-} (x + 2) = 4.$$

The derivative from the right is

$$\lim_{x \to 2^+} \frac{f(x) - f(2)}{x - 2} = \lim_{x \to 2^+} \frac{(4x - 3) - 5}{x - 2} = \lim_{x \to 2^+} 4 = 4.$$

The one-sided limits are equal. So, $f$ is differentiable at $x = 2$. $\left(f'(2) = 4\right)$

**98.** Note that $f$ is continuous at $x = 2$.

$f(x) = \begin{cases} \frac{1}{2}x + 1, & x < 2 \\ \sqrt{2x}, & x \geq 2 \end{cases}$

The derivative from the left is

$$\lim_{x \to 2^-} \frac{f(x) - f(2)}{x - 2} = \lim_{x \to 2^-} \frac{\left(\frac{1}{2}x + 1\right) - 2}{x - 2}$$

$$= \lim_{x \to 2^-} \frac{\frac{1}{2}(x - 2)}{x - 2} = \frac{1}{2}.$$

The derivative from the right is

$$\lim_{x \to 2^+} \frac{f(x) - f(2)}{x - 2} = \lim_{x \to 2^+} \frac{\sqrt{2x} - 2}{x - 2} \cdot \frac{\sqrt{2x} + 2}{\sqrt{2x} + 2}$$

$$= \lim_{x \to 2^+} \frac{2x - 4}{(x - 2)\left(\sqrt{2x} + 2\right)}$$

$$= \lim_{x \to 2^+} \frac{2(x - 2)}{(x - 2)\left(\sqrt{2x} + 2\right)}$$

$$= \lim_{x \to 2^+} \frac{2}{\sqrt{2x} + 2} = \frac{1}{2}.$$

The one-sided limits are equal. So, $f$ is differentiable at $x = 2$. $\left(f'(2) = \frac{1}{2}\right)$

**99.** 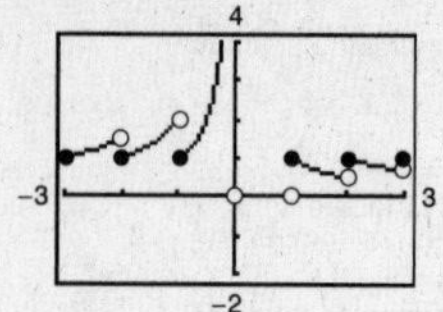


Let $g(x) = \dfrac{[\![x]\!]}{x}$.

For $f(x) = [\![x]\!]$,

$$\begin{aligned}\lim_{x\to 0^-}\frac{f(x)-f(0)}{x-0} &= \lim_{x\to 0^-}\frac{[\![x]\!]-0}{x}\\ &= \lim_{x\to 0^-}\frac{[\![x]\!]}{x}\\ &= \lim_{x\to 0^-}[\![x]\!]\cdot\lim_{x\to 0^-}\frac{1}{x}\\ &= -1\cdot\lim_{x\to 0^-}\frac{1}{x}\\ &= \lim_{x\to 0^-}\frac{-1}{x}\\ &= \infty.\end{aligned}$$

On the other hand,

$$\begin{aligned}\lim_{x\to 0^+}\frac{f(x)-f(0)}{x-0} &= \lim_{x\to 0^+}\frac{[\![x]\!]-0}{x}\\ &= \lim_{x\to 0^+}\frac{[\![x]\!]}{x}\\ &= \lim_{x\to 0^+}[\![x]\!]\cdot\lim_{x\to 0^+}\frac{1}{x}\\ &= 0\cdot\lim_{x\to 0^+}\frac{1}{x}\\ &= 0.\end{aligned}$$

So, $f$ is not differentiable at $x = 0$ because $\displaystyle\lim_{x\to 0}\frac{f(x)-f(0)}{x-0}$ does not exist. $f$ is differentiable for all $x \neq n$, $n$ an integer.

**100.** (a) $f(x) = x^2$ and $f'(x) = 2x$

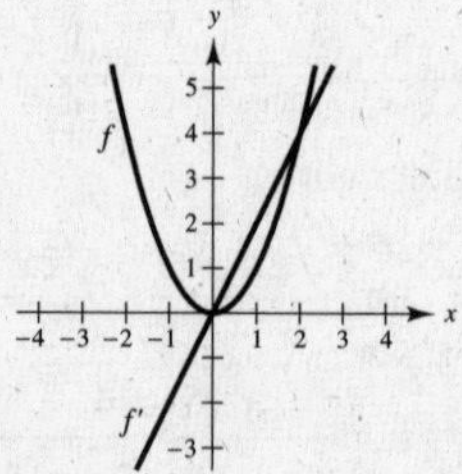


(b) $g(x) = x^3$ and $g'(x) = 3x^2$

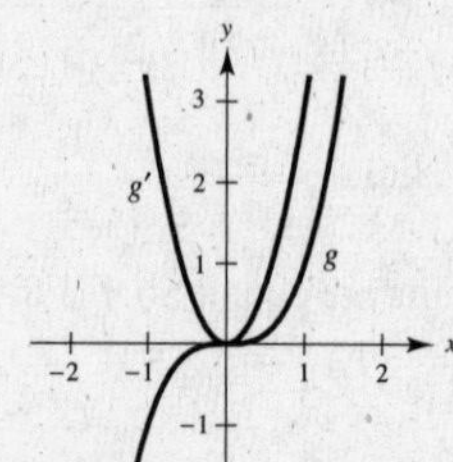

(c) The derivative is a polynomial of degree 1 less than the original function. If $h(x) = x^n$, then $h'(x) = nx^{n-1}$.

(d) If $f(x) = x^4$, then

$$\begin{aligned} f'(x) &= \lim_{\Delta x \to 0} \frac{f(x + \Delta x) - f(x)}{\Delta x} \\ &= \lim_{\Delta x \to 0} \frac{(x + \Delta x)^4 - x^4}{\Delta x} \\ &= \lim_{\Delta x \to 0} \frac{x^4 + 4x^3(\Delta x) + 6x^2(\Delta x)^2 + 4x(\Delta x)^3 + (\Delta x)^4 - x^4}{\Delta x} \\ &= \lim_{\Delta x \to 0} \frac{\Delta x\left(4x^3 + 6x^2(\Delta x) + 4x(\Delta x)^2 + (\Delta x)^3\right)}{\Delta x} = \lim_{\Delta x \to 0}\left(4x^3 + 6x^2(\Delta x) + 4x(\Delta x)^2 + (\Delta x)^3\right) = 4x^3. \end{aligned}$$

So, if $f(x) = x^4$, then $f'(x) = 4x^3$ which is consistent with the conjecture. However, this is not a proof because you must verify the conjecture for all integer values of $n$, $n \ge 2$.

**101.** False. The slope is $\lim_{\Delta x \to 0} \dfrac{f(2 + \Delta x) - f(2)}{\Delta x}$.

**102.** False. $y = |x - 2|$ is continuous at $x = 2$, but is not differentiable at $x = 2$. (Sharp turn in the graph)

**103.** False. If the derivative from the left of a point does not equal the derivative from the right of a point, then the derivative does not exist at that point. For example, if $f(x) = |x|$, then the derivative from the left at $x = 0$ is $-1$ and the derivative from the right at $x = 0$ is 1. At $x = 0$, the derivative does not exist.

**104.** True—see Theorem 2.1.

**105.** $f(x) = \begin{cases} x\sin(1/x), & x \ne 0 \\ 0, & x = 0 \end{cases}$

Using the Squeeze Theorem, you have $-|x| \le x\sin(1/x) \le |x|$, $x \ne 0$. So, $\lim_{x \to 0} x\sin(1/x) = 0 = f(0)$ and $f$ is continuous at $x = 0$. Using the alternative form of the derivative, you have

$$\lim_{x \to 0} \frac{f(x) - f(0)}{x - 0} = \lim_{x \to 0} \frac{x\sin(1/x) - 0}{x - 0} = \lim_{x \to 0}\left(\sin\frac{1}{x}\right).$$

Because this limit does not exist ($\sin(1/x)$ oscillates between $-1$ and 1), the function is not differentiable at $x = 0$.

$g(x) = \begin{cases} x^2\sin(1/x), & x \ne 0 \\ 0, & x = 0 \end{cases}$

Using the Squeeze Theorem again, you have $-x^2 \le x^2\sin(1/x) \le x^2$, $x \ne 0$. So, $\lim_{x \to 0} x^2\sin(1/x) = 0 = g(0)$ and $g$ is continuous at $x = 0$. Using the alternative form of the derivative again, you have

$$\lim_{x \to 0} \frac{g(x) - g(0)}{x - 0} = \lim_{x \to 0} \frac{x^2\sin(1/x) - 0}{x - 0} = \lim_{x \to 0} x\sin\frac{1}{x} = 0.$$

Therefore, $g$ is differentiable at $x = 0$, $g'(0) = 0$.

**106.**

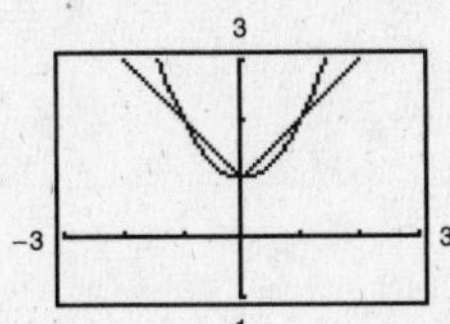


As you zoom in, the graph of $y_1 = x^2 + 1$ appears to be locally the graph of a horizontal line, whereas the graph of $y_2 = |x| + 1$ always has a sharp corner at $(0, 1)$. $y_2$ is not differentiable at $(0, 1)$.

## Section 3.2 Basic Differentiation Rules and Rates of Change

**1.** (a) $y = x^{1/2}$

$y' = \frac{1}{2}x^{-1/2}$

$y'(1) = \frac{1}{2}$

(b) $y = x^3$

$y' = 3x^2$

$y'(1) = 3$

**2.** (a) $y = x^{-1/2}$

$y' = -\frac{1}{2}x^{-3/2}$

$y'(1) = -\frac{1}{2}$

(b) $y = x^{-1}$

$y' = -x^{-2}$

$y'(1) = -1$

**3.** $y = 12$

$y' = 0$

**4.** $f(x) = -9$

$f'(x) = 0$

**5.** $y = x^7$

$y' = 7x^6$

**6.** $y = x^{16}$

$y' = 16x^{15}$

**7.** $y = \frac{1}{x^5} = x^{-5}$

$y' = -5x^{-6} = -\frac{5}{x^6}$

**8.** $y = \frac{1}{x^8} = x^{-8}$

$y' = -8x^{-9} = -\frac{8}{x^9}$

**9.** $y = \sqrt[5]{x} = x^{1/5}$

$y' = \frac{1}{5}x^{-4/5} = \frac{1}{5x^{4/5}}$

**10.** $g(x) = \sqrt[6]{x} = x^{1/6}$

$g'(x) = \frac{1}{6}x^{-5/6} = \frac{1}{6x^{5/6}}$

**11.** $f(x) = x + 11$

$f'(x) = 1$

**12.** $g(x) = 3x - 1$

$g'(x) = 3$

**13.** $f(t) = -2t^2 + 3t - 6$

$f'(t) = -4t + 3$

**14.** $y = t^2 + 2t - 3$

$y' = 2t + 2$

**15.** $g(x) = x^2 + 4x^3$

$g'(x) = 2x + 12x^2$

**16.** $y = 8 - x^3$

$y' = -3x^2$

**17.** $s(t) = t^3 + 5t^2 - 3t + 8$

$s'(t) = 3t^2 + 10t - 3$

**18.** $f(x) = 2x^3 - 4x^2 + 3x$

$f'(x) = 6x^2 - 8x + 3$

**19.** $f(x) = 6x - 5e^x$

$f'(x) = 6 - 5e^x$

**20.** $h(t) = t^3 + 2e^t$

$h'(t) = 3t^2 + 2e^t$

**21.** $y = \frac{\pi}{2}\sin\theta - \cos\theta$

$y' = \frac{\pi}{2}\cos\theta + \sin\theta$

**22.** $g(t) = \pi\cos t$

$g'(t) = -\pi\sin t$

**23.** $y = x^2 - \frac{1}{2}\cos x$

$y' = 2x + \frac{1}{2}\sin x$

**24.** $y = 7 + \sin x$

$y' = \cos x$

**25.** $y = \frac{1}{2}e^x - 3\sin x$

$y' = \frac{1}{2}e^x - 3\cos x$

**26.** $y = \frac{3}{4}e^x + 2\cos x$

$y' = \frac{3}{4}e^x - 2\sin x$

| Function | Rewrite | Differentiate | Simplify |
|---|---|---|---|
| **27.** $y = \frac{5}{2x^2}$ | $y = \frac{5}{2}x^{-2}$ | $y' = -5x^{-3}$ | $y' = -\frac{5}{x^3}$ |
| **28.** $y = \frac{4}{3x^2}$ | $y = \frac{4}{3}x^{-2}$ | $y' = -\frac{8}{3}x^{-3}$ | $y' = -\frac{8}{3x^3}$ |
| **29.** $y = \frac{6}{(5x)^3}$ | $y = \frac{6}{125}x^{-3}$ | $y' = -\frac{18}{125}x^{-4}$ | $y' = -\frac{18}{125x^4}$ |
| **30.** $y = \frac{\pi}{(5x)^2}$ | $y = \frac{\pi}{25}x^{-2}$ | $y' = -\frac{2\pi}{25}x^{-3}$ | $y' = -\frac{2\pi}{25x^3}$ |
| **31.** $y = \frac{\sqrt{x}}{x}$ | $y = x^{-1/2}$ | $y' = -\frac{1}{2}x^{-3/2}$ | $y' = -\frac{1}{2x^{3/2}}$ |
| **32.** $y = \frac{4}{x^{-3}}$ | $y = 4x^3$ | $y' = 12x^2$ | $y' = 12x^2$ |

**33.** $f(x) = \frac{8}{x^2} = 8x^{-2}, (2, 2)$

$f'(x) = -16x^{-3} = -\frac{16}{x^3}$

$f'(2) = -2$

**34.** $f(t) = 3 - \frac{3}{5t}, \left(\frac{3}{5}, 2\right)$

$f'(t) = \frac{3}{5t^2}$

$f'\left(\frac{3}{5}\right) = \frac{5}{3}$

**35.** $f(x) = -\frac{1}{2} + \frac{7}{5}x^3, \left(0, -\frac{1}{2}\right)$

$f'(x) = \frac{21}{5}x^2$

$f'(0) = 0$

**36.** $f(x) = 3(5 - x)^2, (5, 0)$

$= 3x^2 - 30x + 75$

$f'(x) = 6x - 30$

$f'(5) = 0$

**37.** $f(\theta) = 4 \sin \theta - \theta, (0, 0)$

$f'(\theta) = 4 \cos \theta - 1$

$f'(0) = 4(1) - 1 = 3$

**38.** $g(t) = -2 \cos t + 5, (\pi, 7)$

$g'(t) = 2 \sin t$

$g'(\pi) = 0$

**39.** $f(t) = \frac{3}{4}e^t, \left(0, \frac{3}{4}\right)$

$f'(t) = \frac{3}{4}e^t$

$f(0) = \frac{3}{4}e^0 = \frac{3}{4}$

**40.** $g(x) = -4e^x, (1, -4e)$

$g'(x) = -4e^x$

$g'(1) = -4e$

**41.** $g(t) = t^2 - \frac{4}{t^3} = t^2 - 4t^{-3}$

$g'(t) = 2t + 12t^{-4} = 2t + \frac{12}{t^4}$

**42.** $f(x) = x + x^{-2}$

$f'(x) = 1 - 2x^{-3}$

$= 1 - \frac{2}{x^3}$

**43.** $f(x) = \frac{4x^3 + 3x^2}{x} = 4x^2 + 3x$

$f'(x) = 8x + 3$

**44.** $f(x) = \frac{x^3 - 6}{x^2} = x - 6x^{-2}$

$f'(x) = 1 + 12x^{-3} = 1 + \frac{12}{x^3}$

**45.** $f(x) = \frac{x^3 - 3x^2 + 4}{x^2} = x - 3 + 4x^{-2}$

$f'(x) = 1 - \frac{8}{x^3} = \frac{x^3 - 8}{x^3}$

**46.** $h(x) = \dfrac{2x^2 - 3x + 1}{x} = 2x - 3 + x^{-1}$

$h'(x) = 2 - \dfrac{1}{x^2} = \dfrac{2x^2 - 1}{x^2}$

**47.** $y = x(x^2 + 1) = x^3 + x$

$y' = 3x^2 + 1$

**48.** $y = 3x(6x - 5x^2) = 18x^2 - 15x^3$

$y' = 36x - 45x^2$

**49.** $f(x) = \sqrt{x} - 6\sqrt[3]{x} = x^{1/2} - 6x^{1/3}$

$f'(x) = \dfrac{1}{2}x^{-1/2} - 2x^{-2/3} = \dfrac{1}{2\sqrt{x}} - \dfrac{2}{x^{2/3}}$

**50.** $f(x) = \sqrt[3]{x} + \sqrt[5]{x} = x^{1/3} + x^{1/5}$

$f'(x) = \dfrac{1}{3}x^{-2/3} + \dfrac{1}{5}x^{-4/5} = \dfrac{1}{3x^{2/3}} + \dfrac{1}{5x^{4/5}}$

**51.** $h(s) = s^{4/5} - s^{2/3}$

$h'(s) = \dfrac{4}{5}s^{-1/5} - \dfrac{2}{3}s^{-1/3} = \dfrac{4}{5s^{1/5}} - \dfrac{2}{3s^{1/3}}$

**52.** $f(t) = t^{2/3} - t^{1/3} + 4$

$f'(t) = \dfrac{2}{3}t^{-1/3} - \dfrac{1}{3}t^{-2/3} = \dfrac{2}{3t^{1/3}} - \dfrac{1}{3t^{2/3}}$

**53.** $f(x) = 6\sqrt{x} + 5\cos x = 6x^{1/2} + 5\cos x$

$f'(x) = 3x^{-1/2} - 5\sin x = \dfrac{3}{\sqrt{x}} - 5\sin x$

**54.** $f(x) = \dfrac{2}{\sqrt[3]{x}} + 5\cos x = 2x^{-1/3} + 5\cos x$

$f'(x) = \dfrac{-2}{3}x^{-4/3} - 5\sin x = \dfrac{-2}{3x^{4/3}} - 5\sin x$

**55.** $f(x) = x^{-2} - 2e^x$

$f'(x) = -2x^{-3} - 2e^x = \dfrac{-2}{x^3} - 2e^x$

**56.** $g(x) = \sqrt{x} - 3e^x$

$g'(x) = \dfrac{1}{2\sqrt{x}} - 3e^x$

**57.** (a) $y = x^4 - x$

$y' = 4x^3 - 1$

At $(-1, 2)$: $y' = 4(-1)^3 - 1 = -5$

Tangent line: $y - 2 = -5(x + 1)$

$y = -5x - 3$

(b)

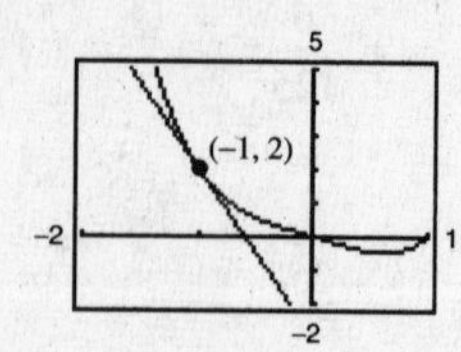


**58.** (a) $f(x) = \dfrac{2}{\sqrt[4]{x^3}} = 2x^{-3/4}$

$f'(x) = -\dfrac{3}{2}x^{-7/4} = -\dfrac{3}{2x^{7/4}}$

At $(1, 2)$: $f'(1) = -\dfrac{3}{2}$

Tangent line: $y - 2 = -\dfrac{3}{2}(x - 1)$

$y = -\dfrac{3}{2}x + \dfrac{7}{2}$

$3x + 2y - 7 = 0$

(b)

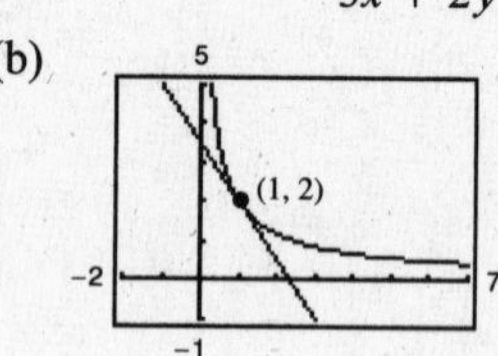


**59.** (a) $g(x) = x + e^x$

$g'(x) = 1 + e^x$

At $(0, 1)$: $g'(0) = 1 + 1 = 2$

Tangent line: $y - 1 = 2(x - 0)$

$y = 2x + 1$

(b)

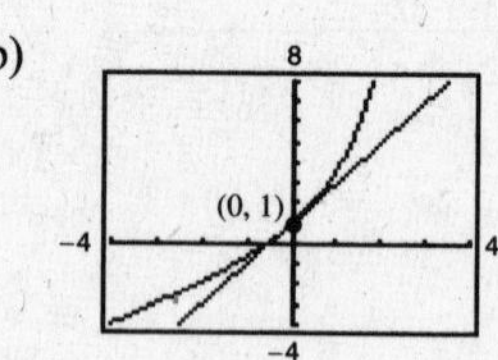

**60.** (a) $h(t) = \sin t + \frac{1}{2}e^t$

$h'(t) = \cos t + \frac{1}{2}e^t$

At $\left(\pi, \frac{1}{2}e^t\right)$: $h'(\pi) = -1 + \frac{1}{2}e^\pi$

Tangent line:

$y - \frac{1}{2}e^\pi = \left(-1 + \frac{1}{2}e^\pi\right)(t - \pi)$

$y = \left(-1 + \frac{1}{2}e^\pi\right)t + \frac{1}{2}e^\pi + \pi - \frac{1}{2}\pi e^\pi$

(b)

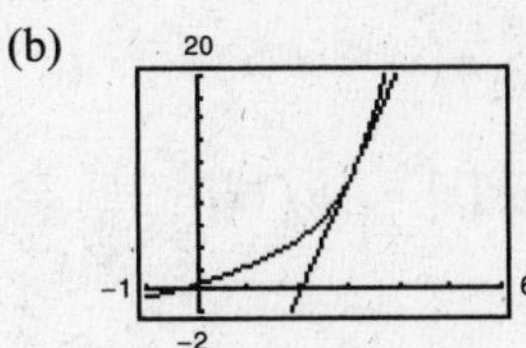


**61.** $y = x^4 - 2x^2 + 3$

$y' = 4x^3 - 4x$

$= 4x(x^2 - 1)$

$= 4x(x - 1)(x + 1)$

$y' = 0 \Rightarrow x = 0, \pm 1$

Horizontal tangents: $(0, 3), (1, 2), (-1, 2)$

**62.** $y = x^3 + x$

$y' = 3x^2 + 1 > 0$ for all $x$.

So, there are no horizontal tangents.

**63.** $y = \dfrac{1}{x^2} = x^{-2}$

$y' = -2x^{-3} = -\dfrac{2}{x^3}$ cannot equal zero.

So, there are no horizontal tangents.

**64.** $y = x^2 + 9$

$y' = 2x = 0 \Rightarrow x = 0$

At $x = 0$: $y = 1$

Horizontal tangent: $(0, 9)$

**65.** $y = x + \sin x, 0 \le x < 2\pi$

$y' = 1 + \cos x = 0$

$\cos x = -1 \Rightarrow x = \pi$

At $x = \pi$: $y = \pi$

Horizontal tangent: $(\pi, \pi)$

**66.** $y = \sqrt{3}x + 2\cos x, 0 \le x < 2\pi$

$y' = \sqrt{3} - 2\sin x = 0$

$\sin x = \dfrac{\sqrt{3}}{2} \Rightarrow x = \dfrac{\pi}{3}$ or $\dfrac{2\pi}{3}$

At $x = \dfrac{\pi}{3}$: $y = \dfrac{\sqrt{3}\pi + 3}{3}$

At $x = \dfrac{2\pi}{3}$: $y = \dfrac{2\sqrt{3}\pi - 3}{3}$

Horizontal tangents: $\left(\dfrac{\pi}{3}, \dfrac{\sqrt{3}\pi + 3}{3}\right), \left(\dfrac{2\pi}{3}, \dfrac{2\sqrt{3}\pi - 3}{3}\right)$

**67.** $y = -4x + e^x$

$y' = -4 + e^x = 0$

$e^x = 4$

$x = \ln 4$

$(\ln 4, -4\ln 4 + 4)$

**68.** $y = x + 4e^x$

$y' = 1 + 4e^x$ cannot equal 0.

So, there are no horizontal tangents.

**69.** $x^2 - kx = 5x - 4$ Equate functions.

$2x - k = 5$ Equate derivatives.

So, $k = 2x - 5$ and

$x^2 - (2x - 5)x = 5x - 4 \Rightarrow -x^2 = -4 \Rightarrow x = \pm 2.$

For $x = 2, k = -1$ and for $x = -2, k = -9$.

**70.** $k - x^2 = -6x + 1$ Equate functions.

$-2x = -6$ Equate derivatives.

So, $x = 3$ and $k - 9 = -18 + 1 \Rightarrow k = -8$.

**71.** $\dfrac{k}{x} = -\dfrac{3}{4}x + 3$ Equate functions.

$-\dfrac{k}{x^2} = -\dfrac{3}{4}$ Equate derivatives.

So, $k = \dfrac{3}{4}x^2$ and

$\dfrac{\frac{3}{4}x^2}{x} = -\dfrac{3}{4}x + 3 \Rightarrow \dfrac{3}{4}x = -\dfrac{3}{4}x + 3$

$\Rightarrow \dfrac{3}{2}x = 3 \Rightarrow x = 2 \Rightarrow k = 3.$

**72.** $k\sqrt{x} = x + 4$ Equate functions.

$\dfrac{k}{2\sqrt{x}} = 1$ Equate derivatives.

So, $k = 2\sqrt{x}$ and

$(2\sqrt{x})\sqrt{x} = x + 4 \Rightarrow 2x = x + 4 \Rightarrow x = 4 \Rightarrow k = 4.$

**73.** $kx^3 = x + 1$ Equate equations.

$3kx^2 = 1$ Equate derivatives.

So, $k = \dfrac{1}{3x^2}$ and

$\left(\dfrac{1}{3x^2}\right)x^3 = x + 1$

$\dfrac{1}{3}x = x + 1$

$x = -\dfrac{3}{2}, k = \dfrac{4}{27}.$

**74.** $kx^4 = 4x - 1$ Equate equations.

$4kx^3 = 4$ Equate derivatives.

So, $k = \dfrac{1}{x^3}$ and

$\left(\dfrac{1}{x^3}\right)x^4 = 4x - 1$

$x = 4x - 1$

$x = \dfrac{1}{3}$ and $k = 27.$

**75.** The graph of a function $f$ such that $f' > 0$ for all $x$ and the rate of change of the function is decreasing (i.e., $f'' < 0$) would, in general, look like the graph below.

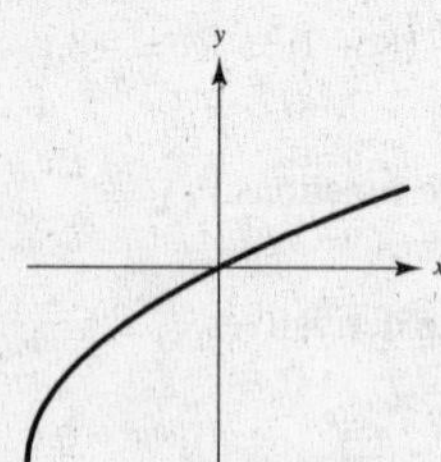


**76.** (a) The slope appears to be steepest between $A$ and $B$.

(b) The average rate of change between $A$ and $B$ is **greater** than the instantaneous rate of change at $B$.

(c)

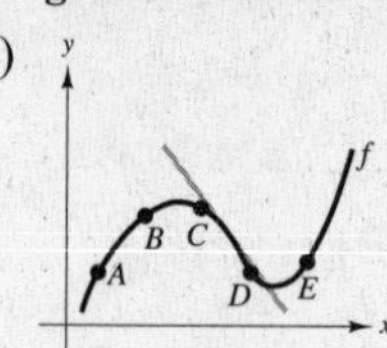


**77.** $g(x) = f(x) + 6 \Rightarrow g'(x) = f'(x)$

**78.** $g(x) = -5f(x) \Rightarrow g'(x) = -5f'(x)$

**79.**

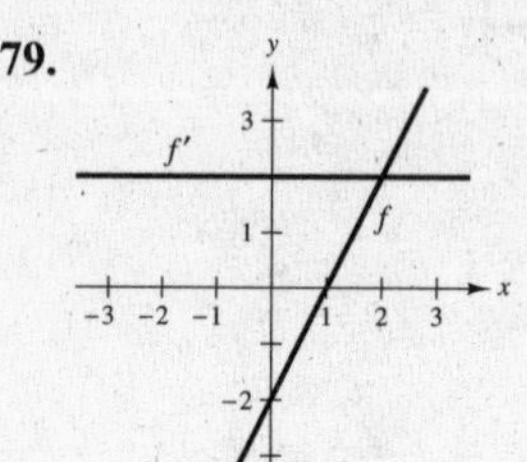


If $f$ is linear then its derivative is a constant function.

$f(x) = ax + b$

$f'(x) = a$

**80.**

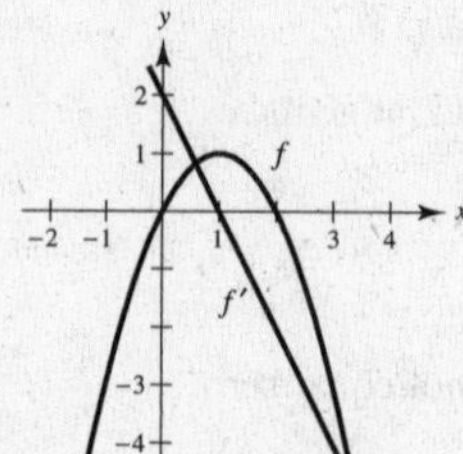


If $f$ is quadratic, then its derivative is a linear function.

$f(x) = ax^2 + bx + c$

$f'(x) = 2ax + b$

**81.** Let $(x_1, y_1)$ and $(x_2, y_2)$ be the points of tangency on $y = x^2$ and $y = -x^2 + 6x - 5$, respectively.

The derivatives of these functions are:

$y' = 2x \Rightarrow m = 2x_1$ and $y' = -2x + 6 \Rightarrow m = -2x_2 + 6$

$m = 2x_1 = -2x_2 + 6$

$x_1 = -x_2 + 3$

Because $y_1 = x_1^2$ and $y_2 = -x_2^2 + 6x_2 - 5$:

$$m = \frac{y_2 - y_1}{x_2 - x_1} = \frac{\left(-x_2^2 + 6x_2 - 5\right) - \left(x_1^2\right)}{x_2 - x_1} = -2x_2 + 6$$

$$\frac{\left(-x_2^2 + 6x_2 - 5\right) - \left(-x_2 + 3\right)^2}{x_2 - \left(-x_2 + 3\right)} = -2x_2 + 6$$

$$\left(-x_2^2 + 6x_2 - 5\right) - \left(x_2^2 - 6x_2 + 9\right) = \left(-2x_2 + 6\right)\left(2x_2 - 3\right)$$

$$-2x_2^2 + 12x_2 - 14 = -4x_2^2 + 18x_2 - 18$$

$$2x_2^2 - 6x_2 + 4 = 0$$

$$2\left(x_2 - 2\right)\left(x_2 - 1\right) = 0$$

$$x_2 = 1 \text{ or } 2$$

$x_2 = 1 \Rightarrow y_2 = 0, x_1 = 2$ and $y_1 = 4$

So, the tangent line through $(1, 0)$ and $(2, 4)$ is

$$y - 0 = \left(\frac{4 - 0}{2 - 1}\right)(x - 1) \Rightarrow y = 4x - 4.$$

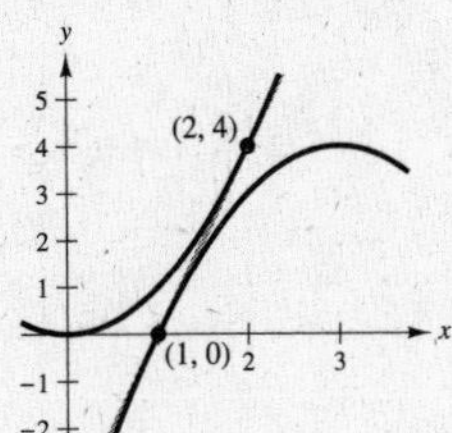


$x_2 = 2 \Rightarrow y_2 = 3, x_1 = 1$ and $y_1 = 1$

So, the tangent line through $(2, 3)$ and $(1, 1)$ is

$$y - 1 = \left(\frac{3 - 1}{2 - 1}\right)(x - 1) \Rightarrow y = 2x - 1.$$

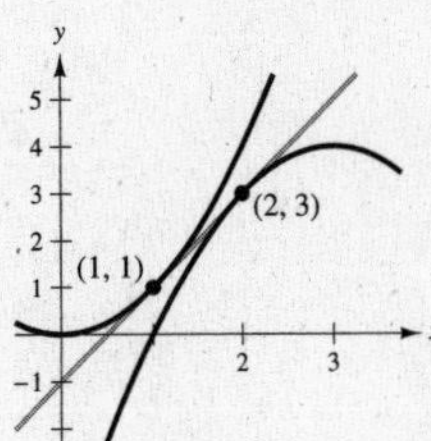


**82.** $m_1$ is the slope of the line tangent to $y = x$. $m_2$ is the slope of the line tangent to $y = 1/x$. Because

$$y = x \Rightarrow y' = 1 \Rightarrow m_1 = 1 \text{ and } y = \frac{1}{x} \Rightarrow y' = -\frac{1}{x^2} \Rightarrow m_2 = -\frac{1}{x^2}.$$

The points of intersection of $y = x$ and $y = 1/x$ are

$$x = \frac{1}{x} \Rightarrow x^2 = 1 \Rightarrow x = \pm 1.$$

At $x = \pm 1$, $m_2 = -1$. Because $m_2 = -1/m_1$, these tangent lines are perpendicular at the points of intersection.

**83.** $f(x) = 3x + \sin x + 2$

$f'(x) = 3 + \cos x$

Because $|\cos x| \le 1$, $f'(x) \ne 0$ for all $x$ and $f$ does not have a horizontal tangent line.

**84.** $f(x) = x^5 + 3x^3 + 5x$

$f'(x) = 5x^4 + 9x^2 + 5$

Because $5x^4 + 9x^2 \ge 0$, $f'(x) \ge 5$. So, $f$ does not have a tangent line with a slope of 3.

**85.** $f(x) = \sqrt{x}, (-4, 0)$

$$f'(x) = \frac{1}{2}x^{-1/2} = \frac{1}{2\sqrt{x}}$$

$$\frac{1}{2\sqrt{x}} = \frac{0 - y}{-4 - x}$$

$$4 + x = 2\sqrt{x}y$$

$$4 + x = 2\sqrt{x}\sqrt{x}$$

$$4 + x = 2x$$

$$x = 4, y = 2$$

The point $(4, 2)$ is on the graph of $f$.

Tangent line: $y - 2 = \dfrac{0 - 2}{-4 - 4}(x - 4)$

$$4y - 8 = x - 4$$

$$0 = x - 4y + 4$$

**86.** $f(x) = \dfrac{2}{x}, (5, 0)$

$$f'(x) = -\frac{2}{x^2}$$

$$-\frac{2}{x^2} = \frac{0 - y}{5 - x}$$

$$-10 + 2x = -x^2y$$

$$-10 + 2x = -x^2\left(\frac{2}{x}\right)$$

$$-10 + 2x = -2x$$

$$4x = 10$$

$$x = \frac{5}{2}, y = \frac{4}{5}$$

The point $\left(\dfrac{5}{2}, \dfrac{4}{5}\right)$ is on the graph of $f$. The slope of the tangent line is $f'\left(\dfrac{5}{2}\right) = -\dfrac{8}{25}$.

Tangent line: $y - \dfrac{4}{5} = -\dfrac{8}{25}\left(x - \dfrac{5}{2}\right)$

$$25y - 20 = -8x + 20$$

$$8x + 25y - 40 = 0$$

**87.** $f'(1)$ appears to be close to $-1$.

$$f'(1) = -1$$

**88.** $f'(4)$ appears to be close to 1.

$$f'(4) = 1$$

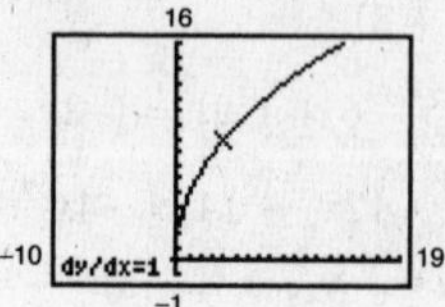


**89.** (a) One possible secant is between $(3.9, 7.7019)$ and $(4, 8)$:

$$y - 8 = \frac{8 - 7.7019}{4 - 3.9}(x - 4)$$

$$y - 8 = 2.981(x - 4)$$

$$y = S(x) = 2.981x - 3.924$$

(b) $f'(x) = \dfrac{3}{2}x^{1/2} \Rightarrow f'(4) = \dfrac{3}{2}(2) = 3$

$$T(x) = 3(x - 4) + 8 = 3x - 4$$

The slope (and equation) of the secant line approaches that of the tangent line at $(4, 8)$ as you choose points closer and closer to $(4, 8)$.

(c) As you move further away from $(4, 8)$, the accuracy of the approximation $T$ gets worse.

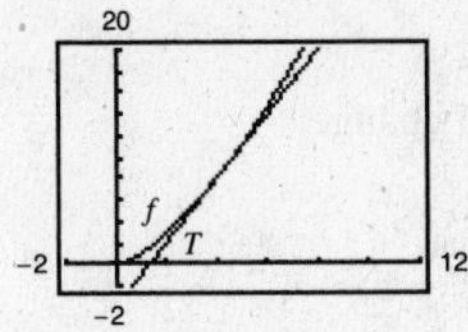


(d)

| $\Delta x$ | −3 | −2 | −1 | −0.5 | −0.1 | 0 | 0.1 | 0.5 | 1 | 2 | 3 |
|---|---|---|---|---|---|---|---|---|---|---|---|
| $f(4 + \Delta x)$ | 1 | 2.828 | 5.196 | 6.548 | 7.702 | 8 | 8.302 | 9.546 | 11.180 | 14.697 | 18.520 |
| $T(4 + \Delta x)$ | −1 | 2 | 5 | 6.5 | 7.7 | 8 | 8.3 | 9.5 | 11 | 14 | 17 |

**90.** (a) Nearby point: $(1.0073138, 1.0221024)$

Secant line: $y - 1 = \dfrac{1.0221024 - 1}{1.0073138 - 1}(x - 1)$

$y = 3.022(x - 1) + 1$

(Answers will vary.)

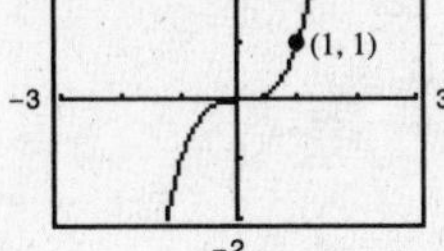


(b) $f'(x) = 3x^2$

$T(x) = 3(x - 1) + 1 = 3x - 2$

(c) The accuracy worsens as you move away from $(1, 1)$.

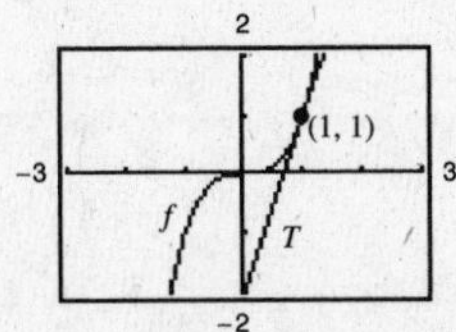


(d)

| $\Delta x$ | −3 | −2 | −1 | −0.5 | −0.1 | 0 | 0.1 | 0.5 | 1 | 2 | 3 |
|---|---|---|---|---|---|---|---|---|---|---|---|
| $f(x)$ | −8 | −1 | 0 | 0.125 | 0.729 | 1 | 1.331 | 3.375 | 8 | 27 | 64 |
| $T(x)$ | −8 | −5 | −2 | −0.5 | 0.7 | 1 | 1.3 | 2.5 | 4 | 7 | 10 |

The accuracy decreases more rapidly than in Exercise 89 because $y = x^3$ is less "linear" than $y = x^{3/2}$.

**91.** False. Let $f(x) = x$ and $g(x) = x + 1$. Then $f'(x) = g'(x) = 1$, but $f(x) \neq g(x)$.

**92.** True. If $f(x) = g(x) + c$, then $f'(x) = g'(x) + 0 = g'(x)$.

**93.** False. If $y = \pi^2$, then $dy/dx = 0$. ($\pi^2$ is a constant.)

**94.** True. If $y = x/\pi = (1/\pi) \cdot x$, then $dy/dx = (1/\pi)(1) = 1/\pi$.

**95.** True. If $g(x) = 3f(x)$, then $g'(x) = 3f'(x)$.

**96.** False. If $f(x) = \dfrac{1}{x_n} = x^{-n}$, then

$f'(x) = -nx^{-n-1} = \dfrac{-n}{x^{n+1}}$.

**97.** $f(x) = -\dfrac{1}{x}$, $[1, 2]$

$f'(x) = \dfrac{1}{x^2}$

Instantaneous rate of change:

$(1, -1) \Rightarrow f'(1) = 1$

$\left(2, -\dfrac{1}{2}\right) \Rightarrow f'(2) = \dfrac{1}{4}$

Average rate of change:

$\dfrac{f(2) - f(1)}{2 - 1} = \dfrac{(-1/2) - (-1)}{2 - 1} = \dfrac{1}{2}$

**98.** $f(x) = \cos x, \quad \left[0, \dfrac{\pi}{3}\right]$

$f'(x) = -\sin x$

Instantaneous rate of change:

$(0, 1) \Rightarrow f'(0) = 0$

$\left(\dfrac{\pi}{3}, \dfrac{1}{2}\right) \Rightarrow f'\left(\dfrac{\pi}{3}\right) = -\dfrac{\sqrt{3}}{2} \approx -0.866$

Average rate of change:

$$\frac{f(\pi/3) - f(0)}{(\pi/6) - 0} = \frac{(1/2) - 1}{(\pi/6)} = -\frac{3}{\pi} \approx -0.955$$

**99.** $g(x) = x^2 + e^x, \quad [0, 1]$

$g'(x) = 2x + e^x$

Instantaneous rate of change:

$(0, 1)$: $g'(0) = 1$

$(1, 1 + e)$: $g'(1) = 2 + e \approx 4.718$

Average rate of change:

$$\frac{g(1) - g(0)}{1 - 0} = \frac{(1 + e) - (1)}{1} = e \approx 2.718$$

**100.** $h(x) = x^3 - \dfrac{1}{2}e^x, \quad [0, 2]$

$h'(x) = 3x^2 - \dfrac{1}{2}e^x$

Instantaneous rate of change:

$\left(0, -\dfrac{1}{2}\right)$: $h'(0) = -\dfrac{1}{2}$

$\left(2, 8 - \dfrac{1}{2}e^2\right)$: $h'(2) = 12 - \dfrac{1}{2}e^2 \approx 8.305$

Average rate of change:

$$\frac{h(2) - h(0)}{2 - 0} = \frac{\left[8 - (1/2)e^2\right] - (-1/2)}{2} = \frac{17 - e^2}{4} \approx 2.403$$

**101.** (a) $s(t) = -16t^2 + 1362$

$v(t) = -32t$

(b) $\dfrac{s(2) - s(1)}{2 - 1} = 1298 - 1346 = -48$ ft/sec

(c) $v(t) = s'(t) = -32t$

When $t = 1$: $v(1) = -32$ ft/sec

When $t = 2$: $v(2) = -64$ ft/sec

(d) $-16t^2 + 1362 = 0$

$t^2 = \dfrac{1362}{16} \Rightarrow t = \dfrac{\sqrt{1362}}{4} \approx 9.226$ sec

(e) $v\left(\dfrac{\sqrt{1362}}{4}\right) = -32\left(\dfrac{\sqrt{1362}}{4}\right)$

$= -8\sqrt{1362} \approx -295.242$ ft/sec

**102.** $s(t) = -16t^2 - 22t + 220$

$v(t) = -32t - 22$

$v(3) = -118$ ft/sec

$s(t) = -16t^2 - 22t + 220$

$= 112$ (height after falling 108 ft)

$-16t^2 - 22t + 108 = 0$

$-2(t - 2)(8t + 27) = 0$

$t = 2$

$v(2) = -32(2) - 22$

$= -86$ ft/sec

**103.** $s(t) = -4.9t^2 + v_0t + s_0$

$= -4.9t^2 + 120t$

$v(t) = -9.8t + 120$

$v(5) = -9.8(5) + 120 = 71$ m/sec

$v(10) = -9.8(10) + 120 = 22$ m/sec

**104.** $s(t) = -4.9t^2 + v_0t + s_0$

$= -4.9t^2 + s_0 = 0$ when $t = 5.6.$

$s_0 = 4.9t^2 = 4.9(5.6)^2 \approx 153.7$ m

**105.** From $(0, 0)$ to $(4, 2)$, $s(t) = \frac{1}{2}t \Rightarrow v(t) = \frac{1}{2}$ mi/min.

$v(t) = \frac{1}{2}(60) = 30$ mi/h for $0 < t < 4$

Similarly, $v(t) = 0$ for $4 < t < 6$. Finally, from $(6, 2)$ to $(10, 6)$,

$s(t) = t - 4 \Rightarrow v(t) = 1$ mi/min. $= 60$ mi/h.

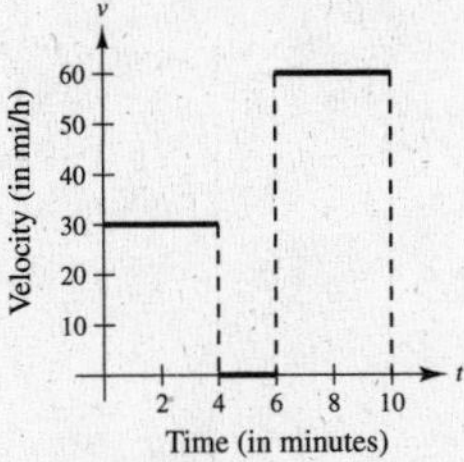


(The velocity has been converted to miles per hour.)

**106.** From $(0, 0)$ to $(6, 5)$, $s(t) = \frac{5}{6}t \Rightarrow v(t) = \frac{5}{6}$ mi/min.

$v(t) = \frac{5}{6}(60) = 50$ mi/h for $0 < t < 6$

Similarly, $v(t) = 0$ for $6 < t < 8$.

Finally, from $(8, 5)$ to $(10, 6)$,

$s(t) = \frac{1}{2}t + 1 \Rightarrow v(t) = \frac{1}{2}$ mi/min $= 30$ mi/h.

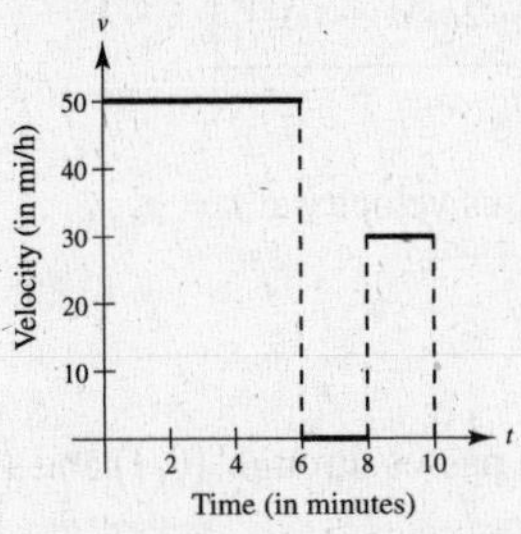


(The velocity has been converted to miles per hour.)

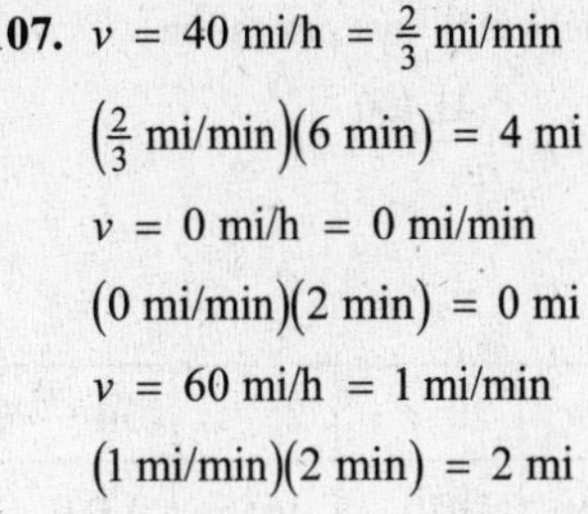

**107.** $v = 40$ mi/h $= \frac{2}{3}$ mi/min

$\left(\frac{2}{3} \text{ mi/min}\right)(6 \text{ min}) = 4$ mi

$v = 0$ mi/h $= 0$ mi/min

$(0 \text{ mi/min})(2 \text{ min}) = 0$ mi

$v = 60$ mi/h $= 1$ mi/min

$(1 \text{ mi/min})(2 \text{ min}) = 2$ mi

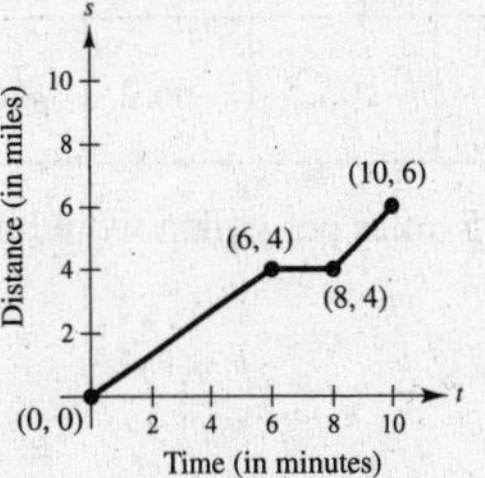


**108.** This graph corresponds with Exercise 105.

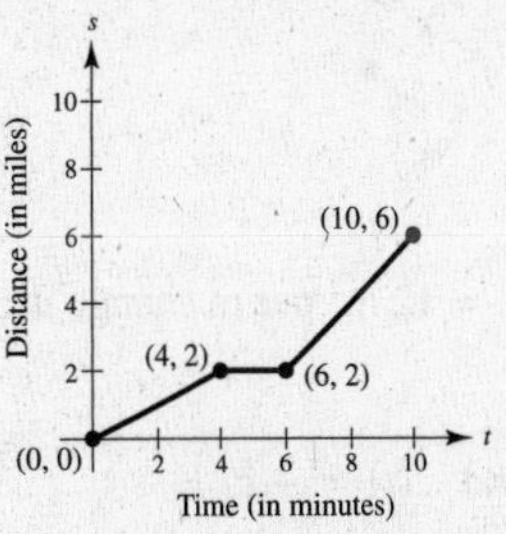


**109.** (a) Using a graphing utility,

$R(v) = 0.417v - 0.02.$

(b) Using a graphing utility,

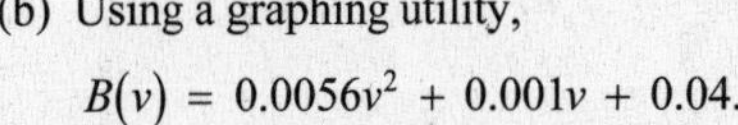

$B(v) = 0.0056v^2 + 0.001v + 0.04.$

(c) $T(v) = R(v) + B(v) = 0.0056v^2 + 0.418v + 0.02$

(d)

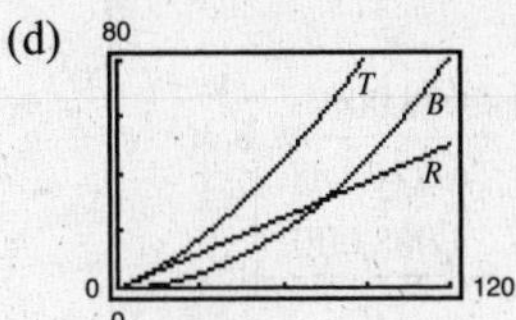


(e) $\dfrac{dT}{dv} = 0.0112v + 0.418$

For $v = 40$, $T'(40) \approx 0.866$

For $v = 80$, $T'(80) \approx 1.314$

For $v = 100$, $T'(100) \approx 1.538$

(f) For increasing speeds, the total stopping distance increases.

**110.** $C = (\text{gallons of fuel used})(\text{cost per gallon})$

$$= \left(\frac{15{,}000}{x}\right)(2.76) = \frac{41{,}400}{x}$$

$$\frac{dC}{dx} = -\frac{41{,}400}{x^2}$$

| $x$ | 10 | 15 | 20 | 25 | 30 | 35 | 40 |
|---|---|---|---|---|---|---|---|
| $C$ | 4140 | 2760 | 2070 | 1656 | 1380 | 1183 | 1035 |
| $\frac{dC}{dx}$ | −414 | −184 | −103.5 | −66.2 | −46 | −33.8 | −25.9 |

The driver who gets 15 miles per gallon would benefit more. The rate of change at $x = 15$ is larger in absolute value than that at $x = 35$.

**111.** $V = s^3, \frac{dV}{ds} = 3s^2$

When $s = 6$ cm, $\frac{dV}{ds} = 108 \text{ cm}^3$ per cm change in $s$.

**112.** $A = s^2, \frac{dA}{ds} = 2s$

When $s = 6$ m, $\frac{dA}{ds} = 12 \text{ m}^2$ per m change in $s$.

**113.** $s(t) = -\frac{1}{2}at^2 + c$ and $s'(t) = -at$

Average velocity: $$\frac{s(t_0 + \Delta t) - s(t_0 - \Delta t)}{(t_0 + \Delta t) - (t_0 - \Delta t)} = \frac{\left[-(1/2)a(t_0 + \Delta t)^2 + c\right] - \left[-(1/2)a(t_0 - \Delta t)^2 + c)\right]}{2\Delta t}$$

$$= \frac{-(1/2)a\left(t_0^2 + 2t_0\Delta t + (\Delta t)^2\right) + (1/2)a\left(t_0^2 - 2t_0\Delta t + (\Delta t)^2\right)}{2\,\Delta t}$$

$$= \frac{-2at_0\,\Delta t}{2\,\Delta t} = -at_0 = s'(t_0) \qquad \text{instantaneous velocity at } t = t_0$$

**114.** $$C = \frac{1{,}008{,}000}{Q} + 6.3Q$$

$$\frac{dC}{dQ} = -\frac{1{,}008{,}000}{Q^2} + 6.3$$

$C(351) - C(350) \approx 5083.095 - 5085 \approx -\$1.91$

When $Q = 350$, $\frac{dC}{dQ} \approx -\$1.93$.

**115.** $N = f(p)$

(a) $f'(2.979)$ is the rate of change of the number of gallons of gasoline sold when the price is \$2.979 per gallon.

(b) $f'(2.979)$ is usually negative. As prices go up, sales go down.

**116.** $\frac{dT}{dt} = K(T - T_a)$

**117.** $y = ax^2 + bx + c$

Because the parabola passes through $(0, 1)$ and $(1, 0)$, you have:

$(0, 1)$: $1 = a(0)^2 + b(0) + c \Rightarrow c = 1$

$(1, 0)$: $0 = a(1)^2 + b(1) + 1 \Rightarrow b = -a - 1$

So, $y = ax^2 + (-a - 1)x + 1$. From the tangent line $y = x - 1$, you know that the derivative is 1 at the point $(1, 0)$.

$$y' = 2ax + (-a - 1)$$
$$1 = 2a(1) + (-a - 1)$$
$$1 = a - 1$$
$$a = 2$$
$$b = -a - 1 = -3$$

Therefore, $y = 2x^2 - 3x + 1$.

**118.** $y = \dfrac{1}{x}, x > 0$

$y' = -\dfrac{1}{x^2}$

At $(a, b)$, the equation of the tangent line is

$$y - \frac{1}{a} = -\frac{1}{a^2}(x - a) \quad \text{or} \quad y = -\frac{x}{a^2} + \frac{2}{a}.$$

The $x$-intercept is $(2a, 0)$.

The $y$-intercept is $\left(0, \dfrac{2}{a}\right)$.

The area of the triangle is $A = \dfrac{1}{2}bh = \dfrac{1}{2}(2a)\left(\dfrac{2}{a}\right) = 2.$

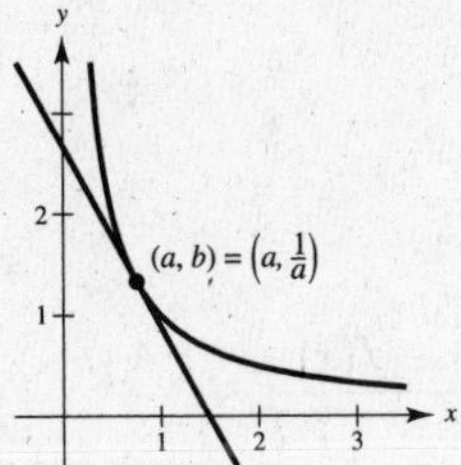


**119.** $y = x^3 - 9x$

$y' = 3x^2 - 9$

Tangent lines through $(1, -9)$:

$$y + 9 = (3x^2 - 9)(x - 1)$$
$$(x^3 - 9x) + 9 = 3x^3 - 3x^2 - 9x + 9$$
$$0 = 2x^3 - 3x^2 = x^2(2x - 3)$$
$$x = 0 \text{ or } x = \tfrac{3}{2}$$

The points of tangency are $(0, 0)$ and $\left(\frac{3}{2}, -\frac{81}{8}\right)$.

At $(0, 0)$, the slope is $y'(0) = -9$. At $\left(\frac{3}{2}, -\frac{81}{8}\right)$, the slope is $y'\left(\frac{3}{2}\right) = -\frac{9}{4}$.

Tangent Lines:

$y - 0 = -9(x - 0)$ and $y + \frac{81}{8} = -\frac{9}{4}\left(x - \frac{3}{2}\right)$

$y = -9x$ $\qquad y = -\frac{9}{4}x - \frac{27}{4}$

$9x + y = 0$ $\qquad 9x + 4y + 27 = 0$

**120.** $y = x^2$

$y' = 2x$

(a) Tangent lines through $(0, a)$:

$$y - a = 2x(x - 0)$$
$$x^2 - a = 2x^2$$
$$-a = x^2$$
$$\pm\sqrt{-a} = x$$

The points of tangency are $\left(\pm\sqrt{-a}, -a\right)$. At $\left(\sqrt{-a}, -a\right)$, the slope is $y'\left(\sqrt{-a}\right) = 2\sqrt{-a}$.

At $\left(-\sqrt{-a}, -a\right)$, the slope is $y'\left(-\sqrt{-a}\right) = -2\sqrt{-a}$.

Tangent lines: $y + a = 2\sqrt{-a}\left(x - \sqrt{-a}\right)$ and $y + a = -2\sqrt{-a}\left(x + \sqrt{-a}\right)$

$y = 2\sqrt{-a}x + a$ $\qquad y = -2\sqrt{-a}x + a$

**Restriction:** $a$ must be negative.

(b) Tangent lines through $(a, 0)$:

$$y - 0 = 2x(x - a)$$
$$x^2 = 2x^2 - 2ax$$
$$0 = x^2 - 2ax = x(x - 2a)$$

The points of tangency are $(0, 0)$ and $(2a, 4a^2)$. At $(0, 0)$, the slope is $y'(0) = 0$. At $(2a, 4a^2)$, the slope is $y'(2a) = 4a$.

Tangent lines: $y - 0 = 0(x - 0)$ and $y - 4a^2 = 4a(x - 2a)$

$y = 0$ $\qquad y = 4ax - 4a^2$

**Restriction:** None, $a$ can be any real number.

**121.** $f(x) = \begin{cases} ax^3, & x \le 2 \\ x^2 + b, & x > 2 \end{cases}$

$f$ must be continuous at $x = 2$ to be differentiable at $x = 2$.

$$\left.\begin{aligned} \lim_{x\to 2^-} f(x) &= \lim_{x\to 2^-} ax^3 = 8a \\ \lim_{x\to 2^+} f(x) &= \lim_{x\to 2^+} (x^2 + b) = 4 + b \end{aligned}\right\} \begin{aligned} 8a &= 4 + b \\ 8a - 4 &= b \end{aligned}$$

$$f'(x) = \begin{cases} 3ax^2, & x < 2 \\ 2x, & x > 2 \end{cases}$$

For $f$ to be differentiable at $x = 2$, the left derivative must equal the right derivative.

$$\begin{aligned} 3a(2)^2 &= 2(2) \\ 12a &= 4 \\ a &= \tfrac{1}{3} \\ b &= 8a - 4 = -\tfrac{4}{3} \end{aligned}$$

**122.** $f(x) = \begin{cases} \cos x, & x < 0 \\ ax + b, & x \ge 0 \end{cases}$

$f(0) = b = \cos(0) = 1 \Rightarrow b = 1$

$$f'(x) = \begin{cases} -\sin x, & x < 0 \\ a, & x > 0 \end{cases}$$

So, $a = 0$.

Answer: $a = 0, b = 1$

**123.** $f_1(x) = |\sin x|$ is differentiable for all $x \ne n\pi$, $n$ an integer.

$f_2(x) = \sin|x|$ is differentiable for all $x \ne 0$.

You can verify this by graphing $f_1$ and $f_2$ and observing the locations of the sharp turns.

**124.** Let $f(x) = \cos x$.

$$\begin{aligned} f'(x) &= \lim_{\Delta x\to 0} \frac{f(x + \Delta x) - f(x)}{\Delta x} \\ &= \lim_{\Delta x\to 0} \frac{\cos x \cos \Delta x - \sin x \sin \Delta x - \cos x}{\Delta x} \\ &= \lim_{\Delta x\to 0} \frac{\cos x(\cos \Delta x - 1)}{\Delta x} - \lim_{\Delta x\to 0} \sin x\left(\frac{\sin \Delta x}{\Delta x}\right) \\ &= 0 - \sin x(1) = -\sin x \end{aligned}$$

## Section 3.3 Product and Quotient Rules and Higher-Order Derivatives

**1.** $g(x) = (x^2 + 3)(x^2 - 4x)$

$$\begin{aligned} g'(x) &= (x^2 + 3)(2x - 4) + (x^2 - 4x)(2x) \\ &= 2x^3 - 4x^2 + 6x - 12 + 2x^3 - 8x^2 \\ &= 4x^3 - 12x^2 + 6x - 12 \\ &= 2(2x^3 - 6x^2 + 3x - 6) \end{aligned}$$

**2.** $f(x) = (6x + 5)(x^3 - 2)$

$$\begin{aligned} f'(x) &= (6x + 5)(3x^2) + (x^3 - 2)(6) \\ &= 18x^3 + 15x^2 + 6x^3 - 12 \\ &= 24x^3 + 15x^2 - 12 \end{aligned}$$

**3.** $h(t) = \sqrt{t}(1 - t^2) = t^{1/2}(1 - t^2)$

$$\begin{aligned} h'(t) &= t^{1/2}(-2t) + (1 - t^2)\frac{1}{2}t^{-1/2} \\ &= -2t^{3/2} + \frac{1}{2t^{1/2}} - \frac{1}{2}t^{3/2} \\ &= -\frac{5}{2}t^{3/2} + \frac{1}{2t^{1/2}} \\ &= \frac{1 - 5t^2}{2t^{1/2}} = \frac{1 - 5t^2}{2\sqrt{t}} \end{aligned}$$

**4.** $g(s) = \sqrt{s}\left(s^2 + 8\right) = s^{1/2}\left(s^2 + 8\right)$

$$g'(s) = s^{1/2}(2s) + \left(s^2 + 8\right)\frac{1}{2}s^{-1/2}$$
$$= 2s^{3/2} + \frac{1}{2}s^{3/2} + 4s^{-1/2}$$
$$= \frac{5}{2}s^{3/2} + \frac{4}{s^{1/2}}$$
$$= \frac{5s^2 + 8}{2\sqrt{s}}$$

**5.** $f(x) = e^x \cos x$

$$f'(x) = e^x(-\sin x) + e^x \cos x$$
$$= e^x(\cos x - \sin x)$$

**6.** $g(x) = \sqrt{x} \sin x$

$$g'(x) = \sqrt{x} \cos x + \sin x\left(\frac{1}{2\sqrt{x}}\right)$$
$$= \sqrt{x} \cos x + \frac{1}{2\sqrt{x}} \sin x$$

**7.** $f(x) = \dfrac{x}{x^2 + 1}$

$$f'(x) = \frac{\left(x^2 + 1\right)(1) - x(2x)}{\left(x^2 + 1\right)^2} = \frac{1 - x^2}{\left(x^2 + 1\right)^2}$$

**8.** $g(t) = \dfrac{t^2 + 4}{5t - 3}$

$$g'(t) = \frac{(5t - 3)(2t) - \left(t^2 + 4\right)(5)}{(5t - 3)^2}$$
$$= \frac{10t^2 - 6t - 5t^2 - 20}{(5t - 3)^2} = \frac{5t^2 - 6t - 20}{(5t - 3)^2}$$

**9.** $h(x) = \dfrac{\sqrt{x}}{x^3 + 1} = \dfrac{x^{1/2}}{x^3 + 1}$

$$h'(x) = \frac{\left(x^3 + 1\right)\frac{1}{2}x^{-1/2} - x^{1/2}\left(3x^2\right)}{\left(x^3 + 1\right)^2}$$
$$= \frac{x^3 + 1 - 6x^3}{2x^{1/2}\left(x^3 + 1\right)^2}$$
$$= \frac{1 - 5x^3}{2\sqrt{x}\left(x^3 + 1\right)^2}$$

**10.** $h(s) = \dfrac{s}{\sqrt{s} - 1}$

$$h'(s) = \frac{\left(\sqrt{s} - 1\right)(1) - s\left(\frac{1}{2}s^{-1/2}\right)}{\left(\sqrt{s} - 1\right)^2}$$
$$= \frac{\sqrt{s} - 1 - \frac{1}{2}\sqrt{s}}{\left(\sqrt{s} - 1\right)^2} = \frac{\sqrt{s} - 2}{2\left(\sqrt{s} - 1\right)^2}$$

**11.** $g(x) = \dfrac{\sin x}{e^x}$

$$g'(x) = \frac{e^x \cos x - \sin x\left(e^x\right)}{\left(e^x\right)^2}$$
$$= \frac{\cos x - \sin x}{e^x}$$

**12.** $f(t) = \dfrac{\cos t}{t^3}$

$$f'(t) = \frac{t^3(-\sin t) - \cos t\left(3t^2\right)}{\left(t^3\right)^2} = -\frac{t \sin t + 3 \cos t}{t^4}$$

**13.** $f(x) = \left(x^3 + 4x\right)\left(3x^2 + 2x - 5\right)$

$$f'(x) = \left(x^3 + 4x\right)(6x + 2) + \left(3x^2 + 2x - 5\right)\left(3x^2 + 4\right)$$
$$= 6x^4 + 24x^2 + 2x^3 + 8x + 9x^4 + 6x^3 - 15x^2 + 12x^2 + 8x - 20$$
$$= 15x^4 + 8x^3 + 21x^2 + 16x - 20$$
$$f'(0) = -20$$

**14.** $f(x) = \dfrac{x + 5}{x - 5}$

$$f'(x) = \frac{(x - 5)(1) - (x + 5)(1)}{(x - 5)^2}$$
$$= \frac{x - 5 - x - 5}{(x - 5)^2}$$
$$= \frac{-10}{(x - 5)^2}$$
$$f'(4) = \frac{-10}{(4 - 5)^2} = -10$$

**15.** $f(x) = x \cos x$

$$f'(x) = (x)(-\sin x) + (\cos x)(1) = \cos x - x \sin x$$
$$f'\left(\frac{\pi}{4}\right) = \frac{\sqrt{2}}{2} - \frac{\pi}{4}\left(\frac{\sqrt{2}}{2}\right) = \frac{\sqrt{2}}{8}(4 - \pi)$$

**16.** $f(x) = \dfrac{\sin x}{x}$

$$f'(x) = \frac{(x)(\cos x) - (\sin x)(1)}{x^2} = \frac{x\cos x - \sin x}{x^2}$$

$$f'\left(\frac{\pi}{6}\right) = \frac{(\pi/6)\left(\sqrt{3}/2\right) - (1/2)}{\pi^2/36} = \frac{3\sqrt{3}\pi - 18}{\pi^2} = \frac{3\left(\sqrt{3}\pi - 6\right)}{\pi^2}$$

**17.** $f(x) = e^x \sin x$

$$f'(x) = e^x \cos x + e^x \sin x = e^x(\cos x + \sin x)$$

$$f'(0) = 1$$

**18.** $f(x) = \dfrac{\cos x}{e^x}$

$$f'(x) = \frac{e^x(-\sin x) - \cos x\left(e^x\right)}{\left(e^x\right)^2} = \frac{-\sin x - \cos x}{e^x}$$

$$f'(0) = \frac{0 - 1}{1} = -1$$

| | *Function* | *Rewrite* | *Differentiate* | *Simplify* |
|---|---|---|---|---|
| **19.** | $y = \dfrac{x^2 + 3x}{7}$ | $y = \dfrac{1}{7}x^2 + \dfrac{3}{7}x$ | $y' = \dfrac{2}{7}x + \dfrac{3}{7}$ | $y' = \dfrac{2x + 3}{7}$ |
| **20.** | $y = \dfrac{5x^2 - 3}{4}$ | $y = \dfrac{5}{4}x^2 - \dfrac{3}{4}$ | $y' = \dfrac{10}{4}x$ | $y' = \dfrac{5x}{2}$ |
| **21.** | $y = \dfrac{6}{7x^2}$ | $y = \dfrac{6}{7}x^{-2}$ | $y' = -\dfrac{12}{7}x^{-3}$ | $y' = -\dfrac{12}{7x^3}$ |
| **22.** | $y = \dfrac{10}{3x^3}$ | $y = \dfrac{10}{3}x^{-3}$ | $y' = -\dfrac{30}{3}x^{-4}$ | $y' = -\dfrac{10}{x^4}$ |
| **23.** | $y = \dfrac{4x^{3/2}}{x}$ | $y = 4x^{1/2},\ x > 0$ | $y' = 2x^{-1/2}$ | $y' = \dfrac{2}{\sqrt{x}},\ x > 0$ |
| **24.** | $y = \dfrac{5x^2 - 8}{11}$ | $y = \dfrac{5}{11}x^2 - \dfrac{8}{11}$ | $y' = \dfrac{5}{11}(2x)$ | $y' = \dfrac{10x}{11}$ |

**25.** $f(x) = \dfrac{4 - 3x - x^2}{x^2 - 1}$

$$f'(x) = \frac{\left(x^2 - 1\right)(-3 - 2x) - \left(4 - 3x - x^2\right)(2x)}{\left(x^2 - 1\right)^2}$$

$$= \frac{-3x^2 + 3 - 2x^3 + 2x - 8x + 6x^2 + 2x^3}{\left(x^2 - 1\right)^2}$$

$$= \frac{3x^2 - 6x + 3}{\left(x^2 - 1\right)^2}$$

$$= \frac{3\left(x^2 - 2x + 1\right)}{\left(x^2 - 1\right)^2}$$

$$= \frac{3(x - 1)^2}{(x - 1)^2(x + 1)^2} = \frac{3}{(x + 1)^2},\ x \neq 1$$

**26.** $f(x) = \dfrac{x^3 + 5x + 3}{x^2 - 1}$

$$f'(x) = \frac{\left(x^2 - 1\right)\left(3x^2 + 5\right) - \left(x^3 + 5x + 3\right)(2x)}{\left(x^2 - 1\right)^2}$$

$$= \frac{3x^4 + 5x^2 - 3x^2 - 5 - 2x^4 - 10x^2 - 6x}{\left(x^2 - 1\right)^2}$$

$$= \frac{x^4 - 8x^2 - 6x - 5}{\left(x^2 - 1\right)^2}$$

**27.** $f(x) = x\left(1 - \dfrac{4}{x+3}\right) = x - \dfrac{4x}{x+3}$

$$f'(x) = 1 - \frac{(x+3)4 - 4x(1)}{(x+3)^2}$$

$$= \frac{(x^2 + 6x + 9) - 12}{(x+3)^2}$$

$$= \frac{x^2 + 6x - 3}{(x+3)^2}$$

**28.** $f(x) = x^4\left[1 - \dfrac{2}{x+1}\right] = x^4\left[\dfrac{x-1}{x+1}\right]$

$$f'(x) = x^4\left[\frac{(x+1) - (x-1)}{(x+1)^2}\right] + \left[\frac{x-1}{x+1}\right](4x^3)$$

$$= x^4\left[\frac{2}{(x+1)^2}\right] + \left[\frac{x^2-1}{(x+1)^2}\right](4x^3)$$

$$= 2x^3\left[\frac{2x^2 + x - 2}{(x+1)^2}\right]$$

**29.** $f(x) = \dfrac{3x - 1}{\sqrt{x}} = 3x^{1/2} - x^{-1/2}$

$$f'(x) = \frac{3}{2}x^{-1/2} + \frac{1}{2}x^{-3/2}$$

$$= \frac{3x + 1}{2x^{3/2}}$$

**Alternate solution:**

$$f(x) = \frac{3x-1}{\sqrt{x}} = \frac{3x-1}{x^{1/2}}$$

$$f'(x) = \frac{x^{1/2}(3) - (3x-1)\left(\frac{1}{2}\right)\left(x^{-1/2}\right)}{x}$$

$$= \frac{\frac{1}{2}x^{-1/2}(3x+1)}{x}$$

$$= \frac{3x+1}{2x^{3/2}}$$

**30.** $f(x) = \sqrt[3]{x}\left(\sqrt{x} + 3\right) = x^{1/3}\left(x^{1/2} + 3\right)$

$$f'(x) = x^{1/3}\left(\frac{1}{2}x^{-1/2}\right) + \left(x^{1/2} + 3\right)\left(\frac{1}{3}x^{-2/3}\right)$$

$$= \frac{5}{6}x^{-1/6} + x^{-2/3}$$

$$= \frac{5}{6x^{1/6}} + \frac{1}{x^{2/3}}$$

**Alternate solution:**

$$f(x) = \sqrt[3]{x}\left(\sqrt{x} + 3\right)$$

$$= x^{5/6} + 3x^{1/3}$$

$$f'(x) = \frac{5}{6}x^{-1/6} + x^{-2/3}$$

$$= \frac{5}{6x^{1/6}} + \frac{1}{x^{2/3}}$$

**31.** $h(s) = \left(s^3 - 2\right)^2 = s^6 - 4s^3 + 4$

$$h'(s) = 6s^5 - 12s^2 = 6s^2\left(s^3 - 2\right)$$

**32.** $h(x) = \left(x^2 + 1\right)^2 = x^4 + 2x^2 + 1$

$$h'(x) = 4x^3 + 4x = 4x\left(x^2 + 1\right)$$

**33.** $f(x) = \dfrac{2 - (1/x)}{x - 3} = \dfrac{2x - 1}{x(x-3)} = \dfrac{2x-1}{x^2 - 3x}$

$$f'(x) = \frac{\left(x^2 - 3x\right)2 - (2x-1)(2x-3)}{\left(x^2 - 3x\right)^2} = \frac{2x^2 - 6x - 4x^2 + 8x - 3}{\left(x^2 - 3x\right)^2}$$

$$= \frac{-2x^2 + 2x - 3}{\left(x^2 - 3x\right)^2} = -\frac{2x^2 - 2x + 3}{x^2(x-3)^2}$$

**34.** $g(x) = x^2\left(\frac{2}{x} - \frac{1}{x+1}\right) = 2x - \frac{x^2}{x+1}$

$$g'(x) = 2 - \frac{(x+1)2x - x^2(1)}{(x+1)^2} = \frac{2(x^2+2x+1) - x^2 - 2x}{(x+1)^2} = \frac{x^2+2x+2}{(x+1)^2}$$

**35.** $f(x) = (2x^3 + 5x)(x-3)(x+2)$

$$\begin{aligned} f'(x) &= (6x^2+5)(x-3)(x+2) + (2x^3+5x)(1)(x+2) + (2x^3+5x)(x-3)(1) \\ &= (6x^2+5)(x^2-x-6) + (2x^3+5x)(x+2) + (2x^3+5x)(x-3) \\ &= (6x^4+5x^2-6x^3-5x-36x^2-30) + (2x^4+4x^3+5x^2+10x) + (2x^4+5x^2-6x^3-15x) \\ &= 10x^4 - 8x^3 - 21x^2 - 10x - 30 \end{aligned}$$

***Note:*** You could simplify first:

$f(x) = (2x^3+5x)(x^2-x-6)$

**36.** $f(x) = (x^3 - x)(x^2+2)(x^2+x-1)$

$$\begin{aligned} f'(x) &= (3x^2-1)(x^2+2)(x^2+x-1) + (x^3-x)(2x)(x^2+x-1) + (x^3-x)(x^2+2)(2x+1) \\ &= (3x^4+5x^2-2)(x^2+x-1) + (2x^4-2x^2)(x^2+x-1) + (x^5+x^3-2x)(2x+1) \\ &= (3x^6+5x^4-2x^2+3x^5+5x^3-2x-3x^4-5x^2+2) \\ &\quad + (2x^6-2x^4+2x^5-2x^3-2x^4+2x^2) \\ &\quad + (2x^6+2x^4-4x^2+x^5+x^3-2x) \\ &= 7x^6+6x^5+4x^3-9x^2-4x+2 \end{aligned}$$

**37.** $f(x) = \frac{x^2+c^2}{x^2-c^2}$

$$f'(x) = \frac{(x^2-c^2)(2x) - (x^2+c^2)(2x)}{(x^2-c^2)^2} = -\frac{4xc^2}{(x^2-c^2)^2}$$

**38.** $f(x) = \frac{c^2-x^2}{c^2+x^2}$

$$f'(x) = \frac{(c^2+x^2)(-2x) - (c^2-x^2)(2x)}{(c^2+x^2)^2} = -\frac{4xc^2}{(c^2+x^2)^2}$$

**39.** $f(t) = t^2 \sin t$

$f'(t) = t^2\cos t + 2t\sin t = t(t\cos t + 2\sin t)$

**40.** $f(\theta) = (\theta+1)\cos\theta$

$$\begin{aligned} f'(\theta) &= (\theta+1)(-\sin\theta) + (\cos\theta)(1) \\ &= \cos\theta - (\theta+1)\sin\theta \end{aligned}$$

**41.** $f(t) = \frac{\cos t}{t}$

$$f'(t) = \frac{-t\sin t - \cos t}{t^2} = -\frac{t\sin t + \cos t}{t^2}$$

**42.** $f(x) = \frac{\sin x}{x^3}$

$$f'(x) = \frac{x^3\cos x - \sin x(3x^2)}{(x^3)^2} = \frac{x\cos x - 3\sin x}{x^4}$$

**43.** $f(x) = -e^x + \tan x$

$f'(x) = -e^x + \sec^2 x$

**44.** $y = e^x - \cot x$

$y' = e^x + \csc^2 x$

**45.** $g(t) = \sqrt[4]{t} + 6\csc t = t^{1/4} + 6\csc t$

$$\begin{aligned} g'(t) &= \frac{1}{4}t^{-3/4} - 6\csc t\cot t \\ &= \frac{1}{4t^{3/4}} - 6\csc t\cot t \end{aligned}$$

**46.** $h(x) = \dfrac{1}{x} - 12\sec x = x^{-1} - 12\sec x$

$h'(x) = -x^{-2} - 12\sec x\tan x$

$= \dfrac{-1}{x^2} - 12\sec x\tan x$

**47.** $y = \dfrac{3(1-\sin x)}{2\cos x} = \dfrac{3 - 3\sin x}{2\cos x}$

$y' = \dfrac{(-3\cos x)(2\cos x) - (3 - 3\sin x)(-2\sin x)}{(2\cos x)^2}$

$= \dfrac{-6\cos^2 x + 6\sin x - 6\sin^2 x}{4\cos^2 x}$

$= \dfrac{3}{2}\left(-1 + \tan x\sec x - \tan^2 x\right)$

$= \dfrac{3}{2}\sec x(\tan x - \sec x)$

**48.** $y = \dfrac{\sec x}{x}$

$y' = \dfrac{x\sec x\tan x - \sec x}{x^2}$

$= \dfrac{\sec x(x\tan x - 1)}{x^2}$

**49.** $y = -\csc x - \sin x$

$y' = \csc x\cot x - \cos x$

$= \dfrac{\cos x}{\sin^2 x} - \cos x$

$= \cos x(\csc^2 x - 1)$

$= \cos x\cot^2 x$

**50.** $y = x\cos x + \sin x$

$y' = -x\sin x + \cos x + \cos x$

$= 2\cos x - x\sin x$

**51.** $f(x) = x^2\tan x$

$f'(x) = x^2\sec^2 x + 2x\tan x$

$= x(x\sec^2 x + 2\tan x)$

**52.** $f(x) = 2\sin x\cos x$

$f'(x) = 2[\sin x(-\sin x) + \cos x(\cos x)]$

$= 2[\cos 2x - \sin 2x] = 2\cos 2x$

**53.** $y = 2x\sin x + x^2e^x$

$y' = 2x(\cos x) + 2\sin x + x^2e^x + 2xe^x$

$= 2x\cos x + 2\sin x + xe^x(x + 2)$

**54.** $h(x) = 2e^x\cos x$

$h'(x) = 2(e^x\cos x - e^x\sin x) = 2e^x(\cos x - \sin x)$

**55.** $y = \dfrac{e^x}{4\sqrt{x}}$

$y' = \dfrac{4\sqrt{x}e^x - e^x\left(4/2\sqrt{x}\right)}{\left(4\sqrt{x}\right)^2} = \dfrac{e^x\left[4\sqrt{x} - \left(2/\sqrt{x}\right)\right]}{16x}$

$= \dfrac{e^x(4x-2)}{16x^{3/2}} = \dfrac{e^x(2x-1)}{8x^{3/2}}$

**56.** $y = \dfrac{2e^x}{x^2+1}$

$y' = \dfrac{(x^2+1)2e^x - 2e^x(2x)}{(x^2+1)^2} = \dfrac{2e^x(x^2 - 2x + 1)}{(x^2+1)^2}$

**57.** $g(x) = \left(\dfrac{x+1}{x+2}\right)(2x-5)$

$g'(x) = \left(\dfrac{x+1}{x+2}\right)(2) + (2x-5)\left[\dfrac{(x+2)(1) - (x+1)(1)}{(x+2)^2}\right]$

$= \dfrac{2x^2 + 8x - 1}{(x+2)^2}$

(Form of answer may vary.)

**58.** $f(x) = \left(\dfrac{x^2 - x - 3}{x^2+1}\right)(x^2 + x + 1)$

$f'(x) = 2\dfrac{x^5 + 2x^3 + 2x^2 - 2}{(x^2+1)^2}$

(Form of answer may vary.)

**59.** $g(\theta) = \dfrac{\theta}{1 - \sin\theta}$

$g'(\theta) = \dfrac{1 - \sin\theta + \theta\cos\theta}{(1-\sin\theta)^2}$

(Form of answer may vary.)

**60.** $f(\theta) = \dfrac{\sin\theta}{1 - \cos\theta}$

$f'(\theta) = \dfrac{1}{\cos\theta - 1} = \dfrac{\cos\theta - 1}{(1-\cos\theta)^2}$ (Form of answer may vary.)

**61.** $y = \dfrac{1 + \csc x}{1 - \csc x}$

$y' = \dfrac{(1 - \csc x)(-\csc x \cot x) - (1 + \csc x)(\csc x \cot x)}{(1 - \csc x)^2} = \dfrac{-2 \csc x \cot x}{(1 - \csc x)^2}$

$y'\left(\dfrac{\pi}{6}\right) = \dfrac{-2(2)(\sqrt{3})}{(1 - 2)^2} = -4\sqrt{3}$

**62.** $f(x) = \tan x \cot x = 1$

$f'(x) = 0$

$f'(1) = 0$

**63.** $h(t) = \dfrac{\sec t}{t}$

$h'(t) = \dfrac{t(\sec t \tan t) - (\sec t)(1)}{t^2} = \dfrac{\sec t(t \tan t - 1)}{t^2}$

$h'(\pi) = \dfrac{\sec \pi(\pi \tan \pi - 1)}{\pi^2} = \dfrac{1}{\pi^2}$

**64.** $f(x) = \sin x(\sin x + \cos x)$

$f'(x) = \sin x(\cos x - \sin x) + (\sin x + \cos x)\cos x$

$= \sin x \cos x - \sin^2 x + \sin x \cos x + \cos^2 x$

$= \sin 2x + \cos 2x$

$f'\left(\dfrac{\pi}{4}\right) = \sin \dfrac{\pi}{2} + \cos \dfrac{\pi}{2} = 1$

**65.** (a) $f(x) = (x^3 + 4x - 1)(x - 2), \quad (1, -4)$

$f'(x) = (x^3 + 4x - 1)(1) + (x - 2)(3x^2 + 4)$

$= x^3 + 4x - 1 + 3x^3 - 6x^2 + 4x - 8$

$= 4x^3 - 6x^2 + 8x - 9$

$f'(1) = -3$; Slope at $(1, -4)$

Tangent line: $y + 4 = -3(x - 1) \Rightarrow y = -3x - 1$

(b)

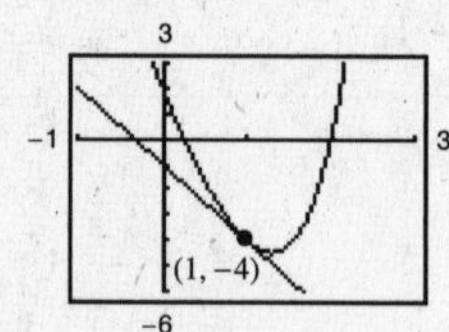


(c) Graphing utility confirms $\dfrac{dy}{dx} = -3$ at $(1, -4)$.

**66.** (a) $f(x) = \dfrac{x - 1}{x + 1}, \quad \left(2, \dfrac{1}{3}\right)$

$f'(x) = \dfrac{(x + 1)(1) - (x - 1)(1)}{(x + 1)^2} = \dfrac{2}{(x + 1)^2}$

$f'(2) = \dfrac{2}{9}$; Slope at $\left(2, \dfrac{1}{3}\right)$

Tangent line: $y - \dfrac{1}{3} = \dfrac{2}{9}(x - 2) \Rightarrow y = \dfrac{2}{9}x - \dfrac{1}{9}$

(b)

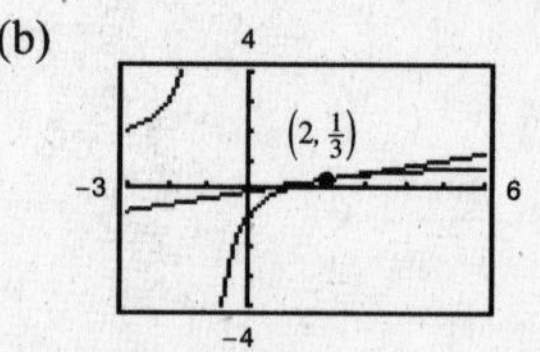


(c) Graphing utility confirms $\dfrac{dy}{dx} = \dfrac{2}{9}$ at $\left(2, \dfrac{1}{3}\right)$.

**67.** (a) $f(x) = \tan x, \quad \left(\dfrac{\pi}{4}, 1\right)$

$f'(x) = \sec^2 x$

$f'\left(\dfrac{\pi}{4}\right) = 2$; Slope at $\left(\dfrac{\pi}{4}, 1\right)$

Tangent line: $y - 1 = 2\left(x - \dfrac{\pi}{4}\right)$

$y - 1 = 2x - \dfrac{\pi}{2}$

$4x - 2y - \pi + 2 = 0$

(b)

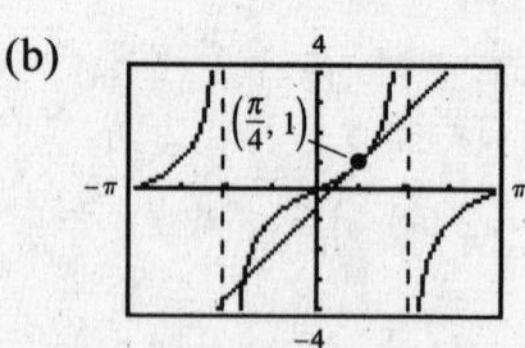


(c) Graphing utility confirms $\dfrac{dy}{dx} = 2$ at $\left(\dfrac{\pi}{4}, 1\right)$.

**68.** (a) $f(x) = \sec x, \quad \left(\dfrac{\pi}{3}, 2\right)$

$f'(x) = \sec x \tan x$

$f'\left(\dfrac{\pi}{3}\right) = 2\sqrt{3}$; Slope at $\left(\dfrac{\pi}{3}, 2\right)$

Tangent line:

$$y - 2 = 2\sqrt{3}\left(x - \frac{\pi}{3}\right)$$

$$6\sqrt{3}x - 3y + 6 - 2\sqrt{3}\pi = 0$$

(b)

(c) Graphing utility confirms $\dfrac{dy}{dx} = 2\sqrt{3}$ at $\left(\dfrac{\pi}{3}, 2\right)$.

**69.** (a) $f(x) = (x - 1)e^x, \quad (1, 0)$

$f'(x) = (x - 1)e^x + e^x = e^x$

$f'(1) = e$

Tangent line: $y - 0 = e(x - 1)$

$y = e(x - 1)$

(b)

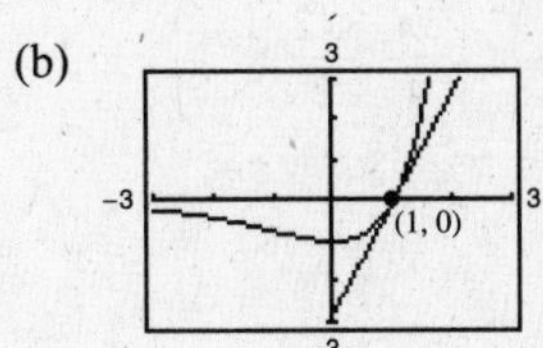

(c) Graphing utility confirms $\dfrac{dy}{dx} = e$ at $(1, 0)$.

**70.** (a) $f(x) = \dfrac{e^x}{x + 4}, \quad \left(0, \dfrac{1}{4}\right)$

$$f'(x) = \frac{(x + 4)e^x - e^x}{(x + 4)^2} = \frac{e^x(x + 3)}{(x + 4)^2}$$

$$f'(0) = \frac{3}{16}$$

Tangent line: $y - \dfrac{1}{4} = \dfrac{3}{16}(x - 0)$

$y = \dfrac{3}{16}x + \dfrac{1}{4}$

(b)

(c) Graphing utility confirms $\dfrac{dy}{dx} = \dfrac{3}{16}$ at $\left(0, \dfrac{1}{4}\right)$.

**71.** $f(x) = \dfrac{8}{x^2 + 4}; \quad (2, 1)$

$$f'(x) = \frac{(x^2 + 4)(0) - 8(2x)}{(x^2 + 4)^2} = \frac{-16x}{(x^2 + 4)^2}$$

$$f'(2) = \frac{-16(2)}{(4 + 4)^2} = -\frac{1}{2}$$

$$y - 1 = -\frac{1}{2}(x - 2)$$

$$y = -\frac{1}{2}x + 2$$

$$2y + x - 4 = 0$$

**72.** $f(x) = \dfrac{27}{x^2 + 9}; \quad \left(-3, \dfrac{3}{2}\right)$

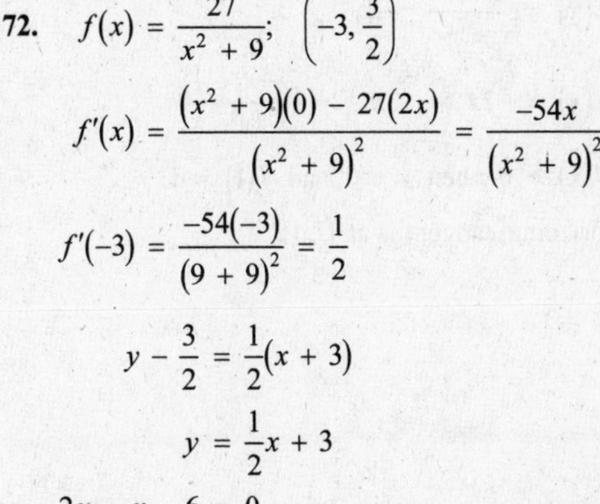

$$f'(x) = \frac{(x^2 + 9)(0) - 27(2x)}{(x^2 + 9)^2} = \frac{-54x}{(x^2 + 9)^2}$$

$$f'(-3) = \frac{-54(-3)}{(9 + 9)^2} = \frac{1}{2}$$

$$y - \frac{3}{2} = \frac{1}{2}(x + 3)$$

$$y = \frac{1}{2}x + 3$$

$$2y - x - 6 = 0$$

**73.** $f(x) = \dfrac{16x}{x^2 + 16}; \quad \left(-2, -\dfrac{8}{5}\right)$

$$f'(x) = \frac{(x^2 + 16)(16) - 16x(2x)}{(x^2 + 16)^2} = \frac{256 - 16x^2}{(x^2 + 16)^2}$$

$$f'(-2) = \frac{256 - 16(4)}{20^2} = \frac{12}{25}$$

$$y + \frac{8}{5} = \frac{12}{25}(x + 2)$$

$$y = \frac{12}{25}x - \frac{16}{25}$$

$$25y - 12x + 16 = 0$$

**74.** $f(x) = \dfrac{4x}{x^2 + 6}; \left(2, \dfrac{4}{5}\right)$

$$f'(x) = \frac{(x^2 + 6)(4) - 4x(2x)}{(x^2 + 6)^2} = \frac{24 - 4x^2}{(x^2 + 6)^2}$$

$$f'(2) = \frac{24 - 16}{10^2} = \frac{2}{25}$$

$$y - \frac{4}{5} = \frac{2}{25}(x - 2)$$

$$y = \frac{2}{25}x + \frac{16}{25}$$

$$25y - 2x - 16 = 0$$

**75.** $f(x) = \dfrac{2x - 1}{x^2} = 2x^{-1} - x^{-2}$

$$f'(x) = -2x^{-2} + 2x^{-3} = \frac{2(-x + 1)}{x^3}$$

$f'(x) = 0$ when $x = 1$, and $f(1) = 1$.

Horizontal tangent is at $(1, 1)$.

**76.** $f(x) = \dfrac{x^2}{x^2 + 1}$

$$f'(x) = \frac{(x^2 + 1)(2x) - (x^2)(2x)}{(x^2 + 1)^2} = \frac{2x}{(x^2 + 1)^2}$$

$f'(x) = 0$ when $x = 0$.

Horizontal tangent is at $(0, 0)$.

**77.** $g(x) = \dfrac{8(x - 2)}{e^x}$

$$g'(x) = \frac{e^x(8) - 8(x - 2)e^x}{e^{2x}} = \frac{24 - 8x}{e^x}$$

$g'(x) = 0$ when $x = 3$.

Horizontal tangent is at $(3, 8e^{-3})$.

**78.** $f(x) = e^x \sin x, \quad 0 \le x \le \pi$

$$f'(x) = e^x \cos x + e^x \sin x = e^x(\cos x + \sin x)$$

$f'(x) = 0$ when $\cos x = -\sin x \Rightarrow x = \dfrac{3\pi}{4}$.

Horizontal tangent is at $\left(\dfrac{3\pi}{4}, \dfrac{\sqrt{2}}{2}e^{3\pi/4}\right)$.

**79.** $f(x) = \dfrac{x + 1}{x - 1}$

$$f'(x) = \frac{(x - 1) - (x + 1)}{(x - 1)^2} = \frac{-2}{(x - 1)^2}$$

$2y + x = 6 \Rightarrow y = -\dfrac{1}{2}x + 3$; Slope: $-\dfrac{1}{2}$

$$\frac{-2}{(x - 1)^2} = -\frac{1}{2}$$

$$(x - 1)^2 = 4$$

$$x - 1 = \pm 2$$

$$x = -1, 3;\ f(-1) = 0,\ f(3) = 2$$

$$y - 0 = -\frac{1}{2}(x + 1) \Rightarrow y = -\frac{1}{2}x - \frac{1}{2}$$

$$y - 2 = -\frac{1}{2}(x - 3) \Rightarrow y = -\frac{1}{2}x + \frac{7}{2}$$

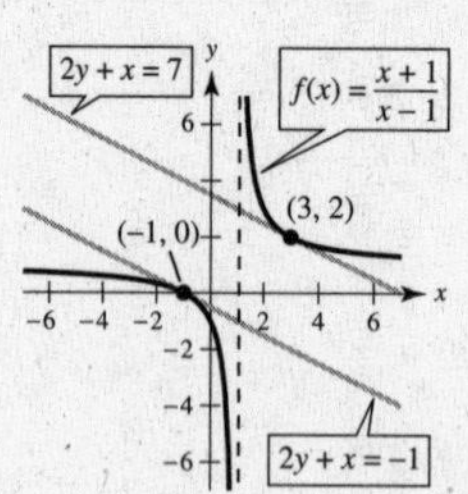

**80.** $f(x) = \dfrac{x}{x - 1}$

$f'(x) = \dfrac{(x - 1) - x}{(x - 1)^2} = \dfrac{-1}{(x - 1)^2}$

Let $(x, y) = (x, x/(x - 1))$ be a point of tangency on the graph of $f$.

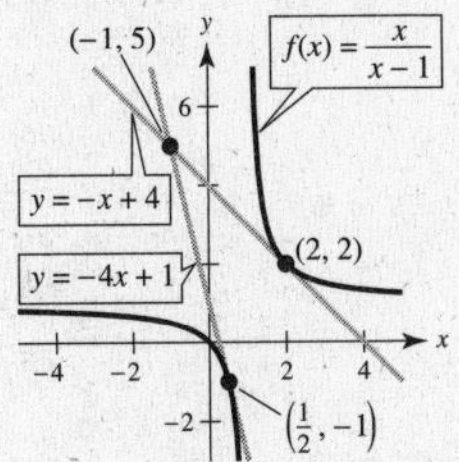


$$\frac{5 - (x/(x - 1))}{-1 - x} = \frac{-1}{(x - 1)^2}$$

$$\frac{4x - 5}{(x - 1)(x + 1)} = \frac{1}{(x - 1)^2}$$

$$(4x - 5)(x - 1) = x + 1$$

$$4x^2 - 10x + 4 = 0$$

$$(x - 2)(2x - 1) = 0 \Rightarrow x = \frac{1}{2}, 2$$

$$f\left(\frac{1}{2}\right) = -1, f(2) = 2; f'\left(\frac{1}{2}\right) = -4, f'(2) = -1$$

Two tangent lines:

$$y + 1 = -4\left(x - \frac{1}{2}\right) \Rightarrow y = -4x + 1$$

$$y - 2 = -1(x - 2) \Rightarrow y = -x + 4$$

**81.** $f'(x) = \dfrac{(x + 2)3 - 3x(1)}{(x + 2)^2} = \dfrac{6}{(x + 2)^2}$

$g'(x) = \dfrac{(x + 2)5 - (5x + 4)(1)}{(x + 2)^2} = \dfrac{6}{(x + 2)^2}$

$g(x) = \dfrac{5x + 4}{(x + 2)} = \dfrac{3x}{(x + 2)} + \dfrac{2x + 4}{(x + 2)} = f(x) + 2$

$f$ and $g$ differ by a constant.

**82.** $f'(x) = \dfrac{x(\cos x - 3) - (\sin x - 3x)(1)}{x^2}$

$= \dfrac{x \cos x - \sin x}{x^2}$

$g'(x) = \dfrac{x(\cos x + 2) - (\sin x + 2x)(1)}{x^2}$

$= \dfrac{x \cos x - \sin x}{x^2}$

$g(x) = \dfrac{\sin x + 2x}{x} = \dfrac{\sin x - 3x + 5x}{x} = f(x) + 5$

$f$ and $g$ differ by a constant.

**83.** (a) $p'(x) = f'(x)g(x) + f(x)g'(x)$

$p'(1) = f'(1)g(1) + f(1)g'(1) = 1(4) + 6\left(-\frac{1}{2}\right) = 1$

(b) $q'(x) = \dfrac{g(x)f'(x) - f(x)g'(x)}{g(x)^2}$

$q'(4) = \dfrac{3(-1) - 7(0)}{3^2} = -\dfrac{1}{3}$

**84.** (a) $p'(x) = f'(x)g(x) + f(x)g'(x)$

$p'(4) = \frac{1}{2}(8) + 1(0) = 4$

(b) $q'(x) = \dfrac{g(x)f'(x) - f(x)g'(x)}{g(x)^2}$

$q'(7) = \dfrac{4(2) - 4(-1)}{4^2} = \dfrac{12}{16} = \dfrac{3}{4}$

**85.** Area $= A(t) = (6t + 5)\sqrt{t} = 6t^{3/2} + 5t^{1/2}$

$A'(t) = 9t^{1/2} + \frac{5}{2}t^{-1/2} = \dfrac{18t + 5}{2\sqrt{t}}$ cm²/sec

**86.** $V = \pi r^2 h = \pi(t + 2)\left(\frac{1}{2}\sqrt{t}\right)$

$= \frac{1}{2}(t^{3/2} + 2t^{1/2})\pi$

$V'(t) = \frac{1}{2}\left(\frac{3}{2}t^{1/2} + t^{-1/2}\right)\pi = \dfrac{3t + 2}{4t^{1/2}}\pi$ in.³/sec

**87.** $C = \dfrac{375{,}000 + 6x^2}{x}, \ x \geq 1$

$= 375{,}000x^{-1} + 6x$

$C' = -375{,}000x^{-2} + 6 = 6 - \dfrac{375{,}000}{x^2}$

(a) $C'(200) = -\dfrac{27}{8} = -\$3.375$ per unit

(b) $C'(250) = \$0$ per unit

(c) $C'(300) = \dfrac{11}{6} \approx \$1.83$ per unit

The rate of change of $C$ is decreasing at a rate of −\$3.38 per unit when the order size is 200 units. The rate of change is not changing when the order size is 250 units. The rate of change of $C$ is increasing at a rate of about \$1.83 per unit when the order size is 300 units.

**88.** $P = \dfrac{k}{V}$

$\dfrac{dP}{dV} = -\dfrac{k}{V^2}$

**89.** $P(t) = 500\left[1 + \dfrac{4t}{50 + t^2}\right]$

$$P'(t) = 500\left[\frac{(50 + t^2)(4) - (4t)(2t)}{(50 + t^2)^2}\right] = 500\left[\frac{200 - 4t^2}{(50 + t^2)^2}\right] = 2000\left[\frac{50 - t^2}{(50 + t^2)^2}\right]$$

$P'(2) \approx 31.55$ bacteria/h

**90.** $F = \dfrac{Gm_1m_2}{d^2} = Gm_1m_2d^{-2}$

$$\frac{dF}{dd} = F'(d) = \frac{-2\,Gm_1m_2}{d^3}$$

**91.** (a) $\sec x = \dfrac{1}{\cos x}$

$$\frac{d}{dx}[\sec x] = \frac{d}{dx}\left[\frac{1}{\cos x}\right] = \frac{(\cos x)(0) - (1)(-\sin x)}{(\cos x)^2} = \frac{\sin x}{\cos x \cos x} = \frac{1}{\cos x}\cdot\frac{\sin x}{\cos x} = \sec x \tan x$$

(b) $\csc x = \dfrac{1}{\sin x}$

$$\frac{d}{dx}[\csc x] = \frac{d}{dx}\left[\frac{1}{\sin x}\right] = \frac{(\sin x)(0) - (1)(\cos x)}{(\sin x)^2} = -\frac{\cos x}{\sin x \sin x} = -\frac{1}{\sin x}\cdot\frac{\cos x}{\sin x} = -\csc x \cot x$$

(c) $\cot x = \dfrac{\cos x}{\sin x}$

$$\frac{d}{dx}[\cot x] = \frac{d}{dx}\left[\frac{\cos x}{\sin x}\right] = \frac{\sin x(-\sin x) - (\cos x)(\cos x)}{(\sin x)^2} = -\frac{\sin^2 x + \cos^2 x}{\sin^2 x} = -\frac{1}{\sin^2 x} = -\csc^2 x$$

**92.** $f(x) = \sec x$

$g(x) = \csc x,\ [0, 2\pi)$

$f'(x) = g'(x)$

$$\sec x \tan x = -\csc x \cot x \Rightarrow \frac{\sec x \tan x}{\csc x \cot x} = -1 \Rightarrow \frac{\dfrac{1}{\cos x}\cdot\dfrac{\sin x}{\cos x}}{\dfrac{1}{\sin x}\cdot\dfrac{\cos x}{\sin x}} = -1 \Rightarrow \frac{\sin^3 x}{\cos^3 x} = -1 \Rightarrow \tan^3 x = -1 \Rightarrow \tan x = -1$$

$$x = \frac{3\pi}{4}, \frac{7\pi}{4}$$

**93.** (a) Using a graphing utility,

$q(t) = -0.0546t^3 + 2.529t^2 - 36.89t + 186.6$

$v(t) = 0.0796t^3 - 2.162t^2 + 15.32t + 5.9.$

(b)

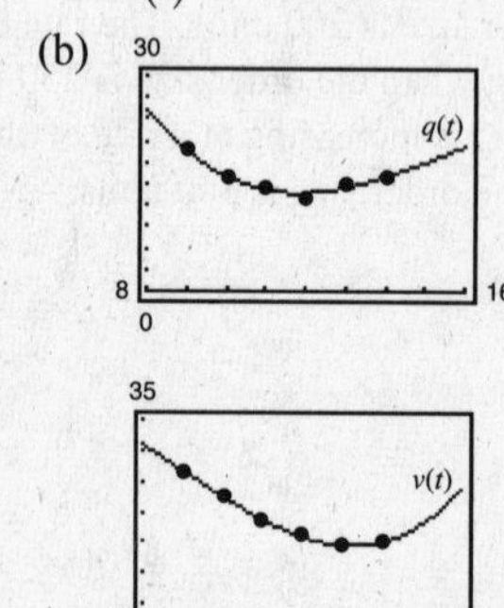


(c) $A = \dfrac{v(t)}{q(t)} = \dfrac{0.0796t^3 - 2.162t^2 + 15.32t + 5.9}{-0.0546t^3 + 2.529t^2 - 36.89t + 186.6}$

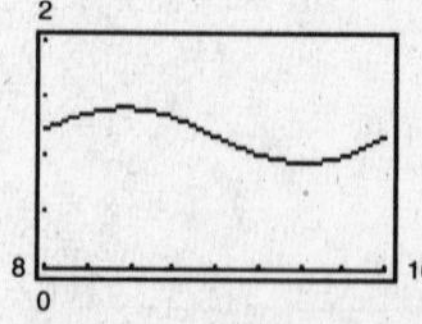


$A$ represents the average value (in billions of dollars) per one million personal computers.

(d) $A'(t)$ represents the rate of change of the average value per one million personal computers for the given year $t$.

**94.** (a) $\sin\theta = \dfrac{r}{r+h}$

$r + h = r\csc\theta$

$h = r\csc\theta - r = r(\csc\theta - 1)$

(b) $h'(\theta) = r(-\csc\theta \cdot \cot\theta)$

$h'(30^\circ) = h'\left(\dfrac{\pi}{6}\right)$

$= -3960\left(2 \cdot \sqrt{3}\right) = -7920\sqrt{3}$ mi/rad

**95.** $f(x) = 4x^{3/2}$

$f'(x) = 6x^{1/2}$

$f''(x) = 3x^{-1/2} = \dfrac{3}{\sqrt{x}}$

**96.** $f(x) = x + \dfrac{32}{x^2}$

$f'(x) = 1 - \dfrac{64}{x^3}$

$f''(x) = \dfrac{192}{x^4}$

**97.** $f(x) = \dfrac{x}{x-1}$

$f'(x) = \dfrac{(x-1)(1) - x(1)}{(x-1)^2} = \dfrac{-1}{(x-1)^2}$

$f''(x) = \dfrac{2}{(x-1)^3}$

**98.** $f(x) = \dfrac{x^2 + 2x - 1}{x} = x + 2 - \dfrac{1}{x}$

$f'(x) = 1 + \dfrac{1}{x^2}$

$f''(x) = -\dfrac{2}{x^3}$

**99.** $f(x) = x\sin x$

$f'(x) = x\cos x + \sin x$

$f''(x) = x(-\sin x) + \cos x + \cos x$

$= -x\sin x + 2\cos x$

**100.** $f(x) = \sec x$

$f'(x) = \sec x\tan x$

$f''(x) = \sec x\left(\sec^2 x\right) + \tan x(\sec x\tan x)$

$= \sec x\left(\sec^2 x + \tan^2 x\right)$

**101.** $g(x) = \dfrac{e^x}{x}$

$g'(x) = \dfrac{xe^x - e^x}{x^2}$

$g''(x) = \dfrac{x^2\left(xe^x + e^x - e^x\right) - 2x\left(xe^x - e^x\right)}{x^4}$

$= \dfrac{e^x}{x^3}\left(x^2 - 2x + 2\right)$

**102.** $h(t) = e^t \sin t$

$h'(t) = e^t\cos t + e^t\sin t = e^t(\cos t + \sin t)$

$h''(t) = e^t(-\sin t + \cos t) + e^t(\cos t + \sin t)$

$= 2e^t\cos t$

**103.** $f'(x) = x^2$

$f''(x) = 2x$

**104.** $f''(x) = 2 - 2x^{-1}$

$f'''(x) = 2x^{-2} = \dfrac{2}{x^2}$

**105.** $f'''(x) = 2\sqrt{x}$

$f^{(4)}(x) = \dfrac{1}{2}(2)x^{-1/2} = \dfrac{1}{\sqrt{x}}$

**106.** $f^{(4)}(x) = 2x + 1$

$f^{(5)}(x) = 2$

$f^{(6)}(x) = 0$

**107.** The graph of a differentiable function $f$ such that $f(2) = 0$, $f' < 0$ for $-\infty < x < 2$, and $f' > 0$ for $2 < x < \infty$ would, in general, look like the graph below.

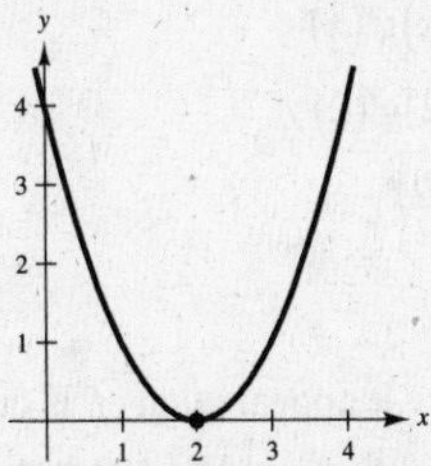


One such function is $f(x) = (x-2)^2$.

**108.** The graph of a differentiable function $f$ such that $f > 0$ and $f' < 0$ for all real numbers $x$ would, in general, look like the graph below.

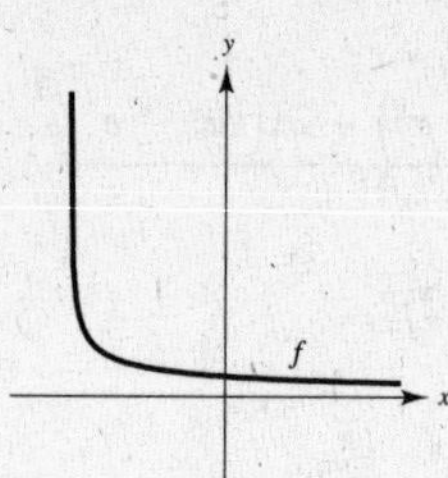


**109.** $f(x) = 2g(x) + h(x)$

$f'(x) = 2g'(x) + h'(x)$

$f'(2) = 2g'(2) + h'(2)$

$= 2(-2) + 4$

$= 0$

**110.** $f(x) = 4 - h(x)$

$f'(x) = -h'(x)$

$f'(2) = -h'(2) = -4$

**111.** $f(x) = \dfrac{g(x)}{h(x)}$

$f'(x) = \dfrac{h(x)g'(x) - g(x)h'(x)}{\left[h(x)\right]^2}$

$f'(2) = \dfrac{h(2)g'(2) - g(2)h'(2)}{\left[h(2)\right]^2}$

$= \dfrac{(-1)(-2) - (3)(4)}{(-1)^2}$

$= -10$

**112.** $f(x) = g(x)h(x)$

$f'(x) = g(x)h'(x) + h(x)g'(x)$

$f'(2) = g(2)h'(2) + h(2)g'(2)$

$= (3)(4) + (-1)(-2)$

$= 14$

**113.** It appears that $f$ is cubic, so $f'$ would be quadratic and $f''$ would be linear.

**114.**

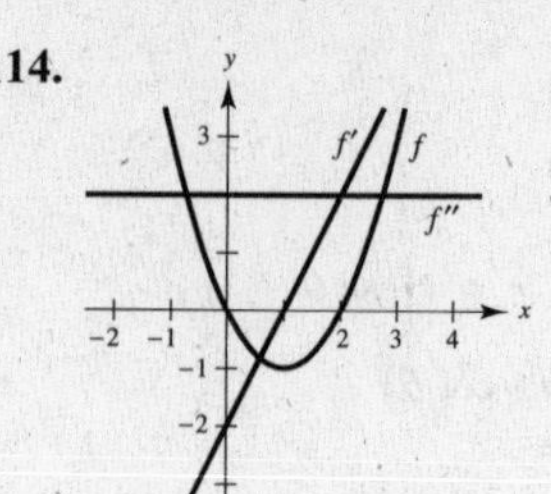


It appears that $f$ is quadratic, so $f'$ would be linear and $f''$ would be constant.

**115.**

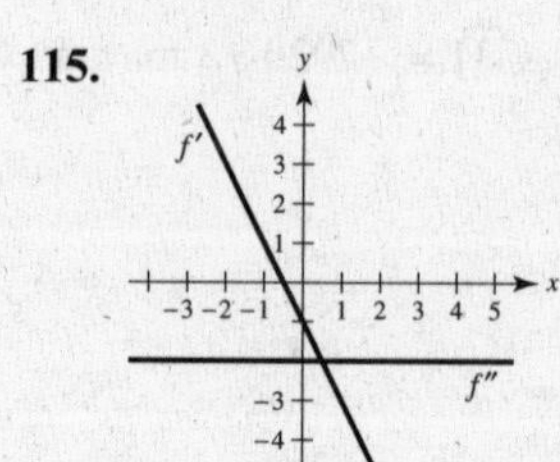


**116.**

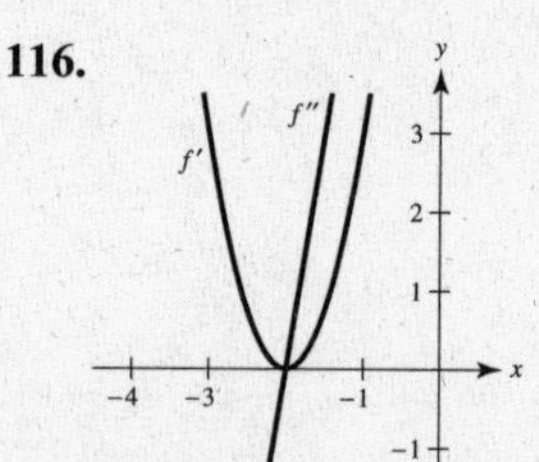


**117.**

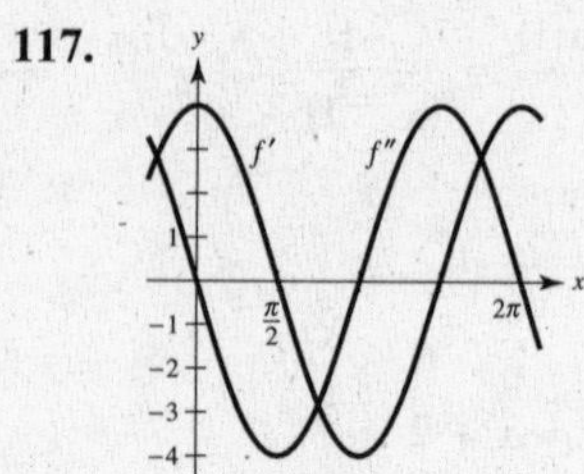


**118.**

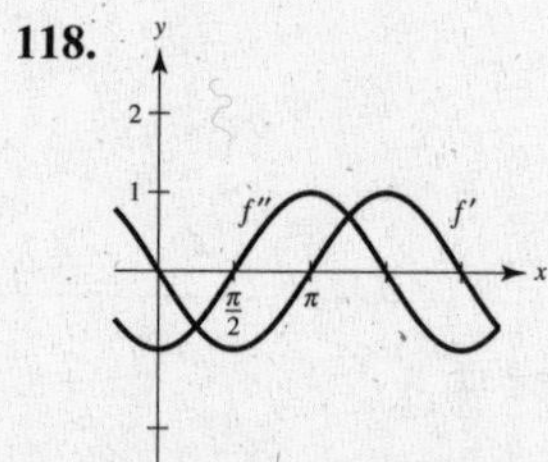


**119.** $v(t) = 36 - t^2, 0 \le t \le 6$

$a(t) = v'(t) = -2t$

$v(3) = 27$ m/sec

$a(3) = -6$ m/sec$^2$

The speed of the object is decreasing.

**120.** (a) 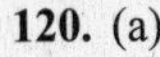

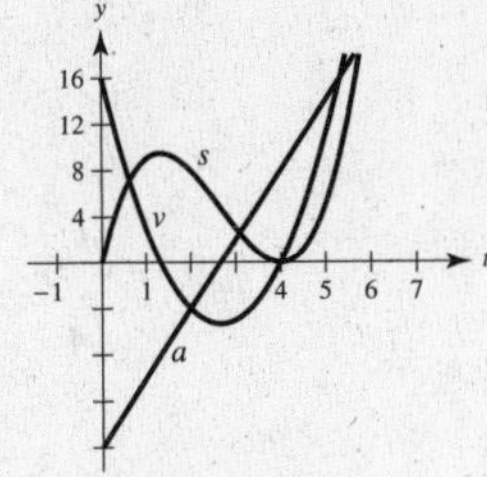


$s$ position function
$v$ velocity function
$a$ acceleration function

(b) The speed of the particle is the absolute value of its velocity. So, the particle's speed is slowing down on the intervals $(0, 4/3)$ and $(8/3, 4)$ and it speeds up on the intervals $(4/3, 8/3)$ and $(4, 6)$.

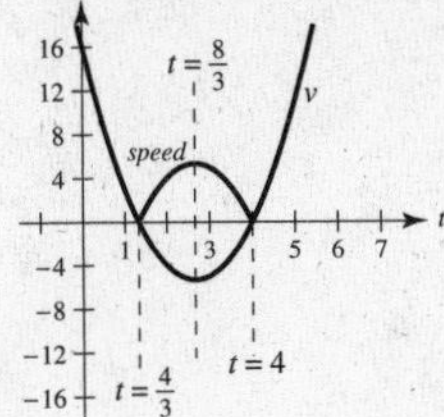


**121.** $f(x) = x^n$

$$f^{(n)}(x) = n(n-1)(n-2)\cdots(2)(1) = n!$$

**Note:** $n! = n(n-1)\cdots 3 \cdot 2 \cdot 1$ (read "$n$ factorial")

**122.** $f(x) = \dfrac{1}{x}$

$$f^{(n)}(x) = \frac{(-1)^n(n)(n-1)(n-2)\cdots(2)(1)}{x^{n+1}} = \frac{(-1)^n n!}{x^{n+1}}$$

**123.** $f(x) = g(x)h(x)$

(a)
$$f'(x) = g(x)h'(x) + h(x)g'(x)$$
$$f''(x) = g(x)h''(x) + g'(x)h'(x) + h(x)g''(x) + h'(x)g'(x)$$
$$= g(x)h''(x) + 2g'(x)h'(x) + h(x)g''(x)$$
$$f'''(x) = g(x)h'''(x) + g'(x)h''(x) + 2g'(x)h''(x) + 2g''(x)h'(x) + h(x)g'''(x) + h'(x)g''(x)$$
$$= g(x)h'''(x) + 3g'(x)h''(x) + 3g''(x)h'(x) + g'''(x)h(x)$$
$$f^{(4)}(x) = g(x)h^{(4)}(x) + g'(x)h'''(x) + 3g'(x)h'''(x) + 3g''(x)h''(x) + 3g''(x)h''(x) + 3g'''(x)h'(x) + g'''(x)h'(x) + g^{(4)}(x)h(x)$$
$$= g(x)h^{(4)}(x) + 4g'(x)h'''(x) + 6g''(x)h''(x) + 4g'''(x)h'(x) + g^{(4)}(x)h(x)$$

(b)
$$f^{(n)}(x) = g(x)h^{(n)}(x) + \frac{n(n-1)(n-2)\cdots(2)(1)}{1[(n-1)(n-2)\cdots(2)(1)]}g'(x)h^{(n-1)}(x) + \frac{n(n-1)(n-2)\cdots(2)(1)}{(2)(1)[(n-2)(n-3)\cdots(2)(1)]}g''(x)h^{(n-2)}(x)$$
$$+ \frac{n(n-1)(n-2)\cdots(2)(1)}{(3)(2)(1)[(n-3)(n-4)\cdots(2)(1)]}g'''(x)h^{(n-3)}(x) + \cdots$$
$$+ \frac{n(n-1)(n-2)\cdots(2)(1)}{[(n-1)(n-2)\cdots(2)(1)](1)}g^{(n-1)}(x)h'(x) + g^{(n)}(x)h(x)$$
$$= g(x)h^{(n)}(x) + \frac{n!}{1!(n-1)!}g'(x)h^{(n-1)}(x) + \frac{n!}{2!(n-2)!}g''(x)h^{(n-2)}(x) + \cdots + \frac{n!}{(n-1)!1!}g^{(n-1)}(x)h'(x) + g^{(n)}(x)h(x)$$

**124.** $[xf(x)]' = xf'(x) + f(x)$

$[xf(x)]'' = xf''(x) + f'(x) + f'(x) = xf''(x) + 2f'(x)$

$[xf(x)]''' = xf'''(x) + f''(x) + 2f''(x) = xf'''(x) + 3f''(x)$

In general, $[xf(x)]^{(n)} = xf^{(n)}(x) + nf^{(n-1)}(x)$.

**125.** $f(x) = x^n \sin x$

$f'(x) = x^n \cos x + nx^{n-1} \sin x$

When $n = 1$: $f'(x) = x \cos x + \sin x$

When $n = 2$: $f'(x) = x^2 \cos x + 2 \sin x$

When $n = 3$: $f'(x) = x^3 \cos x + 3x^2 \sin x$

When $n = 4$: $f'(x) = x^4 \cos x + 4x^3 \sin x$

For general $n$, $f'(x) = x^n \cos x + nx^{n-1} \sin x$.

**126.** $f(x) = \dfrac{\cos x}{x^n} = x^{-n} \cos x$

$$\begin{aligned} f'(x) &= -x^{-n} \sin x - nx^{-n-1} \cos x \\ &= -x^{-n-1}(x \sin x + n \cos x) \\ &= -\frac{x \sin x + n \cos x}{x^{n+1}} \end{aligned}$$

When $n = 1$: $f'(x) = -\dfrac{x \sin x + \cos x}{x^2}$

When $n = 2$: $f'(x) = -\dfrac{x \sin x + 2 \cos x}{x^3}$

When $n = 3$: $f'(x) = -\dfrac{x \sin x + 3 \cos x}{x^4}$

When $n = 4$: $f'(x) = -\dfrac{x \sin x + 4 \cos x}{x^5}$

For general $n$, $f'(x) = -\dfrac{x \sin x + n \cos x}{x^{n+1}}$.

**127.** $y = \dfrac{1}{x}, y' = -\dfrac{1}{x^2}, y'' = \dfrac{2}{x^3}$

$$x^3y'' + 2x^2y' = x^3\left[\frac{2}{x^3}\right] + 2x^2\left[-\frac{1}{x^2}\right] = 2 - 2 = 0$$

**128.**

$$\begin{aligned} y &= 2x^3 - 6x + 10 \\ y' &= 6x^2 - 6 \\ y'' &= 12x \\ y''' &= 12 \end{aligned}$$

$$-y''' - xy'' - 2y' = -12 - x(12x) - 2(6x^2 - 6) = -24x^2$$

**129.**

$$\begin{aligned} y &= 2 \sin x + 3 \\ y' &= 2 \cos x \\ y'' &= -2 \sin x \\ y'' + y &= -2 \sin x + (2 \sin x + 3) = 3 \end{aligned}$$

**130.**

$$\begin{aligned} y &= 3 \cos x + \sin x \\ y' &= -3 \sin x + \cos x \\ y'' &= -3 \cos x - \sin x \\ y'' + y &= (-3 \cos x - \sin x) + (3 \cos x + \sin x) = 0 \end{aligned}$$

**131.** False. If $y = f(x)g(x)$, then

$$\frac{dy}{dx} = f(x)g'(x) + g(x)f'(x).$$

**132.** True. $y$ is a fourth-degree polynomial.

$$\frac{d^n y}{dx^n} = 0 \text{ when } n > 4.$$

**133.** True

$$\begin{aligned} h'(c) &= f(c)g'(c) + g(c)f'(c) \\ &= f(c)(0) + g(c)(0) \\ &= 0 \end{aligned}$$

**134.** True

**135.** True

**136.** True. If $v(t) = c$, then $a(t) = v'(t) = 0$.

**137.** $f(x) = ax^2 + bx + c$

$f'(x) = 2ax + b$

$x$-intercept at $(1, 0)$: $0 = a + b + c$

$(2, 7)$ on graph: $7 = 4a + 2b + c$

Slope 10 at $(2, 7)$: $10 = 4a + b$

Subtracting the third equation from the second, $-3 = b + c$. Subtracting this equation from the first, $3 = a$. Then, $10 = 4(3) + b \Rightarrow b = -2$. Finally, $-3 = (-2) + c \Rightarrow c = -1$.

$f(x) = 3x^2 - 2x - 1$

**138.** $f(x) = ax^3 + bx^2 + cx + d, a \neq 0$

$f'(x) = 3ax^2 + 2bx + c$

$f'(x) = 0 \Rightarrow x = \dfrac{-2b \pm \sqrt{4b^2 - 12ac}}{6a}$

(a) No horizontal tangents: $f'(x) \neq 0$

$4b^2 - 12ac < 0$

Example: $a = c = 1, b = 0$:

$f(x) = x^3 + x$

(b) Exactly one horizontal tangent $4b^2 - 12ac = 0$

Example: $a = 1, b = 3, c = 3$:

$f(x) = x^3 + 3x^2 + 3x$

(c) Exactly two horizontal tangents

$4b^2 - 12ac > 0$

Example: $b = 1, a = 1, c = 0$:

$f(x) = x^3 + x^2$

**139.** $f(x) = x|x| = \begin{cases} x^2, & \text{if } x \geq 0 \\ -x^2, & \text{if } x < 0 \end{cases}$

$f'(x) = \begin{Bmatrix} 2x, & \text{if } x \geq 0 \\ -2x, & \text{if } x < 0 \end{Bmatrix} = 2|x|$

$f''(x) = \begin{cases} 2, & \text{if } x > 0 \\ -2, & \text{if } x < 0 \end{cases}$

$f''(0)$ does not exist because the left and right derivatives are not equal.

**140.** (a) $(fg' - f'g)' = fg'' + f'g' - f'g' - f''g$

$= fg'' - f''g$ True

(b) $(fg)'' = (fg' + f'g)'$

$= fg'' + f'g' + f'g' + f''g$

$= fg'' + 2f'g' + f''g$

$\neq fg'' + f''g$ False

**141.**
$$\begin{aligned}\frac{d}{dx}[f(x)g(x)h(x)] &= \frac{d}{dx}[(f(x)g(x))h(x)] \\ &= \frac{d}{dx}[f(x)g(x)]h(x) + f(x)g(x)h'(x) \\ &= [f(x)g'(x) + g(x)f'(x)]h(x) + f(x)g(x)h'(x) \\ &= f'(x)g(x)h(x) + f(x)g'(x)h(x) + f(x)g(x)h'(x)\end{aligned}$$

## Section 3.4 The Chain Rule

| | $y = f(g(x))$ | $u = g(x)$ | $y = f(u)$ |
|---|---|---|---|
| **1.** | $y = (5x - 8)^4$ | $u = 5x - 8$ | $y = u^4$ |
| **2.** | $y = \dfrac{1}{\sqrt{x + 1}}$ | $u = x + 1$ | $y = u^{-1/2}$ |
| **3.** | $y = \sqrt{x^3 - 7}$ | $u = x^3 - 7$ | $y = \sqrt{u}$ |

| $y = f(g(x))$ | $u = g(x)$ | $y = f(u)$ |
|---|---|---|
| **4.** $y = 3\tan(\pi x^2)$ | $u = \pi x^2$ | $y = 3\tan u$ |
| **5.** $y = \csc^3 x$ | $u = \csc x$ | $y = u^3$ |
| **6.** $y = \sin\frac{5x}{2}$ | $u = \frac{5x}{2}$ | $y = \sin u$ |
| **7.** $y = e^{-2x}$ | $u = -2x$ | $y = e^u$ |
| **8.** $y = (\ln x)^3$ | $u = \ln x$ | $y = u^3$ |

**9.** $y = (4x - 1)^3$

$y' = 3(4x - 1)^2(4) = 12(4x - 1)^2$

**10.** $y = 2(6 - x^2)^5$

$y' = 2(5)(6 - x^2)^4(-2x) = -20x(6 - x^2)^4$

**11.** $g(x) = 3(4 - 9x)^4$

$g'(x) = 12(4 - 9x)^3(-9) = -108(4 - 9x)^3$

**12.** $y = 3(5 - x^2)^5$

$y' = 15(5 - x^2)^4(-2x) = -30x(5 - x^2)^4$

**13.** $f(x) = (9 - x^2)^{2/3}$

$f'(x) = \frac{2}{3}(9 - x^2)^{-1/3}(-2x) = -\frac{4x}{3(9 - x^2)^{1/3}}$

**14.** $f(t) = (9t + 7)^{2/3}$

$f'(t) = \frac{2}{3}(9t + 7)^{-1/3}(9) = \frac{6}{\sqrt[3]{9t + 7}}$

**15.** $f(t) = \sqrt{5 - t} = (5 - t)^{1/2}$

$f'(t) = \frac{1}{2}(5 - t)^{-1/2}(-1) = \frac{-1}{2\sqrt{5 - t}}$

**16.** $g(x) = \sqrt{9 - 4x} = (9 - 4x)^{1/2}$

$g'(x) = \frac{1}{2}(9 - 4x)^{-1/2}(-4) = \frac{-2}{\sqrt{9 - 4x}}$

**17.** $y = \sqrt[3]{6x^2 + 1} = (6x^2 + 1)^{1/3}$

$y' = \frac{1}{3}(6x^2 + 1)^{-2/3}(12x) = \frac{4x}{(6x^2 + 1)^{2/3}} = \frac{4x}{\sqrt[3]{(6x^2 + 1)^2}}$

**18.** $g(x) = \sqrt{x^2 - 2x + 1} = \sqrt{(x - 1)^2} = |x - 1|$

$g'(x) = \begin{cases} 1, & x > 1 \\ -1, & x < 1 \end{cases}$

**19.** $y = 2\sqrt[4]{9 - x^2} = 2(9 - x^2)^{1/4}$

$y' = 2\left(\frac{1}{4}\right)(9 - x^2)^{-3/4}(-2x)$

$= \frac{-x}{(9 - x^2)^{3/4}} = \frac{-x}{\sqrt[4]{(9 - x^2)^3}}$

**20.** $f(x) = -3\sqrt[4]{2 - 9x}$

$f(x) = -3(2 - 9x)^{1/4}$

$f'(x) = -\frac{3}{4}(2 - 9x)^{-3/4}(-9)$

$= \frac{27}{4(2 - 9x)^{3/4}} = \frac{27}{4\sqrt[4]{(2 - 9x)^3}}$

**21.** $y = (x - 2)^{-1}$

$y' = -1(x - 2)^{-2}(1) = \frac{-1}{(x - 2)^2}$

**22.** $s(t) = \frac{1}{t^2 + 3t - 1}$

$s(t) = (t^2 + 3t - 1)^{-1}$

$s'(t) = -1(t^2 + 3t - 1)^{-2}(2t + 3) = \frac{-(2t + 3)}{(t^2 + 3t - 1)^2}$

**23.** $f(t) = (t - 3)^{-2}$

$f'(t) = -2(t - 3)^{-3}(1) = \frac{-2}{(t - 3)^3}$

**24.** $y = -8(t+3)^{-3}$

$$y' = 24(t+3)^{-4} = \frac{24}{(t+3)^4}$$

**25.** $y = (x+2)^{-1/2}$

$$\frac{dy}{dx} = -\frac{1}{2}(x+2)^{-3/2}$$

$$= -\frac{1}{2(x+2)^{3/2}}$$

$$= -\frac{1}{2\sqrt{(x+2)^3}}$$

**26.** $g(t) = \sqrt{\dfrac{1}{t^2-2}}$

$$g(t) = (t^2-2)^{-1/2}$$

$$g'(t) = -\frac{1}{2}(t^2-2)^{-3/2}(2t)$$

$$= -\frac{t}{(t^2-2)^{3/2}} = -\frac{t}{\sqrt{(t^2-2)^3}}$$

**27.** $f(x) = x^2(x-2)^4$

$$f'(x) = x^2\left[4(x-2)^3(1)\right] + (x-2)^4(2x)$$

$$= 2x(x-2)^3\left[2x + (x-2)\right]$$

$$= 2x(x-2)^3(3x-2)$$

**28.** $f(x) = x(3x-7)^3$

$$f'(x) = x\left[3(3x-7)^2(3)\right] + (3x-7)^3(1)$$

$$= (3x-7)^2[9x + 3x - 7]$$

$$= (3x-7)^2(12x-7)$$

**29.** $y = x\sqrt{1-x^2} = x(1-x^2)^{1/2}$

$$y' = x\left[\frac{1}{2}(1-x^2)^{-1/2}(-2x)\right] + (1-x^2)^{1/2}(1)$$

$$= -x^2(1-x^2)^{-1/2} + (1-x^2)^{1/2}$$

$$= (1-x^2)^{-1/2}\left[-x^2 + (1-x^2)\right]$$

$$= \frac{1-2x^2}{\sqrt{1-x^2}}$$

**30.** $y = \dfrac{1}{2}x^2\sqrt{16-x^2}$

$$y' = \frac{1}{2}x^2\left(\frac{1}{2}(16-x^2)^{-1/2}(-2x)\right) + x(16-x^2)^{1/2}$$

$$= \frac{-x^3}{2\sqrt{16-x^2}} + x\sqrt{16-x^2} = \frac{-x(3x^2-32)}{2\sqrt{16-x^2}}$$

**31.** $y = \dfrac{x}{\sqrt{x^2+1}} = \dfrac{x}{(x^2+1)^{1/2}}$

$$y' = \frac{(x^2+1)^{1/2}(1) - x\left(\frac{1}{2}\right)(x^2+1)^{-1/2}(2x)}{\left[(x^2+1)^{1/2}\right]^2}$$

$$= \frac{(x^2+1)^{1/2} - x^2(x^2+1)^{-1/2}}{x^2+1}$$

$$= \frac{(x^2+1)^{-1/2}\left[x^2+1-x^2\right]}{x^2+1}$$

$$= \frac{1}{(x^2+1)^{3/2}} = \frac{1}{\sqrt{(x^2+1)^3}}$$

**32.** $y = \dfrac{x}{\sqrt{x^4+2}}$

$$y' = \frac{(x^4+2)^{1/2}(1) - x(1/2)(x^4+2)^{-1/2}(4x^3)}{x^4+2}$$

$$= \frac{x^4+2-2x^4}{(x^4+2)^{3/2}} = \frac{2-x^4}{(x^4+2)^{3/2}}$$

**33.** $g(x) = \left(\dfrac{x+5}{x^2+2}\right)^2$

$$g'(x) = 2\left(\frac{x+5}{x^2+2}\right)\left(\frac{(x^2+2)-(x+5)(2x)}{(x^2+2)^2}\right)$$

$$= \frac{2(x+5)(2-10x-x^2)}{(x^2+2)^3}$$

$$= \frac{-2(x+5)(x^2+10x-2)}{(x^2+2)^3}$$

**34.** $g(x) = \left(\dfrac{3x^2-1}{2x+5}\right)^3$

$$g'(x) = 3\left(\frac{3x^2-1}{2x+5}\right)^2\left(\frac{(2x+5)(6x)-(3x^2-1)(2)}{(2x+5)^2}\right) = \frac{3(3x^2-1)^2(6x^2+30x+2)}{(2x+5)^4} = \frac{6(3x^2-1)^2(3x^2+15x+1)}{(2x+5)^4}$$

**35.** $f(x) = \left((x^2+3)^5 + x\right)^2$

$f'(x) = 2\left((x^2+3)^5 + x\right)\left(5(x^2+3)^4(2x) + 1\right)$

$= 2\left[10x(x^2+3)^9 + (x^2+3)^5 + 10x^2(x^2+3)^4 + x\right] = 20x(x^2+3)^9 + 2(x^2+3)^5 + 20x^2(x^2+3)^4 + 2x$

**36.** $g(x) = \left(2 + (x^2+1)^4\right)^3$

$g'(x) = 3\left(2 + (x^2+1)^4\right)^2\left(4(x^2+1)^3(2x)\right) = 24x(x^2+1)^3\left(2 + (x^2+1)^4\right)^2$

**37.** $f(x) = \sqrt{2 + \sqrt{2 + \sqrt{x}}}$

$= \left[2 + \left(2 + x^{1/2}\right)^{1/2}\right]^{1/2}$

$f'(x) = \frac{1}{2}\left[2 + \left(2 + x^{1/2}\right)^{1/2}\right]^{-1/2}\left[\frac{1}{2}\left(2 + x^{1/2}\right)^{-1/2}\left(\frac{1}{2}x^{-1/2}\right)\right]$

$= \dfrac{1}{8\sqrt{x}\sqrt{2+\sqrt{x}}\sqrt{2+\sqrt{2+\sqrt{x}}}}$

**38.** $g(t) = \sqrt{\sqrt{t+1} + 1} = \left[(t+1)^{1/2} + 1\right]^{1/2}$

$g'(t) = \frac{1}{2}\left[(t+1)^{1/2} + 1\right]^{-1/2}\left[\frac{1}{2}(t+1)^{-1/2}\right]$

$= \dfrac{1}{4\sqrt{t+1}\sqrt{\sqrt{t+1}+1}}$

**39.** $y = \dfrac{\sqrt{x}+1}{x^2+1}$

$y' = \dfrac{1 - 3x^2 - 4x^{3/2}}{2\sqrt{x}(x^2+1)^2}$

The zero of $y'$ corresponds to the point on the graph of $y$ where the tangent line is horizontal.

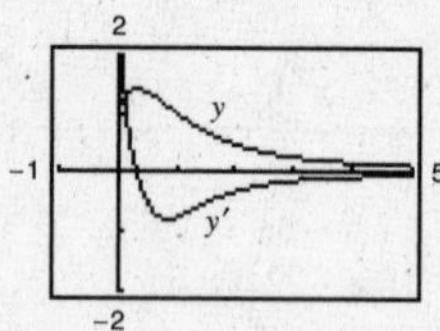


**40.** $y = \sqrt{\dfrac{2x}{x+1}}$

$y' = \dfrac{1}{\sqrt{2x}(x+1)^{3/2}}$

$y'$ has no zeros.

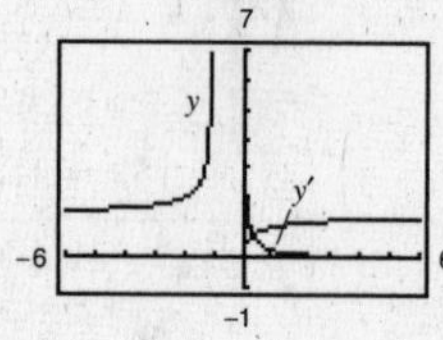


**41.** $g(t) = \dfrac{3t^2}{\sqrt{t^2+2t-1}}$

$g'(t) = \dfrac{3t(t^2+3t-2)}{(t^2+2t-1)^{3/2}}$

The zeros of $g'$ correspond to the points on the graph of $g$ where the tangent lines are horizontal.

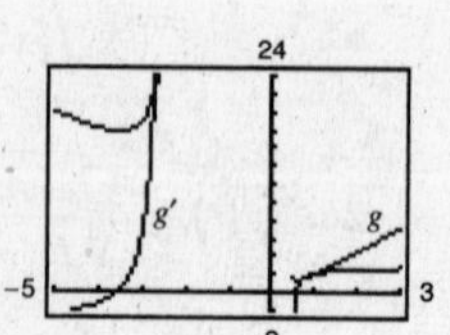


**42.** $f(x) = \sqrt{x}(2-x)^2$

$f'(x) = \dfrac{(x-2)(5x-2)}{2\sqrt{x}}$

The zeros of $f'$ correspond to the points on the graph of $f$ where the tangent lines are horizontal.

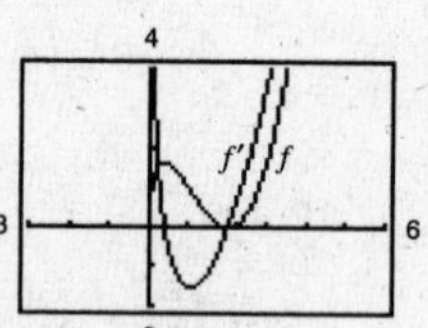


**43.** $y = \sqrt{\dfrac{x+1}{x}}$

$y' = -\dfrac{\sqrt{(x+1)/x}}{2x(x+1)}$

$y'$ has no zeros.

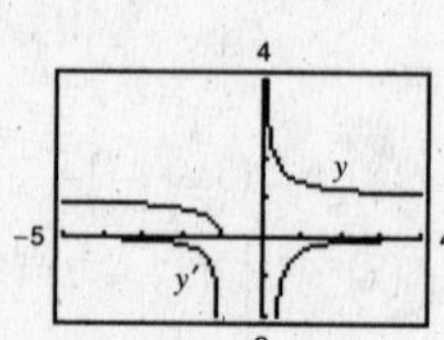


**44.** $y = (t^2-9)\sqrt{t+2}$

$y' = \dfrac{5t^2+8t-9}{2\sqrt{t+2}}$

The zero of $y'$ corresponds to the point on the graph of $y$ where the tangent line is horizontal.

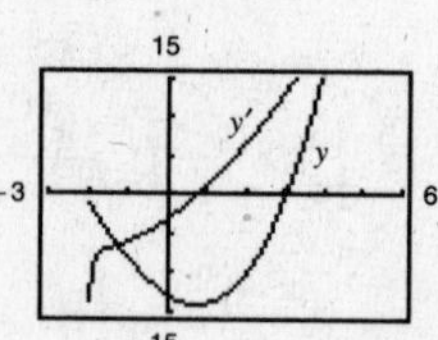


**45.** $s(t) = \dfrac{-2(2-t)\sqrt{1+t}}{3}$

$s'(t) = \dfrac{t}{\sqrt{1+t}}$

The zero of $s'(t)$ corresponds to the point on the graph of $s(t)$ where the tangent line is horizontal.

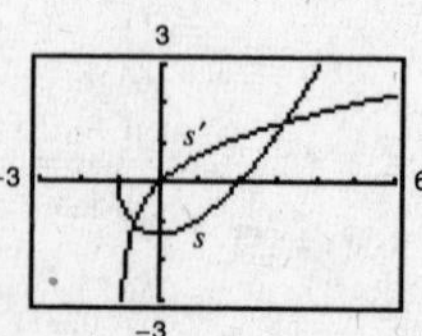

**46.** $g(x) = \sqrt{x-1} + \sqrt{x+1}$

$$g'(x) = \frac{1}{2\sqrt{x-1}} + \frac{1}{2\sqrt{x+1}}$$

$g'$ has no zeros.

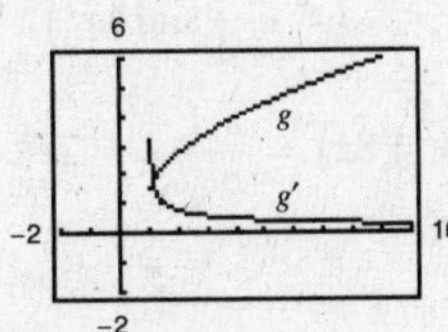


**47.** $y = \dfrac{\cos \pi x + 1}{x}$

$$\frac{dy}{dx} = \frac{-\pi x \sin \pi x - \cos \pi x - 1}{x^2}$$

$$= -\frac{\pi x \sin \pi x + \cos \pi x + 1}{x^2}$$

The zeros of $y'$ correspond to the points on the graph of $y$ where the tangent lines are horizontal.

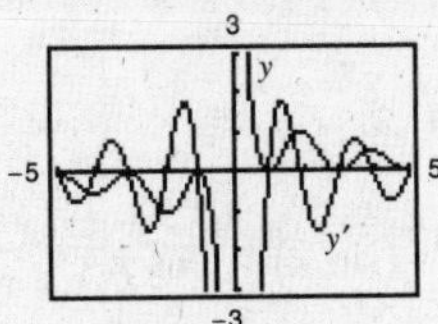


**48.** $y = x^2 \tan \dfrac{1}{x}$

$$\frac{dy}{dx} = 2x \tan \frac{1}{x} - \sec^2 \frac{1}{x}$$

The zeros of $y'$ correspond to the points on the graph of $y$ where the tangent lines are horizontal.

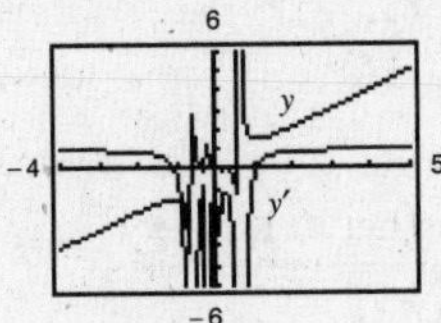


**49.** (a) $y = \sin x$

$y' = \cos x$

$y'(0) = 1$

1 cycle in $[0, 2\pi]$

(b) $y = \sin 2x$

$y' = 2 \cos 2x$

$y'(0) = 2$

2 cycles in $[0, 2\pi]$

The slope of sin $ax$ at the origin is $a$.

**50.** (a) $y = \sin 3x$

$y' = 3 \cos 3x$

$y'(0) = 3$

3 cycles in $[0, 2\pi]$

(b) $y = \sin\left(\dfrac{x}{2}\right)$

$y' = \left(\dfrac{1}{2}\right)\cos\left(\dfrac{x}{2}\right)$

$y'(0) = \dfrac{1}{2}$

Half cycle in $[0, 2\pi]$

The slope of sin $ax$ at the origin is $a$.

**51.** (a) $y = e^{3x}$

$y' = 3e^{3x}$

At $(0, 1)$, $y' = 3$.

(b) $y = e^{-3x}$

$y' = -3e^{-3x}$

At $(0, 1)$, $y' = -3$.

**52.** (a) $y = e^{2x}$

$y' = 2e^{2x}$

At $(0, 1)$, $y' = 2$.

(b) $y = e^{-2x}$

$y' = -2e^{-2x}$

At $(0, 1)$, $y' = -2$.

**53.** $y = \ln x^3 = 3 \ln x$

$y' = \dfrac{3}{x}$

At $(1, 0)$, $y' = 3$.

**54.** $y = \ln x^{3/2} = \dfrac{3}{2} \ln x$

$y' = \dfrac{3}{2}\left(\dfrac{1}{x}\right) = \dfrac{3}{2x}$

At $(1, 0)$, $y' = \dfrac{3}{2}$.

**55.** $y = \ln x^2 = 2 \ln x$

$y' = \dfrac{2}{x}$

At $(1, 0)$, $y' = 2$.

**56.** $y = \ln x^{1/2} = \frac{1}{2}\ln x$.

$y' = \frac{1}{2}\left(\frac{1}{x}\right) = \frac{1}{2x}$

At $(1, 0)$, $y' = \frac{1}{2}$.

**57.** $y = \cos 4x$

$\frac{dy}{dx} = -4\sin 4x$

**58.** $y = \sin \pi x$

$\frac{dy}{dx} = \pi \cos \pi x$

**59.** $g(x) = 5\tan 3x$

$g'(x) = 15\sec^2 3x$

**60.** $h(x) = \sec(x^3)$

$h'(x) = 3x^2\sec(x^3)\tan(x^3)$

**61.** $f(\theta) = \tan^2 5\theta = (\tan 5\theta)^2$

$f'(\theta) = 2(\tan 5\theta)(\sec^2 5\theta)5 = 10\tan 5\theta\sec^2 5\theta$

**62.** $g(\theta) = \cos^2 8\theta = (\cos 8\theta)^2$

$g'(\theta) = 2(\cos 8\theta)(-\sin 8\theta)8 = -16\cos 8\theta\sin 8\theta$

**63.** $f(\theta) = \frac{1}{4}\sin^2 2\theta = \frac{1}{4}(\sin 2\theta)^2$

$f'(\theta) = 2\left(\frac{1}{4}\right)(\sin 2\theta)(\cos 2\theta)(2)$

$= \sin 2\theta\cos 2\theta = \frac{1}{2}\sin 4\theta$

**64.** $g(t) = 5\cos^3 \pi t = 5(\cos \pi t)^3$

$g'(t) = 15(\cos \pi t)^2(-\sin \pi t)(\pi)$

$= -15\pi\cos^2 \pi t\sin \pi t$

**65.** $y = \sqrt{x} + \frac{1}{4}\sin(2x)^2 = \sqrt{x} + \frac{1}{4}\sin(4x^2)$

$\frac{dy}{dx} = \frac{1}{2}x^{-1/2} + \frac{1}{4}\cos(4x^2)(8x) = \frac{1}{2\sqrt{x}} + 2x\cos(2x)^2$

**66.** $y = 3x - 5\cos(2x)^2$

$= 3x - 5\cos(4x^2)$

$y' = 3 + 5\sin(4x^2)(8x)$

$= 3 + 40x\sin(2x)^2$

**67.** $y = \sin(\cos x)$

$\frac{dy}{dx} = \cos(\cos x)\cdot(-\sin x)$

$= -\sin x\cos(\cos x)$

**68.** $y = \sin x^{1/3} + (\sin x)^{1/3}$

$y' = \cos x^{1/3}\left(\frac{1}{3}x^{-2/3}\right) + \frac{1}{3}(\sin x)^{-2/3}\cos x$

$= \frac{1}{3}\left[\frac{\cos x^{1/3}}{x^{2/3}} + \frac{\cos x}{(\sin x)^{2/3}}\right]$

**69.** $y = \sin(\tan 2x)$

$y' = \cos(\tan 2x)(\sec^2 2x)(2) = 2\cos(\tan 2x)\sec^2 2x$

**70.** $y = \cos\sqrt{\sin(\tan \pi x)}$

$$y' = -\sin\sqrt{\sin(\tan \pi x)}\cdot\frac{1}{2}(\sin(\tan \pi x))^{-1/2}\cos(\tan \pi x)\sec^2 \pi x(\pi) = \frac{-\pi\sin\sqrt{\sin(\tan \pi x)}\cos(\tan \pi x)\sec^2 \pi x}{2\sqrt{\sin(\tan \pi x)}}$$

**71.** $f(x) = e^{2x}$

$f'(x) = 2e^{2x}$

**72.** $y = e^{-x^2}$

$\frac{dy}{dx} = -2xe^{-x^2}$

**73.** $y = e^{\sqrt{x}}$

$\frac{dy}{dx} = \frac{e^{\sqrt{x}}}{2\sqrt{x}}$

**74.** $y = x^2e^{-x}$

$\frac{dy}{dx} = -x^2e^{-x} + 2xe^{-x}$

$= xe^{-x}(2 - x)$

**75.** $g(t) = (e^{-t} + e^t)^3$

$g'(t) = 3(e^{-t} + e^t)^2(e^t - e^{-t})$

**76.** $g(t) = e^{-3/t^2} = e^{-3t^{-2}}$

$g'(t) = e^{-3/t^2}(6t^{-3}) = \frac{6}{t^3e^{3/t^2}} = \frac{6e^{-3/t^2}}{t^3}$

**77.** $y = \ln e^{x^2} = x^2$

$$\frac{dy}{dx} = 2x$$

**78.** $y = \ln\left(\frac{1 + e^x}{1 - e^x}\right)$

$$= \ln(1 + e^x) - \ln(1 - e^x)$$

$$\frac{dy}{dx} = \frac{e^x}{1 + e^x} + \frac{e^x}{1 - e^x}$$

$$= \frac{2e^x}{1 - e^{2x}}$$

**79.** $y = \frac{2}{e^x + e^{-x}} = 2(e^x + e^{-x})^{-1}$

$$\frac{dy}{dx} = -2(e^x + e^{-x})^{-2}(e^x - e^{-x})$$

$$= \frac{-2(e^x - e^{-x})}{(e^x + e^{-x})^2}$$

**80.** $y = \frac{e^x - e^{-x}}{2}$

$$\frac{dy}{dx} = \frac{e^x + e^{-x}}{2}$$

**81.** $y = x^2e^x - 2xe^x + 2e^x = e^x(x^2 - 2x + 2)$

$$\frac{dy}{dx} = e^x(2x - 2) + e^x(x^2 - 2x + 2) = x^2e^x$$

**82.** $y = xe^x - e^x = e^x(x - 1)$

$$\frac{dy}{dx} = e^x + e^x(x - 1) = xe^x$$

**83.** $f(x) = e^{-x} \ln x$

$$f'(x) = e^{-x}\left(\frac{1}{x}\right) - e^{-x} \ln x = e^{-x}\left(\frac{1}{x} - \ln x\right)$$

**84.** $f(x) = e^3 \ln x$

$$f'(x) = \frac{e^3}{x}$$

**85.** $y = e^x(\sin x + \cos x)$

$$\frac{dy}{dx} = e^x(\cos x - \sin x) + (\sin x + \cos x)(e^x)$$

$$= e^x(2 \cos x) = 2e^x \cos x$$

**86.** $y = \ln e^x = x$

$$\frac{dy}{dx} = 1$$

**87.** $g(x) = \ln x^2 = 2 \ln x$

$$g'(x) = \frac{2}{x}$$

**88.** $h(x) = \ln(2x^2 + 3)$

$$h'(x) = \frac{4x}{2x^2 + 3}$$

**89.** $y = (\ln x)^4$

$$\frac{dy}{dx} = 4(\ln x)^3\left(\frac{1}{x}\right) = \frac{4(\ln x)^3}{x}$$

**90.** $y = x \ln x$

$$\frac{dy}{dx} = x\left(\frac{1}{x}\right) + \ln x = 1 + \ln x$$

**91.** $y = \ln x\sqrt{x^2 - 1} = \ln x + \frac{1}{2}\ln(x^2 - 1)$

$$\frac{dy}{dx} = \frac{1}{x} + \frac{1}{2}\left(\frac{2x}{x^2 - 1}\right) = \frac{2x^2 - 1}{x(x^2 - 1)}$$

**92.** $y = \ln \sqrt{x^2 - 9} = \frac{1}{2}\ln(x^2 - 9)$

$$y' = \frac{1}{2}\frac{1}{x^2 - 9}(2x) = \frac{x}{x^2 - 9}$$

**93.** $f(x) = \ln\frac{x}{x^2 + 1} = \ln x - \ln(x^2 + 1)$

$$f'(x) = \frac{1}{x} - \frac{2x}{x^2 + 1} = \frac{1 - x^2}{x(x^2 + 1)}$$

**94.** $f(x) = \ln\left(\frac{2x}{x + 3}\right) = \ln(2x) - \ln(x + 3)$

$$f'(x) = \frac{1}{2x}(2) - \frac{1}{x + 3} = \frac{1}{x} - \frac{1}{x + 3}$$

**95.** $g(t) = \frac{\ln t}{t^2}$

$$g'(t) = \frac{t^2(1/t) - 2t \ln t}{t^4} = \frac{1 - 2 \ln t}{t^3}$$

**96.** $h(t) = \frac{\ln t}{t}$

$$h'(t) = \frac{t(1/t) - \ln t}{t^2} = \frac{1 - \ln t}{t^2}$$

**97.** $y = \ln\sqrt{\frac{x + 1}{x - 1}} = \frac{1}{2}\left[\ln(x + 1) - \ln(x - 1)\right]$

$$\frac{dy}{dx} = \frac{1}{2}\left[\frac{1}{x + 1} - \frac{1}{x - 1}\right] = \frac{1}{1 - x^2}$$

**98.** $y = \ln\sqrt[3]{\dfrac{x-2}{x+2}} = \dfrac{1}{3}\left[\ln(x-2) - \ln(x+2)\right]$

$$y' = \frac{1}{3}\left[\frac{1}{x-2} - \frac{1}{x+2}\right] = \frac{4}{3(x^2-4)}$$

**99.** $y = \dfrac{-\sqrt{x^2+1}}{x} + \ln\left(x + \sqrt{x^2+1}\right)$

$$\frac{dy}{dx} = \frac{-x\left(x/\sqrt{x^2+1}\right) + \sqrt{x^2+1}}{x^2} + \left(\frac{1}{x+\sqrt{x^2+1}}\right)\left(1 + \frac{x}{\sqrt{x^2+1}}\right)$$

$$= \frac{1}{x^2\sqrt{x^2+1}} + \left(\frac{1}{x+\sqrt{x^2+1}}\right)\left(\frac{\sqrt{x^2+1}+x}{\sqrt{x^2+1}}\right)$$

$$= \frac{1}{x^2\sqrt{x^2+1}} + \frac{1}{\sqrt{x^2+1}} = \frac{1+x^2}{x^2\sqrt{x^2+1}} = \frac{\sqrt{x^2+1}}{x^2}$$

**100.** $y = \dfrac{-\sqrt{x^2+4}}{2x^2} - \dfrac{1}{4}\ln\left(\dfrac{2+\sqrt{x^2+4}}{x}\right) = \dfrac{-\sqrt{x^2+4}}{2x^2} - \dfrac{1}{4}\ln\left(2+\sqrt{x^2+4}\right) + \dfrac{1}{4}\ln x$

$$\frac{dy}{dx} = \frac{-2x^2\left(x/\sqrt{x^2+4}\right) + 4x\sqrt{x^2+4}}{4x^4} - \frac{1}{4}\left(\frac{1}{2+\sqrt{x^2+4}}\right)\left(\frac{x}{\sqrt{x^2+4}}\right) + \frac{1}{4x}$$

Note that $\dfrac{1}{2+\sqrt{x^2+4}} = \dfrac{1}{2+\sqrt{x^2+4}} \cdot \dfrac{2-\sqrt{x^2+4}}{2-\sqrt{x^2+4}} = \dfrac{2-\sqrt{x^2+4}}{-x^2}$.

So, $\dfrac{dy}{dx} = \dfrac{-1}{2x\sqrt{x^2+4}} + \dfrac{\sqrt{x^2+4}}{x^3} - \dfrac{1}{4}\dfrac{\left(2-\sqrt{x^2+4}\right)}{-x^2}\left(\dfrac{x}{\sqrt{x^2+4}}\right) + \dfrac{1}{4x}$

$$= \frac{-1 + (1/2)\left(2-\sqrt{x^2+4}\right)}{2x\sqrt{x^2+4}} + \frac{\sqrt{x^2+4}}{x^3} + \frac{1}{4x}$$

$$= \frac{-\sqrt{x^2+4}}{4x\sqrt{x^2+4}} + \frac{\sqrt{x^2+4}}{x^3} + \frac{1}{4x} = \frac{\sqrt{x^2+4}}{x^3}.$$

**101.** $y = \ln|\sin x|$

$$\frac{dy}{dx} = \frac{\cos x}{\sin x} = \cot x$$

**102.** $y = \ln|\csc x|$

$$y' = \frac{1}{\csc x}(-\csc x \cot x) = -\cot x$$

**103.** $y = \ln\left|\dfrac{\cos x}{\cos x - 1}\right|$

$$= \ln|\cos x| - \ln|\cos x - 1|$$

$$\frac{dy}{dx} = \frac{-\sin x}{\cos x} - \frac{-\sin x}{\cos x - 1} = -\tan x + \frac{\sin x}{\cos x - 1}$$

**104.** $y = \ln|\sec x + \tan x|$

$$\frac{dy}{dx} = \frac{\sec x \tan x + \sec^2 x}{\sec x + \tan x}$$

$$= \frac{\sec x(\sec x + \tan x)}{\sec x + \tan x} = \sec x$$

**105.** $y = \ln\left|\dfrac{-1+\sin x}{2+\sin x}\right|$

$$= \ln|-1+\sin x| - \ln|2+\sin x|$$

$$\frac{dy}{dx} = \frac{\cos x}{-1+\sin x} - \frac{\cos x}{2+\sin x}$$

$$= \frac{3\cos x}{(\sin x - 1)(\sin x + 2)}$$

**106.** $y = \ln\sqrt{1 + \sin^2 x} = \frac{1}{2}\ln(1 + \sin^2 x)$

$$\frac{dy}{dx} = \left(\frac{1}{2}\right)\frac{2\sin x\cos x}{1 + \sin^2 x} = \frac{\sin x \cos x}{1 + \sin^2 x}$$

**107.** $f(x) = 5(2 - 7x)^4$

$$f'(x) = 20(2 - 7x)^3(-7) = -140(2 - 7x)^3$$

$$f''(x) = -420(2 - 7x)^2(-7) = 2940(2 - 7x)^2$$

**108.** $f(x) = 4(x^2 - 2)^3$

$$f'(x) = 12(x^2 - 2)^2(2x) = 24x(x^2 - 2)^2$$

$$\begin{aligned} f''(x) &= 24x(2)(x^2 - 2)(2x) + 24(x^2 - 2)^2 \\ &= (x^2 - 2)(96x^2 + 24(x^2 - 2)) \\ &= (x^2 - 2)(120x^2 - 48) \\ &= 24(x^2 - 2)(5x^2 - 2) \end{aligned}$$

**109.** $f(x) = \frac{1}{x - 6} = (x - 6)^{-1}$

$$f'(x) = -(x - 6)^{-2}$$

$$f''(x) = 2(x - 6)^{-3} = \frac{2}{(x - 6)^3}$$

**110.** $f(x) = \frac{4}{(x + 2)^3} = 4(x + 2)^{-3}$

$$f'(x) = -12(x + 2)^{-4}$$

$$f''(x) = 48(x + 2)^{-5} = \frac{48}{(x + 2)^5}$$

**111.** $f(x) = \sin x^2$

$$f'(x) = 2x\cos x^2$$

$$\begin{aligned} f''(x) &= 2x\left[2x(-\sin x^2)\right] + 2\cos x^2 \\ &= 2(\cos x^2 - 2x^2 \sin x^2) \end{aligned}$$

**112.** $f(x) = \sec^2 \pi x$

$$\begin{aligned} f'(x) &= 2\sec \pi x(\pi \sec \pi x \tan \pi x) \\ &= 2\pi \sec^2 \pi x \tan \pi x \end{aligned}$$

$$\begin{aligned} f''(x) &= 2\pi \sec^2 \pi x(\sec^2 \pi x)(\pi) + 2\pi \tan \pi x(2\pi \sec^2 \pi x \tan \pi x) \\ &= 2\pi^2 \sec^4 \pi x + 4\pi^2 \sec^2 \pi x \tan^2 \pi x \\ &= 2\pi^2 \sec^2 \pi x(\sec^2 \pi x + 2\tan^2 \pi x) \\ &= 2\pi^2 \sec^2 \pi x(3\sec^2 \pi x - 2) \end{aligned}$$

**113.** $f(x) = (3 + 2x)e^{-3x}$

$$\begin{aligned} f'(x) &= (3 + 2x)(-3e^{-3x}) + 2e^{-3x} \\ &= (-7 - 6x)e^{-3x} \end{aligned}$$

$$\begin{aligned} f''(x) &= (-7 - 6x)(-3e^{-3x}) - 6e^{-3x} \\ &= 3(6x + 5)e^{-3x} \end{aligned}$$

**114.** $g(x) = \sqrt{x} + e^x \ln x$

$$g'(x) = \frac{1}{2\sqrt{x}} + \frac{e^x}{x} + e^x \ln x$$

$$\begin{aligned} g''(x) &= -\frac{1}{4x^{3/2}} + \frac{xe^x - e^x}{x^2} + \frac{e^x}{x} + e^x \ln x \\ &= -\frac{1}{4x\sqrt{x}} + \frac{e^x(2x - 1)}{x^2} + e^x \ln x \end{aligned}$$

**115.** $s(t) = (t^2 + 6t - 2)^{1/2}$, $(3, 5)$

$$\begin{aligned} s'(t) &= \frac{1}{2}(t^2 + 6t - 2)^{-1/2}(2t + 6) \\ &= \frac{t + 3}{\sqrt{t^2 + 6t - 2}} \end{aligned}$$

$$s'(3) = \frac{6}{5}$$

**116.** $y = (3x^3 + 4x)^{1/5}$, $(2, 2)$

$$\begin{aligned} y' &= \frac{1}{5}(3x^3 + 4x)^{-4/5}(9x^2 + 4) \\ &= \frac{9x^2 + 4}{5(3x^3 + 4x)^{4/5}} \end{aligned}$$

$$y'(2) = \frac{1}{2}$$

**117.** $f(x) = \dfrac{5}{x^3 - 2} = 5(x^3 - 2)^{-1}, \quad \left(-2, -\dfrac{1}{2}\right)$

$f'(x) = -5(x^3 - 2)^{-2}(3x^2) = \dfrac{-15x^2}{(x^3 - 2)^2}$

$f'(-2) = -\dfrac{60}{100} = -\dfrac{3}{5}$

**118.** $f(x) = \dfrac{1}{(x^2 - 3x)^2} = (x^2 - 3x)^{-2}, \quad \left(4, \dfrac{1}{16}\right)$

$f'(x) = -2(x^2 - 3x)^{-3}(2x - 3) = \dfrac{-2(2x - 3)}{(x^2 - 3x)^3}$

$f'(4) = -\dfrac{5}{32}$

**119.** $f(t) = \dfrac{3t + 2}{t - 1}, \quad (0, -2)$

$f'(t) = \dfrac{(t - 1)(3) - (3t + 2)(1)}{(t - 1)^2} = \dfrac{-5}{(t - 1)^2}$

$f'(0) = -5$

**120.** $f(x) = \dfrac{x + 1}{2x - 3}, \quad (2, 3)$

$f'(x) = -\dfrac{(2x - 3)(1) - (x + 1)(2)}{(2x - 3)^2} = \dfrac{-5}{(2x - 3)^2}$

$f'(2) = -5$

**121.** $y = 26 - \sec^3 4x, \quad (0, 25)$

$y' = -3\sec^2 4x \sec 4x \tan 4x\ 4$

$= -12\sec^3 4x \tan 4x$

$y'(0) = 0$

**122.** $y = \dfrac{1}{x} + \sqrt{\cos x}, \quad \left(\dfrac{\pi}{2}, \dfrac{2}{\pi}\right)$

$y' = -\dfrac{1}{x^2} - \dfrac{\sin x}{2\sqrt{\cos x}}$

$y'(\pi/2)$ is undefined.

**123.** (a) $f(x) = (2x^2 - 7)^{1/2}, \quad (4, 5)$

$f'(x) = \dfrac{1}{2}(2x^2 - 7)^{-1/2}(4x) = \dfrac{2x}{\sqrt{2x^2 - 7}}$

$f'(4) = \dfrac{8}{5}$

Tangent line:

$y - 5 = \dfrac{8}{5}(x - 4) \Rightarrow 8x - 5y - 7 = 0$

(b)

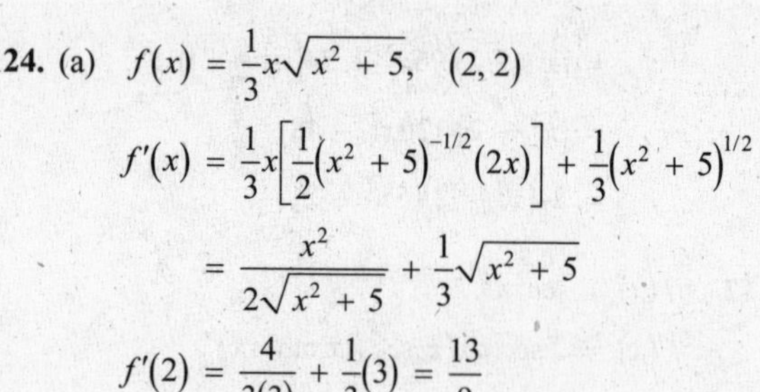


**124.** (a) $f(x) = \dfrac{1}{3}x\sqrt{x^2 + 5}, \quad (2, 2)$

$f'(x) = \dfrac{1}{3}x\left[\dfrac{1}{2}(x^2 + 5)^{-1/2}(2x)\right] + \dfrac{1}{3}(x^2 + 5)^{1/2}$

$= \dfrac{x^2}{2\sqrt{x^2 + 5}} + \dfrac{1}{3}\sqrt{x^2 + 5}$

$f'(2) = \dfrac{4}{3(3)} + \dfrac{1}{3}(3) = \dfrac{13}{9}$

Tangent line:

$y - 2 = \dfrac{13}{9}(x - 2) \Rightarrow 13x - 9y - 8 = 0$

(b)

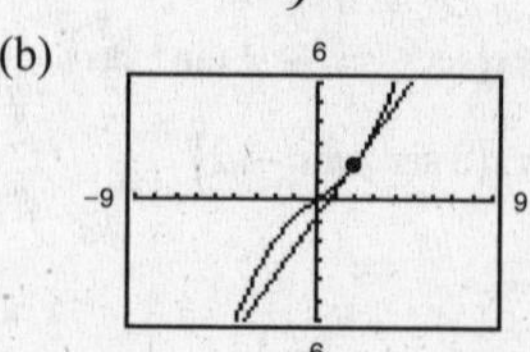


**125.** (a) $f(x) = \sin 2x, \quad (\pi, 0)$

$f'(x) = 2\cos 2x$

$f'(\pi) = 2$

Tangent line:

$y = 2(x - \pi) \Rightarrow 2x - y - 2\pi = 0$

(b)

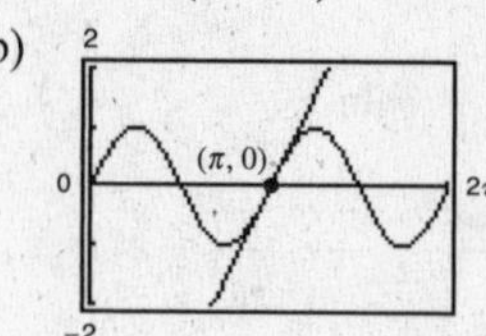

**126.** (a) $y = \cos 3x, \quad \left(\frac{\pi}{4}, -\frac{\sqrt{2}}{2}\right)$

$$y' = -3 \sin 3x$$

$$y'\left(\frac{\pi}{4}\right) = -3 \sin\left(\frac{3\pi}{4}\right) = \frac{-3\sqrt{2}}{2}$$

Tangent line: $y + \frac{\sqrt{2}}{2} = \frac{-3\sqrt{2}}{2}\left(x - \frac{\pi}{4}\right)$

$$y = \frac{-3\sqrt{2}}{2}x + \frac{3\sqrt{2}\pi}{8} - \frac{\sqrt{2}}{2}$$

(b)

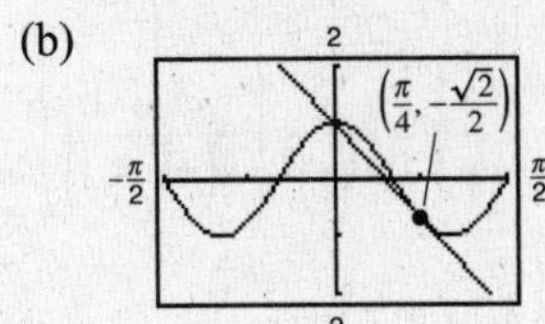

**127.** (a) $y = 2 \tan^3 x, \quad \left(\frac{\pi}{4}, 2\right)$

$$y' = 6 \tan^2 x \cdot \sec^2 x$$

$$y'\left(\frac{\pi}{4}\right) = 6(1)(2) = 12$$

Tangent line:

$$y - 2 = 12\left(x - \frac{\pi}{4}\right) \Rightarrow 12x - y + (2 - 3\pi) = 0$$

(b)

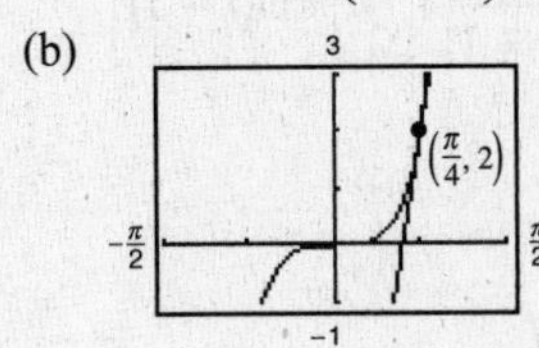

**128.** (a) $f(x) = \tan^2 x, \quad \left(\frac{\pi}{4}, 1\right)$

$$f'(x) = 2 \tan x \sec^2 x$$

$$f'\left(\frac{\pi}{4}\right) = 2(1)(2) = 4$$

Tangent line:

$$y - 1 = 4\left(x - \frac{\pi}{4}\right) \Rightarrow 4x - y + (1 - \pi) = 0$$

(b)

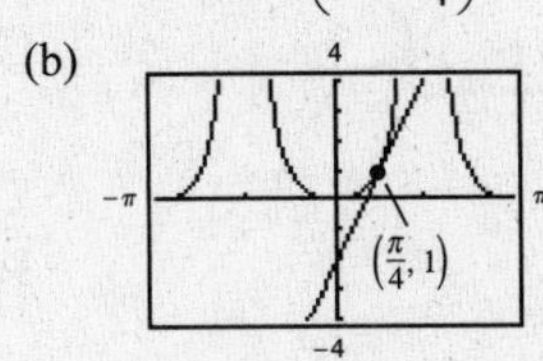

**129.** (a) $y = 4 - x^2 - \ln\left(\frac{1}{2}x + 1\right), \quad (0, 4)$

$$\frac{dy}{dx} = -2x - \frac{1}{(1/2)x + 1}\left(\frac{1}{2}\right)$$

$$= -2x - \frac{1}{x + 2}$$

When $x = 0$, $\frac{dy}{dx} = -\frac{1}{2}$.

Tangent line: $y - 4 = -\frac{1}{2}(x - 0)$

$$y = -\frac{1}{2}x + 4$$

(b)

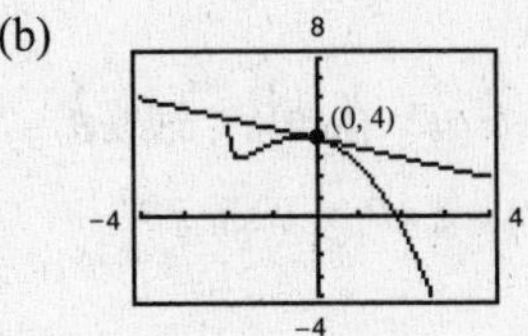

**130.** (a) $y = 2e^{1-x^2}, \quad (1, 2)$

$$y' = 2e^{1-x^2}(-2x) = -4xe^{1-x^2}$$

$$y'(1) = -4$$

Tangent line: $y - 2 = -4(x - 1)$

$$y = -4x + 6$$

(b)

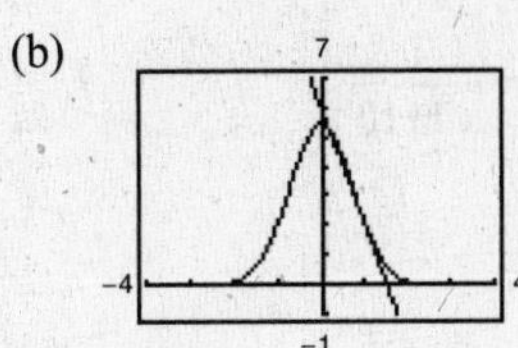

**131.** $f(x) = 4^x$

$$f'(x) = (\ln 4)4^x$$

**132.** $g(x) = 5^{-x}$

$$g'(x) = -(\ln 5)5^{-x}$$

**133.** $y = 5^{x-2}$

$$\frac{dy}{dx} = (\ln 5)5^{x-2}$$

**134.** $y = x(6^{-2x})$

$$y' = x(-2 \ln 6)6^{-2x} + 6^{-2x}$$

$$= 6^{-2x}(-2x \ln 6 + 1)$$

**135.** $g(t) = t^2 2^t$

$g'(t) = t^2(\ln 2)2^t + (2t)2^t$

$= t2^t(t \ln 2 + 2)$

$= 2^t t(2 + t \ln 2)$

**136.** $f(t) = \dfrac{3^{2t}}{t}$

$f'(t) = \dfrac{t(2 \ln 3)3^{2t} - 3^{2t}}{t^2}$

$= \dfrac{3^{2t}(2t \ln 3 - 1)}{t^2}$

**137.** $h(\theta) = 2^{-\theta} \cos \pi\theta$

$h'(\theta) = 2^{-\theta}(-\pi \sin \pi\theta) - (\ln 2)2^{-\theta} \cos \pi\theta$

$= -2^{-\theta}\left[(\ln 2) \cos \pi\theta + \pi \sin \pi\theta\right]$

**138.** $g(\alpha) = 5^{-\alpha/2} \sin 2\alpha$

$g'(\alpha) = 5^{-\alpha/2}\, 2 \cos 2\alpha - \frac{1}{2}(\ln 5)5^{-\alpha/2} \sin 2\alpha$

**139.** $y = \log_3 x$

$\dfrac{dy}{dx} = \dfrac{1}{x \ln 3}$

**140.** $y = \log_{10}(2x) = \log_{10} 2 + \log_{10} x$

$\dfrac{dy}{dx} = 0 + \dfrac{1}{x \ln 10} = \dfrac{1}{x \ln 10}$

**141.** $f(x) = \log_2 \dfrac{x^2}{x - 1}$

$= 2 \log_2 x - \log_2(x - 1)$

$f'(x) = \dfrac{2}{x \ln 2} - \dfrac{1}{(x - 1) \ln 2}$

$= \dfrac{x - 2}{(\ln 2)x(x - 1)}$

**142.** $h(x) = \log_3 \dfrac{x\sqrt{x - 1}}{2}$

$= \log_3 x + \dfrac{1}{2} \log_3(x - 1) - \log_3 2$

$h'(x) = \dfrac{1}{x \ln 3} + \dfrac{1}{2} \cdot \dfrac{1}{(x - 1) \ln 3} - 0$

$= \dfrac{1}{\ln 3}\left[\dfrac{1}{x} + \dfrac{1}{2(x - 1)}\right]$

$= \dfrac{1}{\ln 3}\left[\dfrac{3x - 2}{2x(x - 1)}\right]$

**143.** $y = \log_5 \sqrt{x^2 - 1} = \dfrac{1}{2} \log_5\left(x^2 - 1\right)$

$\dfrac{dy}{dx} = \dfrac{1}{2} \cdot \dfrac{2x}{\left(x^2 - 1\right) \ln 5} = \dfrac{x}{\left(x^2 - 1\right) \ln 5}$

**144.** $y = \log_{10} \dfrac{x^2 - 1}{x}$

$= \log_{10}\left(x^2 - 1\right) - \log_{10} x$

$\dfrac{dy}{dx} = \dfrac{2x}{\left(x^2 - 1\right) \ln 10} - \dfrac{1}{x \ln 10}$

$= \dfrac{1}{\ln 10}\left[\dfrac{2x}{x^2 - 1} - \dfrac{1}{x}\right] = \dfrac{1}{\ln 10}\left[\dfrac{x^2 + 1}{x\left(x^2 - 1\right)}\right]$

**145.** $g(t) = \dfrac{10 \log_4 t}{t} = \dfrac{10}{\ln 4}\left(\dfrac{\ln t}{t}\right)$

$g'(t) = \dfrac{10}{\ln 4}\left[\dfrac{t(1/t) - \ln t}{t^2}\right]$

$= \dfrac{10}{t^2 \ln 4}[1 - \ln t] = \dfrac{5}{t^2 \ln 2}(1 - \ln t)$

**146.** $f(t) = t^{3/2} \log_2 \sqrt{t + 1} = t^{3/2} \dfrac{1}{2} \dfrac{\ln(t + 1)}{\ln 2}$

$f'(t) = \dfrac{1}{2 \ln 2}\left[t^{3/2} \dfrac{1}{t + 1} + \dfrac{3}{2} t^{1/2} \ln(t + 1)\right]$

**147.**

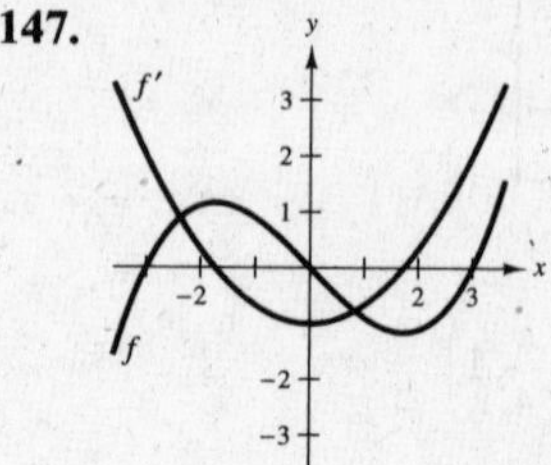


The zeros of $f'$ correspond to the points where the graph of $f$ has horizontal tangents.

**148.**

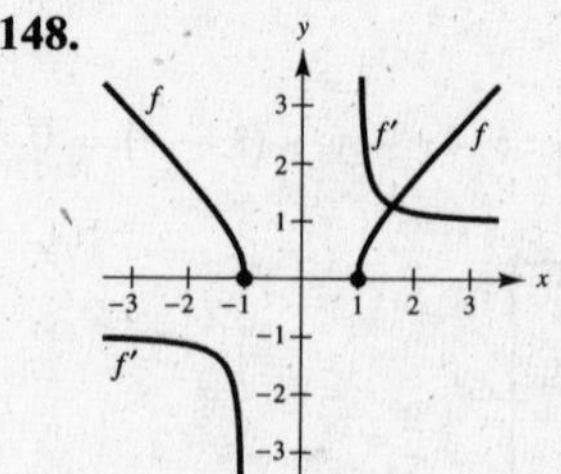


$f$ is decreasing on $(-\infty, -1)$ so $f'$ must be negative there.

$f$ is increasing on $(1, \infty)$ so $f'$ must be positive there.

**149.**

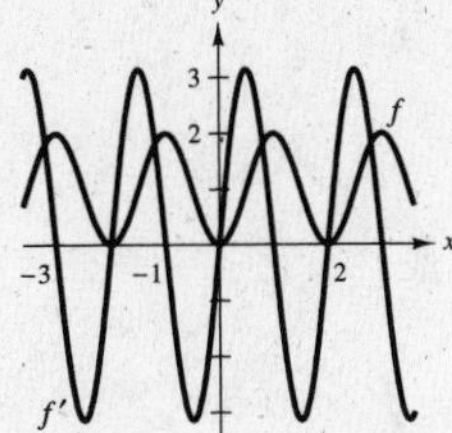

The zeros of $f'$ correspond to the points where the graph of $f$ has horizontal tangents.

**150.**

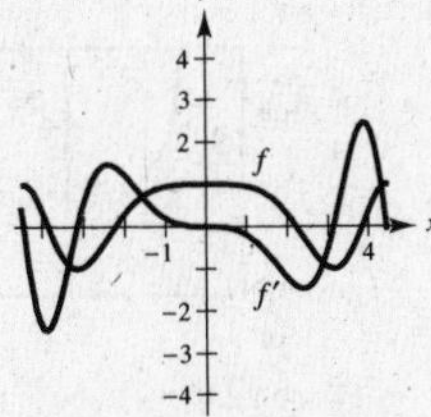

The zeros of $f'$ correspond to the points where the graph of $f$ has horizontal tangents.

**151.** $g(x) = f(3x)$

$g'(x) = f'(3x)(3) \Rightarrow g'(x) = 3f'(3x)$

**152.** $g(x) = f(x^2)$

$g'(x) = f'(x^2)(2x) \Rightarrow g'(x) = 2xf'(x^2)$

**153.** (a) $g(x) = \sin^2 x + \cos^2 x = 1 \Rightarrow g'(x) = 0$

$g'(x) = 2 \sin x \cos x + 2 \cos x(-\sin x) = 0$

(b) $\tan^2 x + 1 = \sec^2 x$

$g(x) + 1 = f(x)$

Taking derivatives of both sides, $g'(x) = f'(x)$. Equivalently,

$f'(x) = 2 \sec x \cdot \sec x \tan x = 2 \sec^2 x \tan x$ and

$g'(x) = 2 \tan x \cdot \sec^2 x = 2 \sec^2 x \tan x$, which are the same.

**154.** (a) $f(x) = g(x)h(x)$

$f'(x) = g(x)h'(x) + g'(x)h(x)$

$f'(5) = (-3)(-2) + (6)(3) = 24$

(b) $f(x) = g(h(x))$

$f'(x) = g'(h(x))h'(x)$

$f'(5) = g'(3)(-2) = -2g'(3)$

Not possible, you need $g'(3)$ to find $f'(5)$.

(c) $f(x) = \dfrac{g(x)}{h(x)}$

$$f'(x) = \frac{h(x)g'(x) - g(x)h'(x)}{[h(x)]^2}$$

$$f'(5) = \frac{(3)(6) - (-3)(-2)}{(3)^2} = \frac{12}{9} = \frac{4}{3}$$

(d) $f(x) = [g(x)]^3$

$f'(x) = 3[g(x)]^2 g'(x)$

$f'(5) = 3(-3)^2(6) = 162$

**155.** (a) $g(t) = \dfrac{3t^2}{\sqrt{t^2 + 2t - 1}}, \quad \left(\dfrac{1}{2}, \dfrac{3}{2}\right)$

$$g'(t) = \frac{3t(t^2 + 3t - 2)}{(t^2 + 2t - 1)^{3/2}}$$

$$g'\left(\frac{1}{2}\right) = -3$$

(b) $y - \dfrac{3}{2} = -3\left(x - \dfrac{1}{2}\right) \Rightarrow 3x + y - 3 = 0$

(c)

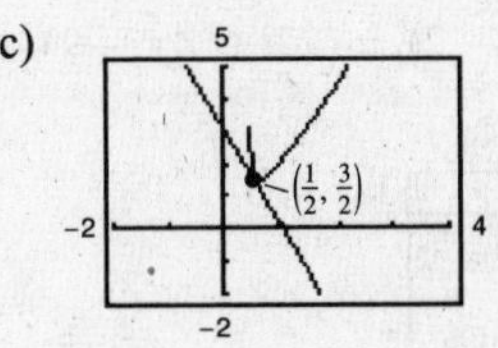


**156.** (a) $f(x) = \sqrt{x}(2 - x)^2, \quad (4, 8)$

$$f'(x) = \frac{(x - 2)(5x - 2)}{2\sqrt{x}}$$

$f'(4) = 9$

(b) $y - 8 = 9(x - 4) \Rightarrow 9x - y - 28 = 0$

(c)

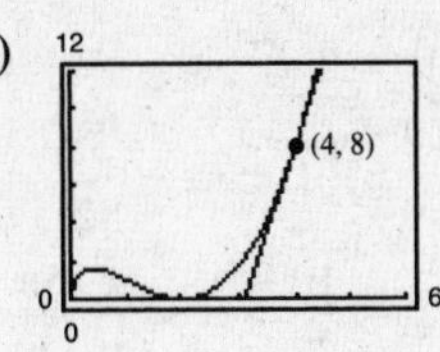

**157.** (a) $s(t) = \dfrac{(4 - 2t)\sqrt{1 + t}}{3}, \quad \left(0, \dfrac{4}{3}\right)$

$$s'(t) = \frac{-2\sqrt{1 + t}}{3} + \frac{2 - t}{3\sqrt{1 + t}}$$

$$s'(0) = 0$$

(b) $y - \dfrac{4}{3} = 0(x - 0)$

$$y = \frac{4}{3}$$

(c)

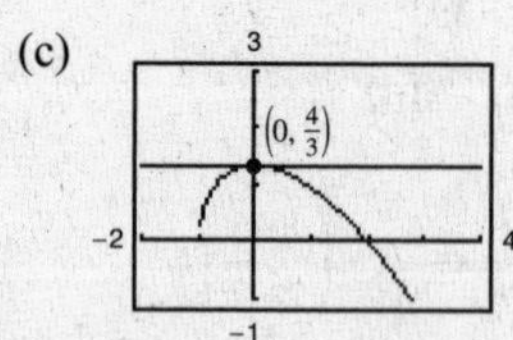


**158.** (a) $y = (t^2 - 9)\sqrt{t + 2}, \quad (2, -10)$

$$y' = \frac{5t^2 + 8t - 9}{2\sqrt{t + 2}}$$

$$y'(2) = \frac{27}{4}$$

(b) $y + 10 = \dfrac{27}{4}(t - 2) \Rightarrow 27t - 4y - 94$

(c)

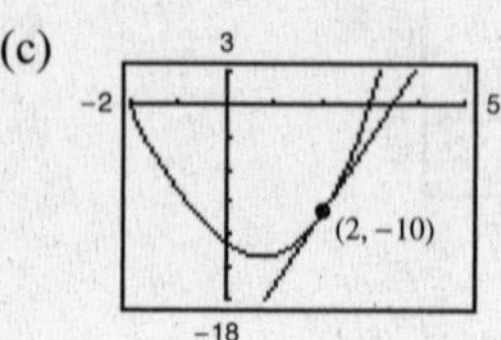


**159.** $f(x) = \sqrt{25 - x^2}, \quad (3, 4)$

$$f'(x) = \frac{-x}{\sqrt{25 - x^2}}$$

$$f'(3) = -\frac{3}{4}$$

Tangent line:

$$y - 4 = -\frac{3}{4}(x - 3) \Rightarrow 3x + 4y - 25 = 0$$

**160.** $f(x) = \dfrac{|x|}{\sqrt{2 - x^2}}, \quad (1, 1)$

$$f'(x) = \frac{2}{(2 - x^2)^{3/2}} \text{ for } x > 0$$

$$f'(1) = 2$$

Tangent line: $y - 1 = 2(x - 1) \Rightarrow 2x - y - 1 = 0$

**161.**

$$f(x) = 2\cos x + \sin 2x, \quad 0 < x < 2\pi$$

$$f'(x) = -2\sin x + 2\cos 2x$$

$$= -2\sin x + 2 - 4\sin^2 x = 0$$

$$2\sin^2 x + \sin x - 1 = 0$$

$$(\sin x + 1)(2\sin x - 1) = 0$$

$$\sin x = -1 \Rightarrow x = \frac{3\pi}{2}$$

$$\sin x = \frac{1}{2} \Rightarrow x = \frac{\pi}{6}, \frac{5\pi}{6}$$

Horizontal tangents at $x = \dfrac{\pi}{6}, \dfrac{3\pi}{2}, \dfrac{5\pi}{6}$

Horizontal tangent at the points $\left(\dfrac{\pi}{6}, \dfrac{3\sqrt{3}}{2}\right), \left(\dfrac{3\pi}{2}, 0\right)$, and $\left(\dfrac{5\pi}{6}, -\dfrac{3\sqrt{3}}{2}\right)$

**162.** $f(x) = \dfrac{x}{\sqrt{2x-1}}$

$f'(x) = \dfrac{(2x-1)^{1/2} - x(2x-1)^{-1/2}}{2x-1}$

$= \dfrac{2x-1-x}{(2x-1)^{3/2}}$

$= \dfrac{x-1}{(2x-1)^{3/2}}$

$\dfrac{x-1}{(2x-1)^{3/2}} = 0 \Rightarrow x = 1$

Horizontal tangent at $(1, 1)$

**163.** $h(x) = \frac{1}{9}(3x+1)^3, \quad \left(1, \frac{64}{9}\right)$

$h'(x) = \frac{1}{9}3(3x+1)^2(3) = (3x+1)^2$

$h''(x) = 2(3x+1)(3) = 18x + 6$

$h''(1) = 24$

**164.** $f(x) = \dfrac{1}{\sqrt{x+4}} = (x+4)^{-1/2}, \quad \left(0, \dfrac{1}{2}\right)$

$f'(x) = -\dfrac{1}{2}(x+4)^{-3/2}$

$f''(x) = \dfrac{3}{4}(x+4)^{-5/2} = \dfrac{3}{4(x+4)^{5/2}}$

$f''(0) = \dfrac{3}{128}$

**165.** $f(x) = \cos x^2, \quad (0, 1)$

$f'(x) = -\sin(x^2)(2x) = -2x\sin(x^2)$

$f''(x) = -2x\cos(x^2)(2x) - 2\sin(x^2)$

$= -4x^2\cos(x^2) - 2\sin(x^2)$

$f''(0) = 0$

**166.** $g(t) = \tan 2t, \quad \left(\dfrac{\pi}{6}, \sqrt{3}\right)$

$g'(t) = 2\sec^2(2t)$

$g''(t) = 4\sec(2t)\cdot\sec(2t)\tan(2t)2$

$= 8\sec^2(2t)\tan(2t)$

$g''\left(\dfrac{\pi}{6}\right) = 32\sqrt{3}$

**167.** (a) $F = 132{,}400(331 - v)^{-1}$

$F' = (-1)(132{,}400)(331 - v)^{-2}(-1) = \dfrac{132{,}400}{(331 - v)^2}$

When $v = 30$, $F' \approx 1.461$.

(b) $F = 132{,}400(331 + v)^{-1}$

$F' = (-1)(132{,}400)(331 + v)^{-2}(-1) = \dfrac{-132{,}400}{(331 + v)^2}$

When $v = 30$, $F' \approx -1.016$.

**168.** $y = \frac{1}{3}\cos 12t - \frac{1}{4}\sin 12t$

$v = y' = \frac{1}{3}[-12\sin 12t] - \frac{1}{4}[12\cos 12t]$

$= -4\sin 12t - 3\cos 12t$

When $t = \pi/8$, $y = 0.25$ ft and $v = 4$ ft/sec.

**169.** $\theta = 0.2\cos 8t$

The maximum angular displacement is $\theta = 0.2$ (because $-1 \le \cos 8t \le 1$).

$\dfrac{d\theta}{dt} = 0.2[-8\sin 8t] = -1.6\sin 8t$

When $t = 3$, $d\theta/dt = -1.6\sin 24 \approx 1.4489$ rad/sec.

**170.** $y = A\cos\omega t$

(a) Amplitude: $A = \dfrac{3.5}{2} = 1.75$

$y = 1.75\cos\omega t$

Period: $10 \Rightarrow \omega = \dfrac{2\pi}{10} = \dfrac{\pi}{5}$

$y = 1.75\cos\dfrac{\pi t}{5}$

(b) $v = y' = 1.75\left[-\dfrac{\pi}{5}\sin\dfrac{\pi t}{5}\right] = -0.35\pi\sin\dfrac{\pi t}{5}$

**171.** $S = C(R^2 - r^2)$

$\dfrac{dS}{dt} = C\left(2R\dfrac{dR}{dt} - 2r\dfrac{dr}{dt}\right)$

Because $r$ is constant, you have $dr/dt = 0$ and

$\dfrac{dS}{dt} = (1.76\times 10^5)(2)(1.2\times 10^{-2})(10^{-5})$

$= 4.224\times 10^{-2} = 0.04224$ cm/sec$^2$.

**172.** (a) Using a graphing utility, you obtain a model similar to $T(t) = 56.1 + 27.6 \sin(0.48t - 1.86)$.

(a)

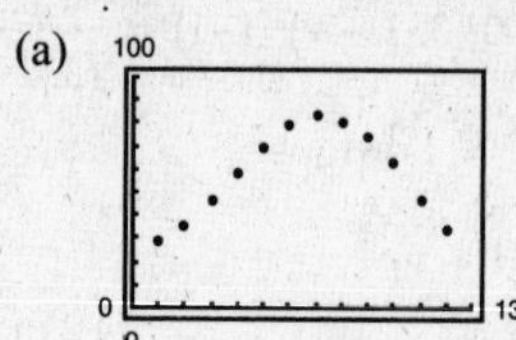

(b)

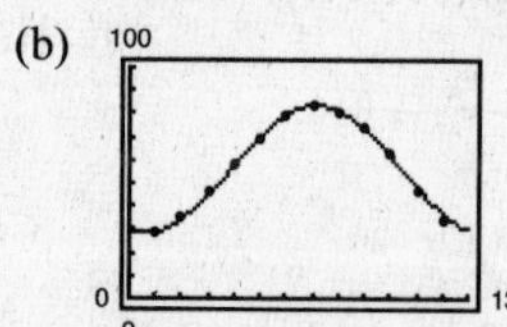

The model is a good fit.

(c)

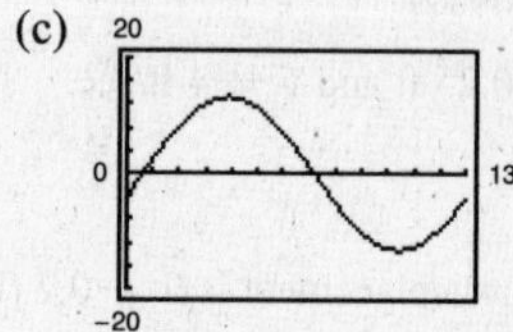

$T'(t) \approx 13.25 \cos(0.48t - 1.86)$

(d) The temperature changes most rapidly around spring (March–May), and fall (Oct–Nov).

**173.** $V = \frac{4}{3}\pi r^3, \quad \frac{dr}{dt} = 3$

$$\frac{dv}{dt} = 4\pi r^2 \frac{dr}{dt}$$
$$= 4\pi(8)^2(3)$$
$$= 768\pi \text{ cubic inches/second}$$

**174.** (a) $g(x) = f(x) - 2 \Rightarrow g'(x) = f'(x)$

(b) $h(x) = 2f(x) \Rightarrow h'(x) = 2f'(x)$

(c) $r(x) = f(-3x) \Rightarrow r'(x) = f'(-3x)(-3) = -3f'(-3x)$

So, you need to know $f'(-3x)$.

$r'(0) = -3f'(0) = (-3)\left(-\frac{1}{3}\right) = 1$

$r'(-1) = -3f'(3) = (-3)(-4) = 12$

(d) $s(x) = f(x + 2) \Rightarrow s'(x) = f'(x + 2)$

So, you need to know $f'(x + 2)$.

$s'(-2) = f'(0) = -\frac{1}{3}$, etc.

| $x$ | $-2$ | $-1$ | $0$ | $1$ | $2$ | $3$ |
|---|---|---|---|---|---|---|
| $f'(x)$ | $4$ | $\frac{2}{3}$ | $-\frac{1}{3}$ | $-1$ | $-2$ | $-4$ |
| $g'(x)$ | $4$ | $\frac{2}{3}$ | $-\frac{1}{3}$ | $-1$ | $-2$ | $-4$ |
| $h'(x)$ | $8$ | $\frac{4}{3}$ | $-\frac{2}{3}$ | $-2$ | $-4$ | $-8$ |
| $r'(x)$ | | $12$ | $1$ | | | |
| $s'(x)$ | $-\frac{1}{3}$ | $-1$ | $-2$ | $-4$ | | |

**175.** (a)

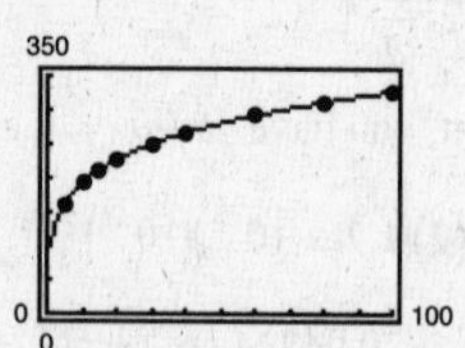

(b) $T'(p) = \frac{34.96}{p} + \frac{3.955}{\sqrt{p}}$

$T'(10) \approx 4.75$ deg/lb/in.$^2$

$T'(70) \approx 0.97$ deg/lb/in.$^2$

**176.** $V(t) = 25{,}000\left(\frac{3}{4}\right)^t$

(a) 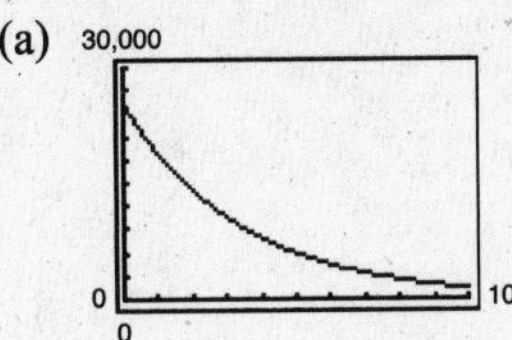


$V(2) = 25{,}000\left(\frac{3}{4}\right)^2 = \$14{,}062.50$

(b) $\frac{dV}{dt} = 25{,}000 \ln\left(\frac{3}{4}\right)\left(\frac{3}{4}\right)^t$

When $t = 1$, $\frac{dV}{dt} \approx -5394.04$.

When $t = 4$, $\frac{dV}{dt} \approx -2275.61$.

**177.** $C(t) = P(1.05)^t$

(a) $C(10) = 29.95(1.05)^{10} \approx \$48.79$

(b) $\frac{dC}{dt} = P\ln(1.05)(1.05)^t$

When $t = 1$, $\frac{dC}{dt} \approx 0.051P$.

When $t = 8$, $\frac{dC}{dt} \approx 0.072P$.

(c) $\frac{dC}{dt} = \ln(1.05)\left[P(1.05)^t\right]$

$= \ln(1.05)C(t)$

The constant of proportionality is $\ln 1.05$.

**178.** $f(x) = \sin\beta x$

(a) $f'(x) = \beta\cos\beta x$

$f''(x) = -\beta^2\sin\beta x$

$f'''(x) = -\beta^3\cos\beta x$

$f^{(4)} = \beta^4\sin\beta x$

(b) $f''(x) + \beta^2 f(x) = -\beta^2\sin\beta x + \beta^2(\sin\beta x) = 0$

(c) $f^{(2k)}(x) = (-1)^k\beta^{2k}\sin\beta x$

$f^{(2k-1)}(x) = (-1)^{k+1}\beta^{2k-1}\cos\beta x$

**179.** (a) Yes, if $f(x + p) = f(x)$ for all $x$, then $f'(x + p) = f'(x)$, which shows that $f'$ is periodic as well.

(b) Yes, if $g(x) = f(2x)$, then $g'(x) = 2f'(2x)$. Because $f'$ is periodic, so is $g'$.

**180.** (a) $r'(x) = f'(g(x))g'(x)$

$r'(1) = f'(g(1))g'(1)$

Note that $g(1) = 4$ and $f'(4) = \frac{5-0}{6-2} = \frac{5}{4}$.

Also, $g'(1) = 0$. So, $r'(1) = 0$.

(b) $s'(x) = g'(f(x))f'(x)$

$s'(4) = g'(f(4))f'(4)$

Note that $f(4) = \frac{5}{2}$, $g'\left(\frac{5}{2}\right) = \frac{6-4}{6-2} = \frac{1}{2}$ and

$f'(4) = \frac{5}{4}$. So, $s'(4) = \frac{1}{2}\left(\frac{5}{4}\right) = \frac{5}{8}$.

**181.** (a) If $f(-x) = -f(x)$, then

$\frac{d}{dx}[f(-x)] = \frac{d}{dx}[-f(x)]$

$f'(-x)(-1) = -f'(x)$

$f'(-x) = f'(x)$.

So, $f'(x)$ is even.

(b) If $f(-x) = f(x)$, then

$\frac{d}{dx}[f(-x)] = \frac{d}{dx}[f(x)]$

$f'(-x)(-1) = f'(x)$

$f'(-x) = -f'(x)$.

So, $f'$ is odd.

**182.** $|u| = \sqrt{u^2}$

$\frac{d}{dx}[|u|] = \frac{d}{dx}\left[\sqrt{u^2}\right] = \frac{1}{2}(u^2)^{-1/2}(2uu')$

$= \frac{uu'}{\sqrt{u^2}} = u'\frac{u}{|u|}, \quad u \neq 0$

**183.** $g(x) = |3x - 5|$

$g'(x) = 3\left(\frac{3x-5}{|3x-5|}\right), \quad x \neq \frac{5}{3}$

**184.** $f(x) = |x^2 - 9|$

$f'(x) = 2x\left(\frac{x^2-9}{|x^2-9|}\right), \quad x \neq \pm 3$

**185.** $h(x) = |x|\cos x$

$h'(x) = -|x|\sin x + \frac{x}{|x|}\cos x, \quad x \neq 0$

**186.** $f(x) = |\sin x|$

$f'(x) = \cos x\left(\frac{\sin x}{|\sin x|}\right), x \neq k\pi$

**187.** (a) $f(x) = \tan x \qquad f(\pi/4) = 1$

$f'(x) = \sec^2 x \qquad f'(\pi/4) = 2$

$f''(x) = 2\sec^2 x \tan x \qquad f''(\pi/4) = 4$

$$P_1(x) = 2(x - \pi/4) + 1$$

$$P_2(x) = \frac{1}{2}(4)(x - \pi/4)^2 + 2(x - \pi/4) + 1$$

$$= 2(x - \pi/4)^2 + 2(x - \pi/4) + 1$$

(b)

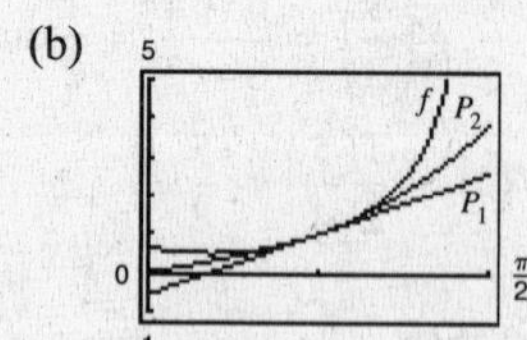


(c) $P_2$ is a better approximation than $P_1$.

(d) The accuracy worsens as you move away from $x = \pi/4$.

**188.** (a) $f(x) = \sec x \qquad f(\pi/6) = \dfrac{2}{\sqrt{3}}$

$f'(x) = \sec x \tan x \qquad f'(\pi/6) = \dfrac{2}{3}$

$f''(x) = \sec x(\sec^2 x) + \tan x(\sec x \tan x) \qquad f''(\pi/6) = \dfrac{10\sqrt{3}}{9}$

$$= \sec^3 x + \sec x \tan^2 x$$

$$P_1(x) = \frac{2}{3}(x - \pi/6) + \frac{2}{\sqrt{3}}$$

$$P_2(x) = \frac{1}{2}\cdot\left(\frac{10}{3\sqrt{3}}\right)\left(x - \frac{\pi}{6}\right)^2 + \frac{2}{3}\left(x - \frac{\pi}{6}\right) + \frac{2}{\sqrt{3}}$$

$$= \left(\frac{5}{3\sqrt{3}}\right)\left(x - \frac{\pi}{6}\right)^2 + \frac{2}{3}\left(x - \frac{\pi}{6}\right) + \frac{2}{\sqrt{3}}$$

(b)

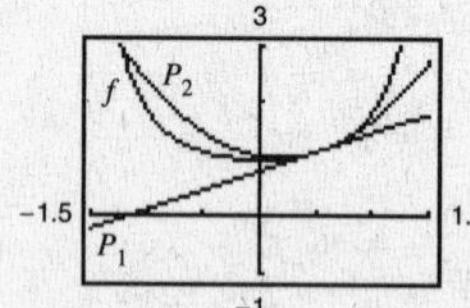


(c) $P_2$ is a better approximation than $P_1$.

(d) The accuracy worsens as you move away from $x = \pi/6$.

**189.** (a) $f(x) = e^x \qquad f(0) = 1$

$f'(x) = e^x \qquad f'(0) = 1$

$f''(x) = e^x \qquad f''(0) = 1$

$$P_1(x) = 1(x - 0) + 1 = x + 1$$

$$P_2(x) = \frac{1}{2}(1)(x - 0)^2 + 1(x - 0) + 1 = \frac{1}{2}x^2 + x + 1$$

(b)

(c) $P_2$ is a better approximation than $P_1$.

(d) The accuracy worsens as you move away from $x = 0$.

**190.** (a) $f(x) = \ln x \qquad f(1) = \ln(1) = 0$

$f'(x) = \dfrac{1}{x} \qquad f'(1) = 1$

$f''(x) = -1/x^2 \qquad f''(1) = -1$

$P_1(x) = 1(x - 1) + 0 = x - 1$

$P_2(x) = \dfrac{1}{2}(-1)(x - 1)^2 + 1(x - 1) + 0 = -\dfrac{1}{2}(x + 1)^2 + x - 1$

(b)

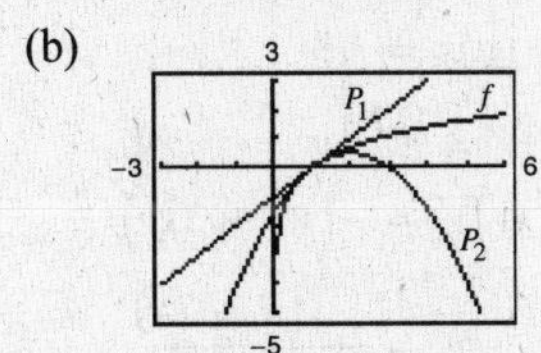


(c) $P_2$ is a better approximation than $P_1$.

(d) The accuracy worsens as you move away from $x = 0$.

**191.** False. If $y = (1 - x)^{1/2}$, then $y' = \frac{1}{2}(1 - x)^{-1/2}(-1)$.

**192.** False. If $f(x) = \sin^2 2x$, then $f'(x) = 2(\sin 2x)(2\cos 2x)$.

**193.** True

**194.** False. Let $f(x) = \sqrt{x}$ and $g(x) = -x^2$. $f$ must be a differentiable function of $u = g(x)$.

**195.**

$$f(x) = a_1 \sin x + a_2 \sin 2x + \cdots + a_n \sin nx$$
$$f'(x) = a_1 \cos x + 2a_2 \cos 2x + \cdots + na_n \cos nx$$
$$f'(0) = a_1 + 2a_2 + \cdots + na_n$$

$$\left|a_1 + 2a_2 + \cdots + na_n\right| = \left|f'(0)\right| = \lim_{x\to 0}\left|\frac{f(x) - f(0)}{x - 0}\right| = \lim_{x\to 0}\left|\frac{f(x)}{\sin x}\right| \cdot \left|\frac{\sin x}{x}\right| = \lim_{x\to 0}\left|\frac{f(x)}{\sin x}\right| \le 1$$

**196.** $\dfrac{d}{dx}\left[\dfrac{P_n(x)}{(x^k-1)^{n+1}}\right] = \dfrac{(x^k-1)^{n+1}P_n'(x) - P_n(x)(n+1)(x^k-1)^n kx^{k-1}}{(x^k-1)^{2n+2}} = \dfrac{(x^k-1)P_n'(x) - (n+1)kx^{k-1}P_n(x)}{(x^k-1)^{n+2}}$

$P_n(x) = (x^k-1)^{n+1}\dfrac{d^n}{dx^n}\left[\dfrac{1}{x^k-1}\right] \Rightarrow$

$P_{n+1}(x) = (x^k-1)^{n+2}\dfrac{d}{dx}\left[\dfrac{d^n}{dx^n}\left[\dfrac{1}{x^k-1}\right]\right] = (x^k-1)P_n'(x) - (n+1)kx^{k-1}P_n(x)$

$P_{n+1}(1) = -(n+1)kP_n(1)$

For $n = 1$, $\dfrac{d}{dx}\left[\dfrac{1}{x^k-1}\right] = \dfrac{-kx^{k-1}}{(x^k-1)^2} = \dfrac{P_1(x)}{(x^k-1)^2} \Rightarrow P_1(1) = -k$. Also, $P_0(1) = 1$.

You now use mathematical induction to verify that $P_n(1) = (-k)^n n!$ for $n \ge 0$. Assume true for $n$. Then

$P_{n+1}(1) = -(n+1)k\,P_n(1) = -(n+1)k(-k)^n n! = (-k)^{n+1}(n+1)!$.

## Section 3.5 Implicit Differentiation

**1.** $x^2 + y^2 = 9$

$2x + 2yy' = 0$

$y' = -\dfrac{x}{y}$

**2.** $x^2 - y^2 = 25$

$2x - 2yy' = 0$

$y' = \dfrac{x}{y}$

**3.** $x^{1/2} + y^{1/2} = 16$

$\dfrac{1}{2}x^{-1/2} + \dfrac{1}{2}y^{-1/2}y' = 0$

$y' = -\dfrac{x^{-1/2}}{y^{-1/2}}$

$= -\sqrt{\dfrac{y}{x}}$

**4.** $x^3 + y^3 = 64$

$3x^2 + 3y^2y' = 0$

$y' = -\dfrac{x^2}{y^2}$

**5.** $x^3 - xy + y^2 = 7$

$3x^2 - xy' - y + 2yy' = 0$

$(2y - x)y' = y - 3x^2$

$y' = \dfrac{y - 3x^2}{2y - x}$

**6.** $x^2y + y^2x = -3$

$x^2y' + 2xy + y^2 + 2yxy' = 0$

$(x^2 + 2xy)y' = -(y^2 + 2xy)$

$y' = \dfrac{-y(y + 2x)}{x(x + 2y)}$

**7.** $xe^y - 10x + 3y = 0$

$xe^y\dfrac{dy}{dx} + e^y - 10 + 3\dfrac{dy}{dx} = 0$

$\dfrac{dy}{dx}(xe^y + 3) = 10 - e^y$

$\dfrac{dy}{dx} = \dfrac{10 - e^y}{xe^y + 3}$

**8.** $e^{xy} + x^2 - y^2 = 10$

$\left(x\dfrac{dy}{dx} + y\right)e^{xy} + 2x - 2y\dfrac{dy}{dx} = 0$

$\dfrac{dy}{dx}(xe^{xy} - 2y) = -ye^{xy} - 2x$

$\dfrac{dy}{dx} = -\dfrac{ye^{xy} + 2x}{xe^{xy} - 2y}$

**9.** $x^3y^3 - y - x = 0$

$3x^3y^2y' + 3x^2y^3 - y' - 1 = 0$

$(3x^3y^2 - 1)y' = 1 - 3x^2y^3$

$y' = \dfrac{1 - 3x^2y^3}{3x^3y^2 - 1}$

**10.** $$\sqrt{xy} = x^2y + 1$$

$$\frac{1}{2}(xy)^{-1/2}(xy' + y) = 2xy + x^2y'$$

$$\frac{x}{2\sqrt{xy}}y' + \frac{y}{2\sqrt{xy}} = 2xy + x^2y'$$

$$\left(\frac{x}{2\sqrt{xy}} - x^2\right)y' = 2xy - \frac{y}{2\sqrt{xy}}$$

$$y' = \frac{2xy - \frac{y}{2\sqrt{xy}}}{\frac{x}{2\sqrt{xy}} - x^2}$$

$$y' = \frac{4xy\sqrt{xy} - y}{x - 2x^2\sqrt{xy}}$$

**11.** $$x^3 - 3x^2y + 2xy^2 = 12$$

$$3x^2 - 3x^2y' - 6xy + 4xyy' + 2y^2 = 0$$

$$(4xy - 3x^2)y' = 6xy - 3x^2 - 2y^2$$

$$y' = \frac{6xy - 3x^2 - 2y^2}{4xy - 3x^2}$$

**12.** $$4\cos x \sin y = 1$$

$$4[-\sin x \sin y + \cos x \cos y\, y'] = 0$$

$$\cos x \cos y\, y' = \sin x \sin y$$

$$y' = \frac{\sin x \sin y}{\cos x \cos y}$$

$$= \tan x \tan y$$

**13.** $$\sin x + 2\cos 2y = 1$$

$$\cos x - 4(\sin 2y)y' = 0$$

$$y' = \frac{\cos x}{4\sin 2y}$$

**14.** $$(\sin \pi x + \cos \pi y)^2 = 2$$

$$2(\sin \pi x + \cos \pi y)[\pi \cos \pi x - \pi(\sin \pi y)y'] = 0$$

$$\pi \cos \pi x - \pi(\sin \pi y)y' = 0$$

$$y' = \frac{\cos \pi x}{\sin \pi y}$$

**15.** $$\sin x = x(1 + \tan y)$$

$$\cos x = x(\sec^2 y)y' + (1 + \tan y)(1)$$

$$y' = \frac{\cos x - \tan y - 1}{x\sec^2 y}$$

**16.** $$\cot y = x - y$$

$$(-\csc^2 y)y' = 1 - y'$$

$$y' = \frac{1}{1 - \csc^2 y} = \frac{1}{-\cot^2 y} = -\tan^2 y$$

**17.** $$y = \sin xy$$

$$y' = [xy' + y]\cos(xy)$$

$$y' - x\cos(xy)y' = y\cos(xy)$$

$$y' = \frac{y\cos(xy)}{1 - x\cos(xy)}$$

**18.** $$x = \sec\frac{1}{y}$$

$$1 = -\frac{y'}{y^2}\sec\frac{1}{y}\tan\frac{1}{y}$$

$$y' = \frac{-y^2}{\sec(1/y)\tan(1/y)} = -y^2\cos\left(\frac{1}{y}\right)\cot\left(\frac{1}{y}\right)$$

**19.** $$x^2 - 3\ln y + y^2 = 10$$

$$2x - \frac{3}{y}\frac{dy}{dx} + 2y\frac{dy}{dx} = 0$$

$$2x = \frac{dy}{dx}\left(\frac{3}{y} - 2y\right)$$

$$\frac{dy}{dx} = \frac{2x}{(3/y) - 2y} = \frac{2xy}{3 - 2y^2}$$

**20.** $$\ln(xy) + 5x = 30$$

$$\ln x + \ln y + 5x = 30$$

$$\frac{1}{x} + \frac{1}{y}\frac{dy}{dx} + 5 = 0$$

$$\frac{1}{y}\frac{dy}{dx} = -\frac{1}{x} - 5$$

$$\frac{dy}{dx} = -\frac{y}{x} - 5y = -\left(\frac{y + 5xy}{x}\right)$$

**21.** $$4x^3 + \ln y^2 + 2y = 2x$$

$$12x^2 + \frac{2}{y}y' + 2y' = 2$$

$$\left(\frac{2}{y} + 2\right)y' = 2 - 12x^2$$

$$y' = \frac{2 - 12x^2}{2/y + 2}$$

$$y' = \frac{y - 6yx^2}{1 + y} = \frac{y(1 - 6x^2)}{1 + y}$$

**22.**

$$4xy + \ln x^2y = 7$$
$$4xy + 2\ln x + \ln y = 7$$
$$4xy' + 4y + \frac{2}{x} + \frac{1}{y}y' = 0$$
$$\left(4x + \frac{1}{y}\right)y' = -4y - \frac{2}{x}$$
$$y' = \frac{-4y - \dfrac{2}{x}}{4x + \dfrac{1}{y}}$$
$$y' = \frac{-4xy^2 - 2y}{4x^2y + x}$$

**23.** (a) $x^2 + y^2 = 64$

$$y^2 = 64 - x^2$$
$$y = \pm\sqrt{64 - x^2}$$

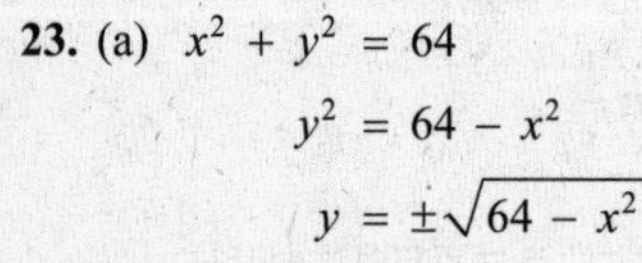

(b)

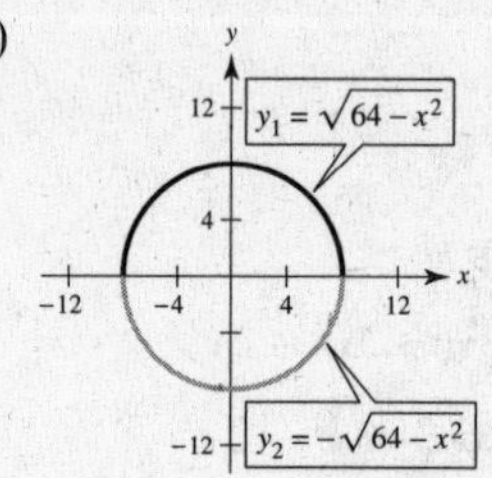


(c) Explicitly:

$$\frac{dy}{dx} = \pm\frac{1}{2}\left(64 - x^2\right)^{-1/2}(-2x) = \frac{\mp x}{\sqrt{64 - x^2}} = \frac{-x}{\pm\sqrt{64 - x^2}} = -\frac{x}{y}$$

(d) Implicitly: $2x + 2yy' = 0$

$$y' = -\frac{x}{y}$$

**24.** (a) $\left(x^2 - 4x + 4\right) + \left(y^2 + 6y + 9\right) = -9 + 4 + 9$

$$(x - 2)^2 + (y + 3)^2 = 4, \quad \text{Circle}$$
$$(y + 3)^2 = 4 - (x - 2)^2$$
$$y = -3 \pm\sqrt{4 - (x - 2)^2}$$

(b)

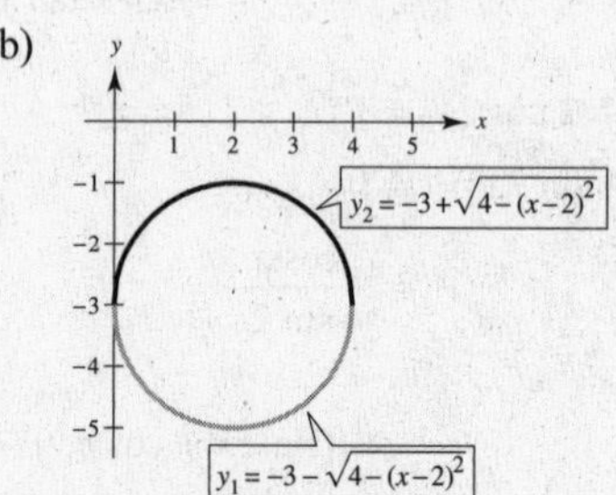


(c) Explicitly:

$$\frac{dy}{dx} = \pm\frac{1}{2}\left[4 - (x - 2)^2\right]^{-1/2}(-2)(x - 2) = \frac{\mp(x - 2)}{\sqrt{4 - (x - 2)^2}} = \frac{-(x - 2)}{\pm\sqrt{4 - (x - 2)^2}}$$
$$= \frac{-(x - 2)}{-3 \pm\sqrt{4 - (x - 2)^2} + 3} = \frac{-(x - 2)}{y + 3}$$

(d) Implicitly:

$$2x + 2yy' - 4 + 6y' = 0$$
$$(2y + 6)y' = -2(x - 2)$$
$$y' = \frac{-(x - 2)}{y + 3}$$

**25.** (a) $16y^2 = 400 - 25x^2$

$$y^2 = \frac{1}{25}(400 - 16x^2) = \frac{16}{25}(25 - x^2)$$

$$y = \pm\frac{4}{5}\sqrt{25 - x^2}$$

(b)

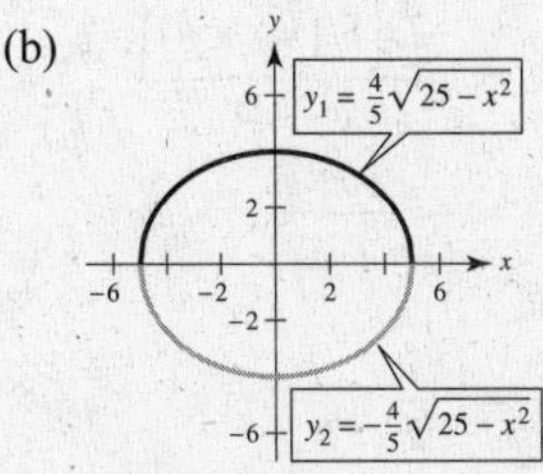


(c) Explicitly:

$$\frac{dy}{dx} = \pm\frac{4}{10}(25 - x^2)^{-1/2}(-2x)$$

$$= \mp\frac{4x}{5\sqrt{25 - x^2}} = \frac{-4x}{5(5/4)y} = -\frac{16x}{25y}$$

(d) Implicitly: $32x + 50yy' = 0$

$$y' = -\frac{16x}{25y}$$

**26.** (a) $16y^2 = x^2 + 16$

$$y^2 = \frac{x^2}{16} + 1 = \frac{x^2 + 16}{16}$$

$$y = \frac{\pm\sqrt{x^2 + 16}}{4}$$

(b)

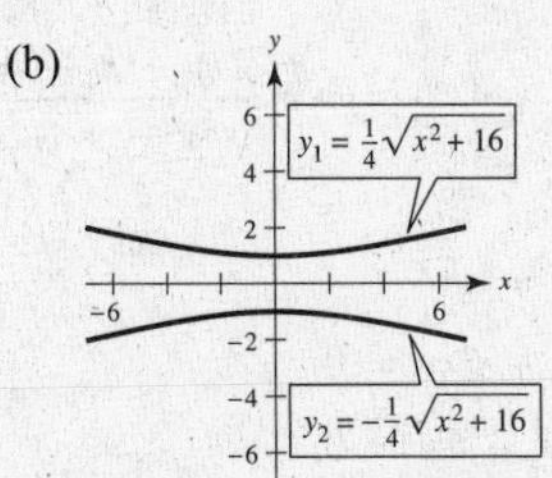


(c) Explicitly:

$$\frac{dy}{dx} = \frac{\pm\frac{1}{2}(x^2 + 16)^{-1/2}(2x)}{4}$$

$$= \frac{\pm x}{4\sqrt{x^2 + 16}} = \frac{\pm x}{4(\pm 4y)} = \frac{x}{16y}$$

(d) Implicitly: $16y^2 - x^2 = 16$

$$32yy' - 2x = 0$$

$$32yy' = 2x$$

$$y' = \frac{2x}{32y} = \frac{x}{16y}$$

**27.**

$$xy = 6$$

$$xy' + y(1) = 0$$

$$xy' = -y$$

$$y' = -\frac{y}{x}$$

At $(-6, -1)$: $y' = -\frac{1}{6}$

**28.**

$$x^3 - y^2 = 0$$

$$3x^2 - 2yy' = 0$$

$$y' = \frac{3x^2}{2y}$$

At $(1, 1)$: $y' = \frac{3}{2}$

**29.**

$$y^2 = \frac{x^2 - 49}{x^2 + 49}$$

$$2yy' = \frac{(x^2 + 49)(2x) - (x^2 - 49)(2x)}{(x^2 + 4)^2}$$

$$2yy' = \frac{196x}{(x^2 + 49)^2}$$

$$y' = \frac{98x}{y(x^2 + 49)^2}$$

At $(7, 0)$: $y'$ is undefined.

**30.**

$$(x + y)^3 = x^3 + y^3$$

$$x^3 + 3x^2y + 3xy^2 + y^3 = x^3 + y^3$$

$$3x^2y + 3xy^2 = 0$$

$$x^2y + xy^2 = 0$$

$$x^2y' + 2xy + 2xyy' + y^2 = 0$$

$$(x^2 + 2xy)y' = -(y^2 + 2xy)$$

$$y' = -\frac{y(y + 2x)}{x(x + 2y)}$$

At $(-1, 1)$: $y' = -1$

**31.**

$$x^{2/3} + y^{2/3} = 5$$

$$\frac{2}{3}x^{-1/3} + \frac{2}{3}y^{-1/3}y' = 0$$

$$y' = \frac{-x^{-1/3}}{y^{-1/3}} = -\sqrt[3]{\frac{y}{x}}$$

At $(8, 1)$: $y' = -\frac{1}{2}$

**32.**
$$x^3 + y^3 = 6xy - 1$$
$$3x^2 + 3y^2y' = 6xy' + 6y$$
$$(3y^2 - 6x)y' = 6y - 3x^2$$
$$y' = \frac{6y - 3x^2}{3y^2 - 6x}$$

At $(2, 3)$, $y' = \dfrac{18 - 12}{27 - 12} = \dfrac{6}{15} = \dfrac{2}{5}$

**33.**
$$\tan(x + y) = x$$
$$(1 + y')\sec^2(x + y) = 1$$
$$y' = \frac{1 - \sec^2(x + y)}{\sec^2(x + y)}$$
$$= \frac{-\tan^2(x + y)}{\tan^2(x + y) + 1}$$
$$= -\sin^2(x + y)$$
$$= -\frac{x^2}{x^2 + 1}$$

At $(0, 0)$: $y' = 0$

**34.**
$$x \cos y = 1$$
$$x[-y' \sin y] + \cos y = 0$$
$$y' = \frac{\cos y}{x \sin y}$$
$$= \frac{1}{x}\cot y$$
$$= \frac{\cot y}{x}$$

At $\left(2, \dfrac{\pi}{3}\right)$: $y' = \dfrac{1}{2\sqrt{3}}$

**35.**
$$3e^{xy} - x = 0$$
$$3e^{xy}[xy' + y] - 1 = 0$$
$$3e^{xy}xy' = 1 - 3ye^{xy}$$
$$y' = \frac{1 - 3ye^{xy}}{3xe^{xy}}$$

At $(3, 0)$: $y' = \dfrac{1}{9}$

**36.**
$$y^2 = \ln x$$
$$2yy' = \frac{1}{x}$$
$$y' = \frac{1}{2xy}$$

At $(e, 1)$: $y' = \dfrac{1}{2e}$

**37.**
$$(x^2 + 4)y = 8$$
$$(x^2 + 4)y' + y(2x) = 0$$
$$y' = \frac{-2xy}{x^2 + 4}$$
$$= \frac{-2x\left[8/(x^2 + 4)\right]}{x^2 + 4}$$
$$= \frac{-16x}{(x^2 + 4)^2}$$

At $(2, 1)$: $y' = \dfrac{-32}{64} = -\dfrac{1}{2}$

$\left(\text{Or, you could just solve for } y\text{: } y = \dfrac{8}{x^2 + 4}\right)$

**38.**
$$(4 - x)y^2 = x^3$$
$$(4 - x)(2yy') + y^2(-1) = 3x^2$$
$$y' = \frac{3x^2 + y^2}{2y(4 - x)}$$

At $(2, 2)$: $y' = 2$

**39.**
$$(x^2 + y^2)^2 = 4x^2y$$
$$2(x^2 + y^2)(2x + 2yy') = 4x^2y' + y(8x)$$
$$4x^3 + 4x^2yy' + 4xy^2 + 4y^3y' = 4x^2y' + 8xy$$
$$4x^2yy' + 4y^3y' - 4x^2y' = 8xy - 4x^3 - 4xy^2$$
$$4y'(x^2y + y^3 - x^2) = 4(2xy - x^3 - xy^2)$$
$$y' = \frac{2xy - x^3 - xy^2}{x^2y + y^3 - x^2}$$

At $(1, 1)$: $y' = 0$

**40.**
$$x^3 + y^3 - 6xy = 0$$
$$3x^2 + 3y^2y' - 6xy' - 6y = 0$$
$$y'(3y^2 - 6x) = 6y - 3x^2$$
$$y' = \frac{6y - 3x^2}{3y^2 - 6x} = \frac{2y - x^2}{y^2 - 2x}$$

At $\left(\dfrac{4}{3}, \dfrac{8}{3}\right)$: $y' = \dfrac{(16/3) - (16/9)}{(64/9) - (8/3)} = \dfrac{32}{40} = \dfrac{4}{5}$

**41.** $4xy = 9, \quad \left(1, \frac{9}{4}\right)$

$$4xy' + 4y = 0$$
$$xy' = -y$$
$$y' = \frac{-y}{x}$$

At $\left(1, \frac{9}{4}\right)$, $y' = \frac{-9/4}{1} = \frac{-9}{4}$

Tangent line: $y - \frac{9}{4} = \frac{-9}{4}(x - 1)$

$$4y - 9 = -9x + 9$$
$$4y + 9x = 18$$
$$y = \frac{-9}{4}x + \frac{9}{2}$$

**42.** $x^2 + xy + y^2 = 4, \quad (2, 0)$

$$2x + xy' + y + 2yy' = 0$$
$$(x + 2y)y' = -2x - y$$
$$y' = \frac{-2x - y}{x + 2y}$$

At $(2, 0)$, $y' = \frac{-4}{2} = -2$

Tangent line: $y - 0 = -2(x - 2)$

$$y = -2x + 4$$

**43.** $x + y - 1 = \ln(x^2 + y^2), \quad (1, 0)$

$$1 + y' = \frac{2x + 2yy'}{x^2 + y^2}$$
$$x^2 + y^2 + (x^2 + y^2)y' = 2x + 2yy'$$

At $(1, 0)$: $1 + y' = 2$

$$y' = 1$$

Tangent line: $y = x - 1$

**44.** $y^2 + \ln(xy) = 2, \quad (e, 1)$

$$2yy' + \frac{xy' + y}{xy} = 0$$
$$2xy^2y' + xy' + y = 0$$

At $(e, 1)$: $2ey' + ey' + 1 = 0$

$$y' = \frac{-1}{3e}$$

Tangent line: $y - 1 = \frac{-1}{3e}(x - e)$

$$y = \frac{-1}{3e}x + \frac{4}{3}$$

**45.** $(y - 3)^2 = 4(x - 5), \quad (6, 1)$

$$2(y - 3)y' = 4$$
$$y' = \frac{2}{y - 3}$$

At $(6, 1)$, $y' = \frac{2}{1 - 3} = -1$

Tangent line: $y - 1 = -1(x - 6)$

$$y = -x + 7$$

**46.** $(x + 2)^2 + (y - 3)^2 = 37, \quad (4, 4)$

$$2(x + 2) + 2(y - 3)y' = 0$$
$$(y - 3)y' = -(x + 2)$$
$$y' = -\frac{(x + 2)}{y - 3}$$

At $(4, 4)$, $y' = -\frac{6}{1} = -6$

Tangent line: $y - 4 = -6(x - 4)$

$$y = -6x + 28$$

**47.** $xy = 1, \quad (1, 1)$

$$xy' + y = 0$$
$$y' = \frac{-y}{x}$$

At $(1, 1)$: $y' = -1$

Tangent line: $y - 1 = -1(x - 1)$

$$y = -x + 2$$

**48.** $7x^2 - 6\sqrt{3}xy + 13y^2 - 16 = 0, \quad \left(\sqrt{3}, 1\right)$

$$14x - 6\sqrt{3}xy' - 6\sqrt{3}y + 26yy' = 0$$
$$y' = \frac{6\sqrt{3}y - 14x}{26y - 6\sqrt{3}x}$$

At $\left(\sqrt{3}, 1\right)$: $y' = \frac{6\sqrt{3} - 14\sqrt{3}}{26 - 6\sqrt{3}\sqrt{3}} = \frac{-8\sqrt{3}}{8} = -\sqrt{3}$

Tangent line: $y - 1 = -\sqrt{3}\left(x - \sqrt{3}\right)$

$$y = -\sqrt{3}x + 4$$

**49.** $x^2y^2 - 9x^2 - 4y^2 = 0, \ \left(-4, 2\sqrt{3}\right)$

$$x^2 2yy' + 2xy^2 - 18x - 8yy' = 0$$

$$y' = \frac{18x - 2xy^2}{2x^2y - 8y}$$

$$\text{At } \left(-4, 2\sqrt{3}\right): y' = \frac{18(-4) - 2(-4)(12)}{2(16)\left(2\sqrt{3}\right) - 16\sqrt{3}}$$

$$= \frac{24}{48\sqrt{3}} = \frac{1}{2\sqrt{3}} = \frac{\sqrt{3}}{6}$$

$$\text{Tangent line: } y - 2\sqrt{3} = \frac{\sqrt{3}}{6}(x + 4)$$

$$y = \frac{\sqrt{3}}{6}x + \frac{8}{3}\sqrt{3}$$

**50.** $x^{2/3} + y^{2/3} = 5, \ (8, 1)$

$$\frac{2}{3}x^{-1/3} + \frac{2}{3}y^{-1/3}y' = 0$$

$$y' = \frac{-x^{-1/3}}{y^{-1/3}} = -\left(\frac{y}{x}\right)^{1/3}$$

$$\text{At } (8, 1): y' = -\frac{1}{2}$$

$$\text{Tangent line: } y - 1 = -\frac{1}{2}(x - 8)$$

$$y = -\frac{1}{2}x + 5$$

**51.** $3\left(x^2 + y^2\right)^2 = 100\left(x^2 - y^2\right), \ (4, 2)$

$$6\left(x^2 + y^2\right)(2x + 2yy') = 100(2x - 2yy')$$

At $(4, 2)$:

$$6(16 + 4)(8 + 4y') = 100(8 - 4y')$$

$$960 + 480y' = 800 - 400y'$$

$$880y' = -160$$

$$y' = -\tfrac{2}{11}$$

$$\text{Tangent line: } y - 2 = -\tfrac{2}{11}(x - 4)$$

$$11y + 2x - 30 = 0$$

$$y = -\tfrac{2}{11}x + \tfrac{30}{11}$$

**52.** $y^2\left(x^2 + y^2\right) = 2x^2, \ (1, 1)$

$$y^2x^2 + y^4 = 2x^2$$

$$2yy'x^2 + 2xy^2 + 4y^3y' = 4x$$

At $(1, 1)$:

$$2y' + 2 + 4y' = 4$$

$$6y' = 2$$

$$y' = \tfrac{1}{3}$$

$$\text{Tangent line: } y - 1 = \tfrac{1}{3}(x - 1)$$

$$y = \tfrac{1}{3}x + \tfrac{2}{3}$$

**53.** (a) $\dfrac{x^2}{2} + \dfrac{y^2}{8} = 1, \ (1, 2)$

$$x + \frac{yy'}{4} = 0$$

$$y' = -\frac{4x}{y}$$

At $(1, 2)$: $y' = -2$

$$\text{Tangent line: } y - 2 = -2(x - 1)$$

$$y = -2x + 4$$

(b) $\dfrac{x^2}{a^2} + \dfrac{y^2}{b^2} = 1 \Rightarrow \dfrac{2x}{a^2} + \dfrac{2yy'}{b^2} = 0 \Rightarrow y' = \dfrac{-b^2x}{a^2y}$

$y - y_0 = \dfrac{-b^2x_0}{a^2y_0}(x - x_0)$, Tangent line at $(x_0, y_0)$

$$\frac{y_0y}{b^2} - \frac{y_0^2}{b^2} = \frac{-x_0x}{a^2} + \frac{x_0^2}{a^2}$$

Because $\dfrac{x_0^2}{a^2} + \dfrac{y_0^2}{b^2} = 1$, you have $\dfrac{y_0y}{b^2} + \dfrac{x_0x}{a^2} = 1$.

**Note:** From part (a),

$\dfrac{1(x)}{2} + \dfrac{2(y)}{8} = 1 \Rightarrow \dfrac{1}{4}y = -\dfrac{1}{2}x + 1 \Rightarrow y = -2x + 4$,

Tangent line.

**54.** (a) $\frac{x^2}{6} - \frac{y^2}{8} = 1, \ (3, -2)$

$$\frac{x}{3} - \frac{y}{4}y' = 0$$

$$\frac{y}{4}y' = \frac{x}{3}$$

$$y' = \frac{4x}{3y}$$

At $(3, -2)$: $y' = \frac{4(3)}{3(-2)} = -2$

Tangent line: $y + 2 = -2(x - 3)$

$$y = -2x + 4$$

(b) $\frac{x^2}{a^2} - \frac{y^2}{b^2} = 1 \Rightarrow \frac{2x}{a^2} - \frac{2yy'}{b^2} = 0 \Rightarrow y' = \frac{xb^2}{ya^2}$

$y - y_0 = \frac{x_0 b^2}{y_0 a^2}(x - x_0)$, Tangent line at $(x_0, y_0)$

$$\frac{yy_0}{b^2} - \frac{y_0^2}{b^2} = \frac{x_0 x}{a^2} - \frac{x_0^2}{a^2}$$

Because $\frac{x_0^2}{a^2} - \frac{y_0^2}{b^2} = 1$, you have $\frac{x_0 x}{a^2} - \frac{yy_0}{b^2} = 1$.

**Note:** From part (a),

$\frac{3x}{6} - \frac{(-2)y}{8} = 1 \Rightarrow \frac{1}{2}x + \frac{y}{4} = 1 \Rightarrow y = -2x + 4$,

Tangent line.

**55.**

$$\tan y = x$$

$$y' \sec^2 y = 1$$

$$y' = \frac{1}{\sec^2 y} = \cos^2 y, \ -\frac{\pi}{2} < y < \frac{\pi}{2}$$

$$\sec^2 y = 1 + \tan^2 y = 1 + x^2$$

$$y' = \frac{1}{1 + x^2}$$

**56.**

$$\cos y = x$$

$$-\sin y \cdot y' = 1$$

$$y' = \frac{-1}{\sin y}, \quad 0 < y < \pi$$

$$\sin^2 y + \cos^2 y = 1$$

$$\sin^2 y = 1 - \cos^2 y$$

$$\sin y = \sqrt{1 - \cos^2 y} = \sqrt{1 - x^2}$$

$$y' = \frac{-1}{\sqrt{1 - x^2}}, \quad -1 < x < 1$$

**57.** $x^2 + y^2 = 4$

$$2x + 2yy' = 0$$

$$y' = \frac{-x}{y}$$

$$y'' = \frac{y(-1) + xy'}{y^2} = \frac{-y + x(-x/y)}{y^2} = \frac{-y^2 - x^2}{y^3} = -\frac{4}{y^3}$$

**58.**

$$x^2y^2 - 2x = 3$$

$$2x^2yy' + 2xy^2 - 2 = 0$$

$$x^2yy' + xy^2 - 1 = 0$$

$$y' = \frac{1 - xy^2}{x^2y}$$

$$2xyy' + x^2(y')^2 + x^2yy'' + 2xyy' + y^2 = 0$$

$$4xyy' + x^2(y')^2 + x^2yy'' + y^2 = 0$$

$$\frac{4 - 4xy^2}{x} + \frac{(1 - xy^2)^2}{x^2y^2} + x^2yy'' + y^2 = 0$$

$$4xy^2 - 4x^2y^4 + 1 - 2xy^2 + x^2y^4 + x^4y^3y'' + x^2y^4 = 0$$

$$x^4y^3y'' = 2x^2y^4 - 2xy^2 - 1$$

$$y'' = \frac{2x^2y^4 - 2xy^2 - 1}{x^4y^3}$$

**59.**
$$\begin{aligned} x^2 - y^2 &= 36 \\ 2x - 2yy' &= 0 \\ y' &= \frac{x}{y} \\ x - yy' &= 0 \\ 1 - yy'' - (y')^2 &= 0 \\ 1 - yy'' - \left(\frac{x}{y}\right)^2 &= 0 \\ y^2 - y^3y'' &= x^2 \\ y'' &= \frac{y^2 - x^2}{y^3} = -\frac{36}{y^3} \end{aligned}$$

**60.**
$$\begin{aligned} 1 - xy &= x - y \\ y - xy &= x - 1 \\ y &= \frac{x - 1}{1 - x} = -1 \\ y' &= 0 \\ y'' &= 0 \end{aligned}$$

**61.**
$$\begin{aligned} y^2 &= x^3 \\ 2yy' &= 3x^2 \\ y' &= \frac{3x^2}{2y} = \frac{3x^2}{2y} \cdot \frac{xy}{xy} = \frac{3y}{2x} \cdot \frac{x^3}{y^2} = \frac{3y}{2x} \\ y'' &= \frac{2x(3y') - 3y(2)}{4x^2} \\ &= \frac{2x[3 \cdot (3y/2x)] - 6y}{4x^2} = \frac{3y}{4x^2} = \frac{3x}{4y} \end{aligned}$$

**62.**
$$\begin{aligned} y^2 &= 10x \\ 2yy' &= 10 \\ y' &= \frac{5}{y} \\ y'' &= -5y^{-2}y' = \left[\frac{-5}{y^2}\right] \cdot \frac{5}{y} = -\frac{25}{y^3} \end{aligned}$$

**63.**
$$\begin{aligned} \sqrt{x} + \sqrt{y} &= 5 \\ \frac{1}{2}x^{-1/2} + \frac{1}{2}y^{-1/2}y' &= 0 \\ y' &= \frac{-\sqrt{y}}{\sqrt{x}} \end{aligned}$$

At $(9, 4)$: $y' = -\dfrac{2}{3}$

Tangent line: $y - 4 = -\dfrac{2}{3}(x - 9)$

$$2x + 3y - 30 = 0$$

**64.**
$$\begin{aligned} y^2 &= \frac{x - 1}{x^2 + 1} \\ 2yy' &= \frac{(x^2 + 1)(1) - (x - 1)(2x)}{(x^2 + 1)^2} = \frac{x^2 + 1 - 2x^2 + 2x}{(x^2 + 1)^2} \\ y' &= \frac{1 + 2x - x^2}{2y(x^2 + 1)^2} \end{aligned}$$

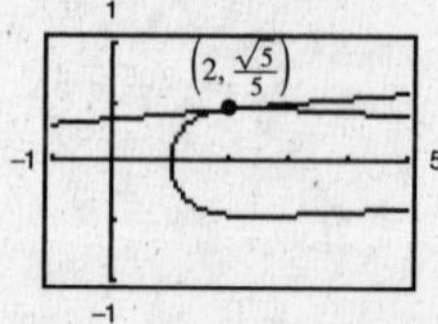


At $\left(2, \dfrac{\sqrt{5}}{5}\right)$: $y' = \dfrac{1 + 4 - 4}{\left[\dfrac{(2\sqrt{5})}{5}\right](4 + 1)^2} = \dfrac{1}{10\sqrt{5}}$

Tangent line:
$$\begin{aligned} y - \frac{\sqrt{5}}{5} &= \frac{1}{10\sqrt{5}}(x - 2) \\ 10\sqrt{5}y - 10 &= x - 2 \\ x - 10\sqrt{5}y + 8 &= 0 \end{aligned}$$

**65.**
$$\begin{aligned} x^2 + y^2 &= 25 \\ 2x + 2yy' &= 0 \\ y' &= \frac{-x}{y} \end{aligned}$$

At $(4, 3)$:

Tangent line:

$$y - 3 = \frac{-4}{3}(x - 4) \Rightarrow 4x + 3y - 25 = 0$$

Normal line: $y - 3 = \dfrac{3}{4}(x - 4) \Rightarrow 3x - 4y = 0$

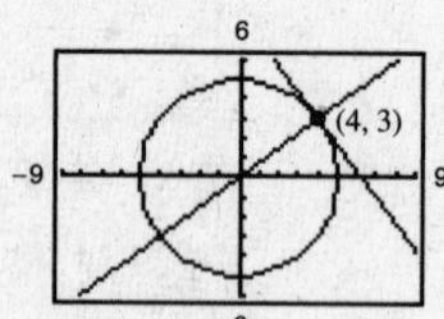


At $(-3, 4)$:

Tangent line:

$$y - 4 = \frac{3}{4}(x + 3) \Rightarrow 3x - 4y + 25 = 0$$

Normal line: $y - 4 = \dfrac{-4}{3}(x + 3) \Rightarrow 4x + 3y = 0$

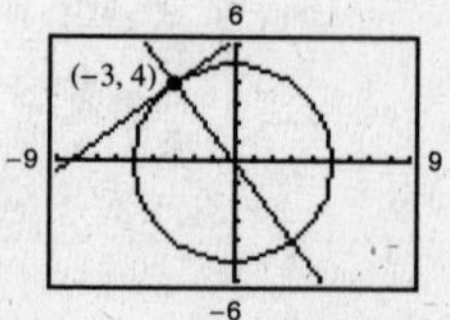

**66.** $x^2 + y^2 = 36$

$2x + 2yy' = 0$

$y' = -\frac{x}{y}$

At $(6, 0)$; slope is undefined.

Tangent line: $x = 6$

Normal line: $y = 0$

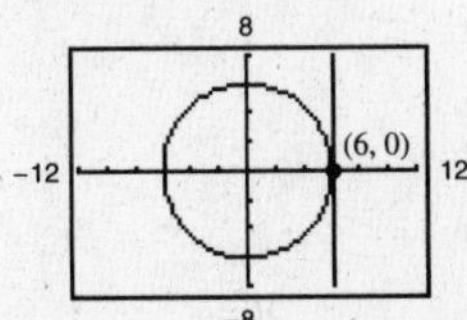


At $(5, \sqrt{11})$, slope is $\frac{-5}{\sqrt{11}}$.

Tangent line: $y - \sqrt{11} = \frac{-5}{\sqrt{11}}(x - 5)$

$\sqrt{11}y - 11 = -5x + 25$

$5x + \sqrt{11}y - 36 = 0$

Normal line: $y - \sqrt{11} = \frac{\sqrt{11}}{5}(x - 5)$

$5y - 5\sqrt{11} = \sqrt{11}x - 5\sqrt{11}$

$5y - \sqrt{11}x = 0$

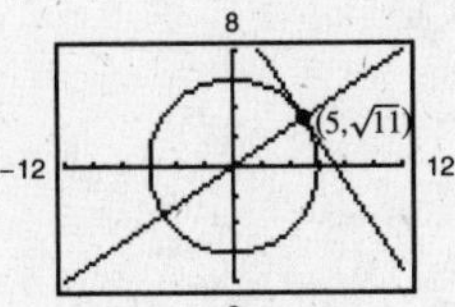


**67.** $x^2 + y^2 = r^2$

$2x + 2yy' = 0$

$y' = \frac{-x}{y}$ = slope of tangent line

$\frac{y}{x}$ = slope of normal line

Let $(x_0, y_0)$ be a point on the circle. If $x_0 = 0$, then the tangent line is horizontal, the normal line is vertical and, so, passes through the origin. If $x_0 \neq 0$, then the equation of the normal line is

$y - y_0 = \frac{y_0}{x_0}(x - x_0)$

$y = \frac{y_0}{x_0}x$

which passes through the origin.

**68.** $y^2 = 4x$

$2yy' = 4$

$y' = \frac{2}{y} = 1$ at $(1, 2)$

Equation of normal line at $(1, 2)$ is $y - 2 = -1(x - 1)$, $y = 3 - x$. The centers of the circles must be on the normal line and at a distance of 4 units from $(1, 2)$. So,

$(x - 1)^2 + [(3 - x) - 2]^2 = 16$

$2(x - 1)^2 = 16$

$x = 1 \pm 2\sqrt{2}.$

Centers of the circles: $(1 + 2\sqrt{2}, 2 - 2\sqrt{2})$ and $(1 - 2\sqrt{2}, 2 + 2\sqrt{2})$

Equations: $(x - 1 - 2\sqrt{2})^2 + (y - 2 + 2\sqrt{2})^2 = 16$

$(x - 1 + 2\sqrt{2})^2 + (y - 2 - 2\sqrt{2})^2 = 16$

**69.** $25x^2 + 16y^2 + 200x - 160y + 400 = 0$

$50x + 32yy' + 200 - 160y' = 0$

$y' = \frac{200 + 50x}{160 - 32y}$

Horizontal tangents occur when $x = -4$:

$25(16) + 16y^2 + 200(-4) - 160y + 400 = 0$

$y(y - 10) = 0 \Rightarrow y = 0, 10$

Horizontal tangents: $(-4, 0)$, $(-4, 10)$

Vertical tangents occur when $y = 5$:

$25x^2 + 400 + 200x - 800 + 400 = 0$

$25x(x + 8) = 0 \Rightarrow x = 0, -8$

Vertical tangents: $(0, 5)$, $(-8, 5)$

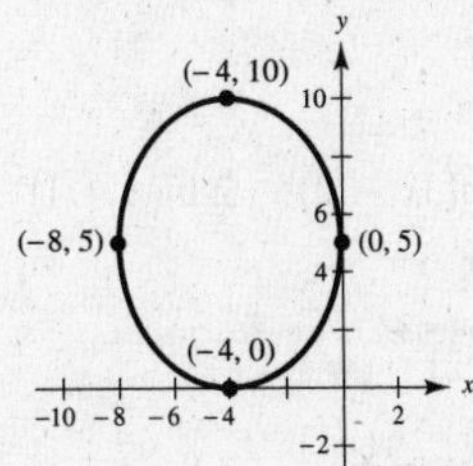

**70.** $4x^2 + y^2 - 8x + 4y + 4 = 0$

$$8x + 2yy' - 8 + 4y' = 0$$

$$y' = \frac{8 - 8x}{2y + 4} = \frac{4 - 4x}{y + 2}$$

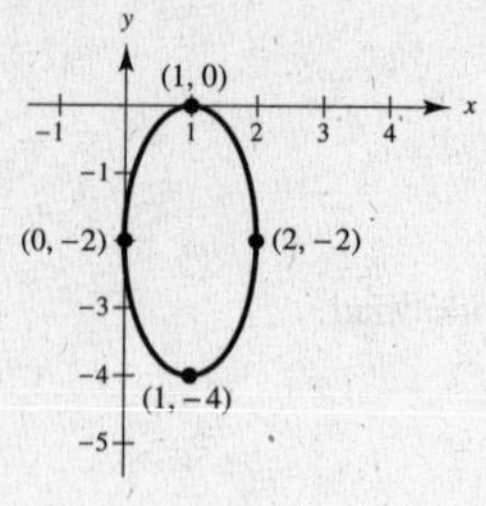


Horizontal tangents occur when $x = 1$:

$$4(1)^2 + y^2 - 8(1) + 4y + 4 = 0$$

$$y^2 + 4y = y(y + 4) = 0 \Rightarrow y = 0, -4$$

Horizontal tangents: $(1, 0), (1, -4)$

Vertical tangents occur when $y = -2$:

$$4x^2 + (-2)^2 - 8x + 4(-2) + 4 = 0$$

$$4x^2 - 8x = 4x(x - 2) = 0 \Rightarrow x = 0, 2$$

Vertical tangents: $(0, -2), (2, -2)$

**71.**
$$y = x\sqrt{x^2 + 1}$$

$$\ln y = \ln x + \frac{1}{2}\ln(x^2 + 1)$$

$$\frac{1}{y}\left(\frac{dy}{dx}\right) = \frac{1}{x} + \frac{x}{x^2 + 1}$$

$$\frac{dy}{dx} = y\left[\frac{2x^2 + 1}{x(x^2 + 1)}\right] = \frac{2x^2 + 1}{\sqrt{x^2 + 1}}$$

**72.**
$$y = \sqrt{x^2(x + 1)(x + 2)},\ x > 0$$

$$y^2 = x^2(x + 1)(x + 2)$$

$$2\ln y = 2\ln x + \ln(x + 1) + \ln(x + 2)$$

$$\frac{2}{y}\frac{dy}{dx} = \frac{2}{x} + \frac{1}{x + 1} + \frac{1}{x + 2}$$

$$\frac{dy}{dx} = \frac{y}{2}\left[\frac{2}{x} + \frac{1}{x + 1} + \frac{1}{x + 2}\right]$$

$$\frac{dy}{dx} = \frac{\sqrt{x^2(x + 1)(x + 2)}}{2}\left[\frac{2(x + 1)(x + 2) + x(x + 2) + x(x + 1)}{x(x + 1)(x + 2)}\right] = \frac{4x^2 + 9x + 4}{2\sqrt{(x + 1)(x + 2)}}$$

**73.**
$$y = \frac{x^2\sqrt{3x - 2}}{(x + 1)^2}$$

$$\ln y = 2\ln x + \frac{1}{2}\ln(3x - 2) - 2\ln(x + 1)$$

$$\frac{1}{y}\left(\frac{dy}{dx}\right) = \frac{2}{x} + \frac{3}{2(3x - 2)} - \frac{2}{x + 1}$$

$$\frac{dy}{dx} = y\left[\frac{3x^2 + 15x - 8}{2x(3x - 2)(x + 1)}\right]$$

$$= \frac{3x^3 + 15x^2 - 8x}{2(x + 1)^3\sqrt{3x - 2}}$$

**74.**
$$y = \sqrt{\frac{x^2 - 1}{x^2 + 1}}$$

$$\ln y = \frac{1}{2}\left[\ln(x^2 - 1) - \ln(x^2 + 1)\right]$$

$$\frac{1}{y}\left(\frac{dy}{dx}\right) = \frac{1}{2}\left[\frac{2x}{x^2 - 1} - \frac{2x}{x^2 + 1}\right]$$

$$\frac{dy}{dx} = \sqrt{\frac{x^2 - 1}{x^2 + 1}}\left[\frac{2x}{x^4 - 1}\right]$$

$$= \frac{(x^2 - 1)^{1/2}2x}{(x^2 + 1)^{1/2}(x^2 - 1)(x^2 + 1)}$$

$$= \frac{2x}{(x^2 + 1)^{3/2}(x^2 - 1)^{1/2}}$$

**75.**

$$y = \frac{x(x-1)^{3/2}}{\sqrt{x+1}}$$

$$\ln y = \ln x + \frac{3}{2}\ln(x-1) - \frac{1}{2}\ln(x+1)$$

$$\frac{1}{y}\left(\frac{dy}{dx}\right) = \frac{1}{x} + \frac{3}{2}\left(\frac{1}{x-1}\right) - \frac{1}{2}\left(\frac{1}{x+1}\right)$$

$$\frac{dy}{dx} = \frac{y}{2}\left[\frac{2}{x} + \frac{3}{x-1} - \frac{1}{x+1}\right]$$

$$= \frac{y}{2}\left[\frac{4x^2+4x-2}{x(x^2-1)}\right] = \frac{(2x^2+2x-1)\sqrt{x-1}}{(x+1)^{3/2}}$$

**76.**

$$y = \frac{(x+1)(x-2)}{(x-1)(x+2)}$$

$$\ln y = \ln(x+1) + \ln(x-2) - \ln(x-1) - \ln(x+2)$$

$$\frac{1}{y}\left(\frac{dy}{dx}\right) = \frac{1}{x+1} + \frac{1}{x-2} - \frac{1}{x-1} - \frac{1}{x+2}$$

$$\frac{dy}{dx} = y\left[\frac{-2}{x^2-1} + \frac{4}{x^2-4}\right] = y\left[\frac{2x^2+4}{(x^2-1)(x^2-4)}\right]$$

$$= \frac{(x+1)(x+2)}{(x-1)(x-2)} \cdot \frac{2x^2+4}{(x+1)(x-1)(x+2)(x-2)}$$

$$= \frac{2(x^2+2)}{(x-1)^2(x-2)^2}$$

**77.**

$$y = x^{2/x}$$

$$\ln y = \frac{2}{x}\ln x$$

$$\frac{1}{y}\left(\frac{dy}{dx}\right) = \frac{2}{x}\left(\frac{1}{x}\right) + \ln x\left(-\frac{2}{x^2}\right) = \frac{2}{x^2}(1 - \ln x)$$

$$\frac{dy}{dx} = \frac{2y}{x^2}(1 - \ln x) = 2x^{(2/x)-2}(1 - \ln x)$$

**78.**

$$y = x^{x-1}$$

$$\ln y = (x-1)(\ln x)$$

$$\frac{1}{y}\left(\frac{dy}{dx}\right) = (x-1)\left(\frac{1}{x}\right) + \ln x$$

$$\frac{dy}{dx} = y\left[\frac{x-1}{x} + \ln x\right]$$

$$= x^{x-2}(x - 1 + x\ln x)$$

**79.**

$$y = (x-2)^{x+1}$$

$$\ln y = (x+1)\ln(x-2)$$

$$\frac{1}{y}\left(\frac{dy}{dx}\right) = (x+1)\left(\frac{1}{x-2}\right) + \ln(x-2)$$

$$\frac{dy}{dx} = y\left[\frac{x+1}{x-2} + \ln(x-2)\right]$$

$$= (x-2)^{x+1}\left[\frac{x+1}{x-2} + \ln(x-2)\right]$$

**80.**

$$y = (1+x)^{1/x}$$

$$\ln y = \frac{1}{x}\ln(1+x)$$

$$\frac{1}{y}\left(\frac{dy}{dx}\right) = \frac{1}{x}\left(\frac{1}{1+x}\right) + \ln(1+x)\left(-\frac{1}{x^2}\right)$$

$$\frac{dy}{dx} = \frac{y}{x}\left[\frac{1}{x+1} - \frac{\ln(x+1)}{x}\right]$$

$$= \frac{(1+x)^{1/x}}{x}\left[\frac{1}{x+1} - \frac{\ln(x+1)}{x}\right]$$

**81.**

$$y = x^{\ln x}, \quad x > 0$$

$$\ln y = \ln x^{\ln x} = (\ln x)(\ln x) = (\ln x)^2$$

$$\frac{y'}{y} = 2\ln x(1/x)$$

$$y' = \frac{2y\ln x}{x} = \frac{2x^{\ln x}\cdot \ln x}{x}$$

**82.**

$$y = (\ln x)^{\ln x}, \quad x > 1$$

$$\ln y = \ln\left[(\ln x)^{\ln x}\right] = (\ln x)\ln(\ln x)$$

$$\frac{y'}{y} = (\ln x)\frac{1}{\ln x}\cdot\frac{1}{x} + \frac{1}{x}\ln(\ln x)$$

$$= \frac{1}{x}(1 + \ln(\ln x))$$

$$y' = \frac{y}{x}(1 + \ln(\ln x))$$

$$= (\ln x)^{\ln x}(1 + \ln(\ln x))/x$$

**83.** Find the points of intersection by letting $y^2 = 4x$ in the equation $2x^2 + y^2 = 6$.

$2x^2 + 4x = 6$ and $(x + 3)(x - 1) = 0$

The curves intersect at $(1, \pm 2)$.

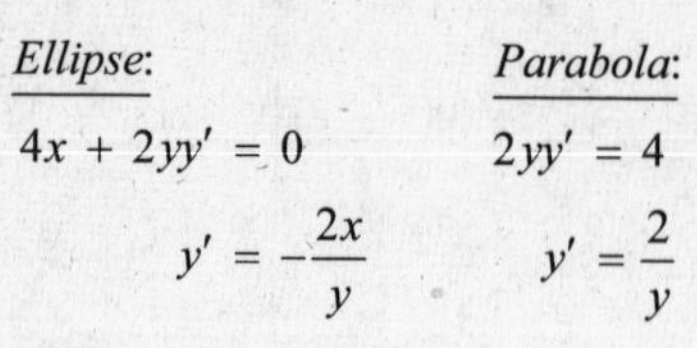

*Ellipse*:

$4x + 2yy' = 0$

$y' = -\frac{2x}{y}$

*Parabola*:

$2yy' = 4$

$y' = \frac{2}{y}$

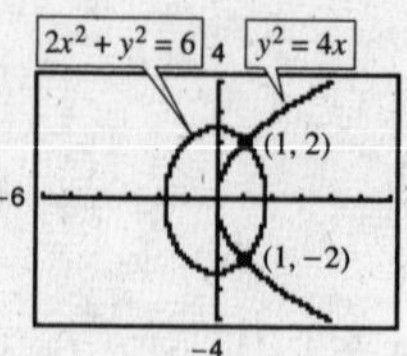


At $(1, 2)$, the slopes are:

$y' = -1$ $\qquad$ $y' = 1$

At $(1, -2)$, the slopes are:

$y' = 1$ $\qquad$ $y' = -1$

Tangents are perpendicular.

**84.** Find the points of intersection by letting $y^2 = x^3$ in the equation $2x^2 + 3y^2 = 5$.

$2x^2 + 3x^3 = 5$ and $3x^3 + 2x^2 - 5 = 0$

Intersect when $x = 1$.

Points of intersection: $(1, \pm 1)$

$y^2 = x^3$:

$2yy' = 3x^2$

$y' = \frac{3x^2}{2y}$

$2x^2 + 3y^2 = 5$:

$4x + 6yy' = 0$

$y' = -\frac{2x}{3y}$

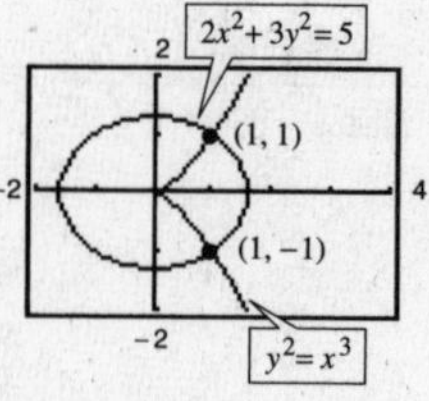


At $(1, 1)$, the slopes are:

$y' = \frac{3}{2}$ $\qquad$ $y' = -\frac{2}{3}$

At $(1, -1)$, the slopes are:

$y' = -\frac{3}{2}$ $\qquad$ $y' = \frac{2}{3}$

Tangents are perpendicular.

**85.** $y = -x$ and $x = \sin y$

Point of intersection: $(0, 0)$

$y = -x$:

$y' = -1$

$x = \sin y$:

$1 = y' \cos y$

$y' = \sec y$

At $(0, 0)$, the slopes are:

$y' = -1$ $\qquad$ $y' = 1$

Tangents are perpendicular.

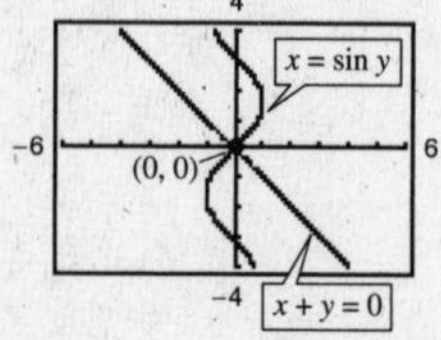


**86.** Rewriting each equation and differentiating:

$x^3 = 3(y - 1)$ $\qquad$ $x(3y - 29) = 3$

$y = \frac{x^3}{3} + 1$ $\qquad$ $y = \frac{1}{3}\left(\frac{3}{x} + 29\right)$

$y' = x^2$ $\qquad$ $y' = -\frac{1}{x^2}$

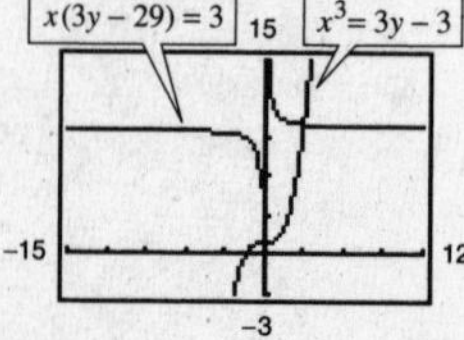


For each value of $x$, the derivatives are negative reciprocals of each other. So, the tangent lines are orthogonal at both points of intersection.

**87.** $xy = C$ $\qquad x^2 - y^2 = K$

$xy' + y = 0 \qquad 2x - 2yy' = 0$

$y' = -\dfrac{y}{x} \qquad y' = \dfrac{x}{y}$

At any point of intersection $(x, y)$, the product of the slopes is $(-y/x)(x/y) = -1$. The curves are orthogonal.

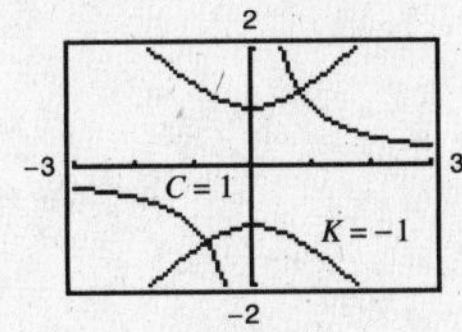


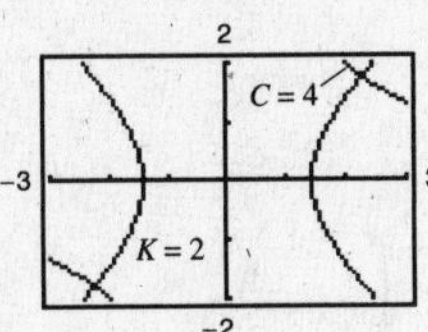


**88.** $x^2 + y^2 = C^2 \qquad y = Kx$

$2x + 2yy' = 0 \qquad y' = K$

$y' = -\dfrac{x}{y}$

At the point of intersection $(x, y)$, the product of the slopes is $(-x/y)(K) = (-x/Kx)(K) = -1$. The curves are orthogonal.

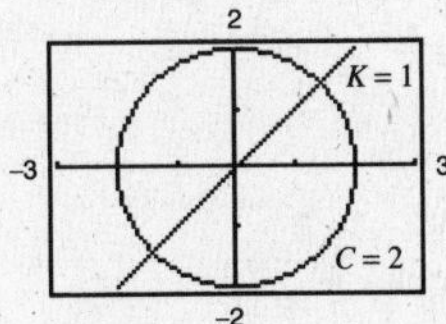


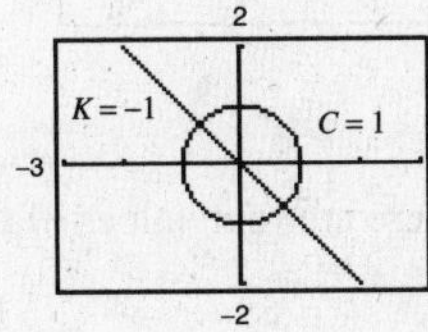


**89.** $2y^2 - 3x^4 = 0$

(a) $4yy' - 12x^3 = 0$

$$4yy' = 12x^3$$

$$y' = \frac{12x^3}{4y} = \frac{3x^3}{y}$$

(b) $4y\dfrac{dy}{dt} - 12x^3\dfrac{dx}{dt} = 0$

$$y\frac{dy}{dt} = 3x^3\frac{dx}{dt}$$

**90.** $x^2 - 3xy^2 + y^3 = 10$

(a) $2x - 3y^2 - 6xyy' + 3y^2y' = 0$

$$(-6xy + 3y^2)y' = 3y^2 - 2x$$

$$y' = \frac{3y^2 - 2x}{3y^2 - 6xy}$$

(b) $2x\dfrac{dx}{dt} - 3y^2\dfrac{dx}{dt} - 6xy\dfrac{dy}{dt} + 3y^2\dfrac{dy}{dt} = 0$

$$(2x - 3y^2)\frac{dx}{dt} = (6xy - 3y^2)\frac{dy}{dt}$$

**91.** $\cos \pi y - 3 \sin \pi x = 1$

(a) $-\pi \sin \pi y(y') - 3\pi \cos \pi x = 0$

$$y' = \frac{-3 \cos \pi x}{\sin \pi y}$$

(b) $-\pi \sin \pi y\left(\dfrac{dy}{dt}\right) - 3\pi \cos \pi x\left(\dfrac{dx}{dt}\right) = 0$

$$-\sin \pi y\left(\frac{dy}{dt}\right) = 3 \cos \pi x\left(\frac{dx}{dt}\right)$$

**92.** $4 \sin x \cos y = 1$

(a) $4 \sin x(-\sin y)y' + 4 \cos x \cos y = 0$

$$y' = \frac{\cos x \cos y}{\sin x \sin y}$$

(b) $4 \sin x(-\sin y)\left(\dfrac{dy}{dt}\right) + 4 \cos x\left(\dfrac{dx}{dt}\right)\cos y = 0$

$$\cos x \cos y\left(\frac{dx}{dt}\right) = \sin x \sin y\left(\frac{dy}{dt}\right)$$

**93.** Answers will vary. *Sample answer:* In the explicit form of a function, the variable is explicitly written as a function of $x$. In an implicit equation, the function is only implied by an equation. An example of an implicit function is $x^2 + xy = 5$. In explicit form, it would be $y = (5 - x^2)/x$.

**94.** Answers will vary. *Sample answer:* Given an implicit equation, first differentiate both sides with respect to $x$. Collect all terms involving $y'$ on the left, and all other terms to the right. Factor out $y'$ on the left side. Finally, divide both sides by the left-hand factor that does not contain $y'$.

**95.** 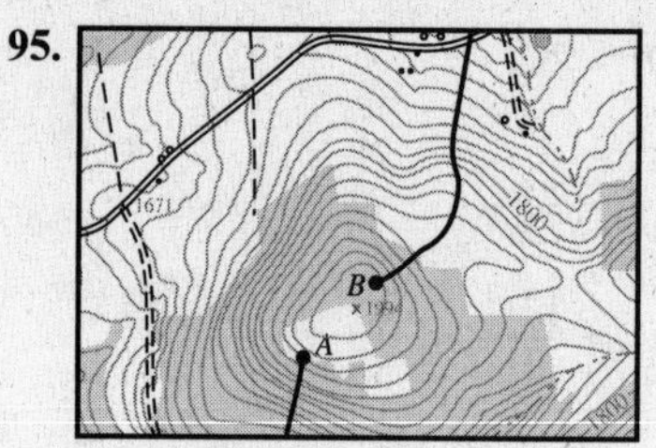


Use starting point $B$.

**96.** Highest wind speed near $L$

**97.** (a)

$$x^4 = 4(4x^2 - y^2)$$
$$4y^2 = 16x^2 - x^4$$
$$y^2 = 4x^2 - \frac{1}{4}x^4$$
$$y = \pm\sqrt{4x^2 - \frac{1}{4}x^4}$$

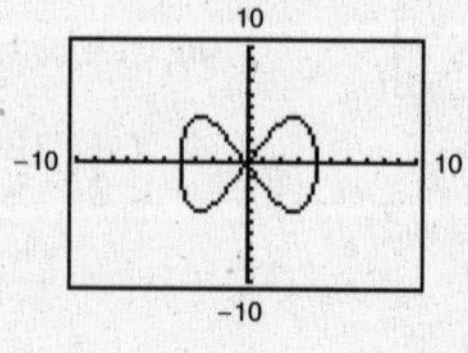


(b)

$$y = 3 \Rightarrow 9 = 4x^2 - \frac{1}{4}x^4$$
$$36 = 16x^2 - x^4$$
$$x^4 - 16x^2 + 36 = 0$$
$$x^2 = \frac{16 \pm \sqrt{256 - 144}}{2} = 8 \pm \sqrt{28}$$

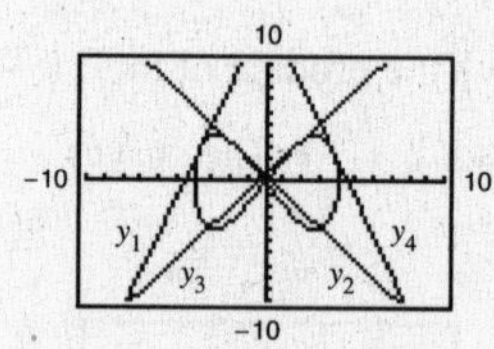


Note that $x^2 = 8 \pm \sqrt{28} = 8 \pm 2\sqrt{7} = \left(1 \pm \sqrt{7}\right)^2$. So, there are four values of $x$:

$-1 - \sqrt{7}, 1 - \sqrt{7}, -1 + \sqrt{7}, 1 + \sqrt{7}$

To find the slope, $2yy' = 8x - x^3 \Rightarrow y' = \dfrac{x(8 - x^2)}{2(3)}$.

For $x = -1 - \sqrt{7}$, $y' = \frac{1}{3}\left(\sqrt{7} + 7\right)$, and the line is

$$y_1 = \frac{1}{3}\left(\sqrt{7} + 7\right)\left(x + 1 + \sqrt{7}\right) + 3 = \frac{1}{3}\left[\left(\sqrt{7} + 7\right)x + 8\sqrt{7} + 23\right].$$

For $x = 1 - \sqrt{7}$, $y' = \frac{1}{3}\left(\sqrt{7} - 7\right)$, and the line is

$$y_2 = \frac{1}{3}\left(\sqrt{7} - 7\right)\left(x - 1 + \sqrt{7}\right) + 3 = \frac{1}{3}\left[\left(\sqrt{7} - 7\right)x + 23 - 8\sqrt{7}\right].$$

For $x = -1 + \sqrt{7}$, $y' = -\frac{1}{3}\left(\sqrt{7} - 7\right)$, and the line is

$$y_3 = -\frac{1}{3}\left(\sqrt{7} - 7\right)\left(x + 1 - \sqrt{7}\right) + 3 = -\frac{1}{3}\left[\left(\sqrt{7} - 7\right)x - \left(23 - 8\sqrt{7}\right)\right].$$

For $x = 1 + \sqrt{7}$, $y' = -\frac{1}{3}\left(\sqrt{7} + 7\right)$, and the line is

$$y_4 = -\frac{1}{3}\left(\sqrt{7} + 7\right)\left(x - 1 - \sqrt{7}\right) + 3 = -\frac{1}{3}\left[\left(\sqrt{7} + 7\right)x - \left(8\sqrt{7} + 23\right)\right].$$

(c) Equating $y_3$ and $y_4$:

$$-\frac{1}{3}\left(\sqrt{7}-7\right)\left(x+1-\sqrt{7}\right)+3=-\frac{1}{3}\left(\sqrt{7}+7\right)\left(x-1-\sqrt{7}\right)+3$$

$$\left(\sqrt{7}-7\right)\left(x+1-\sqrt{7}\right)=\left(\sqrt{7}+7\right)\left(x-1-\sqrt{7}\right)$$

$$\sqrt{7}x+\sqrt{7}-7-7x-7+7\sqrt{7}=\sqrt{7}x-\sqrt{7}-7+7x-7-7\sqrt{7}$$

$$16\sqrt{7}=14x$$

$$x=\frac{8\sqrt{7}}{7}$$

If $x=\dfrac{8\sqrt{7}}{7}$, then $y=5$ and the lines intersect at $\left(\dfrac{8\sqrt{7}}{7}, 5\right)$.

**98.** (a) True

(b) False. $\dfrac{d}{dy}\cos\left(y^2\right)=-2y\sin\left(y^2\right)$.

(c) False. $\dfrac{d}{dx}\cos\left(y^2\right)=-2yy'\sin\left(y^2\right)$.

**99.**

$$\sqrt{x}+\sqrt{y}=\sqrt{c}$$

$$\frac{1}{2\sqrt{x}}+\frac{1}{2\sqrt{y}}\frac{dy}{dx}=0$$

$$\frac{dy}{dx}=-\frac{\sqrt{y}}{\sqrt{x}}$$

Tangent line at $(x_0, y_0)$: $y-y_0=-\dfrac{\sqrt{y_0}}{\sqrt{x_0}}(x-x_0)$

$x$-intercept: $\left(x_0+\sqrt{x_0}\sqrt{y_0}, 0\right)$

$y$-intercept: $\left(0, y_0+\sqrt{x_0}\sqrt{y_0}\right)$

Sum of intercepts:

$$\left(x_0+\sqrt{x_0}\sqrt{y_0}\right)+\left(y_0+\sqrt{x_0}\sqrt{y_0}\right)=x_0+2\sqrt{x_0}\sqrt{y_0}+y_0=\left(\sqrt{x_0}+\sqrt{y_0}\right)^2=\left(\sqrt{c}\right)^2=c$$

**100.** (a)

$$y=x^{p/q};\ p, q \text{ integers and } q>0$$

$$y^q=x^p$$

$$qy^{q-1}y'=px^{p-1}$$

$$y'=\frac{p}{q}\cdot\frac{x^{p-1}}{y^{q-1}}=\frac{p}{q}\cdot\frac{x^{p-1}y}{y^q}$$

$$=\frac{p}{q}\cdot\frac{x^{p-1}}{x^p}x^{p/q}=\frac{p}{q}x^{p/q-1}$$

So, if $y=x^n$, $n=p/q$, then $y'=nx^{n-1}$.

(b) $y=x^r$, $r$ real

$$\ln y=\ln\left(x^r\right)=r\ln x$$

$$\frac{y'}{y}=\frac{r}{x}$$

$$y'=\frac{yr}{x}=\frac{x^r\cdot r}{x}=rx^{r-1}.$$

**101.**

$$x^2+y^2=100,\ \text{slope}=\frac{3}{4}$$

$$2x+2yy'=0$$

$$y'=-\frac{x}{y}=\frac{3}{4}\Rightarrow y=-\frac{4}{3}x.$$

$$x^2+\left(\frac{16}{9}x^2\right)=100$$

$$\frac{25}{9}x^2=100$$

$$x=\pm 6$$

Points: $(6, -8)$ and $(-6, 8)$

**102.** $y^4 = y^2 - x^2$

$4y^3y' = 2yy' - 2x$

$2x = (2y - 4y^3)y'$

$y' = \dfrac{2x}{2y - 4y^3} = 0 \Rightarrow x = 0$

Horizontal tangents at $(0, 1)$ and $(0, -1)$

**Note:** $y^4 - y^2 + x^2 = 0$

$$y^2 = \frac{1 \pm \sqrt{1 - 4x^2}}{2}$$

If you graph these four equations, you will see that these are horizontal tangents at $(0, \pm 1)$, but not at $(0, 0)$.

**103.** $\dfrac{x^2}{4} + \dfrac{y^2}{9} = 1, \quad (4, 0)$

$\dfrac{2x}{4} + \dfrac{2yy'}{9} = 0$

$y' = \dfrac{-9x}{4y}$

$\dfrac{-9x}{4y} = \dfrac{y - 0}{x - 4}$

$-9x(x - 4) = 4y^2$

But, $9x^2 + 4y^2 = 36 \Rightarrow 4y^2 = 36 - 9x^2$. So,

$-9x^2 + 36x = 4y^2 = 36 - 9x^2 \Rightarrow x = 1.$

Points on ellipse: $\left(1, \pm \dfrac{3}{2}\sqrt{3}\right)$

At $\left(1, \dfrac{3}{2}\sqrt{3}\right)$: $y' = \dfrac{-9x}{4y} = \dfrac{-9}{4\left[(3/2)\sqrt{3}\right]} = -\dfrac{\sqrt{3}}{2}$

At $\left(1, -\dfrac{3}{2}\sqrt{3}\right)$: $y' = \dfrac{\sqrt{3}}{2}$

Tangent lines: $y = -\dfrac{\sqrt{3}}{2}(x - 4) = -\dfrac{\sqrt{3}}{2}x + 2\sqrt{3}$

$y = \dfrac{\sqrt{3}}{2}(x - 4) = \dfrac{\sqrt{3}}{2}x - 2\sqrt{3}$

**104.** $x = y^2$

$1 = 2yy'$

$y' = \dfrac{1}{2y}$, slope of tangent line

Consider the slope of the normal line joining $(x_0, 0)$ and $(x, y) = (y^2, y)$ on the parabola.

$-2y = \dfrac{y - 0}{y^2 - x_0}$

$y^2 - x_0 = -\dfrac{1}{2}$

$y^2 = x_0 - \dfrac{1}{2}$

(a) If $x_0 = \frac{1}{4}$, then $y^2 = \frac{1}{4} - \frac{1}{2} = -\frac{1}{4}$, which is impossible. So, the only normal line is the $x$-axis $(y = 0)$.

(b) If $x_0 = \frac{1}{2}$, then $y^2 = 0 \Rightarrow y = 0$. Same as part (a).

(c) If $x_0 = 1$, then $y^2 = \frac{1}{2} = x$ and there are three normal lines.

The $x$-axis, the line joining $(x_0, 0)$ and $\left(\dfrac{1}{2}, \dfrac{1}{\sqrt{2}}\right)$, and the line joining $(x_0, 0)$ and $\left(\dfrac{1}{2}, -\dfrac{1}{\sqrt{2}}\right)$

If two normals are perpendicular, then their slopes are $-1$ and 1. So,

$-2y = -1 = \dfrac{y - 0}{y^2 - x_0} \Rightarrow y = \dfrac{1}{2}$

and

$\dfrac{1/2}{(1/4) - x_0} = -1 \Rightarrow \dfrac{1}{4} - x_0 = -\dfrac{1}{2} \Rightarrow x_0 = \dfrac{3}{4}.$

The perpendicular normal lines are $y = -x + \dfrac{3}{4}$ and $y = x - \dfrac{3}{4}$.

**105.** (a) $\dfrac{x^2}{32} + \dfrac{y^2}{8} = 1$

$\dfrac{2x}{32} + \dfrac{2yy'}{8} = 0 \Rightarrow y' = \dfrac{-x}{4y}$

At $(4, 2)$: $y' = \dfrac{-4}{4(2)} = -\dfrac{1}{2}$

Slope of normal line is 2.

$y - 2 = 2(x - 4)$

$y = 2x - 6$

(b)

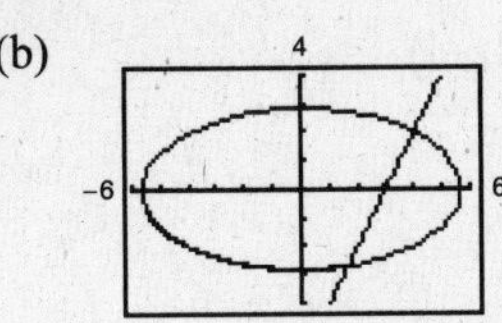


(c) $$\frac{x^2}{32} + \frac{(2x-6)^2}{8} = 1$$

$$x^2 + 4(4x^2 - 24x + 36) = 32$$

$$17x^2 - 96x + 112 = 0$$

$$(17x - 28)(x - 4) = 0 \Rightarrow x = 4, \frac{28}{17}$$

Second point: $\left(\frac{28}{17}, -\frac{46}{17}\right)$

## Section 3.6 Derivatives and Inverse Functions

**1.** $f(x) = x^3 - 1, \quad a = 26$

$f'(x) = 3x^2$

$f$ is monotonic (increasing) on $(-\infty, \infty)$ therefore $f$ has an inverse.

$$f(3) = 26 \Rightarrow f^{-1}(26) = 3$$

$$(f^{-1})'(26) = \frac{1}{f'(f^{-1}(26))} = \frac{1}{f'(3)} = \frac{1}{3(3^2)} = \frac{1}{27}$$

**2.** $f(x) = 5 - 2x^3, \quad a = 7$

$f'(x) = -6x^2$

$f$ is monotonic (decreasing) on $(-\infty, \infty)$ therefore $f$ has an inverse.

$$f(-1) = 7 \Rightarrow f^{-1}(7) = -1$$

$$(f^{-1})'(7) = \frac{1}{f'(f^{-1}(7))} = \frac{1}{f'(-1)} = \frac{1}{-6(-1)^2} = \frac{-1}{6}$$

**3.** $f(x) = x^3 + 2x - 1, \quad a = 2$

$f'(x) = 3x^2 + 2 > 0$

$f$ is monotonic (increasing) on $(-\infty, \infty)$ therefore $f$ has an inverse.

$$f(1) = 2 \Rightarrow f^{-1}(2) = 1$$

$$(f^{-1})'(2) = \frac{1}{f'(f^{-1}(2))} = \frac{1}{f'(1)} = \frac{1}{3(1^2) + 2} = \frac{1}{5}$$

**4.** $f(x) = \frac{1}{27}(x^5 + 2x^3), \quad a = -11$

$f'(x) = \frac{1}{27}(5x^4 + 6x^2)$

$f$ is monotonic (increasing) on $(-\infty, \infty)$ therefore $f$ has an inverse.

$$f(-3) = \frac{1}{27}(-243 - 54) = -11 \Rightarrow f^{-1}(-11) = -3$$

$$(f^{-1})'(-11) = \frac{1}{f'(f^{-1}(-11))} = \frac{1}{f'(-3)}$$

$$= \frac{1}{\frac{1}{27}\left(5(-3)^4 + 6(-3)^2\right)} = \frac{1}{\frac{1}{27}(459)} = \frac{1}{17}$$

**5.** $f(x) = \sin x, \quad a = 1/2, -\frac{\pi}{2} \le x \le \frac{\pi}{2}$

$f'(x) = \cos x > 0$ on $\left(-\frac{\pi}{2}, \frac{\pi}{2}\right)$

$f$ is monotonic (increasing) on $\left[-\frac{\pi}{2}, \frac{\pi}{2}\right]$ therefore $f$ has an inverse.

$$f\left(\frac{\pi}{6}\right) = \sin\frac{\pi}{6} = \frac{1}{2} \Rightarrow f^{-1}\left(\frac{1}{2}\right) = \frac{\pi}{6}$$

$$(f^{-1})'\left(\frac{1}{2}\right) = \frac{1}{f'\left(f^{-1}\left(\frac{1}{2}\right)\right)}$$

$$= \frac{1}{f'\left(\frac{\pi}{6}\right)} = \frac{1}{\cos\left(\frac{\pi}{6}\right)} = \frac{2}{\sqrt{3}} = \frac{2\sqrt{3}}{3}$$

**6.** $f(x) = \cos 2x, \quad a = 1, 0 \le x \le \pi/2$

$f'(x) = -2\sin 2x < 0$ on $(0, \pi/2)$

$f$ is monotonic (decreasing) on $[0, \pi/2]$ therefore $f$ has an inverse.

$$f(0) = 1 \Rightarrow f^{-1}(1) = 0$$

$$(f^{-1})'(1) = \frac{1}{f'(f^{-1}(1))} = \frac{1}{f'(0)} = \frac{1}{-2\sin 0} = \frac{1}{0}$$

So, $(f^{-1})'(1)$ is undefined.

**7.** $f(x) = \dfrac{x+6}{x-2}, \quad x > 0, a = 3$

$$f'(x) = \frac{(x-2)(1) - (x+6)(1)}{(x-2)^2}$$

$$= \frac{-8}{(x-2)^2} < 0 \text{ on } (2, \infty)$$

$f$ is monotonic (decreasing) on $(2, \infty)$ therefore $f$ has an inverse.

$$f(6) = 3 \Rightarrow f^{-1}(3) = 6$$

$$(f^{-1})'(3) = \frac{1}{f'(f^{-1}(3))} = \frac{1}{f'(6)} = \frac{1}{-8/(6-2)^2} = -2$$

**8.** $f(x) = \sqrt{x-4}, \quad a = 2, \quad x \ge 4$

$$f'(x) = \frac{1}{2\sqrt{x-4}} > 0 \text{ on } (4, \infty)$$

$f$ is monotonic (increasing) on $[4, \infty)$ therefore $f$ has an inverse.

$$f(8) = 2 \Rightarrow f^{-1}(2) = 8$$

$$f'(8) = \frac{1}{2\sqrt{8-4}} = \frac{1}{4}$$

$$(f^{-1})'(2) = \frac{1}{f'(f^{-1}(2))} = \frac{1}{f'(8)} = \frac{1}{1/4} = 4$$

**9.** $f(x) = x^3, \quad \left(\dfrac{1}{2}, \dfrac{1}{8}\right)$

$$f'(x) = 3x^2$$

$$f'\left(\frac{1}{2}\right) = \frac{3}{4}$$

$$f^{-1}(x) = \sqrt[3]{x}, \quad \left(\frac{1}{8}, \frac{1}{2}\right)$$

$$(f^{-1})'(x) = \frac{1}{3\sqrt[3]{x}}$$

$$(f^{-1})'\left(\frac{1}{8}\right) = \frac{4}{3}$$

**10.** $f(x) = 3 - 4x, \quad (1, -1)$

$$f'(x) = -4$$

$$f'(1) = -4$$

$$f^{-1}(x) = \frac{3-x}{4}, \quad (-1, 1)$$

$$(f^{-1})'(x) = -\frac{1}{4}$$

$$(f^{-1})'(-1) = -\frac{1}{4}$$

**11.** $f(x) = \sqrt{x-4}, \quad (5, 1)$

$$f'(x) = \frac{1}{2\sqrt{x-4}}$$

$$f'(5) = \frac{1}{2}$$

$$f^{-1}(x) = x^2 + 4, \quad (1, 5)$$

$$(f^{-1})'(x) = 2x$$

$$(f^{-1})'(1) = 2$$

**12.** $f(x) = \dfrac{4}{1+x^2}$

$$f'(x) = \frac{-8x}{(x^2+1)^2}$$

$$f'(1) = -2$$

$$f^{-1}(x) = \sqrt{\frac{4-x}{x}}$$

$$(f^{-1})'(x) = \frac{-2}{x^2\sqrt{(4-x)/x}}$$

$$(f^{-1})'(2) = -\frac{1}{2}$$

**13.** (a) $f(x) = \arccos(x^2)$

$$f'(x) = \frac{-1}{\sqrt{1-x^4}}(2x) = \frac{-2x}{\sqrt{1-x^4}}$$

$$f'(0) = 0$$

$$y - \frac{\pi}{2} = 0(x - 0)$$

$$y = \frac{\pi}{2}, \quad \text{tangent line}$$

(b)

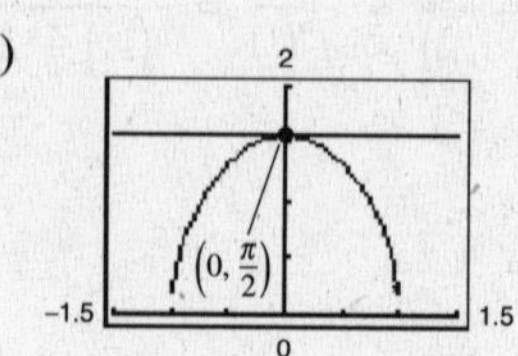

**14.** (a) $f(x) = \arctan x$

$$f'(x) = \frac{1}{1 + x^2}$$

$$f'(-1) = \frac{1}{2}$$

$$y + \frac{\pi}{4} = \frac{1}{2}(x + 1)$$

$$y = \frac{1}{2}x + \frac{1}{2} - \frac{\pi}{4}, \quad \text{tangent line}$$

(b)

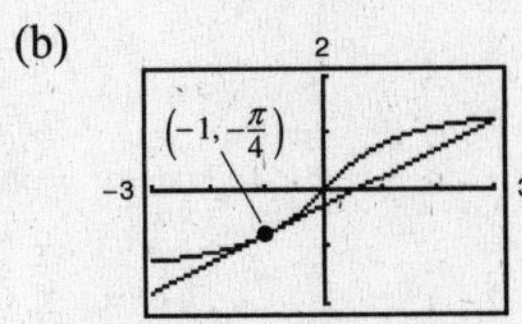


**15.** (a) $f(x) = \arcsin 3x$

$$f'(x) = \frac{1}{\sqrt{1 - (3x)^2}}(3) = \frac{3}{\sqrt{1 - 9x^2}}$$

$$f'\left(\sqrt{2}/6\right) = \frac{3}{\sqrt{1 - 9(1/18)}} = \frac{3}{\sqrt{1/2}} = 3\sqrt{2}$$

$$y - \frac{\pi}{4} = 3\sqrt{2}\left(x - \sqrt{2}/6\right)$$

$$y = 3\sqrt{2}x + \frac{\pi}{4} - 1, \quad \text{Tangent line}$$

(b)

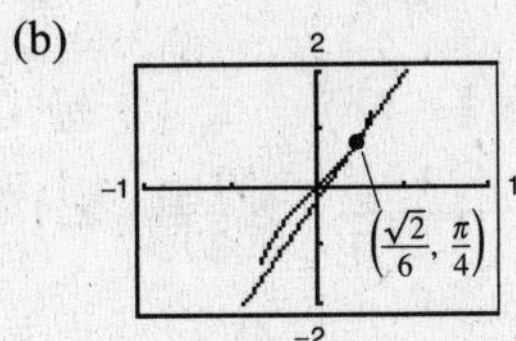


**16.** (a) $f(x) = \operatorname{arcsec} x$

$$f'(x) = \frac{1}{|x|\sqrt{x^2 - 1}}$$

$$f'\left(\sqrt{2}\right) = \frac{1}{\sqrt{2}} = \frac{\sqrt{2}}{2}$$

$$y - \frac{\pi}{4} = \frac{\sqrt{2}}{2}\left(x - \sqrt{2}\right)$$

$$y = \frac{\sqrt{2}}{2}x + \frac{\pi}{4} - 1, \quad \text{tangent line}$$

(b)

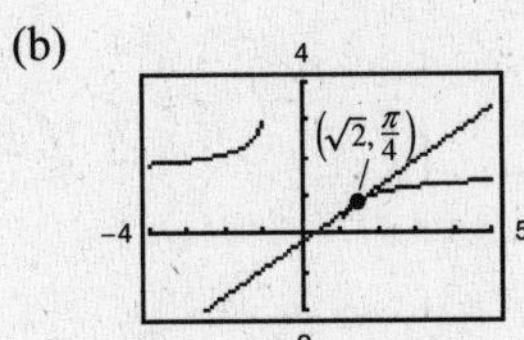


**17.** $x = y^3 - 7y^2 + 2$

$$1 = 3y^2\frac{dy}{dx} - 14y\frac{dy}{dx}$$

$$\frac{dy}{dx} = \frac{1}{3y^2 - 14y}$$

At $(-4, 1)$: $\dfrac{dy}{dx} = \dfrac{1}{3 - 14} = \dfrac{-1}{11}$.

**Alternate Solution:**

Let $f(x) = x^3 - 7x^2 + 2$. Then

$f'(x) = 3x^2 - 14x$ and $f'(1) = -11$. So,

$$\frac{dy}{dx} = \frac{1}{-11} = \frac{-1}{11}.$$

**18.** $x = 2\ln\left(y^2 - 3\right)$

$$1 = 2\frac{1}{y^2 - 3}2y\frac{dy}{dx}$$

$$\frac{dy}{dx} = \frac{y^2 - 3}{4y}$$

At $(0, 2)$: $\dfrac{dy}{dx} = \dfrac{4 - 3}{8} = \dfrac{1}{8}$

**19.** $x \arctan x = e^y$

$$x\frac{1}{1 + x^2} + \arctan x = e^y \cdot \frac{dy}{dx}$$

At $\left(1, \ln\frac{\pi}{4}\right)$: $\dfrac{1}{2} + \dfrac{\pi}{4} = \dfrac{\pi}{4}\dfrac{dy}{dx}$

$$\frac{dy}{dx} = \frac{\pi + 2}{\pi}$$

**20.** $\arctan(xy) = \dfrac{2}{3}\arctan(2x)$

$$\frac{1}{\sqrt{1 - (xy)^2}}\left(x\frac{dy}{dx} + y\right) = \frac{2}{3}\frac{1}{1 + 4x^2}(2)$$

At $\left(\frac{1}{2}, 1\right)$: $\dfrac{1}{\sqrt{3/4}}\left(\dfrac{1}{2}y' + 1\right) = \dfrac{2}{3}$

$$\frac{2}{\sqrt{3}}\left(\frac{1}{2}y' + 1\right) = \frac{2}{3}$$

$$y' = \left(\frac{\sqrt{3}}{3} - 1\right)2 = \frac{2\sqrt{3} - 6}{3}$$

**21.** $f(x) = \arcsin(x + 1)$

$$f'(x) = \frac{1}{\sqrt{1 - (x + 1)^2}} = \frac{1}{\sqrt{-x^2 - 2x}}$$

**22.** $f(t) = \arcsin t^2$

$$f'(t) = \frac{2t}{\sqrt{1 - t^4}}$$

**23.** $g(x) = 3 \arccos \dfrac{x}{2}$

$$g'(x) = \frac{-3(1/2)}{\sqrt{1 - (x^2/4)}} = \frac{-3}{\sqrt{4 - x^2}}$$

**24.** $f(x) = \operatorname{arcsec} 4x$

$$f'(x) = \frac{4}{|4x|\sqrt{16x^2 - 1}} = \frac{1}{|x|\sqrt{16x^2 - 1}}$$

**25.** $f(x) = \arctan(e^x)$

$$f'(x) = \frac{1}{1 + (e^x)^2}e^x = \frac{e^x}{1 + e^{2x}}$$

**26.** $f(x) = \operatorname{arccot} \sqrt{2x} = \operatorname{arccot} (2x)^{1/2}$

$$f'(x) = \frac{-1}{1 + \left(\sqrt{2x}\right)^2}\left[\frac{1}{2}(2x)^{-1/2}(2)\right]$$

$$= \frac{-1}{\sqrt{2x}(1 + 2x)} = \frac{-\sqrt{2}}{2\sqrt{x}(1 + 2x)}$$

**27.** $g(x) = \dfrac{\arcsin 3x}{x}$

$$g'(x) = \frac{x\left(3/\sqrt{1 - 9x^2}\right) - \arcsin 3x}{x^2}$$

$$= \frac{3x - \sqrt{1 - 9x^2} \arcsin 3x}{x^2\sqrt{1 - 9x^2}}$$

**28.** $h(x) = x^2 \arctan(5x)$

$$h'(x) = 2x \arctan(5x) + x^2\frac{1}{1 + (5x)^2}(5)$$

$$= 2x \arctan(5x) + \frac{5x^2}{1 + 25x^2}$$

**29.** $g(x) = \dfrac{\arccos x}{x + 1}$

$$g'(x) = \frac{(x + 1)\dfrac{-1}{\sqrt{1 - x^2}} - \arccos x}{(x + 1)^2}$$

$$= -\frac{x + 1 + \sqrt{1 - x^2} \arccos x}{(x + 1)^2\sqrt{1 - x^2}}$$

**30.** $g(x) = e^{2x} \arcsin x$

$$g'(x) = e^{2x}\frac{1}{\sqrt{1 - x^2}} + 2e^{2x} \arcsin x$$

$$= e^{2x}\left[2 \arcsin x + \frac{1}{\sqrt{1 - x^2}}\right]$$

**31.** $h(x) = \operatorname{arccot} 6x$

$$h'(x) = \frac{-6}{1 + 36x^2}$$

**32.** $f(x) = \operatorname{arccsc} 3x$

$$f'(x) = \frac{-3}{|3x|\sqrt{9x^2 - 1}}$$

$$= \frac{-1}{|x|\sqrt{9x^2 - 1}}$$

**33.** $h(t) = \sin(\arccos t) = \sqrt{1 - t^2}$

$$h'(t) = \frac{1}{2}(1 - t^2)^{-1/2}(-2t)$$

$$= \frac{-t}{\sqrt{1 - t^2}}$$

**34.** $f(x) = \arcsin x + \arccos x = \dfrac{\pi}{2}$

$$f'(x) = 0$$

**35.** $y = 2x \arccos x - 2\sqrt{1 - x^2}$

$$y' = 2 \arccos x - 2x\frac{1}{\sqrt{1 - x^2}} - 2\left(\frac{1}{2}\right)(1 - x^2)^{-1/2}(-2x)$$

$$= 2 \arccos x - \frac{2x}{\sqrt{1 - x^2}} + \frac{2x}{\sqrt{1 - x^2}} = 2 \arccos x$$

**36.** $y = \ln(t^2 + 4) - \dfrac{1}{2} \arctan \dfrac{t}{2}$

$$y' = \frac{2t}{t^2 + 4} - \frac{1}{2} \cdot \frac{1}{1 + (t/2)^2}\left(\frac{1}{2}\right)$$

$$= \frac{2t}{t^2 + 4} - \frac{1}{t^2 + 4} = \frac{2t - 1}{t^2 + 4}$$

**37.** $y = \frac{1}{2}\left(\frac{1}{2}\ln\frac{x+1}{x-1} + \arctan x\right) = \frac{1}{4}\left[\ln(x+1) - \ln(x-1)\right] + \frac{1}{2}\arctan x$

$$\frac{dy}{dx} = \frac{1}{4}\left(\frac{1}{x+1} - \frac{1}{x-1}\right) + \frac{1/2}{1+x^2} = \frac{1}{1-x^4}$$

**38.** $y = \frac{1}{2}\left[x\sqrt{4-x^2} + 4\arcsin\left(\frac{x}{2}\right)\right]$

$$y' = \frac{1}{2}\left[x\frac{1}{2}\left(4-x^2\right)^{-1/2}(-2x) + \sqrt{4-x^2} + 2\frac{1}{\sqrt{1-(x/2)^2}}\right] = \frac{1}{2}\left[\frac{-x^2}{\sqrt{4-x^2}} + \sqrt{4-x^2} + \frac{4}{\sqrt{4-x^2}}\right] = \sqrt{4-x^2}$$

**39.** $g(t) = \tan(\arcsin t) = \frac{t}{\sqrt{1-t^2}}$

$$g'(t) = \frac{\sqrt{1-t^2} - t\left(-t/\sqrt{1-t^2}\right)}{1-t^2}$$

$$= \frac{1}{\left(1-t^2\right)^{3/2}}$$

**40.** $f(x) = \operatorname{arcsec} x + \operatorname{arccsc} x = \frac{\pi}{2}$

$$f'(x) = 0$$

**41.** $y = x\arcsin x + \sqrt{1-x^2}$

$$\frac{dy}{dx} = x\left(\frac{1}{\sqrt{1-x^2}}\right) + \arcsin x - \frac{x}{\sqrt{1-x^2}} = \arcsin x$$

**42.** $y = x\arctan 2x - \frac{1}{4}\ln\left(1+4x^2\right)$

$$\frac{dy}{dx} = \frac{2x}{1+4x^2} + \arctan(2x) - \frac{1}{4}\left(\frac{8x}{1+4x^2}\right) = \arctan(2x)$$

**43.** $y = 8\arcsin\frac{x}{4} - \frac{x\sqrt{16-x^2}}{2}$

$$y' = 2\frac{1}{\sqrt{1-(x/4)^2}} - \frac{\sqrt{16-x^2}}{2} - \frac{x}{4}\left(16-x^2\right)^{-1/2}(-2x)$$

$$= \frac{8}{\sqrt{16-x^2}} - \frac{\sqrt{16-x^2}}{2} + \frac{x^2}{2\sqrt{16-x^2}} = \frac{16 - \left(16-x^2\right) + x^2}{2\sqrt{16-x^2}} = \frac{x^2}{\sqrt{16-x^2}}$$

**44.** $y = 25\arcsin\frac{x}{5} - x\sqrt{25-x^2}$

$$y' = 5\frac{1}{\sqrt{1-(x/2)^2}} - \sqrt{25-x^2} - x\frac{1}{2}\left(25-x^2\right)^{-1/2}(-2x)$$

$$= \frac{25}{\sqrt{25-x^2}} - \frac{\left(25-x^2\right)}{\sqrt{25-x^2}} + \frac{x^2}{\sqrt{25-x^2}} = \frac{2x^2}{\sqrt{25-x^2}}$$

**45.** $y = \arctan x + \dfrac{x}{1+x^2}$

$$y' = \frac{1}{1+x^2} + \frac{(1+x^2) - x(2x)}{(1+x^2)^2}$$

$$= \frac{(1+x^2) + (1-x^2)}{(1+x^2)^2}$$

$$= \frac{2}{(1+x^2)^2}$$

**46.** $y = \arctan \dfrac{x}{2} - \dfrac{1}{2(x^2+4)}$

$$y' = \frac{1}{2}\frac{1}{1+(x/2)^2} + \frac{1}{2}(x^2+4)^{-2}(2x)$$

$$= \frac{2}{x^2+4} + \frac{x}{(x^2+4)^2}$$

$$= \frac{2x^2+8+x}{(x^2+4)^2}$$

**47.** $y = 2 \arcsin x, \quad \left(\dfrac{1}{2}, \dfrac{\pi}{3}\right)$

$$y' = \frac{2}{\sqrt{1-x^2}}$$

At $\left(\dfrac{1}{2}, \dfrac{\pi}{3}\right)$, $y' = \dfrac{2}{\sqrt{1-(1/4)}} = \dfrac{4}{\sqrt{3}}$.

Tangent line: $y - \dfrac{\pi}{3} = \dfrac{4}{\sqrt{3}}\left(x - \dfrac{1}{2}\right)$

$$y = \frac{4}{\sqrt{3}}x + \frac{\pi}{3} - \frac{2}{\sqrt{3}}$$

$$y = \frac{4\sqrt{3}}{3}x + \frac{\pi}{3} - \frac{2\sqrt{3}}{3}$$

**48.** $y = \dfrac{1}{2} \arccos x, \quad \left(-\dfrac{\sqrt{2}}{2}, \dfrac{3\pi}{8}\right)$

$$y' = \frac{-1}{2\sqrt{1-x^2}}$$

At $\left(-\dfrac{\sqrt{2}}{2}, \dfrac{3\pi}{8}\right)$, $y' = \dfrac{-1}{2\sqrt{1/2}} = -\dfrac{\sqrt{2}}{2}$.

Tangent line: $y - \dfrac{3\pi}{8} = -\dfrac{\sqrt{2}}{2}\left(x + \dfrac{\sqrt{2}}{2}\right)$

$$y = -\frac{\sqrt{2}}{2}x + \frac{3\pi}{8} - \frac{1}{2}$$

**49.** $y = \arcsin\left(\dfrac{x}{2}\right), \quad \left(2, \dfrac{\pi}{4}\right)$

$$y' = \frac{1}{1+(x^2/4)}\left(\frac{1}{2}\right) = \frac{2}{4+x^2}$$

At $\left(2, \dfrac{\pi}{4}\right)$, $y' = \dfrac{2}{4+4} = \dfrac{1}{4}$.

Tangent line: $y - \dfrac{\pi}{4} = \dfrac{1}{4}(x-2)$

$$y = \frac{1}{4}x + \frac{\pi}{4} - \frac{1}{2}$$

**50.** $y = \operatorname{arcsec}(4x), \quad \left(\dfrac{\sqrt{2}}{4}, \dfrac{\pi}{4}\right)$

$$y' = \frac{4}{|4x|\sqrt{16x^2-1}} = \frac{1}{x\sqrt{16x^2-1}} \text{ for } x > 0$$

At $\left(\dfrac{\sqrt{2}}{4}, \dfrac{\pi}{4}\right)$, $y' = \dfrac{1}{\left(\sqrt{2}/4\right)\sqrt{2-1}} = 2\sqrt{2}$.

Tangent line: $y - \dfrac{\pi}{4} = 2\sqrt{2}\left(x - \dfrac{\sqrt{2}}{4}\right)$

$$y = 2\sqrt{2}x + \frac{\pi}{4} - 1$$

**51.** $y = 4x \arccos(x-1), \quad (1, 2\pi)$

$$y' = 4x\frac{-1}{\sqrt{1-(x-1)^2}} + 4\arccos(x-1)$$

At $(1, 2\pi)$, $y' = -4 + 2\pi$.

Tangent line: $y - 2\pi = (2\pi - 4)(x-1)$

$$y = (2\pi - 4)x + 4$$

**52.** $y = 3x \arcsin x, \quad \left(\dfrac{1}{2}, \dfrac{\pi}{4}\right)$

$$y' = 3x\frac{1}{\sqrt{1-x^2}} + 3\arcsin x$$

At $\left(\dfrac{1}{2}, \dfrac{\pi}{4}\right)$, $y' = \dfrac{3}{2}\dfrac{1}{\sqrt{3/4}} + 3\left(\dfrac{\pi}{6}\right) = \sqrt{3} + \dfrac{\pi}{2}$.

Tangent line: $y - \dfrac{\pi}{4} = \left(\sqrt{3} + \dfrac{\pi}{2}\right)\left(x - \dfrac{1}{2}\right)$

$$y = \left(\sqrt{3} + \frac{\pi}{2}\right)x - \frac{\sqrt{3}}{2}$$

**53.** $f(x) = \arccos x$

$$f'(x) = \frac{-1}{\sqrt{1-x^2}} = -2 \text{ when } x = \pm\frac{\sqrt{3}}{2}.$$

When $x = \sqrt{3}/2$, $f\left(\sqrt{3}/2\right) = \pi/6$. When $x = -\sqrt{3}/2$, $f\left(-\sqrt{3}/2\right) = 5\pi/6$.

Tangent lines: $y - \frac{\pi}{6} = -2\left(x - \frac{\sqrt{3}}{2}\right) \Rightarrow y = -2x + \left(\frac{\pi}{6} + \sqrt{3}\right)$

$$y - \frac{5\pi}{6} = -2\left(x + \frac{\sqrt{3}}{2}\right) \Rightarrow y = -2x + \left(\frac{5\pi}{6} - \sqrt{3}\right)$$

**54.** $g(x) = \arctan x$, $g'(x) = \frac{1}{1+x^2}$, $g'(1) = \frac{1}{2}$

Tangent line: $y - \frac{\pi}{4} = \frac{1}{2}(x - 1)$

$$y = \frac{1}{2}x + \frac{\pi}{4} - \frac{1}{2}$$

**55.** $f(x) = \arcsin x$, $a = \frac{1}{2}$

$$f'(x) = \frac{1}{\sqrt{1-x^2}}$$

$$f''(x) = \frac{x}{\left(1-x^2\right)^{3/2}}$$

$$P_1(x) = f\left(\frac{1}{2}\right) + f'\left(\frac{1}{2}\right)\left(x - \frac{1}{2}\right) = \frac{\pi}{6} + \frac{2\sqrt{3}}{3}\left(x - \frac{1}{2}\right)$$

$$P_2(x) = f\left(\frac{1}{2}\right) + f'\left(\frac{1}{2}\right)\left(x - \frac{1}{2}\right) + \frac{1}{2}f''\left(\frac{1}{2}\right)\left(x - \frac{1}{2}\right)^2 = \frac{\pi}{6} + \frac{2\sqrt{3}}{3}\left(x - \frac{1}{2}\right) + \frac{2\sqrt{3}}{9}\left(x - \frac{1}{2}\right)^2$$

**56.** $f(x) = \arcsin x$, $a = 1$

$$f'(x) = \frac{1}{1+x^2}$$

$$f''(x) = \frac{-2x}{\left(1+x^2\right)^2}$$

$$P_1(x) = f(1) + f'(1)(x-1) = \frac{\pi}{4} + \frac{1}{2}(x-1)$$

$$P_2(x) = f(1) + f'(1)(x-1) + \frac{1}{2}f''(1)(x-1)^2 = \frac{\pi}{4} + \frac{1}{2}(x-1) - \frac{1}{4}(x-1)^2$$

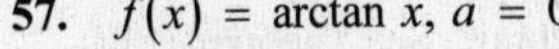

**57.** $f(x) = \arctan x$, $a = 0$

$f(0) = 0$

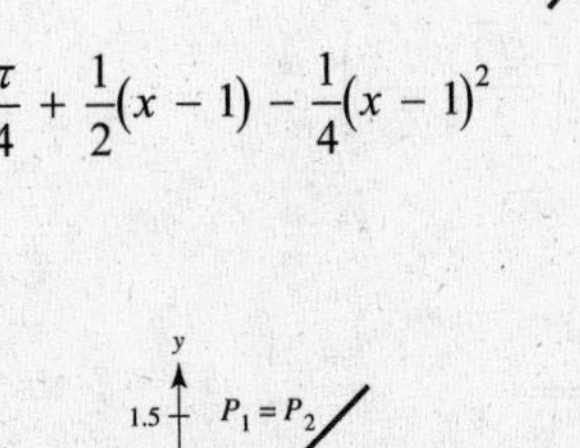

$f'(x) = \frac{1}{1+x^2}$, $\quad f'(0) = 1$

$f''(x) = \frac{-2x}{\left(1+x^2\right)^2}$, $\quad f''(0) = 0$

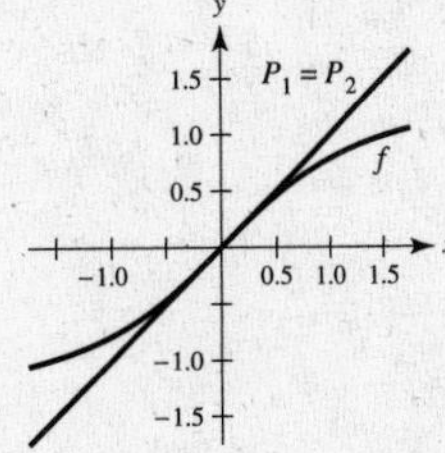


$P_1(x) = f(0) + f'(0)x = x$

$P_2(x) = f(0) + f'(0)x + \frac{1}{2}f''(0)x^2 = x$

**58.** $f(x) = \arccos x,\ a = 0$

$f(0) = \dfrac{\pi}{2}$

$f'(x) = \dfrac{-1}{\sqrt{1 - x^2}}, \quad f'(0) = -1$

$f''(x) = \dfrac{-x}{\left(1 - x^2\right)^{3/2}}, \quad f''(0) = 0$

$P_1(x) = f(0) + f'(0)x = \dfrac{\pi}{2} - x$

$P_2(x) = f(0) + f'(0)x + \dfrac{1}{2}f''(0)x^2 = \dfrac{\pi}{2} - x$

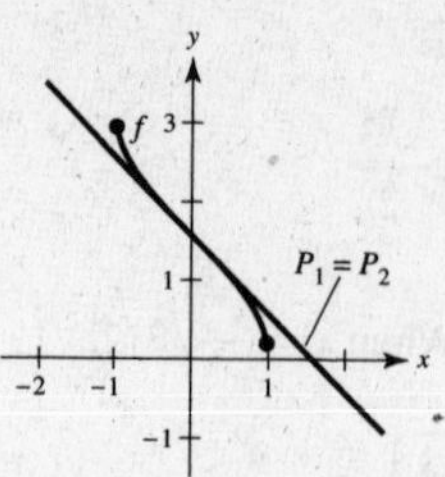


**59.** $x^2 + x\arctan y = y - 1, \quad \left(-\dfrac{\pi}{4}, 1\right)$

$2x + \arctan y + \dfrac{x}{1 + y^2}y' = y'$

$\left(1 - \dfrac{x}{1 + y^2}\right)y' = 2x + \arctan y$

$y' = \dfrac{2x + \arctan y}{1 - \dfrac{x}{1 + y^2}}$

At $\left(-\dfrac{\pi}{4}, 1\right)$: $y' = \dfrac{-\dfrac{\pi}{2} + \dfrac{\pi}{4}}{1 - \dfrac{-\pi/4}{2}} = \dfrac{-\dfrac{\pi}{2}}{2 + \dfrac{\pi}{4}} = \dfrac{-2\pi}{8 + \pi}$

Tangent line: $y - 1 = \dfrac{-2\pi}{8 + \pi}\left(x + \dfrac{\pi}{4}\right)$

$y = \dfrac{-2\pi}{8 + \pi}x + 1 - \dfrac{\pi^2}{16 + 2\pi}$

**60.** $\arctan(xy) = \arcsin(x + y), \quad (0, 0)$

$\dfrac{1}{1 + (xy)^2}[y + xy'] = \dfrac{1}{\sqrt{1 - (x + y)^2}}[1 + y']$

At $(0, 0)$: $0 = 1 + y' \Rightarrow y' = -1$

Tangent line: $y = -x$

**61.** $\arcsin x + \arcsin y = \dfrac{\pi}{2}, \quad \left(\dfrac{\sqrt{2}}{2}, \dfrac{\sqrt{2}}{2}\right)$

$\dfrac{1}{\sqrt{1 - x^2}} + \dfrac{1}{\sqrt{1 - y^2}}y' = 0$

$\dfrac{1}{\sqrt{1 - y^2}}y' = \dfrac{-1}{\sqrt{1 - x^2}}$

At $\left(\dfrac{\sqrt{2}}{2}, \dfrac{\sqrt{2}}{2}\right)$: $y' = -1$

Tangent line: $y - \dfrac{\sqrt{2}}{2} = -1\left(x - \dfrac{\sqrt{2}}{2}\right)$

$y = -x + \sqrt{2}$

**62.** $\arctan(x + y) = y^2 + \dfrac{\pi}{4}, \quad (1, 0)$

$\dfrac{1}{1 + (x + y)^2}[1 + y'] = 2yy'$

At $(1, 0)$: $\dfrac{1}{2}[1 + y'] = 0 \Rightarrow y' = -1$

Tangent line: $y - 0 = -1(x - 1)$

$y = -x + 1$

**63.** $f$ is not one-to-one because many different $x$-values yield the same $y$-value.

Example: $f(0) = f(\pi) = 0$

Not continuous at $\dfrac{(2n - 1)\pi}{2}$, where $n$ is an integer.

**64.** $f$ is not one-to-one because different $x$-values yield the same $y$-value.

Example: $f(3) = f\left(-\dfrac{4}{3}\right) = \dfrac{3}{5}$

Not continuous at $\pm 2$.

**65.** Theorem 3.17: Let $f$ be a function that is differentiable on an interval $I$. If $f$ has an inverse function $g$, then $g$ is differentiable at any $x$ for which $f'(g(x)) \neq 0$.

Moreover, $g'(x) = \dfrac{1}{f'(g(x))}, \ f'(g(x)) \neq 0.$

**66.** The derivatives are algebraic. See Theorem 3.18.

**67.** (a) $\cot\theta = \dfrac{x}{5}$

$$\theta = \operatorname{arccot}\left(\frac{x}{5}\right)$$

(b) $$\frac{d\theta}{dt} = \frac{-1/5}{1 + (x/5)^2}\frac{dx}{dt} = \frac{-5}{x^2 + 25}\frac{dx}{dt}$$

If $\dfrac{dx}{dt} = -400$ and $x = 10$, $\dfrac{d\theta}{dt} = 16$ rad/h.

If $\dfrac{dx}{dt} = -400$ and $x = 3$, $\dfrac{d\theta}{dt} \approx 58.824$ rad/h.

**68.** (a) $\cot\theta = \dfrac{x}{3}$

$$\theta = \operatorname{arccot}\left(\frac{x}{3}\right)$$

(b) $$\frac{d\theta}{dt} = \frac{-3}{x^2 + 9}\frac{dx}{dt}$$

If $x = 10$, $\dfrac{d\theta}{dt} \approx 11.001$ rad/h.

If $x = 3$, $\dfrac{d\theta}{dt} \approx 66.667$ rad/h.

A lower altitude results in a greater rate of change of $\theta$.

**69.** (a) $$h(t) = -16t^2 + 256$$

$-16t^2 + 256 = 0$ when $t = 4$ sec

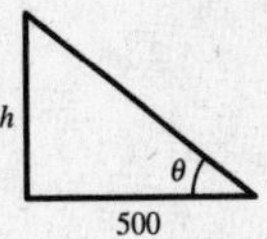


(b) $\tan\theta = \dfrac{h}{500} = \dfrac{-16t^2 + 256}{500}$

$$\theta = \arctan\left[\frac{16}{500}\left(-t^2 + 16\right)\right]$$

$$\frac{d\theta}{dt} = \frac{-8t/125}{1 + \left[(4/125)\left(-t^2 + 16\right)\right]^2}$$

$$= \frac{-1000t}{15{,}625 + 16\left(16 - t^2\right)^2}$$

When $t = 1$, $d\theta/dt \approx -0.0520$ rad/sec.

When $t = 2$, $d\theta/dt \approx -0.1116$ rad/sec.

**70.** $\cos\theta = \dfrac{800}{s}$

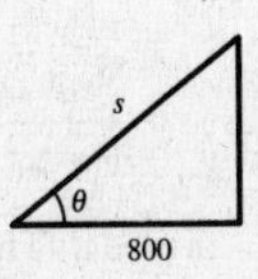


$$\theta = \arccos\left(\frac{800}{s}\right)$$

$$\frac{d\theta}{dt} = \frac{d\theta}{ds}\cdot\frac{ds}{dt} = \frac{-1}{\sqrt{1 - (800/s)^2}}\left(\frac{-800}{s^2}\right)\frac{ds}{dt} = \frac{800}{s\sqrt{s^2 - 800^2}}\frac{ds}{dt}, \quad s > 800$$

**71.** $\tan\theta = \dfrac{h}{300}$

$$\frac{dh}{dt} = 5 \text{ ft/sec}$$

$$\theta = \arctan\left(\frac{h}{300}\right)$$

$$\frac{d\theta}{dt} = \frac{1/300}{1 + \left(h^2/300^2\right)}\left(\frac{dh}{dt}\right) = \frac{300}{300^2 + h^2}(5)$$

$$= \frac{1500}{300^2 + h^2} = \frac{3}{200} \text{ rad/sec when } h = 100$$

**72.** $\dfrac{d\theta}{dt} = 30(2\pi) = 60\pi$ rad/min

$$\tan\theta = \frac{x}{50}$$

$$\theta = \arctan\left(\frac{x}{50}\right)$$

$$\frac{d\theta}{dt} = \frac{d\theta}{dx}\frac{dx}{dt} = \frac{50}{x^2 + 2500}\frac{dx}{dt}$$

$$\frac{dx}{dt} = \frac{x^2 + 2500}{50}\frac{d\theta}{dt}$$

When $\theta = 45° = \dfrac{\pi}{4}$, $x = 50$:

$$\frac{dx}{dt} = \frac{(50)^2 + 2500}{50}(60\pi) = 6000\pi \text{ ft/min}$$

**73.** (a) Let $y = \arccos u$. Then

$$\cos y = u$$

$$-\sin y\frac{dy}{dx} = u'$$

$$\frac{dy}{dx} = -\frac{u'}{\sin y} = -\frac{u'}{\sqrt{1 - u^2}}.$$

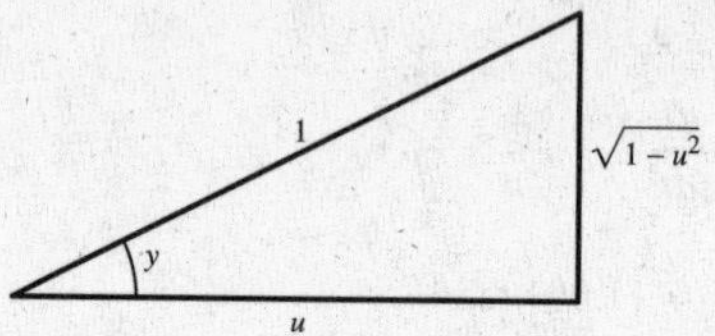


(b) Let $y = \arctan u$. Then

$$\tan y = u$$

$$\sec^2 y\frac{dy}{dx} = u'$$

$$\frac{dy}{dx} = \frac{u'}{\sec^2 y} = \frac{u'}{1 - u^2}.$$

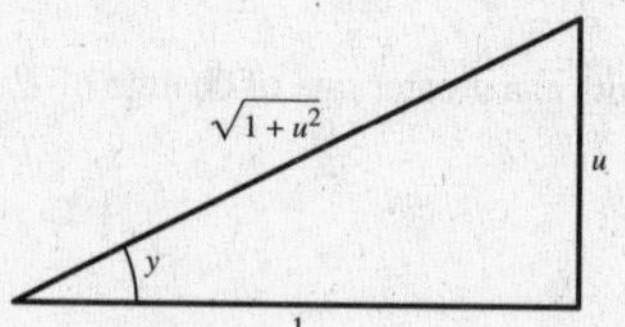


(c) Let $y = \operatorname{arcsec} u$. Then

$$\sec y = u$$

$$\sec y\tan y\frac{dy}{dx} = u'$$

$$\frac{dy}{dx} = \frac{u'}{\sec y\tan y} = \frac{u'}{|u|\sqrt{u^2 - 1}}.$$

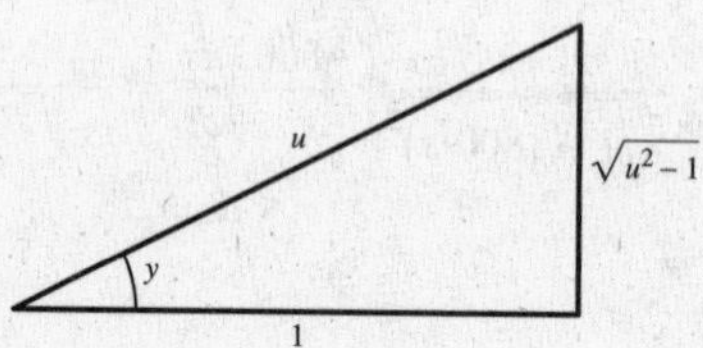


**Note:** The absolute value sign in the formula for the derivative of arcsec $u$ is necessary because the inverse secant function has a positive slope at every value in its domain.

(d) Let $y = \operatorname{arccot} u$. Then

$$\cot y = u$$

$$-\csc^2 y\frac{dy}{dx} = u'$$

$$\frac{dy}{dx} = \frac{u'}{-\csc^2 y} = -\frac{u'}{1 + u^2}.$$

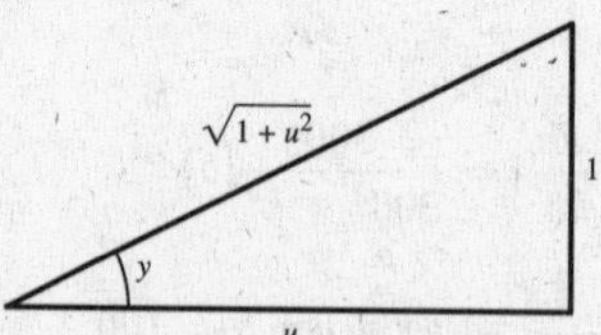


(e) Let $y = \operatorname{arccsc} u$. Then

$$\csc y = u$$

$$-\csc y\cot y\frac{dy}{dx} = u'$$

$$\frac{dy}{dx} = \frac{u'}{-\csc y\cot y} = -\frac{u'}{|u|\sqrt{u^2 - 1}}.$$

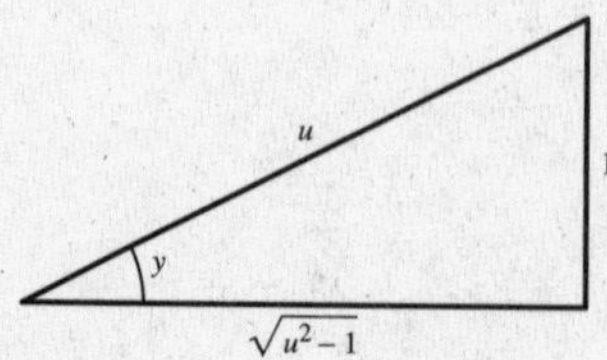


**Note:** The absolute value sign in the formula for the derivative of arccsc $u$ is necessary because the inverse cosecant function has a negative slope at every value in its domain.

**74.** $f(x) = kx + \sin x$

$f'(x) = k + \cos x \geq 0$ for $k \geq 1$

$f'(x) = k + \cos x \leq 0$ for $k \leq -1$

Therefore, $f(x) = kx + \sin x$ is strictly monotonic and has an inverse for $k \leq -1$ or $k \geq 1$.

**75.** True

$\frac{d}{dx}[\arctan x] = \frac{1}{1 + x^2} > 0$ for all $x$.

**76.** True

$\frac{d}{dx}[\arctan(\tan x)] = \frac{\sec^2 x}{1 + \tan^2 x} = \frac{\sec^2 x}{\sec^2 x} = 1$

**77.** Let $\theta = \arctan\left(\frac{x}{\sqrt{1 - x^2}}\right), \quad -1 < x < 1$

$\tan \theta = \frac{x}{\sqrt{1 - x^2}}$

$\sin \theta = \frac{x}{1} = x$

$\arcsin x = \theta.$

So, $\arcsin x = \arctan\left(\frac{x}{\sqrt{1 - x^2}}\right)$ for $-1 < x < 1$.

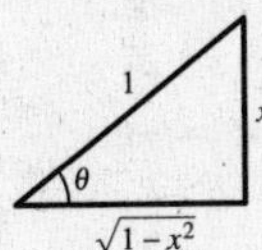


**78.** Let $\theta = \arctan \frac{x}{\sqrt{1 - x^2}}, \quad |x| < 1.$

Then $\tan \theta = \frac{x}{\sqrt{1 - x^2}}$, as indicated in the figure.

So, $\cos\left(\frac{\pi}{2} - \theta\right) = x$ and $\frac{\pi}{2} - \theta = \arccos x$ which gives $\arccos x = \frac{\pi}{2} - \arctan \frac{x}{\sqrt{1 - x^2}}$.

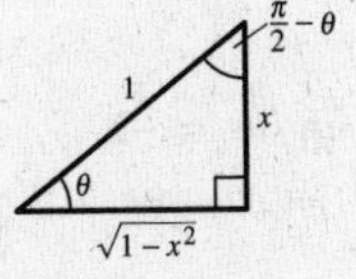


**79.** $f(x) = \sec x, \quad 0 \leq x < \frac{\pi}{2}, \pi \leq x < \frac{3\pi}{2}$

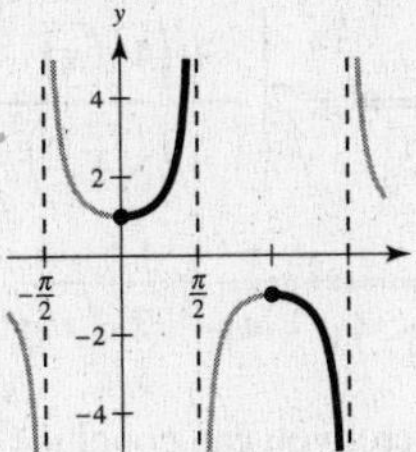


(a) $y = \operatorname{arcsec} x, \quad x \leq -1$ or $x \geq 1$

$0 \leq y < \frac{\pi}{2}$ or $\pi \leq y < \frac{3\pi}{2}$

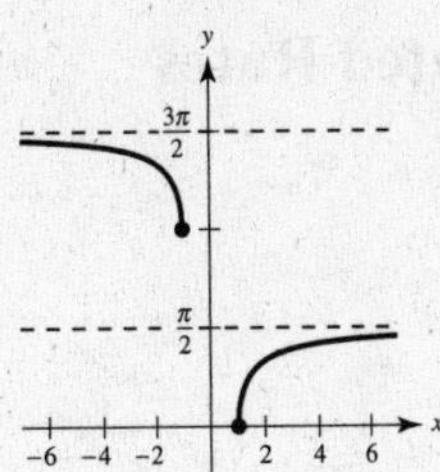


(b)
$$\begin{aligned} y &= \operatorname{arcsec} x \\ x &= \sec y \\ 1 &= \sec y \tan y \cdot y' \\ y' &= \frac{1}{\sec y \tan y} \\ &= \frac{1}{x\sqrt{x^2 - 1}} \end{aligned}$$

$$\tan^2 y + 1 = \sec^2 y$$

$$\tan y = \pm\sqrt{\sec^2 y - 1}$$

On $0 \leq y < \pi/2$ and $\pi \leq y < 3\pi/2$, $\tan y \geq 0$.

**80.** $y_1 = \sin(\arcsin x) = x$

Domain: $[-1, 1]$

Range: $[-1, 1]$

$y_2 = \arcsin(\sin x)$

Domain: $(-\infty, \infty)$

Range: $\left[-\frac{\pi}{2}, \frac{\pi}{2}\right]$

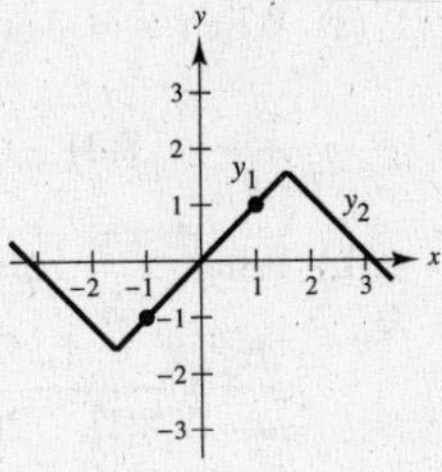

**81.** $f(x) = \arcsin\left(\frac{x-2}{2}\right) - 2\arcsin\frac{\sqrt{x}}{2}, \quad 0 \le x \le 4$

$$f'(x) = \frac{1/2}{\sqrt{1-[(x-2)/2]^2}} - 2\left[\frac{1/(4\sqrt{x})}{\sqrt{1-(\sqrt{x}/2)^2}}\right]$$

$$= \frac{1}{2\sqrt{1-(1/4)(x^2-4x+4)}} - \frac{1}{2\sqrt{x}\sqrt{1-(x/4)}} = \frac{1}{2\sqrt{x-(x^2/4)}} - \frac{1}{2\sqrt{x-(x^2/4)}} = 0$$

Because the derivative is zero, you can conclude that the function is constant. (By letting $x = 0$ in $f(x)$, you can see that the constant is $-\pi/2$.)

**82.** Because the slope of $f$ at $(1, 3)$ is $m = 2$, the slope of $f^{-1}$ at $(3, 1)$ is $1/2$.

## Section 3.7 Related Rates

**1.** $y = \sqrt{x}$

$$\frac{dy}{dt} = \left(\frac{1}{2\sqrt{x}}\right)\frac{dx}{dt}$$

$$\frac{dx}{dt} = 2\sqrt{x}\,\frac{dy}{dt}$$

(a) When $x = 4$ and $dx/dt = 3$,

$$\frac{dy}{dt} = \frac{1}{2\sqrt{4}}(3) = \frac{3}{4}.$$

(b) When $x = 25$ and $dy/dt = 2$,

$$\frac{dx}{dt} = 2\sqrt{25}(2) = 20.$$

**2.** $y = 4(x^2 - 5x)$

$$\frac{dy}{dt} = (8x - 20)\frac{dx}{dt}$$

$$\frac{dx}{dt} = \frac{1}{8x-20}\frac{dy}{dt}$$

(a) When $x = 3$ and $dx/dt = 2$,

$$\frac{dy}{dt} = [8(3) - 20](2) = 8.$$

(b) When $x = 1$ and $dy/dt = 5$,

$$\frac{dx}{dt} = \frac{1}{8(1)-20}(5) = -\frac{5}{12}.$$

**3.** $xy = 4$

$$x\frac{dy}{dt} + y\frac{dx}{dt} = 0$$

$$\frac{dy}{dt} = \left(-\frac{y}{x}\right)\frac{dx}{dt}$$

$$\frac{dx}{dt} = \left(-\frac{x}{y}\right)\frac{dy}{dt}$$

(a) When $x = 8$, $y = 1/2$, and $dx/dt = 10$,

$$\frac{dy}{dt} = -\frac{1/2}{8}(10) = -\frac{5}{8}.$$

(b) When $x = 1$, $y = 4$, and $dy/dt = -6$,

$$\frac{dx}{dt} = -\frac{1}{4}(-6) = \frac{3}{2}.$$

**4.** $x^2 + y^2 = 25$

$$2x\frac{dx}{dt} + 2y\frac{dy}{dt} = 0$$

$$\frac{dy}{dt} = \left(-\frac{x}{y}\right)\frac{dx}{dt}$$

$$\frac{dx}{dt} = \left(-\frac{y}{x}\right)\frac{dy}{dt}$$

(a) When $x = 3$, $y = 4$, and $dx/dt = 8$,

$$\frac{dy}{dt} = -\frac{3}{4}(8) = -6.$$

(b) When $x = 4$, $y = 3$, and $dy/dt = -2$,

$$\frac{dx}{dt} = -\frac{3}{4}(-2) = \frac{3}{2}.$$

**5.** $y = 2x^2 + 1$

$$\frac{dx}{dt} = 2$$

$$\frac{dy}{dt} = 4x\frac{dx}{dt}$$

(a) When $x = -1$,

$$\frac{dy}{dt} = 4(-1)(2) = -8 \text{ cm/sec.}$$

(b) When $x = 0$,

$$\frac{dy}{dt} = 4(0)(2) = 0 \text{ cm/sec.}$$

(c) When $x = 1$,

$$\frac{dy}{dt} = 4(1)(2) = 8 \text{ cm/sec.}$$

**6.** $y = \dfrac{1}{1 + x^2}$

$$\frac{dx}{dt} = 2$$

$$\frac{dy}{dt} = \left[\frac{-2x}{\left(1 + x^2\right)^2}\right]\frac{dx}{dt}$$

(a) When $x = -2$,

$$\frac{dy}{dt} = \frac{-2(-2)(2)}{25} = \frac{8}{25} \text{ cm/sec.}$$

(b) When $x = 0$,

$$\frac{dy}{dt} = 0 \text{ cm/sec.}$$

(c) When $x = 2$,

$$\frac{dy}{dt} = \frac{-2(2)(2)}{25} = \frac{-8}{25} \text{ cm/sec.}$$

**7.** $y = \tan x$

$$\frac{dx}{dt} = 2$$

$$\frac{dy}{dt} = \sec^2 x\frac{dx}{dt}$$

(a) When $x = -\pi/3$,

$$\frac{dy}{dt} = (2)^2(2) = 8 \text{ cm/sec.}$$

(b) When $x = -\pi/4$,

$$\frac{dy}{dt} = \left(\sqrt{2}\right)^2(2) = 4 \text{ cm/sec.}$$

(c) When $x = 0$,

$$\frac{dy}{dt} = (1)^2(2) = 2 \text{ cm/sec.}$$

**8.** $y = \cos x$

$$\frac{dx}{dt} = 2$$

$$\frac{dy}{dt} = -\sin x\frac{dx}{dt}$$

(a) When $x = \pi/6$,

$$\frac{dy}{dt} = \left(-\sin\frac{\pi}{6}\right)(2) = -1 \text{ cm/sec.}$$

(b) When $x = \pi/4$,

$$\frac{dy}{dt} = \left(-\sin\frac{\pi}{4}\right)(2) = -\sqrt{2} \text{ cm/sec.}$$

(c) When $x = \pi/3$,

$$\frac{dy}{dt} = \left(-\sin\frac{\pi}{3}\right)(2) = -\sqrt{3} \text{ cm/sec.}$$

**9.** Yes, $y$ changes at a constant rate.

$$\frac{dy}{dt} = a \cdot \frac{dx}{dt}$$

No, the rate $dy/dt$ is a multiple of $dx/dt$.

**10.** Answers will vary. See page 183.

**11.** $D = \sqrt{x^2 + y^2} = \sqrt{x^2 + \left(x^2 + 1\right)^2} = \sqrt{x^4 + 3x^2 + 1}$

$$\frac{dx}{dt} = 2$$

$$\frac{dD}{dt} = \frac{1}{2}\left(x^4 + 3x^2 + 1\right)^{-1/2}\left(4x^3 + 6x\right)\frac{dx}{dt}$$

$$= \frac{2x^3 + 3x}{\sqrt{x^4 + 3x^2 + 1}}\frac{dx}{dt}$$

$$= \frac{4x^3 + 6x}{\sqrt{x^4 + 3x^2 + 1}}$$

**12.** $D = \sqrt{x^2 + y^2} = \sqrt{x^2 + \sin^2 x}$

$$\frac{dx}{dt} = 2$$

$$\frac{dD}{dt} = \frac{1}{2}\left(x^2 + \sin^2 x\right)^{-1/2}(2x + 2\sin x\cos x)\frac{dx}{dt}$$

$$= \frac{x + \sin x\cos x}{\sqrt{x^2 + \sin^2 x}}\frac{dx}{dt}$$

$$= \frac{2x + 2\sin x\cos x}{\sqrt{x^2 + \sin^2 x}}$$

**13.** $A = \pi r^2$

$\dfrac{dr}{dt} = 4$

$\dfrac{dA}{dt} = 2\pi r \dfrac{dr}{dt}$

(a) When $r = 8, \dfrac{dA}{dt} = 2\pi(8)(4) = 64\pi$ cm²/min.

(b) When $r = 32, \dfrac{dA}{dt} = 2\pi(32)(4) = 256\pi$ cm²/min.

**14.** $A = \pi r^2$

$\dfrac{dA}{dt} = 2\pi r \dfrac{dr}{dt}$

If $dr/dt$ is constant, $dA/dt$ is not constant.

$dA/dt$ depends on $r$ and $dr/dt$.

**15.** (a) $\sin\dfrac{\theta}{2} = \dfrac{(1/2)b}{s} \Rightarrow b = 2s\sin\dfrac{\theta}{2}$

$\cos\dfrac{\theta}{2} = \dfrac{h}{s} \Rightarrow h = s\cos\dfrac{\theta}{2}$

$A = \dfrac{1}{2}bh = \dfrac{1}{2}\left(2s\sin\dfrac{\theta}{2}\right)\left(s\cos\dfrac{\theta}{2}\right)$

$= \dfrac{s^2}{2}\left(2\sin\dfrac{\theta}{2}\cos\dfrac{\theta}{2}\right) = \dfrac{s^2}{2}\sin\theta$

(b) $\dfrac{dA}{dt} = \dfrac{s^2}{2}\cos\theta\dfrac{d\theta}{dt}$ where $\dfrac{d\theta}{dt} = \dfrac{1}{2}$ rad/min.

When $\theta = \dfrac{\pi}{6}, \dfrac{dA}{dt} = \dfrac{s^2}{2}\left(\dfrac{\sqrt{3}}{2}\right)\left(\dfrac{1}{2}\right) = \dfrac{\sqrt{3}s^2}{8}$.

When $\theta = \dfrac{\pi}{3}, \dfrac{dA}{dt} = \dfrac{s^2}{2}\left(\dfrac{1}{2}\right)\left(\dfrac{1}{2}\right) = \dfrac{s^2}{8}$.

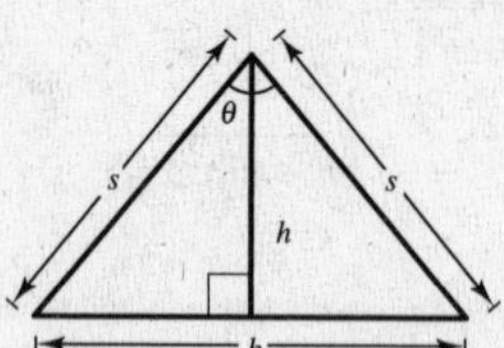


(c) If $s$ and $\dfrac{d\theta}{dt}$ are constant, $\dfrac{dA}{dt}$ is proportional to $\cos\theta$.

**16.** $V = \dfrac{4}{3}\pi r^3$

$\dfrac{dr}{dt} = 3$

$\dfrac{dV}{dt} = 4\pi r^2\dfrac{dr}{dt}$

(a) When $r = 9$,

$\dfrac{dV}{dt} = 4\pi(9)^2(3) = 972\pi$ in.³/min.

When $r = 36$,

$\dfrac{dV}{dt} = 4\pi(36)^2(3) = 15{,}552\pi$ in.³/min.

(b) If $dr/dt$ is constant, $dV/dt$ is proportional to $r^2$.

**17.** $V = \dfrac{1}{3}\pi h(108 - h^2) = 36\pi h - \dfrac{1}{3}\pi h^3,\ 0 < h < 6$

$\dfrac{dV}{dt} = 36\pi\dfrac{dh}{dt} - \pi h^2\dfrac{dh}{dt}$

When $\dfrac{dV}{dt} = 3$ and $h = 2$,

$3 = 36\pi\dfrac{dh}{dt} - 4\pi\dfrac{dh}{dt} \Rightarrow$

$\dfrac{dh}{dt} = \dfrac{3}{36\pi - 4\pi} = \dfrac{3}{32\pi} \approx 0.0298$ m/min.

**18.** $V = x^3$

$\dfrac{dx}{dt} = 6$

$\dfrac{dV}{dt} = 3x^2\dfrac{dx}{dt}$

(a) When $x = 2$,

$\dfrac{dV}{dt} = 3(2)^2(6) = 72$ cm³/sec.

(b) When $x = 10$,

$\dfrac{dV}{dt} = 3(10)^2(6) = 1800$ cm³/sec.

**19.** $s = 6x^2$

$\dfrac{dx}{dt} = 6$

$\dfrac{ds}{dt} = 12x\dfrac{dx}{dt}$

(a) When $x = 2$,

$\dfrac{ds}{dt} = 12(2)(6) = 144$ cm²/sec.

(b) When $x = 10$,

$\dfrac{ds}{dt} = 12(10)(6) = 720$ cm²/sec.

**20.** $V = \frac{1}{3}\pi r^2 h = \frac{1}{3}\pi r^2(3r) = \pi r^3$

$\frac{dr}{dt} = 2$

$\frac{dV}{dt} = 3\pi r^2 \frac{dr}{dt}$

(a) When $r = 6$,

$\frac{dV}{dt} = 3\pi(6)^2(2) = 216\pi$ in.³/min.

(b) When $r = 24$,

$\frac{dV}{dt} = 3\pi(24)^2(2) = 3456\pi$ in.³/min.

**21.** $V = \frac{1}{3}\pi r^2 h = \frac{1}{3}\pi\left(\frac{9}{4}h^2\right)h$ [because $2r = 3h$]

$= \frac{3\pi}{4}h^3$

$\frac{dV}{dt} = 10$

$\frac{dV}{dt} = \frac{9\pi}{4}h^2\frac{dh}{dt} \Rightarrow \frac{dh}{dt} = \frac{4(dV/dt)}{9\pi h^2}$

When $h = 15$,

$\frac{dh}{dt} = \frac{4(10)}{9\pi(15)^2} = \frac{8}{405\pi}$ ft/min.

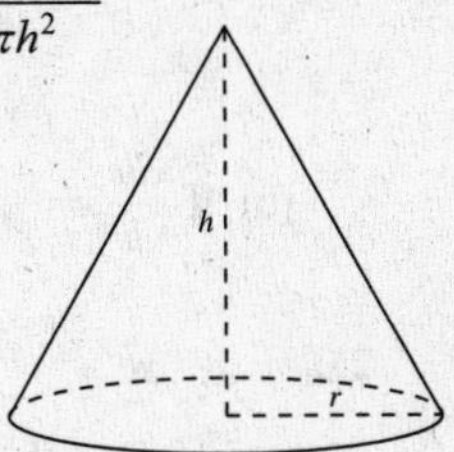


**22.** $V = \frac{1}{3}\pi r^2 h = \frac{1}{3}\pi\frac{25}{144}h^3 = \frac{25\pi}{3(144)}h^3$ $\left(\text{By similar triangles, } \frac{r}{5} = \frac{h}{12} \Rightarrow r = \frac{5}{12}h.\right)$

$\frac{dV}{dt} = 10$

$\frac{dV}{dt} = \frac{25\pi}{144}h^2\frac{dh}{dt} \Rightarrow \frac{dh}{dt} = \left(\frac{144}{25\pi h^2}\right)\frac{dV}{dt}$

When $h = 8$, $\frac{dh}{dt} = \frac{144}{25\pi(64)}(10) = \frac{9}{10\pi}$ ft/min.

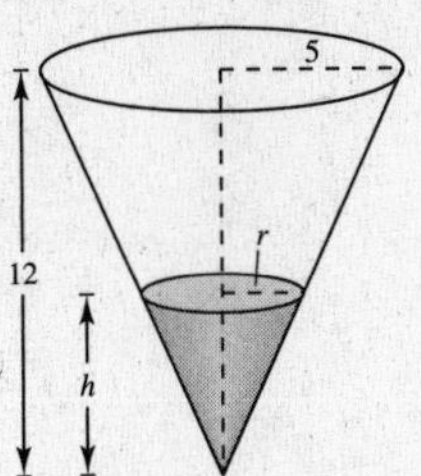

**23.**

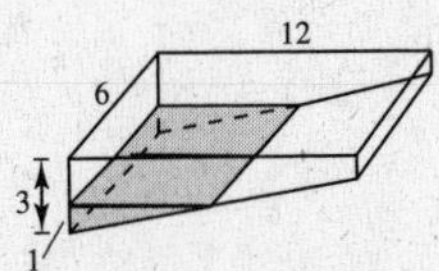


(a) Total volume of pool $= \frac{1}{2}(2)(12)(6) + (1)(6)(12) = 144$ m³

Volume of 1 m of water $= \frac{1}{2}(1)(6)(6) = 18$ m³ (see similar triangle diagram)

% pool filled $= \frac{18}{144}(100\%) = 12.5\%$

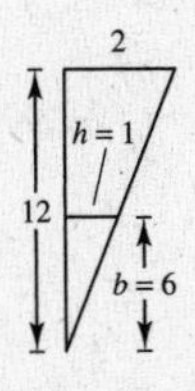


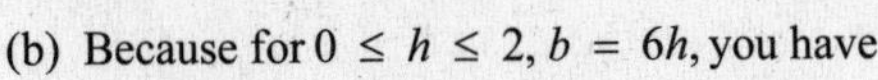
(b) Because for $0 \le h \le 2$, $b = 6h$, you have

$V = \frac{1}{2}bh(6) = 3bh = 3(6h)h = 18h^2$

$\frac{dV}{dt} = 36h\frac{dh}{dt} = \frac{1}{4} \Rightarrow \frac{dh}{dt} = \frac{1}{144h} = \frac{1}{144(1)} = \frac{1}{144}$ m/min.

**24.** $V = \frac{1}{2}bh(12) = 6bh = 6h^2$ (because $b = h$)

(a) $\frac{dV}{dt} = 12h\frac{dh}{dt} \Rightarrow \frac{dh}{dt} = \frac{1}{12h}\frac{dV}{dt}$

When $h = 1$ and $\frac{dV}{dt} = 2$, $\frac{dh}{dt} = \frac{1}{12(1)}(2) = \frac{1}{6}$ ft/min.

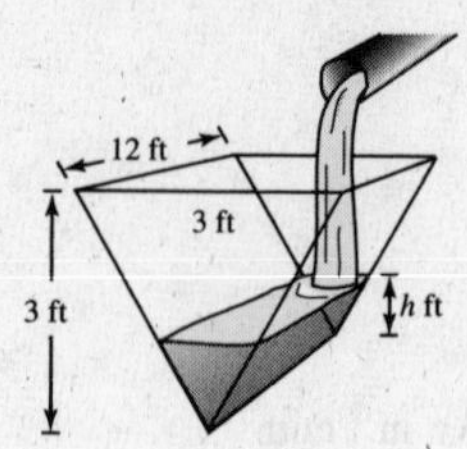


(b) If $\frac{dh}{dt} = \frac{3}{8}$ in./min $= \frac{1}{32}$ ft/min and $h = 2$ ft, then $\frac{dV}{dt} = (12)(2)\left(\frac{1}{32}\right) = \frac{3}{4}$ ft³/min.

**25.** $x^2 + y^2 = 25^2$

$$2x\frac{dx}{dt} + 2y\frac{dy}{dt} = 0$$

$$\frac{dy}{dt} = \frac{-x}{y} \cdot \frac{dx}{dt} = \frac{-2x}{y} \quad \text{because } \frac{dx}{dt} = 2.$$

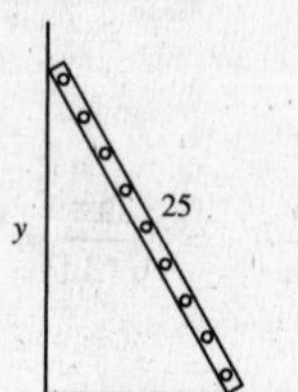


(a) When $x = 7$, $y = \sqrt{576} = 24$, $\frac{dy}{dt} = \frac{-2(7)}{24} = -\frac{7}{12}$ ft/sec.

When $x = 15$, $y = \sqrt{400} = 20$, $\frac{dy}{dt} = \frac{-2(15)}{20} = -\frac{3}{2}$ ft/sec.

When $x = 24$, $y = 7$, $\frac{dy}{dt} = \frac{-2(24)}{7} = -\frac{48}{7}$ ft/sec.

(b) $A = \frac{1}{2}xy$

$$\frac{dA}{dt} = \frac{1}{2}\left(x\frac{dy}{dt} + y\frac{dx}{dt}\right)$$

From part (a) you have $x = 7$, $y = 24$, $\frac{dx}{dt} = 2$, and $\frac{dy}{dt} = -\frac{7}{12}$. So,

$$\frac{dA}{dt} = \frac{1}{2}\left[7\left(-\frac{7}{12}\right) + 24(2)\right] = \frac{527}{24} \text{ ft}^2/\text{sec}.$$

(c) $\tan\theta = \frac{x}{y}$

$$\sec^2\theta\frac{d\theta}{dt} = \frac{1}{y} \cdot \frac{dx}{dt} - \frac{x}{y^2} \cdot \frac{dy}{dt}$$

$$\frac{d\theta}{dt} = \cos^2\theta\left[\frac{1}{y} \cdot \frac{dx}{dt} - \frac{x}{y^2} \cdot \frac{dy}{dt}\right]$$

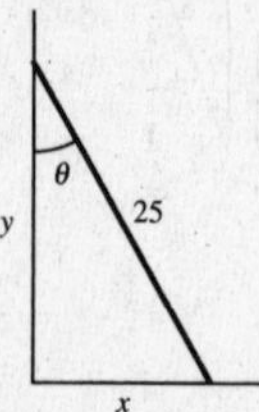


Using $x = 7$, $y = 24$, $\frac{dx}{dt} = 2$, $\frac{dy}{dt} = -\frac{7}{12}$ and $\cos\theta = \frac{24}{25}$, you have

$$\frac{d\theta}{dt} = \left(\frac{24}{25}\right)^2\left[\frac{1}{24}(2) - \frac{7}{(24)^2}\left(-\frac{7}{12}\right)\right] = \frac{1}{12} \text{ rad/sec}.$$

**26.**

$$x^2 + y^2 = 25$$

$$2x\frac{dx}{dt} + 2y\frac{dy}{dt} = 0$$

$$\frac{dx}{dt} = -\frac{y}{x} \cdot \frac{dy}{dt} = -\frac{0.15y}{x} \quad \left(\text{because } \frac{dy}{dt} = 0.15\right)$$

When $x = 2.5$, $y = \sqrt{18.75}$, $\frac{dx}{dt} = -\frac{\sqrt{18.75}}{2.5} 0.15 \approx -0.26$ m/sec.

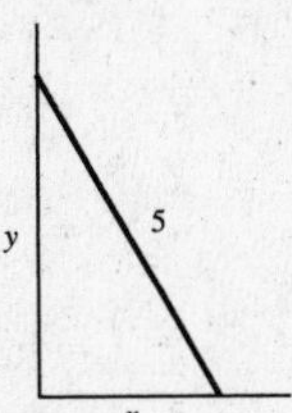


**27.** When $y = 6$, $x = \sqrt{12^2 - 6^2} = 6\sqrt{3}$, and $s = \sqrt{x^2 + (12 - y)^2} = \sqrt{108 + 36} = 12$.

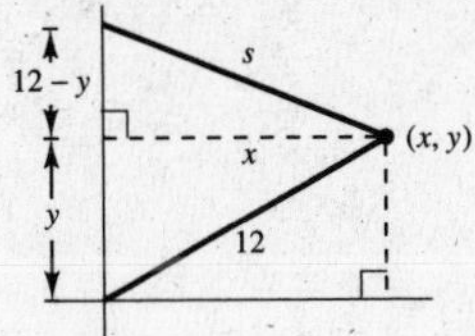


$$x^2 + (12 - y)^2 = s^2$$

$$2x\frac{dx}{dt} + 2(12 - y)(-1)\frac{dy}{dt} = 2s\frac{ds}{dt}$$

$$x\frac{dx}{dt} + (y - 12)\frac{dy}{dt} = s\frac{ds}{dt}$$

Also, $x^2 + y^2 = 12^2$.

$$2x\frac{dx}{dt} + 2y\frac{dy}{dt} = 0 \Rightarrow \frac{dy}{dt} = \frac{-x}{y}\frac{dx}{dt}$$

So, $x\frac{dx}{dt} + (y - 12)\left(\frac{-x}{y}\frac{dx}{dt}\right) = s\frac{ds}{dt}$.

$$\frac{dx}{dt}\left[x - x + \frac{12x}{y}\right] = s\frac{ds}{dt} \Rightarrow \frac{dx}{dt} = \frac{sy}{12x} \cdot \frac{ds}{dt} = \frac{(12)(6)}{(12)(6\sqrt{3})}(-0.2) = \frac{-1}{5\sqrt{3}} = \frac{-\sqrt{3}}{15} \text{ m/sec (horizontal)}$$

$$\frac{dy}{dt} = \frac{-x}{y}\frac{dx}{dt} = \frac{-6\sqrt{3}}{6} \cdot \frac{\left(-\sqrt{3}\right)}{15} = \frac{1}{5} \text{ m/sec (vertical)}$$

**28.** Let $L$ be the length of the rope.

(a)
$$L^2 = 144 + x^2$$
$$2L\frac{dL}{dt} = 2x\frac{dx}{dt}$$
$$\frac{dx}{dt} = \frac{L}{x}\cdot\frac{dL}{dt} = -\frac{4L}{x} \quad \left(\text{because } \frac{dL}{dt} = -4 \text{ ft/sec}\right)$$

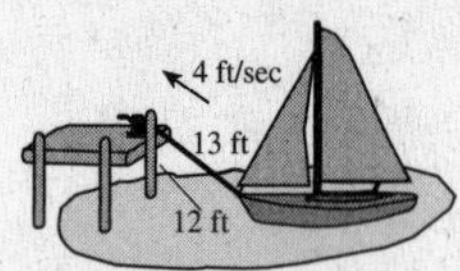


When $L = 13$:

$$x = \sqrt{L^2 - 144} = \sqrt{169 - 144} = 5$$
$$\frac{dx}{dt} = -\frac{4(13)}{5} = -\frac{52}{5} = -10.4 \text{ ft/sec}$$

Speed of the boat increases as it approaches the dock.

(b) If $\frac{dx}{dt} = -4$, and $L = 13$:

$$\frac{dL}{dt} = \frac{x}{L}\frac{dx}{dt} = \frac{5}{13}(-4) = \frac{-20}{13} \text{ ft/sec}$$
$$\frac{dL}{dt} = \frac{x}{L}\frac{dx}{dt} = \frac{\sqrt{L^2 - 144}}{L}(-4)$$
$$\lim_{L\to 12^+}\frac{dL}{dt} = \lim_{L\to 12^+}\frac{-4}{L}\sqrt{L^2 - 144} = 0$$

**29.** (a)
$$s^2 = x^2 + y^2$$
$$\frac{dx}{dt} = -450$$
$$\frac{dy}{dt} = -600$$
$$2s\frac{ds}{dt} = 2x\frac{dx}{dt} + 2y\frac{dy}{dt}$$
$$\frac{ds}{dt} = \frac{x(dx/dt) + y(dy/dt)}{s}$$

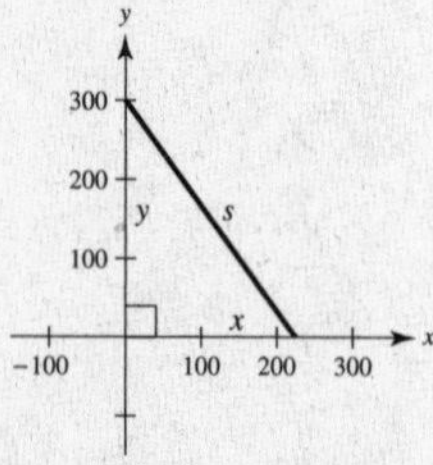


When $x = 225$ and $y = 300$, $s = 375$ and

$$\frac{ds}{dt} = \frac{225(-450) + 300(-600)}{375} = -750 \text{ mi/h}.$$

(b) $t = \frac{375}{750} = \frac{1}{2}\text{ h} = 30 \text{ min}$

**30.**
$$x^2 + y^2 = s^2$$
$$2x\frac{dx}{dt} + 0 = 2s\frac{ds}{dt} \quad \left(\text{because } \frac{dy}{dt} = 0\right)$$
$$\frac{dx}{dt} = \frac{s}{x}\cdot\frac{ds}{dt}$$

When $s = 10$, $x = \sqrt{100 - 25} = \sqrt{75} = 5\sqrt{3}$,

$$\frac{dx}{dt} = \frac{10}{5\sqrt{3}}(240) = \frac{480}{\sqrt{3}} = 160\sqrt{3} \approx 277.13 \text{ mi/h}.$$

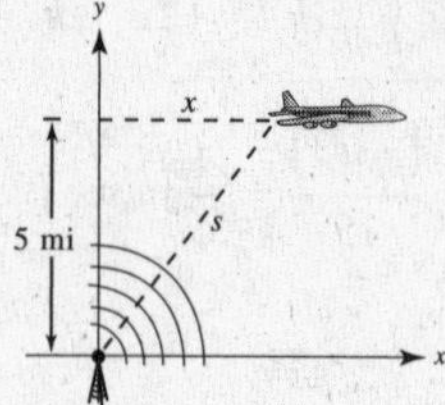

**31.** $s^2 = 90^2 + x^2$

$x = 30$

$\frac{dx}{dt} = -25$

$2s\frac{ds}{dt} = 2x\frac{dx}{dt} \Rightarrow \frac{ds}{dt} = \frac{x}{s}\cdot\frac{dx}{dt}$

When $x = 20$, $s = \sqrt{90^2 + 20^2} = 10\sqrt{85}$,

$\frac{ds}{dt} = \frac{20}{10\sqrt{85}}(-25) = \frac{-50}{\sqrt{85}} \approx -5.42$ ft/sec.

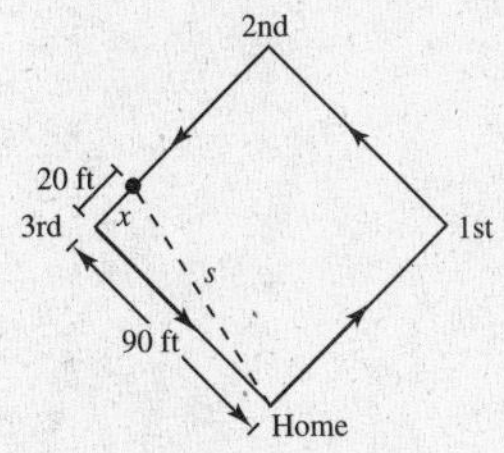


**32.** $s^2 = 90^2 + x^2$

$x = 90 - 20 = 70$

$\frac{dx}{dt} = 25$

$\frac{ds}{dt} = \frac{x}{s}\cdot\frac{dx}{dt}$

When $x = 70$, $s = \sqrt{90^2 + 70^2} = 10\sqrt{130}$,

$\frac{ds}{dt} = \frac{70}{10\sqrt{130}}(25) = \frac{175}{\sqrt{130}} \approx 15.35$ ft/sec.

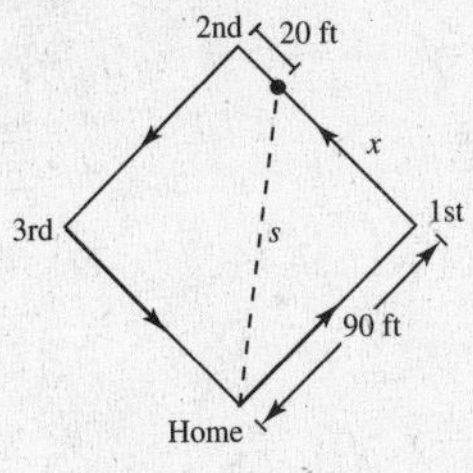


**33.** (a) $\frac{15}{6} = \frac{y}{y - x} \Rightarrow 15y - 15x = 6y$

$y = \frac{5}{3}x$

$\frac{dx}{dt} = 5$

$\frac{dy}{dt} = \frac{5}{3}\cdot\frac{dx}{dt} = \frac{5}{3}(5) = \frac{25}{3}$ ft/sec

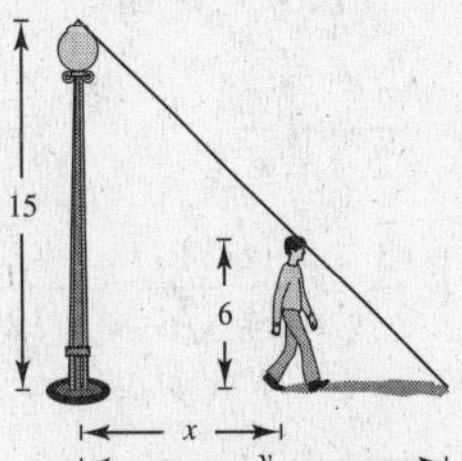


(b) $\frac{d(y - x)}{dt} = \frac{dy}{dt} - \frac{dx}{dt} = \frac{25}{3} - 5 = \frac{10}{3}$ ft/sec

**34.** (a) $\frac{20}{6} = \frac{y}{y - x}$

$20y - 20x = 6y$

$14y = 20x$

$y = \frac{10}{7}x$

$\frac{dx}{dt} = -5$

$\frac{dy}{dt} = \frac{10}{7}\frac{dx}{dt} = \frac{10}{7}(-5) = \frac{-50}{7}$ ft/sec

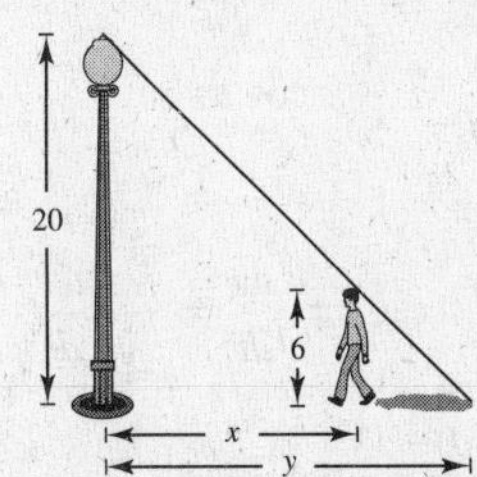


(b) $\frac{d(y - x)}{dt} = \frac{dy}{dt} - \frac{dx}{dt}$

$= \frac{-50}{7} - (-5)$

$= \frac{-50}{7} + \frac{35}{7} = \frac{-15}{7}$ ft/sec

**35.** $x(t) = \frac{1}{2}\sin\frac{\pi t}{6}$, $x^2 + y^2 = 1$

(a) Period: $\frac{2\pi}{\pi/6} = 12$ seconds

(b) When $x = \frac{1}{2}$, $y = \sqrt{1^2 - \left(\frac{1}{2}\right)^2} = \frac{\sqrt{3}}{2}$ m.

Lowest point: $\left(0, \frac{\sqrt{3}}{2}\right)$

(c) When $x = \frac{1}{4}$, $y = \sqrt{1 - \left(\frac{1}{4}\right)^2} = \frac{\sqrt{15}}{4}$ and $t = 1$:

$$\frac{dx}{dt} = \frac{1}{2}\left(\frac{\pi}{6}\right)\cos\frac{\pi t}{6} = \frac{\pi}{12}\cos\frac{\pi t}{6}.$$

$$x^2 + y^2 = 1$$

$$2x\frac{dx}{dt} + 2y\frac{dy}{dt} = 0 \Rightarrow \frac{dy}{dt} = \frac{-x}{y}\frac{dx}{dt}$$

So, $\frac{dy}{dt} = -\frac{1/4}{\sqrt{15}/4} \cdot \frac{\pi}{12}\cos\left(\frac{\pi}{6}\right)$

$$= \frac{-\pi}{\sqrt{15}}\left(\frac{1}{12}\right)\frac{\sqrt{3}}{2} = \frac{-\pi}{24}\frac{1}{\sqrt{5}} = \frac{-\sqrt{5}\pi}{120}.$$

Speed $= \left|\frac{-\sqrt{5}\pi}{120}\right| = \frac{\sqrt{5}\pi}{120}$ m/sec

**36.** $x(t) = \frac{3}{5}\sin \pi t,\ x^2 + y^2 = 1$

(a) Period: $\frac{2\pi}{\pi} = 2$ seconds

(b) When $x = \frac{3}{5}$, $y = \sqrt{1 - \left(\frac{3}{5}\right)^2} = \frac{4}{5}$ m.

Lowest point: $\left(0, \frac{4}{5}\right)$

(c) When $x = \frac{3}{10}$, $y = \sqrt{1 - \left(\frac{1}{4}\right)^2} = \frac{\sqrt{15}}{4}$ and $\frac{3}{10} = \frac{3}{5}\sin \pi t \Rightarrow \sin \pi t = \frac{1}{2} \Rightarrow t = \frac{1}{6}$:

$$\frac{dx}{dt} = \frac{3}{5}\pi\cos \pi t$$

$$x^2 + y^2 = 1$$

$$2x\frac{dx}{dt} + 2y\frac{dy}{dt} = 0 \Rightarrow \frac{dy}{dt} = \frac{-x}{y}\frac{dx}{dt}$$

So, $\frac{dy}{dt} = \frac{-3/10}{\sqrt{15}/4} \cdot \frac{3}{5}\pi\cos\left(\frac{\pi}{6}\right)$

$$= \frac{-9\pi}{25\sqrt{5}} = \frac{-9\sqrt{5}\pi}{125}.$$

Speed $= \left|\frac{-9\sqrt{5}\pi}{125}\right| \approx 0.5058$ m/sec

**37.** Because the evaporation rate is proportional to the surface area, $dV/dt = k(4\pi r^2)$. However, because $V = (4/3)\pi r^3$, you have

$$\frac{dV}{dt} = 4\pi r^2\frac{dr}{dt}.$$

Therefore, $k(4\pi r^2) = 4\pi r^2\frac{dr}{dt} \Rightarrow k = \frac{dr}{dt}.$

**38.** $$\frac{1}{R} = \frac{1}{R_1} + \frac{1}{R_2}$$

$$\frac{dR_1}{dt} = 1$$

$$\frac{dR_2}{dt} = 1.5$$

$$\frac{1}{R^2} \cdot \frac{dR}{dt} = \frac{1}{R_1^2} \cdot \frac{dR_1}{dt} + \frac{1}{R_2^2} \cdot \frac{dR_2}{dt}$$

When $R_1 = 50$ and $R_2 = 75$:

$R = 30$

$$\frac{dR}{dt} = (30)^2\left[\frac{1}{(50)^2}(1) + \frac{1}{(75)^2}(1.5)\right] = 0.6 \text{ ohm/sec}$$

**39.** $$pV^{1.3} = k$$

$$1.3pV^{0.3}\frac{dV}{dt} + V^{1.3}\frac{dp}{dt} = 0$$

$$V^{0.3}\left(1.3p\frac{dV}{dt} + V\frac{dp}{dt}\right) = 0$$

$$1.3p\frac{dV}{dt} = -V\frac{dp}{dt}$$

**40.** $rg \tan\theta = v^2$

$32r \tan\theta = v^2$, $\quad r$ is a constant.

$$32r \sec^2\theta \frac{d\theta}{dt} = 2v\frac{dv}{dt}$$

$$\frac{dv}{dt} = \frac{16r}{v}\sec^2\theta\frac{d\theta}{dt}$$

Likewise, $\dfrac{d\theta}{dt} = \dfrac{v}{16r}\cos^2\theta\dfrac{dv}{dt}$.

**41.** $$\tan\theta = \frac{y}{50}$$

$$\frac{dy}{dt} = 4 \text{ m/sec}$$

$$\sec^2\theta \cdot \frac{d\theta}{dt} = \frac{1}{50}\frac{dy}{dt}$$

$$\frac{d\theta}{dt} = \frac{1}{50}\cos^2\theta \cdot \frac{dy}{dt}$$

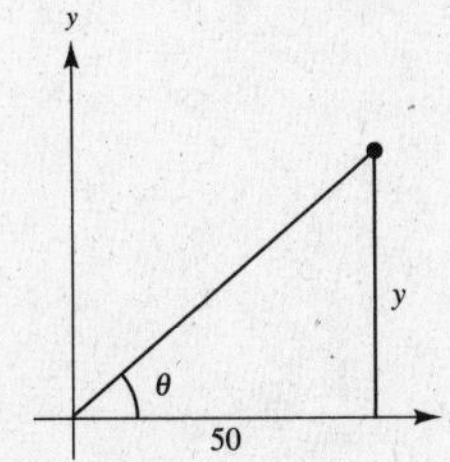


When $y = 50$, $\theta = \dfrac{\pi}{4}$, and $\cos\theta = \dfrac{\sqrt{2}}{2}$. So,

$$\frac{d\theta}{dt} = \frac{1}{50}\left(\frac{\sqrt{2}}{2}\right)^2(4) = \frac{1}{25} \text{ rad/sec.}$$

**42.** $$\sin\theta = \frac{10}{x}$$

$$\frac{dx}{dt} = (-1) \text{ ft/sec}$$

$$\cos\theta\left(\frac{d\theta}{dt}\right) = \frac{-10}{x^2} \cdot \frac{dx}{dt}$$

$$\frac{d\theta}{dt} = \frac{-10}{x^2}\frac{dx}{dt}(\sec\theta)$$

$$= \frac{-10}{25^2}(-1)\frac{25}{\sqrt{25^2 - 10^2}}$$

$$= \frac{10}{25}\frac{1}{5\sqrt{21}} = \frac{2}{25\sqrt{21}}$$

$$= \frac{2\sqrt{21}}{525} \approx 0.017 \text{ rad/sec}$$

**43.** $$H = \frac{4347}{400{,}000{,}000}e^{369{,}444/(50t+19{,}793)}$$

(a) $t = 65° \Rightarrow H \approx 99.79\%$

$t = 80° \Rightarrow H \approx 60.20\%$

(b) $$H' = H \cdot \left(\frac{-369{,}444(50)}{(50t + 19{,}793)^2}\right)t'$$

At $t = 75$ and $t' = 2$, $H' \approx -4.7\%/h$.

**44.** $$\tan\theta = \frac{x}{50}$$

$$\frac{d\theta}{dt} = 30(2\pi) = 60\pi \text{ rad/min} = \pi \text{ rad/sec}$$

$$\sec^2\theta\left(\frac{d\theta}{dt}\right) = \frac{1}{50}\left(\frac{dx}{dt}\right)$$

$$\frac{dx}{dt} = 50\sec^2\theta\left(\frac{d\theta}{dt}\right)$$

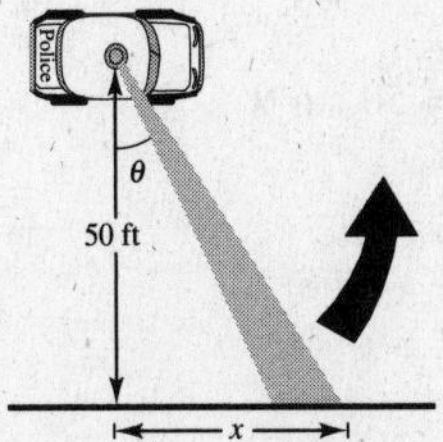


(a) When $\theta = 30°$, $\dfrac{dx}{dt} = \dfrac{200\pi}{3}$ ft/sec.

(b) When $\theta = 60°$, $\dfrac{dx}{dt} = 200\pi$ ft/sec.

(c) When $\theta = 70°$, $\dfrac{dx}{dt} \approx 427.43\pi$ ft/sec.

**45.** $\dfrac{d\theta}{dt} = (10\text{ rev/sec})(2\pi\text{ rad/rev}) = 20\pi\text{ rad/sec}$

(a)
$$\cos\theta = \frac{x}{30}$$
$$-\sin\theta\frac{d\theta}{dt} = \frac{1}{30}\frac{dx}{dt}$$
$$\frac{dx}{dt} = -30\sin\theta\frac{d\theta}{dt}$$
$$= -30\sin\theta(20\pi)$$
$$= -600\pi\sin\theta$$

(b)

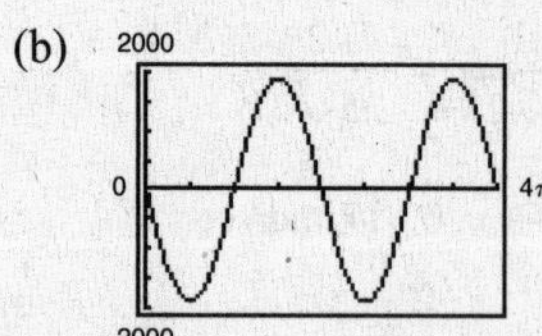


(c) $|dx/dt| = |-600\pi\sin\theta|$ is greatest when

$|\sin\theta| = 1 \Rightarrow \theta = \dfrac{\pi}{2} + n\pi$ (or $90° + n\cdot 180°$).

$|dx/dt|$ is least when $\theta = n\pi$ (or $n\cdot 180°$).

(d) For $\theta = 30°$,
$$\frac{dx}{dt} = -600\pi\sin(30°) = -600\pi\frac{1}{2} = -300\pi\text{ cm/sec.}$$
For $\theta = 60°$,
$$\frac{dx}{dt} = -600\pi\sin(60°)$$
$$= -600\pi\frac{\sqrt{3}}{2} = -300\sqrt{3}\pi\text{ cm/sec.}$$

**46.** $\sin 18° = \dfrac{x}{y}$
$$0 = -\frac{x}{y^2}\cdot\frac{dy}{dt} + \frac{1}{y}\cdot\frac{dx}{dt}$$
$$\frac{dx}{dt} = \frac{x}{y}\cdot\frac{dy}{dt} = (\sin 18°)(275) \approx 84.9797\text{ mi/hr}$$

**47.** $\tan\theta = \dfrac{x}{50} \Rightarrow x = 50\tan\theta$
$$\frac{dx}{dt} = 50\sec^2\theta\frac{d\theta}{dt}$$
$$2 = 50\sec^2\theta\frac{d\theta}{dt}$$
$$\frac{d\theta}{dt} = \frac{1}{25}\cos^2\theta,\quad -\frac{\pi}{4} \le \theta \le \frac{\pi}{4}$$

**48 (i)** (a) $\dfrac{dx}{dt}$ negative $\Rightarrow \dfrac{dy}{dt}$ positive

(b) $\dfrac{dy}{dt}$ positive $\Rightarrow \dfrac{dx}{dt}$ negative

**(ii)** (a) $\dfrac{dx}{dt}$ negative $\Rightarrow \dfrac{dy}{dt}$ negative

(b) $\dfrac{dy}{dt}$ positive $\Rightarrow \dfrac{dx}{dt}$ positive

**49.** $\tan\theta = \dfrac{y}{x},\ y = 5$
$$\frac{dx}{dt} = -600\text{ mi/h}$$
$$(\sec^2\theta)\frac{d\theta}{dt} = -\frac{5}{x^2}\cdot\frac{dx}{dt}$$
$$\frac{d\theta}{dt} = \cos^2\theta\left(-\frac{5}{x^2}\right)\frac{dx}{dt} = \frac{x^2}{L^2}\left(-\frac{5}{x^2}\right)\frac{dx}{dt}$$
$$= \left(-\frac{5^2}{L^2}\right)\left(\frac{1}{5}\right)\frac{dx}{dt}$$
$$= \left(-\sin^2\theta\right)\left(\frac{1}{5}\right)(-600) = 120\sin^2\theta$$

(a) When $\theta = 30°$,
$$\frac{d\theta}{dt} = \frac{120}{4} = 30\text{ rad/h} = \frac{1}{2}\text{ rad/min.}$$
(b) When $\theta = 60°$,
$$\frac{d\theta}{dt} = 120\left(\frac{3}{4}\right) = 90\text{ rad/h} = \frac{3}{2}\text{ rad/min.}$$
(c) When $\theta = 75°$,
$$\frac{d\theta}{dt} = 120\sin^2 75° \approx 111.96\text{ rad/h} \approx 1.87\text{ rad/min.}$$

**50.** $y(t) = -4.9t^2 + 20$

$$\frac{dy}{dt} = -9.8t$$

$$y(1) = -4.9 + 20 = 15.1$$

$$y'(1) = -9.8$$

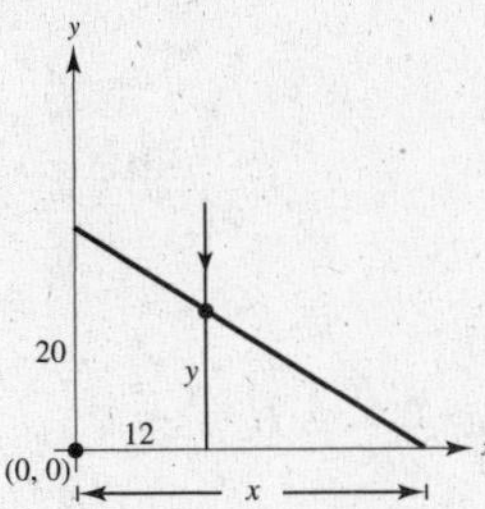


By similar triangles: $\dfrac{20}{x} = \dfrac{y}{x - 12}$

$$20x - 240 = xy$$

When $y = 15.1$: $20x - 240 = x(15.1)$

$$(20 - 15.1)x = 240$$

$$x = \frac{240}{4.9}$$

$$20x - 240 = xy$$

$$20\frac{dx}{dt} = x\frac{dy}{dt} + y\frac{dx}{dt}$$

$$\frac{dx}{dt} = \frac{x}{20 - y}\frac{dy}{dt}$$

At $t = 1$, $\dfrac{dx}{dt} = \dfrac{240/4.9}{20 - 15.1}(-9.8) \approx -97.96$ m/sec.

**51.** $x^2 + y^2 = 25$; acceleration of the top of the ladder $= \dfrac{d^2y}{dt^2}$

First derivative: $2x\dfrac{dx}{dt} + 2y\dfrac{dy}{dt} = 0$

$$x\frac{dx}{dt} + y\frac{dy}{dt} = 0$$

Second derivative: $x\dfrac{d^2x}{dt^2} + \dfrac{dx}{dt}\cdot\dfrac{dx}{dt} + y\dfrac{d^2y}{dt^2} + \dfrac{dy}{dt}\cdot\dfrac{dy}{dt} = 0$

$$\frac{d^2y}{dt^2} = \left(\frac{1}{y}\right)\left[-x\frac{d^2x}{dt^2} - \left(\frac{dx}{dt}\right)^2 - \left(\frac{dy}{dt}\right)^2\right]$$

When $x = 7$, $y = 24$, $\dfrac{dy}{dt} = -\dfrac{7}{12}$, and $\dfrac{dx}{dt} = 2$ (see Exercise 25). Because $\dfrac{dx}{dt}$ is constant, $\dfrac{d^2x}{dt^2} = 0$.

$$\frac{d^2y}{dt^2} = \frac{1}{24}\left[-7(0) - (2)^2 - \left(-\frac{7}{12}\right)^2\right] = \frac{1}{24}\left[-4 - \frac{49}{144}\right] = \frac{1}{24}\left[-\frac{625}{144}\right] \approx -0.1808 \text{ ft/sec}^2$$

**52.** $L^2 = 144 + x^2$; acceleration of the boat $= \dfrac{d^2x}{dt^2}$

First derivative: $2L\dfrac{dL}{dt} = 2x\dfrac{dx}{dt}$

$$L\frac{dL}{dt} = x\frac{dx}{dt}$$

Second derivative: $L\dfrac{d^2L}{dt^2} + \dfrac{dL}{dt}\cdot\dfrac{dL}{dt} = x\dfrac{d^2x}{dt^2} + \dfrac{dx}{dt}\cdot\dfrac{dx}{dt}$

$$\frac{d^2x}{dt^2} = \left(\frac{1}{x}\right)\left[L\frac{d^2L}{dt^2} + \left(\frac{dL}{dt}\right)^2 - \left(\frac{dx}{dt}\right)^2\right]$$

When $L = 13$, $x = 5$, $\dfrac{dx}{dt} = -10.4$, and $\dfrac{dL}{dt} = -4$ (see Exercise 28). Because $\dfrac{dL}{dt}$ is constant, $\dfrac{d^2L}{dt^2} = 0$.

$$\frac{d^2x}{dt^2} = \frac{1}{5}\left[13(0) + (-4)^2 - (-10.4)^2\right]$$

$$= \frac{1}{5}[16 - 108.16] = \frac{1}{5}[-92.16] = -18.432 \text{ ft/sec}^2$$

**53.** (a) $dy/dt = 3(dx/dt)$ means that $y$ changes three times as fast as $x$ changes.

(b) $y$ changes slowly when $x \approx 0$ or $x \approx L$. $y$ changes more rapidly when $x$ is near the middle of the interval.

## Section 3.8 Newton's Method

**The following solutions may vary depending on the software or calculator used, and on rounding.**

**1.** $f(x) = x^2 - 5$

$f'(x) = 2x$

$x_1 = 2.2$

| $n$ | $x_n$ | $f(x_n)$ | $f'(x_n)$ | $\dfrac{f(x_n)}{f'(x_n)}$ | $x_n - \dfrac{f(x_n)}{f'(x_n)}$ |
|---|---|---|---|---|---|
| 1 | 2.2000 | –0.1600 | 4.4000 | –0.0364 | 2.2364 |
| 2 | 2.2364 | 0.0013 | 4.4727 | 0.0003 | 2.2361 |

**2.** $f(x) = x^3 - 3$

$f'(x) = 3x^2$

$x_1 = 1.4$

| $n$ | $x_n$ | $f(x_n)$ | $f'(x_n)$ | $\dfrac{f(x_n)}{f'(x_n)}$ | $x_n - \dfrac{f(x_n)}{f'(x_n)}$ |
|---|---|---|---|---|---|
| 1 | 1.4000 | –0.2560 | 5.8800 | –0.0435 | 1.4435 |
| 2 | 1.4435 | 0.0080 | 6.2514 | 0.0013 | 1.4423 |

**3.** $f(x) = \cos x$

$f'(x) = -\sin x$

$x_1 = 1.6$

| $n$ | $x_n$ | $f(x_n)$ | $f'(x_n)$ | $\frac{f(x_n)}{f'(x_n)}$ | $x_n - \frac{f(x_n)}{f'(x_n)}$ |
|---|---|---|---|---|---|
| 1 | 1.6000 | –0.0292 | –0.9996 | 0.0292 | 1.5708 |
| 2 | 1.5708 | 0.0000 | –1.0000 | 0.0000 | 1.5708 |

**4.** $f(x) = \tan x$

$f'(x) = \sec^2 x$

$x_1 = 0.1$

| $n$ | $x_n$ | $f(x_n)$ | $f'(x_n)$ | $\frac{f(x_n)}{f'(x_n)}$ | $x_n - \frac{f(x_n)}{f'(x_n)}$ |
|---|---|---|---|---|---|
| 1 | 0.1000 | 0.1003 | 1.0101 | 0.0993 | 0.0007 |
| 2 | 0.0007 | 0.0007 | 1.0000 | 0.0007 | 0.0000 |

**5.** $f(x) = x^3 + 4$

$f'(x) = 3x^2$

$x_1 = -2$

| $n$ | $x_n$ | $f(x_n)$ | $f'(x_n)$ | $\frac{f(x_n)}{f'(x_n)}$ | $x_n - \frac{f(x_n)}{f'(x_n)}$ |
|---|---|---|---|---|---|
| 1 | –2.0000 | –4.0000 | 12.0000 | –0.3333 | –1.6667 |
| 2 | –1.6667 | –0.6296 | 8.3333 | –0.0756 | –1.5911 |
| 3 | –1.5911 | –0.0281 | 7.5949 | –0.0037 | –1.5874 |
| 4 | –1.5874 | –0.0000 | 7.5596 | 0.0000 | –1.5874 |

Approximation of the zero of $f$ is –1.587.

**6.** $f(x) = 2 - x^3$

$f'(x) = -3x^2$

$x_1 = 1.0$

| $n$ | $x_n$ | $f(x_n)$ | $f'(x_n)$ | $\frac{f(x_n)}{f'(x_n)}$ | $x_n - \frac{f(x_n)}{f'(x_n)}$ |
|---|---|---|---|---|---|
| 1 | 1.0000 | 1.0000 | –3.0000 | –0.3333 | 1.3333 |
| 2 | 1.3333 | –0.3704 | –5.3333 | 0.0694 | 1.2639 |
| 3 | 1.2639 | –0.0190 | –4.7922 | 0.0040 | 1.2599 |
| 4 | 1.2599 | 0.0001 | –4.7623 | 0.0000 | 1.2599 |

Approximation of the zero of $f$ is 1.260.

**7.** $f(x) = x^3 + x - 1$

$f'(x) = 3x^2 + 1$

| $n$ | $x_n$ | $f(x_n)$ | $f'(x_n)$ | $\dfrac{f(x_n)}{f'(x_n)}$ | $x_n - \dfrac{f(x_n)}{f'(x_n)}$ |
|---|---|---|---|---|---|
| 1 | 0.5000 | –0.3750 | 1.7500 | –0.2143 | 0.7143 |
| 2 | 0.7143 | 0.0788 | 2.5307 | 0.0311 | 0.6832 |
| 3 | 0.6832 | 0.0021 | 2.4003 | 0.0009 | 0.6823 |

Approximation of the zero of $f$ is 0.682.

**8.** $f(x) = x^5 + x - 1$

$f'(x) = 5x^4 + 1$

| $n$ | $x_n$ | $f(x_n)$ | $f'(x_n)$ | $\dfrac{f(x_n)}{f'(x_n)}$ | $x_n - \dfrac{f(x_n)}{f'(x_n)}$ |
|---|---|---|---|---|---|
| 1 | 0.5000 | –0.4688 | 1.3125 | –0.3571 | 0.8571 |
| 2 | 0.8571 | 0.3196 | 3.6983 | 0.0864 | 0.7707 |
| 3 | 0.7707 | 0.0426 | 2.7641 | 0.0154 | 0.7553 |
| 4 | 0.7553 | 0.0011 | 2.6272 | 0.0004 | 0.7549 |

Approximation of the zero of $f$ is 0.755.

**9.** $f(x) = 5\sqrt{x-1} - 2x$

$$f'(x) = \frac{5}{2\sqrt{x-1}} - 2$$

Using a graphing utility, you can see that there are two zeros. Begin with $x = 1.2$.

| $n$ | $x_n$ | $f(x_n)$ | $f'(x_n)$ | $\dfrac{f(x_n)}{f'(x_n)}$ | $x_n - \dfrac{f(x_n)}{f'(x_n)}$ |
|---|---|---|---|---|---|
| 1 | 1.2000 | –0.1639 | 3.5902 | –0.0457 | 1.2457 |
| 2 | 1.2457 | –0.0131 | 3.0440 | –0.0043 | 1.2500 |
| 3 | 1.2500 | –0.0001 | 3.0003 | –0.0003 | 1.2500 |

Approximation of the zero of $f$ is 1.250.

Similarly, the other zero is approximately 5.000.

(**Note:** These answers are exact)

**10.** $f(x) = x - 2\sqrt{x+1}$

$$f'(x) = 1 - \frac{1}{\sqrt{x+1}}$$

| $n$ | $x_n$ | $f(x_n)$ | $f'(x_n)$ | $\dfrac{f(x_n)}{f'(x_n)}$ | $x_n - \dfrac{f(x_n)}{f'(x_n)}$ |
|---|---|---|---|---|---|
| 1 | 5.0000 | 0.1010 | 0.5918 | 0.1707 | 4.8293 |
| 2 | 4.8293 | 0.0005 | 0.5858 | 0.00085 | 4.8284 |

Approximation of the zero of $f$ is 4.828.

**11.** $f(x) = x - e^{-x}$

$f'(x) = 1 + e^{-x}$

$x_1 = 0.5$

| $n$ | $x_n$ | $f(x_n)$ | $f'(x_n)$ | $\frac{f(x_n)}{f'(x_n)}$ | $x_n - \frac{f(x_n)}{f'(x_n)}$ |
|---|---|---|---|---|---|
| 1 | 0.5 | –0.1065 | 1.6065 | –0.0663 | 0.5663 |
| 2 | 0.5663 | 0.0013 | 1.5676 | 0.0008 | 0.5671 |
| 3 | 0.5671 | 0.0001 | 1.5672 | –0.0000 | 0.5671 |

Approximation of the zero of $f$ is 0.567.

**12.** $f(x) = x - 3 + \ln x$

$f'(x) = 1 + \frac{1}{x}$

$x_1 = 2.0$

| $n$ | $x_n$ | $f(x_n)$ | $f'(x_n)$ | $\frac{f(x_n)}{f'(x_n)}$ | $x_n - \frac{f(x_n)}{f'(x_n)}$ |
|---|---|---|---|---|---|
| 1 | 2.0 | –0.3069 | 1.5 | –0.2046 | 2.2046 |
| 2 | 2.2046 | –0.0049 | 1.4536 | –0.0033 | 2.2079 |
| 3 | 2.2079 | –0.0001 | 1.4529 | –0.0000 | 2.2079 |

Approximation of the zero of $f$ is 2.208.

**13.** $f(x) = x^3 - 3.9x^2 + 4.79x - 1.881$

$f'(x) = 3x^2 - 7.8x + 4.79$

| $n$ | $x_n$ | $f(x_n)$ | $f'(x_n)$ | $\frac{f(x_n)}{f'(x_n)}$ | $x_n - \frac{f(x_n)}{f'(x_n)}$ |
|---|---|---|---|---|---|
| 1 | 0.5000 | –0.3360 | 1.6400 | –0.2049 | 0.7049 |
| 2 | 0.7049 | –0.0921 | 0.7824 | –0.1177 | 0.8226 |
| 3 | 0.8226 | –0.0231 | 0.4037 | –0.0573 | 0.8799 |
| 4 | 0.8799 | –0.0045 | 0.2495 | –0.0181 | 0.8980 |
| 5 | 0.8980 | –0.0004 | 0.2048 | –0.0020 | 0.9000 |
| 6 | 0.9000 | 0.0000 | 0.2000 | 0.0000 | 0.9000 |

Approximation of the zero of $f$ is 0.900.

| $n$ | $x_n$ | $f(x_n)$ | $f'(x_n)$ | $\frac{f(x_n)}{f'(x_n)}$ | $x_n - \frac{f(x_n)}{f'(x_n)}$ |
|---|---|---|---|---|---|
| 1 | 1.1 | 0.0000 | –0.1600 | –0.0000 | 1.1000 |

Approximation of the zero of $f$ is 1.100.

| $n$ | $x_n$ | $f(x_n)$ | $f'(x_n)$ | $\frac{f(x_n)}{f'(x_n)}$ | $x_n - \frac{f(x_n)}{f'(x_n)}$ |
|---|---|---|---|---|---|
| 1 | 1.9 | 0.0000 | 0.8000 | 0.0000 | 1.9000 |

Approximation of the zero of $f$ is 1.900.

**14.** $f(x) = x^4 + x^3 - 1$

$f'(x) = 4x^3 + 3x^2$

Using a graphing utility, you can see that there are two zeros. Begin with $x_1 = 1.0$.

| $n$ | $x_n$ | $f(x_n)$ | $f'(x_n)$ | $\frac{f(x_n)}{f'(x_n)}$ | $x_n - \frac{f(x_n)}{f'(x_n)}$ |
|---|---|---|---|---|---|
| 1 | 1.0000 | 1.0000 | 7.0000 | 0.1429 | 0.8571 |
| 2 | 0.8571 | 0.1695 | 4.7230 | 0.0359 | 0.8213 |
| 3 | 0.8213 | 0.0088 | 4.2390 | 0.0021 | 0.8192 |
| 4 | 0.8192 | 0.0003 | 4.2120 | 0.0000 | 0.8192 |

Approximation of the zero of $f$ is 0.819.

Similarly, the other zero is approximately $-1.380$.

**15.** $f(x) = 1 - x + \sin x$

$f'(x) = -1 + \cos x$

$x_1 = 2$

| $n$ | $x_n$ | $f(x_n)$ | $f'(x_n)$ | $\frac{f(x_n)}{f'(x_n)}$ | $x_n - \frac{f(x_n)}{f'(x_n)}$ |
|---|---|---|---|---|---|
| 1 | 2.0000 | −0.0907 | −1.4161 | 0.0640 | 1.9360 |
| 2 | 1.9360 | −0.0019 | −1.3571 | 0.0014 | 1.9346 |
| 3 | 1.9346 | 0.0000 | −1.3558 | 0.0000 | 1.9346 |

Approximation of the zero of $f$ is 1.935.

**16.** $f(x) = x^3 - \cos x$

$f'(x) = 3x^2 + \sin x$

| $n$ | $x_n$ | $f(x_n)$ | $f'(x_n)$ | $\frac{f(x_n)}{f'(x_n)}$ | $x_n - \frac{f(x_n)}{f'(x_n)}$ |
|---|---|---|---|---|---|
| 1 | 0.9000 | 0.1074 | 3.2133 | 0.0334 | 0.8666 |
| 2 | 0.8666 | 0.0034 | 3.0151 | 0.0011 | 0.8655 |
| 3 | 0.8655 | 0.0000 | 3.0087 | 0.0000 | 0.8655 |

Approximation of the zero of $f$ is 0.866.

**17.** $h(x) = f(x) - g(x) = 2x + 1 - \sqrt{x + 4}$

$h'(x) = 2 - \dfrac{1}{2\sqrt{x + 4}}$

| $n$ | $x_n$ | $h(x_n)$ | $h'(x_n)$ | $\frac{h(x_n)}{h'(x_n)}$ | $x_n - \frac{h(x_n)}{h'(x_n)}$ |
|---|---|---|---|---|---|
| 1 | 0.6000 | 0.0552 | 1.7669 | 0.0313 | 0.5687 |
| 2 | 0.5687 | 0.0000 | 1.7661 | 0.0000 | 0.5687 |

Point of intersection of the graphs of $f$ and $g$ occurs when $x \approx 0.569$.

**18.** $h(x) = f(x) - g(x) = 3 - x - \dfrac{1}{x^2 + 1}$

$h'(x) = -1 + \dfrac{2x}{\left(x^2 + 1\right)^2}$

| $n$ | $x_n$ | $h(x_n)$ | $h'(x_n)$ | $\dfrac{h(x_n)}{h'(x_n)}$ | $x_n - \dfrac{h(x_n)}{h'(x_n)}$ |
|---|---|---|---|---|---|
| 1 | 2.9000 | –0.0063 | –0.9345 | 0.0067 | 2.8933 |
| 2 | 2.8933 | 0.0000 | –0.9341 | 0.0000 | 2.8933 |

Point of intersection of the graphs of $f$ and $g$ occurs when $x \approx 2.893$.

**19.** $h(x) = f(x) - g(x) = x - \tan x$

$h'(x) = 1 - \sec^2 x$

| $n$ | $x_n$ | $h(x_n)$ | $h'(x_n)$ | $\dfrac{h(x_n)}{h'(x_n)}$ | $x_n - \dfrac{h(x_n)}{h'(x_n)}$ |
|---|---|---|---|---|---|
| 1 | 4.5000 | –0.1373 | –21.5048 | 0.0064 | 4.4936 |
| 2 | 4.4936 | –0.0039 | –20.2271 | 0.0002 | 4.4934 |

Point of intersection of the graphs of $f$ and $g$ occurs when $x \approx 4.493$.

**Note:** $f(x) = x$ and $g(x) = \tan x$ intersect infinitely often.

**20.** $h(x) = f(x) - g(x) = x^2 - \cos x$

$h'(x) = 2x + \sin x$

| $n$ | $x_n$ | $h(x_n)$ | $h'(x_n)$ | $\dfrac{h(x_n)}{h'(x_n)}$ | $x_n - \dfrac{h(x_n)}{h'(x_n)}$ |
|---|---|---|---|---|---|
| 1 | 0.8000 | –0.0567 | 2.3174 | –0.0245 | 0.8245 |
| 2 | 0.8245 | 0.0009 | 2.3832 | 0.0004 | 0.8241 |

One point of intersection of the graphs of $f$ and $g$ occurs when $x \approx 0.824$. Because $f(x) = x^2$ and $g(x) = \cos x$ are both symmetric with respect to the $y$-axis, the other point of intersection occurs when $x \approx -0.824$.

**21.** $h(x) = \ln x + x$

$h'(x) = \dfrac{1}{x} + 1$

$x_1 = 0.5$

| $n$ | $x_n$ | $h(x_n)$ | $h'(x_n)$ | $\dfrac{h(x_n)}{h'(x_n)}$ | $x_n - \dfrac{h(x_n)}{h'(x_n)}$ |
|---|---|---|---|---|---|
| 1 | 0.5 | –0.1931 | 3.0000 | –0.0644 | 0.5644 |
| 2 | 0.5644 | –0.0076 | 2.7718 | –0.0027 | 0.5671 |
| 3 | 0.5671 | 0.0001 | 2.7634 | –0.0000 | 0.5671 |

Point of intersection of the graphs of $f$ and $g$ occurs when $x \approx 0.567$.

**22.** $h(x) = e^{x/2} - 2 + x^2$

$h'(x) = \frac{1}{2}e^{x/2} + 2x$

Two points of intersection

| $n$ | $x_n$ | $h(x_n)$ | $h'(x_n)$ | $\frac{h(x_n)}{h'(x_n)}$ | $x_n - \frac{h(x_n)}{h'(x_n)}$ |
|---|---|---|---|---|---|
| 1 | −1 | −0.3935 | −1.6967 | 0.2319 | −1.2319 |
| 2 | −1.2319 | 0.0577 | −2.1937 | −0.0263 | −1.2056 |
| 3 | −1.2056 | 0.0007 | −2.1376 | −0.0004 | −1.2052 |

One point of intersection of the graphs of $f$ and $g$ occurs when $x \approx -1.205$.

| $n$ | $x_n$ | $h(x_n)$ | $h'(x_n)$ | $\frac{h(x_n)}{h'(x_n)}$ | $x_n - \frac{h(x_n)}{h'(x_n)}$ |
|---|---|---|---|---|---|
| 1 | 1 | 0.6487 | 2.8244 | 0.2297 | 0.7703 |
| 2 | 0.7703 | 0.0632 | 2.2755 | 0.0277 | 0.7425 |
| 3 | 0.7425 | 0.0009 | 2.2098 | 0.0004 | 0.7421 |

Another point of intersection of the graphs of $f$ and $g$ occurs when $x \approx 0.742$.

**23.** $h(x) = \arctan x - \arccos x$

$h'(x) = \frac{1}{1 + x^2} + \frac{1}{\sqrt{1 - x^2}}$

| $n$ | $x_n$ | $h(x_n)$ | $h'(x_n)$ | $\frac{h(x_n)}{h'(x_n)}$ | $x_n - \frac{h(x_n)}{h'(x_n)}$ |
|---|---|---|---|---|---|
| 1 | 0.5 | −0.5835 | 1.9547 | −0.2985 | 0.7985 |
| 2 | 0.7985 | 0.0278 | 2.2718 | 0.0122 | 0.7863 |
| 3 | 0.7863 | 0.0003 | 2.2365 | 0.0001 | 0.7862 |

Point of intersection of the graphs of $f$ and $g$ occurs when $x \approx 0.786$.

**24.** $h(x) = \arcsin x - 1 + x$

$h'(x) = \frac{1}{\sqrt{1 - x^2}} + 1$

| $n$ | $x_n$ | $h(x_n)$ | $h'(x_n)$ | $\frac{h(x_n)}{h'(x_n)}$ | $x_n - \frac{h(x_n)}{h'(x_n)}$ |
|---|---|---|---|---|---|
| 1 | 0.5 | 0.0236 | 2.1547 | 0.0110 | 0.4890 |
| 2 | 0.4890 | 0.0001 | 2.1465 | 0.0000 | 0.4890 |

Point of intersection of the graphs of $f$ and $g$ occurs when $x \approx 0.489$.

**25.** (a) $f(x) = x^2 - a, a > 0$

$f'(x) = 2x$

$$x_{n+1} = x_n - \frac{f(x_n)}{f'(x_n)}$$

$$= x_n - \frac{x_n^2 - a}{2x_n}$$

$$= \frac{1}{2}\left(x_n + \frac{a}{x_n}\right)$$

(b) $\sqrt{5}$: $x_{n+1} = \frac{1}{2}\left(x_n + \frac{5}{x_n}\right), x_1 = 2$

| $n$ | 1 | 2 | 3 | 4 |
|---|---|---|---|---|
| $x_n$ | 2 | 2.25 | 2.2361 | 2.2361 |

For example, given $x_1 = 2$,

$$x_2 = \frac{1}{2}\left(2 + \frac{5}{2}\right) = \frac{9}{4} = 2.25.$$

$\sqrt{5} \approx 2.236$

$\sqrt{7}$: $x_{n+1} = \frac{1}{2}\left(x_n + \frac{7}{x_n}\right), x_1 = 2$

| $n$ | 1 | 2 | 3 | 4 | 5 |
|---|---|---|---|---|---|
| $x_n$ | 2 | 2.75 | 2.6477 | 2.6458 | 2.6458 |

$\sqrt{7} \approx 2.646$

**26.** (a) $f(x) = x^n - a, a > 0$

$f'(x) = nx^{n-1}$

$$x_{i+1} = x_i - \frac{f(x_i)}{f'(x_i)}$$

$$= x_i - \frac{x_i^n - a}{nx_i^{n-1}}$$

$$= \frac{(n-1)x_i^n + a}{nx_i^{n-1}}$$

(b) $\sqrt[4]{6}$: $x_{i+1} = \frac{3x_i^4 + 6}{4x_i^3}, x_1 = 1.5$

| $i$ | 1 | 2 | 3 | 4 |
|---|---|---|---|---|
| $x_i$ | 1.5 | 1.5694 | 1.5651 | 1.5651 |

$\sqrt[4]{6} \approx 1.565$

$\sqrt[3]{15}$: $x_{i+1} = \frac{2x_i^3 + 15}{3x_i^2}, x_1 = 2.5$

| $i$ | 1 | 2 | 3 | 4 |
|---|---|---|---|---|
| $x_i$ | 2.5 | 2.4667 | 2.4662 | 2.4662 |

$\sqrt[3]{15} \approx 2.466$

**27.** $y = 2x^3 - 6x^2 + 6x - 1 = f(x)$

$y' = 6x^2 - 12x + 6 = f'(x)$

$x_1 = 1$

$f'(x) = 0$; therefore, the method fails.

| $n$ | $x_n$ | $f(x_n)$ | $f'(x_n)$ |
|---|---|---|---|
| 1 | 1 | 1 | 0 |

**28.** $y = x^3 - 2x - 2, x_1 = 0$

$y' = 3x^2 - 2$

$x_1 = 0$

$x_2 = -1$

$x_3 = 0$

$x_4 = -1$ and so on.

Fails to converge

**29.** $y = -x^3 + 6x^2 - 10x + 6 = f(x)$

$y' = -3x^2 + 12x - 10 = f'(x)$

$x_1 = 2$

$x_2 = 1$

$x_3 = 2$

$x_4 = 1$ and so on.

Fails to converge

**30.** $f(x) = 2\sin x + \cos 2x$

$f'(x) = 2\cos x - 2\sin 2x$

$$x_1 = \frac{3\pi}{2}$$

$f'(x_1) = 0$; therefore, the method fails.

| $n$ | $x_n$ | $f(x_n)$ | $f'(x_n)$ |
|---|---|---|---|
| 1 | $\frac{3\pi}{2}$ | $-3$ | 0 |

**31.** Let $g(x) = f(x) - x = \cos x - x$

$g'(x) = -\sin x - 1.$

| $n$ | $x_n$ | $g(x_n)$ | $g'(x_n)$ | $\dfrac{g(x_n)}{g'(x_n)}$ | $x_n - \dfrac{g(x_n)}{g'(x_n)}$ |
|---|---|---|---|---|---|
| 1 | 1.0000 | –0.4597 | –1.8415 | 0.2496 | 0.7504 |
| 2 | 0.7504 | –0.0190 | –1.6819 | 0.0113 | 0.7391 |
| 3 | 0.7391 | 0.0000 | –1.6736 | 0.0000 | 0.7391 |

The fixed point is approximately 0.74.

**32.** Let $g(x) = f(x) - x = \cot x - x$

$g'(x) = -\csc^2 x - 1.$

| $n$ | $x_n$ | $g(x_n)$ | $g'(x_n)$ | $\dfrac{g(x_n)}{g'(x_n)}$ | $x_n - \dfrac{g(x_n)}{g'(x_n)}$ |
|---|---|---|---|---|---|
| 1 | 1.0000 | –0.3579 | –2.4123 | 0.1484 | 0.8516 |
| 2 | 0.8516 | 0.0240 | –2.7668 | –0.0087 | 0.8603 |
| 3 | 0.8603 | 0.0001 | –2.7403 | 0.0000 | 0.8603 |

The fixed point is approximately 0.86.

**33.** Let $g(x) = e^{x/10} - x$

$g'(x) = \dfrac{1}{10}e^{x/10} - 1$

| $n$ | $x_n$ | $g(x_n)$ | $g'(x_n)$ | $\dfrac{g(x_n)}{g'(x_n)}$ | $x_n - \dfrac{g(x_n)}{g'(x_n)}$ |
|---|---|---|---|---|---|
| 1 | 1.0 | 0.1052 | –0.8895 | –0.1182 | 1.1182 |
| 2 | 1.1182 | 0.0001 | –0.8882 | –0.0001 | 1.1183 |

The fixed point is approximately 1.12.

**34.** Let $g(x) = x + \ln x$

$g'(x) = \dfrac{1}{x} + 1$

| $n$ | $x_n$ | $g(x_n)$ | $g'(x_n)$ | $\dfrac{g(x_n)}{g'(x_n)}$ | $x_n - \dfrac{g(x_n)}{g'(x_n)}$ |
|---|---|---|---|---|---|
| 1 | 0.5 | –0.1931 | 3 | –0.0644 | 0.5644 |
| 2 | 0.5644 | –0.0076 | 2.7718 | –0.0027 | 0.5671 |

The fixed point is approximately 0.57.

**35.** $f(x) = x^3 - 3x^2 + 3, f'(x) = 3x^2 - 6x$

(a)

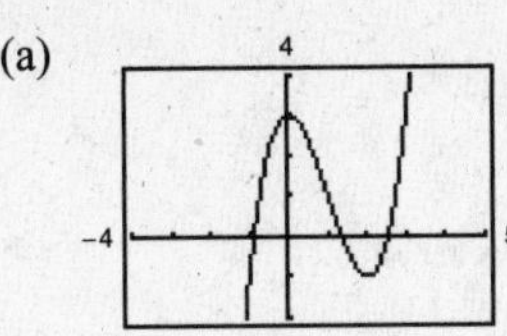

(b) $x_1 = 1$

$$x_2 = x_1 - \frac{f(x_1)}{f'(x_1)} \approx 1.333$$

Continuing, the zero is 1.347.

(c) $x_1 = \frac{1}{4}$

$$x_2 = x_1 - \frac{f(x_1)}{f'(x_1)} \approx 2.405$$

Continuing, the zero is 2.532.

(d)

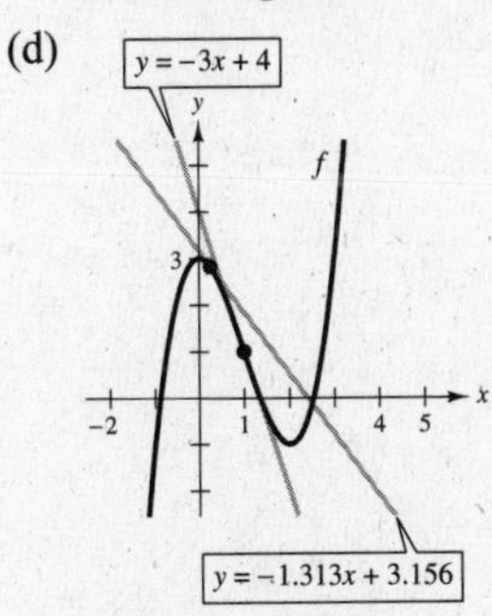


The $x$-intercept of $y = -3x + 4$ is $\frac{4}{3}$. The $x$-intercept of $y = 1.313x + 3.156$ is approximately 2.405.

The $x$-intercepts correspond to the values resulting from the first iteration of Newton's Method.

(e) If the initial guess $x_1$ is not "close to" the desired zero of the function, the $x$-intercept of the tangent line may approximate another zero of the function.

**36.** $f(x) = \sin x, f'(x) = \cos x$

(a)

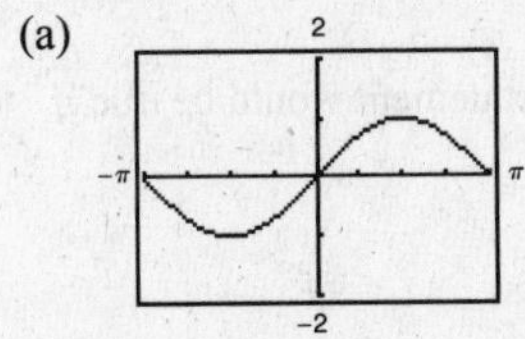

(b) $x_1 = 1.8$

$$x_2 = x_1 - \frac{f(x_1)}{f'(x_1)} \approx 6.086$$

(c) $x_1 = 3$

$$x_2 = x_1 - \frac{f(x_1)}{f'(x_1)} \approx 3.143$$

(d)

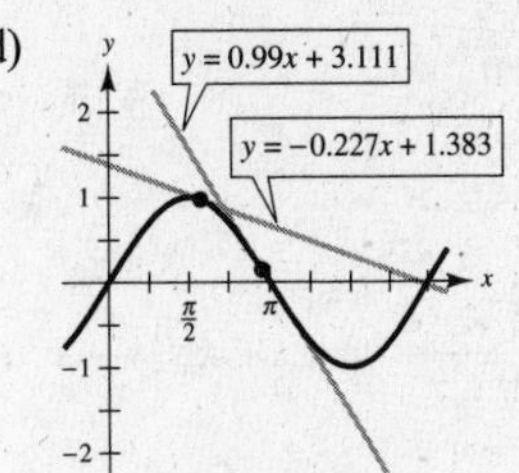


The $x$-intercept of $y = -0.227x + 1.383$ is approximately 6.086. The $x$-intercept of $y = 0.99x + 3.111$ is approximately 3.143.

The $x$-intercepts correspond to the values resulting from the first iteration of Newton's Method.

(e) If the initial guess $x_1$ is not "close to" the desired zero of the function, the $x$-intercept of the tangent line may approximate another zero of the function.

**37.** Answers will vary. See page 191.

If $f$ is a function continuous on $[a, b]$ and differentiable on $(a, b)$ where $c \in [a, b]$ and $f(c) = 0$, Newton's Method uses tangent lines to approximate $c$ such that $f(c) = 0$.

First, estimate an initial $x_1$ close to $c$ (see graph).

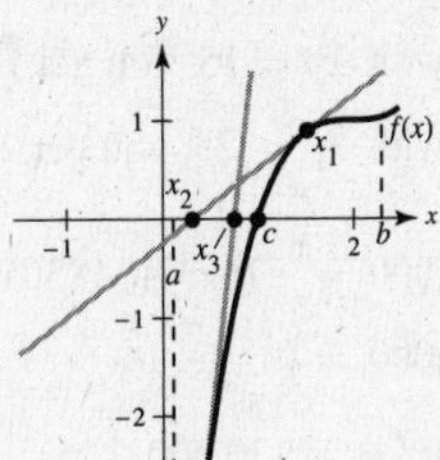

Then determine $x_2$ by $x_2 = x_1 - \frac{f(x_1)}{f'(x_1)}$.

Calculate a third estimate by $x_3 = x_2 - \frac{f(x_2)}{f'(x_2)}$.

Continue this process until $|x_n - x_{n+1}|$ is within the desired accuracy.

Let $x_{n+1}$ be the final approximation of $c$.

**38.** Newton's Method could fail if $f'(c) \approx 0$, or if the initial value $x_1$ is far from $c$.

**39.** $f(x) = \frac{1}{x} - a = 0$

$f'(x) = -\frac{1}{x^2}$

$$x_{n+1} = x_n - \frac{(1/x_n) - a}{-1/x_n^2} = x_n + x_n^2\left(\frac{1}{x_n} - a\right) = x_n + x_n - x_n^2 a = 2x_n - x_n^2 a = x_n(2 - ax_n)$$

**40.** (a) $x_{n+1} = x_n(2 - 3x_n)$

| $i$ | 1 | 2 | 3 | 4 |
|---|---|---|---|---|
| $x_i$ | 0.3000 | 0.3300 | 0.3333 | 0.3333 |

$\frac{1}{3} \approx 0.333$

(b) $x_{n+1} = x_n(2 - 11x_n)$

| $i$ | 1 | 2 | 3 | 4 |
|---|---|---|---|---|
| $x_i$ | 0.1000 | 0.0900 | 0.0909 | 0.0909 |

$\frac{1}{11} \approx 0.091$

**41.** $225 = 0.602x^3 - 41.44x^2 + 922.8x - 6330, 14 \le x \le 27.$

$0.602x^3 - 41.44x^2 + 922.8x - 6555 = 0$

Using Newton's Method with $x_1 = 15$, you get 15.1 years

Using Newton's Method with $x_1 = 25$, you get 26.8 years

**42.**
$$2{,}500{,}000 = -76x^3 + 4830x^2 - 320{,}000$$

$76x^3 - 4830x^2 + 2{,}820{,}000 = 0$

Let $f(x) = 76x^3 - 4830x^2 + 2{,}820{,}000$

$f'(x) = 228x^2 - 9660x.$

From the graph, choose $x_1 = 40.$

The zero occurs when $x \approx 38.4356$ which corresponds to \$384,356.

| $n$ | $x_n$ | $f(x_n)$ | $f'(x_n)$ | $\frac{f(x_n)}{f'(x_n)}$ | $x_n - \frac{f(x_n)}{f'(x_n)}$ |
|---|---|---|---|---|---|
| 1 | 40.0000 | −44000.0000 | −21600.0000 | 2.0370 | 37.9630 |
| 2 | 37.9630 | 17157.6209 | −38131.4039 | −0.4500 | 38.4130 |
| 3 | 38.4130 | 780.0914 | −34642.2263 | −0.0225 | 38.4355 |
| 4 | 38.4355 | 2.6308 | −34465.3435 | −0.0001 | 38.4356 |

**43.** False. Let $f(x) = (x^2 - 1)/(x - 1)$. $x = 1$ is a discontinuity. It is not a zero of $f(x)$. This statement would be true if $f(x) = p(x)/q(x)$ was given in **reduced** form.

**44.** True

**45.** True

**46.** True

**47.** $f(x) = \frac{1}{4}x^3 - 3x^2 + \frac{3}{4}x - 2$

$f'(x) = \frac{3}{4}x^2 - 6x + \frac{3}{4}$

Let $x_1 = 12$.

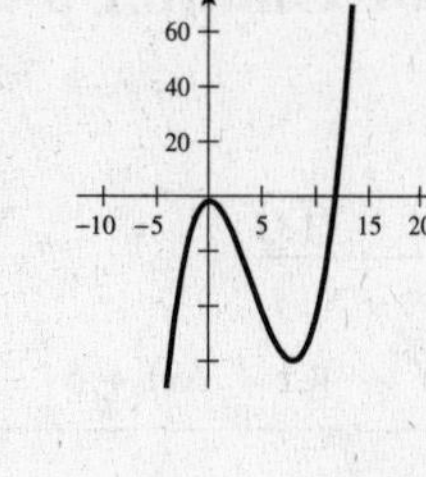

| $n$ | $x_n$ | $f(x_n)$ | $f'(x_n)$ | $\frac{f(x_n)}{f'(x_n)}$ | $x_n - \frac{f(x_n)}{f'(x_n)}$ |
|---|---|---|---|---|---|
| 1 | 12.0000 | 7.0000 | 36.7500 | 0.1905 | 11.8095 |
| 2 | 11.8095 | 0.2151 | 34.4912 | 0.0062 | 11.8033 |
| 3 | 11.8033 | 0.0015 | 34.4186 | 0.0000 | 11.8033 |

Approximation: $x \approx 11.803$

**48.** $f(x) = \sqrt{4 - x^2}\sin(x - 2)$

Domain: $[-2, 2]$

$x = -2$ and $x = 2$ are both zeros.

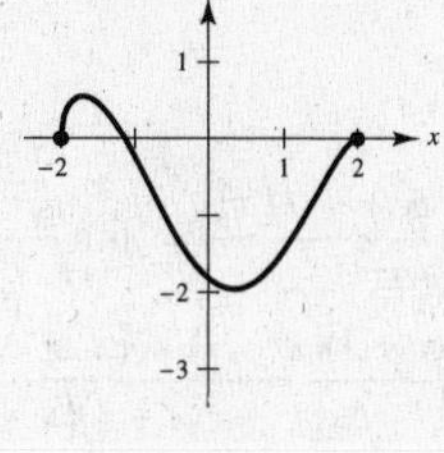

$$f'(x) = \sqrt{4 - x^2}\cos(x - 2) - \frac{x}{\sqrt{4 - x^2}}\sin(x - 2)$$

Let $x_1 = -1$.

| $n$ | $x_n$ | $f(x_n)$ | $f'(x_n)$ | $\frac{f(x_n)}{f'(x_n)}$ | $x_n - \frac{f(x_n)}{f'(x_n)}$ |
|---|---|---|---|---|---|
| 1 | −1.0000 | −0.2444 | −1.7962 | 0.1361 | −1.1361 |
| 2 | −1.1361 | −0.0090 | −1.6498 | 0.0055 | −1.1416 |
| 3 | −1.1416 | 0.0000 | −1.6422 | 0.0000 | −1.1416 |

Zeros: $x = \pm 2, x \approx -1.142$

**49.** $f(x) = -\sin x$

$f'(x) = -\cos x$

Let $(x_0, y_0) = (x_0, -\sin(x_0))$ be a point on the graph of $f$. If $(x_0, y_0)$ is a point of tangency, then

$$-\cos(x_0) = \frac{y_0 - 0}{x_0 - 0} = \frac{y_0}{x_0} = \frac{-\sin(x_0)}{x_0}.$$

So, $x_0 = \tan(x_0)$.

$x_0 \approx 4.4934$

Slope $= -\cos(x_0) \approx 0.217$

You can verify this answer by graphing $y_1 = -\sin x$ and the tangent line $y_2 = 0.217x$.

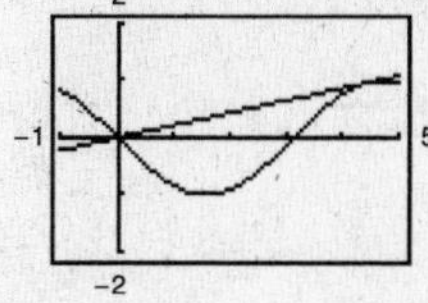


**50.** Let $(x_1, y_1)$ be the point of tangency.

$f(x) = \cos x,\ f'(x) = -\sin x,\ f'(x_1) = -\sin(x_1)$.

At the point of tangency,

$$f'(x_1) = \frac{y_1 - 0}{x_1 - 0}$$

$$-\sin(x_1) = \cos(x_1)/x_1$$

$$\cos(x_1) + x_1\sin(x_1) = 0$$

Using Newton's method with initial guess 3, you obtain $x_1 \approx 2.798$ and $y_1 \approx -0.942$.

# Review Exercises for Chapter 3

1. $f(x) = x^2 - 4x + 5$

$$f'(x) = \lim_{\Delta x \to 0} \frac{f(x + \Delta x) - f(x)}{\Delta x}$$

$$= \lim_{\Delta x \to 0} \frac{\left[(x + \Delta x)^2 - 4(x + \Delta x) + 5\right] - \left[x^2 - 4x + 5\right]}{\Delta x}$$

$$= \lim_{\Delta x \to 0} \frac{\left(x^2 + 2x(\Delta x) + (\Delta x)^2 - 4x - 4(\Delta x) + 5\right) - \left(x^2 - 4x + 5\right)}{\Delta x}$$

$$= \lim_{\Delta x \to 0} \frac{2x(\Delta x) + (\Delta x)^2 - 4(\Delta x)}{\Delta x} = \lim_{\Delta x \to 0} (2x + \Delta x - 4) = 2x - 4$$

2. $f(x) = \dfrac{x + 1}{x - 1}$

$$f'(x) = \lim_{\Delta x \to 0} \frac{f(x + \Delta x) - f(x)}{\Delta x} = \lim_{\Delta x \to 0} \frac{\dfrac{x + \Delta x + 1}{x + \Delta x - 1} - \dfrac{x + 1}{x - 1}}{\Delta x}$$

$$= \lim_{\Delta x \to 0} \frac{(x + \Delta x + 1)(x - 1) - (x + \Delta x - 1)(x + 1)}{\Delta x(x + \Delta x - 1)(x - 1)}$$

$$= \lim_{\Delta x \to 0} \frac{\left(x^2 + x\,\Delta x + x - x - \Delta x - 1\right) - \left(x^2 + x\,\Delta x - x + x + \Delta x - 1\right)}{\Delta x(x + \Delta x - 1)(x - 1)}$$

$$= \lim_{\Delta x \to 0} \frac{-2\,\Delta x}{\Delta x(x + \Delta x - 1)(x - 1)} = \lim_{\Delta x \to 0} \frac{-2}{(x + \Delta x - 1)(x - 1)} = \frac{-2}{(x - 1)^2}$$

3. $f(x) = \sqrt{x} + 1$

$$f'(x) = \lim_{\Delta x \to 0} \frac{f(x + \Delta x) - f(x)}{\Delta x}$$

$$= \lim_{\Delta x \to 0} \frac{\left(\sqrt{x + \Delta x} + 1\right) - \left(\sqrt{x} + 1\right)}{\Delta x}$$

$$= \lim_{\Delta x \to 0} \frac{\sqrt{x + \Delta x} - \sqrt{x}}{\Delta x} \cdot \frac{\sqrt{x + \Delta x} + \sqrt{x}}{\sqrt{x + \Delta x} + \sqrt{x}}$$

$$= \lim_{\Delta x \to 0} \frac{(x + \Delta x) - x}{\Delta x\left(\sqrt{x + \Delta x} + \sqrt{x}\right)}$$

$$= \lim_{\Delta x \to 0} \frac{1}{\sqrt{x + \Delta x} + \sqrt{x}} = \frac{1}{2\sqrt{x}} = \frac{\sqrt{x}}{2x}$$

4. $f(x) = \dfrac{6}{x}$

$$f'(x) = \lim_{\Delta x \to 0} \frac{f(x + \Delta x) - f(x)}{\Delta x}$$

$$= \lim_{\Delta x \to 0} \frac{\dfrac{6}{x + \Delta x} - \dfrac{6}{x}}{\Delta x} = \lim_{\Delta x \to 0} \frac{6x - (6x + 6\,\Delta x)}{\Delta x(x + \Delta x)x} = \lim_{\Delta x \to 0} \frac{-6\,\Delta x}{\Delta x(x + \Delta x)x} = \lim_{\Delta x \to 0} \frac{-6}{(x + \Delta x)x} = \frac{-6}{x^2}$$

**5.** $f$ is differentiable for all $x \neq 3$.

**6.** $f$ is differentiable for all $x \neq -1$.

**7.** $f(x) = 4 - |x - 2|$

(a) Continuous at $x = 2$

(b) Not differentiable at $x = 2$ because of the sharp turn in the graph. Also, the derivatives from the left and right are not equal.

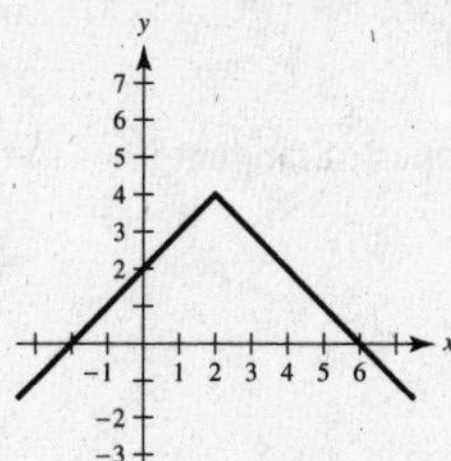

**8.** $f(x) = \begin{cases} x^2 + 4x + 2, & \text{if } x < -2 \\ 1 - 4x - x^2, & \text{if } x \geq -2 \end{cases}$

(a) Nonremovable discontinuity at $x = -2$

(b) Not differentiable at $x = -2$ because the function is discontinuous there.

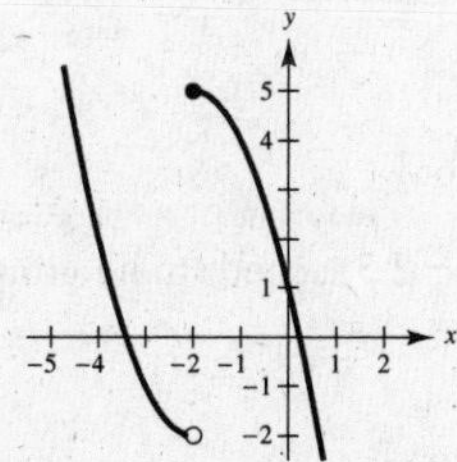

**9.** Using the limit definition, you obtain $g'(x) = \frac{4}{3}x - \frac{1}{6}$. At $x = -1$,

$g'(-1) = -\frac{4}{3} - \frac{1}{6} = -\frac{3}{2}$.

**10.** Using the limit definition, you obtain $h'(x) = \frac{3}{8} - 4x$. At $x = -2$,

$h'(-2) = \frac{3}{8} - 4(-2) = \frac{67}{8}$.

**11.** (a) Using the limit definition, $f'(x) = 3x^2$. At $x = -1$, $f'(-1) = 3$. The tangent line is

$$y - (-2) = 3(x - (-1))$$
$$y = 3x + 1.$$

(b)

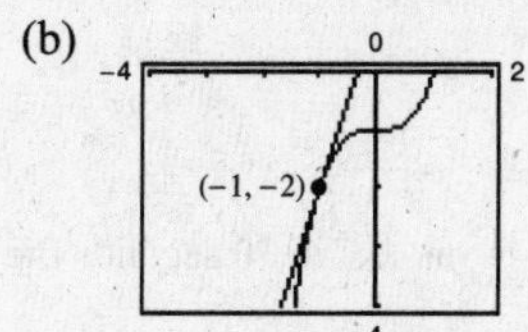

**12.** (a) Using the limit definition,

$$f'(x) = \frac{-2}{(x + 1)^2}.$$

At $x = 0$, $f'(0) = -2$. The tangent line is

$$y - 2 = -2(x - 0)$$
$$y = -2x + 2.$$

(b)

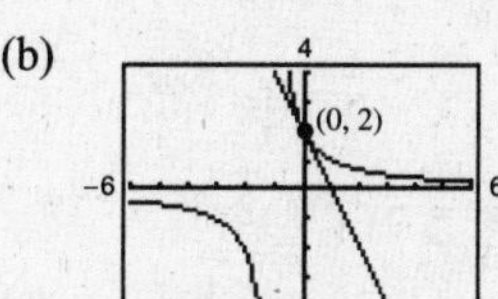

**13.**
$$\begin{aligned} g'(2) &= \lim_{x \to 2} \frac{g(x) - g(2)}{x - 2} \\ &= \lim_{x \to 2} \frac{x^2(x - 1) - 4}{x - 2} \\ &= \lim_{x \to 2} \frac{x^3 - x^2 - 4}{x - 2} \\ &= \lim_{x \to 2} \frac{(x - 2)(x^2 + x + 2)}{x - 2} \\ &= \lim_{x \to 2}(x^2 + x + 2) = 8 \end{aligned}$$

**14.**
$$\begin{aligned} f'(3) &= \lim_{x \to 3} \frac{f(x) - f(3)}{x - 3} \\ &= \lim_{x \to 3} \frac{\frac{1}{x + 4} - \frac{1}{7}}{x - 3} \\ &= \lim_{x \to 3} \frac{7 - x - 4}{(x - 3)(x + 4)7} \\ &= \lim_{x \to 3} \frac{-1}{(x + 4)7} = -\frac{1}{49} \end{aligned}$$

**15.** $y = 25$

$y' = 0$

**16.** $y = -30$

$y' = 0$

**17.** $f(x) = x^8$

$f'(x) = 8x^7$

**18.** $g(x) = x^{20}$

$g'(x) = 20x^{19}$

**19.** $h(t) = 3t^4$

$h'(t) = 12t^3$

**20.** $f(t) = -8t^5$

$f'(t) = -40t^4$

**21.** $f(x) = x^3 - 3x^2$

$f'(x) = 3x^2 - 6x = 3x(x - 2)$

**22.** $g(s) = 4s^4 - 5s^2$

$g'(s) = 16s^3 - 10s$

**23.** $h(x) = 6\sqrt{x} + 3\sqrt[3]{x} = 6x^{1/2} + 3x^{1/3}$

$h'(x) = 3x^{-1/2} + x^{-2/3} = \dfrac{3}{\sqrt{x}} + \dfrac{1}{\sqrt[3]{x^2}}$

**24.** $f(x) = x^{1/2} - x^{-1/2}$

$f'(x) = \dfrac{1}{2}x^{-1/2} + \dfrac{1}{2}x^{-3/2} = \dfrac{x + 1}{2x^{3/2}}$

**25.** $g(t) = \dfrac{2}{3}t^{-2}$

$g'(t) = \dfrac{-4}{3}t^{-3} = -\dfrac{4}{3t^3}$

**26.** $h(x) = \dfrac{10}{49}x^{-2}$

$h'(x) = \dfrac{-20}{49}x^{-3} = -\dfrac{20}{49x^3}$

**27.** $f(\theta) = 4\theta - 5 \sin \theta$

$f'(\theta) = 4 - 5 \cos \theta$

**28.** $g(\alpha) = 4 \cos \alpha + 6$

$g'(\alpha) = -4 \sin \alpha$

**29.** $f(t) = 3 \cos t - 4e^t$

$f'(t) = -3 \sin t - 4e^t$

**30.** $g(s) = \frac{5}{3} \sin s - 2e^s$

$g'(s) = \frac{5}{3} \cos s - 2e^s$

**31.**

$f' > 0$ where the slopes of tangent lines to the graph of $f$ are positive.

**32.**

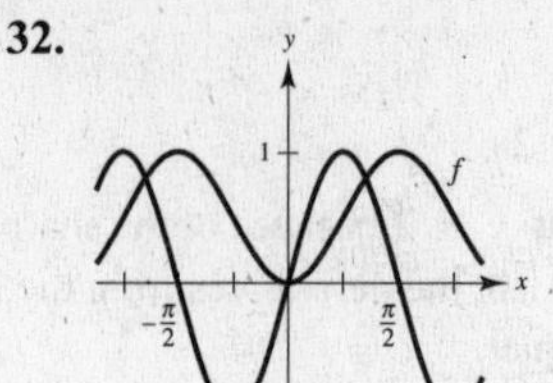


$f' = 0$ where the slopes of tangent lines to the graph of $f$ are 0.

**33.** $F = 200\sqrt{T}$

$F'(t) = \dfrac{100}{\sqrt{T}}$

(a) When $T = 4$, $F'(4) = 50$ vibrations/sec/lb.

(b) When $T = 9$, $F'(9) = 33\frac{1}{3}$ vibrations/sec/lb.

**34.** $s = -16t^2 + s_0$

First ball:

$-16t^2 + 100 = 0$

$t = \sqrt{\dfrac{100}{16}}$

$= \dfrac{10}{4} = 2.5$ seconds to hit ground

Second ball:

$-16t^2 + 75 = 0$

$t^2 = \sqrt{\dfrac{75}{16}}$

$= \dfrac{5\sqrt{3}}{4} \approx 2.165$ seconds to hit ground

Because the second ball was released one second after the first ball, the first ball will hit the ground first. The second ball will hit the ground $3.165 - 2.5 = 0.665$ second later.

**35.** $s(t) = -16t^2 + s_0$

$s(9.2) = -16(9.2)^2 + s_0 = 0$

$s_0 = 1354.24$

The building is approximately 1354 feet high (or 415 m).

**36.** $s(t) = -16t^2 + 14{,}400 = 0$

$16t^2 = 14{,}400$

$t = 30$ sec

Because 600 mi/h $= \frac{1}{6}$ mi/sec, in 30 seconds the bomb will move horizontally $\left(\frac{1}{6}\right)(30) = 5$ miles.

**37.** (a)

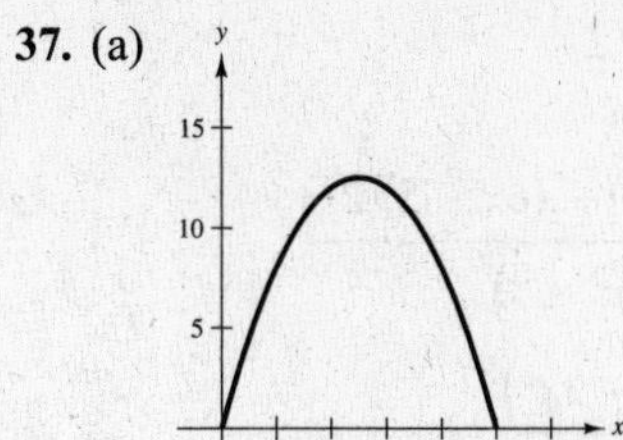


Total horizontal distance: 50

(b) $0 = x - 0.02x^2$

$0 = x\left(1 - \dfrac{x}{50}\right)$ implies $x = 50$.

(c) Ball reaches maximum height when $x = 25$.

(d) $y = x - 0.02x^2$

$y' = 1 - 0.04x$

$y'(0) = 1$

$y'(10) = 0.6$

$y'(25) = 0$

$y'(30) = -0.2$

$y'(50) = -1$

(e) $y'(25) = 0$

**38.**

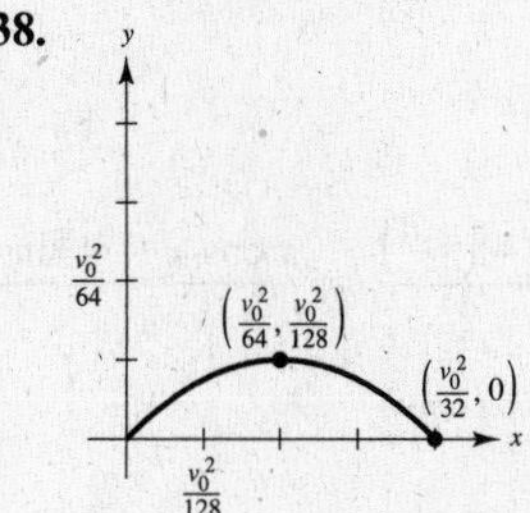


(a) $y = x - \dfrac{32}{v_0^2}x^2 = x\left(1 - \dfrac{32}{v_0^2}x\right)$

$= 0$ if $x = 0$ or $x = \dfrac{v_0^2}{32}$

Projectile strikes the ground when $x = v_0^2/32$.

Projectile reaches its maximum height at $x = v_0^2/64$ (one-half the distance).

(b) $y' = 1 - \dfrac{64}{v_0^2}x$

When $x = \dfrac{v_0^2}{64}$, $y' = 1 - \dfrac{64}{v_0^2}\left(\dfrac{v_0^2}{64}\right) = 0$.

(c) $y = x - \dfrac{32}{v_0^2}x^2 = x\left(1 - \dfrac{32}{v_0^2}x\right) = 0$

when $x = 0$ and $x = s_0^2/32$. Therefore, the range is $x = v_0^2/32$. When the initial velocity is doubled the range is

$$x = \frac{(2v_0)^2}{32} = \frac{4v_0^2}{32}$$

or four times the initial range. From part (a), the maximum height occurs when $x = v_0^2/64$. The maximum height is

$$y\left(\frac{v_0^2}{64}\right) = \frac{v_0^2}{64} - \frac{32}{v_0^2}\left(\frac{v_0^2}{64}\right)^2 = \frac{v_0^2}{64} - \frac{v_0^2}{128} = \frac{v_0^2}{128}.$$

If the initial velocity is doubled, the maximum height is

$$y\left[\frac{(2v_0)^2}{64}\right] = \frac{(2v_0)^2}{128} = 4\left(\frac{v_0^2}{128}\right)$$

or four times the original maximum height.

(d) $v_0 = 70$ ft/sec

Range: $x = \dfrac{v_0^2}{32} = \dfrac{(70)^2}{32} = 153.125$ ft

Maximum height: $y = \dfrac{v_0^2}{128} = \dfrac{(70)^2}{128} \approx 38.28$ ft

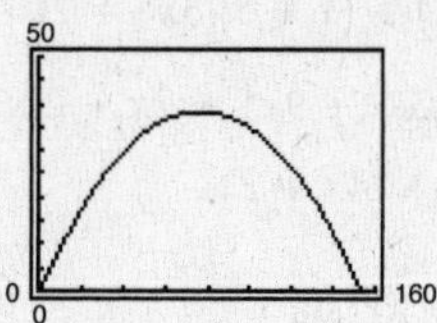


**39.** $x(t) = t^2 - 3t + 2 = (t - 2)(t - 1)$

(a) $v(t) = x'(t) = 2t - 3$

(b) $v(t) < 0$ for $t < \frac{3}{2}$

(c) $v(t) = 0$ for $t = \frac{3}{2}$

$x = \left(\frac{3}{2} - 2\right)\left(\frac{3}{2} - 1\right) = \left(-\frac{1}{2}\right)\left(\frac{1}{2}\right) = -\frac{1}{4}$

(d) $x(t) = 0$ for $t = 1, 2$

$|v(1)| = |2(1) - 3| = 1$

$|v(2)| = |2(2) - 3| = 1$

The speed is 1 when the position is 0.

**40.** (a) $y = 0.14x^2 - 4.43x + 58.4$

(b)

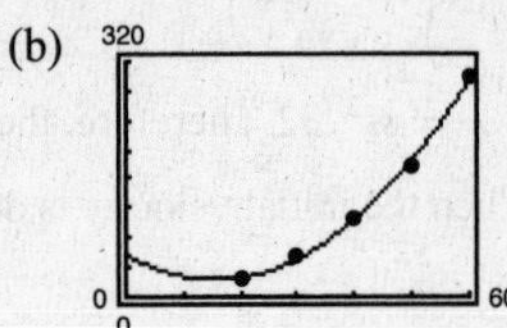


(c)

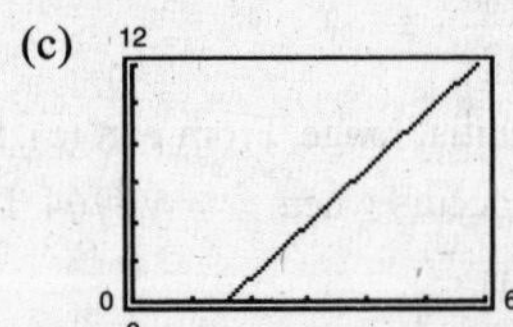


(d) If $x = 65$, $y \approx 362$ feet.

(e) As the speed increases, the stopping distance increases at an increasing rate.

**41.** $f(x) = (5x^2 + 8)(x^2 - 4x - 6)$

$$f'(x) = (5x^2 + 8)(2x - 4) + (x^2 - 4x - 6)(10x)$$
$$= 10x^3 + 16x - 20x^2 - 32 + 10x^3 - 40x^2 - 60x$$
$$= 20x^3 - 60x^2 - 44x - 32$$
$$= 4(5x^3 - 15x^2 - 11x - 8)$$

**42.** $g(x) = (x^3 + 7x)(x + 3)$

$$g'(x) = (x^3 + 7x)(1) + (x + 3)(3x^2 + 7)$$
$$= x^3 + 7x + 3x^3 + 9x^2 + 7x + 21$$
$$= 4x^3 + 9x^2 + 14x + 21$$

**43.** $h(x) = \sqrt{x}\sin x = x^{1/2}\sin x$

$$h'(x) = \frac{1}{2\sqrt{x}}\sin x + \sqrt{x}\cos x$$

**44.** $f(t) = 2t^5 \cos t$

$$f'(t) = 2t^5(-\sin t) + \cos t(10t^4)$$
$$= -2t^5 \sin t + 10t^4 \cos t$$

**45.** $f(x) = \dfrac{x^2 + x - 1}{x^2 - 1}$

$$f'(x) = \frac{(x^2 - 1)(2x + 1) - (x^2 + x - 1)(2x)}{(x^2 - 1)^2}$$
$$= \frac{-(x^2 + 1)}{(x^2 - 1)^2}$$

**46.** $f(x) = \dfrac{6x - 5}{x^2 + 1}$

$$f'(x) = \frac{(x^2 + 1)(6) - (6x - 5)(2x)}{(x^2 + 1)^2}$$
$$= \frac{2(3 + 5x - 3x^2)}{(x^2 + 1)^2}$$

**47.** $f(x) = (9 - 4x^2)^{-1}$

$$f'(x) = -(9 - 4x^2)^{-2}(-8x) = \frac{8x}{(9 - 4x^2)^2}$$

**48.** $f(x) = 9(3x^2 - 2x)^{-1}$

$$f'(x) = -9(3x^2 - 2x)^{-2}(6x - 2) = \frac{18(1 - 3x)}{(3x^2 - 2x)^2}$$

**49.** $y = \dfrac{x^4}{\cos x}$

$$y' = \frac{(\cos x)\,4x^3 - x^4(-\sin x)}{\cos^2 x}$$
$$= \frac{4x^3 \cos x + x^4 \sin x}{\cos^2 x}$$

**50.** $y = \dfrac{\sin x}{x^4}$

$$y' = \frac{(x^4)\cos x - (\sin x)(4x^3)}{(x^4)^2} = \frac{x\cos x - 4\sin x}{x^5}$$

**51.** $y = 3x^2 \sec x$

$$y' = 3x^2 \sec x \tan x + 6x \sec x$$

**52.** $y = 2x - x^2 \tan x$

$$y' = 2 - x^2 \sec^2 x - 2x \tan x$$

**53.** $y = x\cos x - \sin x$

$$y' = -x\sin x + \cos x - \cos x = -x\sin x$$

**54.** $g(x) = 3x\sin x + x^2 \cos x$

$$g'(x) = 3x\cos x + 3\sin x - x^2 \sin x + 2x\cos x$$
$$= 5x\cos x + (3 - x^2)\sin x$$

**55.** $y = 4xe^x$

$$y' = 4xe^x + 4e^x = 4e^x(x + 1)$$

**56.** $y = \dfrac{1 + \sin x}{1 - \sin x}$

$$y' = \frac{(1 - \sin x)\cos x - (1 + \sin x)(-\cos x)}{(1 - \sin x)^2}$$

$$= \frac{2\cos x}{(1 - \sin x)^2}$$

**57.** $f(x) = \dfrac{2x^3 - 1}{x^2} = 2x - x^{-2}, \quad (1, 1)$

$f'(x) = 2 + 2x^{-3}$

$f'(1) = 4$

Tangent line: $y - 1 = 4(x - 1)$

$y = 4x - 3$

**58.** $f(x) = \dfrac{x + 1}{x - 1}, \left(\dfrac{1}{2}, -3\right)$

$$f'(x) = \frac{(x - 1) - (x + 1)}{(x - 1)^2} = \frac{-2}{(x - 1)^2}$$

$$f'\left(\frac{1}{2}\right) = \frac{-2}{(1/4)} = -8$$

Tangent line: $y + 3 = -8\left(x - \dfrac{1}{2}\right)$

$y = -8x + 1$

**59.** $f(x) = -x\tan x, \quad (0, 0)$

$f'(x) = -x\sec^2 x - \tan x$

$f'(0) = 0$

Tangent line: $y - 0 = 0(x - 0)$

$y = 0$

**60.** $f(x) = \dfrac{1 + \cos x}{1 - \cos x}, \left(\dfrac{\pi}{2}, 1\right)$

$$f'(x) = \frac{(1 - \cos x)(-\sin x) - (1 + \cos x)(\sin x)}{(1 - \cos x)^2}$$

$$= \frac{-2\sin x}{(1 - \cos x)^2}$$

$$f'\left(\frac{\pi}{2}\right) = \frac{-2}{1} = -2$$

Tangent line: $y - 1 = -2\left(x - \dfrac{\pi}{2}\right)$

$y = -2x + 1 + \pi$

**61.** $v(t) = 36 - t^2, \quad 0 \le t \le 6$

$a(t) = v'(t) = -2t$

$v(4) = 36 - 16 = 20$ m/sec

$a(4) = -8$ m/sec$^2$

**62.** $v(t) = \dfrac{90t}{4t + 10}$

$$a(t) = \frac{(4t + 10)90 - 90t(4)}{(4t + 10)^2}$$

$$= \frac{900}{(4t + 10)^2} = \frac{225}{(2t + 5)^2}$$

(a) $v(1) = \dfrac{90}{14} \approx 6.43$ ft/sec

$a(1) = \dfrac{225}{49} \approx 4.59$ ft/sec$^2$

(b) $v(5) = \dfrac{90(5)}{30} = 15$ ft/sec

$a(5) = \dfrac{225}{15^2} = 1$ ft/sec$^2$

(c) $v(10) = \dfrac{90(10)}{50} = 18$ ft/sec

$a(10) = \dfrac{225}{25^2} = 0.36$ ft/sec$^2$

**63.** $g(t) = -8t^3 - 5t + 12$

$g'(t) = -24t^2 - 5$

$g''(t) = -48t$

**64.** $h(x) = 21x^{-3} + 3x$

$h'(x) = -63x^{-4} + 3$

$h''(x) = 252x^{-5} = \dfrac{252}{x^5}$

**65.** $f(x) = 15x^{5/2}$

$f'(x) = \frac{75}{2}x^{3/2}$

$f''(x) = \frac{225}{4}x^{1/2} = \frac{225}{4}\sqrt{x}$

**66.** $f(x) = 20\sqrt[5]{x} = 20x^{1/5}$

$f'(x) = 4x^{-4/5}$

$f''(x) = \dfrac{-16}{5}x^{-9/5} = -\dfrac{16}{5x^{9/5}}$

**67.** $f(\theta) = 3\tan\theta$

$f'(\theta) = 3\sec^2\theta$

$f''(\theta) = 6\sec\theta(\sec\theta\tan\theta)$

$= 6\sec^2\theta\tan\theta$

**68.** $h(t) = 10\cos t - 15\sin t$

$h'(t) = -10\sin t - 15\cos t$

$h''(t) = -10\cos t + 15\sin t$

69.
$$y = 2\sin x + 3\cos x$$
$$y' = 2\cos x - 3\sin x$$
$$y'' = -2\sin x - 3\cos x$$
$$y'' + y = -(2\sin x + 3\cos x) + (2\sin x + 3\cos x) = 0$$

70.
$$y = \frac{(10 - \cos x)}{x}$$
$$xy + \cos x = 10$$
$$xy' + y - \sin x = 0$$
$$xy' + y = \sin x$$

71. $f(x) = \sec x,\ g(x) = \csc x,\ f'(x) = g'(x)$ on $[0, 2\pi)$
$$\sec x \tan x = -\csc x \cot x$$
$$\frac{\sec x \tan x}{\csc x \cot x} = -1$$
$$\frac{\frac{1}{\cos x}\frac{\sin x}{\cos x}}{\frac{1}{\sin x}\frac{\cos x}{\sin x}} = -1$$
$$\frac{\sin^3 x}{\cos^3 x} = -1$$
$$\tan^3 x = -1$$
$$\tan x = -1$$
$$x = \frac{3\pi}{4}, \frac{7\pi}{4}$$

72.
$$V = \pi r^2 h = \pi(t + 2)\left(\frac{1}{2}\sqrt{t}\right)$$
$$= \frac{1}{2}\pi\left(t^{3/2} + 2t^{1/2}\right)$$
$$\frac{dV}{dt} = \frac{1}{2}\pi\left(\frac{3}{2}t^{1/2} + t^{-1/2}\right)$$
$$= \frac{3t + 2}{4\sqrt{t}}\pi \text{ cubic inch/sec}$$

73.
$$h(x) = \left(\frac{x + 5}{x^2 + 3}\right)^2$$
$$h'(x) = 2\left(\frac{x + 5}{x^2 + 3}\right)\left(\frac{(x^2 + 3)(1) - (x + 5)(2x)}{(x^2 + 3)^2}\right)$$
$$= \frac{2(x + 5)(-x^2 - 10x + 3)}{(x^2 + 3)^3}$$

74.
$$f(x) = \left(x^2 + \frac{1}{x}\right)^5$$
$$f'(x) = 5\left(x^2 + \frac{1}{x}\right)^4\left(2x - \frac{1}{x^2}\right)$$

75.
$$f(s) = \left(s^2 - 1\right)^{5/2}\left(s^3 + 5\right)$$
$$f'(s) = \left(s^2 - 1\right)^{5/2}\left(3s^2\right) + \left(s^3 + 5\right)\left(\frac{5}{2}\right)\left(s^2 - 1\right)^{3/2}(2s)$$
$$= s\left(s^2 - 1\right)^{3/2}\left[3s\left(s^2 - 1\right) + 5\left(s^3 + 5\right)\right]$$
$$= s\left(s^2 - 1\right)^{3/2}\left(8s^3 - 3s + 25\right)$$

76.
$$h(\theta) = \frac{\theta}{(1 - \theta)^3}$$
$$h'(\theta) = \frac{(1 - \theta)^3 - \theta\left[3(1 - \theta)^2(-1)\right]}{(1 - \theta)^6}$$
$$= \frac{(1 - \theta)^2(1 - \theta + 3\theta)}{(1 - \theta)^6} = \frac{2\theta + 1}{(1 - \theta)^4}$$

77.
$$y = 5\cos(9x + 1)$$
$$y' = -5\sin(9x + 1)(9) = -45\sin(9x + 1)$$

78.
$$y = 1 - \cos 2x + 2\cos^2 x$$
$$y' = 2\sin 2x - 4\cos x \sin x$$
$$= 2[2\sin x \cos x] - 4\sin x \cos x$$
$$= 0$$

79.
$$y = \frac{x}{2} - \frac{\sin 2x}{4}$$
$$y' = \frac{1}{2} - \frac{1}{4}\cos 2x(2) = \frac{1}{2}(1 - \cos 2x) = \sin^2 x$$

80.
$$y = \frac{\sec^7 x}{7} - \frac{\sec^5 x}{5}$$
$$y' = \sec^6 x(\sec x \tan x) - \sec^4 x(\sec x \tan x)$$
$$= \sec^5 x \tan x\left(\sec^2 x - 1\right)$$
$$= \sec^5 x \tan^3 x$$

81.
$$y = \frac{2}{3}\sin^{3/2} x - \frac{2}{7}\sin^{7/2} x$$
$$y' = \sin^{1/2} x \cos x - \sin^{5/2} x \cos x$$
$$= (\cos x)\sqrt{\sin x}\left(1 - \sin^2 x\right)$$
$$= \cos^3 x\sqrt{\sin x}$$

82.
$$f(x) = \frac{3x}{\sqrt{x^2 + 1}}$$
$$f'(x) = \frac{3\left(x^2 + 1\right)^{1/2} - 3x\frac{1}{2}\left(x^2 + 1\right)^{-1/2}(2x)}{x^2 + 1}$$
$$= \frac{3\left(x^2 + 1\right) - 3x^2}{\left(x^2 + 1\right)^{3/2}} = \frac{3}{\left(x^2 + 1\right)^{3/2}}$$

**83.** $y = \dfrac{\sin \pi x}{x + 2}$

$y' = \dfrac{(x + 2)\pi \cos \pi x - \sin \pi x}{(x + 2)^2}$

**84.** $y = \dfrac{\cos(x - 1)}{x - 1}$

$y' = \dfrac{-(x - 1)\sin(x - 1) - \cos(x - 1)(1)}{(x - 1)^2}$

$= -\dfrac{1}{(x - 1)^2}\left[(x - 1)\sin(x - 1) + \cos(x - 1)\right]$

**85.** $g(t) = t^2 e^{t/4}$

$g'(t) = \frac{1}{4}t^2 e^{t/4} + 2te^{t/4}$

$= \frac{1}{4}te^{t/4}[t + 8]$

**86.** $h(z) = e^{-z^2/2}$

$h'(z) = -ze^{-z^2/2}$

**87.** $y = \sqrt{e^{2x} + e^{-2x}} = \left(e^{2x} + e^{-2x}\right)^{1/2}$

$y' = \dfrac{1}{2}\left(e^{2x} + e^{-2x}\right)^{-1/2}\left(2e^{2x} - 2e^{-2x}\right)$

$= \dfrac{e^{2x} - e^{-2x}}{\sqrt{e^{2x} + e^{-2x}}}$

**88.** $y = 3e^{-3/t}$

$y' = 3e^{-3/t}\left(3t^{-2}\right) = \dfrac{9e^{-3/t}}{t^2}$

**89.** $g(x) = \dfrac{x^2}{e^x}$

$g'(x) = \dfrac{e^x(2x) - x^2e^x}{e^{2x}} = \dfrac{x(2 - x)}{e^x}$

**90.** $f(\theta) = \frac{1}{2}e^{\sin 2\theta}$

$f'(\theta) = \cos 2\theta e^{\sin 2\theta}$

**91.** $g(x) = \ln\sqrt{x} = \dfrac{1}{2}\ln x$

$g'(x) = \dfrac{1}{2x}$

**92.** $h(x) = \ln\dfrac{x(x - 1)}{x - 2} = \ln x + \ln(x - 1) - \ln(x - 2)$

$h'(x) = \dfrac{1}{x} + \dfrac{1}{x - 1} - \dfrac{1}{x - 2} = \dfrac{x^2 - 4x + 2}{x^3 - 3x^2 + 2x}$

**93.** $f(x) = x\sqrt{\ln x}$

$f'(x) = \left(\dfrac{x}{2}\right)(\ln x)^{-1/2}\left(\dfrac{1}{x}\right) + \sqrt{\ln x}$

$= \dfrac{1}{2\sqrt{\ln x}} + \sqrt{\ln x} = \dfrac{1 + 2\ln x}{2\sqrt{\ln x}}$

**94.** $f(x) = \ln\left[x\left(x^2 - 2\right)^{2/3}\right] = \ln x + \dfrac{2}{3}\ln\left(x^2 - 2\right)$

$f'(x) = \dfrac{1}{x} + \dfrac{2}{3}\left(\dfrac{2x}{x^2 - 2}\right) = \dfrac{7x^2 - 6}{3x^3 - 6x}$

**95.** $y = \dfrac{1}{b^2}\left[\ln(a + bx) + \dfrac{a}{a + bx}\right]$

$\dfrac{dy}{dx} = \dfrac{1}{b^2}\left[\dfrac{b}{a + bx} - \dfrac{ab}{(a + bx)^2}\right] = \dfrac{x}{(a + bx)^2}$

**96.** $y = \dfrac{1}{b^2}\left[a + bx - a\ln(a + bx)\right]$

$\dfrac{dy}{dx} = \dfrac{1}{b^2}\left(b - \dfrac{ab}{a + bx}\right) = \dfrac{x}{a + bx}$

**97.** $y = -\dfrac{1}{a}\ln\left(\dfrac{a + bx}{x}\right) = -\dfrac{1}{a}\left[\ln(a + bx) - \ln x\right]$

$\dfrac{dy}{dx} = -\dfrac{1}{a}\left(\dfrac{b}{a + bx} - \dfrac{1}{x}\right) = \dfrac{1}{x(a + bx)}$

**98.** $y = -\dfrac{1}{ax} + \dfrac{b}{a^2}\ln\dfrac{a + bx}{x}$

$= -\dfrac{1}{ax} + \dfrac{b}{a^2}\left[\ln(a + bx) - \ln x\right]$

$\dfrac{dy}{dx} = -\dfrac{1}{a}\left(-\dfrac{1}{x^2}\right) + \dfrac{b}{a^2}\left[\dfrac{b}{a + bx} - \dfrac{1}{x}\right]$

$= \dfrac{1}{ax^2} + \dfrac{b}{a^2}\left[\dfrac{-a}{x(a + bx)}\right] = \dfrac{1}{ax^2} - \dfrac{b}{ax(a + bx)}$

$= \dfrac{(a + bx) - bx}{ax^2(a + bx)} = \dfrac{1}{x^2(a + bx)}$

**99.** $f(x) = \sqrt{1 - x^3}$

$f'(x) = \dfrac{1}{2}\left(1 - x^3\right)^{-1/2}\left(-3x^2\right) = \dfrac{-3x^2}{2\sqrt{1 - x^3}}$

$f'(-2) = \dfrac{-12}{2(3)} = -2$

**100.** $f(x) = \sqrt[3]{x^2 - 1}$

$f'(x) = \frac{1}{3}(x^2 - 1)^{-2/3}(2x) = \frac{2x}{3(x^2 - 1)^{2/3}}$

$f'(3) = \frac{2(3)}{3(4)} = \frac{1}{2}$

**101.** $y = \frac{1}{2}\csc 2x$

$y' = -\csc 2x \cot 2x$

$y'\left(\frac{\pi}{4}\right) = 0$

**102.** $y = \csc 3x + \cot 3x$

$y' = -3\csc 3x \cot 3x - 3\csc^2 3x$

$y'\left(\frac{\pi}{6}\right) = 0 - 3 = -3$

**103.** $f(t) = t^2(t - 1)^5$

$f'(t) = t(t - 1)^4(7t - 2)$

The zeros of $f'$ correspond to the points on the graph of $f$ where the tangent line is horizontal.

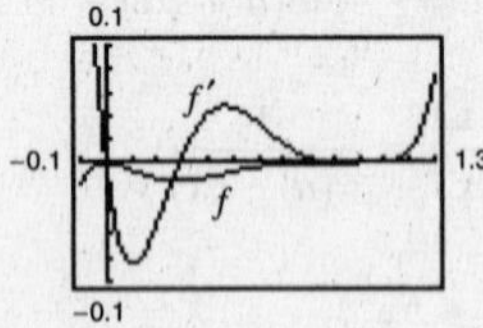


**104.** $f(x) = [(x - 2)(x + 4)]^2 = (x^2 + 2x - 8)^2$

$f'(x) = 4(x^3 + 3x^2 - 6x - 8)$

$= 4(x - 2)(x + 1)(x + 4)$

The zeros of $f'$ correspond to the points on the graph of $f$ where the tangent line is horizontal.

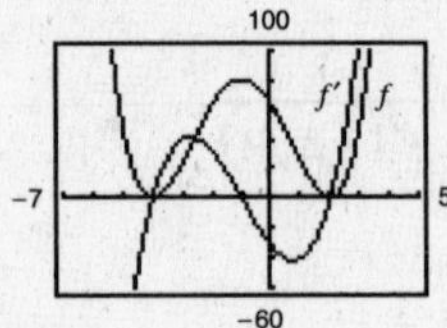


**105.** $g(x) = 2x(x + 1)^{-1/2}$

$g'(x) = \frac{x + 2}{(x + 1)^{3/2}}$

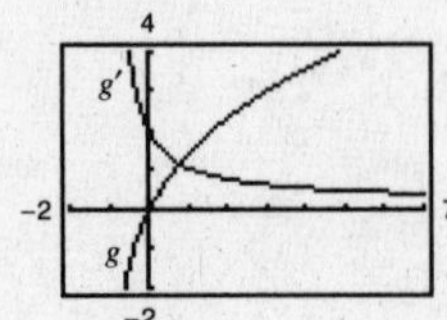


$g'$ does not equal zero for any value of $x$ in the domain. The graph of $g$ has no horizontal tangent lines.

**106.** $g(x) = x(x^2 + 1)^{1/2}$

$g'(x) = \frac{2x^2 + 1}{\sqrt{x^2 + 1}}$

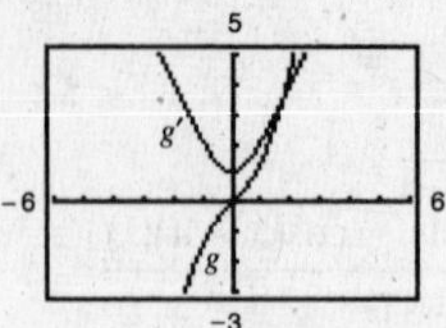


$g'$ does not equal zero for any value of $x$. The graph of $g$ has no horizontal tangent lines.

**107.** $f(t) = \sqrt{t + 1}\sqrt[3]{t + 1}$

$f(t) = (t + 1)^{1/2}(t + 1)^{1/3} = (t + 1)^{5/6}$

$f'(t) = \frac{5}{6(t + 1)^{1/6}}$

$f'$ does not equal zero for any $x$ in the domain. The graph of $f$ has no horizontal tangent lines.

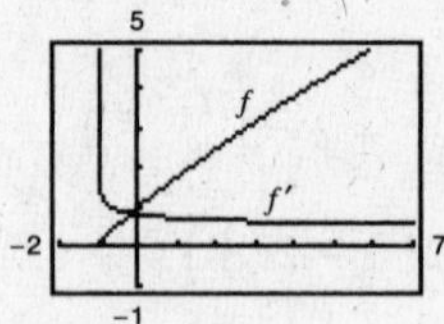


**108.** $y = \sqrt{3x}(x + 2)^3$

$y' = \frac{3(x + 2)^2(7x + 2)}{2\sqrt{3x}}$

$y'$ does not equal zero for any $x$ in the domain. The graph has no horizontal tangent lines.

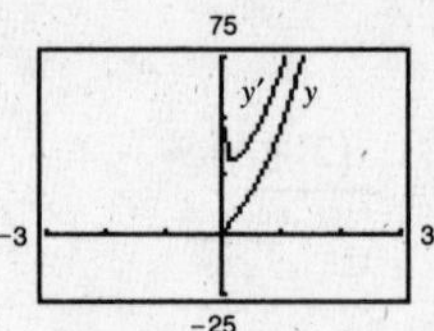


**109.** $y = \tan\sqrt{1 - x}$

$y' = -\frac{\sec^2\sqrt{1 - x}}{2\sqrt{1 - x}}$

$y'$ does not equal zero for any $x$ in the domain. The graph has no horizontal tangent lines.

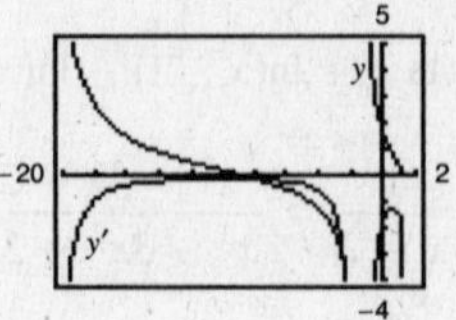

**110.** $y = 2\csc^3(\sqrt{x})$

$$y' = -\frac{3}{\sqrt{x}}\csc^3\sqrt{x}\cot\sqrt{x}$$

The zero of $y'$ corresponds to the point on the graph of $y$ where the tangent line is horizontal.

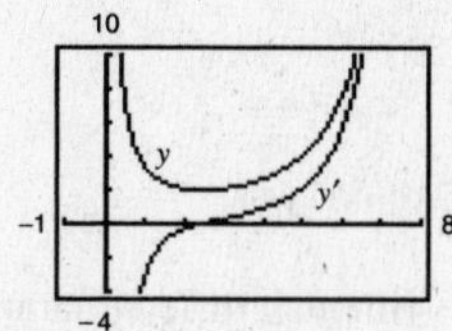


**111.** $y = 7x^2 + \cos 2x$

$y' = 14x - 2\sin 2x$

$y'' = 14 - 4\cos 2x$

**112.** $y = x^{-1} + \tan x$

$y' = -x^{-2} + \sec^2 x$

$y'' = 2x^{-3} + 2\sec x(\sec x\tan x)$

$= \dfrac{2}{x^3} + 2\sec^2 x\tan x$

**113.** $f(x) = \cot x$

$f'(x) = -\csc^2 x$

$f''(x) = -2\csc x(-\csc x \cdot \cot x)$

$= 2\csc^2 x\cot x$

**114.** $y = \sin^2 x$

$y' = 2\sin x\cos x = \sin 2x$

$y'' = 2\cos 2x$

**115** $f(t) = \dfrac{4t^2}{(1-t)^2}$

$f'(t) = \dfrac{8t}{(1-t)^3}$

$f''(t) = \dfrac{8(2t+1)}{(1-t)^4}$

**116.** $g(x) = \dfrac{6x-5}{x^2+1}$

$g'(x) = \dfrac{2(-3x^2+5x+3)}{(x^2+1)^2}$

$g''(x) = \dfrac{2(6x^3-15x^2-18x+5)}{(x^2+1)^3}$

**117.** $g(\theta) = \tan 3\theta - \sin(\theta - 1)$

$g'(\theta) = 3\sec^2 3\theta - \cos(\theta - 1)$

$g''(\theta) = 18\sec^2 3\theta\tan 3\theta + \sin(\theta - 1)$

**118.** $h(x) = 5x\sqrt{x^2 - 16}$

$h'(x) = \dfrac{10x^2 - 80}{\sqrt{x^2 - 16}}$

$h''(x) = \dfrac{10x^3 - 240x}{(x^2 - 16)^{3/2}}$

**119.** $g(x) = x^3\ln x$

$g'(x) = 3x^2\ln x + x^3\left(\dfrac{1}{x}\right) = x^2(3\ln x + 1)$

$g''(x) = 2x(3\ln x + 1) + x^2\left(\dfrac{3}{x}\right)$

$= 6x\ln x + 5x$

**120.** $f(x) = 6x^2e^{-x/3}$

$f'(x) = (12x - 2x^2)e^{-x/3}$

$f''(x) = \left(\dfrac{2x^2}{3} - 8x + 12\right)e^{-x/3}$

**121.** $T = \dfrac{700}{t^2 + 4t + 10}$

$T = 700(t^2 + 4t + 10)^{-1}$

$T' = \dfrac{-1400(t+2)}{(t^2 + 4t + 10)^2}$

(a) When $t = 1$,

$T' = \dfrac{-1400(1+2)}{(1+4+10)^2} \approx -18.667$ deg/h.

(b) When $t = 3$,

$T' = \dfrac{-1400(3+2)}{(9+12+10)^2} \approx -7.284$ deg/h.

(c) When $t = 5$,

$T' = \dfrac{-1400(5+2)}{(25+20+10)^2} \approx -3.240$ deg/h.

(d) When $t = 10$,

$T' = \dfrac{-1400(10+2)}{(100+40+10)^2} \approx -0.747$ deg/h.

**122.** $v = \sqrt{2gh} = \sqrt{2(32)h} = 8\sqrt{h}$

$\dfrac{dv}{dh} = \dfrac{4}{\sqrt{h}}$

(a) When $h = 9$, $\dfrac{dv}{dh} = \dfrac{4}{3}$ ft/sec.

(b) When $h = 4$, $\dfrac{dv}{dh} = 2$ ft/sec.

**123.** (a) You get an error message because $\ln h$ does not exist for $h = 0$.

(b) Reversing the data, you obtain $h = 0.8627 - 6.4474 \ln p$.

(c)

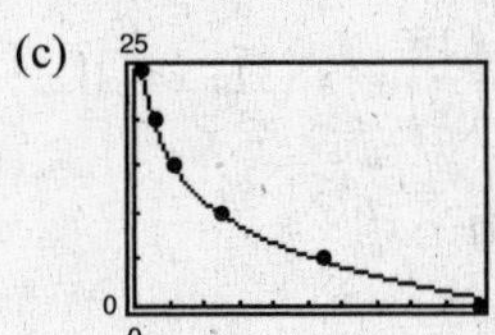


(d) If $p = 0.75$, $h \approx 2.72$ km.

(e) If $h = 13$ km, $p \approx 0.15$ atmosphere.

(f) $h = 0.8627 - 6.4474 \ln p$

$1 = -6.4474 \dfrac{1}{p}\dfrac{dp}{dh}$ (implicit differentiation)

$\dfrac{dp}{dh} = \dfrac{p}{-6.4474}$

For $h = 5$,

$p = 0.5264$ and $\dfrac{dp}{dh} = -0.0816$ atm/km

For $h = 20$,

$p = 0.0514$ and $\dfrac{dp}{dh} = -0.0080$ atm/km

As the altitude increases, the rate of change of pressure decreases.

**124.** $y = 10\ln\left(\dfrac{10 + \sqrt{100 - x^2}}{x}\right) - \sqrt{100 - x^2} = 10\left[\ln\left(10 + \sqrt{100 - x^2}\right) - \ln x\right] - \sqrt{100 - x^2}$

(a)

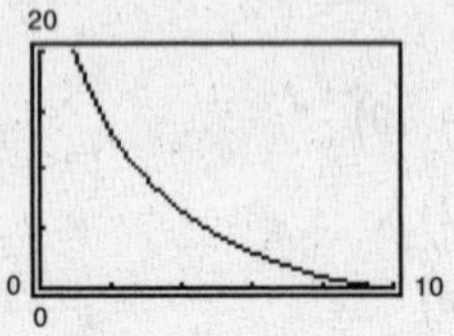

(b) $$\frac{dy}{dx} = 10\left[\frac{-x}{\sqrt{100 - x^2}\left(10 + \sqrt{100 - x^2}\right)} - \frac{1}{x}\right] + \frac{x}{\sqrt{100 - x^2}}$$

$$= \frac{x}{\sqrt{100 - x^2}}\left[\frac{-10}{10 + \sqrt{100 - x^2}}\right] - \frac{10}{x} + \frac{x}{\sqrt{100 - x^2}}$$

$$= \frac{x}{\sqrt{100 - x^2}}\left[\frac{-10}{10 + \sqrt{100 - x^2}} + 1\right] - \frac{10}{x}$$

$$= \frac{x}{\sqrt{100 - x^2}}\left[\frac{\sqrt{100 - x^2}}{10 + \sqrt{100 - x^2}}\right] - \frac{10}{x}$$

$$= \frac{x}{10 + \sqrt{100 - x^2}} - \frac{10}{x}$$

$$= \frac{x\left(10 - \sqrt{100 - x^2}\right)}{x^2} - \frac{10}{x} = -\frac{\sqrt{100 - x^2}}{x}$$

When $x = 5$, $dy/dx = -\sqrt{3}$. When $x = 9$, $dy/dx = -\sqrt{19}/9$.

(c) $\displaystyle\lim_{x\to 10^-} \frac{dy}{dx} = 0$

**125.**
$$x^2 + 3xy + y^3 = 10$$
$$2x + 3xy' + 3y + 3y^2y' = 0$$
$$3(x + y^2)y' = -(2x + 3y)$$
$$y' = \frac{-(2x + 3y)}{3(x + y^2)}$$

**126.**
$$y^2 = x^3 - x^2y + xy - y^2$$
$$0 = x^3 - x^2y + xy - 2y^2$$
$$0 = 3x^2 - x^2y' - 2xy + xy' + y - 4yy'$$
$$(x^2 - x + 4y)y' = 3x^2 - 2xy + y$$
$$y' = \frac{3x^2 - 2xy + y}{x^2 - x + 4y}$$

**127.**
$$\cos x^2 = xe^y$$
$$-\sin x^2(2x) = xe^y y' + e^y$$
$$xe^y y' = -e^y - 2x \sin x^2$$
$$y' = -\frac{e^y + 2x \sin x^2}{xe^y} = -\frac{1}{x} - 2e^{-y} \sin x^2$$

**128.**
$$ye^x + xe^y = xy$$
$$y'e^x + ye^x + xe^y y' + e^y = xy' + y$$
$$(e^x + xe^y - x)y' = y - e^y - ye^x$$
$$y' = \frac{y - e^y - ye^x}{e^x + xe^y - x}$$

**129.**
$$\sqrt{xy} = x - 4y$$
$$\frac{\sqrt{x}}{2\sqrt{y}}y' + \frac{\sqrt{y}}{2\sqrt{x}} = 1 - 4y'$$
$$xy' + y = 2\sqrt{xy} - 8\sqrt{xy}y'$$
$$x + 8\sqrt{xy}y' = 2\sqrt{xy} - y$$
$$y' = \frac{2\sqrt{xy} - y}{x + 8\sqrt{xy}} = \frac{2(x - 4y) - y}{x + 8(x - 4y)} = \frac{2x - 9y}{9x - 32y}$$

**130.**
$$y\sqrt{x} - x\sqrt{y} = 25$$
$$y\left(\frac{1}{2}x^{-1/2}\right) + x^{1/2}y' - x\left(\frac{1}{2}y^{-1/2}y'\right) - y^{1/2} = 0$$
$$\left(\sqrt{x} - \frac{x}{2\sqrt{y}}\right)y' = \sqrt{y} - \frac{y}{2\sqrt{x}}$$
$$\left(\frac{2\sqrt{xy} - x}{2\sqrt{y}}\right)y' = \frac{2\sqrt{xy} - y}{2\sqrt{x}}$$
$$y' = \frac{2\sqrt{xy} - y}{2\sqrt{x}} \cdot \frac{2\sqrt{y}}{2\sqrt{xy} - x}$$
$$= \frac{2y\sqrt{x} - y\sqrt{y}}{2x\sqrt{y} - x\sqrt{x}}$$

**131.**
$$x \sin y = y \cos x$$
$$(x \cos y)y' + \sin y = -y \sin x + y' \cos x$$
$$y'(x \cos y - \cos x) = -y \sin x - \sin y$$
$$y' = \frac{y \sin x + \sin y}{\cos x - x \cos y}$$

**132.**
$$\cos(x + y) = x$$
$$-(1 + y')\sin(x + y) = 1$$
$$-y'\sin(x + y) = 1 + \sin(x + y)$$
$$y' = -\frac{1 + \sin(x + y)}{\sin(x + y)} = -\csc(x + 1) - 1$$

**133.** $x^2 + y^2 = 10$

$2x + 2yy' = 0$

$y' = \frac{-x}{y}$

At $(3, 1)$, $y' = -3$

Tangent line: $y - 1 = -3(x - 3) \Rightarrow 3x + y - 10 = 0$

Normal line: $y - 1 = \frac{1}{3}(x - 3) \Rightarrow x - 3y = 0$

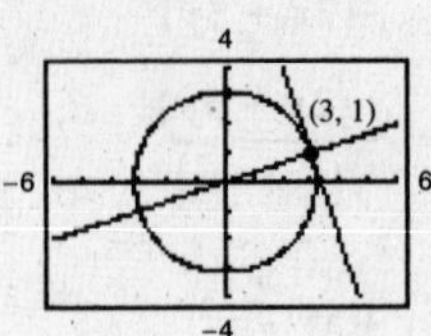


**134.** $x^2 - y^2 = 20$

$2x - 2yy' = 0$

$y' = \frac{x}{y}$

At $(6, 4)$, $y' = \frac{3}{2}$

Tangent line: $y - 4 = \frac{3}{2}(x - 6)$

$y = \frac{3}{2}x - 5$

$2y - 3x + 10 = 0$

Normal line: $y - 4 = -\frac{2}{3}(x - 6)$

$y = -\frac{2}{3}x + 8$

$3y + 2x - 24 = 0$

**135.** $y \ln x + y^2 = 0, \quad (e, -1)$

$y' \ln x + \frac{y}{x} + 2yy' = 0$

$y'(\ln x + 2y) = \frac{-y}{x}$

$y' = \frac{-y}{x(\ln x + 2y)}$

At $(e, -1)$: $y' = \frac{-1}{e}$

Tangent line: $y + 1 = \frac{-1}{e}(x - e)$

$y = \frac{-1}{e}x$

Normal line: $y + 1 = e(x - e)$

$y = ex - e^2 - 1$

**136.** $\ln(x + y) = x, \ (0, 1)$

$\frac{1}{x + y}(1 + y') = 1$

$1 + y' = x + y$

$y' = x + y - 1$

At $(0, 1)$: $y' = 0$

Tangent line: $y - 1 = 0 \Rightarrow y = 1$

Normal line: $x = 0$

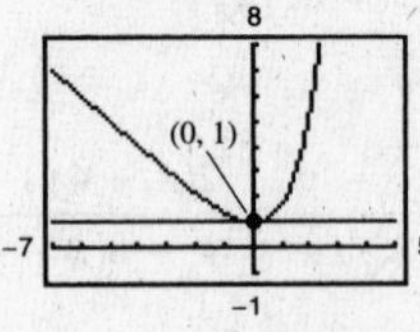


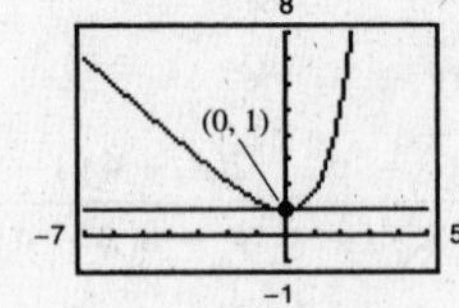

**137.** $y = \frac{x\sqrt{x^2 + 1}}{x + 4}$

$\ln y = \ln x + \frac{1}{2}\ln(x^2 + 1) - \ln(x + 4)$

$\frac{y'}{y} = \frac{1}{x} + \frac{x}{x^2 + 1} - \frac{1}{x + 4}$

$y' = \frac{x\sqrt{x^2 + 1}}{x + 4}\left(\frac{1}{x} + \frac{x}{x^2 + 1} - \frac{1}{x + 4}\right)$

$= \frac{x^3 + 8x^2 + 4}{(x + 4)^2\sqrt{x^2 + 1}}$

**138.** $y = \frac{(2x + 1)^3(x^2 - 1)^2}{x + 3}$

$\ln y = 3\ln(2x + 1) + 2\ln(x^2 - 1) - \ln(x + 3)$

$\frac{y'}{y} = \frac{6}{2x + 1} + \frac{4x}{x^2 - 1} - \frac{1}{x + 3}$

$y' = \frac{(2x + 1)^3(x^2 - 1)^2}{x + 3}\left(\frac{6}{2x + 1} + \frac{4x}{x^2 - 1} - \frac{1}{x + 3}\right)$

$= \frac{(2x + 1)^2(x^2 - 1)(12x^3 + 45x^2 + 8x - 17)}{(x + 3)^2}$

**139.** $f(x) = x^3 + 2, \quad a = -1$

$f'(x) = 3x^2 > 0$

$f$ is monotonic (increasing) on $(-\infty, \infty)$ therefore $f$ has an inverse.

$f(-3^{1/3}) = -1 \Rightarrow f^{-1}(-1) = -3^{1/3}$

$f'(-3^{1/3}) = 3^{2/3}$

$$(f^{-1})'(-1) = \frac{1}{f'(f^{-1}(-1))} = \frac{1}{f'(-3^{1/3})} = \frac{1}{3(3^{2/3})} = \frac{1}{3^{5/3}}$$

**140.** $f(x) = x\sqrt{x-3}, \quad a = 4$

$f'(x) = \frac{1}{2}x\frac{1}{\sqrt{x-3}} + \sqrt{x-3} > 0$

$f$ is monotonic (increasing) on $[3, \infty)$ therefore $f$ has an inverse.

$f(4) = 4 \Rightarrow f^{-1}(4) = 4$

$f'(4) = 2 + 1 = 3$

$$(f^{-1})'(4) = \frac{1}{f'(f^{-1}(4))} = \frac{1}{f'(4)} = \frac{1}{3}$$

**141.** $f(x) = \tan x, \quad a = \frac{\sqrt{3}}{3}, -\frac{\pi}{4} \le x \le \frac{\pi}{4}$

$f'(x) = \sec^2 x > 0$ on $\left(-\frac{\pi}{4}, \frac{\pi}{4}\right)$

$f$ is monotonic (increasing) on $\left[-\frac{\pi}{4}, \frac{\pi}{4}\right]$ therefore $f$ has an inverse.

$f\left(\frac{\pi}{6}\right) = \frac{\sqrt{3}}{3} \Rightarrow f^{-1}\left(\frac{\sqrt{3}}{3}\right) = \frac{\pi}{6}$

$f'\left(\frac{\pi}{6}\right) = \frac{4}{3}$

$$(f^{-1})\left(\frac{\sqrt{3}}{3}\right) = \frac{1}{f'\left(f^{-1}\left(\frac{\sqrt{3}}{3}\right)\right)} = \frac{1}{f'\left(\frac{\pi}{6}\right)} = \frac{1}{\left(\frac{4}{3}\right)} = \frac{3}{4}$$

**142.** $f(x) = \cos x, \quad a = 0, 0 \le x \le \pi$

$f'(x) = -\sin x < 0$ on $(0, \pi)$

$f$ is monotonic (decreasing) on $[0, \pi]$ therefore $f$ has an inverse.

$f\left(\frac{\pi}{2}\right) = 0 \Rightarrow f^{-1}(0) = \frac{\pi}{2}$

$f'\left(\frac{\pi}{2}\right) = -1$

$$(f^{-1})(0) = \frac{1}{f'(f^{-1}(0))} = \frac{1}{f'\left(\frac{\pi}{2}\right)} = \frac{1}{-1} = -1$$

**143.** $y = \tan(\arcsin x) = \frac{x}{\sqrt{1-x^2}}$

$$y' = \frac{(1-x^2)^{1/2} + x^2(1-x^2)^{-1/2}}{1-x^2} = (1-x^2)^{-3/2}$$

**144.** $y = \arctan(x^2 - 1)$

$$y' = \frac{2x}{1 + (x^2-1)^2} = \frac{2x}{x^4 - 2x^2 + 2}$$

**145.** $y = x \operatorname{arcsec} x$

$$y' = \frac{x}{|x|\sqrt{x^2-1}} + \operatorname{arcsec} x$$

**146.** $y = \frac{1}{2}\arctan e^{2x}$

$$y' = \frac{1}{2}\left(\frac{1}{1+e^{4x}}\right)(2e^{2x}) = \frac{e^{2x}}{1+e^{4x}}$$

**147.** $y = x(\arcsin x)^2 - 2x + 2\sqrt{1-x^2}\arcsin x$

$$y' = \frac{2x\arcsin x}{\sqrt{1-x^2}} + (\arcsin x)^2 - 2 + \frac{2\sqrt{1-x^2}}{\sqrt{1-x^2}} - \frac{2x}{\sqrt{1-x^2}}\arcsin x = (\arcsin x)^2$$

**148.** $y = \sqrt{x^2-4} - 2\operatorname{arcsec}\frac{x}{2}, 2 < x < 4$

$$y' = \frac{x}{\sqrt{x^2-4}} - \frac{1}{(|x|/2)\sqrt{(x/2)^2 - 1}} = \frac{x}{\sqrt{x^2-4}} - \frac{4}{|x|\sqrt{x^2-4}} = \frac{x^2-4}{|x|\sqrt{x^2-4}} = \frac{\sqrt{x^2-4}}{x}$$

**149.** $y = \sqrt{x}$

$$\frac{dy}{dt} = 2 \text{ units/sec}$$

$$\frac{dy}{dt} = \frac{1}{2\sqrt{x}}\frac{dx}{dt} \Rightarrow \frac{dx}{dt} = 2\sqrt{x}\frac{dy}{dt} = 4\sqrt{x}$$

(a) When $x = \frac{1}{2}$, $\frac{dx}{dt} = 2\sqrt{2}$ units/sec.

(b) When $x = 1$, $\frac{dx}{dt} = 4$ units/sec.

(c) When $x = 4$, $\frac{dx}{dt} = 8$ units/sec.

**150.** Surface area $= A = 6x^2$, $x =$ length of edge

$$\frac{dx}{dt} = 8$$

$$\frac{dA}{dt} = 12x\frac{dx}{dt} = 12(6.5)(8) = 624 \text{ cm}^2/\text{sec}$$

**151.** $\frac{s}{h} = \frac{1/2}{2}$

$$s = \frac{1}{4}h$$

$$\frac{dV}{dt} = 1$$

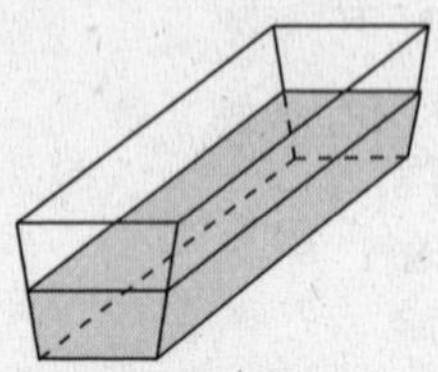

Width of water at depth $h$:

$$w = 2 + 2s = 2 + 2\left(\frac{1}{4}h\right) = \frac{4 + h}{2}$$

$$V = \frac{5}{2}\left(2 + \frac{4 + h}{2}\right)h = \frac{5}{4}(8 + h)h$$

$$\frac{dV}{dt} = \frac{5}{2}(4 + h)\frac{dh}{dt}$$

$$\frac{dh}{dt} = \frac{2(dV/dt)}{5(4 + h)}$$

When $h = 1$, $\frac{dh}{dt} = \frac{2}{25}$ m/min.

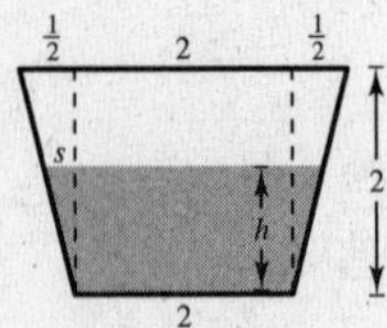


**152.** $\tan\theta = x$

$$\frac{d\theta}{dt} = 3(2\pi) \text{ rad/min}$$

$$\sec^2\theta\left(\frac{d\theta}{dt}\right) = \frac{dx}{dt}$$

$$\frac{dx}{dt} = (\tan^2\theta + 1)(6\pi) = 6\pi(x^2 + 1)$$

When $x = \frac{1}{2}$,

$$\frac{dx}{dt} = 6\pi\left(\frac{1}{4} + 1\right) = \frac{15\pi}{2} \text{km/min} = 450\pi \text{ km/h}.$$

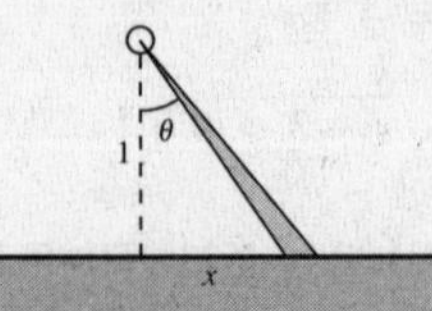


**153.** $s(t) = 60 - 4.9t^2$

$$s'(t) = -9.8t$$

$$s = 35 = 60 - 4.9t^2$$

$$4.9t^2 = 25$$

$$t = \frac{5}{\sqrt{4.9}}$$

$$\tan 30° = \frac{1}{\sqrt{3}} = \frac{s(t)}{x(t)}$$

$$x(t) = \sqrt{3}s(t)$$

$$\frac{dx}{dt} = \sqrt{3}\frac{ds}{dt} = \sqrt{3}(-9.8)\frac{5}{\sqrt{4.9}} \approx -38.34 \text{ m/sec}$$

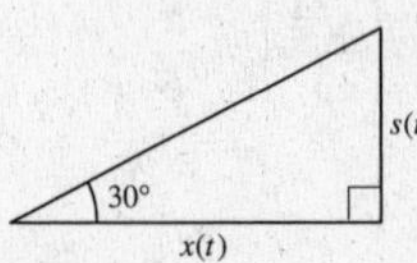


**154.** (a) $A = (\text{base})(\text{height}) = 2xe^{-x^2/2}$

(b) $$\frac{dA}{dt} = \left[2x\left(-xe^{-x^2/2}\right) + 2e^{-x^2/2}\right]\frac{dx}{dt}$$

$$= \left(-2x^2 + 2\right)e^{-x^2/2}\frac{dx}{dt}$$

For $x = 2$ and $\frac{dx}{dt} = 4$,

$$\frac{dA}{dt} = -6e^{-2}(4) = \frac{-24}{e^2} \approx -3.25 \text{ cm}^2/\text{min}.$$

**155.** $f(x) = x^3 - 3x - 1$

From the graph you can see that $f(x)$ has three real zeros.

$f'(x) = 3x^2 - 3$

| $n$ | $x_n$ | $f(x_n)$ | $f'(x_n)$ | $\frac{f(x_n)}{f'(x_n)}$ | $x_n - \frac{f(x_n)}{f'(x_n)}$ |
|---|---|---|---|---|---|
| 1 | –1.5000 | 0.1250 | 3.7500 | 0.0333 | –1.5333 |
| 2 | –1.5333 | –0.0049 | 4.0530 | –0.0012 | –1.5321 |

| $n$ | $x_n$ | $f(x_n)$ | $f'(x_n)$ | $\frac{f(x_n)}{f'(x_n)}$ | $x_n - \frac{f(x_n)}{f'(x_n)}$ |
|---|---|---|---|---|---|
| 1 | –0.5000 | 0.3750 | –2.2500 | –0.1667 | –0.3333 |
| 2 | –0.3333 | –0.0371 | –2.6667 | 0.0139 | –0.3472 |
| 3 | –0.3472 | –0.0003 | –2.6384 | 0.0001 | –0.3473 |

| $n$ | $x_n$ | $f(x_n)$ | $f'(x_n)$ | $\frac{f(x_n)}{f'(x_n)}$ | $x_n - \frac{f(x_n)}{f'(x_n)}$ |
|---|---|---|---|---|---|
| 1 | 1.9000 | 0.1590 | 7.8300 | 0.0203 | 1.8797 |
| 2 | 1.8797 | 0.0024 | 7.5998 | 0.0003 | 1.8794 |

The three real zeros of $f(x)$ are $x \approx -1.532$, $x \approx -0.347$, and $x \approx 1.879$.

**156.** $f(x) = x^3 + 2x + 1$

From the graph, you can see that $f(x)$ has one real zero.

$f'(x) = 3x^2 + 2$

$f$ changes sign in $[-1, 0]$.

| $n$ | $x_n$ | $f(x_n)$ | $f'(x_n)$ | $\frac{f(x_n)}{f'(x_n)}$ | $x_n - \frac{f(x_n)}{f'(x_n)}$ |
|---|---|---|---|---|---|
| 1 | –0.5000 | –0.1250 | 2.7500 | –0.0455 | –0.4545 |
| 2 | –0.4545 | –0.0029 | 2.6197 | –0.0011 | –0.4534 |

On the interval $[-1, 0]$: $x \approx -0.453$.

**157.** $g(x) = xe^x - 4$

$g'(x) = (x + 1)e^x$

From the graph, there is one zero near 1.

| $n$ | $x_n$ | $g(x_n)$ | $g'(x_n)$ | $\frac{g(x_n)}{g'(x_n)}$ | $x_n - \frac{g(x_n)}{g'(x_n)}$ |
|---|---|---|---|---|---|
| 1 | 1.0 | –1.2817 | 5.4366 | –0.2358 | 1.2358 |
| 2 | 1.2358 | 0.2525 | 7.6937 | 0.0328 | 1.2030 |
| 3 | 1.2030 | 0.0059 | 7.3359 | 0.0008 | 1.2022 |

To three decimal places, $x = 1.202$.

**158.** $f(x) = 3 - x \ln x$

$f'(x) = -1 - \ln x$

From the graph, there is one zero near 3.

| $n$ | $x_n$ | $f(x_n)$ | $f'(x_n)$ | $\frac{f(x_n)}{f'(x_n)}$ | $x_n - \frac{f(x_n)}{f'(x_n)}$ |
|---|---|---|---|---|---|
| 1 | 3 | –0.2958 | –2.0986 | 0.1410 | 2.8590 |
| 2 | 2.8590 | –0.0034 | –2.0505 | 0.0016 | 2.8574 |
| 3 | 2.8574 | –0.0000 | –2.0499 | 0.0000 | 2.8574 |

To three decimal places, $x = 2.857$.

**159.** Find the zeros of $f(x) = x^4 - x - 3$.

$f'(x) = 4x^3 - 1$

From the graph you can see that $f(x)$ has two real zeros.

$f$ changes sign in $[-2, -1]$.

| $n$ | $x_n$ | $f(x_n)$ | $f'(x_n)$ | $\frac{f(x_n)}{f'(x_n)}$ | $x_n - \frac{f(x_n)}{f'(x_n)}$ |
|---|---|---|---|---|---|
| 1 | –1.2000 | 0.2736 | –7.9120 | –0.0346 | –1.1654 |
| 2 | –1.1654 | 0.0100 | –7.3312 | –0.0014 | –1.1640 |

On the interval $[-2, -1]$: $x \approx -1.164$.

$f$ changes sign in $[1, 2]$.

| $n$ | $x_n$ | $f(x_n)$ | $f'(x_n)$ | $\frac{f(x_n)}{f'(x_n)}$ | $x_n - \frac{f(x_n)}{f'(x_n)}$ |
|---|---|---|---|---|---|
| 1 | 1.5000 | 0.5625 | 12.5000 | 0.0450 | 1.4550 |
| 2 | 1.4550 | 0.0268 | 11.3211 | 0.0024 | 1.4526 |
| 3 | 1.4526 | –0.0003 | 11.2602 | 0.0000 | 1.4526 |

On the interval $[1, 2]$: $x \approx 1.453$.

**160.** Find the zeros of $f(x) = \sin \pi x + x - 1$.

$f'(x) = \pi \cos \pi x + 1$

From the graph you can see that $f(x)$ has three real zeros.

| $n$ | $x_n$ | $f(x_n)$ | $f'(x_n)$ | $\dfrac{f(x_n)}{f'(x_n)}$ | $x_n - \dfrac{f(x_n)}{f'(x_n)}$ |
|---|---|---|---|---|---|
| 1 | 0.2000 | –0.2122 | 3.5416 | –0.0599 | 0.2599 |
| 2 | 0.2599 | –0.0113 | 3.1513 | –0.0036 | 0.2635 |
| 3 | 0.2635 | 0.0000 | 3.1253 | 0.0000 | 0.2635 |

| $n$ | $x_n$ | $f(x_n)$ | $f'(x_n)$ | $\dfrac{f(x_n)}{f'(x_n)}$ | $x_n - \dfrac{f(x_n)}{f'(x_n)}$ |
|---|---|---|---|---|---|
| 1 | 1.0000 | 0.0000 | –2.1416 | 0.0000 | 1.0000 |

| $n$ | $x_n$ | $f(x_n)$ | $f'(x_n)$ | $\dfrac{f(x_n)}{f'(x_n)}$ | $x_n - \dfrac{f(x_n)}{f'(x_n)}$ |
|---|---|---|---|---|---|
| 1 | 1.8000 | 0.2122 | 3.5416 | 0.0599 | 1.7401 |
| 2 | 1.7401 | 0.0113 | 3.1513 | 0.0036 | 1.7365 |
| 3 | 1.7365 | 0.0000 | 3.1253 | 0.0000 | 1.7365 |

The three real zeros of $f(x)$ are $x \approx 0.264$, $x = 1$, and $x \approx 1.737$.

# Problem Solving for Chapter 3

**1.** (a) $x^2 + (y - r)^2 = r^2$, Circle

$x^2 = y$, Parabola

Substituting:

$$(y - r)^2 = r^2 - y$$
$$y^2 - 2ry + r^2 = r^2 - y$$
$$y^2 - 2ry + y = 0$$
$$y(y - 2r + 1) = 0$$

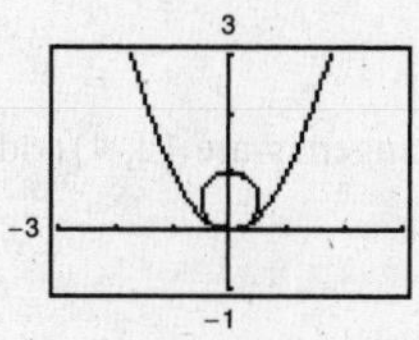


Because you want only one solution, let $1 - 2r = 0 \Rightarrow r = \dfrac{1}{2}$.

(b) Let $(x, y)$ be a point of tangency:

$$x^2 + (y - b)^2 = 1 \Rightarrow 2x + 2(y - b)y' = 0 \Rightarrow y' = \frac{x}{b - y}, \text{ Circle}$$

$y = x^2 \Rightarrow y' = 2x$, Parabola

Equating:

$$2x = \frac{x}{b - y}$$

$$2(b - y) = 1$$

$$b - y = \frac{1}{2} \Rightarrow b = y + \frac{1}{2}$$

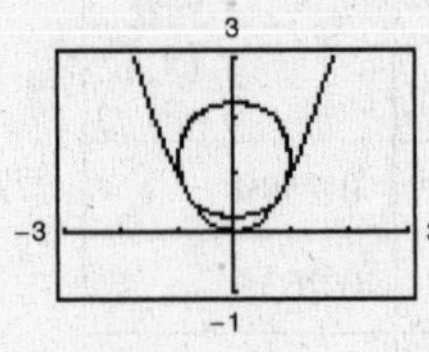


Also, $x^2 + (y - b)^2 = 1$ and $y = x^2$ imply:

$$y + (y - b)^2 = 1 \Rightarrow y + \left[y - \left(y + \frac{1}{2}\right)\right]^2 = 1 \Rightarrow y + \frac{1}{4} = 1 \Rightarrow y = \frac{3}{4} \text{ and } b = \frac{5}{4}$$

Center: $\left(0, \frac{5}{4}\right)$

**2.** Let $(a, a^2)$ and $(b, -b^2 + 2b - 5)$ be the points of tangency. For $y = x^2$, $y' = 2x$ and for $y = -x^2 + 2x - 5$, $y' = -2x + 2$. So, $2a = -2b + 2 \Rightarrow a + b = 1$, or $a = 1 - b$. Furthermore, the slope of the common tangent line is

$$\frac{a^2 - (-b^2 + 2b - 5)}{a - b} = \frac{(1 - b)^2 + b^2 - 2b + 5}{(1 - b) - b} = -2b + 2$$

$$\Rightarrow \frac{1 - 2b + b^2 + b^2 - 2b + 5}{1 - 2b} = -2b + 2$$

$$\Rightarrow 2b^2 - 4b + 6 = 4b^2 - 6b + 2$$

$$\Rightarrow 2b^2 - 2b - 4 = 0$$

$$\Rightarrow b^2 - b - 2 = 0$$

$$\Rightarrow (b - 2)(b + 1) = 0$$

$$b = 2, -1$$

For $b = 2$, $a = 1 - b = -1$ and the points of tangency are $(-1, 1)$ and $(2, -5)$. The tangent line has slope $-2$: $y - 1 = -2(x - 1) \Rightarrow y = -2x - 1$

For $b = -1$, $a = 1 - b = 2$ and the points of tangency are $(2, 4)$ and $(-1, -8)$. The tangent line has slope $4$: $y - 4 = 4(x - 2) \Rightarrow y = 4x - 4$

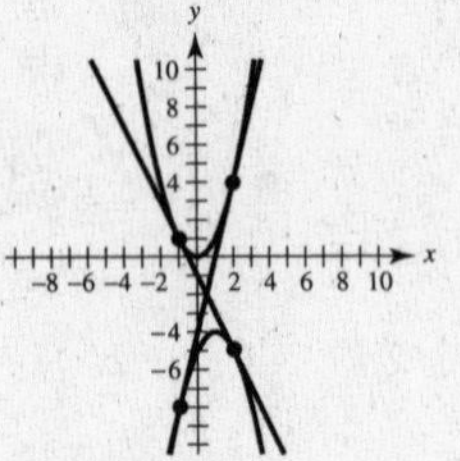

**3.** (a) $f(x) = \cos x$ $\qquad P_1(x) = a_0 + a_1x$

$f(0) = 1$ $\qquad P_1(0) = a_0 \Rightarrow a_0 = 1$

$f'(0) = 0$ $\qquad P_1'(0) = a_1 \Rightarrow a_1 = 0$

$P_1(x) = 1$

(b) $f(x) = \cos x$ $\qquad P_2(x) = a_0 + a_1x + a_2x^2$

$f(0) = 1$ $\qquad P_2(0) = a_0 \Rightarrow a_0 = 1$

$f'(0) = 0$ $\qquad P_2'(0) = a_1 \Rightarrow a_1 = 0$

$f''(0) = -1$ $\qquad P_2''(0) = 2a_2 \Rightarrow a_2 = -\frac{1}{2}$

$P_2(x) = 1 - \frac{1}{2}x^2$

(c)

| $x$ | $-1.0$ | $-0.1$ | $-0.001$ | 0 | 0.001 | 0.1 | 1.0 |
|---|---|---|---|---|---|---|---|
| $\cos x$ | 0.5403 | 0.9950 | $\approx 1$ | 1 | $\approx 1$ | 0.9950 | 0.5403 |
| $P_2(x)$ | 0.5 | 0.9950 | $\approx 1$ | 1 | $\approx 1$ | 0.9950 | 0.5 |

$P_2(x)$ is a good approximation of $f(x) = \cos x$ when $x$ is near 0.

(d) $f(x) = \sin x$ $\qquad P_3(x) = a_0 + a_1x + a_2x^2 + a_3x^3$

$f(0) = 0$ $\qquad P_3(0) = a_0 \Rightarrow a_0 = 0$

$f'(0) = 1$ $\qquad P_3'(0) = a_1 \Rightarrow a_1 = 1$

$f''(0) = 0$ $\qquad P_3''(0) = 2a_2 \Rightarrow a_2 = 0$

$f'''(0) = -1$ $\qquad P_3'''(0) = 6a_3 \Rightarrow a_3 = -\frac{1}{6}$

$P_3(x) = x - \frac{1}{6}x^3$

**4.** (a) $y = x^2$, $y' = 2x$, Slope $= 4$ at $(2, 4)$

Tangent line: $y - 4 = 4(x - 2)$

$$y = 4x - 4$$

(b) Slope of normal line: $-\dfrac{1}{4}$

Normal line: $y - 4 = -\dfrac{1}{4}(x - 2)$

$$y = -\frac{1}{4}x + \frac{9}{2}$$

$$y = -\frac{1}{4}x + \frac{9}{2} = x^2$$

$$\Rightarrow 4x^2 + x - 18 = 0$$

$$\Rightarrow (4x + 9)(x - 2) = 0$$

$x = 2, -\dfrac{9}{4}$

Second intersection point: $\left(-\dfrac{9}{4}, \dfrac{81}{16}\right)$

(c) Tangent line: $y = 0$

Normal line: $x = 0$

(d) Let $(a, a^2)$, $a \neq 0$, be a point on the parabola $y = x^2$. Tangent line at $(a, a^2)$ is $y = 2a(x - a) + a^2$. Normal line at $(a, a^2)$ is $y = -(1/2a)(x - a) + a^2$. To find points of intersection, solve:

$$x^2 = -\frac{1}{2a}(x - a) + a^2$$

$$x^2 + \frac{1}{2a}x = a^2 + \frac{1}{2}$$

$$x^2 + \frac{1}{2a}x + \frac{1}{16a^2} = a^2 + \frac{1}{2} + \frac{1}{16a^2}$$

$$\left(x + \frac{1}{4a}\right)^2 = \left(a + \frac{1}{4a}\right)^2$$

$$x + \frac{1}{4a} = \pm\left(a + \frac{1}{4a}\right)$$

$$x + \frac{1}{4a} = a + \frac{1}{4a} \Rightarrow x = a \quad \text{(Point of tangency)}$$

$$x + \frac{1}{4a} = -\left(a + \frac{1}{4a}\right) \Rightarrow x = -a - \frac{1}{2a} = -\frac{2a^2 + 1}{2a}$$

The normal line intersects a second time at $x = -\dfrac{2a^2 + 1}{2a}$.

**5.** Let $p(x) = Ax^3 + Bx^2 + Cx + D$

$p'(x) = 3Ax^2 + 2Bx + C.$

At $(1, 1)$:

$A + B + C + D = 1$ Equation 1

$3A + 2B + C = 14$ Equation 2

At $(-1, -3)$:

$A + B - C + D = -3$ Equation 3

$3A + 2B + C = -2$ Equation 4

Adding Equations 1 and 3: $2B + 2D = -2$

Subtracting Equations 1 and 3: $2A + 2C = 4$

Adding Equations 2 and 4: $6A + 2C = 12$

Subtracting Equations 2 and 4: $4B = 16$

So, $B = 4$ and $D = \frac{1}{2}(-2 - 2B) = -5$. Subtracting $2A + 2C = 4$ and $6A + 2C = 12$, you obtain $4A = 8 \Rightarrow A = 2$. Finally, $C = \frac{1}{2}(4 - 2A) = 0$.

So, $p(x) = 2x^3 + 4x^2 - 5$.

**6.** $f(x) = a + b\cos cx$

$f'(x) = -bc\sin cx$

At $(0, 1)$: $a + b = 1$ Equation 1

At $\left(\frac{\pi}{4}, \frac{3}{2}\right)$: $a + b\cos\left(\frac{c\pi}{4}\right) = \frac{3}{2}$ Equation 2

$-bc\sin\left(\frac{c\pi}{4}\right) = 1$ Equation 3

From Equation 1, $a = 1 - b$. Equation 2 becomes

$$(1 - b) + b\cos\left(\frac{c\pi}{4}\right) = \frac{3}{2} \Rightarrow -b + b\cos\frac{c\pi}{4} = \frac{1}{2}.$$

From Equation 3, $b = \dfrac{-1}{c\sin(c\pi/4)}$. So:

$$\frac{1}{c\sin(c\pi/4)} + \frac{-1}{c\sin(c\pi/4)}\cos\left(\frac{c\pi}{4}\right) = \frac{1}{2}$$

$$1 - \cos\left(\frac{c\pi}{4}\right) = \frac{1}{2}c\sin\left(\frac{c\pi}{4}\right)$$

Graphing the equation

$$g(c) = \frac{1}{2}c\sin\left(\frac{c\pi}{4}\right) + \cos\left(\frac{c\pi}{4}\right) - 1,$$

you see that many values of $c$ will work. One answer:

$$c = 2, b = -\frac{1}{2}, a = \frac{3}{2} \Rightarrow f(x) = \frac{3}{2} - \frac{1}{2}\cos 2x$$

**7.** (a)
$$x^4 = a^2x^2 - a^2y^2$$
$$a^2y^2 = a^2x^2 - x^4$$
$$y = \frac{\pm\sqrt{a^2x^2 - x^4}}{a}$$

Graph: $y_1 = \dfrac{\sqrt{a^2x^2 - x^4}}{a}$ and

$y_2 = -\dfrac{\sqrt{a^2x^2 - x^4}}{a}$.

(b)

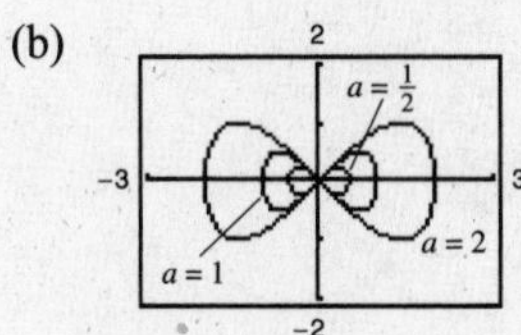


$(\pm a, 0)$ are the $x$-intercepts, along with $(0, 0)$.

(c) Differentiating implicitly:

$$4x^3 = 2a^2x - 2a^2yy'$$
$$y' = \frac{2a^2x - 4x^3}{2a^2y}$$
$$= \frac{x(a^2 - 2x^2)}{a^2y} = 0 \Rightarrow 2x^2 = a^2 \Rightarrow x = \frac{\pm a}{\sqrt{2}}$$
$$\left(\frac{a^2}{2}\right)^2 = a^2\left(\frac{a^2}{2}\right) - a^2y^2$$
$$\frac{a^4}{4} = \frac{a^4}{2} - a^2y^2$$
$$a^2y^2 = \frac{a^4}{4}$$
$$y^2 = \frac{a^2}{4}$$
$$y = \pm\frac{a}{2}$$

Four points: $\left(\dfrac{a}{\sqrt{2}}, \dfrac{a}{2}\right), \left(\dfrac{a}{\sqrt{2}}, -\dfrac{a}{2}\right), \left(\dfrac{-a}{\sqrt{2}}, \dfrac{a}{2}\right),$

$\left(\dfrac{-a}{\sqrt{2}}, -\dfrac{a}{2}\right)$

**8.** (a) $b^2y^2 = x^3(a - x); \quad a, b > 0$

$$y^2 = \frac{x^3(a - x)}{b^2}$$

Graph: $y_1 = \dfrac{\sqrt{x^3(a - x)}}{b}$ and

$y_2 = -\dfrac{\sqrt{x^3(a - x)}}{b}$.

(b) $a$ determines the $x$-intercept on the right: $(a, 0)$.

$b$ affects the height.

(c) Differentiating implicitly:

$$2b^2yy' = 3x^2(a - x) - x^3 = 3ax^2 - 4x^3$$
$$y' = \frac{(3ax^2 - 4x^3)}{2b^2y} = 0$$
$$\Rightarrow 3ax^2 = 4x^3$$
$$3a = 4x$$
$$x = \frac{3a}{4}$$
$$b^2y^2 = \left(\frac{3a}{4}\right)^3\left(a - \frac{3a}{4}\right) = \frac{27a^3}{64}\left(\frac{1}{4}a\right)$$
$$y^2 = \frac{27a^4}{256b^2} \Rightarrow y = \pm\frac{3\sqrt{3}a^2}{16b}$$

Two points: $\left(\dfrac{3a}{4}, \dfrac{3\sqrt{3}a^2}{16b}\right), \left(\dfrac{3a}{4}, \dfrac{-3\sqrt{3}a^2}{16b}\right)$

**9.** $f(x) = \dfrac{a + bx}{1 + cx}$

$f(0) = a = e^0 = 1 \Rightarrow a = 1$

$f'(x) = \dfrac{(1 + cx)(b) - (a + bx)c}{(1 + cx)^2} = \dfrac{b - ac}{(1 + cx)^2}$

$f'(0) = b - ac = 1 \Rightarrow b = 1 + c$

$f''(x) = \dfrac{(1 + cx)^2(0) - (b - ac)2c(1 + cx)}{(1 + cx)^4} = \dfrac{2c(ac - b)}{(1 + cx)^3}$

$f''(0) = 2c(ac - b) = 2c(c - (1 + c)) = 2c(-1) = 1 \Rightarrow c = -\dfrac{1}{2}$

So, $b = 1 + c = 1 - \dfrac{1}{2} = \dfrac{1}{2}$.

$f(x) = \dfrac{1 + \frac{1}{2}x}{1 - \frac{1}{2}x}$

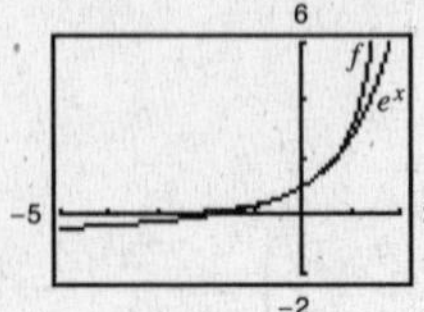
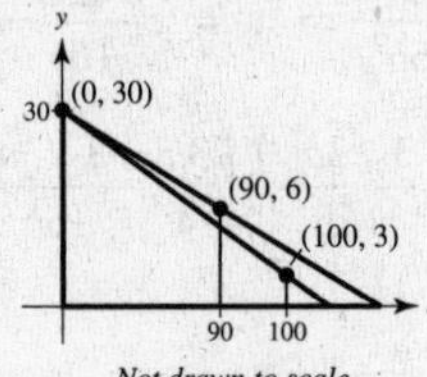


**10.** (a)

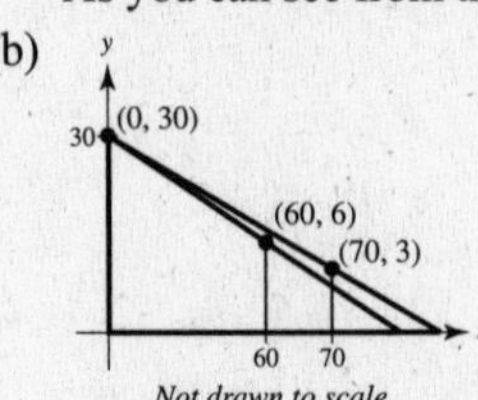

*Not drawn to scale*

Line determined by $(0, 30)$ and $(90, 6)$:

$y - 30 = \dfrac{30 - 6}{0 - 90}(x - 0)$

$= -\dfrac{24}{90}x = -\dfrac{4}{15}x \Rightarrow y = -\dfrac{4}{15}x + 30$

When $x = 100$:

$y = -\dfrac{4}{15}(100) + 30 = \dfrac{10}{3} > 3$

As you can see from the figure, the shadow determined by the man extends beyond the shadow determined by the child.

(b)


*Not drawn to scale*

Line determined by $(0, 30)$ and $(60, 6)$:

$y - 30 = \dfrac{30 - 6}{0 - 60}(x - 0) = -\dfrac{2}{5}x \Rightarrow y = -\dfrac{2}{5}x + 30$

When $x = 70$: $y = -\dfrac{2}{5}(70) + 30 = 2 < 3$

As you can see from the figure, the shadow determined by the child extends beyond the shadow determined by the man.

(c) Need $(0, 30), (d, 6), (d + 10, 3)$ collinear.

$$\frac{30-6}{0-d} = \frac{6-3}{d-(d+10)} \Rightarrow \frac{24}{d} = \frac{3}{10} \Rightarrow d = 80 \text{ feet}$$

(d) Let $y$ be the distance from the base of the street light to the tip of the shadow. You know that $dx/dt = -5$.

For $x > 80$, the shadow is determined by the man.

$$\frac{y}{30} = \frac{y-x}{6} \Rightarrow y = \frac{5}{4}x \text{ and } \frac{dy}{dt} = \frac{5}{4}\frac{dx}{dt} = \frac{-25}{4}$$

For $x < 80$, the shadow is determined by the child.

$$\frac{y}{30} = \frac{y-x-10}{3} \Rightarrow y = \frac{10}{9}x + \frac{100}{9} \text{ and } \frac{dy}{dt} = \frac{10}{9}\frac{dx}{dt} = -\frac{50}{9}$$

Therefore:

$$\frac{dy}{dt} = \begin{cases} -\dfrac{25}{4}, & x > 80 \\ -\dfrac{50}{9}, & 0 < x < 80 \end{cases}$$

$dy/dt$ is not continuous at $x = 80$.

**ALTERNATE SOLUTION for parts (a) and (b):**

(a) As before, the line determined by the man's shadow is

$$y_m = -\frac{4}{15}x + 30$$

The line determined by the child's shadow is obtained by finding the line through $(0, 30)$ and $(100, 3)$:

$$y - 30 = \frac{30-3}{0-100}(x-0) \Rightarrow y_c = -\frac{27}{100}x + 30$$

By setting $y_m = y_c = 0$, you can determine how far the shadows extend:

Man: $y_m = 0 \Rightarrow \frac{4}{15}x = 30 \Rightarrow x = 112.5 = 112\frac{1}{2}$

Child: $y_c = 0 \Rightarrow \frac{27}{100}x = 30 \Rightarrow x = 111.\overline{11} = 111\frac{1}{9}$

The man's shadow is $112\frac{1}{2} - 111\frac{1}{9} = 1\frac{7}{18}$ ft beyond the child's shadow.

(b) As before, the line determined by the man's shadow is

$$y_m = -\frac{2}{5}x + 30$$

For the child's shadow,

$$y - 30 = \frac{30-3}{0-70}(x-0) \Rightarrow y_c = -\frac{27}{70}x + 30$$

Man: $y_m = 0 \Rightarrow \frac{2}{5}x = 30 \Rightarrow x = 75$

Child: $y_c = 0 \Rightarrow \frac{27}{70}x = 30 \Rightarrow x = \frac{700}{9} = 77\frac{7}{9}$

So the child's shadow is $77\frac{7}{9} - 75 = 2\frac{7}{9}$ ft beyond the man's shadow.

**11.** (a) $y = x^{1/3} \Rightarrow \dfrac{dy}{dt} = \dfrac{1}{3}x^{-2/3}\dfrac{dx}{dt}$

$1 = \dfrac{1}{3}(8)^{-2/3}\dfrac{dx}{dt}$

$\dfrac{dx}{dt} = 12 \text{ cm/sec}$

(b) $D = \sqrt{x^2 + y^2} \Rightarrow \dfrac{dD}{dt} = \dfrac{1}{2}\left(x^2 + y^2\right)\left(2x\dfrac{dx}{dt} + 2y\dfrac{dy}{dt}\right) = \dfrac{x(dx/dt) + y(dy/dt)}{\sqrt{x^2 + y^2}}$

$= \dfrac{8(12) + 2(1)}{\sqrt{64 + 4}} = \dfrac{98}{\sqrt{68}} = \dfrac{49}{\sqrt{17}} \text{ cm/sec}$

(c) $\tan\theta = \dfrac{y}{x} \Rightarrow \sec^2\theta \cdot \dfrac{d\theta}{dt} = \dfrac{x(dy/dt) - y(dx/dt)}{x^2}$

$\sqrt{68}$ 2 $\theta$ 8

From the triangle, $\sec\theta = \sqrt{68}/8$. So $\dfrac{d\theta}{dt} = \dfrac{8(1) - 2(12)}{64(68/64)} = \dfrac{-16}{68} = -\dfrac{4}{17}$ rad/sec.

**12.**
$y = \ln x$

$y' = \dfrac{1}{x}$

$y - b = \dfrac{1}{a}(x - a)$

$y = \dfrac{1}{a}x + b - 1$, Tangent line

If $x = 0$, $c = b - 1$. So, $b - c = b - (b - 1) = 1$.

**13.**
$y = e^x$

$y' = e^x$

$y - b = e^a(x - a)$

$y = e^a x - ae^a + b$, Tangent line

If $y = 0$, $e^a x = ae^a - b$.

$bx = ab - b, \quad (b = e^a)$

$x = a - 1$

$c = a - 1$

So, $a - c = 1$ always.

**14.** (a)

| z (degrees) | 0.1 | 0.01 | 0.0001 |
|---|---|---|---|
| $\dfrac{\sin z}{z}$ | 0.0174524 | 0.0174533 | 0.0174533 |

(b) $\lim\limits_{z\to 0}\dfrac{\sin z}{z} \approx 0.0174533$

In fact, $\lim\limits_{z\to 0}\dfrac{\sin z}{z} = \dfrac{\pi}{180}$.

(c) $\dfrac{d}{dz}(\sin z) = \lim\limits_{\Delta z\to 0}\dfrac{\sin(z + \Delta z) - \sin z}{\Delta z}$

$= \lim\limits_{\Delta z\to 0}\dfrac{\sin z \cdot \cos\Delta z + \sin\Delta z \cdot \cos z - \sin z}{\Delta z}$

$= \lim\limits_{\Delta z\to 0}\left[\sin z\left(\dfrac{\cos\Delta z - 1}{\Delta z}\right)\right] + \lim\limits_{\Delta z\to 0}\left[\cos z\left(\dfrac{\sin\Delta z}{\Delta z}\right)\right]$

$= (\sin z)(0) + (\cos z)\left(\dfrac{\pi}{180}\right) = \dfrac{\pi}{180}\cos z$

(d) $S(90) = \sin\left(\frac{\pi}{180}90\right) = \sin\frac{\pi}{2} = 1$

$C(180) = \cos\left(\frac{\pi}{180}180\right) = -1$

$\frac{d}{dz}S(z) = \frac{d}{dz}\sin(cz) = c \cdot \cos(cz) = \frac{\pi}{180}C(z)$

(e) The formulas for the derivatives are more complicated in degrees.

**15.** (a) $v(t) = -\frac{27}{5}t + 27$ ft/sec

$a(t) = -\frac{27}{5}$ ft/sec$^2$

(b) $v(t) = -\frac{27}{5}t + 27 = 0 \Rightarrow \frac{27}{5}t = 27 \Rightarrow t = 5$ seconds

$s(5) = -\frac{27}{10}(5)^2 + 27(5) + 6 = 73.5$ feet

(c) The acceleration due to gravity on Earth is greater in magnitude than that on the moon.

**16.** $j(t) = a'(t)$

(a) $j(t)$ is the rate of change of acceleration.

The acceleration is constant, so $j(t) = 0$.

(b) $a$ is position.

$b$ is acceleration.

$c$ is jerk.

$d$ is velocity.

# CHAPTER 4
# Applications of Differentiation

# CHAPTER 4
# Applications of Differentiation

## Section 4.1 Extrema on an Interval

**1.** $f(x) = \dfrac{x^2}{x^2 + 4}$

$f'(x) = \dfrac{(x^2 + 4)(2x) - (x^2)(2x)}{(x^2 + 4)^2} = \dfrac{8x}{(x^2 + 4)^2}$

$f'(0) = 0$

**2.** $f(x) = \cos \dfrac{\pi x}{2}$

$f'(x) = -\dfrac{\pi}{2} \sin \dfrac{\pi x}{2}$

$f'(0) = 0$

$f'(2) = 0$

**3.** $g(x) = x + \dfrac{4}{x^2} = x + 4x^{-2}$

$g'(x) = 1 - 8x^{-3} = 1 - \dfrac{8}{x^3}$

$g'(2) = 0$

**4.** $f(x) = -3x\sqrt{x + 1}$

$f'(x) = -3x\left[\frac{1}{2}(x + 1)^{-1/2}\right] + \sqrt{x + 1}(-3)$

$= -\frac{3}{2}(x + 1)^{-1/2}\left[x + 2(x + 1)\right]$

$= -\frac{3}{2}(x + 1)^{-1/2}(3x + 2)$

$f'\left(-\frac{2}{3}\right) = 0$

**5.** $f(x) = (x + 2)^{2/3}$

$f'(x) = \frac{2}{3}(x + 2)^{-1/3}$

$f'(-2)$ is undefined.

**6.** Using the limit definition of the derivative,

$$\lim_{x \to 0^-} \frac{f(x) - f(0)}{x - 0} = \lim_{x \to 0^-} \frac{(4 - |x|) - 4}{x} = 1$$

$$\lim_{x \to 0^+} \frac{f(x) - f(0)}{x - 0} = \lim_{x \to 0^+} \frac{(4 - |x|) - 4}{x - 0} = -1$$

$f'(0)$ does not exist, because the one-sided derivatives are not equal.

**7.** Critical number: $x = 2$

$x = 2$: absolute maximum (and relative maximum)

**8.** Critical number: $x = 0$

$x = 0$: neither

**9.** Critical numbers: $x = 1, 2, 3$

$x = 1, 3$: absolute maxima (and relative maxima)

$x = 2$: absolute minimum (and relative minimum)

**10.** Critical numbers: $x = 2, 5$

$x = 2$: neither

$x = 5$: absolute maximum (and relative maximum)

**11.** $f(x) = x^3 - 3x^2$

$f'(x) = 3x^2 - 6x = 3x(x - 2)$

Critical numbers: $x = 0, 2$

**12.** $g(x) = x^4 - 4x^2$

$g'(x) = 4x^3 - 8x = 4x(x^2 - 2)$

Critical numbers: $x = 0, \pm\sqrt{2}$

**13.** $g(t) = t\sqrt{4 - t},\ t < 3$

$g'(t) = t\left[\dfrac{1}{2}(4 - t)^{-1/2}(-1)\right] + (4 - t)^{1/2}$

$= \dfrac{1}{2}(4 - t)^{-1/2}\left[-t + 2(4 - t)\right]$

$= \dfrac{8 - 3t}{2\sqrt{4 - t}}$

Critical number: $t = \dfrac{8}{3}$

**14.** $f(x) = \dfrac{4x}{x^2 + 1}$

$f'(x) = \dfrac{(x^2 + 1)(4) - (4x)(2x)}{(x^2 + 1)^2} = \dfrac{4(1 - x^2)}{(x^2 + 1)^2}$

Critical numbers: $x = \pm 1$

**15.** $h(x) = \sin^2 x + \cos x,\quad 0 < x < 2\pi$

$h'(x) = 2 \sin x \cos x - \sin x = \sin x(2 \cos x - 1)$

Critical numbers in $(0, 2\pi)$: $x = \dfrac{\pi}{3}, \pi, \dfrac{5\pi}{3}$

**16.** $f(\theta) = 2\sec\theta + \tan\theta,\ 0 < \theta < 2\pi$

$$f'(\theta) = 2\sec\theta\tan\theta + \sec^2\theta$$
$$= \sec\theta(2\tan\theta + \sec\theta)$$
$$= \sec\theta\left[2\left(\frac{\sin\theta}{\cos\theta}\right) + \frac{1}{\cos\theta}\right]$$
$$= \sec^2\theta(2\sin\theta + 1)$$

Critical numbers in $(0, 2\pi)$: $\theta = \frac{7\pi}{6}, \frac{11\pi}{6}$

**17.** $f(t) = te^{-2t}$

$f'(t) = e^{-2t} - 2te^{-2t} = e^{-2t}(1 - 2t)$

Critical number: $t = \frac{1}{2}$

**18.** $g(t) = 2t\ln t$

$g'(t) = 2\ln t + 2t\left(\frac{1}{t}\right) = 2\ln t + 2$

Critical number: $t = \frac{1}{e}$

**19.** $f(x) = x^2\log_2(x^2 + 1) = x^2\frac{\ln(x^2 + 1)}{\ln 2}$

$$f'(x) = 2x\frac{\ln(x^2 + 1)}{\ln 2} + x^2\frac{2x}{(\ln 2)(x^2 + 1)}$$
$$= \frac{2x}{\ln 2}\left[\ln(x^2 + 1) + \frac{x^2}{x^2 + 1}\right]$$

Critical number: $x = 0$

**20.** $g(x) = 4x^2(3^x)$

$g'(x) = 8x(3^x) + 4x^2 3^x \ln 3 = 4x(3^x)(2 + x\ln 3)$

Critical numbers: $x = 0, -1.82$

**21.** $f(x) = 3 - x,\ [-1, 2]$

$f'(x) = -1 \Rightarrow$ no critical numbers

Left endpoint: $(-1, 4)$ Maximum

Right endpoint: $(2, 1)$ Minimum

**22.** $f(x) = \frac{2x + 5}{3},\ [0, 5]$

$f'(x) = \frac{2}{3} \Rightarrow$ No critical numbers

Left endpoint: $\left(0, \frac{5}{3}\right)$ Minimum

Right endpoint: $(5, 5)$ Maximum

**23.** $g(x) = x^2 - 2x,\ [0, 4]$

$g'(x) = 2x - 2 = 2(x - 1)$

Critical number: $x = 1$

Left endpoint: $(0, 0)$

Critical number: $(1, -1)$ Minimum

Right endpoint: $(4, 8)$ Maximum

**24.** $h(x) = -x^2 + 3x - 5,\ [-2, 1]$

$h'(x) = -2x + 3$

Critical number: $x = \frac{3}{2}$ (not in interval)

Left endpoint: $(-2, -15)$ Minimum

Right endpoint: $(1, -3)$ Maximum

**25.** $f(x) = x^3 - \frac{3}{2}x^2,\ [-1, 2]$

$f'(x) = 3x^2 - 3x = 3x(x - 1)$

Left endpoint: $\left(-1, -\frac{5}{2}\right)$ Minimum

Critical number: $(0, 0)$

Critical number: $\left(1, -\frac{1}{2}\right)$

Right endpoint: $(2, 2)$ Maximum

**26.** $f(x) = x^3 - 12x,\ [0, 4]$

$f'(x) = 3x^2 - 12 = 3(x^2 - 4)$

Left endpoint: $(0, 0)$

Critical number: $(2, -16)$ Minimum

Right endpoint: $(4, 16)$ Maximum

**Note:** $x = -2$ is not in the interval.

**27.** $f(x) = 3x^{2/3} - 2x,\ [-1, 1]$

$f'(x) = 2x^{-1/3} - 2 = \frac{2(1 - \sqrt[3]{x})}{\sqrt[3]{x}}$

Left endpoint: $(-1, 5)$ Maximum

Critical number: $(0, 0)$ Minimum

Right endpoint: $(1, 1)$

**28.** $g(x) = \sqrt[3]{x},\ [-1, 1]$

$g'(x) = \frac{1}{3x^{2/3}}$

Left endpoint: $(-1, -1)$ Minimum

Critical number: $(0, 0)$

Right endpoint: $(1, 1)$ Maximum

**29.** $h(s) = \dfrac{1}{s - 2}, \quad [0, 1]$

$h'(s) = \dfrac{-1}{(s - 2)^2}$

Left endpoint: $\left(0, -\dfrac{1}{2}\right)$ Maximum

Right endpoint: $(1, -1)$ Minimum

**30.** $h(t) = \dfrac{t}{t - 2}, \quad [3, 5]$

$h'(t) = \dfrac{-2}{(t - 2)^2}$

Left endpoint: $(3, 3)$ Maximum

Right endpoint: $\left(5, \dfrac{5}{3}\right)$ Minimum

**31.** $g(t) = \dfrac{t^2}{t^2 + 3}, \quad [-1, 1]$

$g'(t) = \dfrac{6t}{(t^2 + 3)^2}$

Left endpoint: $\left(-1, \dfrac{1}{4}\right)$ Maximum

Critical number: $(0, 0)$ Minimum

Right endpoint: $\left(1, \dfrac{1}{4}\right)$ Maximum

**32.** $y = 3 - |t - 3|, \quad [-1, 5]$

For $x < 3$, $y = 3 + (t - 3) = t$

and $y' = 1 \neq 0$ on $[-1, 3)$

For $x > 3$, $y = 3 - (t - 3) = 6 - t$

and $y' = -1 \neq 0$ on $(3, 5]$

So, $x = 3$ is the only critical number.

Left endpoint: $(-1, -1)$ Minimum

Right endpoint: $(5, 1)$

Critical number: $(3, 3)$ Maximum

**33.** $f(x) = \cos \pi x, \left[0, \dfrac{1}{6}\right]$

$f'(x) = -\pi \sin \pi x$

Left endpoint: $(0, 1)$ Maximum

Right endpoint: $\left(\dfrac{1}{6}, \dfrac{\sqrt{3}}{2}\right)$ Minimum

**34.** $g(x) = \sec x, \quad \left[-\dfrac{\pi}{6}, \dfrac{\pi}{3}\right]$

$g'(x) = \sec x \tan x$

Left endpoint: $\left(-\dfrac{\pi}{6}, \dfrac{2}{\sqrt{3}}\right) \approx \left(-\dfrac{\pi}{6}, 1.1547\right)$

Right endpoint: $\left(\dfrac{\pi}{3}, 2\right)$ Maximum

Critical number: $(0, 1)$ Minimum

**35.** $y = 3 \cos x, \quad [0, 2\pi]$

$y' = -3 \sin x$

Critical number in $(0, 2\pi)$: $x = \pi$

Left endpoint: $(0, 3)$ Maximum

Critical number: $(\pi, -3)$ Minimum

Right endpoint: $(2\pi, 3)$ Maximum

**36.** $y = \tan\left(\dfrac{\pi x}{8}\right), \quad [0, 2]$

$y' = \dfrac{\pi}{8} \sec^2\left(\dfrac{\pi x}{8}\right) \neq 0$

Left endpoint: $(0, 0)$ Minimum

Right endpoint: $(2, 1)$ Maximum

**37.** $f(x) = \arctan x^2, [-2, 1]$

$f'(x) = \dfrac{2x}{1 + x^4}$

Critical number: $x = 0$

Left endpoint: $(-2, \arctan 4) \approx (-2, 1.326)$ Maximum

Right endpoint: $(1, \arctan 1) = \left(1, \dfrac{\pi}{4}\right) \approx (1, 0.785)$

Critical number: $(0, 0)$ Minimum

**38.** $g(x) = \dfrac{\ln x}{x}, [1, 4]$

$g'(x) = \dfrac{x\left(\dfrac{1}{x}\right) - \ln x}{x^2} = \dfrac{1 - \ln x}{x^2}$

Critical number: $x = e$

Left endpoint: $(1, 0)$ Minimum

Right endpoint: $\left(4, \dfrac{\ln 4}{4}\right) \approx (4, 0.347)$

Critical number: $\left(e, \dfrac{1}{e}\right) \approx (2.718, 0.368)$ Maximum

**39.** $h(x) = 5e^x - e^{2x}, [-1, 2]$

$h'(x) = 5e^x - 2e^{2x} = e^x(5 - 2e^x)$

$5 - 2e^x = 0 \Rightarrow e^x = \frac{5}{2} \Rightarrow x = \ln\left(\frac{5}{2}\right) \approx 0.916$

Critical number: $x = \ln\left(\frac{5}{2}\right)$

Left endpoint: $\left(-1, \frac{5}{e} - \frac{1}{e^2}\right) \approx (-1, 1.704)$

Right endpoint: $(2, 5e^2 - e^4) \approx (2, -17.653)$ Minimum

Critical number: $\left(\ln\left(\frac{5}{2}\right), \frac{25}{4}\right)$ Maximum

**Note:** $h\left(\ln\left(\frac{5}{2}\right)\right) = 5e^{\ln(5/2)} - e^{2\ln(5/2)}$

$= 5\left(\frac{5}{2}\right) - \left(\frac{5}{2}\right)^2 = \frac{25}{4}$

**40.** $y = x^2 - 8\ln x, [1, 5]$

$y' = 2x - \frac{8}{x}$

$2x - \frac{8}{x} = 0 \Rightarrow 2x^2 = 8 \Rightarrow x = 2$

$(x = -2$ not in domain$)$

Critical number: $x = 2$

Left endpoint: $(1, 1)$

Right endpoint: $(5, 25 - 8\ln 5) \approx (5, 12.124)$ Maximum

Critical number: $(2, 4 - 8\ln 2) \approx (2, -1.545)$ Minimum

**41.** $y = e^x \sin x, [0, \pi]$

$y' = e^x \sin x + e^x \cos x = e^x(\sin x + \cos x)$

Left endpoint: $(0, 0)$ Minimum

Critical number:

$\left(\frac{3\pi}{4}, \frac{\sqrt{2}}{2}e^{3\pi/4}\right) \approx \left(\frac{3\pi}{4}, 7.46\right)$ Maximum

Right endpoint: $(\pi, 0)$ Minimum

**42.** $y = x\ln(x + 3), [0, 3]$

$y' = x\left(\frac{1}{x + 3}\right) + \ln(x + 3)$

Left endpoint: $(0, 0)$ Minimum

Right endpoint: $(3, 3\ln 6) \approx (3, 5.375)$ Maximum

**43.** $f(x) = 2x - 3$

(a) Minimum: $(0, -3)$

Maximum: $(2, 1)$

(b) Minimum: $(0, -3)$

(c) Maximum: $(2, 1)$

(d) No extrema

**44.** $f(x) = \sqrt{9 - x^2}$

(a) Minima: $(-3, 0)$ and $(3, 0)$

Maximum: $(0, 3)$

(b) Minimum: $(-3, 0)$

(c) Maximum: $(0, 3)$

(d) Maximum: $(1, \sqrt{8})$

**45.** $f(x) = \begin{cases} 2x + 2, & 0 \le x \le 1 \\ 4x^2, & 1 < x \le 3 \end{cases}$

Left endpoint: $(0, 2)$ Minimum

Right endpoint: $(3, 36)$ Maximum

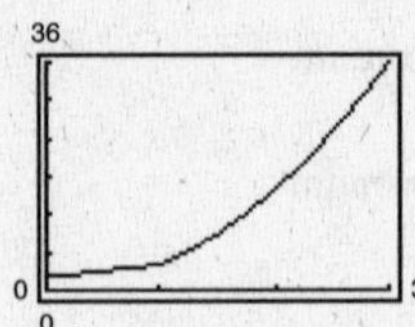


**46.** $f(x) = \begin{cases} 2 - x^2, & 1 \le x < 3 \\ 2 - 3x, & 3 \le x \le 5 \end{cases}$

Left endpoint: $(1, 1)$ Maximum

Right endpoint: $(5, -13)$ Minimum

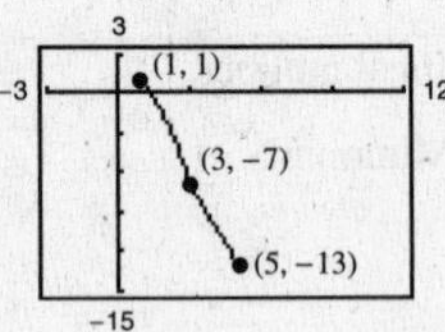

**47.** $f(x) = \dfrac{3}{x-1}, \quad (1, 4]$

Right endpoint: $(4, 1)$ Minimum

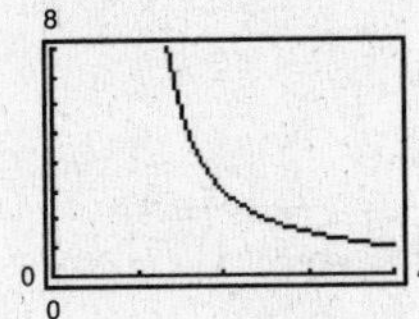

**48.** $f(x) = \dfrac{2}{2-x}, \quad [0, 2)$

Left endpoint: $(0, 1)$ Minimum

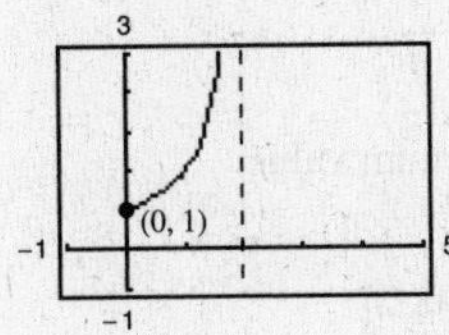


**49.** $f(x) = x^4 - 2x^3 + x + 1, \quad [-1, 3]$

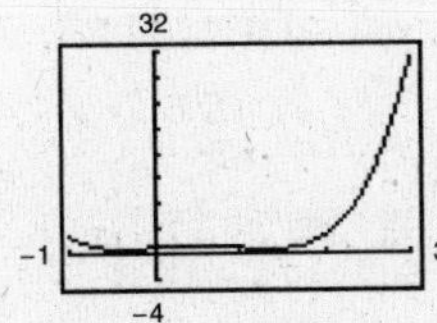

$f'(x) = 4x^3 - 6x^2 + 1 = (2x - 1)(2x^2 - 2x - 1) = 0$

$x = \dfrac{1}{2}, \dfrac{1 \pm \sqrt{3}}{2} \approx 0.5, -0.366, 1.366$

Right endpoint: $(3, 31)$ Maximum

Critical points: $\left(\dfrac{1 \pm \sqrt{3}}{2}, \dfrac{3}{4}\right)$ Minima

**50.** $f(x) = \sqrt{x} + \cos\dfrac{x}{2}, \quad [0, 2\pi]$

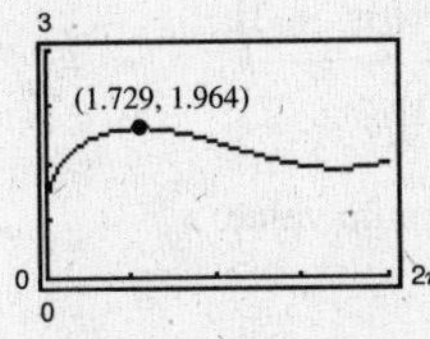


$f'(x) = \dfrac{1}{2\sqrt{x}} - \dfrac{1}{2}\sin\dfrac{x}{2}$

Left endpoint: $(0, 1)$ Minimum

Graphing utility: $(1.729, 1.964)$ Maximum

**51.** (a)

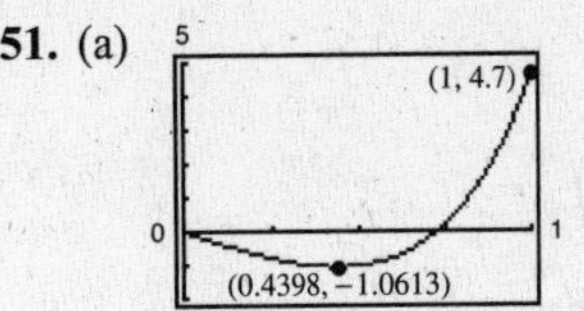


(b) Critical point: $(0.4398, -1.0613)$ Minimum

**52.** (a)

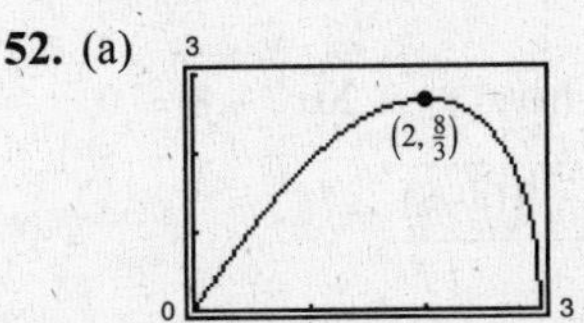


(b) Critical point: $\left(2, \dfrac{8}{3}\right)$ Maximum

**53.** (a)

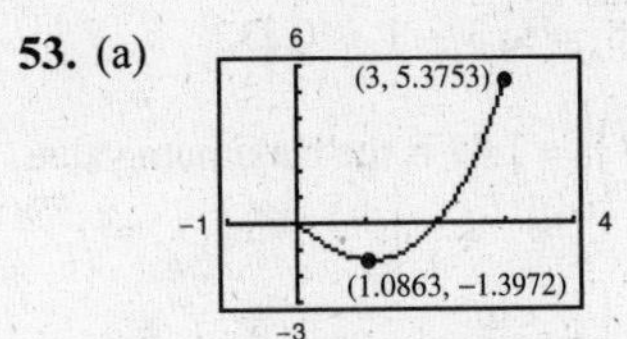


(b) Critical point: $(1.8063, -1.3972)$ Minimum

**54.** (a)

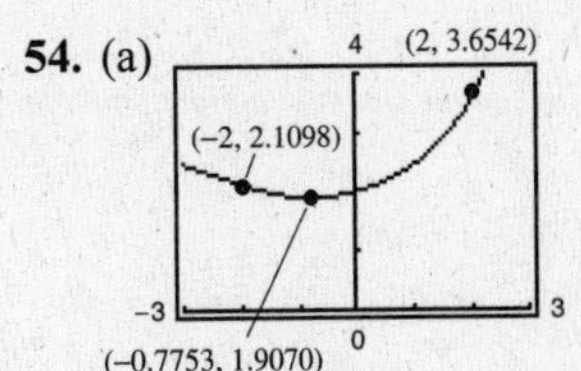


(b) Critical point: $(-0.7753, 1.9070)$ Minimum

**55.** (a)

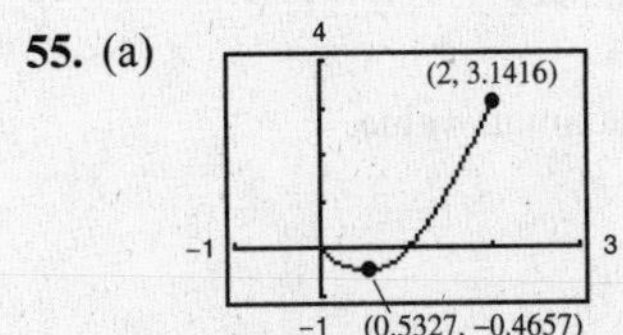


(b) Critical point: $(0.5327, -0.4657)$ Minimum

**56.** (a)

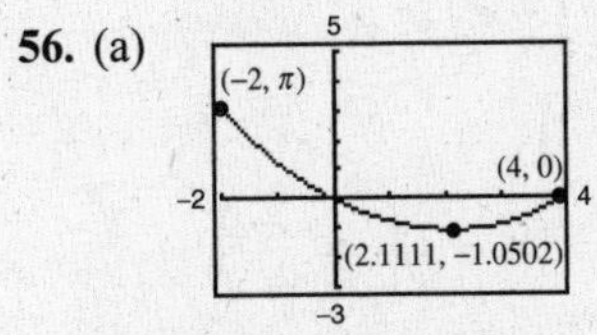


(b) Critical point: $(2.1111, -1.0502)$ Minimum

**57.** $f(x) = (1 + x^3)^{1/2}, \quad [0, 2]$

$f'(x) = \frac{3}{2}x^2(1 + x^3)^{-1/2}$

$f''(x) = \frac{3}{4}(x^4 + 4x)(1 + x^3)^{-3/2}$

$f'''(x) = -\frac{3}{8}(x^6 + 20x^3 - 8)(1 + x^3)^{-5/2}$

Setting $f''' = 0$, you have $x^6 + 20x^3 - 8 = 0$.

$x^3 = \frac{-20 \pm \sqrt{400 - 4(1)(-8)}}{2}$

$x = \sqrt[3]{-10 \pm \sqrt{108}} = \sqrt{3} - 1$

In the interval $[0, 2]$, choose

$x = \sqrt[3]{-10 \pm \sqrt{108}} = \sqrt{3} - 1 \approx 0.732$.

$\left|f''\left(\sqrt[3]{-10 + \sqrt{108}}\right)\right| \approx 1.47$ is the maximum value.

**58.** $f(x) = \frac{1}{x^2 + 1}, \quad \left[\frac{1}{2}, 3\right]$

$f'(x) = \frac{-2x}{(x^2 + 1)^2}$

$f''(x) = \frac{-2(1 - 3x^2)}{(x^2 + 1)^3}$

$f'''(x) = \frac{24x - 24x^3}{(x^2 + 1)^4}$

Setting $f''' = 0$, you have $x = 0, \pm 1$.

$|f''(1)| = \frac{1}{2}$ is the maximum value.

**59.** $f(x) = e^{-x^2/2}, [0, 1]$

$f'(x) = -xe^{-x^2/2}$

$f''(x) = -x\left(-xe^{-x^2/2}\right) - e^{-x^2/2}$

$= e^{-x^2/2}(x^2 - 1)$

$f'''(x) = e^{-x^2/2}(2x) + (x^2 - 1)\left(-xe^{-x^2/2}\right)$

$= xe^{-x^2/2}(3 - x^2)$

Left endpoint: $f''(0) = -1$

Right endpoint: $f''(1) = 0$

$|f''(0)| = 1$ is the maximum value.

**60.** $f(x) = x\ln(x + 1), [0, 2]$

$f'(x) = \frac{x}{(x + 1)} + \ln(x + 1)$

$f''(x) = \frac{x + 1 - x}{(x + 1)^2} + \frac{1}{x + 1}$

$= \frac{1}{(x + 1)^2} + \frac{1}{x + 1} = \frac{x + 2}{(x + 1)^2}$

$f'''(x) = \frac{(x + 1)^2 - (x + 2)2(x + 1)}{(x + 1)^4} = \frac{-x - 3}{(x + 1)^3}$

Left endpoint: $f''(0) = 2$

Right endpoint: $f''(2) = \frac{4}{9}$

$|f''(0)| = 2$ is the maximum value.

**61.** $f(x) = (x + 1)^{2/3}, \quad [0, 2]$

$f'(x) = \frac{2}{3}(x + 1)^{-1/3}$

$f''(x) = -\frac{2}{9}(x + 1)^{-4/3}$

$f'''(x) = \frac{8}{27}(x + 1)^{-7/3}$

$f^{(4)}(x) = -\frac{56}{81}(x + 1)^{-10/3}$

$f^{(5)}(x) = \frac{560}{243}(x + 1)^{-13/3}$

$|f^{(4)}(0)| = \frac{56}{81}$ is the maximum value.

**62.** $f(x) = \frac{1}{x^2 + 1}, \quad [-1, 1]$

$f'''(x) = \frac{24x - 24x^3}{(x^2 + 1)^4}$

$f^{(4)}(x) = \frac{24(5x^4 - 10x^2 + 1)}{(x^2 + 1)^5}$

$f^{(5)}(x) = \frac{-240x(3x^4 - 10x^2 + 3)}{(x^2 + 1)^6}$

$|f^{(4)}(0)| = 24$ is the maximum value.

**63.** Answers will vary. *Sample answer*:

$y = \frac{1}{x}$ on the interval $(0, 1)$

There is no maximum or minimum value.

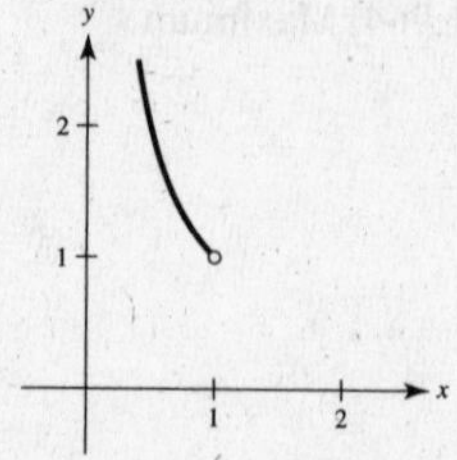

**64.** A: absolute minimum
B: relative maximum
C: neither
D: relative minimum
E: relative maximum
F: relative minimum
G: neither

**65.**

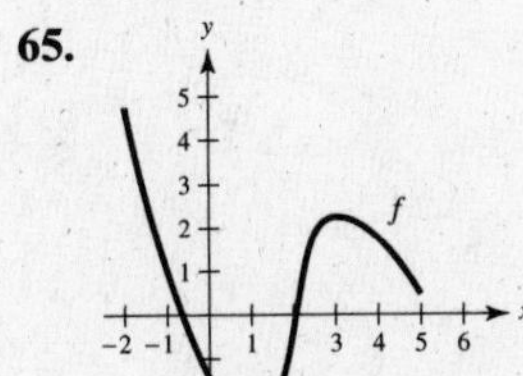

**66.**

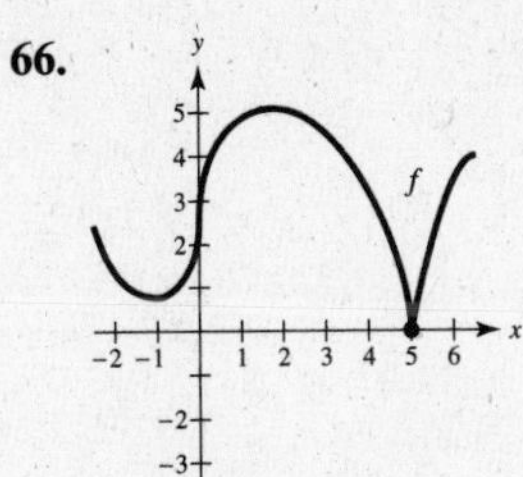

**67.** (a) Yes
(b) No

**68.** (a) No
(b) Yes

**69.** (a) No
(b) Yes

**70.** $f(x) = \tan x$

$f$ is continuous on $[0, \pi/4]$ but not on $[0, \pi]$.

$\lim_{x\to(\pi/2)^-} \tan x = \infty.$

**71.** $x = \dfrac{v^2 \sin 2\theta}{32}, \dfrac{\pi}{4} \le \theta \le \dfrac{3\pi}{4}$

$\dfrac{d\theta}{dt}$ is constant.

$\dfrac{dx}{dt} = \dfrac{dx}{d\theta}\dfrac{d\theta}{dt}$ (by the Chain Rule) $= \dfrac{v^2 \cos 2\theta}{16}\dfrac{d\theta}{dt}$

In the interval $[\pi/4, 3\pi/4]$, $\theta = \pi/4, 3\pi/4$ indicate minimums for $dx/dt$ and $\theta = \pi/2$ indicates a maximum for $dx/dt$. This implies that the sprinkler waters longest when $\theta = \pi/4$ and $3\pi/4$. So, the lawn farthest from the sprinkler gets the most water.

**72.** $S = 6hs + \dfrac{3s^2}{2}\left(\dfrac{\sqrt{3} - \cos\theta}{\sin\theta}\right), \dfrac{\pi}{6} \le \theta \le \dfrac{\pi}{2}$

$$\frac{dS}{d\theta} = \frac{3s^2}{2}\left(-\sqrt{3}\csc\theta\cot\theta + \csc^2\theta\right)$$
$$= \frac{3s^2}{2}\csc\theta\left(-\sqrt{3}\cot\theta + \csc\theta\right) = 0$$
$$\csc\theta = \sqrt{3}\cot\theta$$
$$\sec\theta = \sqrt{3}$$
$$\theta = \text{arcsec}\sqrt{3} \approx 0.9553 \text{ radians}$$
$$S\left(\frac{\pi}{6}\right) = 6hs + \frac{3s^2}{2}\left(\sqrt{3}\right)$$
$$S\left(\frac{\pi}{6}\right) = 6hs + \frac{3s^2}{2}\left(\sqrt{3}\right)$$
$$S\left(\text{arcsec}\sqrt{3}\right) = 6hs + \frac{3s^2}{2}\left(\sqrt{2}\right)$$

$S$ is minimum when $\theta = \text{arcsec}\sqrt{3} \approx 0.9553$ radian.

**73.** True. See Exercise 31.

**74.** True. This is stated in the Extreme Value Theorem.

**75.** True

**76.** False. Let $f(x) = x^2$. $x = 0$ is a critical number of $f$.

$g(x) = f(x - k) = (x - k)^2$

$x = k$ is a critical number of $g$.

**77.** If $f$ has a maximum value at $x = c$, then $f(c) \ge f(x)$ for all $x$ in $I$. So, $-f(c) \le -f(x)$ for all $x$ in $I$. So, $-f$ has a minimum value at $x = c$.

**78.** $f(x) = ax^3 + bx^2 + cx + d, \quad a \neq 0$

$f'(x) = 3ax^2 + 2bx + c$

The quadratic polynomial can have zero, one, or two zeros.

$$x = \frac{-2b \pm \sqrt{4b^2 - 12ac}}{6a} = \frac{-b \pm \sqrt{b^2 - 3ac}}{3a}$$

Zero critical numbers: $b^2 < 3ac$.

Example: $(a = b = c = 1, d = 0) f(x) = x^3 + x^2 + x$ has no critical numbers.

One critical number: $b^2 = 3ac$.

Example: $(a = 1, b = c = d = 0) f(x) = x^3$ has one critical number, $x = 0$.

Two critical numbers: $b^2 > 3ac$.

Example: $(a = c = 1, b = 2, d = 0) f(x) = x^3 + 2x^2 + x$ has two critical numbers: $x = -1, -\frac{1}{3}$.

**79.** (a) Because the grade at $A$ is 9%, $A(-500, 45)$.

The grade at $B$ is 6%, $B(500, 30)$.

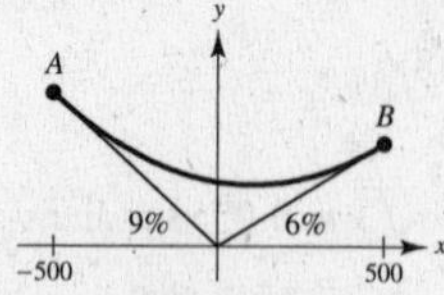


(b) $y = ax^2 + bx + c$

$y' = 2ax + b$

At $A$: $2a(-500) + b = -0.09$

At $B$: $2a(500) + b = 0.06$

Solving these two equations, you obtain

$$a = \frac{3}{40{,}000} \quad \text{and} \quad b = -\frac{3}{200}.$$

Using the points $A(-500, 45)$ and $B(500, 30)$, you obtain

$$45 = \frac{3}{40{,}000}(-500)^2 + \left(-\frac{3}{200}\right)(-500) + C$$

$$30 = \frac{3}{40{,}000}(500)^2 + \left(-\frac{3}{200}\right)(500) + C.$$

In both cases, $C = 18.75 = \frac{75}{4}$. So, $y = \frac{3}{40{,}000}x^2 - \frac{3}{200}x + \frac{75}{4}$

(c)

| $x$ | -500 | -400 | -300 | -200 | -100 | 0 | 100 | 200 | 300 | 400 | 500 |
|---|---|---|---|---|---|---|---|---|---|---|---|
| $d$ | 0 | 0.75 | 3 | 6.75 | 12 | 18.75 | 12 | 6.75 | 3 | 0.75 | 0 |

For $-500 \leq x \leq 0$, $d = (ax^2 + bx + c) - (-0.09x)$.

For $0 \leq x \leq 500$, $d = (ax^2 + bx + c) - (0.06x)$.

(d) $y' = \frac{3}{20{,}000}x - \frac{3}{200} = 0$

$$x = \frac{3}{200} \cdot \frac{20{,}000}{3} = 100$$

The lowest point on the highway is $(100, 18)$, which is not directly over the origin.

**80.** First do an example: Let $a = 4$ and $f(x) = 4$. Then $R$ is the square $0 \le x \le 4, 0 \le y \le 4$.

Its area and perimeter are both $k = 16$.

Claim that all real numbers $a > 2$ work. On the one hand, if $a > 2$ is given, then let $f(x) = 2a/(a - 2)$.

Then the rectangle

$$R = \left\{(x, y): 0 \le x \le a, 0 \le y \le \frac{2a}{a - 2}\right\}$$

has $k = \dfrac{2a^2}{a - 2}$:

$$\text{Area} = a\left(\frac{2a}{a - 2}\right) = \frac{2a^2}{a - 2}$$

$$\text{Perimeter} = 2a + 2\left(\frac{2a}{a - 2}\right) = \frac{2a(a - 2) + 2(2a)}{a - 2} = \frac{2a^2}{a - 2}.$$

To see that $a$ must be greater than 2, consider

$R = \{(x, y): 0 \le x \le a, 0 \le y \le f(x)\}$.

$f$ attains its maximum value on $[0, a]$ at some point $P(x_0, y_0)$, as indicated in the figure.

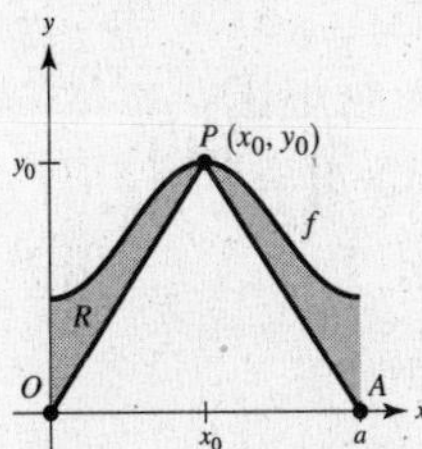


Draw segments $\overline{OP}$ and $\overline{PA}$. The region $R$ is bounded by the rectangle $0 \le x \le a, 0 \le y \le y_0$, so

$\text{area}(R) = k \le ay_0$. Furthermore, from the figure, $y_0 < \overline{OP}$ and $y_0 < \overline{PA}$. So,

$k = \text{Perimeter}(R) > \overline{OP} + \overline{PA} > 2y_0$. Combining, $2y_0 < k \le ay_0 \Rightarrow a > 2$.

## Section 4.2 Rolle's Theorem and the Mean Value Theorem

**1.** $f(x) = \left|\dfrac{1}{x}\right|$

$f(-1) = f(1) = 1$. But, $f$ is not continuous on $[-1, 1]$.

**2.** Rolle's Theorem does not apply to $f(x) = \cot(x/2)$ over $[\pi, 3\pi]$ because $f$ is not continuous at $x = 2\pi$.

**3.** Rolle's Theorem does not apply to $f(x) = 1 - |x - 1|$ over $[0, 2]$ because $f$ is not differentiable at $x = 1$.

**4.** $f(x) = \sqrt{(2 - x^{2/3})^3}$

$f(-1) = f(1) = 1$

$$f'(x) = \frac{-\sqrt{(2 - x^{2/3})}}{x^{1/3}}$$

$f$ is not differentiable at $x = 0$.

**5.** $f(x) = x^2 - x - 2 = (x - 2)(x + 1)$

$x$-intercepts: $(-1, 0), (2, 0)$

$f'(x) = 2x - 1 = 0$ at $x = \frac{1}{2}$.

**6.** $f(x) = x(x - 3)$

$x$-intercepts: $(0, 0), (3, 0)$

$f'(x) = 2x - 3 = 0$ at $x = \frac{3}{2}$.

**7.** $f(x) = x\sqrt{x + 4}$

$x$-intercepts: $(-4, 0), (0, 0)$

$$f'(x) = x\frac{1}{2}(x + 4)^{-1/2} + (x + 4)^{1/2}$$

$$= (x + 4)^{-1/2}\left(\frac{x}{2} + (x + 4)\right)$$

$$f'(x) = \left(\frac{3}{2}x + 4\right)(x + 4)^{-1/2} = 0 \text{ at } x = -\frac{8}{3}$$

**8.** $f(x) = -3x\sqrt{x+1}$

$x$-intercepts: $(-1, 0), (0, 0)$

$$f'(x) = -3x\frac{1}{2}(x+1)^{-1/2} - 3(x+1)^{1/2}$$

$$= -3(x+1)^{-1/2}\left(\frac{x}{2} + (x+1)\right)$$

$$f'(x) = -3(x+1)^{-1/2}\left(\frac{3}{2}x + 1\right) = 0 \text{ at } x = -\frac{2}{3}$$

**9.** $f(x) = x^2 + 2x - 3 = (x+3)(x-1)$

$f(-3) = f(1) = 0$

$f'(x) = 2x + 2 = 0$ at $x = -1$

$c = -1$ and $f'(-1) = 0$.

**10.** $f(x) = \sin 2x$

$$f(0) = f\left(\frac{\pi}{2}\right) = 0$$

$$f'(x) = 2\cos 2x = 0 \text{ at } x = \frac{\pi}{4}$$

$$c = \frac{\pi}{4} \text{ and } f'\left(\frac{\pi}{4}\right) = 0.$$

**11.** $f(x) = -x^2 + 3x, \quad [0, 3]$

$f(0) = f(3) = 0$

$f$ is continuous on $[0, 3]$ and differentiable on $(0, 3)$. Rolle's Theorem applies.

$f'(x) = -2x + 3$

$-2x + 3 = 0 \Rightarrow x = \frac{3}{2}$

$c$-value: $\frac{3}{2}$

**12.** $f(x) = x^2 - 5x + 4, [1, 4]$

$f(1) = f(4) = 0$

$f$ is continuous on $[1, 4]$. $f$ is differentiable on $(1, 4)$. Rolle's Theorem applies.

$f'(x) = 2x - 5$

$2x - 5 = 0 \Rightarrow x = \frac{5}{2}$

$c$-value: $\frac{5}{2}$

**13.** $f(x) = (x-1)(x-2)(x-3), [1, 3]$

$f(1) = f(3) = 0$

$f$ is continuous on $[1, 3]$. $f$ is differentiable on $(1, 3)$. Rolle's Theorem applies.

$$f(x) = x^3 - 6x^2 + 11x - 6$$

$$f'(x) = 3x^2 - 12x + 11$$

$$3x^2 - 12x + 11 = 0 \Rightarrow x = \frac{6 \pm \sqrt{3}}{3}$$

$c$-values: $\dfrac{6-\sqrt{3}}{3}, \dfrac{6+\sqrt{3}}{3}$

**14.** $f(x) = (x-3)(x+1)^2, [-1, 3]$

$f(-1) = f(3) = 0$

$f$ is continuous on $[-1, 3]$. $f$ is differentiable on $(-1, 3)$. Rolle's Theorem applies.

$$f'(x) = (x-3)(2)(x+1) + (x+1)^2$$

$$= (x+1)[2x - 6 + x + 1]$$

$$= (x+1)(3x-5)$$

$c$-value: $\frac{5}{3}$

**15.** $f(x) = x^{2/3} - 1, [-8, 8]$

$f(-8) = f(8) = 3$

$f$ is continuous on $[-8, 8]$. $f$ is not differentiable on $(-8, 8)$ because $f'(0)$ does not exist. Rolle's Theorem does not apply.

**16.** $f(x) = 3 - |x - 3|, [0, 6]$

$f(0) = f(6) = 0$

$f$ is continuous on $[0, 6]$. $f$ is not differentiable on $(0, 6)$ because $f'(3)$ does not exist. Rolle's Theorem does not apply.

**17.** $f(x) = \dfrac{x^2 - 2x - 3}{x + 2}, [-1, 3]$

$f(-1) = f(3) = 0$

$f$ is continuous on $[-1, 3]$. (**Note:** the discontinuity, $x = -2$, is not in the interval.) $f$ is differentiable on $(-1, 3)$. Rolle's Theorem applies.

$$f'(x) = \frac{(x + 2)(2x - 2) - (x^2 - 2x - 3)(1)}{(x + 2)^2} = 0$$

$$\frac{x^2 + 4x - 1}{(x + 2)^2} = 0$$

$$x = \frac{-4 \pm 2\sqrt{5}}{2} = -2 \pm \sqrt{5}$$

$c$-value: $-2 + \sqrt{5}$

**18.** $f(x) = \dfrac{x^2 - 1}{x}, [-1, 1]$

$f(-1) = f(1) = 0$

$f$ is not continuous on $[-1, 1]$ because $f(0)$ does not exist. Rolle's Theorem does not apply.

**19.** $f(x) = (x^2 - 2x)e^x, [0, 2]$

$f(0) = f(2) = 0$

$f$ is continuous on $[0, 2]$ and differentiable on $(0, 2)$, so Rolle's Theorem applies.

$$f'(x) = (x^2 - 2x)e^x + (2x - 2)e^x = e^x(x^2 - 2)$$
$$= 0 \Rightarrow x = \sqrt{2}$$

$c$-value: $\sqrt{2} \approx 1.414$

**20.** $f(x) = x - 2 \ln x, [1, 3]$

$f(1) = 1$

$f(3) = 3 - 2 \ln 3 \neq 1$

Because $f(1) \neq f(3)$, Rolle's Theorem does not apply on $[1, 3]$.

**21.** $f(x) = \sin x, [0, 2\pi]$

$f(0) = f(2\pi) = 0$

$f$ is continuous on $[0, 2\pi]$. $f$ is differentiable on $(0, 2\pi)$. Rolle's Theorem applies.

$f'(x) = \cos x$

$c$-values: $\dfrac{\pi}{2}, \dfrac{3\pi}{2}$

**22.** $f(x) = \cos x, [0, 2\pi]$

$f(0) = f(2\pi) = 1$

$f$ is continuous on $[0, 2\pi]$. $f$ is differentiable on $(0, 2\pi)$. Rolle's Theorem applies.

$f'(x) = -\sin x$

$c$-value: $\pi$

**23.** $f(x) = \dfrac{6x}{\pi} - 4 \sin^2 x, \left[0, \dfrac{\pi}{6}\right]$

$f(0) = f\left(\dfrac{\pi}{6}\right) = 0$

$f$ is continuous on $[0, \pi/6]$. $f$ is differentiable on $(0, \pi/6)$. Rolle's Theorem applies.

$$f'(x) = \frac{6}{\pi} - 8 \sin x \cos x = 0$$

$$\frac{6}{\pi} = 8 \sin x \cos x$$

$$\frac{6}{\pi} = 4 \sin 2x$$

$$\frac{3}{2\pi} = \sin 2x$$

$$\frac{1}{2} \arcsin\left(\frac{3}{2\pi}\right) = x$$

$$x \approx 0.2489$$

$c$-value: 0.2489

**24.** $f(x) = \cos 2x, [-\pi, \pi]$

$f(-\pi) = f(\pi) = 1$

$f$ is continuous on $[-\pi, \pi]$ and differentiable on $(-\pi, \pi)$. Rolle's Theorem applies.

$$f'(x) = -2\sin 2x$$
$$-2\sin 2x = 0$$
$$\sin 2x = 0$$
$$x = -\pi, -\frac{\pi}{2}, 0, \frac{\pi}{2}, \pi$$

$c$-values: $-\frac{\pi}{2}, 0, \frac{\pi}{2}$

**25.** $f(x) = \tan x, [0, \pi]$

$f(0) = f(\pi) = 0$

$f$ is not continuous on $[0, \pi]$ because $f(\pi/2)$ does not exist. Rolle's Theorem does not apply.

**26.** $f(x) = \sec x, [\pi, 2\pi]$

$f$ is not continuous on $[\pi, 2\pi]$ because $f(3\pi/2) = \sec(3\pi/2)$ does not exist. Rolle's Theorem does not apply.

**27.** $f(x) = |x| - 1, [-1, 1]$

$f(-1) = f(1) = 0$

$f$ is continuous on $[-1, 1]$. $f$ is not differentiable on $(-1, 1)$ because $f'(0)$ does not exist. Rolle's Theorem does not apply.

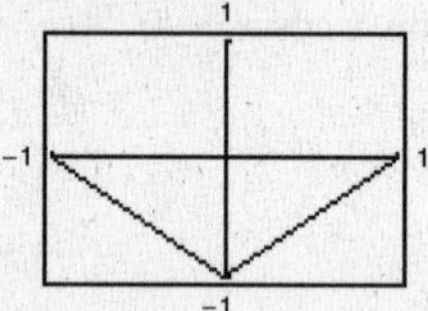


**28.** $f(x) = x - x^{-1/3}, [0, 1]$

$f(0) = f(1) = 0$

$f$ is continuous on $[0, 1]$. $f$ is differentiable on $(0, 1)$. (**Note:** $f$ is not differentiable at $x = 0$.) Rolle's Theorem applies.

$$f'(x) = 1 - \frac{1}{3\sqrt[3]{x^2}} = 0$$
$$1 = \frac{1}{3\sqrt[3]{x^2}}$$
$$\sqrt[3]{x^2} = \frac{1}{3}$$
$$x^2 = \frac{1}{27}$$
$$x = \sqrt{\frac{1}{27}} = \frac{\sqrt{3}}{9}$$

$c$-value: $\frac{\sqrt{3}}{9} \approx 0.1925$

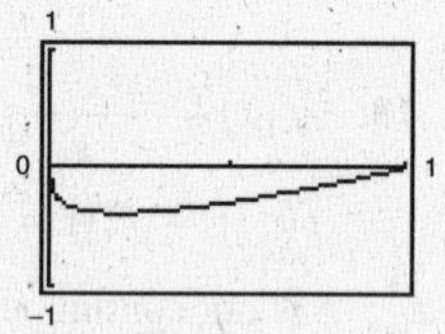

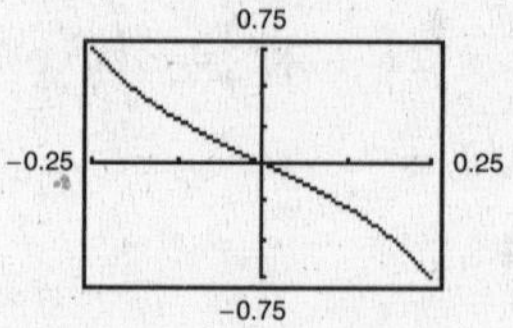


**29.** $f(x) = x - \tan \pi x, \left[-\frac{1}{4}, \frac{1}{4}\right]$

$f\left(-\frac{1}{4}\right) = -\frac{1}{4} + 1 = \frac{3}{4}$

$f\left(\frac{1}{4}\right) = \frac{1}{4} - 1 = -\frac{3}{4}$

Rolle's Theorem does not apply.

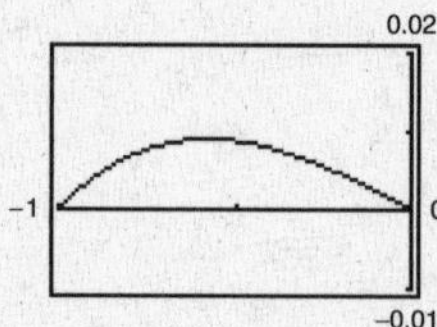


**30.** $f(x) = \frac{x}{2} - \sin\frac{\pi x}{6}, [-1, 0]$

$f(-1) = f(0) = 0$

$f$ is continuous on $[-1, 0]$. $f$ is differentiable on $(-1, 0)$. Rolle's Theorem applies.

$$f'(x) = \frac{1}{2} - \frac{\pi}{6}\cos\frac{\pi x}{6} = 0$$
$$\cos\frac{\pi x}{6} = \frac{3}{\pi}$$
$$x = -\frac{6}{\pi}\arccos\frac{3}{\pi} \text{ [Value needed in } (-1, 0).]$$
$$\approx -0.5756 \text{ radian}$$

$c$-value: $-0.5756$

0.02

−1 0

−0.01

**31.** $f(x) = 2 + \arcsin(x^2 - 1), [-1, 1]$

$f(-1) = f(1) = 2$

$$f'(x) = \frac{2x}{\sqrt{1 - (x^2 - 1)^2}} = \frac{2x}{\sqrt{2x^2 - x^4}}$$

$f'(0)$ does not exist. Rolle's Theorem does not apply.

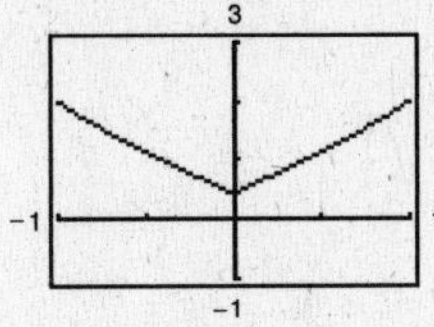


**32.** $f(x) = 2 + (x^2 - 4x)(2^{-x/4}), [0, 4]$

$f(0) = f(4) = 2$

$f$ is continuous on $[0, 4]$. $f$ is differentiable on $(0, 4)$. Rolle's Theorem applies.

$$f'(x) = (2x - 4)2^{-x/4} + (x^2 - 4x)\ln 2 \cdot 2^{-x/4}\left(-\frac{1}{4}\right)$$

$$= 2^{-x/4}\left[2x - 4 - (\ln 2)\left(\frac{x^2}{4} - x\right)\right]$$

$$= 0 \Rightarrow x \approx 1.6633$$

$c$-value: 1.6633

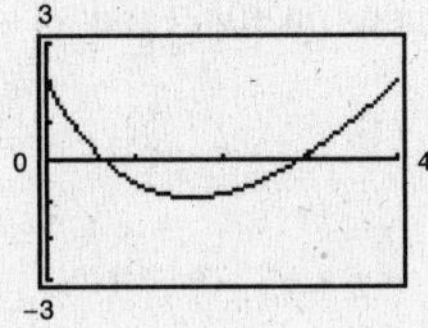


**33.** $f(t) = -16t^2 + 48t + 6$

(a) $f(1) = f(2) = 38$

(b) $v = f'(t)$ must be 0 at some time in $(1, 2)$.

$f'(t) = -32t + 48 = 0$

$t = \frac{3}{2}$ sec

**34.** $C(x) = 10\left(\frac{1}{x} + \frac{x}{x + 3}\right)$

(a) $C(3) = C(6) = \frac{25}{3}$

(b) $$C'(x) = 10\left(-\frac{1}{x^2} + \frac{3}{(x + 3)^2}\right) = 0$$

$$\frac{3}{x^2 + 6x + 9} = \frac{1}{x^2}$$

$$2x^2 - 6x - 9 = 0$$

$$x = \frac{6 \pm \sqrt{108}}{4}$$

$$= \frac{6 \pm 6\sqrt{3}}{4} = \frac{3 \pm 3\sqrt{3}}{2}$$

In the interval

$(3, 6)$: $c = \dfrac{3 + 3\sqrt{3}}{2} \approx 4.098 \approx 410$ components

**35.**

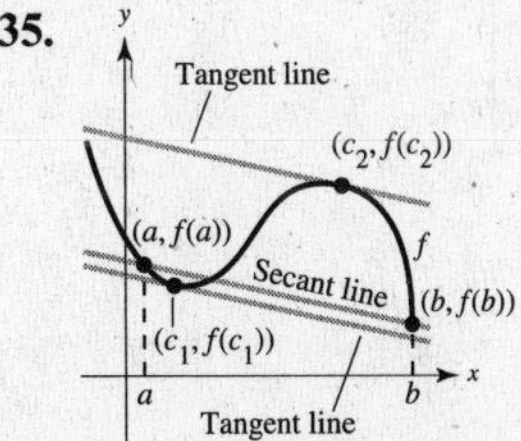


**36.**

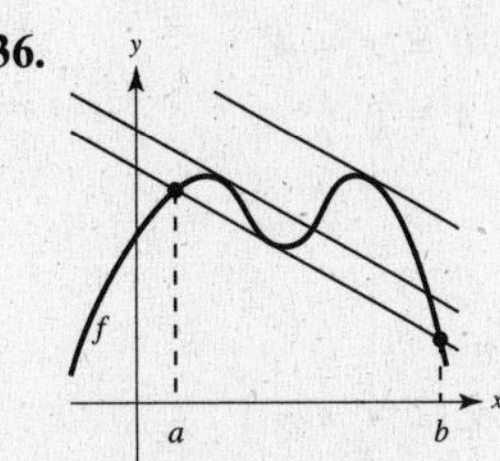


**37.** $f$ is not continuous on the interval $[0, 6]$. ($f$ is not continuous at $x = 2$.)

**38.** $f$ is not differentiable at $x = 2$. The graph of $f$ is not smooth at $x = 2$.

**39.** $f(x) = \frac{1}{x - 3}, [0, 6]$

$f$ has a discontinuity at $x = 3$.

**40.** $f(x) = |x - 3|, [0, 6]$

$f$ is not differentiable at $x = 3$.

**41.** $f(x) = -x^2 + 5$

(a) Slope $= \dfrac{1 - 4}{2 + 1} = -1$

Secant line: $y - 4 = -(x + 1)$

$y = -x + 3$

$x + y - 3 = 0$

(b) $f'(x) = -2x = -1 \Rightarrow x = c = \dfrac{1}{2}$

(c) $f(c) = f\left(\dfrac{1}{2}\right) = -\dfrac{1}{4} + 5 = \dfrac{19}{4}$

Tangent line: $y - \dfrac{19}{4} = -\left(x - \dfrac{1}{2}\right)$

$4y - 19 = -4x + 2$

$4x + 4y - 21 = 0$

(d)

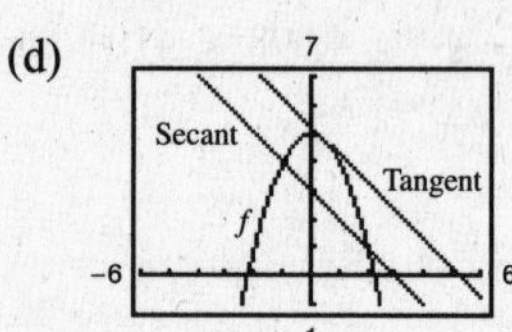


**42.** $f(x) = x^2 - x - 12$

(a) Slope $= \dfrac{-6 - 0}{-2 - 4} = 1$

Secant line: $y - 0 = x - 4$

$x - y - 4 = 0$

(b) $f'(x) = 2x - 1 = 1 \Rightarrow x = c = 1$

(c) $f(c) = f(1) = -12$

Tangent line: $y + 12 = x - 1$

$x - y - 13 = 0$

(d)

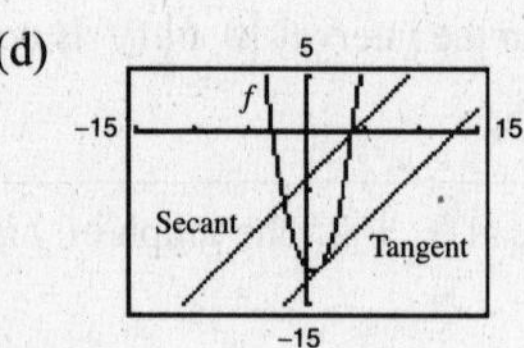


**43.** $f(x) = x^2$ is continuous on $[-2, 1]$ and differentiable on $(-2, 1)$.

$\dfrac{f(1) - f(-2)}{1 - (-2)} = \dfrac{1 - 4}{3} = -1$

$f'(x) = 2x = -1$

$x = -\dfrac{1}{2}$

$c = -\dfrac{1}{2}$

**44.** $f(x) = x^3$ is continuous on $[0, 1]$ and differentiable on $(0, 1)$.

$\dfrac{f(1) - f(0)}{1 - 0} = \dfrac{1 - 0}{1} = 1$

$f'(x) = 3x^2 = 1$

$x = \pm\dfrac{\sqrt{3}}{3}$

In the interval $(0, 1)$: $c = \dfrac{\sqrt{3}}{3}$

**45.** $f(x) = x^3 + 2x$ is continuous on $[-1, 1]$ and differentiable on $(-1, 1)$.

$\dfrac{f(1) - f(-1)}{1 - (-1)} = \dfrac{3 - (-3)}{2} = 3$

$f'(x) = 3x^2 + 2 = 3$

$3x^2 = 1$

$x = \pm\dfrac{\sqrt{3}}{3}$

$c = \pm\dfrac{\sqrt{3}}{3}$

**46.** $f(x) = x^4 - 8x$ is continuous on $[0, 2]$ and differentiable on $(0, 2)$.

$\dfrac{f(2) - f(0)}{2 - 0} = \dfrac{0 - 0}{2} = 0$

$f'(x) = 4x^3 - 8 = 4(x^3 - 2) = 0$

$x^3 = 2$

$x = \sqrt[3]{2}$

$c = \sqrt[3]{2}$

**47.** $f(x) = x^{2/3}$ is continuous on $[0, 1]$ and differentiable on $(0, 1)$.

$\dfrac{f(1) - f(0)}{1 - 0} = 1$

$f'(x) = \dfrac{2}{3}x^{-1/3} = 1$

$x = \left(\dfrac{2}{3}\right)^3 = \dfrac{8}{27}$

$c = \dfrac{8}{27}$

**48.** $f(x) = \dfrac{x + 1}{x}$ is not continuous at $x = 0$. The Mean Value Theorem does not apply.

**49.** $f(x) = |2x + 1|$ is not differentiable at $x = -1/2$. The Mean Value Theorem does not apply.

**50.** $f(x) = \sqrt{2 - x}$ is continuous on $[-7, 2]$ and differentiable on $(-7, 2)$.

$$\frac{f(2) - f(-7)}{2 - (-7)} = \frac{0 - 3}{9} = -\frac{1}{3}$$

$$f'(x) = \frac{-1}{2\sqrt{2 - x}} = -\frac{1}{3}$$

$$2\sqrt{2 - x} = 3$$

$$\sqrt{2 - x} = \frac{3}{2}$$

$$2 - x = \frac{9}{4}$$

$$x = -\frac{1}{4}$$

$$c = -\frac{1}{4}$$

**51.** $f(x) = \sin x$ is continuous on $[0, \pi]$ and differentiable on $(0, \pi)$.

$$\frac{f(\pi) - f(0)}{\pi - 0} = \frac{0 - 0}{\pi} = 0$$

$$f'(x) = \cos x = 0$$

$$x = \pi/2$$

$$c = \frac{\pi}{2}$$

**52.** $f(x) = \cos x + \tan x$ is not continuous at $x = \pi/2$. The Mean Value Theorem does not apply.

**53.** $f(x) = e^{-3x}$ is continued on $[0, 2]$ and differentiable on $(0, 2)$.

$$\frac{f(2) - f(0)}{2 - 0} = \frac{e^{-6} - 1}{2}$$

$$f'(x) = -3e^{-3x} = \frac{e^{-6} - 1}{2}$$

$$e^{-3x} = \frac{e^{-6} - 1}{-6} = \frac{1 - e^{-6}}{6}$$

$$-3x = \ln\left(\frac{1 - e^{-6}}{6}\right)$$

$$x = -\frac{1}{3}\ln\left(\frac{1 - e^{-6}}{6}\right) = \frac{1}{3}\ln\left(\frac{6}{1 - e^{-6}}\right)$$

$$c = \frac{1}{3}\ln\left(\frac{6}{1 - e^{-6}}\right) = \ln\sqrt[3]{\frac{6}{1 - e^{-6}}}$$

**54.** $f(x) = (x + 3)\ln(x + 3)$ is continuous on $[-2, -1]$ and differentiable on $(-2, -1)$.

$$\frac{f(-1) - f(-2)}{-1 - (-2)} = \frac{2\ln 2 - 0}{1} = \ln 4$$

$$f'(x) = (x + 3)\frac{1}{x + 3} + \ln(x + 3) = 1 + \ln(x + 3)$$

$$1 + \ln(x + 3) = \ln 4$$

$$\ln(x + 3) = \ln 4 - 1 = \ln 4 - \ln e = \ln\frac{4}{e}$$

$$x + 3 = \frac{4}{e}$$

$$x = \frac{4}{e} - 3 \approx 1.386$$

$$c = \frac{4 - 3e}{e}$$

**55.** $f(x) = x\log_2 x = x\dfrac{\ln x}{\ln 2}$

$f$ is continuous on $[1, 2]$ and differentiable on $(1, 2)$.

$$\frac{f(2) - f(1)}{2 - 1} = \frac{2 - 0}{2 - 1} = 2$$

$$f'(x) = x\frac{1}{x\ln 2} + \frac{\ln x}{\ln 2} = \frac{1 + \ln x}{\ln 2} = 2$$

$$1 + \ln x = 2\ln 2 = \ln 4$$

$$xe = 4$$

$$x = \frac{4}{e}$$

$$c = \frac{4}{e}$$

**56.** $f(x) = \arctan(1 - x)$

$f$ is continuous on $[0, 1]$ and differentiable on $(0, 1)$.

$$\frac{f(1) - f(0)}{1 - 0} = \frac{0 - (\pi/4)}{1 - 0} = -\frac{\pi}{4}$$

$$f'(x) = \frac{-1}{1 + (1 - x)^2}$$

$$= \frac{-1}{x^2 - 2x + 2} = -\frac{\pi}{4}$$

$$x^2 - 2x + 2 = \frac{4}{\pi}$$

$$x^2 - 2x - \frac{4}{\pi} + 2 = 0$$

$$x \approx 1.5227, 0.4773$$

$$c = 0.4773$$

**57.** $f(x) = \dfrac{x}{x+1}, \left[-\dfrac{1}{2}, 2\right]$

(a)–(c)

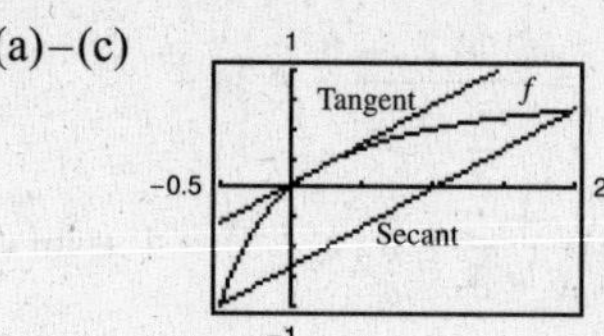


(b) Secant line:

$$\text{slope} = \frac{f(2) - f(-1/2)}{2 - (-1/2)} = \frac{2/3 - (-1)}{5/2} = \frac{2}{3}$$

$$y - \frac{2}{3} = \frac{2}{3}(x - 2)$$

$$y = \frac{2}{3}(x - 1)$$

(c) $f'(x) = \dfrac{1}{(x+1)^2} = \dfrac{2}{3}$

$$(x+1)^2 = \frac{3}{2}$$

$$x = -1 \pm \sqrt{\frac{3}{2}} = -1 \pm \frac{\sqrt{6}}{2}$$

In the interval $[-1/2, 2]$: $c = -1 + \left(\sqrt{6}/2\right)$

$$f(c) = \frac{-1 + \left(\sqrt{6}/2\right)}{\left[-1 + \left(\sqrt{6}/2\right)\right] + 1} = \frac{-2 + \sqrt{6}}{\sqrt{6}} = \frac{-2}{\sqrt{6}} + 1$$

Tangent line: $y - 1 + \dfrac{2}{\sqrt{6}} = \dfrac{2}{3}\left(x - \dfrac{\sqrt{6}}{2} + 1\right)$

$$y - 1 + \frac{\sqrt{6}}{3} = \frac{2}{3}x - \frac{\sqrt{6}}{3} + \frac{2}{3}$$

$$y = \frac{1}{3}\left(2x + 5 - 2\sqrt{6}\right)$$

**58.** $f(x) = x - 2\sin x, [-\pi, \pi]$

(a)–(c)

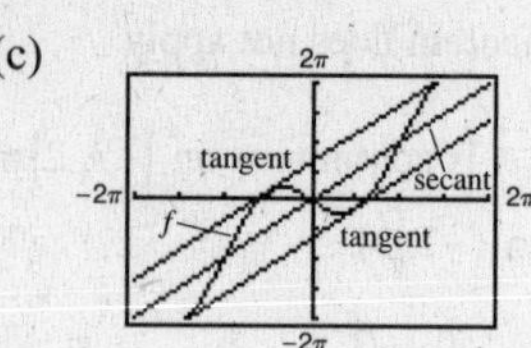


(b) Secant line:

$$\text{slope} = \frac{f(\pi) - f(-\pi)}{\pi - (-\pi)} = \frac{\pi - (-\pi)}{2\pi} = 1$$

$$y - \pi = 1(x - \pi)$$

$$y = x$$

(c) $f'(x) = 1 - 2\cos x = 1$

$$\cos x = 0$$

$$x = c = \pm\frac{\pi}{2}$$

$$f\left(\frac{\pi}{2}\right) = \frac{\pi}{2} - 2$$

$$f\left(-\frac{\pi}{2}\right) = -\frac{\pi}{2} + 2$$

Tangent lines: $y - \left(\dfrac{\pi}{2} - 2\right) = 1\left(x - \dfrac{\pi}{2}\right)$

$$y = x - 2$$

$$y - \left(-\frac{\pi}{2} + 2\right) = 1\left(x + \frac{\pi}{2}\right)$$

$$y = x + 2$$

**59.** $f(x) = \sqrt{x}, [1, 9]$

(a)–(c)

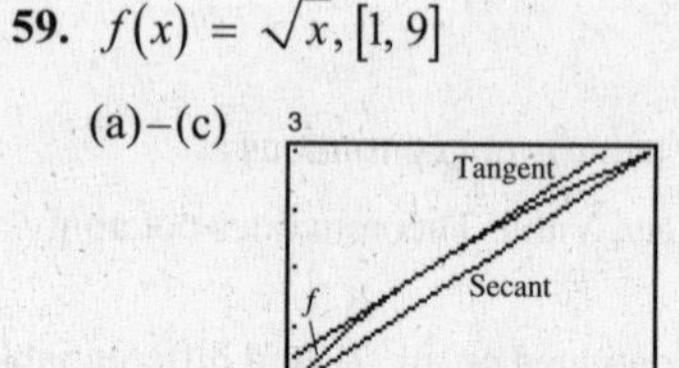


(b) Secant line:

$$\text{slope} = \frac{f(9) - f(1)}{9 - 1} = \frac{3 - 1}{8} = \frac{1}{4}$$

$$y - 1 = \frac{1}{4}(x - 1)$$

$$y = \frac{1}{4}x + \frac{3}{4}$$

(c) $f'(x) = \dfrac{1}{2\sqrt{x}} = \dfrac{1}{4}$

$$x = c = 4$$

$$f(4) = 2$$

Tangent line: $y - 2 = \dfrac{1}{4}(x - 4)$

$$y = \frac{1}{4}x + 1$$

**60.** $f(x) = x^4 - 2x^3 + x^2, [0, 6]$

(a)–(c)

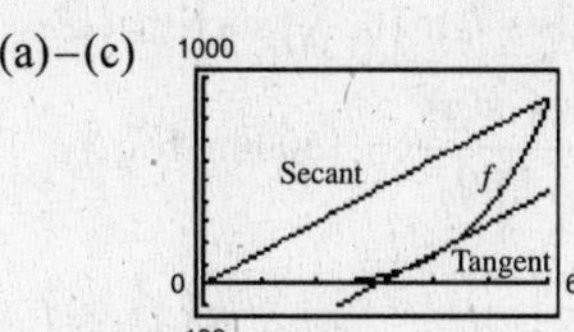


(b) Secant line:

$$\text{slope} = \frac{f(6) - f(0)}{6 - 0} = \frac{900 - 0}{6} = 150$$

$$y - 0 = 150(x - 0)$$

$$y = 150x$$

(c) $f'(x) = 4x^3 - 6x^2 + 2x = 150$

Using a graphing utility, there is one solution in $(0, 6)$, $x = c \approx 3.8721$ and $f(c) \approx 123.6721$.

Tangent line: $y - 123.6721 = 150(x - 3.8721)$

$$y = 150x - 457.143$$

**61.** $f(x) = 2e^{x/4} \cos \dfrac{\pi x}{4}, 0 \le x \le 2$

$f(0) = 2, f(2) = 0$

$$m = \frac{0 - 2}{2 - 0} = -1$$

(a)–(c)

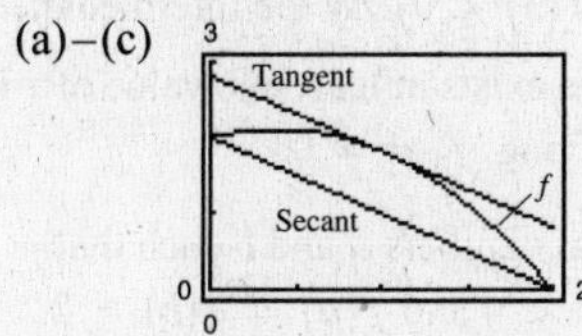


(b) Secant line: $y - 2 = -1(x - 0)$

$$y = -x + 2$$

(c) $f'(x) = 2\left(\dfrac{1}{4}e^{x/4} \cos \dfrac{\pi x}{4}\right) + 2e^{x/4}\left(-\sin \dfrac{\pi x}{4}\right)\dfrac{\pi}{4}$

$$= e^{x/4}\left[\frac{1}{2} \cos \frac{\pi x}{4} - \frac{\pi}{2} \sin \frac{\pi x}{4}\right]$$

$f'(c) = -1 \Rightarrow c \approx 1.0161, f(c) \approx 1.8$

Tangent line: $y - 1.8 = -1(x - 1.0161)$

$$y = -x + 2.8161$$

**62.** $f(x) = \ln|\sec \pi x|$

$f(0) = 0, f\left(\dfrac{1}{4}\right) = \ln \sqrt{2} \approx 0.3466$

$$m = \frac{f(1/4) - f(0)}{(1/4) - 0} = 4 \ln \sqrt{2} = 2 \ln 2 \approx 1.3863$$

(a)–(c)

(b) Secant line: $y - 0 = (2 \ln 2)(x - 0)$

$$y = (\ln 4)x$$

(c) $f'(x) = \dfrac{1}{\sec \pi x} \cdot \sec \pi x \cdot \tan \pi x \cdot \pi$

$$= \pi \tan \pi x$$

$f'(c) = \pi \tan \pi c = \ln 4$

$$c = \frac{1}{\pi}\tan^{-1}\frac{\ln 4}{\pi} \approx 0.1323$$

$f(c) \approx 0.0889$

Tangent line: $y - 0.0889 = 1.3863(x - 0.1323)$

$$y = 1.3863x - 0.0945$$

**63.** No. Let $f(x) = x^2$ on $[-1, 2]$.

$f'(x) = 2x$

$f'(0) = 0$ and zero is in the interval $(-1, 2)$ but $f(-1) \ne f(2)$.

**64.** $f(a) = f(b)$ and $f'(c) = 0$ where $c$ is in the interval $(a, b)$.

(a) $g(x) = f(x) + k$

$g(a) = g(b) = f(a) + k$

$g'(x) = f'(x) \Rightarrow g'(c) = 0$

Interval: $[a, b]$

Critical number of $g$: $c$

(b) $g(x) = f(x - k)$

$g(a + k) = g(b + k) = f(a)$

$g'(x) = f'(x - k)$

$g'(c + k) = f'(c) = 0$

Interval: $[a + k, b + k]$

Critical number of $g$: $c + k$

(c) $g(x) = f(kx)$

$g\left(\frac{a}{k}\right) = g\left(\frac{b}{k}\right) = f(a)$

$g'(x) = kf'(kx)$

$g'\left(\frac{c}{k}\right) = kf'(c) = 0$

Interval: $\left[\frac{a}{k}, \frac{b}{k}\right]$

Critical number of $g$: $\frac{c}{k}$

**65.** $f(x) = \begin{cases} 0, & x = 0 \\ 1 - x, & 0 < x \le 1 \end{cases}$

No, this does not contradict Rolle's Theorem. $f$ is not continuous on $[0, 1]$.

**66.** No. If such a function existed, then the Mean Value Theorem would say that there exists $c \in (-2, 2)$ such that

$$f'(c) = \frac{f(2) - f(-2)}{2 - (-2)} = \frac{6 + 2}{4} = 2.$$

But, $f'(x) < 1$ for all $x$.

**67.** Let $S(t)$ be the position function of the plane. If $t = 0$ corresponds to 2 P.M., $S(0) = 0$, $S(5.5) = 2500$ and the Mean Value Theorem says that there exists a time $t_0$, $0 < t_0 < 5.5$, such that

$$S'(t_0) = v(t_0) = \frac{2500 - 0}{5.5 - 0} \approx 454.54.$$

Applying the Intermediate Value Theorem to the velocity function on the intervals $[0, t_0]$ and $[t_0, 5.5]$, you see that there are at least two times during the flight when the speed was 400 miles per hour. $(0 < 400 < 454.54)$

**68.** Let $T(t)$ be the temperature of the object. Then $T(0) = 1500°$ and $T(5) = 390°$. The average temperature over the interval $[0, 5]$ is

$$\frac{390 - 1500}{5 - 0} = -222° \text{ F/h}.$$

By the Mean Value Theorem, there exist a time $t_0$, $0 < t_0 < 5$, such that $T'(t_0) = -222°$F/h.

**69.** Let $S(t)$ be the difference in the positions of the 2 bicyclists, $S(t) = S_1(t) - S_2(t)$. Because $S(0) = S(2.25) = 0$, there must exist a time $t_0 \in (0, 2.25)$ such that $S'(t_0) = v(t_0) = 0$.

At this time, $v_1(t_0) = v_2(t_0)$.

**70.** Let $t = 0$ correspond to 9:13 A.M. By the Mean Value Theorem, there exists $t_0$ in $\left(0, \frac{1}{30}\right)$ such that

$$v'(t_0) = a(t_0) = \frac{85 - 35}{1/30} = 1500 \text{ mi/h}^2.$$

**71.** $f(x) = 3\cos^2\left(\frac{\pi x}{2}\right)$, $f'(x) = 6\cos\left(\frac{\pi x}{2}\right)\left(-\sin\left(\frac{\pi x}{2}\right)\right)\left(\frac{\pi}{2}\right)$

$$= -3\pi\cos\left(\frac{\pi x}{2}\right)\sin\left(\frac{\pi x}{2}\right)$$

(a)

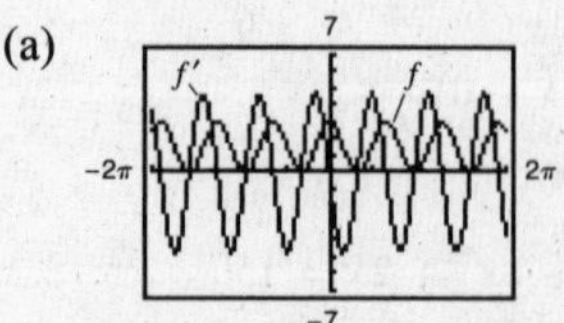


(b) $f$ and $f'$ are both continuous on the entire real line.

(c) Because $f(-1) = f(1) = 0$, Rolle's Theorem applies on $[-1, 1]$. Because $f(1) = 0$ and $f(2) = 3$, Rolle's Theorem does not apply on $[1, 2]$.

(d) $\lim_{x \to 3^-} f'(x) = 0$

$\lim_{x \to 3^+} f'(x) = 0$

**72.** (a) $f$ is continuous on $[-10, 4]$ and changes sign, $(f(-8) > 0, f(3) < 0)$. By the Intermediate Value Theorem, there exists at least one value of $x$ in $[-10, 4]$ satisfying $f(x) = 0$.

(b) There exist real numbers $a$ and $b$ such that $-10 < a < b < 4$ and $f(a) = f(b) = 2$. Therefore, by Rolle's Theorem there exists at least one number $c$ in $(-10, 4)$ such that $f'(c) = 0$. This is called a critical number.

(c)

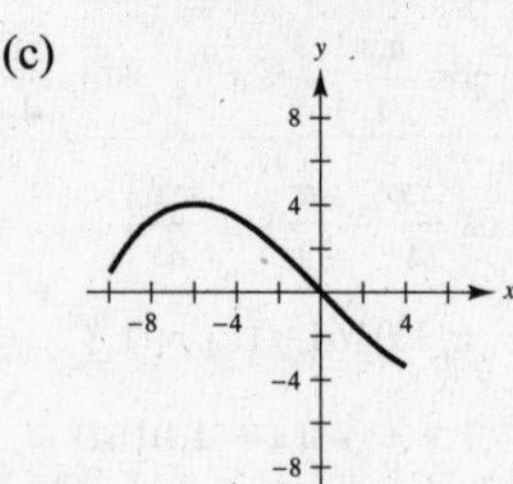


(d)

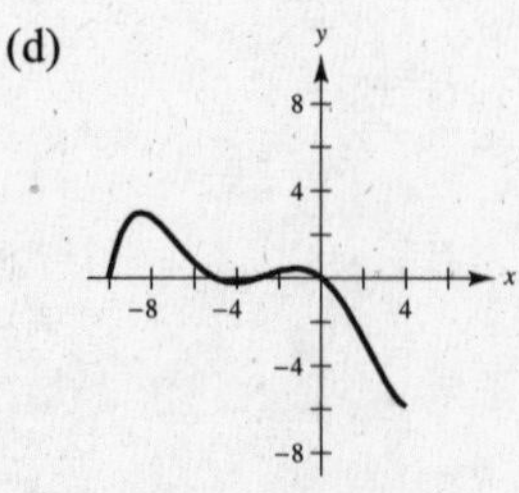


(e) No, $f'$ did not have to be continuous on $[-10, 4]$.

**73.** $f$ is continuous on $[-5, 5]$ and does not satisfy the conditions of the Mean Value Theorem. $\Rightarrow$ $f$ is not differentiable on $(-5, 5)$. Example: $f(x) = |x|$

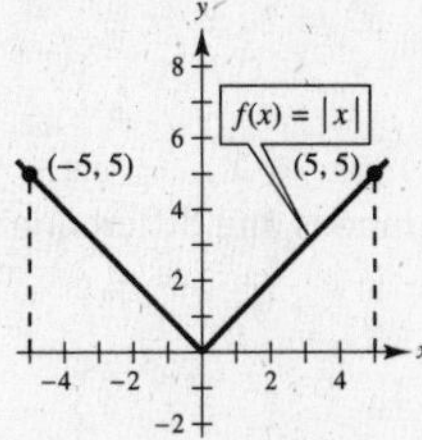


**74.** $f$ is not continuous on $[-5, 5]$.

Example: $f(x) = \begin{cases} 1/x, & x \neq 0 \\ 0, & x = 0 \end{cases}$

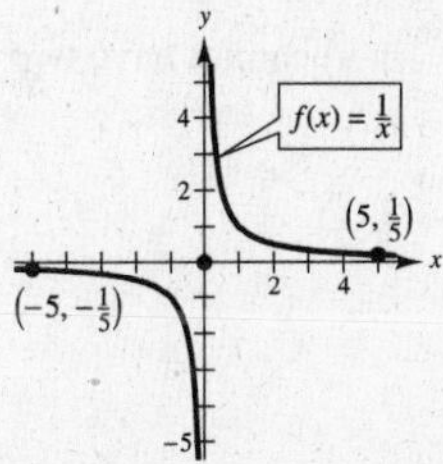


**75.** $f(x) = x^5 + x^3 + x + 1$

$f$ is differentiable for all $x$.

$f(-1) = -2$ and $f(0) = 1$, so the Intermediate Value Theorem implies that $f$ has at least one zero $c$ in $[-1, 0]$, $f(c) = 0$.

Suppose $f$ had 2 zeros, $f(c_1) = f(c_2) = 0$. Then Rolle's Theorem would guarantee the existence of a number $a$ such that

$f'(a) = f(c_2) - f(c_1) = 0$.

But, $f'(x) = 5x^4 + 3x^2 + 1 > 0$ for all $x$. So, $f$ has exactly one real solution.

**76.** $f(x) = 2x^5 + 7x - 1$

$f$ is differentiable for all $x$.

$f(0) = -1$ and $f(1) = 8$, so the Intermediate Value Theorem implies that $f$ has at least one zero $c$ in $[0, 1]$, $f(c) = 0$.

Suppose $f$ had 2 zeros, $f(c_1) = f(c_2) = 0$. Then Rolle's Theorem would guarantee the existence of a number $a$ such that

$f'(a) = f(c_2) - f(c_1) = 0$.

But $f'(x) = 10x^4 + 7 > 0$ for all $x$. So, $f(x) = 0$ has exactly one real solution.

**77.** $f(x) = 3x + 1 - \sin x$

$f$ is differentiable for all $x$.

$f(-\pi) = -3\pi + 1 < 0$ and $f(0) = 1 > 0$, so the Intermediate Value Theorem implies that $f$ has at least one zero $c$ in $[-\pi, 0]$, $f(c) = 0$.

Suppose $f$ had 2 zeros, $f(c_1) = f(c_2) = 0$. Then Rolle's Theorem would guarantee the existence of a number $a$ such that

$f'(a) = f(c_2) - f(c_1) = 0$.

But $f'(x) = 3 - \cos x > 0$ for all $x$. So, $f(x) = 0$ has exactly one real solution.

**78.** $f(x) = 2x - 2 - \cos x$

$f(0) = -3$, $f(\pi) = 2\pi - 2 + 1 = 2\pi - 1 > 0$. By the Intermediate Value Theorem, $f$ has at least one zero.

Suppose $f$ had 2 zeros, $f(c_1) = f(c_2) = 0$. Then Rolle's Theorem would guarantee the existence of a number $a$ such that

$f'(a) = f(c_2) - f(c_1) = 0$.

But, $f'(x) = 2 + \sin x \geq 1$ for all $x$. So, $f$ has exactly one real solution.

**79.** $f$ continuous at $x = 0$: $1 = b$

$f$ continuous at $x = 1$: $a + 1 = 5 + c$

$f$ differentiable at $x = 1$: $a = 2 + 4 = 6$. So, $c = 2$.

$$f(x) = \begin{cases} 1, & x = 0 \\ 6x + 1, & 0 < x \leq 1 \\ x^2 + 4x + 2, & 1 < x \leq 3 \end{cases}$$

$$= \begin{cases} 6x + 1, & 0 \leq x \leq 1 \\ x^2 + 4x + 2, & 1 < x \leq 3 \end{cases}$$

**80.** $f$ continuous at $x = -1$: $a = 2$

$f$ continuous at $x = 0$: $2 = c$

$f$ continuous at $x = 1$: $b + 2 = d + 4 \Rightarrow b = d + 2$

$f$ differentiable at $x = 0$: $0 = 0$

$f$ differentiable at $x = 1$: $2b = d$

So, $b = -2$ and $d = -4$.

**81.** $f'(x) = 0$

$f(x) = c$

$f(2) = 5$

So, $f(x) = 5$.

**82.** $f'(x) = 4$

$f(x) = 4x + c$

$f(0) = 1 \Rightarrow c = 1$

So, $f(x) = 4x + 1$.

**83.** $f'(x) = 2x$

$f(x) = x^2 + c$

$f(1) = 0 \Rightarrow 0 = 1 + c \Rightarrow c = -1$

So, $f(x) = x^2 - 1$.

**84.** $f'(x) = 2x + 3$

$f(x) = x^2 + 3x + c$

$f(1) = 0 \Rightarrow 0 = 1 + 3 + c \Rightarrow c = -4$

So, $f(x) = x^2 + 3x - 4$.

**85.** False. $f(x) = 1/x$ has a discontinuity at $x = 0$.

**86.** False. $f$ must also be continuous *and* differentiable on each interval. Let

$$f(x) = \frac{x^3 - 4x}{x^2 - 1}.$$

**87.** True. A polynomial is continuous and differentiable everywhere.

**88.** True

**89.** Suppose that $p(x) = x^{2n+1} + ax + b$ has two real roots $x_1$ and $x_2$. Then by Rolle's Theorem, because $p(x_1) = p(x_2) = 0$, there exists $c$ in $(x_1, x_2)$ such that $p'(c) = 0$. But $p'(x) = (2n + 1)x^{2n} + a \neq 0$, because $n > 0, a > 0$. Therefore, $p(x)$ cannot have two real roots.

**90.** Suppose $f(x)$ is not constant on $(a, b)$. Then there exists $x_1$ and $x_2$ in $(a, b)$ such that $f(x_1) \neq f(x_2)$. Then by the Mean Value Theorem, there exists $c$ in $(a, b)$ such that

$$f'(c) = \frac{f(x_2) - f(x_1)}{x_2 - x_1} \neq 0.$$

This contradicts the fact that $f'(x) = 0$ for all $x$ in $(a, b)$.

**91.** If $p(x) = Ax^2 + Bx + C$, then

$$\begin{aligned} p'(x) = 2Ax + B = \frac{f(b) - f(a)}{b - a} &= \frac{(Ab^2 + Bb + C) - (Aa^2 + Ba + C)}{b - a} \\ &= \frac{A(b^2 - a^2) + B(b - a)}{b - a} \\ &= \frac{(b - a)[A(b + a) + B]}{b - a} \\ &= A(b + a) + B. \end{aligned}$$

So, $2Ax = A(b + a)$ and $x = (b + a)/2$ which is the midpoint of $[a, b]$.

**92.** (a) $f(x) = x^2, g(x) = -x^3 + x^2 + 3x + 2$

$f(-1) = g(-1) = 1, f(2) = g(2) = 4$

Let $h(x) = f(x) - g(x)$. Then, $h(-1) = h(2) = 0$. So, by Rolle's Theorem these exists $c \in (-1, 2)$ such that $h'(c) = f'(c) - g'(c) = 0$.

So, at $x = c$, the tangent line to $f$ is parallel to the tangent line to $g$.

$h(x) = x^3 - 3x - 2, h'(x) = 3x^2 - 3 = 0 \Rightarrow x = c = 1$

(b) Let $h(x) = f(x) - g(x)$. Then $h(a) = h(b) = 0$. So, by Rolle's Theorem, there exists $c$ in $(a, b)$ such that $h'(c) = f'(c) - g'(c) = 0$.

So, at $x = c$, the tangent line to $f$ is parallel to the tangent line to $g$.

**93.** Suppose $f(x)$ has two fixed points $c_1$ and $c_2$. Then, by the Mean Value Theorem, there exists $c$ such that

$$f'(c) = \frac{f(c_2) - f(c_1)}{c_2 - c_1} = \frac{c_2 - c_1}{c_2 - c_1} = 1.$$

This contradicts the fact that $f'(x) < 1$ for all $x$.

**94.** $f(x) = \frac{1}{2}\cos x$ differentiable on $(-\infty, \infty)$.

$f'(x) = -\frac{1}{2}\sin x$

$-\frac{1}{2} \le f'(x) \le \frac{1}{2} \Rightarrow f'(x) < 1$ for all real numbers.

So, from Exercise 93, $f$ has, at most, one fixed point. $(x \approx 0.4502)$

**95.** Let $f(x) = \cos x$. $f$ is continuous and differentiable for all real numbers. By the Mean Value Theorem, for any interval $[a, b]$, there exists $c$ in $(a, b)$ such that

$$\frac{f(b) - f(a)}{b - a} = f'(c)$$

$$\frac{\cos b - \cos a}{b - a} = -\sin c$$

$$\cos b - \cos a = (-\sin c)(b - a)$$

$$|\cos b - \cos a| = |-\sin c||b - a|$$

$$|\cos b - \cos a| \le |b - a| \text{ because } |-\sin c| \le 1.$$

**96.** Let $f(x) = \sin x$. $f$ is continuous and differentiable for all real numbers. By the Mean Value Theorem, for any interval $[a, b]$, there exists $c$ in $(a, b)$ such that

$$\frac{f(b) - f(a)}{b - a} = f'(c)$$

$$\sin b - \sin a = (b - a)\cos c$$

$$|\sin b - \sin a| = |b - a||\cos c|$$

$$|\sin a - \sin b| \le |a - b|.$$

**97.** Let $0 < a < b$. $f(x) = \sqrt{x}$ satisfies the hypotheses of the Mean Value Theorem on $[a, b]$. So, there exists $c$ in $(a, b)$ such that

$$f'(c) = \frac{1}{2\sqrt{c}} = \frac{f(b) - f(a)}{b - a} = \frac{\sqrt{b} - \sqrt{a}}{b - a}.$$

So $\sqrt{b} - \sqrt{a} = (b - a)\frac{1}{2\sqrt{c}} < \frac{b - a}{2\sqrt{a}}$.

## Section 4.3 Increasing and Decreasing Functions and the First Derivative Test

**1.** (a) Increasing: $(0, 6)$ and $(8, 9)$. Largest: $(0, 6)$

(b) Decreasing: $(6, 8)$ and $(9, 10)$. Largest: $(6, 8)$

**2.** (a) Increasing: $(4, 5), (6, 7)$. Largest: $(4, 5), (6, 7)$

(b) Decreasing: $(-3, 1), (1, 4), (5, 6)$. Largest: $(-3, 1)$

**3.** $f(x) = x^2 - 6x + 8$

From the graph, $f$ is decreasing on $(-\infty, 3)$ and increasing on $(3, \infty)$.

Analytically, $f'(x) = 2x - 6$.

Critical number: $x = 3$

| Test Intervals: | $-\infty < x < 3$ | $3 < x < \infty$ |
|---|---|---|
| Sign of $f'(x)$: | $f' < 0$ | $f' > 0$ |
| Conclusion: | Decreasing | Increasing |

**4.** $y = -(x + 1)^2$

From the graph, $f$ is increasing on $(-\infty, -1)$ and decreasing on $(-1, \infty)$.

Analytically, $y' = -2(x + 1)$.

Critical number: $x = -1$

| Test Intervals: | $-\infty < x < -1$ | $-1 < x < \infty$ |
|---|---|---|
| Sign of $y'$: | $y' > 0$ | $y' < 0$ |
| Conclusion: | Increasing | Decreasing |

**5.** $y = \dfrac{x^3}{4} - 3x$

From the graph, $y$ is increasing on $(-\infty, -2)$ and $(2, \infty)$, and decreasing on $(-2, 2)$.

Analytically, $y' = \dfrac{3x^2}{4} - 3 = \dfrac{3}{4}(x^2 - 4) = \dfrac{3}{4}(x - 2)(x + 2)$

Critical numbers: $x = \pm 2$

| Test Intervals: | $-\infty < x < -2$ | $-2 < x < 2$ | $2 < x < \infty$ |
|---|---|---|---|
| Sign of $y'$: | $y' > 0$ | $y' < 0$ | $y' > 0$ |
| Conclusion: | Increasing | Decreasing | Increasing |

**6.** $f(x) = x^4 - 2x^2$

From the graph, $f$ is decreasing on $(-\infty, -1)$ and $(0, 1)$, and increasing on $(-1, 0)$ and $(1, \infty)$.

Analytically, $f'(x) = 4x^3 - 4x = 4x(x - 1)(x + 1)$.

Critical numbers: $x = 0, \pm 1$.

| Test Intervals: | $-\infty < x < -1$ | $-1 < x < 0$ | $0 < x < 1$ | $1 < x < \infty$ |
|---|---|---|---|---|
| Sign of $f'$: | $f' < 0$ | $f' > 0$ | $f' < 0$ | $f' > 0$ |
| Conclusion: | Decreasing | Increasing | Decreasing | Increasing |

**7.** $f(x) = \dfrac{1}{(x + 1)^2}$

From the graph, $f$ is increasing on $(-\infty, -1)$ and decreasing on $(-1, \infty)$.

Analytically, $f'(x) = \dfrac{-2}{(x + 1)^3}$.

No critical numbers. Discontinuity: $x = -1$

| Test Intervals: | $-\infty < x < -1$ | $-1 < x < \infty$ |
|---|---|---|
| Sign of $f'(x)$: | $f' > 0$ | $f' < 0$ |
| Conclusion: | Increasing | Decreasing |

**8.** $y = \dfrac{x^2}{2x - 1}$

From the graph, $y$ is increasing on $(-\infty, 0)$ and $(1, \infty)$, and decreasing on $(0, 1/2)$ and $(1/2, 1)$.

Analytically, $y' = \dfrac{(2x - 1)2x - x^2(2)}{(2x - 1)^2} = \dfrac{2x^2 - 2x}{(2x - 1)^2} = \dfrac{2x(x - 1)}{(2x - 1)^2}$

Critical numbers: $x = 0, 1$

Discontinuity: $x = 1/2$

| Test Intervals: | $-\infty < x < 0$ | $0 < x < 1/2$ | $1/2 < x < 1$ | $1 < x < \infty$ |
|---|---|---|---|---|
| Sign of $y'$: | $y' > 0$ | $y' < 0$ | $y' < 0$ | $y' > 0$ |
| Conclusion: | Increasing | Decreasing | Decreasing | Increasing |

**9.** $g(x) = x^2 - 2x - 8$

$g'(x) = 2x - 2$

Critical number: $x = 1$

| Test Intervals: | $-\infty < x < 1$ | $1 < x < \infty$ |
|---|---|---|
| Sign of $g'(x)$: | $g' < 0$ | $g' > 0$ |
| Conclusion: | Decreasing | Increasing |

Increasing on: $(1, \infty)$

Decreasing on: $(-\infty, 1)$

**10.** $h(x) = 27x - x^3$

$h'(x) = 27 - 3x^2 = 3(3 - x)(3 + x)$

$h'(x) = 0$

Critical numbers: $x = \pm 3$

| Test Intervals: | $-\infty < x < -3$ | $-3 < x < 3$ | $3 < x < \infty$ |
|---|---|---|---|
| Sign of $h'(x)$: | $h' < 0$ | $h' > 0$ | $h' < 0$ |
| Conclusion: | Decreasing | Increasing | Decreasing |

Increasing on: $(-3, 3)$

Decreasing on: $(-\infty, -3), (3, \infty)$

**11.** $y = x\sqrt{16 - x^2}$ Domain: $[-4, 4]$

$$y' = \frac{-2(x^2 - 8)}{\sqrt{16 - x^2}} = \frac{-2}{\sqrt{16 - x^2}}(x - 2\sqrt{2})(x + 2\sqrt{2})$$

Critical numbers: $x = \pm 2\sqrt{2}$

| Test intervals: | $-4 < x < -2\sqrt{2}$ | $-2\sqrt{2} < x < 2\sqrt{2}$ | $2\sqrt{2} < x < 4$ |
|---|---|---|---|
| Sign of $y'$: | $y' < 0$ | $y' > 0$ | $y' < 0$ |
| Conclusion: | Decreasing | Increasing | Decreasing |

Increasing on: $(-2\sqrt{2}, 2\sqrt{2})$

Decreasing on: $(-4, -2\sqrt{2}), (2\sqrt{2}, 4)$

**12.** $y = x + \dfrac{4}{x}$

$y' = \dfrac{(x-2)(x+2)}{x^2}$

Critical numbers: $x = \pm 2$ Discontinuity: 0

| Test intervals: | $-\infty < x < -2$ | $-2 < x < 0$ | $0 < x < 2$ | $2 < x < \infty$ |
|---|---|---|---|---|
| Sign of $y'$: | $y' > 0$ | $y' < 0$ | $y' < 0$ | $y' > 0$ |
| Conclusion: | Increasing | Decreasing | Decreasing | Increasing |

Increasing on: $(-\infty, -2), (2, \infty)$

Decreasing on: $(-2, 0), (0, 2)$

**13.** $f(x) = \sin x - 1, \quad 0 < x < 2\pi$

$f'(x) = \cos x$

Critical numbers: $x = \dfrac{\pi}{2}, \dfrac{3\pi}{2}$

| Test intervals: | $0 < x < \dfrac{\pi}{2}$ | $\dfrac{\pi}{2} < x < \dfrac{3\pi}{2}$ | $\dfrac{3\pi}{2} < x < 2\pi$ |
|---|---|---|---|
| Sign of $f'(x)$: | $f' > 0$ | $f' < 0$ | $f' > 0$ |
| Conclusion: | Increasing | Decreasing | Increasing |

Increasing on: $\left(0, \dfrac{\pi}{2}\right), \left(\dfrac{3\pi}{2}, 2\pi\right)$

Decreasing on: $\left(\dfrac{\pi}{2}, \dfrac{3\pi}{2}\right)$

**14.** $h(x) = \cos\dfrac{x}{2}, \quad 0 < x < 2\pi$

$h'(x) = -\dfrac{1}{2}\sin\dfrac{x}{2}$

Critical numbers: none

| Test interval: | $0 < x < 2\pi$ |
|---|---|
| Sign of $h'(x)$: | $h' < 0$ |
| Conclusion: | Decreasing |

Decreasing on: $(0, 2\pi)$

**15.** $y = x - 2\cos x, \quad 0 < x < 2\pi$

$y' = 1 + 2\sin x$

$y' = 0\text{: } \sin x = -\dfrac{1}{2}$

Critical numbers: $x = \dfrac{7\pi}{6}, \dfrac{11\pi}{6}$

| Test intervals: | $0 < x < \dfrac{7\pi}{6}$ | $\dfrac{7\pi}{6} < x < \dfrac{11\pi}{6}$ | $\dfrac{11\pi}{6} < x < 2\pi$ |
|---|---|---|---|
| Sign of $y'$: | $y' > 0$ | $y' < 0$ | $y' > 0$ |
| Conclusion: | Increasing | Decreasing | Increasing |

Increasing on: $\left(0, \dfrac{7\pi}{6}\right), \left(\dfrac{11\pi}{6}, 2\pi\right)$

Decreasing on: $\left(\dfrac{7\pi}{6}, \dfrac{11\pi}{6}\right)$

**16.** $f(x) = \cos^2 x - \cos x, \qquad 0 < x < 2\pi$

$f'(x) = -2\cos x \sin x + \sin x = \sin x(1 - 2\cos x)$

$\sin x = 0 \Rightarrow x = \pi$

$1 - 2\cos x = 0 \Rightarrow \cos x = \dfrac{1}{2} \Rightarrow x = \dfrac{\pi}{3}, \dfrac{5\pi}{3}$

Critical numbers: $x = \dfrac{\pi}{3}, \pi, \dfrac{5\pi}{3}$

| Test intervals: | $0 < x < \dfrac{\pi}{3}$ | $\dfrac{\pi}{3} < x < \pi$ | $\pi < x < \dfrac{5\pi}{3}$ | $\dfrac{5\pi}{3} < x < 2\pi$ |
|---|---|---|---|---|
| Sign of $f'(x)$: | $f' < 0$ | $f' > 0$ | $f' < 0$ | $f' > 0$ |
| Conclusion: | Decreasing | Increasing | Decreasing | Increasing |

Increasing on: $\left(\dfrac{\pi}{3}, \pi\right), \left(\dfrac{5\pi}{3}, 2\pi\right)$

Decreasing on: $\left(0, \dfrac{\pi}{3}\right), \left(\pi, \dfrac{5\pi}{3}\right)$

**17.** $g(x) = e^{-x} + e^{3x}$

$g'(x) = -e^{-x} + 3e^{3x}$

Critical number: $x = -\frac{1}{4}\ln 3$

| Test intervals: | $-\infty < x < -\frac{1}{4}\ln 3$ | $-\frac{1}{4}\ln 3 < x < \infty$ |
|---|---|---|
| Sign of $g'(x)$: | $g' < 0$ | $g' > 0$ |
| Conclusion: | Decreasing | Increasing |

Increasing on: $\left(-\frac{1}{4}\ln 3, \infty\right)$

Decreasing on: $\left(-\infty, -\frac{1}{4}\ln 3\right)$

**18.** $h(x) = \sqrt{x}e^{-x}, \quad x \geq 0$

$$h'(x) = -\sqrt{x}e^{-x} + \frac{1}{2\sqrt{x}}e^{-x} = e^{-x}\left(\frac{1}{2\sqrt{x}} - \sqrt{x}\right) = e^{-x} - \frac{1-2x}{2\sqrt{x}}$$

Critical number: $x = \frac{1}{2}$ ($x = 0$ is an endpoint)

| Test intervals: | $0 < x < \frac{1}{2}$ | $\frac{1}{2} < x < \infty$ |
|---|---|---|
| Sign of $h'(x)$: | $h' > 0$ | $h' < 0$ |
| Conclusion: | Increasing | Decreasing |

Increasing on: $\left(0, \frac{1}{2}\right)$

Decreasing on: $\left(\frac{1}{2}, \infty\right)$

**19.** $f(x) = x^2 \ln\left(\frac{x}{2}\right), \quad x > 0$

$$f'(x) = 2x \ln\left(\frac{x}{2}\right) + \frac{x^2}{x} = 2x \ln\left(\frac{x}{2}\right) + x$$

Critical number: $x = \frac{2}{\sqrt{e}}$

| Test intervals: | $0 < x < \frac{2}{\sqrt{e}}$ | $\frac{2}{\sqrt{e}} < x < \infty$ |
|---|---|---|
| Sign of $f'(x)$: | $f' < 0$ | $f' > 0$ |
| Conclusion: | Decreasing | Increasing |

Increasing on: $\left(\frac{2}{\sqrt{e}}, \infty\right)$

Decreasing on: $\left(0, \frac{2}{\sqrt{e}}\right)$

**20.** $f(x) = \frac{\ln x}{\sqrt{x}}, \quad x > 0$

$$f'(x) = \frac{\frac{\sqrt{x}}{x} - \ln x \frac{1}{2\sqrt{x}}}{x} = \frac{2 - \ln x}{2x^{3/2}}$$

Critical number: $x = e^2$

| Test intervals: | $0 < x < e^2$ | $e^2 < x < \infty$ |
|---|---|---|
| Sign of $f'(x)$: | $f' > 0$ | $f' < 0$ |
| Conclusion: | Increasing | Decreasing |

Increasing on: $(0, e^2)$

Decreasing on: $(e^2, \infty)$

**21.** $f(x) = x^2 - 4x$

$f'(x) = 2x - 4$

Critical number: $x = 2$

| Test intervals: | $-\infty < x < 2$ | $2 < x < \infty$ |
|---|---|---|
| Sign of $f'(x)$: | $f' < 0$ | $f' > 0$ |
| Conclusion: | Decreasing | Increasing |

Increasing on: $(2, \infty)$

Decreasing on: $(-\infty, 2)$

Relative minimum: $(2, -4)$

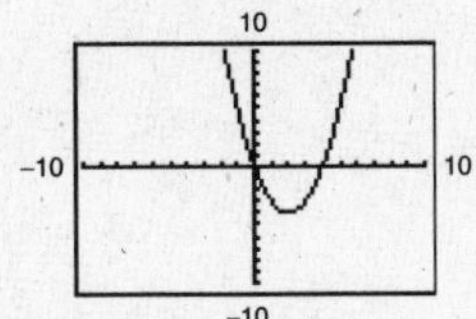


**22.** $f(x) = x^2 + 6x + 10$

$f'(x) = 2x + 6$

Critical number: $x = -3$

| Test intervals: | $-\infty < x < -3$ | $-3 < x < \infty$ |
|---|---|---|
| Sign of $f'(x)$: | $f' < 0$ | $f' > 0$ |
| Conclusion: | Decreasing | Increasing |

Increasing on: $(-3, \infty)$

Decreasing on: $(-\infty, -3)$

Relative minimum: $(-3, 1)$

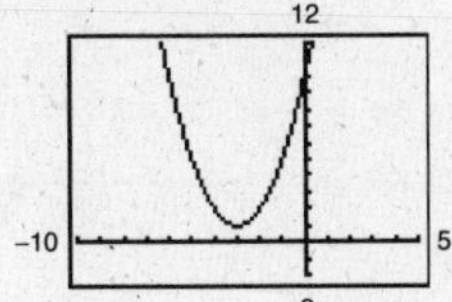


**23.** $f(x) = -2x^2 + 4x + 3$

$f'(x) = -4x + 4 = 0$

Critical number: $x = 1$

| Test intervals: | $-\infty < x < 1$ | $1 < x < \infty$ |
|---|---|---|
| Sign of $f'(x)$: | $f' > 0$ | $f' < 0$ |
| Conclusion: | Increasing | Decreasing |

Increasing on: $(-\infty, 1)$

Decreasing on: $(1, \infty)$

Relative maximum: $(1, 5)$

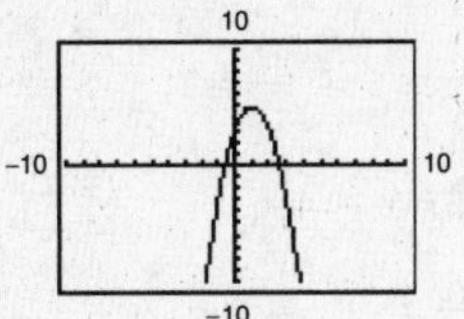


**24.** $f(x) = -(x^2 + 8x + 12)$

$f'(x) = -2x - 8 = 0$

Critical number: $x = -4$

| Test intervals: | $-\infty < x < -4$ | $-4 < x < \infty$ |
|---|---|---|
| Sign of $f'(x)$: | $f' > 0$ | $f' < 0$ |
| Conclusion: | Increasing | Decreasing |

Increasing on: $(-\infty, -4)$

Decreasing on: $(-4, \infty)$

Relative maximum: $(-4, 4)$

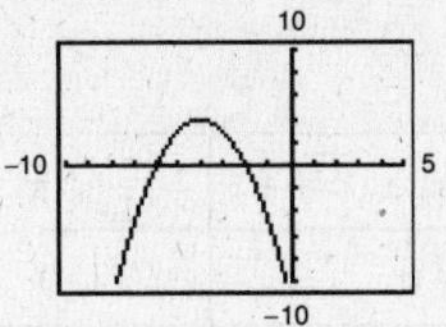

**25.** $f(x) = 2x^3 + 3x^2 - 12x$

$f'(x) = 6x^2 + 6x - 12 = 6(x + 2)(x - 1) = 0$

Critical numbers: $x = -2, 1$

| Test intervals: | $-\infty < x < -2$ | $-2 < x < 1$ | $1 < x < \infty$ |
|---|---|---|---|
| Sign of $f'(x)$: | $f' > 0$ | $f' < 0$ | $f' > 0$ |
| Conclusion: | Increasing | Decreasing | Increasing |

Increasing on: $(-\infty, -2), (1, \infty)$

Decreasing on: $(-2, 1)$

Relative maximum: $(-2, 20)$

Relative minimum: $(1, -7)$

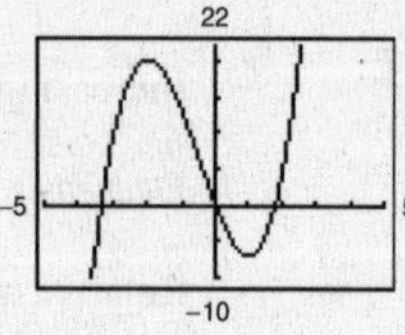


**26.** $f(x) = x^3 - 6x^2 + 15$

$f'(x) = 3x^2 - 12x = 3x(x - 4)$

Critical numbers: $x = 0, 4$

| Test intervals: | $-\infty < x < 0$ | $0 < x < 4$ | $4 < x < \infty$ |
|---|---|---|---|
| Sign of $f'(x)$: | $f' > 0$ | $f' < 0$ | $f' > 0$ |
| Conclusion: | Increasing | Decreasing | Increasing |

Increasing on: $(-\infty, 0), (4, \infty)$

Decreasing on: $(0, 4)$

Relative maximum: $(0, 15)$

Relative minimum: $(4, -17)$

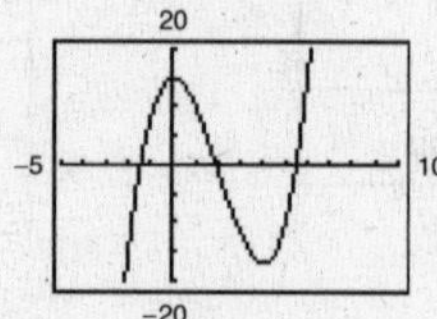


**27.** $f(x) = (x - 1)^2(x + 3) = x^3 + x^2 - 5x + 3$

$f'(x) = 3x^2 + 2x - 5 = (x - 1)(3x + 5)$

Critical numbers: $x = 1, -\frac{5}{3}$

| Test intervals: | $-\infty < x < -\frac{5}{3}$ | $-\frac{5}{3} < x < 1$ | $1 < x < \infty$ |
|---|---|---|---|
| Sign of $f'(x)$: | $f' > 0$ | $f' < 0$ | $f' > 0$ |
| Conclusion: | Increasing | Decreasing | Increasing |

Increasing on: $\left(-\infty, -\frac{5}{3}\right)$ and $(1, \infty)$

Decreasing on: $\left(-\frac{5}{3}, 1\right)$

Relative maximum: $\left(-\frac{5}{3}, \frac{256}{27}\right)$

Relative minimum: $(1, 0)$

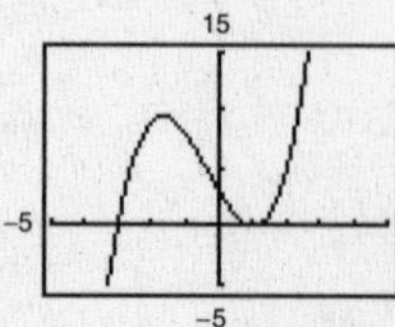

**28.** $f(x) = (x + 2)^2(x - 1)$

$f'(x) = 3x(x + 2)$

Critical numbers: $x = -2, 0$

| Test intervals: | $-\infty < x < -2$ | $-2 < x < 0$ | $0 < x < \infty$ |
|---|---|---|---|
| Sign of $f'(x)$: | $f' > 0$ | $f' < 0$ | $f' > 0$ |
| Conclusion: | Increasing | Decreasing | Increasing |

Increasing on: $(-\infty, -2), (0, \infty)$

Decreasing on: $(-2, 0)$

Relative maximum: $(-2, 0)$

Relative minimum: $(0, -4)$

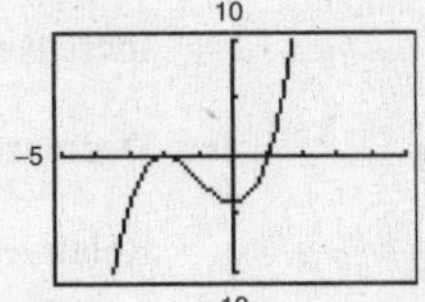


**29.** $f(x) = \dfrac{x^5 - 5x}{5}$

$f'(x) = x^4 - 1$

Critical numbers: $x = -1, 1$

| Test intervals: | $-\infty < x < -1$ | $-1 < x < 1$ | $1 < x < \infty$ |
|---|---|---|---|
| Sign of $f'(x)$: | $f' > 0$ | $f' < 0$ | $f' > 0$ |
| Conclusion: | Increasing | Decreasing | Increasing |

Increasing on: $(-\infty, -1), (1, \infty)$

Decreasing on: $(-1, 1)$

Relative maximum: $\left(-1, \dfrac{4}{5}\right)$

Relative minimum: $\left(1, -\dfrac{4}{5}\right)$

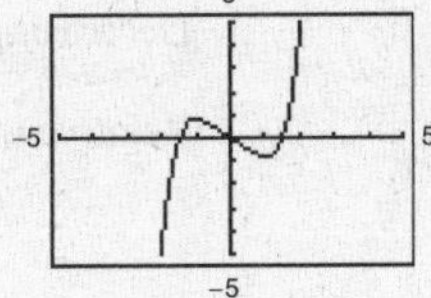


**30.** $f(x) = x^4 - 32x + 4$

$f'(x) = 4x^3 - 32 = 4(x^3 - 8)$

Critical number: $x = 2$

| Test intervals: | $-\infty < x < 2$ | $2 < x < \infty$ |
|---|---|---|
| Sign of $f'(x)$: | $f' < 0$ | $f' > 0$ |
| Conclusion: | Decreasing | Increasing |

Increasing on: $(2, \infty)$

Decreasing on: $(-\infty, 2)$

Relative minimum: $(2, -44)$

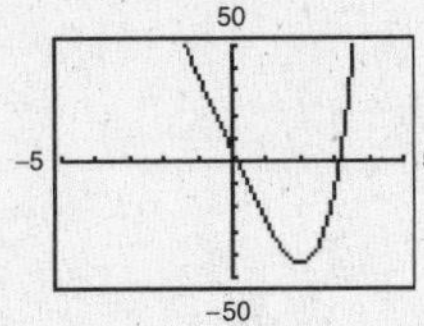


**31.** $f(x) = x^{1/3} + 1$

$f'(x) = \dfrac{1}{3}x^{-2/3} = \dfrac{1}{3x^{2/3}}$

Critical number: $x = 0$

| Test intervals: | $-\infty < x < 0$ | $0 < x < \infty$ |
|---|---|---|
| Sign of $f'(x)$: | $f' > 0$ | $f' > 0$ |
| Conclusion: | Increasing | Increasing |

Increasing on: $(-\infty, \infty)$

No relative extrema

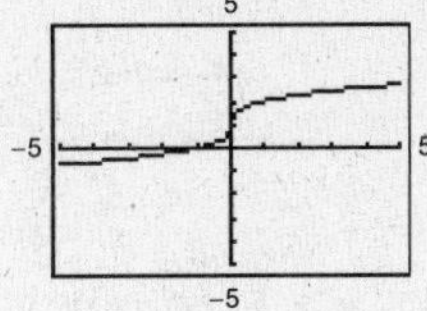

**32.** $f(x) = x^{2/3} - 4$

$f'(x) = \frac{2}{3}x^{-1/3} = \frac{2}{3x^{1/3}}$

Critical number: $x = 0$

| Test intervals: | $-\infty < x < 0$ | $0 < x < \infty$ |
|---|---|---|
| Sign of $f'(x)$: | $f' < 0$ | $f' > 0$ |
| Conclusion: | Decreasing | Increasing |

Increasing on: $(0, \infty)$

Decreasing on: $(-\infty, 0)$

Relative minimum: $(0, -4)$

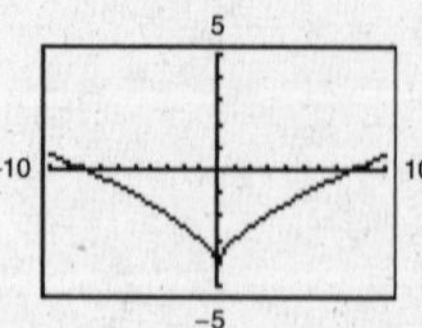


**33.** $f(x) = (x + 2)^{2/3}$

$f'(x) = \frac{2}{3}(x + 2)^{-1/3} = \frac{2}{3(x + 2)^{1/3}}$

Critical number: $x = -2$

| Test intervals: | $-\infty < x < -2$ | $-2 < x < \infty$ |
|---|---|---|
| Sign of $f'(x)$: | $f' < 0$ | $f' > 0$ |
| Conclusion: | Decreasing | Increasing |

Increasing on: $(-2, \infty)$

Decreasing on: $(-\infty, -2)$

Relative minimum: $(-2, 0)$

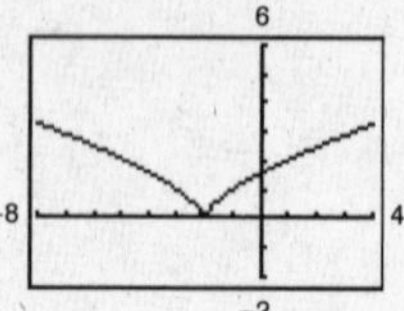


**34.** $f(x) = (x - 3)^{1/3}$

$f'(x) = \frac{1}{3}(x - 3)^{-2/3} = \frac{1}{3(x - 3)^{2/3}}$

Critical number: $x = 3$

| Test intervals: | $-\infty < x < 3$ | $3 < x < \infty$ |
|---|---|---|
| Sign of $f'(x)$: | $f' > 0$ | $f' > 0$ |
| Conclusion: | Increasing | Increasing |

Increasing on: $(-\infty, \infty)$

No relative extrema

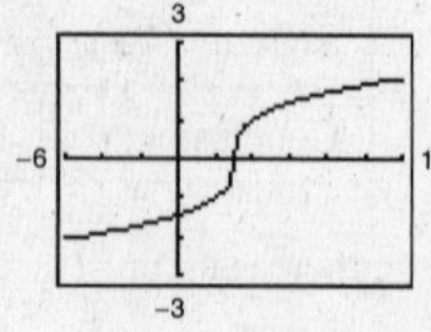


**35.** $f(x) = 5 - |x - 5|$

$f'(x) = -\frac{x - 5}{|x - 5|} = \begin{cases} 1, & x < 5 \\ -1, & x > 5 \end{cases}$

Critical number: $x = 5$

| Test intervals: | $-\infty < x < 5$ | $5 < x < \infty$ |
|---|---|---|
| Sign of $f'(x)$: | $f' > 0$ | $f' < 0$ |
| Conclusion: | Increasing | Decreasing |

Increasing on: $(-\infty, 5)$

Decreasing on: $(5, \infty)$

Relative maximum: $(5, 5)$

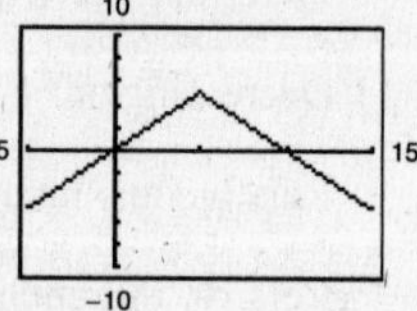


**36.** $f(x) = |x + 3| - 1$

$f'(x) = \frac{x + 3}{|x + 3|} = \begin{cases} 1, & x > -3 \\ -1, & x < -3 \end{cases}$

Critical number: $x = -3$

| Test intervals: | $-\infty < x < -3$ | $-3 < x < \infty$ |
|---|---|---|
| Sign of $f'(x)$: | $f' < 0$ | $f' > 0$ |
| Conclusion: | Decreasing | Increasing |

Increasing on: $(-3, \infty)$

Decreasing on: $(-\infty, -3)$

Relative minimum: $(-3, -1)$

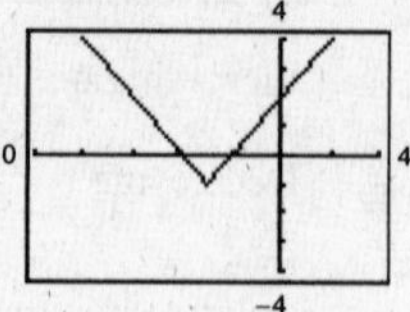

**37.** $f(x) = 2x + \frac{1}{x}$

$f'(x) = 2 - \frac{1}{x^2} = \frac{2x^2 - 1}{x^2}$

Critical numbers: $x = \pm\frac{\sqrt{2}}{2}$

Discontinuity: $x = 0$

| Test intervals: | $-\infty < x < -\frac{\sqrt{2}}{2}$ | $-\frac{\sqrt{2}}{2} < x < 0$ | $0 < x < \frac{\sqrt{2}}{2}$ | $\frac{\sqrt{2}}{2} < x < \infty$ |
|---|---|---|---|---|
| Sign of $f'(x)$: | $f' > 0$ | $f' < 0$ | $f' < 0$ | $f' > 0$ |
| Conclusion: | Increasing | Decreasing | Decreasing | Increasing |

Increasing on: $\left(-\infty, -\frac{\sqrt{2}}{2}\right)$ and $\left(\frac{\sqrt{2}}{2}, \infty\right)$

Decreasing on: $\left(-\frac{\sqrt{2}}{2}, 0\right)$ and $\left(0, \frac{\sqrt{2}}{2}\right)$

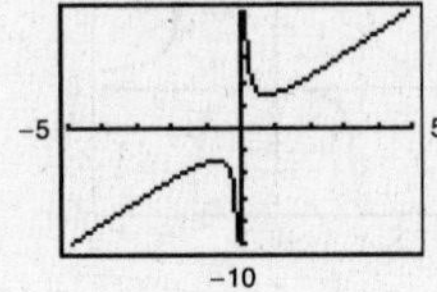


Relative maximum: $\left(-\frac{\sqrt{2}}{2}, -2\sqrt{2}\right)$

Relative minimum: $\left(\frac{\sqrt{2}}{2}, 2\sqrt{2}\right)$

**38.** $f(x) = \frac{x}{x + 3}$

$f'(x) = \frac{(x + 3) - x}{(x + 3)^2} = \frac{3}{(x + 3)^2}$

No critical numbers

Discontinuity: $x = -3$

| Test intervals: | $-\infty < x < -3$ | $-3 < x < \infty$ |
|---|---|---|
| Sign of $f'(x)$: | $f' > 0$ | $f' > 0$ |
| Conclusion: | Increasing | Increasing |

Increasing on: $(-\infty, -3)$ and $(-3, \infty)$

No relative extrema

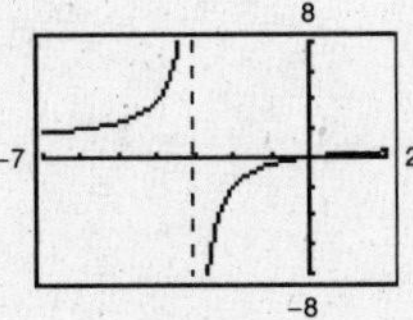

**39.** $f(x) = \dfrac{x^2}{x^2 - 9}$

$$f'(x) = \frac{(x^2 - 9)(2x) - (x^2)(2x)}{(x^2 - 9)^2} = \frac{-18x}{(x^2 - 9)^2}$$

Critical number: $x = 0$

Discontinuities: $x = -3, 3$

| Test intervals: | $-\infty < x < -3$ | $-3 < x < 0$ | $0 < x < 3$ | $3 < x < \infty$ |
|---|---|---|---|---|
| Sign of $f'(x)$: | $f' > 0$ | $f' > 0$ | $f' < 0$ | $f' < 0$ |
| Conclusion: | Increasing | Increasing | Decreasing | Decreasing |

Increasing on: $(-\infty, -3), (-3, 0)$

Decreasing on: $(0, 3), (3, \infty)$

Relative maximum: $(0, 0)$

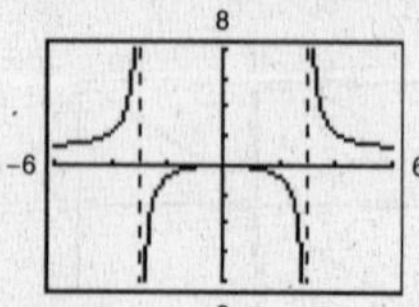


**40.** $f(x) = \dfrac{x + 4}{x^2}$

$$f'(x) = \frac{x^2 - (x + 4)(2x)}{x^4} = \frac{-x^2 - 8x}{x^4} = \frac{-(x + 8)}{x^3}$$

Critical number: $x = -8$

Discontinuity: $x = 0$

| Test intervals: | $-\infty < x < -8$ | $-8 < x < 0$ | $0 < x < \infty$ |
|---|---|---|---|
| Sign of $f'(x)$: | $f' < 0$ | $f' > 0$ | $f' < 0$ |
| Conclusion: | Decreasing | Increasing | Decreasing |

Increasing on: $(-8, 0)$

Decreasing on: $(-\infty, -8), (0, \infty)$

Relative minimum: $\left(-8, -\dfrac{1}{16}\right)$

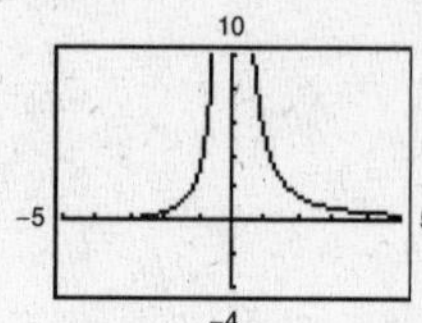

**41.** $f(x) = \dfrac{x^2 - 2x + 1}{x + 1}$

$f'(x) = \dfrac{(x + 1)(2x - 2) - (x^2 - 2x + 1)(1)}{(x + 1)^2} = \dfrac{x^2 + 2x - 3}{(x + 1)^2} = \dfrac{(x + 3)(x - 1)}{(x + 1)^2}$

Critical numbers: $x = -3, 1$

Discontinuity: $x = -1$

| Test intervals: | $-\infty < x < -3$ | $-3 < x < -1$ | $-1 < x < 1$ | $1 < x < \infty$ |
|---|---|---|---|---|
| Sign of $f'(x)$: | $f' > 0$ | $f' < 0$ | $f' < 0$ | $f' > 0$ |
| Conclusion: | Increasing | Decreasing | Decreasing | Increasing |

Increasing on: $(-\infty, -3), (1, \infty)$

Decreasing on: $(-3, -1), (-1, 1)$

Relative maximum: $(-3, -8)$

Relative minimum: $(1, 0)$

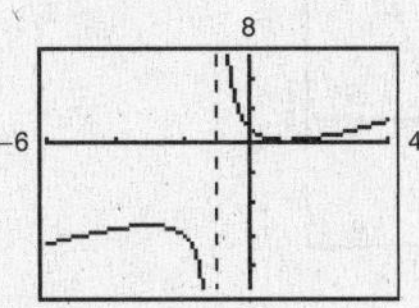


**42.** $f(x) = \dfrac{x^2 - 3x - 4}{x - 2}$

$f'(x) = \dfrac{(x - 2)(2x - 3) - (x^2 - 3x - 4)(1)}{(x - 2)^2} = \dfrac{x^2 - 4x + 10}{(x - 2)^2}$

Discontinuity: $x = 2$

| Test intervals: | $-\infty < x < 2$ | $2 < x < \infty$ |
|---|---|---|
| Sign of $f'(x)$: | $f' > 0$ | $f' > 0$ |
| Conclusion: | Increasing | Increasing |

Increasing on: $(-\infty, 2), (2, \infty)$

No relative extrema

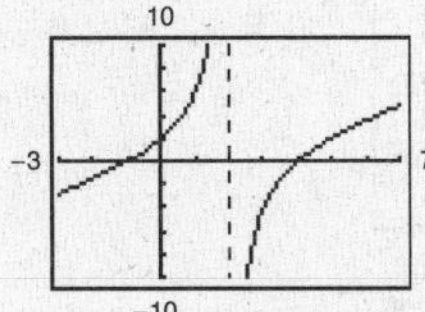


**43.** $f(x) = \begin{cases} 4 - x^2, & x \le 0 \\ -2x, & x > 0 \end{cases}$

$f'(x) = \begin{cases} -2x, & x < 0 \\ -2, & x > 0 \end{cases}$

Critical number: $x = 0$

| Test intervals: | $-\infty < x < 0$ | $0 < x < \infty$ |
|---|---|---|
| Sign of $f'(x)$: | $f' > 0$ | $f' < 0$ |
| Conclusion: | Increasing | Decreasing |

Increasing on: $(-\infty, 0)$

Decreasing on: $(0, \infty)$

No relative extrema. (Note: $(0, 4)$ is an absolute maximum)

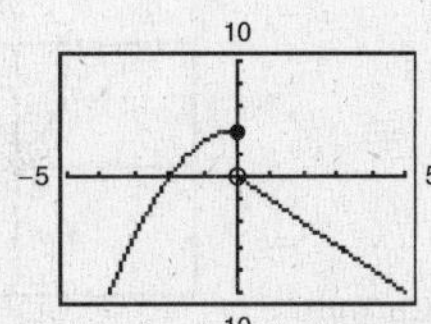

**44.** $f(x) = \begin{cases} 2x + 1, & x \le -1 \\ x^2 - 2, & x > -1 \end{cases}$

$f'(x) = \begin{cases} 2, & x < -1 \\ 2x, & x > -1 \end{cases}$

Critical numbers: $x = -1, 0$

| Test intervals: | $-\infty < x < -1$ | $-1 < x < 0$ | $0 < x < \infty$ |
|---|---|---|---|
| Sign of $f'(x)$: | $f' > 0$ | $f' < 0$ | $f' > 0$ |
| Conclusion: | Increasing | Decreasing | Increasing |

Increasing on: $(-\infty, -1), (0, \infty)$

Decreasing on: $(-1, 0)$

Relative maximum: $(-1, -1)$

Relative minimum: $(0, -2)$

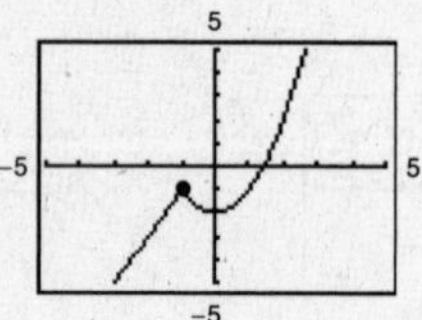

**45.** $f(x) = \begin{cases} 3x + 1, & x \le 1 \\ 5 - x^2, & x > 1 \end{cases}$

$f'(x) = \begin{cases} 3, & x < 1 \\ -2x, & x > 1 \end{cases}$

Critical number: $x = 1$

| Test intervals: | $-\infty < x < 1$ | $1 < x < \infty$ |
|---|---|---|
| Sign of $f'(x)$: | $f' > 0$ | $f' < 0$ |
| Conclusion: | Increasing | Decreasing |

Increasing on: $(-\infty, 1)$

Decreasing on: $(1, \infty)$

Relative maximum: $(1, 4)$

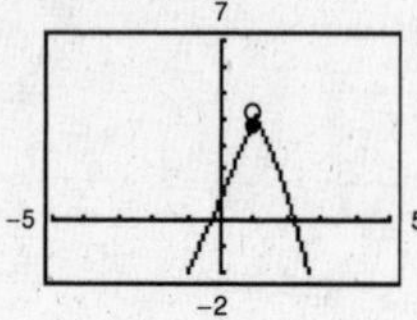

**46.** $f(x) = \begin{cases} -x^3 + 1, & x \le 0 \\ -x^2 + 2x, & x > 0 \end{cases}$

$f'(x) = \begin{cases} -3x^2, & x < 0 \\ -2x + 2, & x > 0 \end{cases}$

Critical numbers: $x = 0, 1$

| Test intervals: | $-\infty < x < 0$ | $0 < x < 1$ | $1 < x < \infty$ |
|---|---|---|---|
| Sign of $f'(x)$: | $f' < 0$ | $f' > 0$ | $f' < 0$ |
| Conclusion: | Decreasing | Increasing | Decreasing |

Increasing on: $(0, 1)$

Decreasing on: $(-\infty, 0), (1, \infty)$

Relative maximum: $(1, 1)$

Note: $(0, 1)$ is not a relative minimum

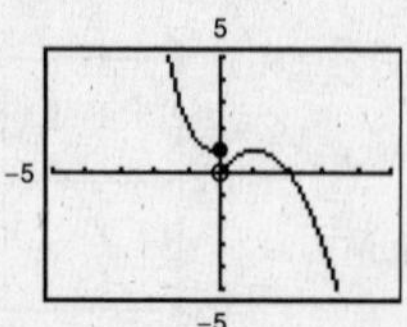

**47.** $f(x) = (3 - x)e^{x-3}$

$f'(x) = (3 - x)e^{x-3} - e^{x-3}$

$= e^{x-3}(2 - x)$

Critical number: $x = 2$

| Test intervals: | $-\infty < x < 2$ | $2 < x < \infty$ |
|---|---|---|
| Sign of $f'(x)$: | $f' > 0$ | $f' < 0$ |
| Conclusion: | Increasing | Decreasing |

Increasing on: $(-\infty, 2)$

Decreasing on: $(2, \infty)$

Relative minimum: $(2, e^{-1})$

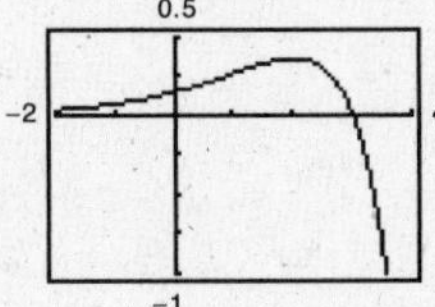


**48.** $f(x) = (x - 1)e^x$

$f'(x) = (x - 1)e^x + e^x = xe^x$

Critical number: $x = 0$

| Test intervals: | $-\infty < x < 0$ | $0 < x < \infty$ |
|---|---|---|
| Sign of $f'(x)$: | $f' < 0$ | $f' > 0$ |
| Conclusion: | Decreasing | Increasing |

Increasing on: $(0, \infty)$

Decreasing on: $(-\infty, 0)$

Relative minimum: $(0, -1)$

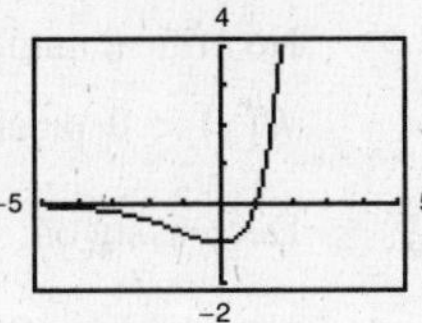


**49.** $f(x) = 4(x - \arcsin x), -1 \le x \le 1$

$f'(x) = 4 - \dfrac{4}{\sqrt{1 - x^2}}$

Critical number: $x = 0$

| Test intervals: | $-1 \le x < 0$ | $0 < x \le 1$ |
|---|---|---|
| Sign of $f'(x)$: | $f' < 0$ | $f' < 0$ |
| Conclusion: | Decreasing | Decreasing |

Decreasing on: $[-1, 1]$

No relative extrema

(Absolute maximum at $x = -1$, absolute minimum at $x = 1$)

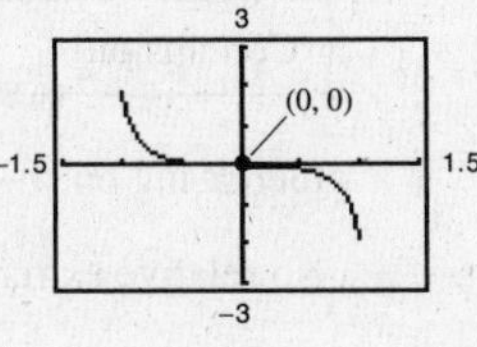


**50.** $f(x) = x \arctan x$

$f'(x) = \dfrac{x}{1 + x^2} + \arctan x$

$f'(x) = 0$

Critical number: $x = 0$

| Test intervals: | $-\infty < x < 0$ | $0 < x < \infty$ |
|---|---|---|
| Sign of $f'(x)$: | $f' < 0$ | $f' > 0$ |
| Conclusion: | Decreasing | Increasing |

Increasing on: $(0, \infty)$

Decreasing on: $(-\infty, 0)$

Relative minimum: $(0, 0)$

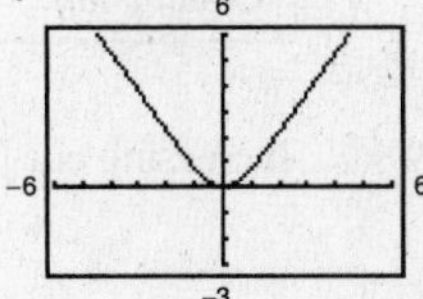


**51.** $g(x) = (x)3^{-x}$

$g'(x) = (1 - x \ln 3)3^{-x}$

Critical number: $x = \dfrac{1}{\ln 3} \approx 0.9102$

| Test intervals: | $-\infty < x < \dfrac{1}{\ln 3}$ | $\dfrac{1}{\ln 3} < x < \infty$ |
|---|---|---|
| Sign of $f'(x)$: | $f' > 0$ | $f' < 0$ |
| Conclusion: | Increasing | Decreasing |

Increasing on: $\left(-\infty, \dfrac{1}{\ln 3}\right)$

Decreasing on: $\left(\dfrac{1}{\ln 3}, \infty\right)$

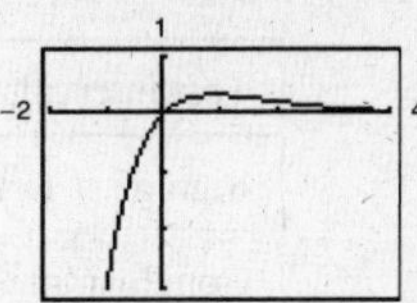


Relative maximum: $\left(\dfrac{1}{\ln 3}, \dfrac{1}{e \ln 3}\right) \approx (0.9102, 0.3349)$

**52.** $f(x) = 2^{x^2-3}$

$f'(x) = (\ln 2)2^{x^2-3}(2x)$

Critical number: $x = 0$

| Test intervals: | $-\infty < x < 0$ | $0 < x < \infty$ |
|---|---|---|
| Sign of $f'(x)$: | $f' < 0$ | $f' > 0$ |
| Conclusion: | Decreasing | Increasing |

Increasing on: $(0, \infty)$

Decreasing on: $(-\infty, 0)$

Relative minimum: $\left(0, \frac{1}{8}\right)$

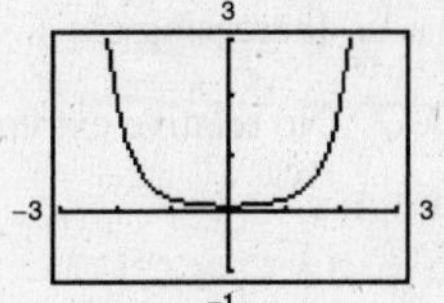

**53.** $f(x) = x - \log_4 x = x - \dfrac{\ln x}{\ln 4}$

$f'(x) = 1 - \dfrac{1}{x \ln 4} = 0 \Rightarrow x \ln 4 = 1 \Rightarrow x = \dfrac{1}{\ln 4}$

Critical number: $x = \dfrac{1}{\ln 4}$

| Test intervals: | $0 < x < \dfrac{1}{\ln 4}$ | $\dfrac{1}{\ln 4} < x < \infty$ |
|---|---|---|
| Sign of $f'(x)$: | $f' < 0$ | $f' > 0$ |
| Conclusion: | Decreasing | Increasing |

Increasing on: $\left(\dfrac{1}{\ln 4}, \infty\right)$

Decreasing on: $\left(0, \dfrac{1}{\ln 4}\right)$

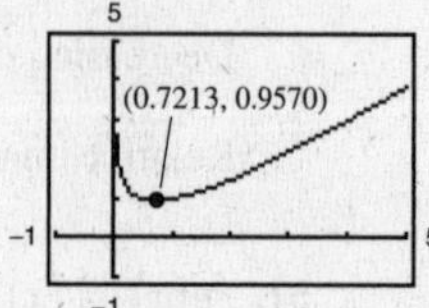


Relative maximum: $\left(\dfrac{1}{\ln 4}, \dfrac{1}{\ln 4} - \log_4\left(\dfrac{1}{\ln 4}\right)\right) = \left(\dfrac{1}{\ln 4}, \dfrac{\ln(\ln 4) + 1}{\ln 4}\right) \approx (0.7213, 0.9570)$

**54.** $f(x) = \dfrac{x^3}{3} - \ln x$

Domain: $x > 0$

$f'(x) = x^2 - \dfrac{1}{x} = \dfrac{x^3 - 1}{x}$

Critical number: $x = 1$

| Test intervals: | $0 < x < 1$ | $1 < x < \infty$ |
|---|---|---|
| Sign of $f'(x)$: | $f' < 0$ | $f' > 0$ |
| Conclusion: | Decreasing | Increasing |

Increasing on: $(1, \infty)$

Decreasing on: $(0, 1)$

Relative minimum: $\left(1, \dfrac{1}{3}\right)$

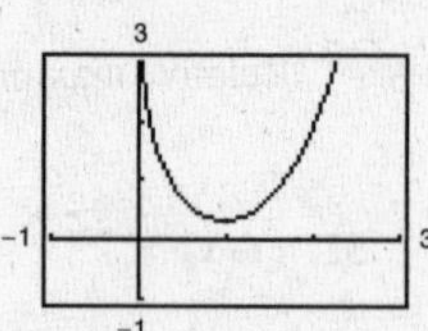


**55.** $g(x) = \dfrac{e^{2x}}{e^{2x} + 1}$

$g'(x) = \dfrac{(e^{2x} + 1)2e^{2x} - e^{2x}(2e^{2x})}{(e^{2x} + 1)^2} = \dfrac{2e^{2x}}{(e^{2x} + 1)^2}$

No critical numbers.

Increasing on: $(-\infty, \infty)$

No relative extrema.

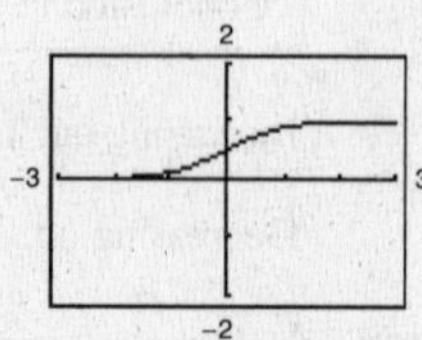


**56.** $h(x) = \ln(2 - \ln x)$

Domain: $x > 0$ and $2 - \ln x > 0 \Rightarrow 0 < x < e^2$

$h'(x) = \dfrac{1}{2 - \ln x}\left(-\dfrac{1}{x}\right) = \dfrac{1}{x \ln x - 2x} = \dfrac{1}{x(\ln x - 2)}$

No critical numbers.

$h'(x) < 0$ on entire domain.

Decreasing on: $(0, e^2)$

No relative extrema.

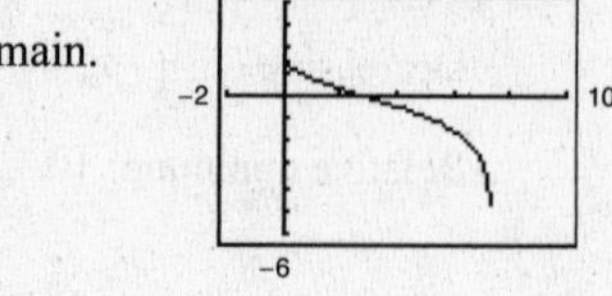


**57.** $f(x) = e^{-1/(x-2)} = e^{1/(2-x)}, x \neq 2$

$f'(x) = e^{1/(2-x)}\left(\dfrac{1}{(2 - x)^2}\right)$

No critical numbers.

$x = 2$ is a vertical asymptote.

| Test intervals: | $-\infty < x < 2$ | $2 < x < \infty$ |
|---|---|---|
| Sign of $f'(x)$: | $f' > 0$ | $f' > 0$ |
| Conclusion: | Increasing | Increasing |

Increasing on: $(-\infty, 2), (2, \infty)$

No relative extrema.

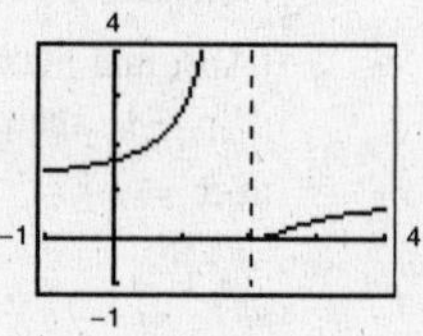

**58.** $f(x) = e^{\arctan x}$

$f'(x) = e^{\arctan x}\left(\dfrac{1}{1 + x^2}\right) \neq 0$

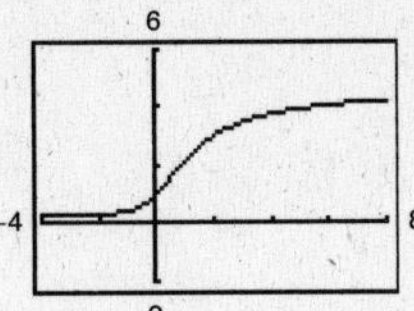


No critical numbers.

Increasing on: $(-\infty, \infty)$

No relative extrema.

**59.** (a) $f(x) = \dfrac{x}{2} + \cos x, 0 < x < 2\pi$

$f'(x) = \dfrac{1}{2} - \sin x = 0$

Critical numbers: $x = \dfrac{\pi}{6}, \dfrac{5\pi}{6}$

| Test intervals: | $0 < x < \dfrac{\pi}{6}$ | $\dfrac{\pi}{6} < x < \dfrac{5\pi}{6}$ | $\dfrac{5\pi}{6} < x < 2\pi$ |
|---|---|---|---|
| Sign of $f'(x)$: | $f' > 0$ | $f' < 0$ | $f' > 0$ |
| Conclusion: | Increasing | Decreasing | Increasing |

Increasing on: $\left(0, \dfrac{\pi}{6}\right), \left(\dfrac{5\pi}{6}, 2\pi\right)$

Decreasing on: $\left(\dfrac{\pi}{6}, \dfrac{5\pi}{6}\right)$

(b) Relative maximum: $\left(\dfrac{\pi}{6}, \dfrac{\pi + 6\sqrt{3}}{12}\right)$

Relative minimum: $\left(\dfrac{5\pi}{6}, \dfrac{5\pi - 6\sqrt{3}}{12}\right)$

(c)

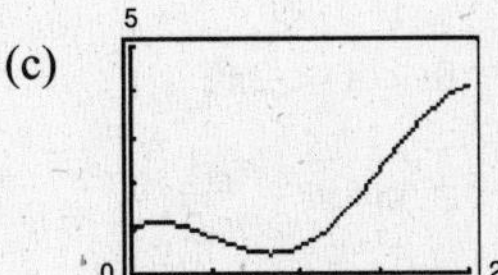


**60.** (a) $f(x) = \sin x \cos x + 5 = \dfrac{1}{2}\sin 2x + 5, 0 < x < 2\pi$

$f'(x) = \cos 2x$

Critical numbers: $\dfrac{\pi}{4}, \dfrac{3\pi}{4}, \dfrac{5\pi}{4}, \dfrac{7\pi}{4}$

| Test intervals: | $0 < x < \dfrac{\pi}{4}$ | $\dfrac{\pi}{4} < x < \dfrac{3\pi}{4}$ | $\dfrac{3\pi}{4} < x < \dfrac{5\pi}{4}$ | $\dfrac{5\pi}{4} < x < \dfrac{7\pi}{4}$ | $\dfrac{7\pi}{4} < x < 2\pi$ |
|---|---|---|---|---|---|
| Sign of $f'(x)$: | $f' > 0$ | $f' < 0$ | $f' > 0$ | $f' < 0$ | $f' > 0$ |
| Conclusion: | Increasing | Decreasing | Increasing | Decreasing | Increasing |

Increasing on: $\left(0, \dfrac{\pi}{4}\right), \left(\dfrac{3\pi}{4}, \dfrac{5\pi}{4}\right), \left(\dfrac{7\pi}{4}, 2\pi\right)$

Decreasing on: $\left(\dfrac{\pi}{4}, \dfrac{3\pi}{4}\right), \left(\dfrac{5\pi}{4}, \dfrac{7\pi}{4}\right)$

(b) Relative maxima: $\left(\dfrac{\pi}{4}, \dfrac{11}{2}\right), \left(\dfrac{5\pi}{4}, \dfrac{11}{2}\right)$

Relative minima: $\left(\dfrac{3\pi}{4}, \dfrac{9}{2}\right), \left(\dfrac{7\pi}{4}, \dfrac{9}{2}\right)$

(c)

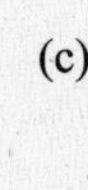

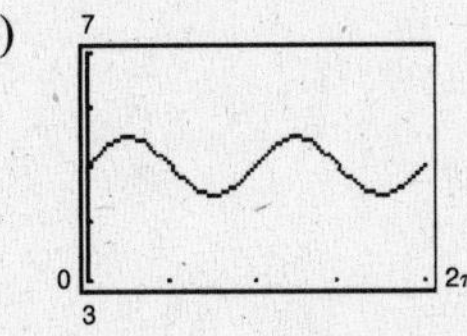

**61.** (a) $f(x) = \sin x + \cos x, \quad 0 < x < 2\pi$

$f'(x) = \cos x - \sin x = 0 \Rightarrow \sin x = \cos x$

Critical numbers: $x = \frac{\pi}{4}, \frac{5\pi}{4}$

| Test intervals: | $0 < x < \frac{\pi}{4}$ | $\frac{\pi}{4} < x < \frac{5\pi}{4}$ | $\frac{5\pi}{4} < x < 2\pi$ |
|---|---|---|---|
| Sign of $f'(x)$: | $f' > 0$ | $f' < 0$ | $f' > 0$ |
| Conclusion: | Increasing | Decreasing | Increasing |

Increasing on: $\left(0, \frac{\pi}{4}\right), \left(\frac{5\pi}{4}, 2\pi\right)$

Decreasing on: $\left(\frac{\pi}{4}, \frac{5\pi}{4}\right)$

(b) Relative maximum: $\left(\frac{\pi}{4}, \sqrt{2}\right)$

Relative minimum: $\left(\frac{5\pi}{4}, -\sqrt{2}\right)$

(c) 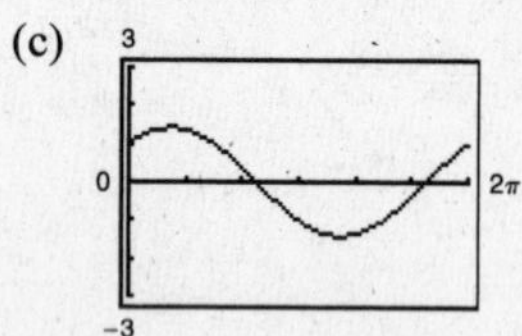


**62.** (a) $f(x) = x + 2 \sin x, \quad 0 < x < 2\pi$

$f'(x) = 1 + 2 \cos x = 0 \Rightarrow \cos x = -\frac{1}{2}$

Critical numbers: $\frac{2\pi}{3}, \frac{4\pi}{3}$

| Test intervals: | $0 < x < \frac{2\pi}{3}$ | $\frac{2\pi}{3} < x < \frac{4\pi}{3}$ | $\frac{4\pi}{3} < x < 2\pi$ |
|---|---|---|---|
| Sign of $f'(x)$: | $f' > 0$ | $f' < 0$ | $f' > 0$ |
| Conclusion: | Increasing | Decreasing | Increasing |

Increasing on: $\left(0, \frac{2\pi}{3}\right), \left(\frac{4\pi}{3}, 2\pi\right)$

Decreasing on: $\left(\frac{2\pi}{3}, \frac{4\pi}{3}\right)$

(b) Relative maximum: $\left(\frac{2\pi}{3}, \frac{2\pi}{3} + \sqrt{3}\right) \approx \left(\frac{2\pi}{3}, 3.826\right)$

Relative minimum: $\left(\frac{4\pi}{3}, \frac{4\pi}{3} - \sqrt{3}\right) \approx \left(\frac{4\pi}{3}, 2.457\right)$

(c) 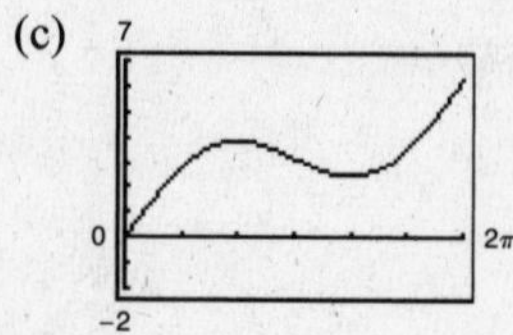

**63.** (a) $f(x) = \cos^2(2x), \quad 0 < x < 2\pi$

$f'(x) = -4\cos 2x \sin 2x = 0 \Rightarrow \cos 2x = 0$ or $\sin 2x = 0$

Critical numbers: $x = \frac{\pi}{4}, \frac{3\pi}{4}, \frac{5\pi}{4}, \frac{7\pi}{4}, \frac{\pi}{2}, \pi, \frac{3\pi}{2}$

| Test intervals: | $0 < x < \frac{\pi}{4}$ | $\frac{\pi}{4} < x < \frac{\pi}{2}$ | $\frac{\pi}{2} < x < \frac{3\pi}{4}$ | $\frac{3\pi}{4} < x < \pi$ |
|---|---|---|---|---|
| Sign of $f'(x)$: | $f' < 0$ | $f' > 0$ | $f' < 0$ | $f' > 0$ |
| Conclusion: | Decreasing | Increasing | Decreasing | Increasing |

| Test intervals: | $\pi < x < \frac{5\pi}{4}$ | $\frac{5\pi}{4} < x < \frac{3\pi}{2}$ | $\frac{3\pi}{2} < x < \frac{7\pi}{4}$ | $\frac{7\pi}{4} < x < 2\pi$ |
|---|---|---|---|---|
| Sign of $f'(x)$: | $f' < 0$ | $f' > 0$ | $f' < 0$ | $f' > 0$ |
| Conclusion: | Decreasing | Increasing | Decreasing | Increasing |

Increasing on: $\left(\frac{\pi}{4}, \frac{\pi}{2}\right), \left(\frac{3\pi}{4}, \pi\right), \left(\frac{5\pi}{4}, \frac{3\pi}{2}\right), \left(\frac{7\pi}{4}, 2\pi\right)$

Decreasing on: $\left(0, \frac{\pi}{4}\right), \left(\frac{\pi}{2}, \frac{3\pi}{4}\right), \left(\pi, \frac{5\pi}{4}\right), \left(\frac{3\pi}{2}, \frac{7\pi}{4}\right)$

(b) Relative maxima: $\left(\frac{\pi}{2}, 1\right), (\pi, 1), \left(\frac{3\pi}{2}, 1\right)$

Relative minima: $\left(\frac{\pi}{4}, 0\right), \left(\frac{3\pi}{4}, 0\right), \left(\frac{5\pi}{4}, 0\right), \left(\frac{7\pi}{4}, 0\right)$

(c)

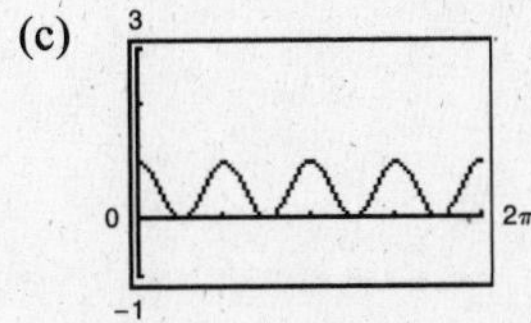


**64.** (a) $f(x) = \sqrt{3}\sin x + \cos x$

$f'(x) = \sqrt{3}\cos x - \sin x = 0 \Rightarrow \tan x = \sqrt{3}$

Critical numbers: $x = \frac{\pi}{3}, \frac{4\pi}{3}$

| Test intervals: | $0 < x < \frac{\pi}{3}$ | $\frac{\pi}{3} < x < \frac{4\pi}{3}$ | $\frac{4\pi}{3} < x < 2\pi$ |
|---|---|---|---|
| Sign of $f'(x)$: | $f' > 0$ | $f' < 0$ | $f' > 0$ |
| Conclusion: | Increasing | Decreasing | Increasing |

Increasing on: $\left(0, \frac{\pi}{3}\right), \left(\frac{4\pi}{3}, 2\pi\right)$

Decreasing on: $\left(\frac{\pi}{3}, \frac{4\pi}{3}\right)$

(b) Relative maximum: $\left(\frac{\pi}{3}, 2\right)$

Relative minimum: $\left(\frac{4\pi}{3}, -2\right)$

(c)

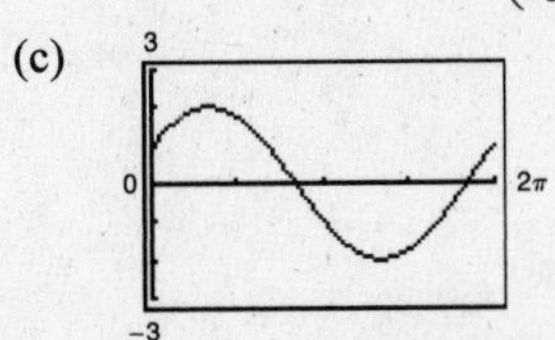

**65.** (a) $f(x) = \sin^2 x + \sin x, \quad 0 < x < 2\pi$

$f'(x) = 2\sin x \cos x + \cos x = \cos x(2\sin x + 1) = 0$

Critical numbers: $x = \frac{\pi}{2}, \frac{7\pi}{6}, \frac{3\pi}{2}, \frac{11\pi}{6}$

| Test intervals: | $0 < x < \frac{\pi}{2}$ | $\frac{\pi}{2} < x < \frac{7\pi}{6}$ | $\frac{7\pi}{6} < x < \frac{3\pi}{2}$ | $\frac{3\pi}{2} < x < \frac{11\pi}{6}$ | $\frac{11\pi}{6} < x < 2\pi$ |
|---|---|---|---|---|---|
| Sign of $f'(x)$: | $f' > 0$ | $f' < 0$ | $f' > 0$ | $f' < 0$ | $f' > 0$ |
| Conclusion: | Increasing | Decreasing | Increasing | Decreasing | Increasing |

Increasing on: $\left(0, \frac{\pi}{2}\right), \left(\frac{7\pi}{6}, \frac{3\pi}{2}\right), \left(\frac{11\pi}{6}, 2\pi\right)$

Decreasing on: $\left(\frac{\pi}{2}, \frac{7\pi}{6}\right), \left(\frac{3\pi}{2}, \frac{11\pi}{6}\right)$

(b) Relative minima: $\left(\frac{7\pi}{6}, -\frac{1}{4}\right), \left(\frac{11\pi}{6}, -\frac{1}{4}\right)$

Relative maxima: $\left(\frac{\pi}{2}, 2\right), \left(\frac{3\pi}{2}, 0\right)$

(c)

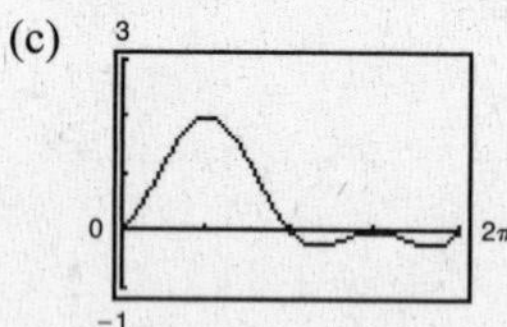


**66.** (a) $f(x) = \dfrac{\sin x}{1 + \cos^2 x}, 0 < x < 2\pi$

$f'(x) = \dfrac{\cos x(2 + \sin^2 x)}{(1 + \cos^2 x)^2} = 0$

Critical numbers: $x = \frac{\pi}{2}, \frac{3\pi}{2}$

| Test intervals: | $0 < x < \frac{\pi}{2}$ | $\frac{\pi}{2} < x < \frac{3\pi}{2}$ | $\frac{3\pi}{2} < x < 2\pi$ |
|---|---|---|---|
| Sign of $f'(x)$: | $f' > 0$ | $f' < 0$ | $f' > 0$ |
| Conclusion: | Increasing | Decreasing | Increasing |

Increasing on: $\left(0, \frac{\pi}{2}\right), \left(\frac{3\pi}{2}, 2\pi\right)$

Decreasing on: $\left(\frac{\pi}{2}, \frac{3\pi}{2}\right)$

(b) Relative maximum: $\left(\frac{\pi}{2}, 1\right)$

Relative minimum: $\left(\frac{3\pi}{2}, -1\right)$

(c)

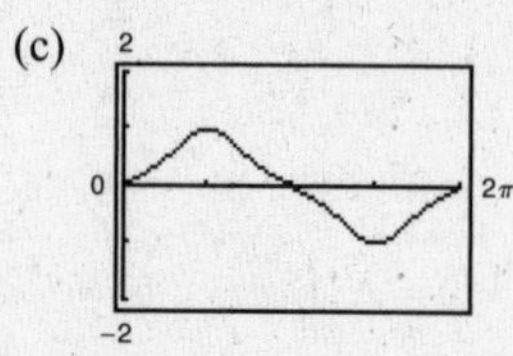

**67.** $f(x) = 2x\sqrt{9 - x^2}, [-3, 3]$

(a) $f'(x) = \dfrac{2(9 - 2x^2)}{\sqrt{9 - x^2}}$

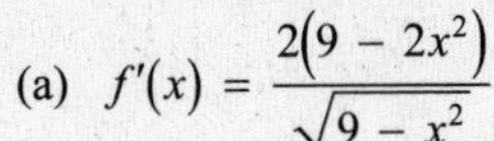

(b)

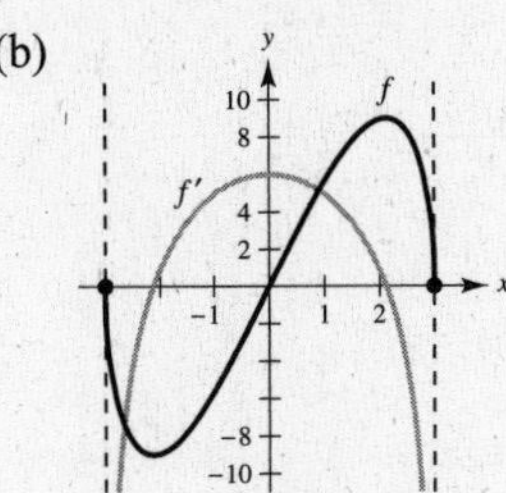


(c) $\dfrac{2(9 - 2x^2)}{\sqrt{9 - x^2}} = 0$

Critical numbers: $x = \pm\dfrac{3}{\sqrt{2}} = \pm\dfrac{3\sqrt{2}}{2}$

(d) Intervals:

| $\left(-3, -\frac{3\sqrt{2}}{2}\right)$ | $\left(-\frac{3\sqrt{2}}{2}, \frac{3\sqrt{2}}{2}\right)$ | $\left(\frac{3\sqrt{2}}{2}, 3\right)$ |
|---|---|---|
| $f'(x) < 0$ | $f'(x) > 0$ | $f'(x) < 0$ |
| Decreasing | Increasing | Decreasing |

(e) $f$ is increasing when $f'$ is positive and decreasing when $f'$ is negative.

**68.** $f(x) = 10\left(5 - \sqrt{x^2 - 3x + 16}\right), [0, 5]$

(a) $f'(x) = -\dfrac{5(2x - 3)}{\sqrt{x^2 - 3x + 16}}$

(b)

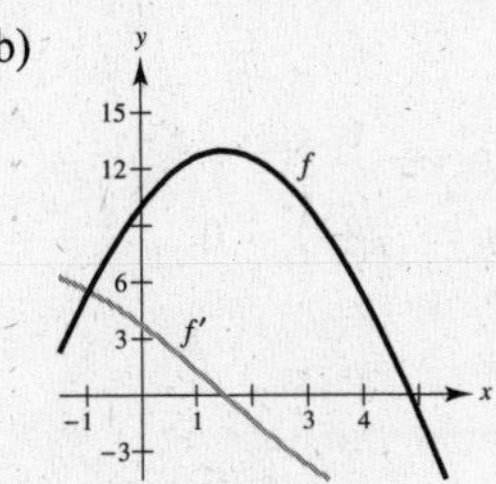


(c) $-\dfrac{5(2x - 3)}{\sqrt{x^2 - 3x + 16}} = 0$

Critical number: $x = \dfrac{3}{2}$

(d) Intervals:

| $\left(0, \frac{3}{2}\right)$ | $\left(\frac{3}{2}, 5\right)$ |
|---|---|
| $f'(x) > 0$ | $f'(x) < 0$ |
| Increasing | Decreasing |

(e) $f$ is increasing when $f'$ is positive and decreasing when $f'$ is negative.

**69.** $f(t) = t^2 \sin t, [0, 2\pi]$

(a) $f'(t) = t^2 \cos t + 2t \sin t = t(t \cos t + 2 \sin t)$

(b)

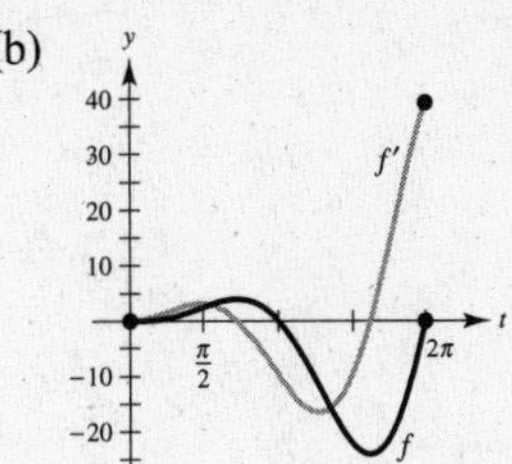


(c) $t(t \cos t + 2 \sin t) = 0$

$t = 0$ or $t = -2 \tan t$

$t \cot t = -2$

$t \approx 2.2889, 5.0870$ (graphing utility)

Critical numbers: $t = 2.2889, 5.0870$

(d) Intervals:

| $(0, 2.2889)$ | $(2.2889, 5.0870)$ | $(5.0870, 2\pi)$ |
|---|---|---|
| $f'(t) > 0$ | $f'(t) < 0$ | $f'(t) > 0$ |
| Increasing | Decreasing | Increasing |

(e) $f$ is increasing when $f'$ is positive and decreasing when $f'$ is negative.

**70.** $f(x) = \dfrac{x}{2} + \cos\dfrac{x}{2}, [0, 4\pi]$

(a) $f'(x) = \dfrac{1}{2} - \dfrac{1}{2}\sin\dfrac{x}{2}$

(b)

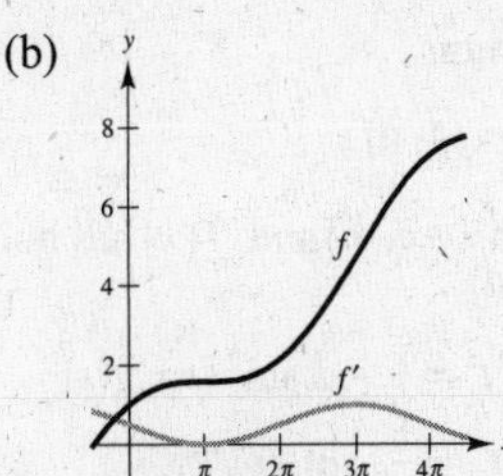


(c) $\dfrac{1}{2} - \dfrac{1}{2}\sin\dfrac{x}{2} = 0$

$\sin\dfrac{x}{2} = 1$

$\dfrac{x}{2} = \dfrac{\pi}{2}$

Critical number: $x = \pi$

(d) Intervals:

| $(0, \pi)$ | $(\pi, 4\pi)$ |
|---|---|
| $f'(x) > 0$ | $f'(x) > 0$ |
| Increasing | Increasing |

(e) $f$ is increasing when $f'$ is positive.

**71.** $f(x) = \frac{1}{2}(x^2 - \ln x), (0, 3]$

(a) $f'(x) = \dfrac{2x^2 - 1}{2x}$

(b)

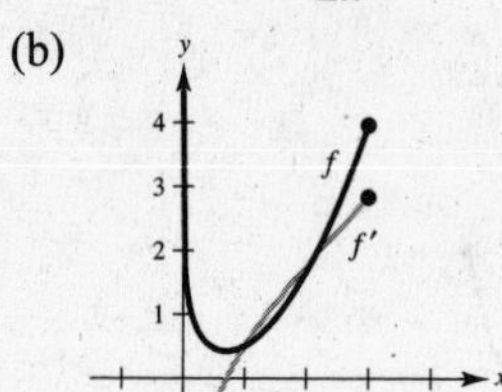


(c) $\dfrac{2x^2 - 1}{2x} = 0$

Critical number: $x = \dfrac{1}{\sqrt{2}} = \dfrac{\sqrt{2}}{2}$

(d) Intervals: $\left(0, \dfrac{\sqrt{2}}{2}\right)$ $\left(\dfrac{\sqrt{2}}{2}, 3\right)$

$f'(x) < 0$ $f'(x) > 0$

Decreasing Increasing

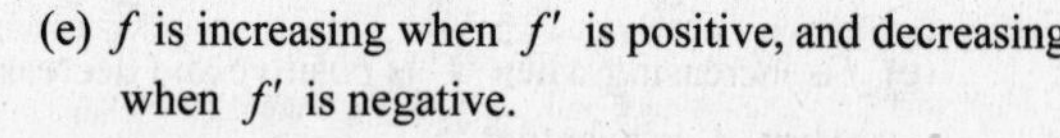

(e) $f$ is increasing when $f'$ is positive, and decreasing when $f'$ is negative.

**72.** $f(x) = (4 - x^2)e^x, [0, 2]$

(a) $f'(x) = (4 - 2x - x^2)e^x$

(b)

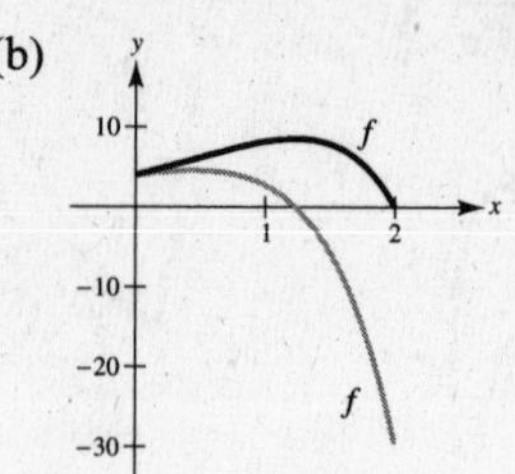


(c) $(4 - 2x - x^2)e^x = 0$

Critical number: $x \approx 1.2361$ $(x = -1 + \sqrt{5})$

(d) Intervals: $(0, 1.2361)$ $(1.2361, 2)$

$f'(x) > 0$ $f'(x) < 0$

Increasing Decreasing

(e) $f$ is increasing when $f'$ is positive, and decreasing when $f'$ is negative.

**73.** $f(x) = \dfrac{x^5 - 4x^3 + 3x}{x^2 - 1} = \dfrac{(x^2 - 1)(x^3 - 3x)}{x^2 - 1} = x^3 - 3x, x \neq \pm 1$

$f(x) = g(x) = x^3 - 3x$ for all $x \neq \pm 1$.

$f'(x) = 3x^2 - 3 = 3(x^2 - 1), x \neq \pm 1 \Rightarrow f'(x) \neq 0$

$f$ symmetric about origin

zeros of $f$: $(0, 0), (\pm\sqrt{3}, 0)$

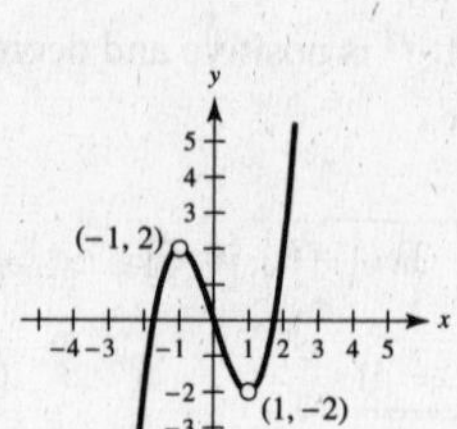


$g(x)$ is continuous on $(-\infty, \infty)$ and $f(x)$ has holes at $(-1, 2)$ and $(1, -2)$.

**74.** $f(t) = \cos^2 t - \sin^2 t = 1 - 2\sin^2 t = g(t)$

$f'(t) = -4 \sin t \cos t = -2 \sin 2t$

$f$ symmetric with respect to $y$-axis

zeros of $f$: $\left(\pm\dfrac{\pi}{4}, 0\right)$

Relative maximum: $(0, 1)$

Relative minimum: $\left(-\dfrac{\pi}{2}, -1\right), \left(\dfrac{\pi}{2}, -1\right)$

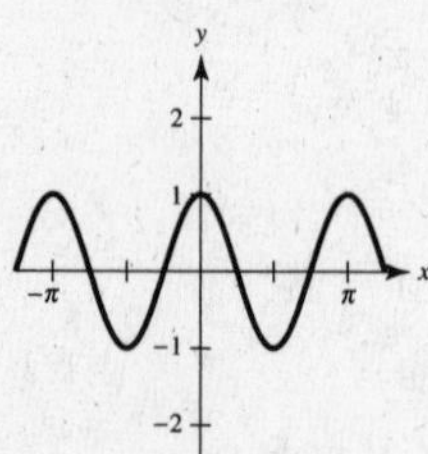


The graphs of $f(x)$ and $g(x)$ are the same.

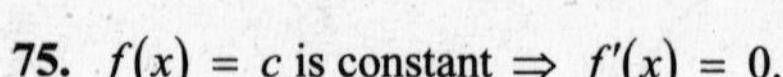

**75.** $f(x) = c$ is constant $\Rightarrow f'(x) = 0$.

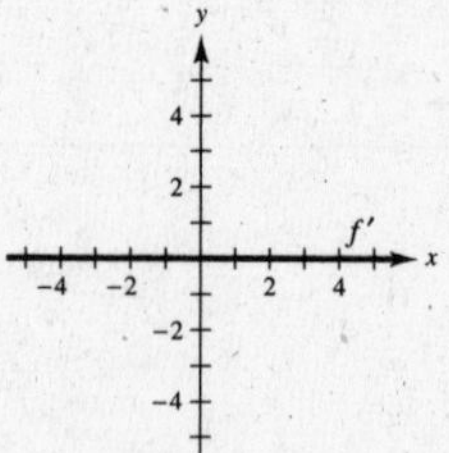


**76.** $f(x)$ is a line of slope $\approx 2 \Rightarrow f'(x) = 2$.

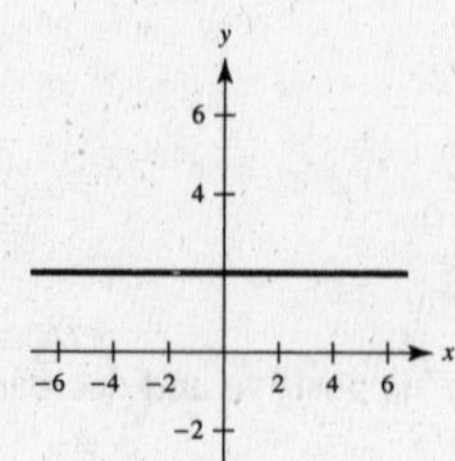

**77.** $f$ is quadratic $\Rightarrow f'$ is a line.

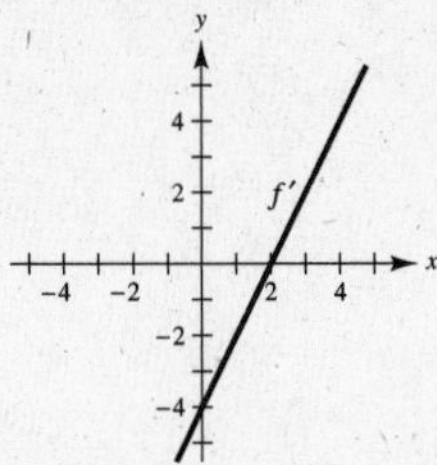

**78.** $f$ is a 4[th] degree polynomial $\Rightarrow f'$ is a cubic polynomial.

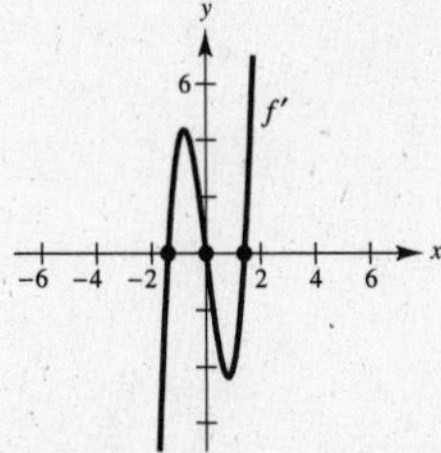

**79.** $f$ has positive, but decreasing slope

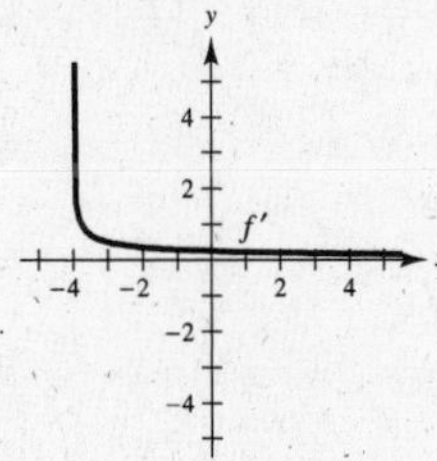

**80.** $f$ has positive slope

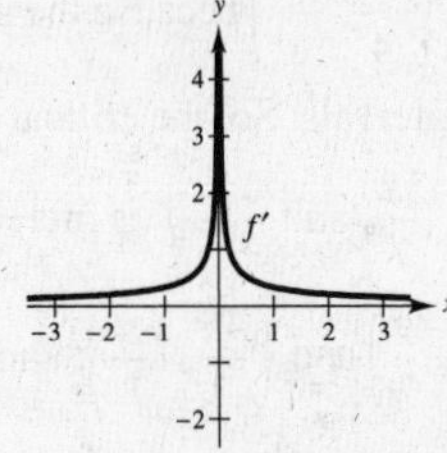

**81.** (a) $f$ is increasing on $(2, \infty)$ because $f' > 0$ on $(2, \infty)$.

$f$ is decreasing on $(-\infty, 2)$ because $f' < 0$ on $(-\infty, 2)$.

(b) $f$ is has a relative minimum at $x = 2$.

**82.** (a) $f$ is increasing on $(-\infty, 0)$ and $(1, \infty)$ because $f' > 0$ on $(-\infty, 0)$ and $(1, \infty)$.

$f$ is decreasing on $(0, 1)$ because $f' < 0$ on $(0, 1)$.

(b) $f$ has a relative maximum at $x = 0$, and a relative minimum at $x = 1$.

**83.** (a) $f$ is increasing on $(-\infty, -1)$ and $(0, 1)$ because $f' > 0$ on $(-\infty, -1)$ and $(0, 1)$.

$f$ is decreasing on $(-1, 0)$ and $(1, \infty)$ because $f' < 0$ on $(-1, 0)$ and $(1, \infty)$.

(b) $f$ has a relative maximum at $x = -1$ and $x = 1$.

$f$ has a relative minimum at $x = 0$.

**84.** (a) $f$ is increasing on $(-1, 0)$ and $(0, \infty)$ because $f' > 0$ on $(-1, 0)$ and $(0, \infty)$.

$f$ is decreasing on $(-\infty, -1)$ because $f' < 0$ on $(-\infty, -1)$.

(b) $f$ has a relative minimum at $x = -1$.

**85.** (a) $f' = 0$ at $x = -1, 1, 2$

Critical numbers: $x = -1, 1, 2$

(b) $x = 1$ is a relative maximum because $f'$ changes from positive to negative.

$x = 2$ is a relative minimum because $f'$ changes from negative to positive. $x = -1$ is not a relative extremum.

**86.** (a) $f' = 0$ at $x = -3, 1$, and 5.

Critical numbers: $x = -3, 1, 5$

(b) $x = -3$ is a relative minimum because $f'$ changes from negative to positive.

$x = 5$ is a relative maximum because $f'$ changes from positive to negative.

$x = 1$ is not a relative extremum.

**In Exercises 87–92, $f'(x) > 0$ on $(-\infty, -4)$, $f'(x) < 0$ on $(-4, 6)$, and $f'(x) > 0$ on $(6, \infty)$.**

**87.** $g(x) = f(x) + 5$

$g'(x) = f'(x)$

$g'(0) = f'(0) < 0$

**88.** $g(x) = 3f(x) - 3$

$g'(x) = 3f'(x)$

$g'(-5) = 3f'(-5) > 0$

**89.** $g(x) = -f(x)$

$g'(x) = -f'(x)$

$g'(-6) = -f'(-6) < 0$

**90.** $g(x) = -f(x)$

$g'(x) = -f'(x)$

$g'(0) = -f'(0) > 0$

**91.** $g(x) = f(x - 10)$

$g'(x) = f'(x - 10)$

$g'(0) = f'(-10) > 0$

**92.** $g(x) = f(x - 10)$

$g'(x) = f'(x - 10)$

$g'(8) = f'(-2) < 0$

**93.** $f'(x) = \begin{cases} > 0, & x < 4 \Rightarrow f \text{ is increasing on } (-\infty, 4). \\ \text{undefined}, & x = 4 \\ < 0, & x > 4 \Rightarrow f \text{ is decreasing on } (4\ \infty). \end{cases}$

Two possibilities for $f(x)$ are given below.

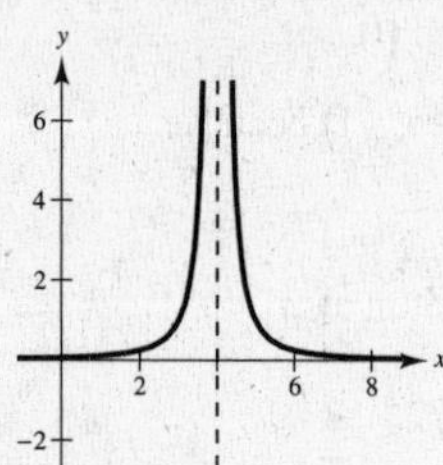
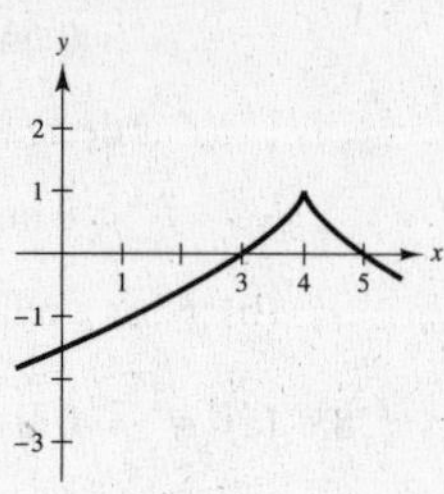

**94.** Critical number: $x = 5$

$f'(4) = -2.5 \Rightarrow f$ is decreasing at $x = 4$.

$f'(6) = 3 \Rightarrow f$ is increasing at $x = 6$.

$(5, f(5))$ is a relative minimum.

**In Exercises 95 and 96, answers will vary.**

*Sample answers*:

**95.** (a)

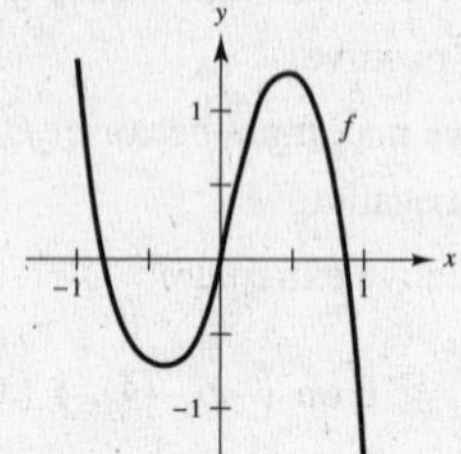

(b) The critical numbers are in intervals $(-0.50, -0.25)$ and $(0.25, 0.50)$ because the sign of $f'$ changes in these intervals. So, the critical numbers are $x \approx -0.40$ and $x \approx 0.48$. $f$ is decreasing on approximately $(-1, -0.40)$ and $(0.48, 1)$, and increasing on $(-0.40, 0.48)$.

(c) Relative minimum when $x \approx -0.40$: $(-0.40, 0.75)$

Relative maximum when $x \approx 0.48$: $(0.48, 1.25)$

**96.** (a)

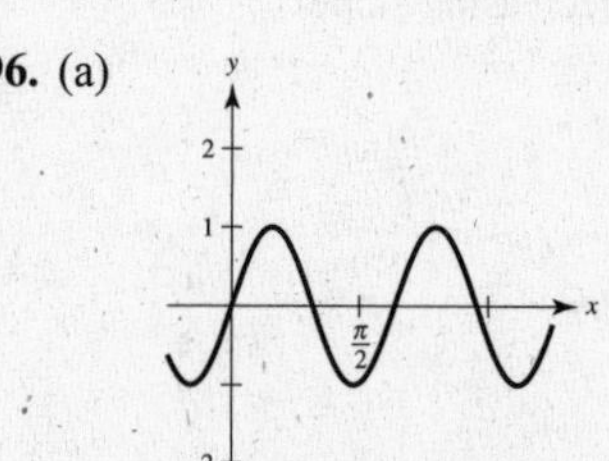

(b) The critical numbers are in the intervals $\left(0, \frac{\pi}{6}\right), \left(\frac{\pi}{3}, \frac{\pi}{2}\right)$, and $\left(\frac{3\pi}{4}, \frac{5\pi}{6}\right)$ because the sign of $f'$ changes in these intervals. So, the critical numbers are $x \approx \frac{\pi}{7}, \frac{3\pi}{7}$, and $\frac{6\pi}{7}$. $f$ is increasing on approximately $\left(0, \frac{\pi}{7}\right)$ and $\left(\frac{3\pi}{7}, \frac{6\pi}{7}\right)$, and decreasing on $\left(\frac{\pi}{7}, \frac{3\pi}{7}\right)$ and $\left(\frac{6\pi}{7}, \pi\right)$.

(c) Relative minima when $x \approx \frac{3\pi}{7}, \pi$

Relative maxima when $x \approx \frac{\pi}{7}, \frac{6\pi}{7}$

**97.** $s(t) = 4.9(\sin\theta)t^2$

(a) $s'(t) = 4.9(\sin\theta)(2t) = 9.8(\sin\theta)t$

speed $= |s'(t)| = |9.8(\sin\theta)t|$

(b)

| $\theta$ | 0 | $\frac{\pi}{4}$ | $\frac{\pi}{3}$ | $\frac{\pi}{2}$ | $\frac{2\pi}{3}$ | $\frac{3\pi}{4}$ | $\pi$ |
|---|---|---|---|---|---|---|---|
| $\lvert s'(t)\rvert$ | 0 | $4.9\sqrt{2}t$ | $4.9\sqrt{3}t$ | $9.8t$ | $4.9\sqrt{3}t$ | $4.9\sqrt{2}t$ | 0 |

The speed is maximum for $\theta = \frac{\pi}{2}$.

**98.** $C = \frac{3t}{27 + t^3}, t \geq 0$

(a)

| $t$ | 0 | 0.5 | 1 | 1.5 | 2 | 2.5 | 3 |
|---|---|---|---|---|---|---|---|
| $C(t)$ | 0 | 0.055 | 0.107 | 0.148 | 0.171 | 0.176 | 0.167 |

The concentration seems greatest near $t = 2.5$ hours.

(b)

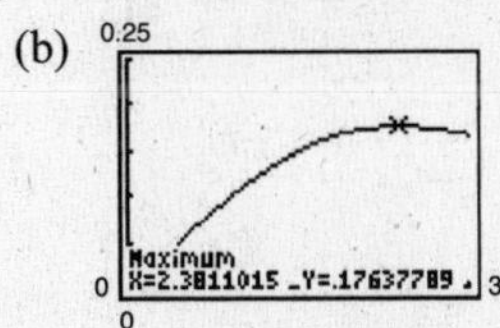


The concentration is greatest when $t \approx 2.38$ hours.

(c) $C' = \frac{(27 + t^3)(3) - (3t)(3t^2)}{(27 + t^3)^2}$

$= \frac{3(27 - 2t^3)}{(27 + t^3)^2}$

$C' = 0$ when $t = 3/\sqrt[3]{2} \approx 2.38$ hours.

By the First Derivative Test, this is a maximum.

**99.** $f(x) = x, g(x) = \sin x, 0 < x < \pi$

(a)

| $x$ | 0.5 | 1 | 1.5 | 2 | 2.5 | 3 |
|---|---|---|---|---|---|---|
| $f(x)$ | 0.5 | 1 | 1.5 | 2 | 2.5 | 3 |
| $g(x)$ | 0.479 | 0.841 | 0.997 | 0.909 | 0.598 | 0.141 |

$f(x)$ seems greater than $g(x)$ on $(0, \pi)$.

(b)

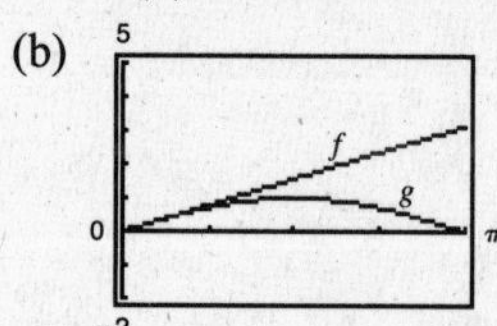


$x > \sin x$ on $(0, \pi)$ so, $f(x) > g(x)$.

(c) Let $h(x) = f(x) - g(x) = x - \sin x$

$h'(x) = 1 - \cos x > 0$ on $(0, \pi)$.

So, $h(x)$ is increasing on $(0, \pi)$. Because $h(0) = 0$ and $h'(x) > 0$ on $(0, \pi)$,

$h(x) > 0$

$x - \sin x > 0$

$x > \sin x$

$f(x) > g(x)$ on $(0, \pi)$.

**100.** $f(x) = x, g(x) = \tan x$

(a)

| $x$ | 0.25 | 0.5 | 0.75 | 1.0 | 1.25 | 1.5 |
|---|---|---|---|---|---|---|
| $f(x)$ | 0.25 | 0.5 | 0.75 | 1.0 | 1.25 | 1.5 |
| $g(x)$ | 0.2553 | 0.5463 | 0.9316 | 1.5574 | 3.0096 | 14.1014 |

$g(x)$ seems greater than $f(x)$ on $\left(0, \frac{\pi}{2}\right)$.

(b)

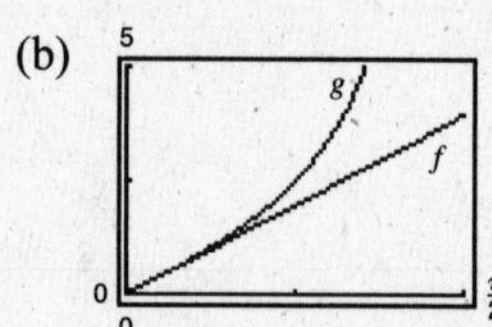


$\tan x > x$ on $\left(0, \frac{\pi}{2}\right)$ so, $g(x) > f(x)$.

(c) Let $h(x) = f(x) - g(x) = \tan x - x$

$h'(x) = \sec^2 x - 1 > 0$ on $\left(0, \frac{\pi}{2}\right)$.

Because $h(0) = 0$ and $h'(x) > 0$ on $\left(0, \frac{\pi}{2}\right)$,

$h(x) > 0$

$\tan x - x > 0$

$\tan x > x$

$g(x) > f(x)$ on $\left(0, \frac{\pi}{2}\right)$.

**101.** $v = k(R - r)r^2 = k(Rr^2 - r^3)$

$v' = k(2Rr - 3r^2)$

$= kr(2R - 3r) = 0$

$r = 0$ or $\frac{2}{3}R$

Maximum when $r = \frac{2}{3}R$.

**102.** (a) $M = 0.03723t^4 - 1.9931t^3 + 37.986t^2 - 282.74t + 825.7$

(b)

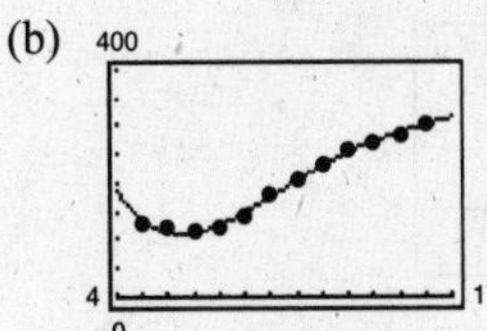


(c) Using a graphing utility, the minimum is (6.5, 111.9) which compares well with the minimum (7, 115.6).

**103.** (a) $s(t) = 6t - t^2, t \geq 0$

$v(t) = 6 - 2t$

(b) $v(t) = 0$ when $t = 3$.

Moving in positive direction for $0 \leq t < 3$ because $v(t) > 0$ on $0 \leq t < 3$.

(c) Moving in negative direction when $t > 3$.

(d) The particle changes direction at $t = 3$.

**104.** (a) $s(t) = t^2 - 7t + 10, t \geq 0$

$v(t) = 2t - 7$

(b) $v(t) = 0$ when $t = \frac{7}{2}$

Particle moving in positive direction for $t > \frac{7}{2}$ because $v'(t) > 0$ on $\left(\frac{7}{2}, \infty\right)$.

(c) Particle moving in negative direction on $\left[0, \frac{7}{2}\right)$.

(d) The particle changes direction at $t = \frac{7}{2}$.

**105.** (a) $s(t) = t^3 - 5t^2 + 4t, t \geq 0$

$v(t) = 3t^2 - 10t + 4$

(b) $v(t) = 0$ for $t = \dfrac{10 \pm \sqrt{100 - 48}}{6} = \dfrac{5 \pm \sqrt{13}}{3}$

Particle is moving in a positive direction on $\left[0, \dfrac{5 - \sqrt{13}}{3}\right) \approx [0, 0.4648)$ and $\left(\dfrac{5 + \sqrt{13}}{3}, \infty\right) \approx (2.8685, \infty)$ because $v > 0$ on these intervals.

(c) Particle is moving in a negative direction on $\left(\dfrac{5 - \sqrt{13}}{3}, \dfrac{5 + \sqrt{13}}{3}\right) \approx (0.4648, 2.8685)$

(d) The particle changes direction at $t = \dfrac{5 \pm \sqrt{13}}{3}$.

**106.** (a) $s(t) = t^3 - 20t^2 + 128t - 280$

$v(t) = 3t^2 - 40t + 128$

(b) $v(t) = (3t - 16)(t - 8)$

$v(t) = 0$ when $t = \frac{16}{3}, 8$

$v(t) > 0$ for $\left[0, \frac{16}{3}\right)$ and $(8, \infty)$

(c) $v(t) < 0$ for $\left(\frac{16}{3}, 8\right)$

(d) The particle changes direction at $t = \frac{16}{3}$ and 8.

**107.** Answers will vary.

**108.** Answers will vary.

**109.** (a) Use a cubic polynomial

$f(x) = a_3x^3 + a_2x^2 + a_1x + a_0$

(b) $f'(x) = 3a_3x^2 + 2a_2x + a_1$.

$f(0) = 0$: $a_3(0)^3 + a_2(0)^2 + a_1(0) + a_0 = 0 \Rightarrow$ $a_0 = 0$

$f'(0) = 0$: $3a_3(0)^2 + 2a_2(0) + a_1 = 0 \Rightarrow$ $a_1 = 0$

$f(2) = 2$: $a_3(2)^3 + a_2(2)^2 + a_1(2) + a_0 = 2 \Rightarrow$ $8a_3 + 4a_2 = 2$

$f'(2) = 0$: $3a_3(2)^2 + 2a_2(2) + a_1 = 0 \Rightarrow$ $12a_3 + 4a_2 = 0$

(c) The solution is $a_0 = a_1 = 0, a_2 = \frac{3}{2}, a_3 = -\frac{1}{2}$:

$f(x) = -\frac{1}{2}x^3 + \frac{3}{2}x^2$.

(d)

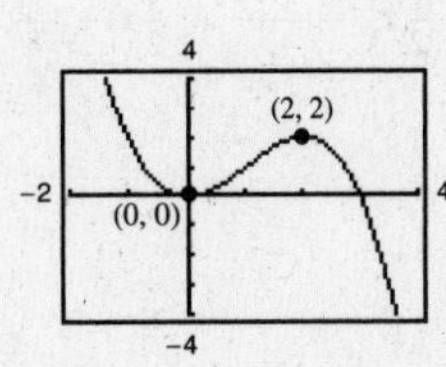

**110.** (a) Use a cubic polynomial

$f(x) = 3a_3x^3 + a_2x^2 + a_1x + a_0$

(b) $f'(x) = 3a_3x^2 + 2a_2x + a_1$

$$\begin{aligned}
f(0) = 0:&\quad a_3(0)^3 + a_2(0)^2 + a_1(0) + a_0 = 0 \Rightarrow &\quad a_0 = 0\\
f'(0) = 0:&\quad 3a_3(0)^2 + 2a_2(0) + a_1 = 0 \Rightarrow &\quad a_1 = 0\\
f(4) = 1000:&\quad a_3(4)^3 + a_2(4)^2 + a_1(4) + a_0 = 1000 \Rightarrow &\quad 64a_3 + 16a_2 = 100\\
f'(4) = 0:&\quad 3a_3(4)^2 + 2a_2(4) + a_1 = 0 \Rightarrow &\quad 48a_3 + 8a_2 = 0
\end{aligned}$$

(c) The solution is $a_0 = a_1 = 0, a_2 = \frac{375}{2}, a_3 = -\frac{125}{4}$:

$f(x) = -\frac{125}{4}x^3 + \frac{375}{2}x^2$.

(d)

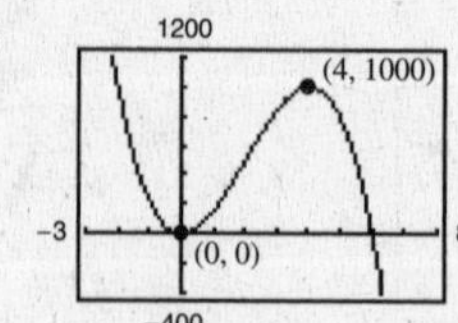


**111.** (a) Use a fourth degree polynomial

$f(x) = a_4x^4 + a_3x^3 + a_2x^2 + a_1x + a_0$.

(b) $f'(x) = 4a_4x^3 + 3a_3x^2 + 2a_2x + a_1$

$$\begin{aligned}
f(0) = 0:&\quad a_4(0)^4 + a_3(0)^3 + a_2(0)^2 + a_1(0) + a_0 = 0 \Rightarrow &\quad a_0 = 0\\
f'(0) = 0:&\quad 4a_4(0)^3 + 3a_3(0)^2 + 2a_2(0) + a_1 = 0 \Rightarrow &\quad a_1 = 0\\
f(4) = 0:&\quad a_4(4)^4 + a_3(4)^3 + a_2(4)^2 + a_1(4) + a_0 = 0 \Rightarrow &\quad 256a_4 + 64a_3 + 16a_2 = 0\\
f'(4) = 0:&\quad 4a_4(4)^3 + 3a_3(4)^2 + 2a_2(4) + a_1 = 0 \Rightarrow &\quad 256a_4 + 48a_3 + 8a_2 = 0\\
f(2) = 4:&\quad a_4(2)^4 + a_3(2)^3 + a_2(2)^2 + a_1(2) + a_0 = 4 \Rightarrow &\quad 16a_4 + 8a_3 + 4a_2 = 4\\
f'(2) = 0:&\quad 4a_4(2)^3 + 3a_3(2)^2 + 2a_2(2) + a_1 = 0 \Rightarrow &\quad 32a_4 + 12a_3 + 4a_2 = 0
\end{aligned}$$

(c) The solution is $a_0 = a_1 = 0, a_2 = 4, a_3 = -2, \quad a_4 = \frac{1}{4}$:

$f(x) = \frac{1}{4}x^4 - 2x^3 + 4x^2$.

(d)

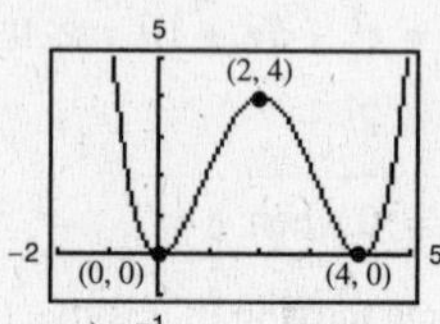


**112.** (a) Use a fourth degree polynomial

$f(x) = a_4x^4 + a_3x^3 + a_2x^2 + a_1x + a_0$.

(b) $f'(x) = 4a_4x^3 + 3a_3x^2 + 2a_2x + a_1$

$$\begin{aligned}
f(1) = 2:&\quad a_4(1)^4 + a_3(1)^3 + a_2(1)^2 + a_1(1) + a_0 = 2 \Rightarrow &\quad a_4 + a_3 + a_2 + a_1 + a_0 = 2\\
f'(1) = 0:&\quad 4a_4(1)^3 + 3a_3(1)^2 + 2a_2(1) + a_1 = 0 \Rightarrow &\quad 4a_4 + 3a_3 + 2a_2 + a_1 = 0\\
f(-1) = 4:&\quad a_4(-1)^4 + a_3(-1)^3 + a_2(-1)^2 + a_1(-1) + a_0 = 4 \Rightarrow &\quad a_4 - a_3 + a_2 - a_1 + a_0 = 4\\
f'(-1) = 0:&\quad 4a_4(-1)^3 + 3a_3(-1)^2 + 2a_2(-1) + a_1 = 0 \Rightarrow &\quad -4a_4 + 3a_3 - 2a_2 + a_1 = 0\\
f(3) = 4:&\quad a_4(3)^4 + a_3(3)^3 + a_2(3)^2 + a_1(3) + a_0 = 4 \Rightarrow &\quad 81a_4 + 27a_3 + 9a_2 + a_1 + a_0 = 4\\
f'(3) = 0:&\quad 4a_4(3)^3 + 3a_3(3)^2 + 2a_2(3) + a_1 = 0 \Rightarrow &\quad 108a_4 + 27a_3 + 6a_2 + a_1 = 0
\end{aligned}$$

(c) The solution is $a_0 = \frac{23}{8}, a_1 = -\frac{3}{2}, a_2 = \frac{1}{4}, a_3 = \frac{1}{2}, a_4 = -\frac{1}{8}$:

$f(x) = -\frac{1}{8}x^4 + \frac{1}{2}x^3 + \frac{1}{4}x^2 - \frac{3}{2}x + \frac{23}{8}$.

(d)

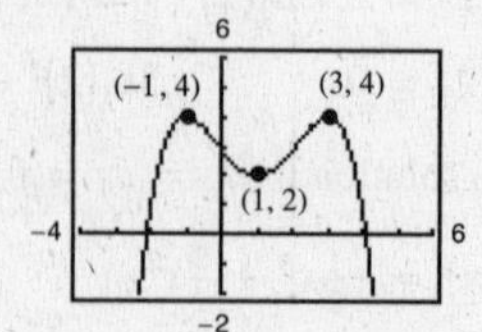

**113.** True.

Let $h(x) = f(x) + g(x)$ where $f$ and $g$ are increasing. Then $h'(x) = f'(x) + g'(x) > 0$ because $f'(x) > 0$ and $g'(x) > 0$.

**114.** False.

Let $h(x) = f(x)g(x)$ where $f(x) = g(x) = x$. Then $h(x) = x^2$ is decreasing on $(-\infty, 0)$.

**115.** False.

Let $f(x) = x^3$, then $f'(x) = 3x^2$ and $f$ only has one critical number. Or, let $f(x) = x^3 + 3x + 1$, then $f'(x) = 3(x^2 + 1)$ has no critical numbers.

**116.** True.

If $f(x)$ is an $n$th-degree polynomial, then the degree of $f'(x)$ is $n - 1$.

**117.** False. For example, $f(x) = x^3$ does not have a relative extrema at the critical number $x = 0$.

**118.** False.

The function might not be continuous.

**119.** Assume that $f'(x) < 0$ for all $x$ in the interval $(a, b)$ and let $x_1 < x_2$ be any two points in the interval. By the Mean Value Theorem, you know there exists a number $c$ such that $x_1 < c < x_2$, and

$$f'(c) = \frac{f(x_2) - f(x_1)}{x_2 - x_1}$$

Because $f'(c) < 0$ and $x_2 - x_1 > 0$, then $f(x_2) - f(x_1) < 0$, which implies that $f(x_2) < f(x_1)$. So, $f$ is decreasing on the interval.

**120.** Suppose $f'(x)$ changes from positive to negative at $c$. Then there exists $a$ and $b$ in $I$ such that $f'(x) > 0$ for all $x$ in $(a, c)$ and $f'(x) < 0$ for all $x$ in $(c, b)$. By Theorem 4.5, $f$ is increasing on $(a, c)$ and decreasing on $(c, b)$. Therefore, $f(c)$ is a maximum of $f$ on $(a, b)$ and so, a relative maximum of $f$.

**121.** Let $f(x) = (1 + x)^n - nx - 1$. Then

$$f'(x) = n(1 + x)^{n-1} - n = n\left[(1 + x)^{n-1} - 1\right] > 0$$

because $x > 0$ and $n > 1$.

So, $f(x)$ is increasing on $(0, \infty)$. Because

$$f(0) = 0 \Rightarrow f(x) > 0 \text{ on } (0, \infty)$$

$$(1 + x)^n - nx - 1 > 0 \Rightarrow (1 + x)^n > 1 + nx.$$

**122.** Let $x_1$ and $x_2$ be two real numbers, $x_1 < x_2$. Then $x_1^3 < x_2^3 \Rightarrow f(x_1) < f(x_2)$. So $f$ is increasing on $(-\infty, \infty)$.

**123.** Let $x_1$ and $x_2$ be two positive real numbers, $0 < x_1 < x_2$. Then

$$\frac{1}{x_1} > \frac{1}{x_2}$$

$$f(x_1) > f(x_2)$$

So, $f$ is decreasing on $(0, \infty)$.

**124.** $f(x) = axe^{bx^2}$

$$f'(x) = ax(2bx)e^{bx^2} + ae^{bx^2} = ae^{bx^2}(1 + 2bx^2)$$

$$f(4) = 2: \ 2 = 4ae^{16b} \Rightarrow 2a = \frac{1}{e^{16b}} \Rightarrow a = \frac{1}{2}e^{-16b}$$

Relative maximum at $x = 4$:

$$f'(4) = 0 \Rightarrow 1 + 2b(16) = 0 \Rightarrow b = -\frac{1}{32}$$

So, $a = \frac{1}{2}e^{1/2} = \frac{\sqrt{e}}{2}$,

$$f(x) = \frac{\sqrt{e}}{2}xe^{-x^2/32}.$$

Notice the $f$ is increasing on $(0, 4)$ and decreasing on $(4, \infty)$, so $(4, 2)$ is a relative maximum.

**125.** First observe that

$$\tan x + \cot x + \sec x + \csc x = \frac{\sin x}{\cos x} + \frac{\cos x}{\sin x} + \frac{1}{\cos x} + \frac{1}{\sin x}$$
$$= \frac{\sin^2 x + \cos^2 x + \sin x + \cos x}{\sin x \cos x}$$
$$= \frac{1 + \sin x + \cos x}{\sin x \cos x}\left(\frac{\sin x + \cos x - 1}{\sin x + \cos x - 1}\right)$$
$$= \frac{(\sin x + \cos x)^2 - 1}{\sin x \cos x(\sin x + \cos x - 1)}$$
$$= \frac{2 \sin x \cos x}{\sin x \cos x(\sin x + \cos x - 1)}$$
$$= \frac{2}{\sin x + \cos x - 1}.$$

Let $t = \sin x + \cos x - 1$. The expression inside the absolute value sign is

$$f(t) = \sin x + \cos x + \frac{2}{\sin x + \cos x - 1}$$
$$= (\sin x + \cos x - 1) + 1 + \frac{2}{\sin x + \cos x - 1}$$
$$= t + 1 + \frac{2}{t}.$$

Because $\sin\left(x + \frac{\pi}{4}\right) = \sin x \cos\frac{\pi}{4} + \cos x \sin\frac{\pi}{4}$

$$= \frac{\sqrt{2}}{2}(\sin x + \cos x),$$

$\sin x + \cos x \in \left[-\sqrt{2}, \sqrt{2}\right]$ and

$t = \sin x + \cos x - 1 \in \left[-1 - \sqrt{2}, -1 + \sqrt{2}\right].$

$$f'(t) = 1 - \frac{2}{t^2} = \frac{t^2 - 2}{t^2} = \frac{(t + \sqrt{2})(t - \sqrt{2})}{t^2}$$

$$f\left(-1 + \sqrt{2}\right) = -1 + \sqrt{2} + 1 + \frac{2}{-1 + \sqrt{2}} = \sqrt{2} + \frac{2}{\sqrt{2} - 1}$$
$$= \frac{4 - \sqrt{2}}{\sqrt{2} - 1}\left(\frac{\sqrt{2} + 1}{\sqrt{2} + 1}\right) = \frac{4\sqrt{2} - 2 + 4 - \sqrt{2}}{1} = 2 + 3\sqrt{2}$$

For $t > 0$, $f$ is decreasing and $f(t) > f\left(-1 + \sqrt{2}\right) = 2 + 3\sqrt{2}$

For $t < 0$, $f$ is increasing on $\left(-\sqrt{2} - 1, -\sqrt{2}\right)$, then decreasing on $\left(-\sqrt{2}, 0\right)$. So $f(t) < f\left(-\sqrt{2}\right) = 1 - 2\sqrt{2}$.

Finally, $|f(t)| \geq 2\sqrt{2} - 1$.

(You can verify this easily with a graphing utility.)

## Section 4.4 Concavity and the Second Derivative Test

**1.** The graph of $f$ is increasing and concave upwards:
$f' > 0, f'' > 0$

**2.** The graph of $f$ is increasing and concave downwards:
$f' > 0, f'' < 0$

**3.** The graph of $f$ is decreasing and concave downward:
$f' < 0, f'' < 0$

**4.** The graph of $f$ is decreasing and concave upward:
$f' < 0, f'' > 0$

5. $y = x^2 - x - 2$

$y' = 2x - 1$

$y'' = 2$

Concave upward: $(-\infty, \infty)$

| Test Interval: | $-\infty < x < \infty$ |
|---|---|
| Sign of $y''$: | $y'' > 0$ |
| Conclusion: | Concave upward |

6. $y = -x^3 + 3x^2 - 2$

$y' = -3x^2 + 6x$

$y'' = -6x + 6$

Concave upward: $(-\infty, 1)$

Concave downward: $(1, \infty)$

| Test Interval: | $-\infty < x < 1$ | $1 < x < \infty$ |
|---|---|---|
| Sign of $y''$: | $y'' > 0$ | $y'' < 0$ |
| Conclusion: | Concave upward | Concave downward |

7. $g(x) = 3x^2 - x^3$

$g'(x) = 6x - 3x^2$

$g''(x) = 6 - 6x$

Concave upward: $(-\infty, 1)$

Concave downward: $(1, \infty)$

| Test Interval: | $-\infty < x < 1$ | $1 < x < \infty$ |
|---|---|---|
| Sign of $g''$: | $g'' > 0$ | $g'' < 0$ |
| Conclusion: | Concave upward | Concave downward |

8. $h(x) = x^5 - 5x + 2$

$h'(x) = 5x^4 - 5$

$h''(x) = 20x^3$

Concave upward: $(0, \infty)$

Concave downward: $(-\infty, 0)$

| Test Interval: | $-\infty < x < 0$ | $0 < x < \infty$ |
|---|---|---|
| Sign of $h''$: | $h'' < 0$ | $h'' > 0$ |
| Conclusion: | Concave downward | Concave upward |

9. $f(x) = -x^3 + 6x^2 - 9x - 1$

$f'(x) = -3x^2 + 12x - 9$

$f''(x) = -6x + 12 = -6(x - 2)$

Concave upward: $(-\infty, 2)$

Concave downward: $(2, \infty)$

| Test Interval: | $-\infty < x < 2$ | $2 < x < \infty$ |
|---|---|---|
| Sign of $f''$: | $f'' > 0$ | $f'' < 0$ |
| Conclusion: | Concave upward | Concave downward |

10. $f(x) = x^5 + 5x^4 - 40x^2$

$f'(x) = 5x^4 + 20x^3 - 80x$

$f''(x) = 20x^3 + 60x^2 - 80$

$= 20(x^3 + 3x^2 - 4)$

$= 20(x - 1)(x + 2)^2$

Concave upward: $(1, \infty)$

Concave downward: $(-\infty, 1)$

| Test Interval: | $-\infty < x < -2$ | $-2 < x < 1$ | $1 < x < \infty$ |
|---|---|---|---|
| Sign of $f''$: | $f'' < 0$ | $f'' < 0$ | $f'' > 0$ |
| Conclusion: | Concave downward | Concave downward | Concave upward |

**11.** $f(x) = \dfrac{24}{x^2 + 12}$

$f'(x) = \dfrac{-48x}{(x^2 + 12)^2}$

$f''(x) = \dfrac{-144(4 - x^2)}{(x^2 + 12)^3}$

| Test Interval: | $-\infty < x < -2$ | $-2 < x < 2$ | $2 < x < \infty$ |
|---|---|---|---|
| Sign of $f''$: | $f'' > 0$ | $f'' < 0$ | $f'' > 0$ |
| Conclusion: | Concave upward | Concave downward | Concave upward |

Concave upward: $(-\infty, -2), (2, \infty)$

Concave downward: $(-2, 2)$

**12.** $f(x) = \dfrac{x^2}{x^2 + 1}$

$f'(x) = \dfrac{2x}{(x^2 + 1)^2}$

$f''(x) = \dfrac{-2(3x^2 - 1)}{(x^2 + 1)^3}$

$= \dfrac{2(1 + \sqrt{3}x)(1 - \sqrt{3}x)}{(x^2 + 1)^3}$

| Test Interval: | $-\infty < x < -\dfrac{\sqrt{3}}{3}$ | $-\dfrac{\sqrt{3}}{3} < x < \dfrac{\sqrt{3}}{3}$ | $\dfrac{\sqrt{3}}{3} < x < \infty$ |
|---|---|---|---|
| Sign of $f''$: | $f'' < 0$ | $f'' > 0$ | $f'' < 0$ |
| Conclusion: | Concave downward | Concave upward | Concave downward |

Concave upward: $\left(-\dfrac{\sqrt{3}}{3}, \dfrac{\sqrt{3}}{3}\right)$

Concave downward: $\left(-\infty, -\dfrac{\sqrt{3}}{3}\right), \left(\dfrac{\sqrt{3}}{3}, \infty\right)$

**13.** $f(x) = \dfrac{x^2 + 1}{x^2 - 1}$

$f'(x) = \dfrac{-4x}{(x^2 - 1)^2}$

$f''(x) = \dfrac{4(3x^2 + 1)}{(x^2 - 1)^3}$

| Test Interval: | $-\infty < x < -1$ | $-1 < x < 1$ | $1 < x < \infty$ |
|---|---|---|---|
| Sign of $f''$: | $f'' > 0$ | $f'' < 0$ | $f'' > 0$ |
| Conclusion: | Concave upward | Concave downward | Concave upward |

Concave upward: $(-\infty, -1), (1, \infty)$

Concave downward: $(-1, 1)$

**14.** $y = \frac{1}{270}(-3x^5 + 40x^3 + 135x)$

$y' = \frac{1}{270}(-15x^4 + 120x^2 + 135)$

$y'' = -\frac{2}{9}x(x - 2)(x + 2)$

| Test Interval: | $-\infty < x < -2$ | $-2 < x < 0$ | $0 < x < 2$ | $2 < x < \infty$ |
|---|---|---|---|---|
| Sign of $y''$: | $y'' > 0$ | $y'' < 0$ | $y'' > 0$ | $y'' < 0$ |
| Conclusion: | Concave upward | Concave downward | Concave upward | Concave downward |

Concave upward: $(-\infty, -2), (0, 2)$

Concave downward: $(-2, 0), (2, \infty)$

**15.** $g(x) = \dfrac{x^2 + 4}{4 - x^2}$

$g'(x) = \dfrac{16x}{(4 - x^2)^2}$

$g''(x) = \dfrac{16(3x^2 + 4)}{(4 - x^2)^3} = \dfrac{16(3x^2 + 4)}{(2 - x)^3(2 + x)^3}$

Concave upward: $(-2, 2)$

Concave downward: $(-\infty, -2), (2, \infty)$

| Test Interval: | $-\infty < x < -2$ | $-2 < x < 2$ | $2 < x < \infty$ |
|---|---|---|---|
| Sign of $g''$: | $g'' < 0$ | $g'' > 0$ | $g'' < 0$ |
| Conclusion: | Concave downward | Concave upward | Concave downward |

**16.** $h(x) = \dfrac{x^2 - 1}{2x - 1}$

$h'(x) = \dfrac{2(x^2 - x + 1)}{(2x - 1)^2}$

$h''(x) = \dfrac{-6}{(2x - 1)^3}$

Concave upward: $\left(-\infty, \dfrac{1}{2}\right)$

Concave downward: $\left(\dfrac{1}{2}, \infty\right)$

| Test Interval: | $-\infty < x < \dfrac{1}{2}$ | $\dfrac{1}{2} < x < \infty$ |
|---|---|---|
| Sign of $h''$: | $h'' > 0$ | $h'' > 0$ |
| Conclusion: | Concave upward | Concave downward |

**17.** $y = 2x - \tan x, \left(-\dfrac{\pi}{2}, \dfrac{\pi}{2}\right)$

$y' = 2 - \sec^2 x$

$y'' = -2\sec^2 x \tan x$

Concave upward: $\left(-\dfrac{\pi}{2}, 0\right)$

Concave downward: $\left(0, \dfrac{\pi}{2}\right)$

| Test Interval: | $-\dfrac{\pi}{2} < x < 0$ | $0 < x < \dfrac{\pi}{2}$ |
|---|---|---|
| Sign of $y''$: | $y'' < 0$ | $y'' > 0$ |
| Conclusion: | Concave upward | Concave downward |

**18.** $y = x + 2\csc x, \quad (-\pi, \pi)$

$y' = 1 - 2\csc x \cot x$

$y'' = -2\csc x(-\csc^2 x) - 2\cot x(-\csc x \cot x)$

$= 2(\csc^3 x + \csc x \cot^2 x)$

Concave upward: $(0, \pi)$

Concave downward: $(-\pi, 0)$

| Test Interval: | $-\pi < x < 0$ | $0 < x < \pi$ |
|---|---|---|
| Sign of $y''$: | $y'' < 0$ | $y'' > 0$ |
| Conclusion: | Concave downward | Concave upward |

**19.** $f(x) = \frac{1}{2}x^4 + 2x^3$

$f'(x) = 2x^3 + 6x^2$

$f''(x) = 6x^2 + 12x = 6x(x + 2)$

$f''(x) = 0$ when $x = 0, -2$.

Points of inflection: $(-2, -8)$ and $(0, 0)$

Concave upward: $(-\infty, -2), (0, \infty)$

Concave downward: $(-2, 0)$

| Test Interval: | $-\infty < x < -2$ | $-2 < x < 0$ | $0 < x < \infty$ |
|---|---|---|---|
| Sign of $f''$: | $f'' > 0$ | $f'' < 0$ | $f'' > 0$ |
| Conclusion: | Concave upward | Concave downward | Concave upward |

**20.** $f(x) = -x^4 + 24x^2$

$f'(x) = -4x^3 + 48x$

$f''(x) = -12x^2 + 48$

$= 12(4 - x^2) = 12(2 + x)(2 - x)$

$f''(x) = 0$ when $x = -2, 2.$

Points of inflection: $(-2, 80), (2, 80)$

Concave upward: $(-2, 2)$

Concave downward: $(-\infty, -2), (2, \infty)$

| Test Interval: | $-\infty < x < -2$ | $-2 < x < 2$ | $2 < x < \infty$ |
|---|---|---|---|
| Sign of $f''$: | $f'' < 0$ | $f'' > 0$ | $f'' < 0$ |
| Conclusion: | Concave downward | Concave upward | Concave downward |

**21.** $f(x) = x^3 - 6x^2 + 12x$

$f'(x) = 3x^2 - 12x + 12$

$f''(x) = 6(x - 2) = 0$ when $x = 2.$

Point of inflection: $(2, 8)$

Concave upward: $(2, \infty)$

Concave downward: $(-\infty, 2)$

| Test Interval: | $-\infty < x < 2$ | $2 < x < \infty$ |
|---|---|---|
| Sign of $y''$: | $y'' < 0$ | $y'' > 0$ |
| Conclusion: | Concave downward | Concave upward |

**22.** $f(x) = 2x^3 - 3x^2 - 12x + 5$

$f'(x) = 6x^2 - 6x - 12$

$f''(x) = 12x - 6$

$f''(x) = 12x - 6 = 0$ when $x = \frac{1}{2}.$

Point of inflection: $\left(\frac{1}{2}, -\frac{13}{2}\right)$

Concave upward: $\left(\frac{1}{2}, \infty\right)$

Concave downward: $\left(-\infty, \frac{1}{2}\right)$

| Test interval: | $-\infty < x < \frac{1}{2}$ | $\frac{1}{2} < x < \infty$ |
|---|---|---|
| Sign of $f''(x)$: | $f''(x) < 0$ | $f''(x) > 0$ |
| Conclusion: | Concave downward | Concave upward |

**23.** $f(x) = \frac{1}{4}x^4 - 2x^2$

$f'(x) = x^3 - 4x$

$f''(x) = 3x^2 - 4$

$f''(x) = 3x^2 - 4 = 0$ when $x = \pm\frac{2}{\sqrt{3}}.$

Points of inflection: $\left(\pm\frac{2}{\sqrt{3}}, -\frac{20}{9}\right)$

Concave upward: $\left(-\infty, -\frac{2}{\sqrt{3}}\right), \left(\frac{2}{\sqrt{3}}, \infty\right)$

Concave downward: $\left(-\frac{2}{\sqrt{3}}, \frac{2}{\sqrt{3}}\right)$

| Test interval: | $-\infty < x < -\frac{2}{\sqrt{3}}$ | $-\frac{2}{\sqrt{3}} < x < \frac{2}{\sqrt{3}}$ | $\frac{2}{\sqrt{3}} < x < \infty$ |
|---|---|---|---|
| Sign of $f''(x)$: | $f''(x) > 0$ | $f''(x) < 0$ | $f''(x) > 0$ |
| Conclusion: | Concave upward | Concave downward | Concave upward |

**24.** $f(x) = 2x^4 - 8x + 3$

$f'(x) = 8x^3 - 8$

$f''(x) = 24x^2 = 0$ when $x = 0$.

However, $(0, 3)$ is not a point of inflection because $f''(x) \geq 0$ for all $x$.

Concave upward: $(-\infty, \infty)$

**25.** $f(x) = x(x - 4)^3$

$f'(x) = x\left[3(x - 4)^2\right] + (x - 4)^3 = (x - 4)^2(4x - 4)$

$f''(x) = 4(x - 1)\left[2(x - 4)\right] + 4(x - 4)^2 = 4(x - 4)\left[2(x - 1) + (x - 4)\right] = 4(x - 4)(3x - 6) = 12(x - 4)(x - 2)$

$f''(x) = 12(x - 4)(x - 2) = 0$ when $x = 2, 4$.

| Test interval: | $-\infty < x < 2$ | $2 < x < 4$ | $4 < x < \infty$ |
|---|---|---|---|
| Sign of $f''(x)$: | $f''(x) > 0$ | $f''(x) < 0$ | $f''(x) > 0$ |
| Conclusion: | Concave upward | Concave downward | Concave upward |

Points of inflection: $(2, -16), (4, 0)$

Concave upward: $(-\infty, 2), (4, \infty)$

Concave downward: $(2, 4)$

**26.** $f(x) = (x - 2)^3(x - 1)$

$f'(x) = (x - 2)^2(4x - 5)$

$f''(x) = 6(x - 2)(2x - 3)$

$f''(x) = 0$ when $x = \frac{3}{2}, 2$

| Test interval: | $-\infty < x < \frac{3}{2}$ | $\frac{3}{2} < x < 2$ | $2 < x < \infty$ |
|---|---|---|---|
| Sign of $f''$: | $f'' > 0$ | $f'' < 0$ | $f'' > 0$ |
| Conclusion: | Concave upward | Concave downward | Concave upward |

Points of inflection: $\left(\frac{3}{2}, -\frac{1}{16}\right), (2, 0)$

Concave upward: $\left(-\infty, \frac{3}{2}\right), (2, \infty)$

Concave downward: $\left(\frac{3}{2}, 2\right)$

**27.** $f(x) = x\sqrt{x + 3}$, Domain: $[-3, \infty)$

$f'(x) = x\left(\frac{1}{2}\right)(x + 3)^{-1/2} + \sqrt{x + 3} = \frac{3(x + 2)}{2\sqrt{x + 3}}$

$f''(x) = \frac{6\sqrt{x + 3} - 3(x + 2)(x + 3)^{-1/2}}{4(x + 3)}$

$= \frac{3(x + 4)}{4(x + 3)^{3/2}}$

$f''(x) > 0$ on the entire domain of $f$ (except for $x = -3$, for which $f''(x)$ is undefined). There are no points of inflection.

Concave upward: $(-3, \infty)$

**28.** $f(x) = x\sqrt{9 - x}$, Domain: $x \leq 9$

$f'(x) = \frac{3(6 - x)}{2\sqrt{9 - x}}$

$f''(x) = \frac{3(x - 12)}{4(9 - x)^{3/2}}$

$f''(x) < 0$ on the entire domain of $f$ (except for $x = 9$, for which $f''(x)$ is undefined). There are no points of inflection.

Concave downward: $(-\infty, 9)$

**29.** $f(x) = \frac{4}{x^2 + 1}$

$f'(x) = \frac{-8x}{(x^2+1)^2}$

$f''(x) = \frac{8(3x^2 - 1)}{(x^2+1)^3}$

$f''(x) = 0$ when $x = \pm\frac{\sqrt{3}}{3}$.

| Test interval: | $-\infty < x < -\frac{\sqrt{3}}{3}$ | $-\frac{\sqrt{3}}{3} < x < \frac{\sqrt{3}}{3}$ | $\frac{\sqrt{3}}{3} < x < \infty$ |
|---|---|---|---|
| Sign of $f''$: | $f'' > 0$ | $f'' < 0$ | $f'' > 0$ |
| Conclusion: | Concave upward | Concave downward | Concave upward |

Points of inflection: $\left(-\frac{\sqrt{3}}{3}, 3\right)$ and $\left(\frac{\sqrt{3}}{3}, 3\right)$

Concave upward: $\left(-\infty, -\frac{\sqrt{3}}{3}\right), \left(\frac{\sqrt{3}}{3}, \infty\right)$

Concave downward: $\left(-\frac{\sqrt{3}}{3}, \frac{\sqrt{3}}{3}\right)$

**30.** $f(x) = \frac{x+1}{\sqrt{x}}$, Domain: $x > 0$

$f'(x) = \frac{x-1}{2x^{3/2}}$

$f''(x) = \frac{3-x}{4x^{5/2}}$

$f''(x) = 0$ when $x = 3$.

| Test intervals: | $0 < x < 3$ | $3 < x < \infty$ |
|---|---|---|
| Sign of $f''(x)$: | $f'' > 0$ | $f'' < 0$ |
| Conclusion: | Concave upward | Concave downward |

Point of inflection: $\left(3, \frac{4\sqrt{3}}{3}\right)$

Concave upward: $(0, 3)$

Concave downward: $(3, \infty)$

**31.** $f(x) = \sin\frac{x}{2}, 0 \le x \le 4\pi$

$f'(x) = \frac{1}{2}\cos\left(\frac{x}{2}\right)$

$f''(x) = -\frac{1}{4}\sin\left(\frac{x}{2}\right)$

$f''(x) = 0$ when $x = 0, 2\pi, 4\pi$.

| Test interval: | $0 < x < 2\pi$ | $2\pi < x < 4\pi$ |
|---|---|---|
| Sign of $f''(x)$: | $f'' < 0$ | $f'' > 0$ |
| Conclusion: | Concave downward | Concave upward |

Point of inflection: $(2\pi, 0)$

Concave upward: $(2\pi, 4\pi)$

Concave downward: $(0, 2\pi)$

**32.** $f(x) = 2\csc\frac{3x}{2}, 0 < x < 2\pi$

$f'(x) = -3\csc\frac{3x}{2}\cot\frac{3x}{2}$

$f''(x) = \frac{9}{2}\left(\csc^3\frac{3x}{2} + \csc\frac{3x}{2}\cot^2\frac{3x}{2}\right) \neq 0$ for any $x$ in the domain of $f$.

| Test interval: | $0 < x < \frac{2\pi}{3}$ | $\frac{2\pi}{3} < x < \frac{4\pi}{3}$ | $\frac{4\pi}{3} < x < 2\pi$ |
|---|---|---|---|
| Sign of $f''$: | $f'' > 0$ | $f'' < 0$ | $f'' > 0$ |
| Conclusion: | Concave upward | Concave downward | Concave upward |

No point of inflection

Concave upward: $\left(0, \frac{2\pi}{3}\right), \left(\frac{4\pi}{3}, 2\pi\right)$

Concave downward: $\left(\frac{2\pi}{3}, \frac{4\pi}{3}\right)$

**33.** $f(x) = \sec\left(x - \frac{\pi}{2}\right), 0 < x < 4\pi$

$f'(x) = \sec\left(x - \frac{\pi}{2}\right)\tan\left(x - \frac{\pi}{2}\right)$

$f''(x) = \sec^3\left(x - \frac{\pi}{2}\right) + \sec\left(x - \frac{\pi}{2}\right)\tan^2\left(x - \frac{\pi}{2}\right) \neq 0$ for any $x$ in the domain of $f$.

| Test interval: | $0 < x < \pi$ | $\pi < x < 2\pi$ | $2\pi < x < 3\pi$ | $3\pi < x < 4\pi$ |
|---|---|---|---|---|
| Sign of $f''$: | $f'' > 0$ | $f'' < 0$ | $f'' > 0$ | $f'' < 0$ |
| Conclusion: | Concave upward | Concave downward | Concave upward | Concave downward |

No point of inflection

Concave upward: $(0, \pi), (2\pi, 3\pi)$

Concave downward: $(\pi, 2\pi), (3\pi, 4\pi)$

**34.** $f(x) = \sin x + \cos x, 0 \le x \le 2\pi$

$f'(x) = \cos x - \sin x$

$f''(x) = \sin x - \cos x$

$f''(x) = 0$ when $x = \frac{3\pi}{4}, \frac{7\pi}{4}$.

| Test interval: | $0 < x < \frac{3\pi}{4}$ | $\frac{3\pi}{4} < x < \frac{7\pi}{4}$ | $\frac{7\pi}{4} < x < 2\pi$ |
|---|---|---|---|
| Sign of $f''(x)$: | $f''(x) < 0$ | $f''(x) > 0$ | $f''(x) < 0$ |
| Conclusion: | Concave downward | Concave upward | Concave downward |

Points of inflection: $\left(\frac{3\pi}{4}, 0\right), \left(\frac{7\pi}{4}, 0\right)$

Concave upward: $\left(\frac{3\pi}{4}, \frac{7\pi}{4}\right)$

Concave downward: $\left(0, \frac{3\pi}{4}\right), \left(\frac{7\pi}{4}, 2\pi\right)$

**35.** $f(x) = 2\sin x + \sin 2x, 0 \le x \le 2\pi$

$f'(x) = 2\cos x + 2\cos 2x$

$f''(x) = -2\sin x - 4\sin 2x = -2\sin x(1 + 4\cos x)$

$f''(x) = 0$ when $x = 0, 1.823, \pi, 4.460$.

| Test interval: | $0 < x < 1.823$ | $1.823 < x < \pi$ | $\pi < x < 4.460$ | $4.460 < x < 2\pi$ |
|---|---|---|---|---|
| Sign of $f''(x)$: | $f'' < 0$ | $f'' > 0$ | $f'' < 0$ | $f'' > 0$ |
| Conclusion: | Concave downward | Concave upward | Concave downward | Concave upward |

Points of inflection: $(1.823, 1.452), (\pi, 0), (4.46, -1.452)$

Concave upward: $(1.823, \pi), (4.460, 2\pi)$

Concave downward: $(0, 1.823), (\pi, 4.460)$

**36.** $f(x) = x + 2\cos x, [0, 2\pi]$

$f'(x) = 1 - 2\sin x$

$f''(x) = -2\cos x$

$f''(x) = 0$ when $x = \frac{\pi}{2}, \frac{3\pi}{2}$.

| Test intervals: | $0 < x < \frac{\pi}{2}$ | $\frac{\pi}{2} < x < \frac{3\pi}{2}$ | $\frac{3\pi}{2} < x < 2\pi$ |
|---|---|---|---|
| Sign of $f''(x)$: | $f'' < 0$ | $f'' > 0$ | $f'' < 0$ |
| Conclusion: | Concave downward | Concave upward | Concave downward |

Points of inflection: $\left(\frac{\pi}{2}, \frac{\pi}{2}\right), \left(\frac{3\pi}{2}, \frac{3\pi}{2}\right)$

Concave upward: $\left(\frac{\pi}{2}, \frac{3\pi}{2}\right)$

Concave downward: $\left(0, \frac{\pi}{2}\right), \left(\frac{3\pi}{2}, 2\pi\right)$

**37.** $y = e^{-3/x}$

$y' = \frac{3}{x^2}e^{-3/x}$

$y'' = \frac{e^{-3/x}(9 - 6x)}{x^4}$

$y'' = 0$ when $x = \frac{3}{2}$. $y$ is not defined at $x = 0$.

| Test intervals: | $-\infty < x < 0$ | $0 < x < \frac{3}{2}$ | $\frac{3}{2} < x < \infty$ |
|---|---|---|---|
| Sign of $y''$: | $y'' > 0$ | $y'' > 0$ | $y'' < 0$ |
| Conclusion: | Concave upward | Concave upward | Concave downward |

Point of inflection: $\left(\frac{3}{2}, e^{-2}\right)$

Concave upward: $(-\infty, 0), \left(0, \frac{3}{2}\right)$

Concave downward: $\left(\frac{3}{2}, \infty\right)$

**38.** $y = \frac{1}{2}\left(e^x - e^{-x}\right)$

$y' = \frac{1}{2}\left(e^x + e^{-x}\right)$

$y'' = \frac{1}{2}\left(e^x - e^{-x}\right)$

$y'' = 0$ when $x = 0$.

| Test interval: | $-\infty < x < 0$ | $0 < x < \infty$ |
|---|---|---|
| Sign of $y''$: | $y'' < 0$ | $y'' > 0$ |
| Conclusion: | Concave downward | Concave upward |

Point of inflection: $(0, 0)$

Concave upward: $(0, \infty)$

Concave downward: $(-\infty, 0)$

**39.** $f(x) = x - \ln x$, Domain: $x > 0$

$f'(x) = 1 - \frac{1}{x}$

$f''(x) = \frac{1}{x^2}$

$f''(x) > 0$ on the entire domain of $f$. There are no points of inflection.

Concave upward: $(0, \infty)$

**40.** $y = \ln\sqrt{x^2 + 9} = \frac{1}{2}\ln\left(x^2 + 9\right)$

$y' = \frac{x}{x^2 + 9}$

$y'' = \frac{9 - x^2}{\left(x^2 + 9\right)^2}$

$y'' = 0$ when $x = \pm 3$.

| Test interval: | $-\infty < x < -3$ | $-3 < x < 3$ | $3 < x < \infty$ |
|---|---|---|---|
| Sign of $y''$: | $y'' < 0$ | $y'' > 0$ | $y'' < 0$ |
| Conclusion: | Concave downward | Concave upward | Concave downward |

Points of inflection: $\left(\pm 3, \frac{1}{2}\ln 18\right)$

Concave upward: $(-3, 3)$

Concave downward: $(-\infty, -3), (3, \infty)$

**41.** $f(x) = \arcsin x^{4/5}, \quad -1 \le x \le 1$

$$f'(x) = \frac{4}{5x^{1/5}\sqrt{1 - x^{8/5}}}$$

$$f''(x) = \frac{20x^{8/5} - 4}{25x^{6/5}\left(1 - x^{8/5}\right)^{3/2}}$$

$f''(x) = 0$ when $20x^{8/5} = 4 \Rightarrow x^{8/5} = \frac{1}{5} \Rightarrow x = \pm\left(\frac{1}{5}\right)^{5/8} \approx \pm 0.3657.$

$f''$ is undefined at $x = 0$.

| Test intervals: | $-1 < x < -\left(\frac{1}{5}\right)^{5/8}$ | $-\left(\frac{1}{5}\right)^{5/8} < x < 0$ | $0 < x < \left(\frac{1}{5}\right)^{5/8}$ | $\left(\frac{1}{5}\right)^{5/8} < x < 1$ |
|---|---|---|---|---|
| Sign of $f''$: | $f'' > 0$ | $f'' < 0$ | $f'' < 0$ | $f'' > 0$ |
| Conclusion: | Concave upward | Concave downward | Concave downward | Concave upward |

Points of inflection: $\left(\pm\left(\frac{1}{5}\right)^{5/8}, \arcsin\sqrt{\frac{1}{5}}\right) \approx (\pm 0.3657, 0.4636)$

Concave upward: $\left(-1, -\left(\frac{1}{5}\right)^{5/8}\right), \left(\left(\frac{1}{5}\right)^{5/8}, 1\right)$

Concave downward: $\left(-\left(\frac{1}{5}\right)^{5/8}, 0\right), \left(0, \left(\frac{1}{5}\right)^{5/8}\right)$

**42.** $f(x) = \arctan\left(x^2\right)$

$$f'(x) = \frac{2x}{x^4 + 1}$$

$$f''(x) = \frac{2\left(1 - 3x^4\right)}{\left(x^4 + 1\right)^2}$$

$f''(x) = 0$ when $3x^4 = 1 \Rightarrow x = \pm\sqrt[4]{\frac{1}{3}} \approx \pm 0.7598.$

| Test interval: | $-\infty < x < -\sqrt[4]{\frac{1}{3}}$ | $-\sqrt[4]{\frac{1}{3}} < x < \sqrt[4]{\frac{1}{3}}$ | $\sqrt[4]{\frac{1}{3}} < x < \infty$ |
|---|---|---|---|
| Sign of $f''(x)$: | $f'' < 0$ | $f'' > 0$ | $f'' < 0$ |
| Conclusion: | Concave downward | Concave upward | Concave downward |

Points of inflection: $\left(\pm\sqrt[4]{\frac{1}{3}}, \arctan\sqrt{\frac{1}{3}}\right) \approx (\pm 0.7598, 0.5236)$

Concave upward: $\left(-\sqrt[4]{\frac{1}{3}}, \sqrt[4]{\frac{1}{3}}\right)$

Concave downward: $\left(-\infty, -\sqrt[4]{\frac{1}{3}}\right), \left(\sqrt[4]{\frac{1}{3}}, \infty\right)$

**43.** $f(x) = (x - 5)^2$

$f'(x) = 2(x - 5)$

$f''(x) = 2$

Critical number: $x = 5$

$f''(5) > 0$

Therefore, $(5, 0)$ is a relative minimum.

**44.** $f(x) = -(x - 5)^2$

$f'(x) = -2(x - 5)$

$f''(x) = -2$

Critical number: $x = 5$

$f''(5) < 0$

Therefore, $(5, 0)$ is a relative maximum.

**45.** $f(x) = 6x - x^2$

$f'(x) = 6 - 2x$

$f''(x) = -2$

Critical number: $x = 3$

$f''(3) < 0$

Therefore, $(3, 9)$ is a relative maximum.

**46.** $f(x) = x^2 + 3x - 8$

$f'(x) = 2x + 3$

$f''(x) = 2$

Critical number: $x = -\frac{3}{2}$

$f''\left(-\frac{3}{2}\right) > 0$

Therefore, $\left(-\frac{3}{2}, -\frac{41}{4}\right)$ is a relative minimum.

**47.** $f(x) = x^3 - 3x^2 + 3$

$f'(x) = 3x^2 - 6x = 3x(x - 2)$

$f''(x) = 6x - 6 = 6(x - 1)$

Critical numbers: $x = 0, x = 2$

$f''(0) = -6 < 0$

Therefore, $(0, 3)$ is a relative maximum.

$f''(2) = 6 > 0$

Therefore, $(2, -1)$ is a relative minimum.

**48.** $f(x) = x^3 - 5x^2 + 7x$

$f'(x) = 3x^2 - 10x + 7 = (3x - 7)(x - 1)$

$f''(x) = 6x - 10$

Critical numbers: $x = \frac{7}{3}, 1$

$f''\left(\frac{7}{3}\right) = 4 > 0$

Therefore, $\left(\frac{7}{3}, \frac{49}{27}\right)$ is a relative minimum.

$f''(1) = -4 < 0$

Therefore, $(1, 3)$ is a relative maximum.

**49.** $f(x) = x^4 - 4x^3 + 2$

$f'(x) = 4x^3 - 12x^2 = 4x^2(x - 3)$

$f''(x) = 12x^2 - 24x = 12x(x - 2)$

Critical numbers: $x = 0, x = 3$

However, $f''(0) = 0$, so you must use the First Derivative Test. $f'(x) < 0$ on the intervals $(-\infty, 0)$ and $(0, 3)$; so, $(0, 2)$ is not an extremum.

$f''(3) > 0$ so $(3, -25)$ is a relative minimum.

**50.** $f(x) = -x^4 + 4x^3 + 8x^2$

$f'(x) = -4x^3 + 12x^2 + 16x = -4x(x - 4)(x + 1)$

$f''(x) = -12x^2 + 24x + 16 = -4(3x^2 - 6x - 4)$

Critical numbers: $x = -1, 0, 4$

$f''(-1) = -20$

Therefore $(-1, 3)$ is a relative maximum.

$f''(0) = 16$

Therefore, $(0, 0)$ is a relative minimum.

$f''(4) = -80$

Therefore, $(4, 128)$ is a relative maximum.

**51.** $g(x) = x^2(6 - x)^3$

$g'(x) = x(x - 6)^2(12 - 5x)$

$g''(x) = 4(6 - x)(5x^2 - 24x + 18)$

Critical numbers: $x = 0, 2.4, 6$

$g''(0) = 432 > 0$

Therefore, $(0, 0)$ is a relative minimum.

$g''(2.4) = -155.52 < 0$

Therefore, $(2.4, 268.74)$ is a relative maximum.

$g''(6) = 0$

Test fails. By the First Derivative Test, $(6, 0)$ is not an extremum.

**52.** $g(x) = -\frac{1}{8}(x + 2)^2(x - 4)^2$

$g'(x) = \dfrac{-(x - 4)(x - 1)(x + 2)}{2}$

$g''(x) = 3 + 3x - \frac{3}{2}x^2$

Critical numbers: $x = -2, 1, 4$

$g''(-2) = -9 < 0$

$(-2, 0)$ is a relative maximum.

$g''(1) = \frac{9}{2} > 0$

$(1, -10.125)$ is a relative minimum.

$g''(4) = -9 < 0$

$(4, 0)$ is a relative maximum.

**53.** $f(x) = x^{2/3} - 3$

$f'(x) = \dfrac{2}{3x^{1/3}}$

$f''(x) = -\dfrac{2}{9x^{4/3}}$

Critical number: $x = 0$

However, $f''(0)$ is undefined, so you must use the First Derivative Test. Because $f'(x) < 0$ on $(-\infty, 0)$ and $f'(x) > 0$ on $(0, \infty)$, $(0, -3)$ is a relative minimum.

**54.** $f(x) = \sqrt{x^2 + 1}$

$f'(x) = \dfrac{x}{\sqrt{x^2 + 1}}$

$f''(x) = \dfrac{1}{(x^2 + 1)^{3/2}}$

Critical number: $x = 0$

$f''(0) = 1 > 0$

Therefore, $(0, 1)$ is a relative minimum.

**55.** $f(x) = x + \dfrac{4}{x}$

$f'(x) = 1 - \dfrac{4}{x^2} = \dfrac{x^2 - 4}{x^2}$

$f''(x) = \dfrac{8}{x^3}$

Critical numbers: $x = \pm 2$

$f''(-2) < 0$

Therefore, $(-2, -4)$ is a relative maximum.

$f''(2) > 0$

Therefore, $(2, 4)$ is a relative minimum.

**56.** $f(x) = \dfrac{x}{x - 1}$

$f'(x) = \dfrac{-1}{(x - 1)^2}$

There are no critical numbers and $x = 1$ is not in the domain. There are no relative extrema.

**57.** $f(x) = \cos x - x, 0 \le x \le 4\pi$

$f'(x) = -\sin x - 1 \le 0$

Therefore, $f$ is non-increasing and there are no relative extrema.

**58.** $f(x) = 2\sin x + \cos 2x, 0 \le x \le 2\pi$

$f'(x) = 2\cos x - 2\sin 2x = 2\cos x - 4\sin x\cos x$

$= 2\cos x(1 - 2\sin x) = 0$ when $x = \dfrac{\pi}{6}, \dfrac{\pi}{2}, \dfrac{5\pi}{6}, \dfrac{3\pi}{2}$.

$f''(x) = -2\sin x - 4\cos 2x$

$f''\left(\frac{\pi}{6}\right) < 0$

$f''\left(\frac{\pi}{2}\right) > 0$

$f''\left(\frac{5\pi}{6}\right) < 0$

$f''\left(\frac{3\pi}{2}\right) > 0$

Relative maxima: $\left(\frac{\pi}{6}, \frac{3}{2}\right), \left(\frac{5\pi}{6}, \frac{3}{2}\right)$

Relative minima: $\left(\frac{\pi}{2}, 1\right), \left(\frac{3\pi}{2}, -3\right)$

**59.** $y = \frac{1}{2}x^2 - \ln x$

Domain: $x > 0$

$y' = x - \frac{1}{x} = \frac{(x+1)(x-1)}{x}$

$y'' = 1 + \frac{1}{x^2}$

Critical number: $x = 1$

$y''(1) > 0$

Relative minimum: $\left(1, \frac{1}{2}\right)$

**60.** $y = x \ln x$

$y' = \ln x + 1$

$y'' = \frac{1}{x}$

Critical number: $\ln x + 1 = 0 \Rightarrow \ln x = -1$

$\Rightarrow x = e^{-1} = \frac{1}{e}$

$y''\left(\frac{1}{e}\right) > 0$

$\left(\frac{1}{e}, -\frac{1}{e}\right)$ is a relative minimum.

**61.** $y = \frac{x}{\ln x}$

Domain: $0 < x < 1, x > 1$

$y' = \frac{(\ln x)(1) - (x)(1/x)}{(\ln x)^2} = \frac{\ln x - 1}{(\ln x)^2}$

$y'' = \frac{2 - \ln x}{x(\ln x)}$

Critical number: $x = e$

$y''(e) > 0$

$(e, e)$ is a relative minimum.

**62.** $y = x^2 \ln \frac{x}{4}$, Domain: $x > 0$

$y' = x^2\left(\frac{1}{x}\right) + 2x \ln \frac{x}{4} = x\left(1 + 2 \ln \frac{x}{4}\right)$

$y'' = 1 + 2 \ln \frac{x}{4} + 2x\left(\frac{1}{x}\right) = 3 + 2 \ln \frac{x}{4}$

Critical number: $x = 4e^{-1/2}$

$y''\left(4e^{-1/2}\right) > 0$

$\left(4e^{-1/2}, -8e^{-1}\right)$ is a relative minimum.

**63.** $f(x) = \frac{e^x + e^{-x}}{2}$

$f'(x) = \frac{e^x - e^{-x}}{2}$

$f''(x) = \frac{e^x + e^{-x}}{2}$

Critical number: $x = 0$

$f''(0) > 0$

$(0, 1)$ is a relative minimum.

**64.** $g(x) = \frac{1}{\sqrt{2\pi}}e^{-(x-3)^2/2}$

$g'(x) = \frac{-1}{\sqrt{2\pi}}(x-3)e^{-(x-3)^2/2}$

$g''(x) = \frac{1}{\sqrt{2\pi}}(x-2)(x-4)e^{-(x-3)^2/2}$

Critical number: $x = 3$

$g''(3) < 0$

$\left(3, \frac{1}{\sqrt{2\pi}}\right) \approx (3, 0.399)$ is a relative minimum.

**65.** $f(x) = x^2e^{-x}$

$f'(x) = -x^2e^{-x} + 2xe^{-x} = xe^{-x}(2 - x)$

$f''(x) = -e^{-x}\left(2x - x^2\right) + e^{-x}(2 - 2x)$

$= e^{-x}\left(x^2 - 4x + 2\right)$

Critical numbers: $x = 0, 2$

$f''(0) > 0$

$(0, 0)$ is a relative minimum.

$f''(2) < 0$

$\left(2, 4e^{-2}\right)$ is a relative maximum.

**66.** $f(x) = xe^{-x}$

$f'(x) = -xe^{-x} + e^{-x} = e^{-x}(1 - x)$

$f''(x) = -e^{-x} + \left(-e^{-x}\right)(1 - x) = e^{-x}(x - 2)$

Critical number: $x = 1$

$f''(1) < 0$

$\left(1, e^{-1}\right)$ is a relative maximum.

**67.** $f(x) = 8x(4^{-x})$

$f'(x) = -8(4^{-x})(x \ln 4 - 1)$

$f''(x) = 8(4^{-x}) \ln 4(x \ln 4 - 2)$

Critical number: $x = \dfrac{1}{\ln 4} = \dfrac{1}{2 \ln 2}$

$f''\left(\dfrac{1}{2 \ln 2}\right) < 0$

$\left(\dfrac{1}{2 \ln 2}, \dfrac{4e^{-1}}{\ln 2}\right)$ is a relative maximum.

**68.** $y = x^2 \log_3 x = x^2 \dfrac{\ln x}{\ln 3}$

$y' = \dfrac{x(2 \ln x + 1)}{\ln 3}$

$y'' = \dfrac{2 \ln x + 3}{\ln 3}$

Critical number: $\ln x = -\dfrac{1}{2} \Rightarrow x = e^{-1/2}$

$y''(e^{-1/2}) > 0$

$(e^{-1/2}, -0.1674)$ is a relative minimum.

**69.** $f(x) = \operatorname{arcsec} x - x$

$f'(x) = \dfrac{1}{|x|\sqrt{x^2 - 1}} - 1 = 0$ when $|x|\sqrt{x^2 - 1} = 1$.

$x^2(x^2 - 1) = 1$

$x^4 - x^2 - 1 = 0$ when $x^2 = \dfrac{1 + \sqrt{5}}{2}$ or $x = \pm\sqrt{\dfrac{1 + \sqrt{5}}{2}} = \pm 1.272$.

$(1.272, -0.606)$ is a relative maximum.

$(-1.272, 3.747)$ is a relative minimum.

**70.** $f(x) = \arcsin x - 2x$

$f'(x) = \dfrac{1}{\sqrt{1 - x^2}} - 2$

$f''(x) = \dfrac{x}{(1 - x^2)^{3/2}}$

Critical numbers: $x = \pm\dfrac{\sqrt{3}}{2}$

$f''\left(\dfrac{\sqrt{3}}{2}\right) > 0$

$\left(\dfrac{\sqrt{3}}{2}, -0.68\right)$ is a relative minimum.

$f''\left(-\dfrac{\sqrt{3}}{2}\right) < 0$

$\left(-\dfrac{\sqrt{3}}{2}, 0.68\right)$ is a relative maximum.

**71.** $f(x) = 0.2x^2(x - 3)^3, [-1, 4]$

(a) $f'(x) = 0.2x(5x - 6)(x - 3)^2$

$f''(x) = (x - 3)(4x^2 - 9.6x + 3.6)$

$= 0.4(x - 3)(10x^2 - 24x + 9)$

(b) $f''(0) < 0 \Rightarrow (0, 0)$ is a relative maximum.

$f''\left(\frac{6}{5}\right) > 0 \Rightarrow (1.2, -1.6796)$ is a relative minimum.

Points of inflection:

$(3, 0), (0.4652, -0.7048), (1.9348, -0.9049)$

(c)

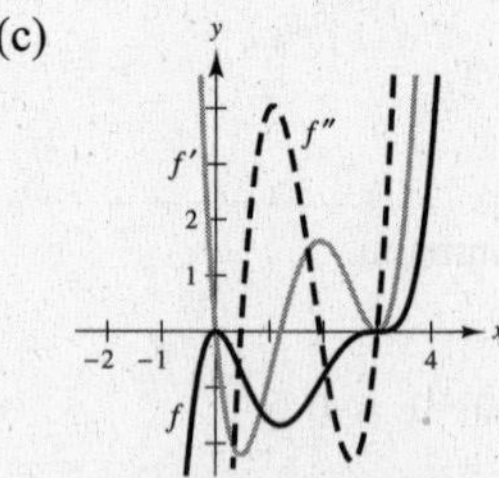


$f$ is increasing when $f' > 0$ and decreasing when $f' < 0$. $f$ is concave upward when $f'' > 0$ and concave downward when $f'' < 0$.

**72.** $f(x) = x^2\sqrt{6 - x^2}, \left[-\sqrt{6}, \sqrt{6}\right]$

(a) $f'(x) = \dfrac{3x(4 - x^2)}{\sqrt{6 - x^2}}$

$f'(x) = 0$ when $x = 0, x = \pm 2$.

$f''(x) = \dfrac{6(x^4 - 9x^2 + 12)}{(6 - x^2)^{3/2}}$

$f''(x) = 0$ when $x = \pm\sqrt{\dfrac{9 - \sqrt{33}}{2}}$.

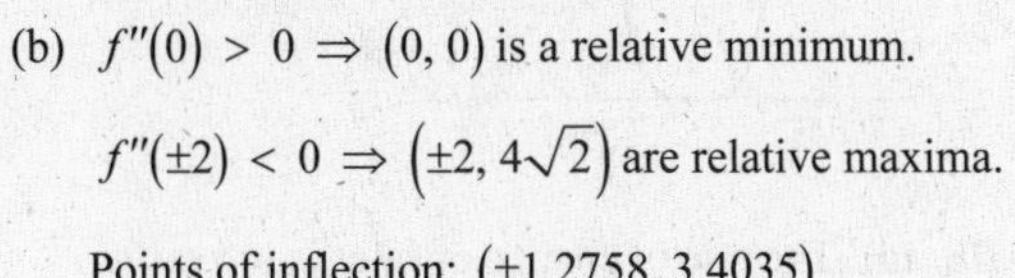

(b) $f''(0) > 0 \Rightarrow (0, 0)$ is a relative minimum.

$f''(\pm 2) < 0 \Rightarrow (\pm 2, 4\sqrt{2})$ are relative maxima.

Points of inflection: $(\pm 1.2758, 3.4035)$

(c)

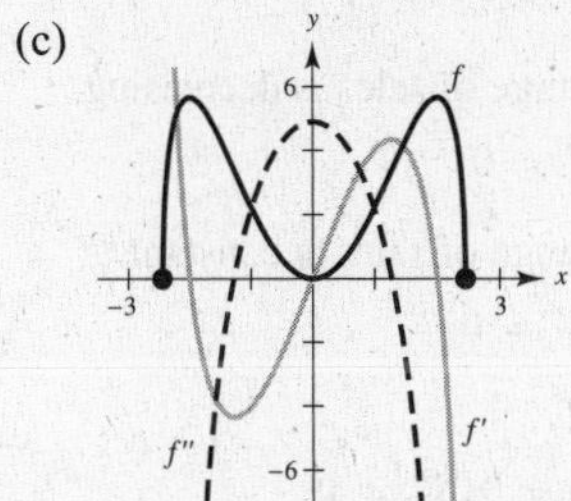


The graph of $f$ is increasing when $f' > 0$ and decreasing when $f' < 0$. $f$ is concave upward when $f'' > 0$ and concave downward when $f'' < 0$.

**73.** $f(x) = \sin x - \dfrac{1}{3}\sin 3x + \dfrac{1}{5}\sin 5x, \quad [0, \pi]$

(a) $f'(x) = \cos x - \cos 3x + \cos 5x$

$f'(x) = 0$ when $x = \dfrac{\pi}{6}, x = \dfrac{\pi}{2}, x = \dfrac{5\pi}{6}$.

$f''(x) = -\sin x + 3\sin 3x - 5\sin 5x$

$f''(x) = 0$ when $x = \dfrac{\pi}{6}, x = \dfrac{5\pi}{6}$,

$x \approx 1.1731, x \approx 1.9685$

(b) $f''\left(\dfrac{\pi}{2}\right) < 0 \Rightarrow \left(\dfrac{\pi}{2}, 1.53333\right)$ is a relative maximum.

Points of inflection: $\left(\dfrac{\pi}{6}, 0.2667\right)$, $(1.1731, 0.9638)$,

$(1.9685, 0.9637)$, $\left(\dfrac{5\pi}{6}, 0.2667\right)$

**Note:** $(0, 0)$ and $(\pi, 0)$ are not points of inflection because they are endpoints.

(c)

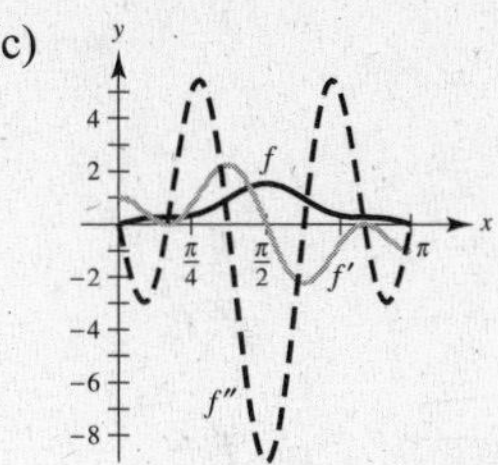


The graph of $f$ is increasing when $f' > 0$ and decreasing when $f' < 0$. $f$ is concave upward when $f'' > 0$ and concave downward when $f'' < 0$.

**74.** $f(x) = \sqrt{2x}\sin x, [0, 2\pi]$

(a) $f'(x) = \sqrt{2x}\cos x + \dfrac{\sin x}{\sqrt{2x}}$

Critical numbers: $x \approx 1.84, 4.82$

$$f''(x) = -\sqrt{2x}\sin x + \frac{\cos x}{\sqrt{2x}} + \frac{\cos x}{\sqrt{2x}} - \frac{\sin x}{2x\sqrt{2x}}$$

$$= \frac{2\cos x}{\sqrt{2x}} - \frac{(4x^2 + 1)\sin x}{2x\sqrt{2x}}$$

$$= \frac{4x\cos x - (4x^2 + 1)\sin x}{2x\sqrt{2x}}$$

(b) Relative maximum: $(1.84, 1.85)$

Relative minimum: $(4.82, -3.09)$

Points of inflection: $(0.75, 0.83), (3.42, -0.72)$

(c)

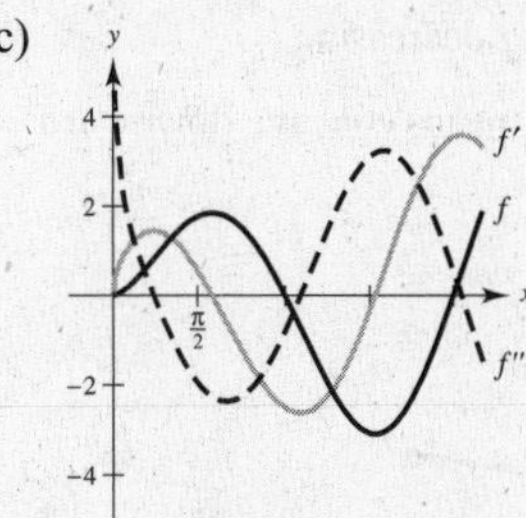

**75.** (a)

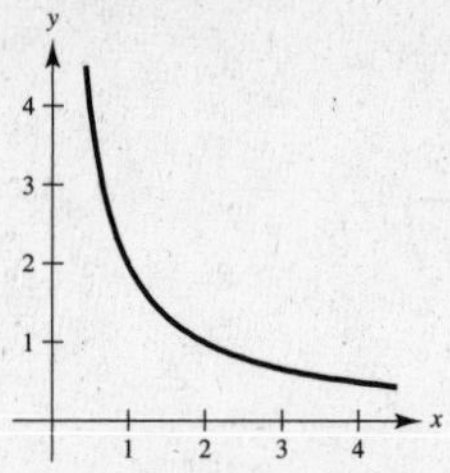

$f' < 0$ means $f$ decreasing

$f'$ increasing means concave upward

(b)

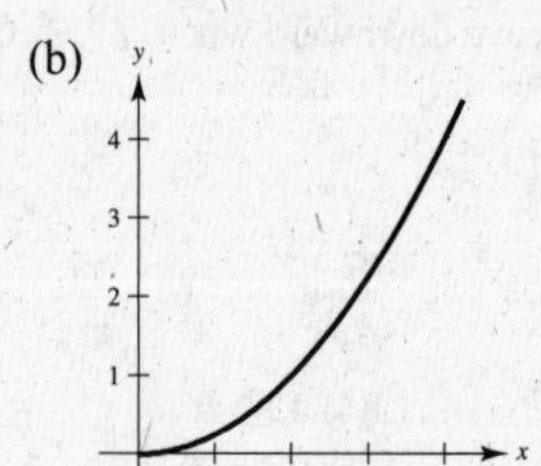

$f' > 0$ means $f$ increasing

$f'$ increasing means concave upward

**76.** (a)

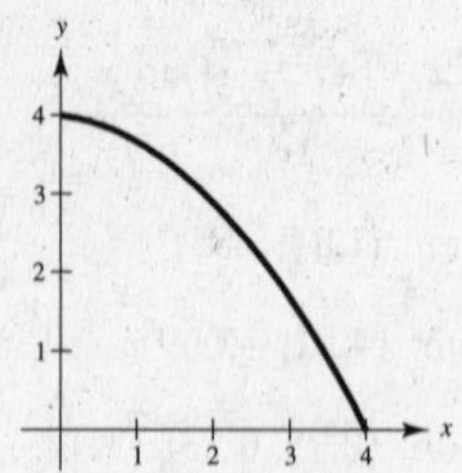

$f' < 0$ means $f$ decreasing

$f'$ decreasing means concave downward

(b)

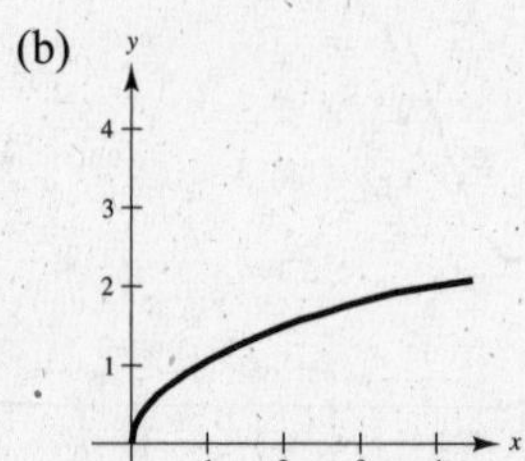

$f' > 0$ means $f$ increasing

$f'$ decreasing means concave downward

**77.** Answers will vary. *Sample answer*:

Let $f(x) = x^4$.

$f''(x) = 12x^2$

$f''(0) = 0$, but $(0, 0)$ is not a point of inflection.

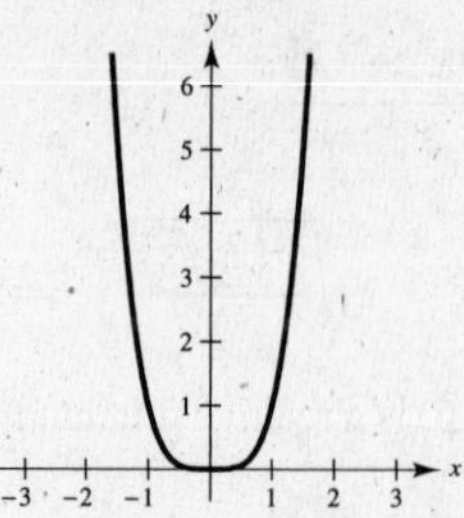

**78.** (a) The rate of change of sales is increasing.

$S'' > 0$

(b) The rate of change of sales is decreasing.

$S' > 0, S'' < 0$

(c) The rate of change of sales is constant.

$S' = C, S'' = 0$

(d) Sales are steady.

$S = C, S' = 0, S'' = 0$

(e) Sales are declining, but at a lower rate.

$S' < 0, S'' > 0$

(f) Sales have bottomed out and have started to rise.

$S' > 0$

**79.**

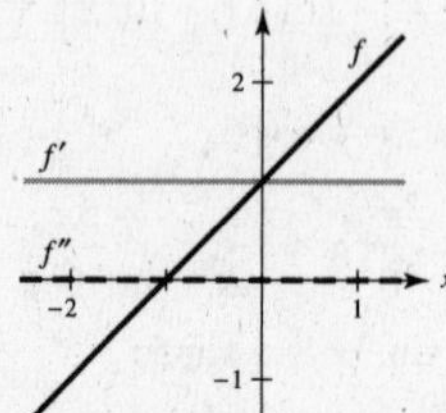


**80.**

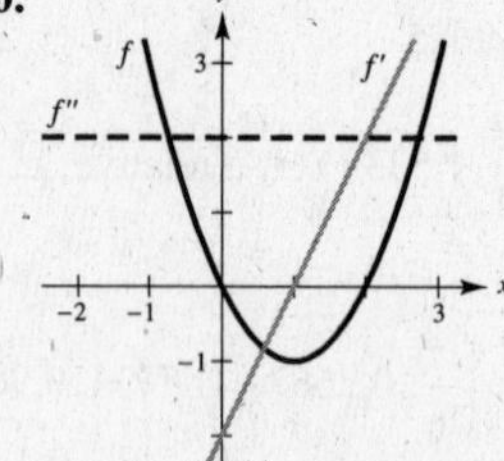


**81.**

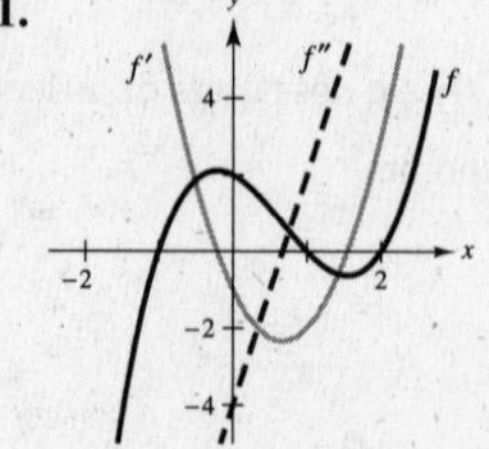

**82.**

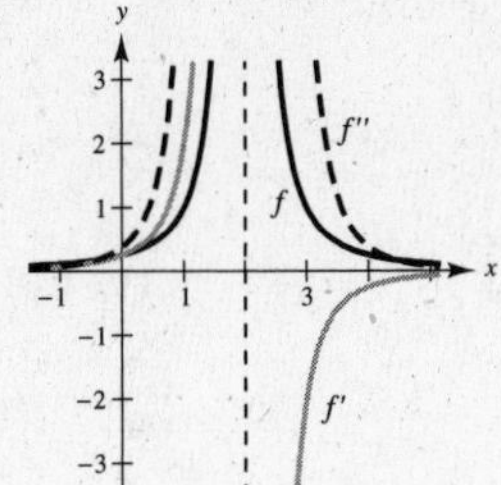


**83.**

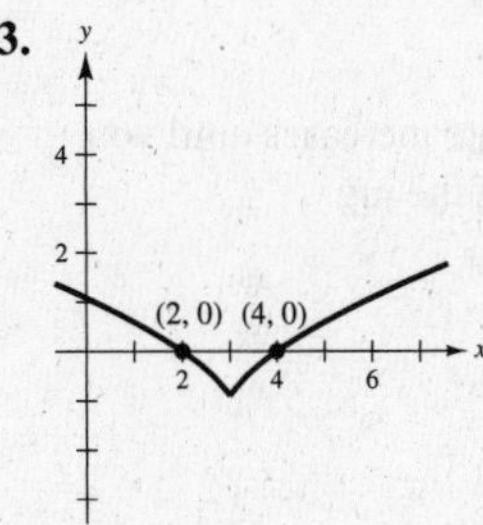


**84.**

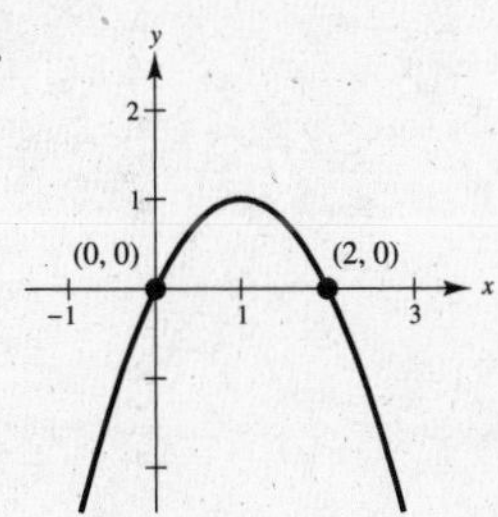


**85.**

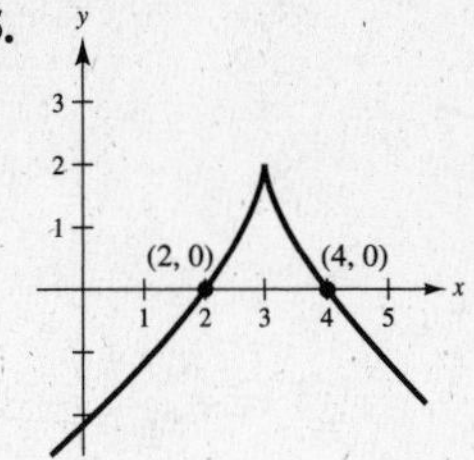


**86.**

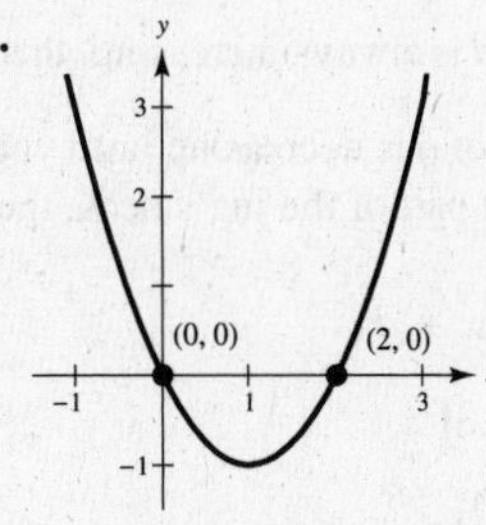


**87.** (a) $n = 1$:

$f(x) = x - 2$

$f'(x) = 1$

$f''(x) = 0$

No point of inflection

$n = 2$:

$f(x) = (x - 2)^2$

$f'(x) = 2(x - 2)$

$f''(x) = 2$

No point of inflection

Relative minimum: $(2, 0)$

$n = 3$:

$f(x) = (x - 2)^3$

$f'(x) = 3(x - 2)^2$

$f''(x) = 6(x - 2)$

Point of inflection: $(2, 0)$

$n = 4$:

$f(x) = (x - 2)^4$

$f'(x) = 4(x - 2)^3$

$f''(x) = 12(x - 2)^2$

No point of inflection

Relative minimum: $(2, 0)$

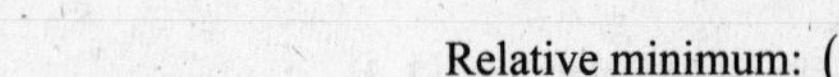

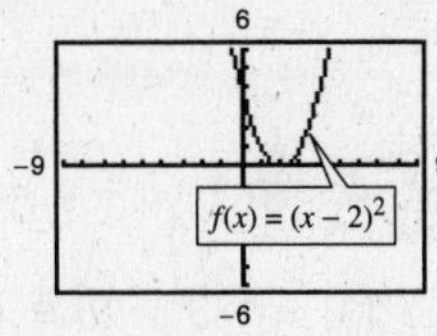


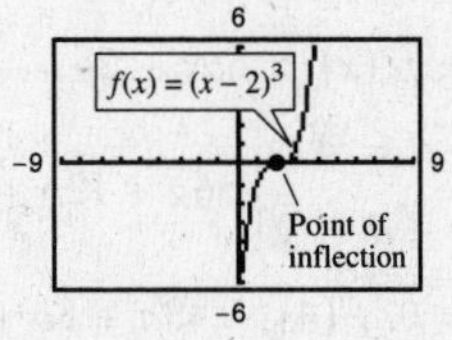


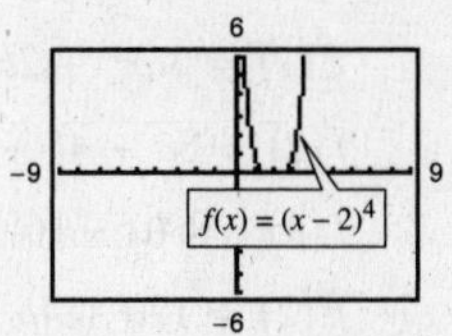


**Conclusion:** If $n \geq 3$ and $n$ is odd, then $(2, 0)$ is point of inflection. If $n \geq 2$ and $n$ is even, then $(2, 0)$ is a relative minimum.

(b) Let $f(x) = (x - 2)^n$, $f'(x) = n(x - 2)^{n-1}$, $f''(x) = n(n - 1)(x - 2)^{n-2}$.

For $n \geq 3$ and odd, $n - 2$ is also odd and the concavity changes at $x = 2$.

For $n \geq 4$ and even, $n - 2$ is also even and the concavity does not change at $x = 2$.

So, $x = 2$ is point of inflection if and only if $n \geq 3$ is odd.

**88.** (a)

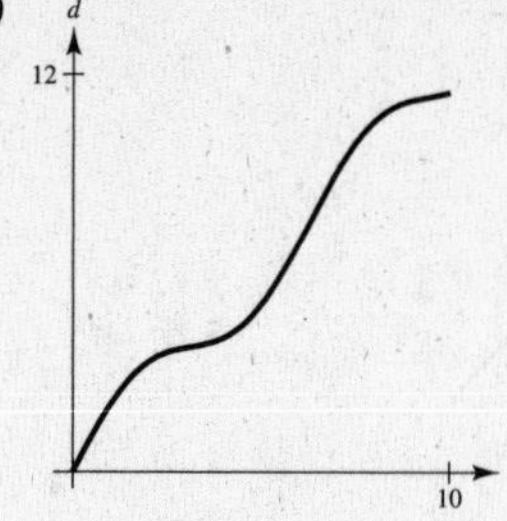


(b) Because the depth $d$ is always increasing, there are no relative extrema. $f'(x) > 0$

(c) The rate of change of $d$ is decreasing until you reach the widest point of the jug, then the rate increases until you reach the narrowest part of the jug's neck, then the rate decreases until you reach the top of the jug.

**89.** $f(x) = ax^3 + bx^2 + cx + d$

Relative maximum: $(3, 3)$

Relative minimum: $(5, 1)$

Point of inflection: $(4, 2)$

$f'(x) = 3ax^2 + 2bx + c,\ f''(x) = 6ax + 2b$

$$\left.\begin{aligned} f(3) &= 27a + 9b + 3c + d = 3 \\ f(5) &= 125a + 25b + 5c + d = 1 \end{aligned}\right\} 98a + 16b + 2c = -2 \Rightarrow 49a + 8b + c = -1$$

$f'(3) = 27a + 6b + c = 0,\ f''(4) = 24a + 2b = 0$

$$\begin{array}{ll} 49a + 8b + c = -1 & 24a + 2b = 0 \\ \underline{27a + 6b + c = 0} & \underline{22a + 2b = -1} \\ 22a + 2b = -1 & 2a = 1 \end{array}$$

$a = \frac{1}{2}, b = -6, c = \frac{45}{2}, d = -24$

$f(x) = \frac{1}{2}x^3 - 6x^2 + \frac{45}{2}x - 24$

**90.** $f(x) = ax^3 + bx^2 + cx + d$

Relative maximum: $(2, 4)$

Relative minimum: $(4, 2)$

Point of inflection: $(3, 3)$

$f'(x) = 3ax^2 + 2bx + c,\ f''(x) = 6ax + 2b$

$$\left.\begin{aligned} f(2) &= 8a + 4b + 2c + d = 4 \\ f(4) &= 64a + 16b + 4c + d = 2 \end{aligned}\right\} 56a + 12b + 2c = -2 \Rightarrow 28a + 6b + c = -1$$

$f'(2) = 12a + 4b + c = 0,\ f'(4) = 48a + 8b + c = 0,\ f''(3) = 18a + 2b = 0$

$$\begin{array}{ll} 28a + 6b + c = -1 & 18a + 2b = 0 \\ \underline{12a + 4b + c = 0} & \underline{16a + 2b = -1} \\ 16a + 2b = -1 & 2a = 1 \end{array}$$

$a = \frac{1}{2}, b = -\frac{9}{2}, c = 12, d = -6$

$f(x) = \frac{1}{2}x^3 - \frac{9}{2}x^2 + 12x - 6$

**91.** $f(x) = ax^3 + bx^2 + cx + d$

Maximum: $(-4, 1)$

Minimum: $(0, 0)$

(a) $f'(x) = 3ax^2 + 2bx + c, \quad f''(x) = 6ax + 2b$

$$\begin{aligned} f(0) &= 0 \Rightarrow d = 0 \\ f(-4) &= 1 \Rightarrow \quad -64a + 16b - 4c = 1 \\ f'(-4) &= 0 \Rightarrow \quad 48a - 8b + c = 0 \\ f'(0) &= 0 \Rightarrow \quad c = 0 \end{aligned}$$

Solving this system yields $a = \frac{1}{32}$ and $b = 6a = \frac{3}{16}$.

$f(x) = \frac{1}{32}x^3 + \frac{3}{16}x^2$

(b) The plane would be descending at the greatest rate at the point of inflection.

$f''(x) = 6ax + 2b = \frac{3}{16}x + \frac{3}{8} = 0 \Rightarrow x = -2.$

Two miles from touchdown.

**92.** (a) line $OA$: $y = -0.06x$ slope: $-0.06$

line $CB$: $y = 0.04x + 50$ slope: $0.04$

$f(x) = ax^3 + bx^2 + cx + d$

$f'(x) = 3ax^2 + 2bx + c$

$(-1000, 60)$: $\quad 60 = (-1000)^3 a + (1000)^2 b - 1000c + d$

$\quad -0.06 = (1000)^2 3a - 2000b + c$

$(1000, 90)$: $\quad 90 = (1000)^3 a + (1000)^2 b + 1000c + d$

$\quad 0.04 = (1000)^2 3a + 2000b + c$

The solution to this system of four equations is $a = -1.25 \times 10^{-8}$, $b = 0.000025$, $c = 0.0275$, and $d = 50$.

(b) $f(x) = -1.25 \times 10^{-8}x^3 + 0.000025x^2 + 0.0275x + 50$

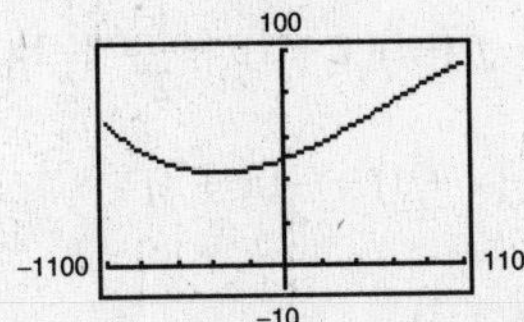


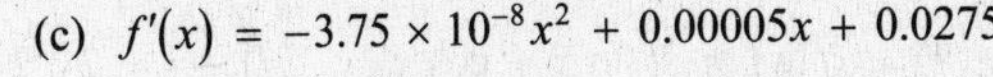
(c) $f'(x) = -3.75 \times 10^{-8}x^2 + 0.00005x + 0.0275$

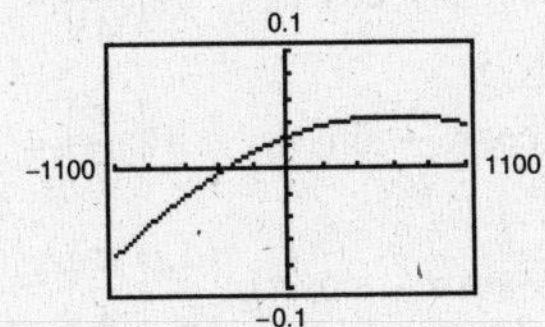


(d) The steepest part of the road is 6% at the point $A$.

**93.** $D = 2x^4 - 5Lx^3 + 3L^2x^2$

$D' = 8x^3 - 15Lx^2 + 6L^2x = x(8x^2 - 15Lx + 6L^2) = 0$

$x = 0$ or $x = \dfrac{15L \pm \sqrt{33}L}{16} = \left(\dfrac{15 \pm \sqrt{33}}{16}\right)L$

By the Second Derivative Test, the deflection is maximum when

$$x = \left(\frac{15 - \sqrt{33}}{16}\right)L \approx 0.578L.$$

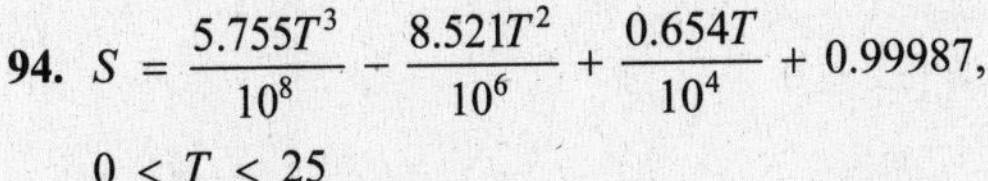
**94.** $S = \dfrac{5.755T^3}{10^8} - \dfrac{8.521T^2}{10^6} + \dfrac{0.654T}{10^4} + 0.99987,$

$0 < T < 25$

(a) The maximum occurs when $T \approx 4°$ and $S \approx 0.999999$.

(b)

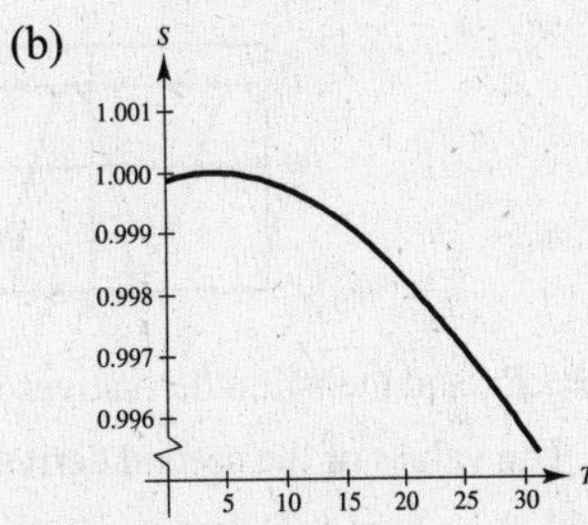


(c) $S(20°) \approx 0.9982$

**95.** $C = 0.5x^2 + 15x + 5000$

$\overline{C} = \dfrac{C}{x} = 0.5x + 15 + \dfrac{5000}{x}$

$\overline{C}$ = average cost per unit

$\dfrac{d\overline{C}}{dx} = 0.5 - \dfrac{5000}{x^2} = 0$ when $x = 100$

By the First Derivative Test, $\overline{C}$ is minimized when $x = 100$ units.

**96.** $S = \dfrac{100t^2}{65 + t^2}, t > 0$

(a)

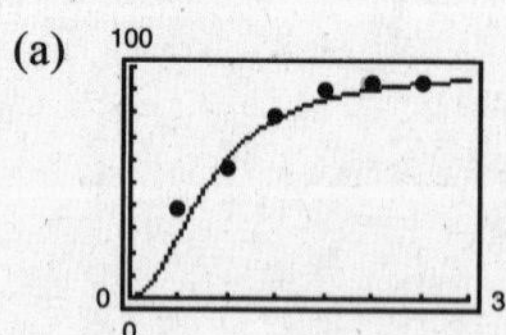


(b) $S'(t) = \dfrac{13{,}000t}{(65 + t^2)^2}$

$S''(t) = \dfrac{13{,}000(65 - 3t^2)}{(65 + t^2)^3} = 0 \Rightarrow t \approx 4.65$

$S$ is concave upward on $(0, 4.65)$ and concave downward on $(4.65, 30)$.

(c) $S'(t) > 0$ for $t > 0$.

As $t$ increases, the speed increases, but at a slower rate.

**97.** $f(x) = 2(\sin x + \cos x)$, $\quad f\left(\dfrac{\pi}{4}\right) = 2\sqrt{2}$

$f'(x) = 2(\cos x - \sin x)$, $\quad f'\left(\dfrac{\pi}{4}\right) = 0$

$f''(x) = 2(-\sin x - \cos x)$, $\quad f''\left(\dfrac{\pi}{4}\right) = -2\sqrt{2}$

$P_1(x) = 2\sqrt{2} + 0\left(x - \dfrac{\pi}{4}\right) = 2\sqrt{2}$

$P_1'(x) = 0$

$P_2(x) = 2\sqrt{2} + 0\left(x - \dfrac{\pi}{4}\right) + \dfrac{1}{2}\left(-2\sqrt{2}\right)\left(x - \dfrac{\pi}{4}\right)^2$

$= 2\sqrt{2} - \sqrt{2}\left(x - \dfrac{\pi}{4}\right)^2$

$P_2'(x) = -2\sqrt{2}\left(x - \dfrac{\pi}{4}\right)$

$P_2''(x) = -2\sqrt{2}$

The values of $f$, $P_1$, $P_2$, and their first derivatives are equal at $x = \pi/4$. The values of the second derivatives of $f$ and $P_2$ are equal at $x = \pi/4$. The approximations worsen as you move away from $x = \pi/4$.

**98.** $f(x) = 2(\sin x + \cos x)$, $\quad f(0) = 2$

$f'(x) = 2(\cos x - \sin x)$, $\quad f'(0) = 2$

$f''(x) = 2(-\sin x - \cos x)$, $\quad f''(0) = -2$

$P_1(x) = 2 + 2(x - 0) = 2(1 + x)$

$P_1'(x) = 2$

$P_2(x) = 2 + 2(x - 0) + \frac{1}{2}(-2)(x - 0)^2$

$= 2 + 2x - x^2$

$P_2'(x) = 2 - 2x$

$P_2''(x) = -2$

The values of $f$, $P_1$, $P_2$, and their first derivatives are equal at $x = 0$. The values of the second derivatives of $f$ and $P_2$ are equal at $x = 0$. The approximations worsen as you move away from $x = 0$.

**99.** $f(x) = \arctan x, a = -1$, $\quad f(-1) = -\dfrac{\pi}{4}$

$f'(x) = \dfrac{1}{1 + x^2}$, $\quad f'(-1) = \dfrac{1}{2}$

$f''(x) = -\dfrac{2x}{(1 + x^2)^2}$, $\quad f''(-1) = \dfrac{1}{2}$

$P_1(x) = f(-1) + f'(-1)(x + 1)$

$= -\dfrac{\pi}{4} + \dfrac{1}{2}(x + 1)$

$P_1'(x) = \dfrac{1}{2}$

$P_2(x) = f(-1) + f'(-1)(x + 1) + \dfrac{1}{2}f''(-1)(x + 1)^2$

$= -\dfrac{\pi}{4} + \dfrac{1}{2}(x + 1) + \dfrac{1}{4}(x + 1)^2$

$P_2'(x) = \dfrac{1}{2} + \dfrac{1}{2}(x + 1)$

$P_2''(x) = \dfrac{1}{2}$

The values of $f$, $P_1$, $P_2$, and their first derivatives are equal when $x = -1$. The approximations worsen as you move away from $x = -1$.

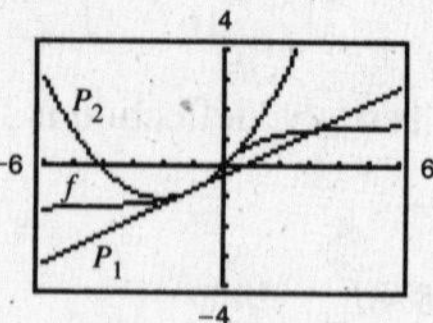

**100.** $f(x) = \dfrac{\sqrt{x}}{x-1}, \quad f(2) = \sqrt{2}$

$f'(x) = \dfrac{-(x+1)}{2\sqrt{x}(x-1)^2}, \quad f'(2) = -\dfrac{3}{2\sqrt{2}} = -\dfrac{3\sqrt{2}}{4}$

$f''(x) = \dfrac{3x^2+6x-1}{4x^{3/2}(x-1)^3}, \quad f''(2) = \dfrac{23}{8\sqrt{2}} = \dfrac{23\sqrt{2}}{16}$

$P_1(x) = \sqrt{2} + \left(-\dfrac{3\sqrt{2}}{4}\right)(x-2) = -\dfrac{3\sqrt{2}}{4}x + \dfrac{5\sqrt{2}}{2}$

$P_1'(x) = -\dfrac{3\sqrt{2}}{4}$

$P_2(x) = \sqrt{2} + \left(-\dfrac{3\sqrt{2}}{4}\right)(x-2) + \dfrac{1}{2}\left(\dfrac{23\sqrt{2}}{16}\right)(x-2)^2 = \sqrt{2} - \dfrac{3\sqrt{2}}{4}(x-2) + \dfrac{23\sqrt{2}}{32}(x-2)^2$

$P_2'(x) = -\dfrac{3\sqrt{2}}{4} + \dfrac{23\sqrt{2}}{16}(x-2)$

$P_2''(x) = \dfrac{23\sqrt{2}}{16}$

The values of $f$, $P_1$, $P_2$ and their first derivatives are equal at $x = 2$. The values of the second derivatives of $f$ and $P_2$ are equal at $x = 2$. The approximations worsen as you move away from $x = 2$.

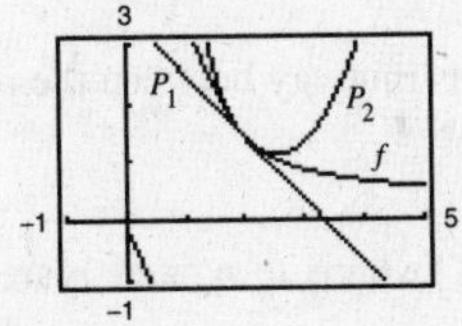


**101.** True. Let $y = ax^3 + bx^2 + cx + d$, $a \neq 0$. Then $y'' = 6ax + 2b = 0$ when $x = -(b/3a)$, and the concavity changes at this point.

**102.** False. $f(x) = 1/x$ has a discontinuity at $x = 0$.

**103.** False.

$f(x) = 3\sin x + 2\cos x$

$f'(x) = 3\cos x - 2\sin x$

$3\cos x - 2\sin x = 0$

$3\cos x = 2\sin x$

$\frac{3}{2} = \tan x$

Critical number: $x = \tan^{-1}\left(\frac{3}{2}\right)$

$f\left(\tan^{-1}\frac{3}{2}\right) \approx 3.60555$ is the maximum value of $y$.

**104.** True.

$y = \sin(bx)$

Slope: $y' = b\cos(bx)$

$-b \le y' \le b$ (Assume $b > 0$.)

**105.** False. Concavity is determined by $f''$. For example, let $f(x) = x$ and $c = 2$. $f'(c) = f'(2) > 0$, but $f$ is not concave upward at $c = 2$.

**106.** False. For example, let $f(x) = (x-2)^4$.

**107.** $f$ and $g$ are concave upward on $(a, b)$ implies that $f'$ and $g'$ are increasing on $(a, b)$, and $f'' > 0$ and $g'' > 0$. So, $(f+g)'' > 0 \Rightarrow f + g$ is concave upward on $(a, b)$ by Theorem 4.7.

**108.** $f$, $g$ are positive, increasing, and concave upward on $(a, b) \Rightarrow f(x) > 0$, $f'(x) \ge 0$ and $f''(x) > 0$, and $g(x) > 0$, $g'(x) \ge 0$ and $g''(x) > 0$ on $(a, b)$. For $x \in (a, b)$,

$(fg)'(x) = f'(x)g(x) + f(x)g'(x)$

$(fg)''(x) = f''(x)g(x) + 2f'(x)g'(x) + f(x)g''(x) > 0$

So, $fg$ is concave upward on $(a, b)$.

**109.** $f(x) = x \sin\left(\frac{1}{x}\right)$

$$f'(x) = x\left[-\frac{1}{x^2}\cos\left(\frac{1}{x}\right)\right] + \sin\left(\frac{1}{x}\right)$$

$$= -\frac{1}{x}\cos\left(\frac{1}{x}\right) + \sin\left(\frac{1}{x}\right)$$

$$f''(x) = -\frac{1}{x}\left[\frac{1}{x^2}\sin\left(\frac{1}{x}\right)\right] + \frac{1}{x^2}\cos\left(\frac{1}{x}\right) - \frac{1}{x^2}\cos\left(\frac{1}{x}\right)$$

$$= -\frac{1}{x^3}\sin\left(\frac{1}{x}\right)$$

$f''(x) = 0$ when $x = \frac{1}{\pi}$.

Point of inflection: $\left(\frac{1}{\pi}, 0\right)$

When $x > 1/\pi$, $f'' < 0$, so the graph is concave downward.

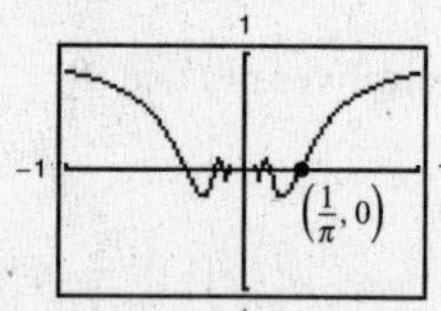


**110.** (a)

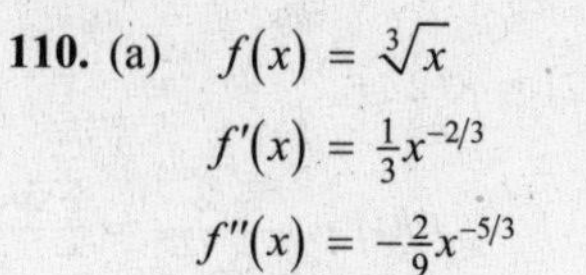

$f(x) = \sqrt[3]{x}$

$f'(x) = \frac{1}{3}x^{-2/3}$

$f''(x) = -\frac{2}{9}x^{-5/3}$

Point of inflection: $(0, 0)$

(b) $f''(x)$ does not exist at $x = 0$.

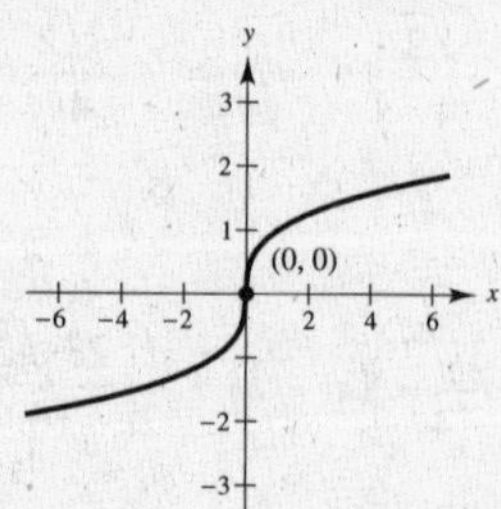


**111.** $f(x) = x(x - 6)^2 = x^3 - 12x^2 + 36x$

$f'(x) = 3x^2 - 24x + 36 = 3(x - 2)(x - 6) = 0$

$f''(x) = 6x - 24 = 6(x - 4) = 0$

Relative extrema: $(2, 32)$ and $(6, 0)$

Point of inflection $(4, 16)$ is midway between the relative extrema of $f$.

**112.** Assume the zeros of $f$ are all real. Then express the function as $f(x) = a(x - r_1)(x - r_2)(x - r_3)$ where $r_1$, $r_2$, and $r_3$ are the distinct zeros of $f$. From the Product Rule for a function involving three factors, we have

$$f'(x) = a\left[(x - r_1)(x - r_2) + (x - r_1)(x - r_3) + (x - r_2)(x - r_3)\right]$$

$$f''(x) = a\left[(x - r_1) + (x - r_2) + (x - r_1) + (x - r_3) + (x - r_2) + (x - r_3)\right] = a\left[6x - 2(r_1 + r_2 + r_3)\right].$$

Consequently, $f''(x) = 0$ if

$$x = \frac{2(r_1 + r_2 + r_3)}{6} = \frac{r_1 + r_2 + r_3}{3} = (\text{Average of } r_1, r_2, \text{ and } r_3).$$

## Section 4.5 Limits at Infinity

**1.** $f(x) = \frac{2x^2}{x^2 + 2}$

No vertical asymptotes

Horizontal asymptote: $y = 2$

Matches (f)

**2.** $f(x) = \frac{2x}{\sqrt{x^2 + 2}}$

No vertical asymptotes

Horizontal asymptotes: $y = \pm 2$

Matches (c)

**3.** $f(x) = \frac{x}{x^2 + 2}$

No vertical asymptotes

Horizontal asymptote: $y = 0$

$f(1) < 1$

Matches (d)

**4.** $f(x) = 2 + \frac{x^2}{x^4 + 1}$

No vertical asymptotes

Horizontal asymptote: $y = 2$

Matches (a)

**5.** $f(x) = \dfrac{4 \sin x}{x^2 + 1}$

No vertical asymptotes

Horizontal asymptote: $y = 0$

$f(1) > 1$

Matches (b)

**6.** $f(x) = \dfrac{2x^2 - 3x + 5}{x^2 + 1}$

No vertical asymptotes

Horizontal asymptote: $y = 2$

Matches (e)

**7.** $f(x) = \dfrac{4x + 3}{2x - 1}$

| $x$ | $10^0$ | $10^1$ | $10^2$ | $10^3$ | $10^4$ | $10^5$ | $10^6$ |
|---|---|---|---|---|---|---|---|
| $f(x)$ | 7 | 2.26 | 2.025 | 2.0025 | 2.0003 | 2 | 2 |

$\lim_{x \to \infty} f(x) = 2$

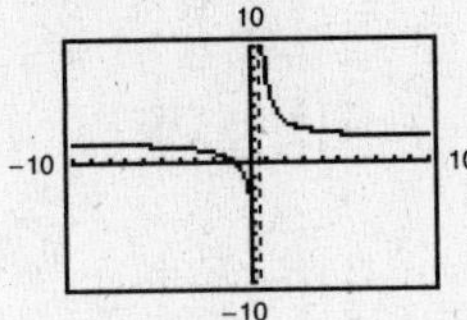


**8.** $f(x) = \dfrac{2x^2}{x + 1}$

| $x$ | $10^0$ | $10^1$ | $10^2$ | $10^3$ | $10^4$ | $10^5$ | $10^6$ |
|---|---|---|---|---|---|---|---|
| $f(x)$ | 1 | 18.18 | 198.02 | 1998.02 | 19,998 | 199,998 | 1,999,998 |

$\lim_{x \to \infty} f(x) = \infty$ (Limit does not exist)

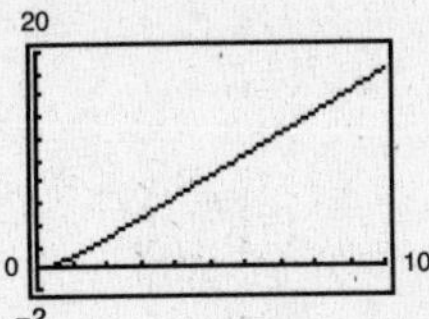


**9.** $f(x) = \dfrac{-6x}{\sqrt{4x^2 + 5}}$

| $x$ | $10^0$ | $10^1$ | $10^2$ | $10^3$ | $10^4$ | $10^5$ | $10^6$ |
|---|---|---|---|---|---|---|---|
| $f(x)$ | −2 | −2.98 | −2.9998 | −3 | −3 | −3 | −3 |

$\lim_{x \to \infty} f(x) = -3$

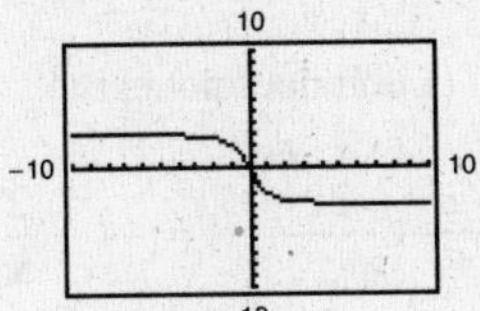

**10.** $f(x) = \dfrac{20x}{\sqrt{9x^2 - 1}}$

| $x$ | $10^0$ | $10^1$ | $10^2$ | $10^3$ | $10^4$ | $10^5$ | $10^6$ |
|---|---|---|---|---|---|---|---|
| $f(x)$ | 7.0711 | 6.6704 | 6.6667 | 6.6667 | 6.6667 | 6.6667 | 6.6667 |

$\lim_{x\to\infty} f(x) = \dfrac{20}{3}$

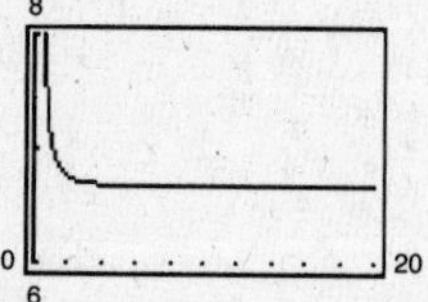

**11.** $f(x) = 5 - \dfrac{1}{x^2 + 1}$

| $x$ | $10^0$ | $10^1$ | $10^2$ | $10^3$ | $10^4$ | $10^5$ | $10^6$ |
|---|---|---|---|---|---|---|---|
| $f(x)$ | 4.5 | 4.99 | 4.9999 | 4.999999 | 5 | 5 | 5 |

$\lim_{x\to\infty} f(x) = 5$

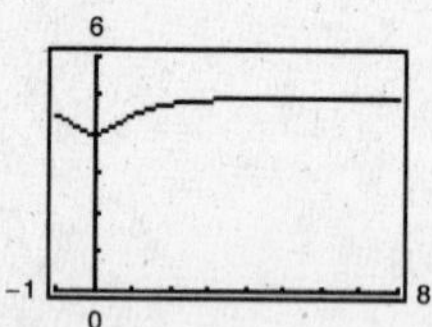

**12.** $f(x) = 4 + \dfrac{3}{x^2 + 2}$

| $x$ | $10^0$ | $10^1$ | $10^2$ | $10^3$ | $10^4$ | $10^5$ | $10^6$ |
|---|---|---|---|---|---|---|---|
| $f(x)$ | 5 | 4.03 | 4.0003 | 4.0 | 4.0 | 4 | 4 |

$\lim_{x\to\infty} f(x) = 4$

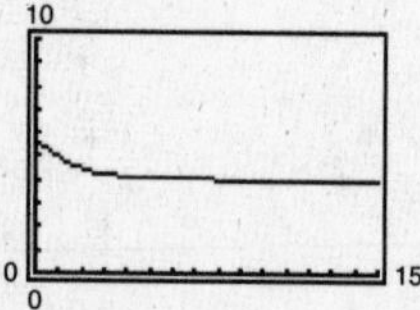

**13.** (a) $h(x) = \dfrac{f(x)}{x^2} = \dfrac{5x^3 - 3x^2 + 10x}{x^2} = 5x - 3 + \dfrac{10}{x}$

$\lim_{x\to\infty} h(x) = \infty$ (Limit does not exist)

(b) $h(x) = \dfrac{f(x)}{x^3} = \dfrac{5x^3 - 3x^2 + 10x}{x^3} = 5 - \dfrac{3}{x} + \dfrac{10}{x^2}$

$\lim_{x\to\infty} h(x) = 5$

(c) $h(x) = \dfrac{f(x)}{x^4} = \dfrac{5x^3 - 3x^2 + 10x}{x^4} = \dfrac{5}{x} - \dfrac{3}{x^2} + \dfrac{10}{x^3}$

$\lim_{x\to\infty} h(x) = 0$

**14.** (a) $h(x) = \dfrac{f(x)}{x} = \dfrac{-4x^2 + 2x - 5}{x} = -4x + 2 - \dfrac{5}{x}$

$\lim_{x\to\infty} h(x) = -\infty$ (Limit does not exist)

(b) $h(x) = \dfrac{f(x)}{x^2} = \dfrac{-4x^2 + 2x - 5}{x^2} = -4 + \dfrac{2}{x} - \dfrac{5}{x^2}$

$\lim_{x\to\infty} h(x) = -4$

(c) $h(x) = \dfrac{f(x)}{x^3} = \dfrac{-4x^2 + 2x - 5}{x^3} = -\dfrac{4}{x} + \dfrac{2}{x^2} - \dfrac{5}{x^3}$

$\lim_{x\to\infty} h(x) = 0$

**15.** (a) $\lim_{x\to\infty} \dfrac{x^2+2}{x^3-1} = 0$

(b) $\lim_{x\to\infty} \dfrac{x^2+2}{x^2-1} = 1$

(c) $\lim_{x\to\infty} \dfrac{x^2+2}{x-1} = \infty$ (Limit does not exist)

**16.** (a) $\lim_{x\to\infty} \dfrac{3-2x}{3x^3-1} = 0$

(b) $\lim_{x\to\infty} \dfrac{3-2x}{3x-1} = -\dfrac{2}{3}$

(c) $\lim_{x\to\infty} \dfrac{3-2x^2}{3x-1} = -\infty$ (Limit does not exist)

**17.** (a) $\lim_{x\to\infty} \dfrac{5-2x^{3/2}}{3x^2-4} = 0$

(b) $\lim_{x\to\infty} \dfrac{5-2x^{3/2}}{3x^{3/2}-4} = -\dfrac{2}{3}$

(c) $\lim_{x\to\infty} \dfrac{5-2x^{3/2}}{3x-4} = -\infty$ (Limit does not exist)

**18.** (a) $\lim_{x\to\infty} \dfrac{5x^{3/2}}{4x^2+1} = 0$

(b) $\lim_{x\to\infty} \dfrac{5x^{3/2}}{4x^{3/2}+1} = \dfrac{5}{4}$

(c) $\lim_{x\to\infty} \dfrac{5x^{3/2}}{4\sqrt{x}+1} = \infty$ (Limit does not exist)

**19.** $\lim_{x\to\infty}\left(4+\dfrac{3}{x}\right) = 4+0 = 4$

**20.** $\lim_{x\to-\infty}\left(\dfrac{5}{x}-\dfrac{x}{3}\right) = \infty$ (Limit does not exist)

**21.** $\lim_{x\to\infty} \dfrac{2x-1}{3x+2} = \lim_{x\to\infty} \dfrac{2-(1/x)}{3+(2/x)} = \dfrac{2-0}{3+0} = \dfrac{2}{3}$

**22.** $\lim_{x\to\infty} \dfrac{x^2+3}{2x^2-1} = \lim_{x\to\infty} \dfrac{1+3/x^2}{2-1/x^2} = \dfrac{1+0}{2-0} = \dfrac{1}{2}$

**23.** $\lim_{x\to\infty} \dfrac{x}{x^2-1} = \lim_{x\to\infty} \dfrac{1/x}{1-\left(1/x^2\right)} = \dfrac{0}{1} = 0$

**24.** $\lim_{x\to\infty} \dfrac{5x^3+1}{10x^3-3x^2+7} = \lim_{x\to\infty} \dfrac{5+1/x^3}{10-3/x+7/x^3}$

$= \dfrac{5+0}{10-0} = \dfrac{1}{2}$

**25.** $\lim_{x\to-\infty} \dfrac{x}{\sqrt{x^2-x}} = \lim_{x\to-\infty} \dfrac{1}{\left(\dfrac{\sqrt{x^2-x}}{-\sqrt{x^2}}\right)} = \lim_{x\to-\infty} \dfrac{-1}{\sqrt{1-(1/x)}} = -1$, $\left(\text{for } x < 0 \text{ you have } x = -\sqrt{x^2}\right)$

**26.** $\lim_{x\to\infty} \dfrac{x}{\sqrt{x^2+1}} = \lim_{x\to\infty} \dfrac{1}{\left(\dfrac{\sqrt{x^2+1}}{\sqrt{x^2}}\right)} = \lim_{x\to\infty} \dfrac{1}{\sqrt{1+\left(1/x^2\right)}} = 1$

**27.** $\lim_{x\to-\infty} \dfrac{2x+1}{\sqrt{x^2-x}} = \lim_{x\to-\infty} \dfrac{2+\dfrac{1}{x}}{\left(\dfrac{\sqrt{x^2-x}}{-\sqrt{x^2}}\right)} = \lim_{x\to-\infty} \dfrac{-2-\left(\dfrac{1}{x}\right)}{\sqrt{1-\dfrac{1}{x}}} = -2$, $\left(\text{for } x < 0,\ x = -\sqrt{x^2}\right)$

**28.** $\lim_{x\to-\infty} \dfrac{-3x+1}{\sqrt{x^2+x}} = \lim_{x\to-\infty} \dfrac{-3+(1/x)}{\left(\dfrac{\sqrt{x^2+x}}{-\sqrt{x^2}}\right)} = \lim_{x\to-\infty} \dfrac{3-(1/x)}{\sqrt{1+(1/x)}} = 3$, $\left(\text{for } x < 0 \text{ you have } -\sqrt{x^2} = x\right)$

**29.** $\lim_{x\to\infty} \dfrac{\sqrt{x^2-1}}{2x-1} = \lim_{x\to\infty} \dfrac{\sqrt{x^2-1}/\sqrt{x^2}}{2-1/x} = \lim_{x\to\infty} \dfrac{\sqrt{1-1/x^2}}{2-1/x} = \dfrac{1}{2}$

**30.** $\lim_{x\to-\infty} \frac{\sqrt{x^4-1}}{x^3-1} = \lim_{x\to-\infty} \frac{\sqrt{x^4-1}}{x^3-1}\left(\frac{1/\left(-\sqrt{x^6}\right)}{1/x^3}\right)$

$= \lim_{x\to-\infty} \frac{\sqrt{1/x^2 - 1/x^6}}{-1 + 1/x^3} = 0,$

$\left(\text{for } x < 0, \text{ you have } -\sqrt{x^6} = x^3\right)$

**31.** $\lim_{x\to\infty} \frac{x+1}{\left(x^2+1\right)^{1/3}} = \lim_{x\to\infty} \frac{x+1}{\left(x^2+1\right)^{1/3}}\left(\frac{1/x^{2/3}}{1/\left(x^2\right)^{1/3}}\right)$

$= \lim_{x\to\infty} \frac{x^{1/3} + 1/x^{2/3}}{\left(1 + 1/x^2\right)^{1/3}} = \infty$

(Limit does not exist)

**32.** $\lim_{x\to-\infty} \frac{2x}{\left(x^6-1\right)^{1/3}} = \lim_{x\to-\infty} \frac{2x}{\left(x^6-1\right)^{1/3}}\left(\frac{\left(1/x^2\right)}{\left(1/\left(x^6\right)^{1/3}\right)}\right)$

$= \lim_{x\to-\infty} \frac{2/x}{\left(1 - 1/x^6\right)^{1/3}} = 0$

**33.** $\lim_{x\to\infty} \frac{1}{2x + \sin x} = 0$

**34.** $\lim_{x\to\infty} \cos\left(\frac{1}{x}\right) = \cos 0 = 1$

**35.** Because $(-1/x) \le (\sin 2x)/x \le (1/x)$ for all $x \ne 0$, you have by the Squeeze Theorem,

$\lim_{x\to\infty} -\frac{1}{x} \le \lim_{x\to\infty} \frac{\sin 2x}{x} \le \lim_{x\to\infty} \frac{1}{x}$

$0 \le \lim_{x\to\infty} \frac{\sin 2x}{x} \le 0.$

Therefore, $\lim_{x\to\infty} \frac{\sin 2x}{x} = 0.$

**36.** $\lim_{x\to\infty} \frac{x - \cos x}{x} = \lim_{x\to\infty}\left(1 - \frac{\cos x}{x}\right)$

$= 1 - 0 = 1$

**Note:**

$\lim_{x\to\infty} \frac{\cos x}{x} = 0$ by the Squeeze Theorem because

$-\frac{1}{x} \le \frac{\cos x}{x} \le \frac{1}{x}.$

**37.** $\lim_{x\to\infty}\left(2 - 5e^{-x}\right) = 2$

**38.** $\lim_{x\to-\infty}\left(2 + 5e^{x}\right) = 2 + 0 = 2$

**39.** $\lim_{x\to-\infty} \frac{3}{1 + 2e^x} = 3$

**40.** $\lim_{x\to\infty} \frac{8}{4 - 10^{-x/2}} = 2$

**41.** $\lim_{x\to\infty} \log_{10}\left(1 + 10^{-x}\right) = 0$

**42.** $\lim_{x\to\infty}\left(\frac{5}{2} + \ln\frac{x^2+1}{x^2}\right) = \frac{5}{2}$

**43.** $\lim_{t\to\infty}\left(8t^{-1} - \arctan t\right) = \lim_{t\to\infty}\left(\frac{8}{t}\right) - \lim_{t\to\infty} \arctan t$

$= 0 - \frac{\pi}{2} = -\frac{\pi}{2}$

**44.** $\lim_{u\to\infty} \operatorname{arcsec}(u+1) = \frac{\pi}{2}$

**45.** $f(x) = \frac{|x|}{x+1}$

$\lim_{x\to\infty} \frac{|x|}{x+1} = 1$

$\lim_{x\to-\infty} \frac{|x|}{x+1} = -1$

Therefore, $y = 1$ and $y = -1$ are both horizontal asymptotes.

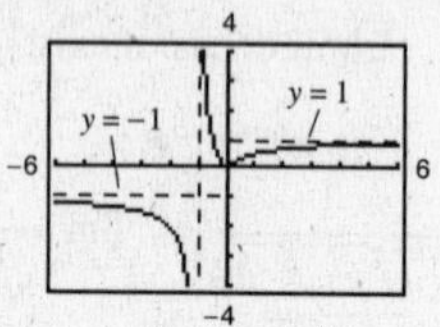


**46.** $f(x) = \frac{|3x + 2|}{x - 2}$

$y = 3$ is a horizontal asymptote (to the right).

$y = -3$ is a horizontal asymptote (to the left).

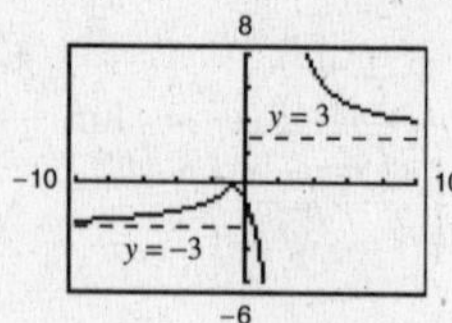

**47.** $f(x) = \dfrac{3x}{\sqrt{x^2 + 2}}$

$\lim_{x\to\infty} f(x) = 3$

$\lim_{x\to-\infty} f(x) = -3$

Therefore, $y = 3$ and $y = -3$ are both horizontal asymptotes.

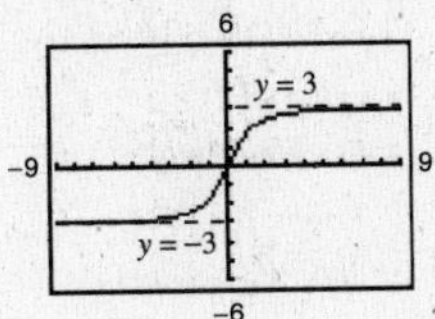


**48.** $f(x) = \dfrac{\sqrt{9x^2 - 2}}{2x + 1}$

$y = \dfrac{3}{2}$ is a horizontal asymptote (to the right).

$y = -\dfrac{3}{2}$ is a horizontal asymptote (to the left).

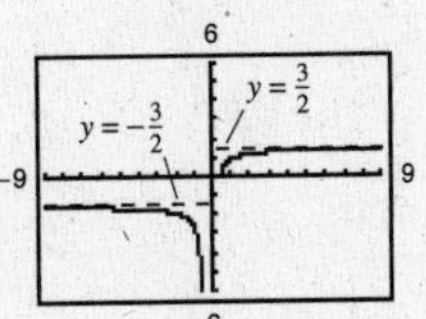


**49.** $\lim_{x\to\infty} x \sin\dfrac{1}{x} = \lim_{t\to 0^+} \dfrac{\sin t}{t} = 1$

(Let $x = 1/t$.)

**50.** $\lim_{x\to\infty} x \tan\dfrac{1}{x} = \lim_{x\to 0^+} \dfrac{\tan t}{t} = \lim_{x\to 0^+}\left[\dfrac{\sin t}{t} \cdot \dfrac{1}{\cos t}\right] = (1)(1) = 1$

(Let $x = 1/t$.)

**51.** $\lim_{x\to-\infty}\left(x + \sqrt{x^2 + 3}\right) = \lim_{x\to-\infty}\left[\left(x + \sqrt{x^2 + 3}\right) \cdot \dfrac{x - \sqrt{x^2 + 3}}{x - \sqrt{x^2 + 3}}\right] = \lim_{x\to-\infty} \dfrac{-3}{x - \sqrt{x^2 + 3}} = 0$

**52.** $\lim_{x\to\infty}\left(2x - \sqrt{4x^2 + 1}\right) = \lim_{x\to\infty}\left[\left(2x - \sqrt{4x^2 + 1}\right) \cdot \dfrac{2x + \sqrt{4x^2 + 1}}{2x + \sqrt{4x^2 + 1}}\right] = \lim_{x\to\infty} \dfrac{-1}{2x + \sqrt{4x^2 + 1}} = 0$

**53.** $\lim_{x\to-\infty}\left(3x + \sqrt{9x^2 - x}\right) = \lim_{x\to-\infty}\left[\left(3x + \sqrt{9x^2 - x}\right) \cdot \dfrac{3x - \sqrt{9x^2 - x}}{3x - \sqrt{9x^2 - x}}\right]$

$= \lim_{x\to-\infty} \dfrac{x}{3x - \sqrt{9x^2 - x}}$

$= \lim_{x\to-\infty} \dfrac{1}{3 - \dfrac{\sqrt{9x^2 - x}}{-\sqrt{x^2}}}$ (for $x < 0$ you have $x = -\sqrt{x^2}$)

$= \lim_{x\to-\infty} \dfrac{1}{3 + \sqrt{9 - (1/x)}} = \dfrac{1}{6}$

**54.** $\lim_{x\to\infty}\left(4x - \sqrt{16x^2 - x}\right)\dfrac{4x + \sqrt{16x^2 - x}}{4x + \sqrt{16x^2 - x}} = \lim_{x\to\infty} \dfrac{16x^2 - \left(16x^2 - x\right)}{4x + \sqrt{\left(16x^2 - x\right)}}$

$= \lim_{x\to\infty} \dfrac{x}{4x + \sqrt{16x^2 - x}}$

$= \lim_{x\to\infty} \dfrac{1}{4 + \sqrt{16 - 1/x}}$

$= \dfrac{1}{4 + 4} = \dfrac{1}{8}$

**55.**

| $x$ | $10^0$ | $10^1$ | $10^2$ | $10^3$ | $10^4$ | $10^5$ | $10^6$ |
|---|---|---|---|---|---|---|---|
| $f(x)$ | 1 | 0.513 | 0.501 | 0.500 | 0.500 | 0.500 | 0.500 |

$$\lim_{x\to\infty}\left(x - \sqrt{x(x-1)}\right) = \lim_{x\to\infty} \frac{x - \sqrt{x^2 - x}}{1} \cdot \frac{x + \sqrt{x^2 - x}}{x + \sqrt{x^2 - x}} = \lim_{x\to\infty} \frac{x}{x + \sqrt{x^2 - x}} = \lim_{x\to\infty} \frac{1}{1 + \sqrt{1 - (1/x)}} = \frac{1}{2}$$

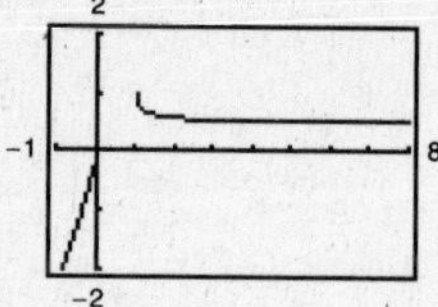


**56.**

| $x$ | $10^0$ | $10^1$ | $10^2$ | $10^3$ | $10^4$ | $10^5$ | $10^6$ |
|---|---|---|---|---|---|---|---|
| $f(x)$ | 1.0 | 5.1 | 50.1 | 500.1 | 5000.1 | 50,000.1 | 500,000.1 |

$$\lim_{x\to\infty} \frac{x^2 - x\sqrt{x^2 - x}}{1} \cdot \frac{x^2 + x\sqrt{x^2 - x}}{x^2 + x\sqrt{x^2 - x}} = \lim_{x\to\infty} \frac{x^3}{x^2 + x\sqrt{x^2 - x}} = \infty$$

Limit does not exist.

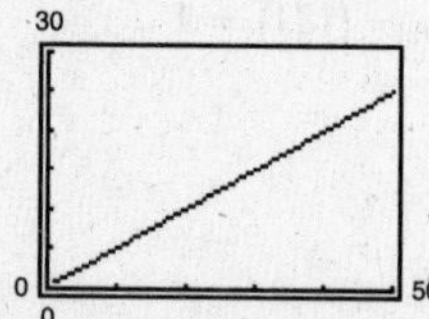


**57.**

| $x$ | $10^0$ | $10^1$ | $10^2$ | $10^3$ | $10^4$ | $10^5$ | $10^6$ |
|---|---|---|---|---|---|---|---|
| $f(x)$ | 0.479 | 0.500 | 0.500 | 0.500 | 0.500 | 0.500 | 0.500 |

Let $x = 1/t$.

$$\lim_{x\to\infty} x \sin\left(\frac{1}{2x}\right) = \lim_{t\to 0^+} \frac{\sin(t/2)}{t} = \lim_{t\to 0^+} \frac{1}{2}\,\frac{\sin(t/2)}{t/2} = \frac{1}{2}$$

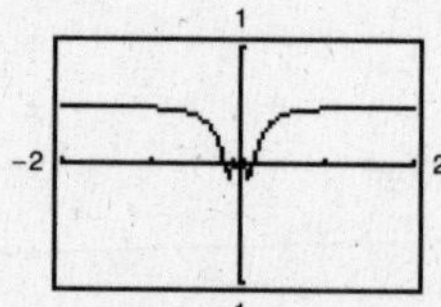


**58.**

| $x$ | $10^0$ | $10^1$ | $10^2$ | $10^3$ | $10^4$ | $10^5$ | $10^6$ |
|---|---|---|---|---|---|---|---|
| $f(x)$ | 2.000 | 0.348 | 0.101 | 0.032 | 0.010 | 0.003 | 0.001 |

$$\lim_{x\to\infty} \frac{x + 1}{x\sqrt{x}} = 0$$

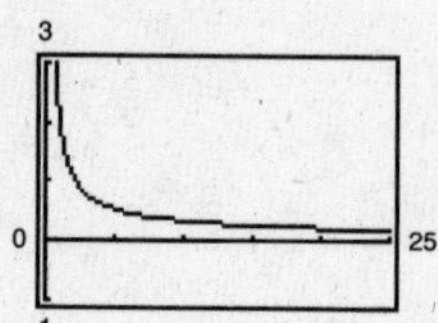

59. $\lim_{x\to\infty} f(x) = 4$ means that $f(x)$ approaches 4 as $x$ becomes large.

60. $\lim_{x\to-\infty} f(x) = 2$ means that $f(x)$ approaches 2 as $x$ becomes very large (in absolute value) and negative.

61. $x = 2$ is a critical number.

$f'(x) < 0$ for $x < 2$.

$f'(x) > 0$ for $x > 2$.

$\lim_{x\to-\infty} f(x) = \lim_{x\to\infty} f(x) = 6$

For example, let $f(x) = \dfrac{-6}{0.1(x-2)^2 + 1} + 6$.

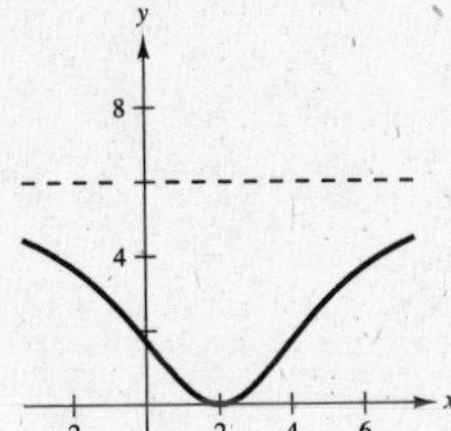

62. Yes. For example, let $f(x) = \dfrac{6|x-2|}{\sqrt{(x-2)^2 + 1}}$.

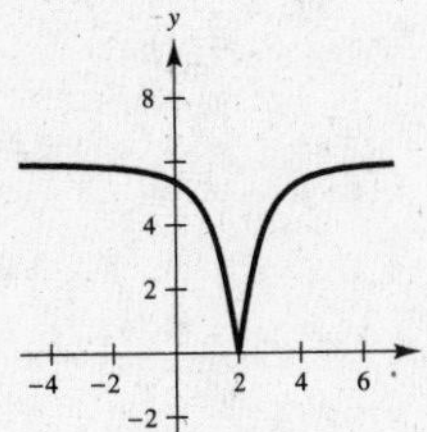

63. (a) The function is even: $\lim_{x\to-\infty} f(x) = 5$

(b) The function is odd: $\lim_{x\to-\infty} f(x) = -5$

64. (a)

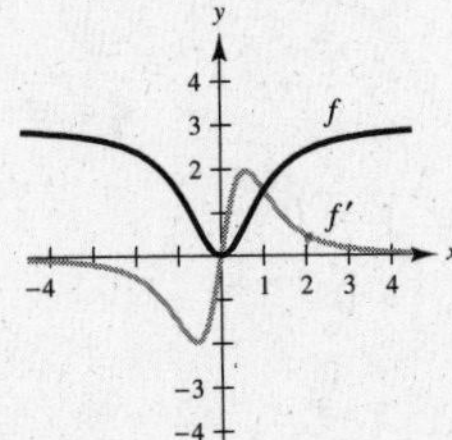


(b) $\lim_{x\to\infty} f(x) = 3 \qquad \lim_{x\to\infty} f'(x) = 0$

(c) Because $\lim_{x\to\infty} f(x) = 3$, the graph approaches that of a horizontal line, $\lim_{x\to\infty} f'(x) = 0$.

65. $y = \dfrac{x}{1-x}$

Intercept: $(0, 0)$

Symmetry: none

Horizontal asymptote: $y = -1$

Vertical asymptote: $x = 1$

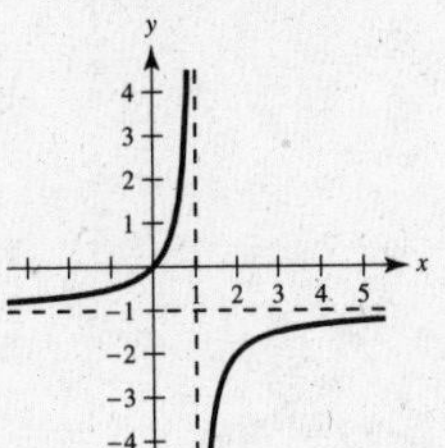

66. $y = \dfrac{x-4}{x-3}$

Intercepts: $(0, 4/3), (4, 0)$

Symmetry: none

Horizontal asymptote: $y = 1$

Vertical asymptote: $x = 3$

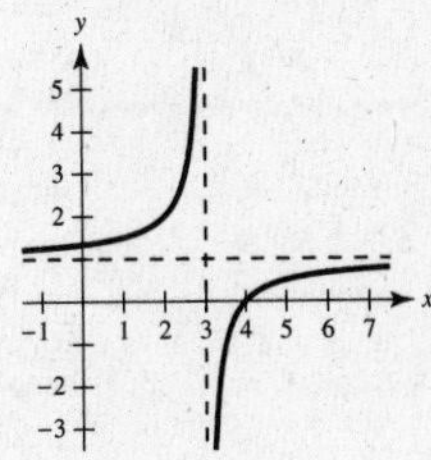

67. $y = \dfrac{x+1}{x^2-4}$

Intercepts: $(0, -1/4), (-1, 0)$

Symmetry: none

Horizontal asymptote: $y = 0$

Vertical asymptotes: $x = \pm 2$

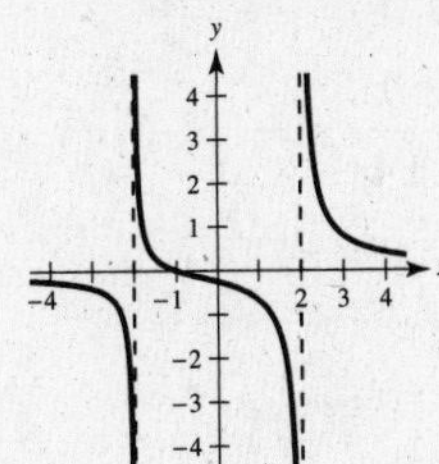

**68.** $y = \dfrac{2x}{9 - x^2}$

Intercept: $(0, 0)$

Symmetry: origin

Horizontal asymptote: $y = 0$

Vertical asymptotes: $x = \pm 3$

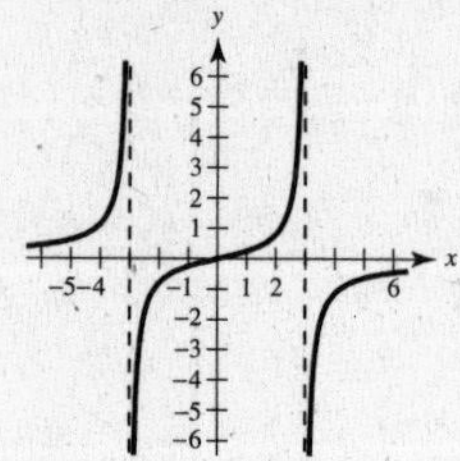

**69.** $y = \dfrac{x^2}{x^2 + 16}$

Intercept: $(0, 0)$

Symmetry: $y$-axis

Horizontal asymptote: $y = 1$

$y' = \dfrac{32x}{(x^2 + 16)^2}$

Relative minimum: $(0, 0)$

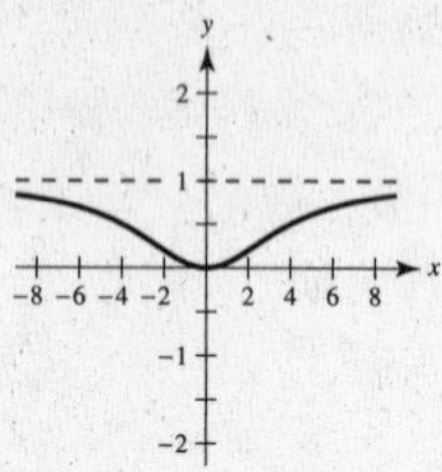

**70.** $y = \dfrac{x^2}{x^2 - 16}$

Intercept: $(0, 0)$

Symmetry: $y$-axis

Horizontal asymptote: $y = 1$

Vertical asymptotes: $x = \pm 4$

$y' = \dfrac{-32x}{(x^2 - 16)^2}$

Relative maximum: $(0, 0)$

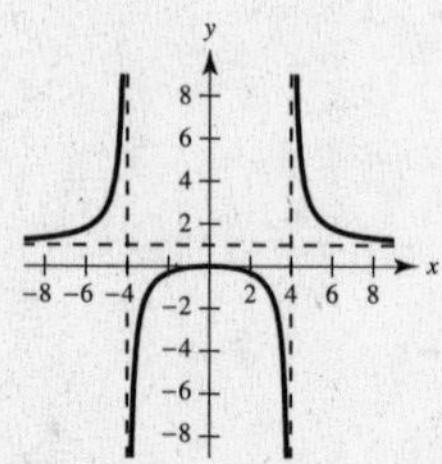

**71.** $y = \dfrac{2x^2}{x^2 - 4}$

Intercept: $(0, 0)$

Symmetry: $y$-axis

Horizontal asymptote: $y = 2$

Vertical asymptotes: $x = \pm 2$

Relative maximum: $(0, 0)$

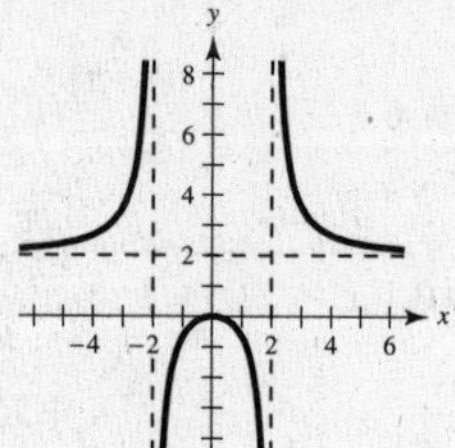

**72.** $y = \dfrac{2x^2}{x^2 + 4}$

Intercept: $(0, 0)$

Symmetry: $y$-axis

Horizontal asymptote: $y = 2$

Relative minimum: $(0, 0)$

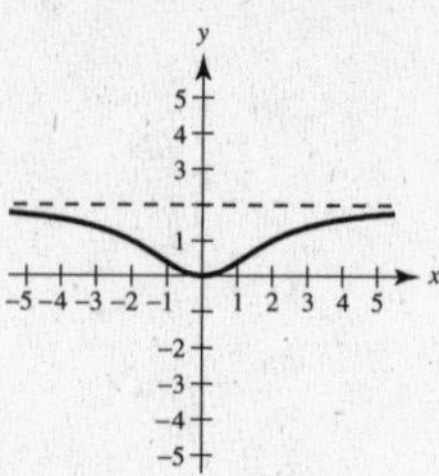

**73.** $xy^2 = 9$

Domain: $x > 0$

Intercepts: none

Symmetry: $x$-axis

$y = \pm \dfrac{3}{\sqrt{x}}$

Horizontal asymptote: $y = 0$

Vertical asymptote: $x = 0$

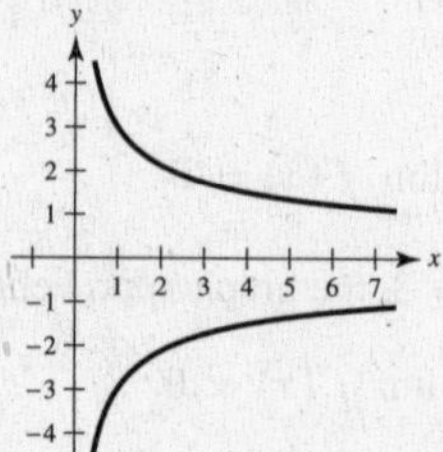

**74.** $x^2y = 9 \Rightarrow y = \dfrac{9}{x^2}$

Intercepts: none

Symmetry: $y$-axis

Horizontal asymptote: $y = 0$

Vertical asymptote: $x = 0$

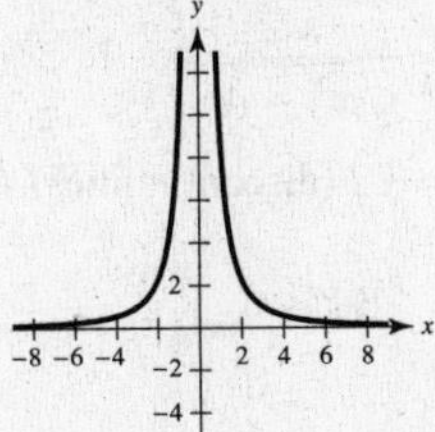

**75.** $y = \dfrac{3x}{1 - x}$

Intercept: $(0, 0)$

Symmetry: none

Horizontal asymptote: $y = -3$

Vertical asymptote: $x = 1$

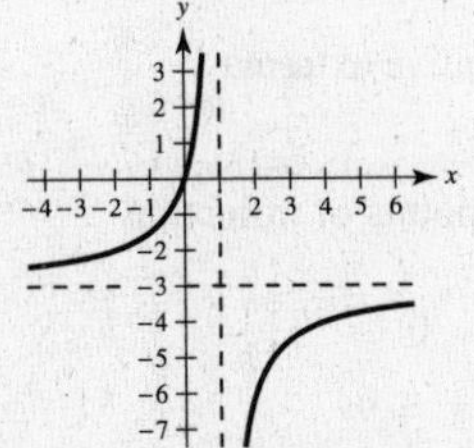

**76.** $y = \dfrac{3x}{1 - x^2}$

Intercept: $(0, 0)$

Symmetry: origin

Horizontal asymptote: $y = 0$

Vertical asymptotes: $x = \pm 1$

$$y' = \frac{3(x^2 + 1)}{(x^2 - 1)^2} > 0$$

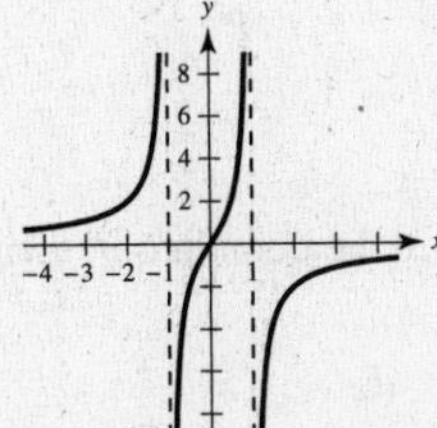

**77.** $y = 2 - \dfrac{3}{x^2}$

Intercepts: $\left(\pm\sqrt{\dfrac{3}{2}}, 0\right)$

Symmetry: $y$-axis

Horizontal asymptote: $y = 2$ because

$$\lim_{x\to-\infty}\left(2 - \frac{3}{x^2}\right) = 2 = \lim_{x\to\infty}\left(2 - \frac{3}{x^2}\right).$$

Discontinuity: $x = 0$ (Vertical asymptote)

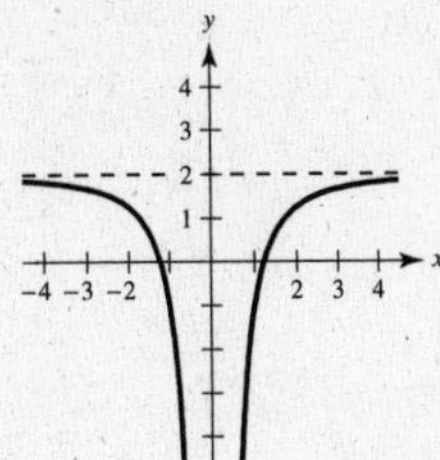

**78.** $y = 1 + \dfrac{1}{x}$

Intercept: $(-1, 0)$

Symmetry: none

Horizontal asymptote: $y = 1$ because

$$\lim_{x\to-\infty}\left(1 + \frac{1}{x}\right) = 1 = \lim_{x\to\infty}\left(1 + \frac{1}{x}\right).$$

Discontinuity: $x = 0$ (Vertical asymptote)

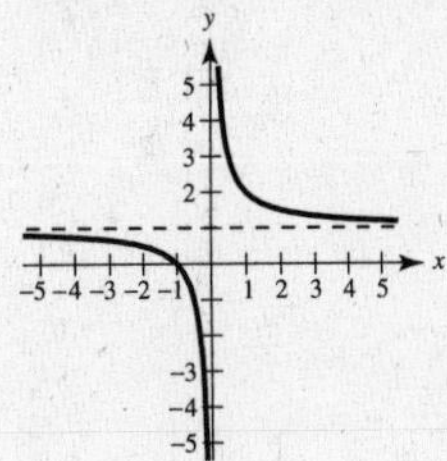

**79.** $y = 3 + \dfrac{2}{x}$

Intercept:

$$y = 0 = 3 + \frac{2}{x} \Rightarrow \frac{2}{x} = -3 \Rightarrow x = -\frac{2}{3}; \left(-\frac{2}{3}, 0\right)$$

Symmetry: none

Horizontal asymptote: $y = 3$

Vertical asymptote: $x = 0$

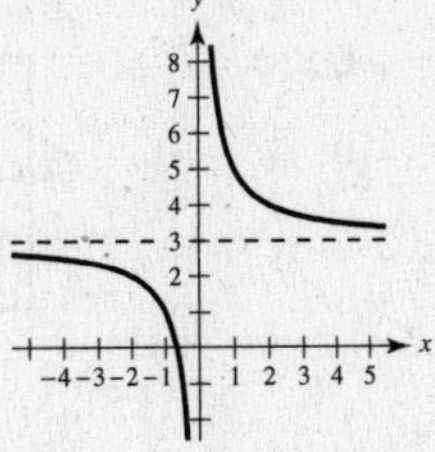

**80.** $y = 4\left(1 - \dfrac{1}{x^2}\right)$

Intercepts: $(\pm 1, 0)$

Symmetry: $y$-axis

Horizontal asymptote: $y = 4$

Vertical asymptote: $x = 0$

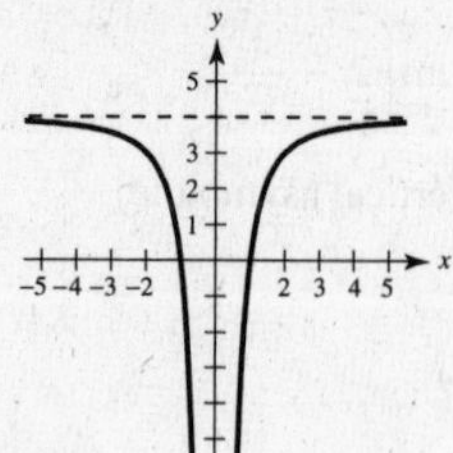

**81.** $y = \dfrac{x^3}{\sqrt{x^2 - 4}}$

Domain: $(-\infty, -2), (2, \infty)$

Intercepts: none

Symmetry: origin

Horizontal asymptote: none

Vertical asymptotes: $x = \pm 2$ (discontinuities)

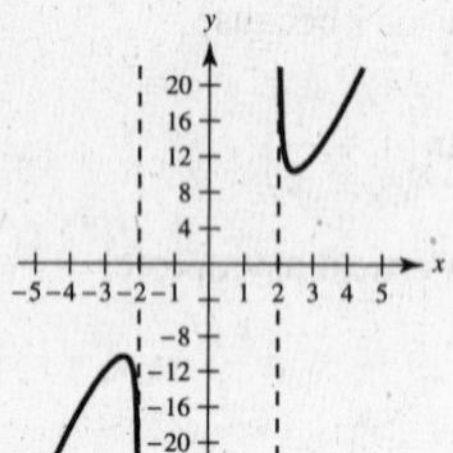

**82.** $y = \dfrac{x}{\sqrt{x^2 - 4}}$

Domain: $(-\infty, -2), (2, \infty)$

Intercepts: none

Symmetry: origin

Horizontal asymptotes: $y = \pm 1$ because

$$\lim_{x \to \infty} \frac{x}{\sqrt{x^2 - 4}} = 1, \quad \lim_{x \to -\infty} \frac{x}{\sqrt{x^2 - 4}} = -1.$$

Vertical asymptotes: $x = \pm 2$ (discontinuities)

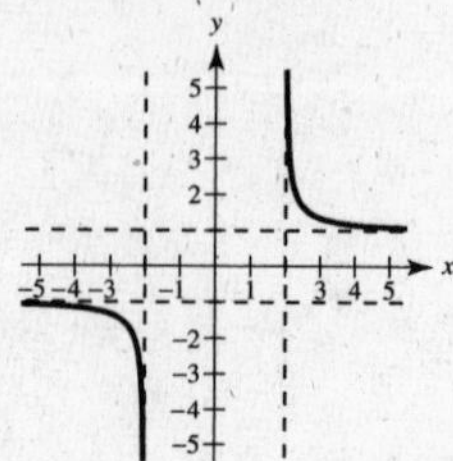

**83.** $f(x) = 9 - \dfrac{5}{x^2}$

Domain: all $x \neq 0$

$f'(x) = \dfrac{10}{x^3} \Rightarrow$ No relative extrema

$f''(x) = -\dfrac{30}{x^4} \Rightarrow$ No points of inflection

Vertical asymptote: $x = 0$

Horizontal asymptote: $y = 9$

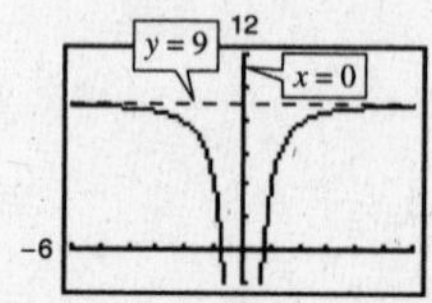


**84.** $f(x) = \dfrac{1}{x^2 - x - 2} = \dfrac{1}{(x + 1)(x - 2)}$

$f'(x) = \dfrac{-(2x - 1)}{(x^2 - x - 2)^2} = 0$ when $x = \dfrac{1}{2}$.

$$f''(x) = \frac{(x^2 - x - 2)^2(-2) + (2x - 1)(2)(x^2 - x - 2)(2x - 1)}{(x^2 - x - 2)^4} = \frac{6(x^2 - x + 1)}{(x^2 - x - 2)^3}$$

Because $f''\left(\dfrac{1}{2}\right) < 0$, $\left(\dfrac{1}{2}, -\dfrac{4}{9}\right)$ is a relative maximum. Because $f''(x) \neq 0$, and it is undefined in the domain of $f$, there are no points of inflection.

Vertical asymptotes: $x = -1, x = 2$

Horizontal asymptote: $y = 0$

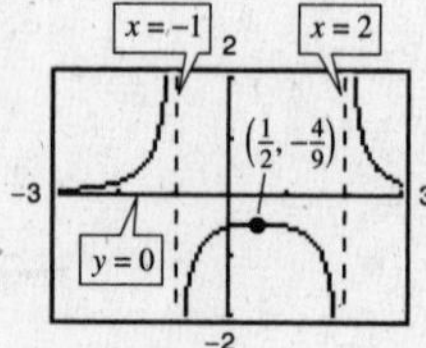

**85.** $f(x) = \dfrac{x-2}{x^2-4x+3} = \dfrac{x-2}{(x-1)(x-3)}$

$$f'(x) = \frac{(x^2-4x+3)-(x-2)(2x-4)}{(x^2-4x+3)^2} = \frac{-x^2+4x-5}{(x^2-4x+3)^2} \neq 0$$

$$f''(x) = \frac{(x^2-4x+3)^2(-2x+4)-(-x^2+4x-5)(2)(x^2-4x+3)(2x-4)}{(x^2-4x+3)^4}$$

$$= \frac{2(x^3-6x^2+15x-14)}{(x^2-4x+3)^3} = \frac{2(x-2)(x^2-4x+7)}{(x^2-4x+3)^3} = 0 \text{ when } x = 2.$$

Because $f''(x) > 0$ on $(1, 2)$ and $f''(x) < 0$ on $(2, 3)$, then $(2, 0)$ is a point of inflection.

Vertical asymptotes: $x = 1, x = 3$

Horizontal asymptote: $y = 0$

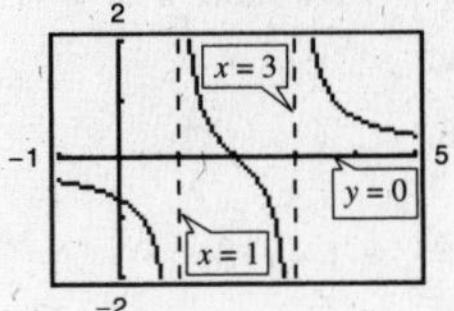


**86.** $f(x) = \dfrac{x+1}{x^2+x+1}$

$$f'(x) = \frac{-x(x+2)}{(x^2+x+1)^2} = 0 \text{ when } x = 0, -2.$$

$$f''(x) = \frac{2(x^3+3x^2-1)}{(x^2+x+1)^3} = 0$$

when $x \approx 0.5321, -0.6527, -2.8794.$

$f''(0) < 0$

Therefore, $(0, 1)$ is a relative maximum.

$f''(-2) > 0$

Therefore,

$\left(-2, -\dfrac{1}{3}\right)$

is a relative minimum.

Points of inflection:
$(0.5321, 0.8440), (-0.6527, 0.4491)$ and
$(-2.8794, -0.2931)$

Horizontal asymptote: $y = 0$

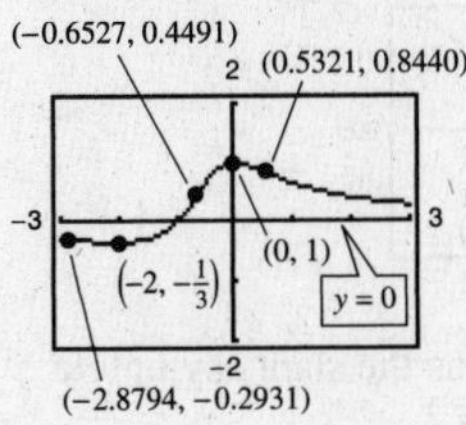


**87.** $f(x) = \dfrac{3x}{\sqrt{4x^2+1}}$

$$f'(x) = \frac{3}{(4x^2+1)^{3/2}} \Rightarrow \text{No relative extrema}$$

$$f''(x) = \frac{-36x}{(4x^2+1)^{5/2}} = 0 \text{ when } x = 0.$$

Point of inflection: $(0, 0)$

Horizontal asymptotes: $y = \pm\dfrac{3}{2}$

No vertical asymptotes

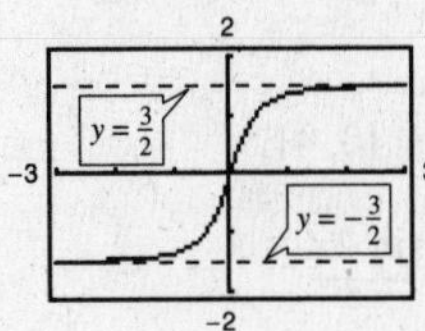

**88.** $g(x) = \dfrac{2x}{\sqrt{3x^2 + 1}}$

$g'(x) = \dfrac{2}{(3x^2 + 1)^{3/2}}$

$g''(x) = \dfrac{-18x}{(3x^2 + 1)^{5/2}}$

No relative extrema. Point of inflection: $(0, 0)$.

Horizontal asymptotes: $y = \pm\dfrac{2}{\sqrt{3}}$

No vertical asymptotes

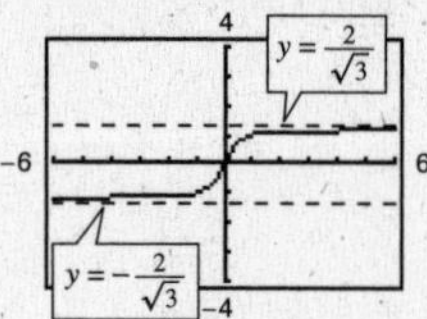


**89.** $g(x) = \sin\left(\dfrac{x}{x - 2}\right),\ 3 < x < \infty$

$g'(x) = \dfrac{-2\cos\left(\dfrac{x}{x - 2}\right)}{(x - 2)^2}$

Horizontal asymptote: $y = \sin(1)$

Relative maximum:

$\dfrac{x}{x - 2} = \dfrac{\pi}{2} \Rightarrow x = \dfrac{2\pi}{\pi - 2} \approx 5.5039$

No vertical asymptotes

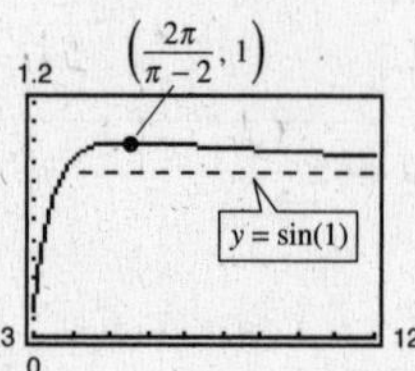


**90.** $f(x) = \dfrac{2 \sin 2x}{x}$; Hole at $(0, 4)$

$f'(x) = \dfrac{4x \cos 2x - 2 \sin 2x}{x^2}$

There are an infinite number of relative extrema. In the interval $(-2\pi, 2\pi)$, you obtain the following.

Relative minima: $(\pm 2.25, -0.869), (\pm 5.45, -0.365)$

Relative maxima: $(\pm 3.87, 0.513)$

Horizontal asymptote: $y = 0$

No vertical asymptotes

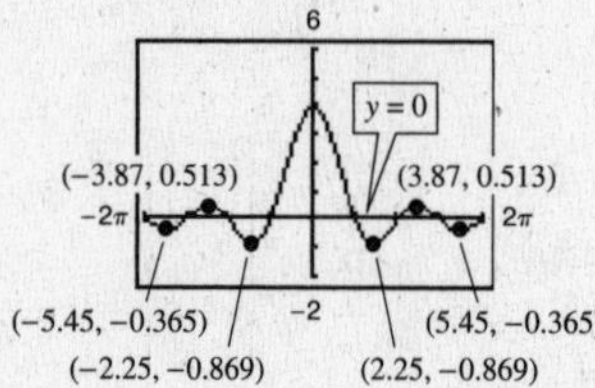


**91.** $f(x) = 2 + (x^2 - 3)e^{-x}$

$f'(x) = -e^{-x}(x + 1)(x - 3)$

Critical numbers: $x = -1, x = 3$

Relative minimum: $(-1, 2 - 2e) \approx (-1, -3.4366)$

Relative maximum: $(3, 2 + 6e^{-3}) \approx (3, 2.2987)$

Horizontal asymptote: $y = 2$

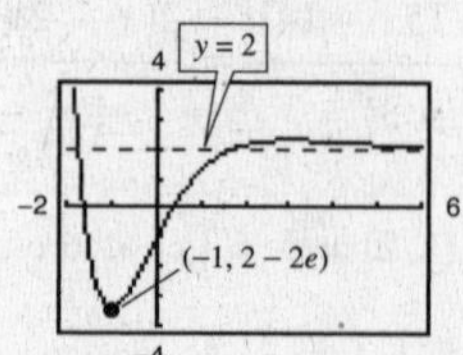


**92.** $f(x) = \dfrac{10 \ln x}{x^2\sqrt{x}} = \dfrac{10 \ln x}{x^{5/2}}$, Domain: $x > 0$

$f'(x) = \dfrac{5}{x^{7/2}}(2 - 5 \ln x)$

Critical number: $x = e^{2/5} \approx 1.4918$

Relative maximum: $(1.4918, 1.4715)$

Horizontal asymptote: $y = 0$

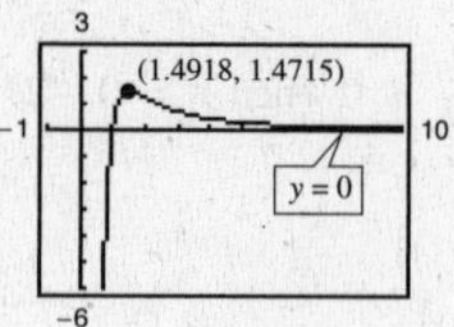


**93.** $f(x) = \dfrac{x^3 - 3x^2 + 2}{x(x - 3)},\ g(x) = x + \dfrac{2}{x(x - 3)}$

(a)

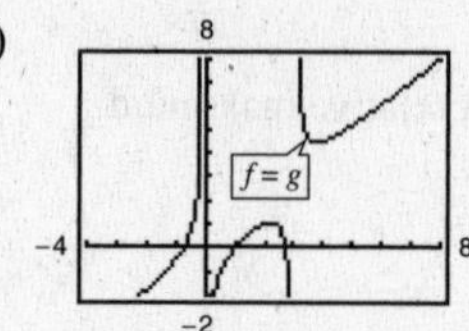


(b) $f(x) = \dfrac{x^3 - 3x^2 + 2}{x(x - 3)}$

$= \dfrac{x^2(x - 3)}{x(x - 3)} + \dfrac{2}{x(x - 3)}$

$= x + \dfrac{2}{x(x - 3)} = g(x)$

(c)

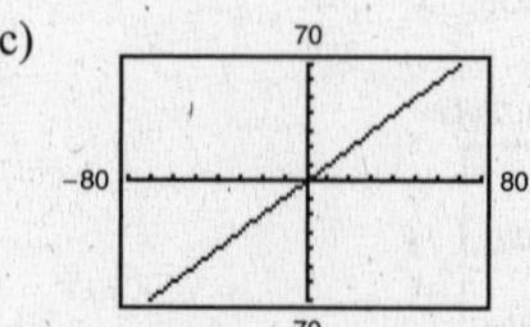


The graph appears as the slant asymptote $y = x$.

**94.** $f(x) = -\dfrac{x^3 - 2x^2 + 2}{2x^2}$, $g(x) = -\dfrac{1}{2}x + 1 - \dfrac{1}{x^2}$

(a)

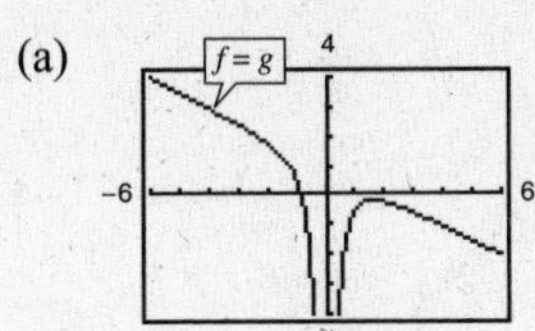


(b) $f(x) = -\dfrac{x^3 - 2x^2 + 2}{2x^2}$

$= -\left[\dfrac{x^3}{2x^2} - \dfrac{2x^2}{2x^2} + \dfrac{2}{2x^2}\right]$

$= -\dfrac{1}{2}x + 1 - \dfrac{1}{x^2} = g(x)$

(c)

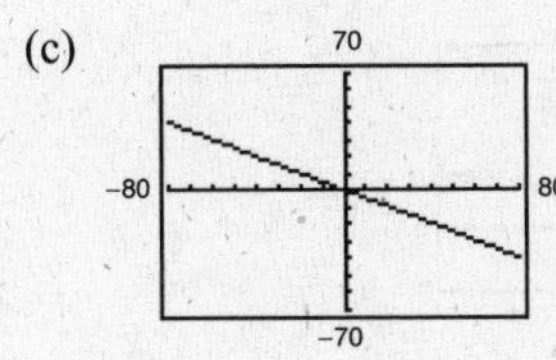


The graph appears as the slant asymptote

$y = -\dfrac{1}{2}x + 1.$

**95.** $\displaystyle\lim_{v_1/v_2 \to \infty} 100\left[1 - \frac{1}{(v_1/v_2)^c}\right] = 100[1 - 0] = 100\%$

**96.** $C = 0.5x + 500$

$\overline{C} = \dfrac{C}{x}$

$\overline{C} = 0.5 + \dfrac{500}{x}$

$\displaystyle\lim_{x\to\infty}\left(0.5 + \frac{500}{x}\right) = 0.5$

**97.** $\displaystyle\lim_{t\to\infty} N(t) = \infty$

$\displaystyle\lim_{t\to\infty} E(t) = c$

**98.** (a) $\displaystyle\lim_{t\to 0^+} T = 1700°$

This is the temperature of the kiln.

(b) $\displaystyle\lim_{t\to\infty} T = 72°$

This is the temperature of the room.

(c) No. $y = 72$ is the horizontal asymptote.

**99.** (a) $T_1(t) = -0.003t^2 + 0.68t + 26.6$

(b)

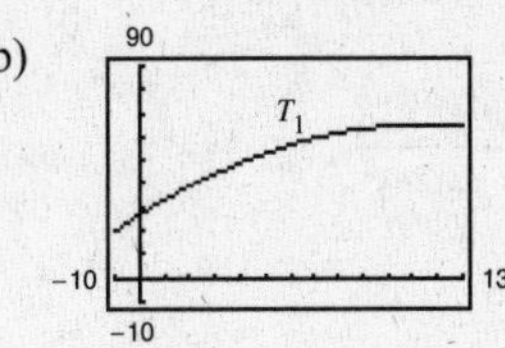


(c)

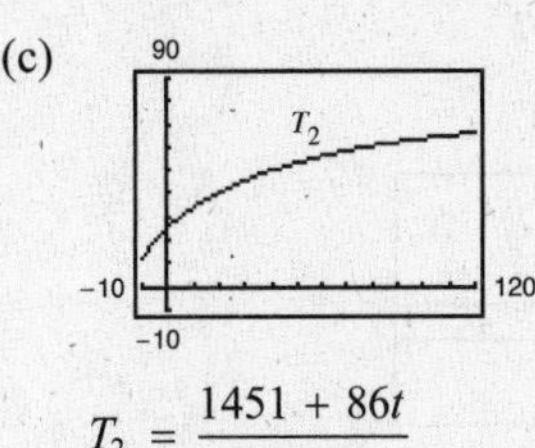


$T_2 = \dfrac{1451 + 86t}{58 + t}$

(d) $T_1(0) \approx 26.6°$

$T_2(0) \approx 25.0°$

(e) $\displaystyle\lim_{t\to\infty} T_2 = \frac{86}{1} = 86$

(f) No. The limiting temperature is 86°.

$T_1$ has no horizontal asymptote.

**100.** (a) Using a graphing utility,

$C_1 = -0.00800x^2 + 0.0865x + 0.252.$

(b)

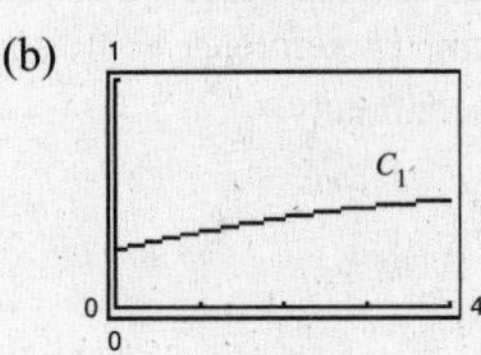


(c) $C_2 = \dfrac{5 + 3x}{20 + 4x}$

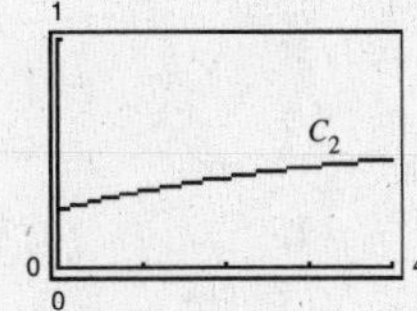


(d) $\displaystyle\lim_{x\to\infty} C_1 = -\infty$

$\displaystyle\lim_{x\to\infty} C_2 = \frac{3}{4}$

Model $C_1$ is unrealistic as $x \to \infty$. Model $C_2$ is better.

(e) The limiting concentration is $3/4 = 75\%$.

**101.** (a) $\displaystyle\lim_{t\to\infty} 7.1e^{-(48.1)/t} = 7.1(e^0) = 7.1$ million ft³/acre

(b) $V'(t) = \dfrac{341.51}{t^2}e^{-(48.1)/t}$

$V'(20) \approx 0.077$ million $\text{ft}^3/\text{yr}$

$V'(60) \approx 0.043$ million $\text{ft}^3/\text{yr}$

**102.** (a) $\lim_{n\to\infty} \frac{0.83}{1 + e^{-0.2n}} = 0.83 = 83\%$

(b) $P' = \frac{0.166e^{-0.2n}}{\left(1 + e^{-0.2n}\right)^2}$

$P'(3) \approx 0.038$

$P'(10) \approx 0.017$

**103.** (a)

(b) When $x$ increases without bound, $1/x$ approaches zero and $e^{1/x}$ approaches 1. Therefore, $f(x)$ approaches $2/(1 + 1) = 1$. So, $f(x)$ has a horizontal asymptote at $y = 1$. As $x$ approaches zero from the right, $1/x$ approaches $\infty$, $e^{1/x}$ approaches $\infty$, and $f(x)$ approaches zero. As $x$ approaches zero from the left, $1/x$ approaches $-\infty$, $e^{1/x}$ approaches zero, and $f(x)$ approaches 2. The limit does not exist because the left limit does not equal the right limit. Therefore, $x = 0$ is a nonremovable discontinuity.

**104.** Answers will vary.

**105.** line: $mx - y + 4 = 0$

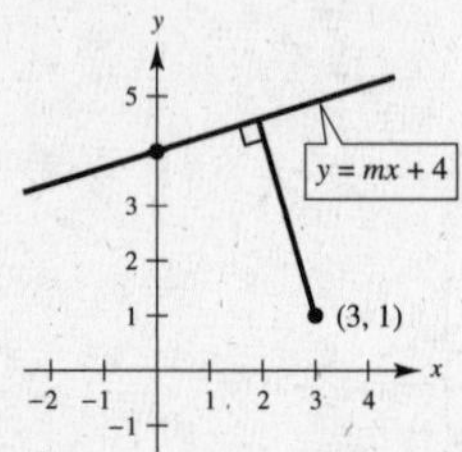


(a) $d = \frac{|Ax_1 + By_1 + C|}{\sqrt{A^2 + B^2}} = \frac{|m(3) - 1(1) + 4|}{\sqrt{m^2 + 1}}$

$= \frac{|3m + 3|}{\sqrt{m^2 + 1}}$

(b)

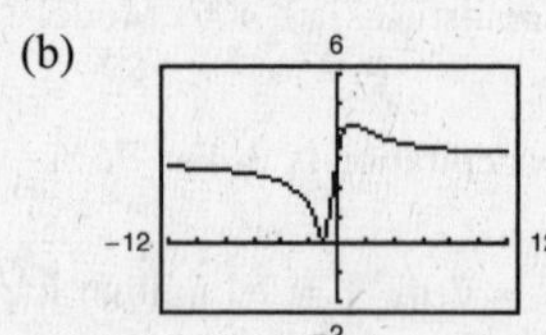


(c) $\lim_{m\to\infty} d(m) = 3 = \lim_{m\to-\infty} d(m)$

The line approaches the vertical line $x = 0$. So, the distance from $(3, 1)$ approaches 3.

**106.** line: $y + 2 = m(x - 0) \Rightarrow mx - y - 2 = 0$

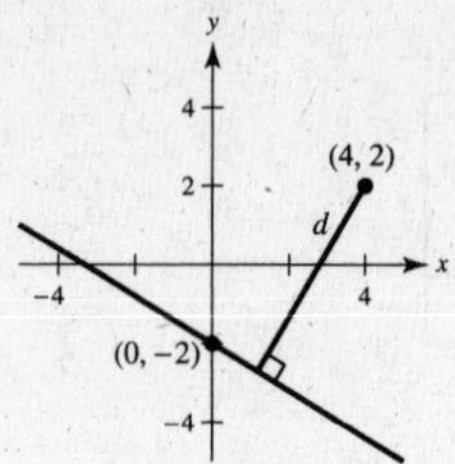


(a) $d = \frac{|Ax_1 + By_1 + C|}{\sqrt{A^2 + B^2}} = \frac{|m(4) - 1(2) - 2|}{\sqrt{m^2 + 1}}$

$= \frac{|4m - 4|}{\sqrt{m^2 + 1}}$

(b)

(c) $\lim_{m\to\infty} d(m) = 4$; $\lim_{m\to-\infty} d(m) = 4$

The line approaches the vertical line $x = 0$. So, the distance from $(4, 2)$ approaches 4.

**107.** $f(x) = \frac{2x^2}{x^2 + 2}$

(a) $\lim_{x\to\infty} f(x) = 2 = L$

(b) $f(x_1) + \varepsilon = \frac{2x_1^2}{x_1^2 + 2} + \varepsilon = 2$

$$2x_1^2 + \varepsilon x_1^2 + 2\varepsilon = 2x_1^2 + 4$$

$$x_1^2\varepsilon = 4 - 2\varepsilon$$

$$x_1 = \sqrt{\frac{4 - 2\varepsilon}{\varepsilon}}$$

$x_2 = -x_1$ by symmetry

(c) Let $M = \sqrt{\frac{4 - 2\varepsilon}{\varepsilon}} > 0$. For $x > M$:

$$x > \sqrt{\frac{4 - 2\varepsilon}{\varepsilon}}$$

$$x^2\varepsilon > 4 - 2\varepsilon$$

$$2x^2 + x^2\varepsilon + 2\varepsilon > 2x^2 + 4$$

$$\frac{2x^2}{x^2 + 2} + \varepsilon > 2$$

$$\left|\frac{2x^2}{x^2 + 2} - 2\right| > |-\varepsilon| = \varepsilon$$

$$|f(x) - L| > \varepsilon$$

(d) Similarly, $N = -\sqrt{\frac{4 - 2\varepsilon}{\varepsilon}}$.

**108.** $f(x) = \dfrac{6x}{\sqrt{x^2 + 2}}$

(a) $\lim_{x\to\infty} f(x) = 6 = L$

$\lim_{x\to-\infty} f(x) = -6 = K$

(b) $f(x_1) + \varepsilon = \dfrac{6x_1}{\sqrt{x_1^2 + 2}} + \varepsilon = 6$

$$6x_1 = (6 - \varepsilon)\sqrt{x_1^2 + 2}$$
$$36x_1^2 = (x_1^2 + 2)(6 - \varepsilon)^2$$
$$36x_1^2 - (6 - \varepsilon)^2 x_1^2 = 2(6 - \varepsilon)^2$$
$$x_1^2\left[36 - 36 + 12\varepsilon - \varepsilon^2\right] = 2(6 - \varepsilon)^2$$
$$x_1^2 = \frac{2(6 - \varepsilon)^2}{12\varepsilon - \varepsilon^2}$$
$$x_1 = (6 - \varepsilon)\sqrt{\frac{2}{12\varepsilon - \varepsilon^2}}$$

$x_2 = -x_1$ by symmetry

(c) $M = x_1 = (6 - \varepsilon)\sqrt{\dfrac{2}{12\varepsilon - \varepsilon^2}}$

(d) $N = x_2 = (\varepsilon - 6)\sqrt{\dfrac{2}{12\varepsilon - \varepsilon^2}}$

**109.** $\lim_{x\to\infty} \dfrac{3x}{\sqrt{x^2 + 3}} = 3$

$f(x_1) + \varepsilon = \dfrac{3x_1}{\sqrt{x_1^2 + 3}} + \varepsilon = 3$

$$3x_1 = (3 - \varepsilon)\sqrt{x_1^2 + 3}$$
$$9x_1^2 = (3 - \varepsilon)^2(x_1^2 + 3)$$
$$9x_1^2 - (3 - \varepsilon)^2 x_1^2 = 3(3 - \varepsilon)^2$$
$$x_1^2(9 - 9 + 6\varepsilon - \varepsilon^2) = 3(3 - \varepsilon)^2$$
$$x_1^2 = \frac{3(3 - \varepsilon)^2}{6\varepsilon - \varepsilon^2}$$
$$x_1 = (3 - \varepsilon)\sqrt{\frac{3}{6\varepsilon - \varepsilon^2}}$$

Let $M = x_1 = (3 - \varepsilon)\sqrt{\dfrac{3}{6\varepsilon - \varepsilon^2}}$

(a) When $\varepsilon = 0.5$:

$$M = (3 - 0.5)\sqrt{\frac{3}{6(0.5) - (0.5)^2}} = \frac{5\sqrt{33}}{11}$$

(b) When $\varepsilon = 0.1$:

$$M = (3 - 0.1)\sqrt{\frac{3}{6(0.1) - (0.1)^2}} = \frac{29\sqrt{177}}{59}$$

**110.** $\lim_{x\to-\infty} \dfrac{3x}{\sqrt{x^2 + 3}} = -3$

$f(x_1) - \varepsilon = \dfrac{3x_1}{\sqrt{x_1^2 + 3}} - \varepsilon = -3$

$$3x_1 = (\varepsilon - 3)\sqrt{x_1^2 + 3}$$
$$9x_1^2 = (\varepsilon - 3)^2(x_1^2 + 3)$$
$$9x_1^2 - (\varepsilon - 3)^2 x_1^2 = 3(\varepsilon - 3)^2$$
$$x_1^2(9 - \varepsilon^2 + 6\varepsilon - 9) = 3(\varepsilon - 3)^2$$
$$x_1^2 = \frac{3(\varepsilon - 3)^2}{6\varepsilon - \varepsilon^2}$$
$$x_1 = (\varepsilon - 3)\sqrt{\frac{3}{6\varepsilon - \varepsilon^2}}$$

Let $x_1 = N = (\varepsilon - 3)\sqrt{\dfrac{3}{6\varepsilon - \varepsilon^2}}$

(a) When $\varepsilon = 0.5$:

$$N = (0.5 - 3)\sqrt{\frac{3}{6(0.5) - (0.5)^2}} = \frac{-5\sqrt{33}}{11}$$

(b) When $\varepsilon = 0.1$:

$$N = (0.1 - 3)\sqrt{\frac{3}{6(0.1) - (0.1)^2}} = \frac{-29\sqrt{177}}{59}$$

**111.** $\lim_{x\to\infty} \dfrac{1}{x^2} = 0$. Let $\varepsilon > 0$ be given. You need $M > 0$ such that

$$|f(x) - L| = \left|\frac{1}{x^2} - 0\right| = \frac{1}{x^2} < \varepsilon \text{ whenever } x > M.$$

$$x^2 > \frac{1}{\varepsilon} \Rightarrow x > \frac{1}{\sqrt{\varepsilon}}$$

Let $M = \dfrac{1}{\sqrt{\varepsilon}}$.

For $x > M$, you have

$$x > \frac{1}{\sqrt{\varepsilon}} \Rightarrow x^2 > \frac{1}{\varepsilon} \Rightarrow \frac{1}{x^2} < \varepsilon \Rightarrow |f(x) - L| < \varepsilon.$$

**112.** $\lim_{x\to\infty} \frac{2}{\sqrt{x}} = 0$. Let $\varepsilon > 0$ be given. You need $M > 0$ such that

$|f(x) - L| = \left|\frac{2}{\sqrt{x}} - 0\right| = \frac{2}{\sqrt{x}} < \varepsilon$ whenever $x > M$.

$$\frac{2}{\sqrt{x}} < \varepsilon \Rightarrow \frac{\sqrt{x}}{2} > \frac{1}{\varepsilon} \Rightarrow x > \frac{4}{\varepsilon^2}$$

Let $M = 4/\varepsilon^2$.

For $x > M = 4/\varepsilon^2$, you have

$$\sqrt{x} > 2/\varepsilon \Rightarrow \frac{2}{\sqrt{x}} < \varepsilon \Rightarrow |f(x) - L| < \varepsilon.$$

**113.** $\lim_{x\to-\infty} \frac{1}{x^3} = 0$. Let $\varepsilon > 0$. You need $N < 0$ such that

$|f(x) - L| = \left|\frac{1}{x^3} - 0\right| = \frac{-1}{x^3} < \varepsilon$ whenever $x < N$.

$$\frac{-1}{x^3} < \varepsilon \Rightarrow -x^3 > \frac{1}{\varepsilon} \Rightarrow x < \frac{-1}{\varepsilon^{1/3}}$$

Let $N = \frac{-1}{\sqrt[3]{\varepsilon}}$.

For $x < N = \frac{-1}{\sqrt[3]{\varepsilon}}$,

$$\frac{1}{x} > -\sqrt[3]{\varepsilon}$$

$$-\frac{1}{x} < \sqrt[3]{\varepsilon}$$

$$-\frac{1}{x^3} < \varepsilon$$

$$\Rightarrow |f(x) - L| < \varepsilon.$$

**114.** $\lim_{x\to-\infty} \frac{1}{x-2} = 0$. Let $\varepsilon > 0$ be given. You need $N < 0$ such that $|f(x) - L| = \left|\frac{1}{x-2} - 0\right| = \frac{-1}{x-2} < \varepsilon$ whenever $x < N$.

$$\frac{-1}{x-2} < \varepsilon \Rightarrow x - 2 < \frac{-1}{\varepsilon} \Rightarrow x < 2 - \frac{1}{\varepsilon}$$

Let $N = 2 - \frac{1}{\varepsilon}$. For $x < N = 2 - \frac{1}{\varepsilon}$,

$$x - 2 < \frac{-1}{\varepsilon}$$

$$\frac{-1}{x-2} < \varepsilon$$

$$\Rightarrow |f(x) - L| < \varepsilon.$$

**115.** $\lim_{x\to\infty} \frac{p(x)}{q(x)} = \lim_{x\to\infty} \frac{a_n x^n + \cdots + a_1 x + a_0}{b_m x^m + \cdots + b_1 x + b_0}$

Divide $p(x)$ and $q(x)$ by $x^m$.

**Case 1:** If $n < m$: $\lim_{x\to\infty} \frac{p(x)}{q(x)} = \lim_{x\to\infty} \frac{\frac{a_n}{x^{m-n}} + \cdots + \frac{a_1}{x^{m-1}} + \frac{a_0}{x^m}}{b_m + \cdots + \frac{b_1}{x^{m-1}} + \frac{b_0}{x^m}} = \frac{0 + \cdots + 0 + 0}{b_m + \cdots + 0 + 0} = \frac{0}{b_m} = 0.$

**Case 2:** If $m = n$: $\lim_{x\to\infty} \frac{p(x)}{q(x)} = \lim_{x\to\infty} \frac{a_n + \cdots + \frac{a_1}{x^{m-1}} + \frac{a_0}{x^m}}{b_m + \cdots + \frac{b_1}{x^{m-1}} + \frac{b_0}{x^m}} = \frac{a_n + \cdots + 0 + 0}{b_m + \cdots + 0 + 0} = \frac{a_n}{b_m}.$

**Case 3:** If $n > m$: $\lim_{x\to\infty} \frac{p(x)}{q(x)} = \lim_{x\to\infty} \frac{a_n x^{n-m} + \cdots + \frac{a_1}{x^{m-1}} + \frac{a_0}{x^m}}{b_m + \cdots + \frac{b_1}{x^{m-1}} + \frac{b_0}{x^m}} = \frac{\pm\infty + \cdots + 0}{b_m + \cdots + 0} = \pm\infty.$

**116.** $\lim_{x\to\infty} x^3 = \infty$. Let $M > 0$ be given. You need $N > 0$ such that $f(x) = x^3 > M$ whenever $x > N$.

$x^3 > M \Rightarrow x > M^{1/3}$. Let $N = M^{1/3}$. For $x > N = M^{1/3}$, $x > M^{1/3} \Rightarrow x^3 > M \Rightarrow f(x) > M$.

**117.** False. Let $f(x) = \dfrac{2x}{\sqrt{x^2 + 2}}$. (See Exercise 60.)

**118.** False. Let $y_1 = \sqrt{x + 1}$, then $y_1(0) = 1$. So $y_1' = 1/\left(2\sqrt{x + 1}\right)$ and $y_1'(0) = 1/2$. Finally, $y_1'' = -\dfrac{1}{4(x + 1)^{3/2}}$ and

$y_1''(0) = -\dfrac{1}{4}$. Let $p = ax^2 + bx + 1$, then $p(0) = 1$. So, $p' = 2ax + b$ and $p'(0) = \dfrac{1}{2} \Rightarrow b = \dfrac{1}{2}$. Finally, $p'' = 2a$ and

$p''(0) = -\dfrac{1}{4} \Rightarrow a = -\dfrac{1}{8}$. Therefore,

$$f(x) = \begin{cases} (-1/8)x^2 + (1/2)x + 1, & x < 0 \\ \sqrt{x + 1}, & x \ge 0 \end{cases} \text{ and } f(0) = 1,$$

$$f'(x) = \begin{cases} (1/2) - (1/4)x, & x < 0 \\ 1/\left(2\sqrt{x + 1}\right), & x > 0 \end{cases} \text{ and } f'(0) = \frac{1}{2}, \text{ and}$$

$$f''(x) = \begin{cases} (-1/4), & x < 0 \\ -1/\left(4(x + 1)^{3/2}\right), & x > 0 \end{cases} \text{ and } f''(0) = -\frac{1}{4}.$$

$f''(x) < 0$ for all real $x$, but $f(x)$ *increases* without bound.

## Section 4.6 A Summary of Curve Sketching

**1.** $f$ has constant negative slope. Matches (d)

**2.** The slope of $f$ approaches $\infty$ as $x \to 0^-$, and approaches $-\infty$ as $x \to 0^+$. Matches (c)

**3.** The slope is periodic, and zero at $x = 0$. Matches (a)

**4.** The slope is positive up to approximately $x = 1.5$. Matches (b)

**5.** $y = \dfrac{1}{x - 2} - 3$

$y' = -\dfrac{1}{(x - 2)^2} < 0$ when $x \neq 2$.

$y'' = \dfrac{2}{(x - 2)^3}$

No relative extrema, no points of inflection

Intercepts: $\left(\dfrac{7}{3}, 0\right), \left(0, -\dfrac{7}{2}\right)$

Vertical asymptote: $x = 2$

Horizontal asymptote: $y = -3$

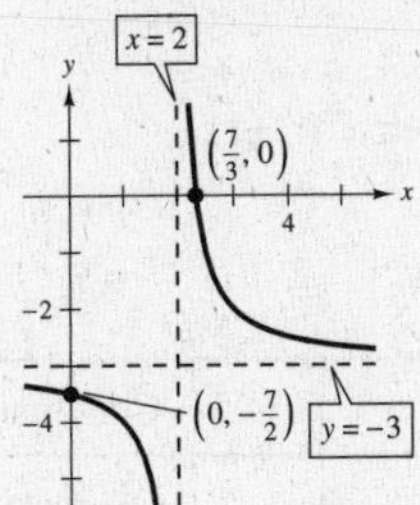

**6.** $y = \dfrac{x}{x^2 + 1}$

$y' = \dfrac{1 - x^2}{(x^2 + 1)^2} = \dfrac{(1 - x)(x + 1)}{(x^2 + 1)^2} = 0$ when $x = \pm 1$.

$y'' = -\dfrac{2x(3 - x^2)}{(x^2 + 1)^3} = 0$ when $x = 0, \pm\sqrt{3}$.

Horizontal asymptote: $y = 0$

| | $y$ | $y'$ | $y''$ | Conclusion |
|---|---|---|---|---|
| $-\infty < x < -\sqrt{3}$ | | $-$ | $-$ | Decreasing, concave down |
| $x = -\sqrt{3}$ | $-\dfrac{\sqrt{3}}{4}$ | $-$ | 0 | Point of inflection |
| $-\sqrt{3} < x < -1$ | | $-$ | $+$ | Decreasing, concave up |
| $x = -1$ | $-\dfrac{1}{2}$ | 0 | $+$ | Relative minimum |
| $-1 < x < 0$ | | $+$ | $+$ | Increasing, concave up |
| $x = 0$ | 0 | $+$ | 0 | Point of inflection |
| $0 < x < 1$ | | $+$ | $-$ | Increasing, concave down |
| $x = 1$ | $\dfrac{1}{2}$ | 0 | $-$ | Relative maximum |
| $1 < x < \sqrt{3}$ | | $-$ | $-$ | Decreasing, concave down |
| $x = \sqrt{3}$ | $\dfrac{\sqrt{3}}{4}$ | $-$ | 0 | Point of inflection |
| $\sqrt{3} < x < \infty$ | | $-$ | $+$ | Decreasing, concave up |

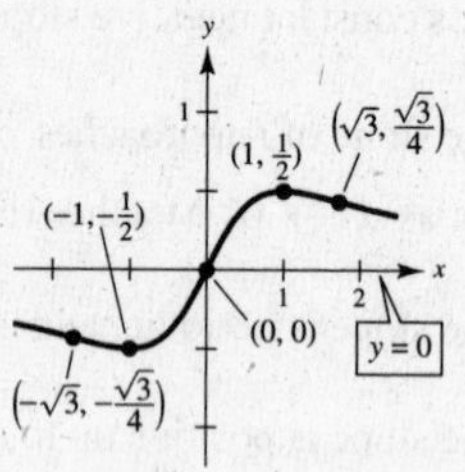


**7.** $y = \dfrac{x^2}{x^2 + 3}$

$y' = \dfrac{6x}{(x^2 + 3)^2} = 0$ when $x = 0$.

$y'' = \dfrac{18(1 - x^2)}{(x^2 + 3)^3} = 0$ when $x = \pm 1$.

Horizontal asymptote: $y = 1$

| | $y$ | $y'$ | $y''$ | Conclusion |
|---|---|---|---|---|
| $-\infty < x < -1$ | | $-$ | $-$ | Decreasing, concave down |
| $x = -1$ | $\dfrac{1}{4}$ | $-$ | 0 | Point of inflection |
| $-1 < x < 0$ | | $-$ | $+$ | Decreasing, concave up |
| $x = 0$ | 0 | 0 | $+$ | Relative minimum |
| $0 < x < 1$ | | $+$ | $+$ | Increasing, concave up |
| $x = 1$ | $\dfrac{1}{4}$ | $+$ | 0 | Point of inflection |
| $1 < x < \infty$ | | $+$ | $-$ | Increasing, concave down |

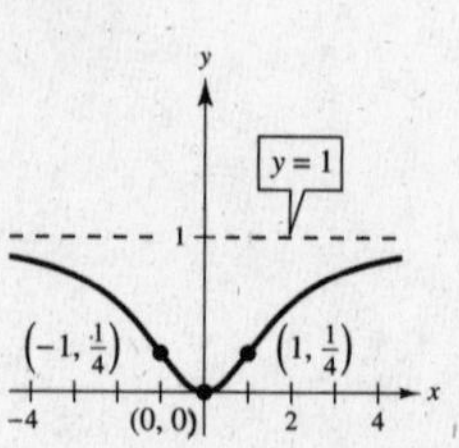

**8.** $y = \dfrac{x^2 + 1}{x^2 - 4}$

$y' = \dfrac{-10x}{(x^2 - 4)^2} = 0$ when $x = 0$

$y'' = \dfrac{10(3x^2 + 4)}{(x^2 - 4)^3} < 0$ when $x = 0$

Therefore, $(0, -1/4)$ is a relative maximum.

Intercept: $(0, -1/4)$

Symmetric about $y$-axis

Vertical asymptotes: $x = \pm 2$

Horizontal asymptote: $y = 1$

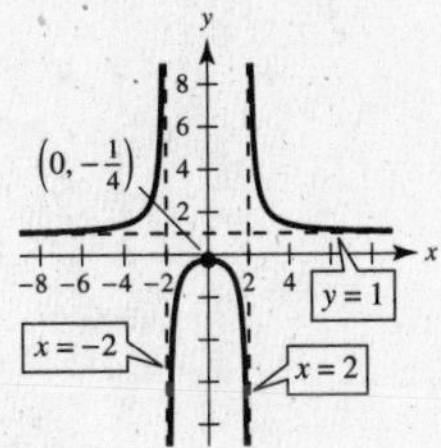


**9.** $y = \dfrac{3x}{x^2 - 1}$

$y' = \dfrac{-3(x^2 + 1)}{(x^2 - 1)^2} < 0$ if $x \neq \pm 1$

$y'' = \dfrac{6x(x^2 + 3)}{(x^2 - 1)^3}$

Inflection point: $(0, 0)$

Intercept: $(0, 0)$

Symmetry with respect to origin

Vertical asymptotes: $x = \pm 1$

Horizontal asymptote: $y = 0$

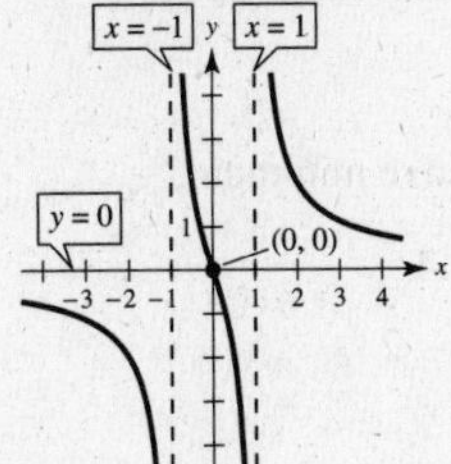


**10.** $f(x) = \dfrac{x - 3}{x} = 1 - \dfrac{3}{x}$

$f'(x) = \dfrac{3}{x^2} > 0$ when $x \neq 0$

$f''(x) = -\dfrac{6}{x^3} \neq 0$

Vertical asymptote: $x = 0$

Intercept: $(3, 0)$

Horizontal asymptote: $y = 1$

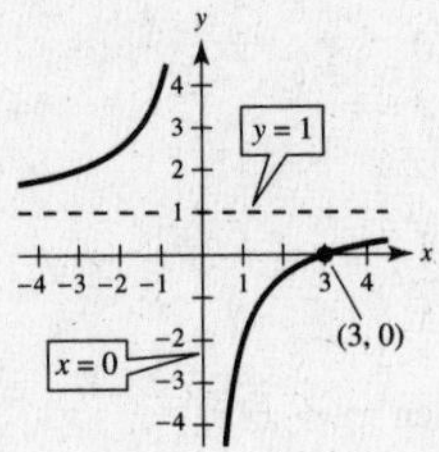


**11.** $g(x) = x - \dfrac{8}{x^2} = \dfrac{x^3 - 8}{x^2}$

$g'(x) = \dfrac{x^3 + 16}{x^3} = 0$ if $x = \sqrt[3]{-16}$

$g''(x) = -48/x^4 < 0$ if $x \neq 0$

Therefore $\left(\sqrt[3]{-16}, -3\sqrt[3]{2}\right) \approx (-2.52, -3.78)$ is a relative maximum.

Intercept: $(2, 0)$

Vertical asymptote: $x = 0$

Slant asymptote: $y = x$

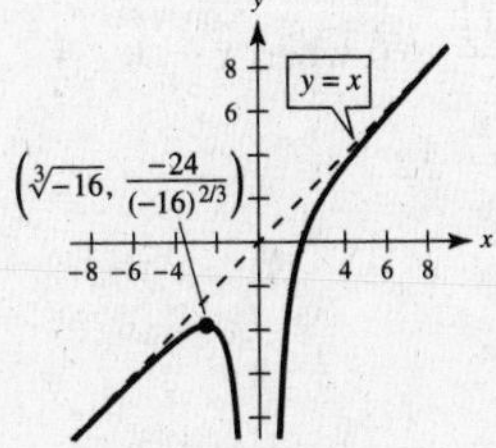

**12.** $f(x) = x + \dfrac{32}{x^2}$

$f'(x) = 1 - \dfrac{64}{x^3} = \dfrac{(x-4)(x^2+4x+16)}{x^3} = 0$ when $x = 4$.

$f''(x) = \dfrac{192}{x^4} > 0$ if $x \neq 0$.

Therefore, $(4, 6)$ is a relative minimum.

Intercept: $\left(-2\sqrt[3]{4}, 0\right)$

Vertical asymptote: $x = 0$

Slant asymptote: $y = x$

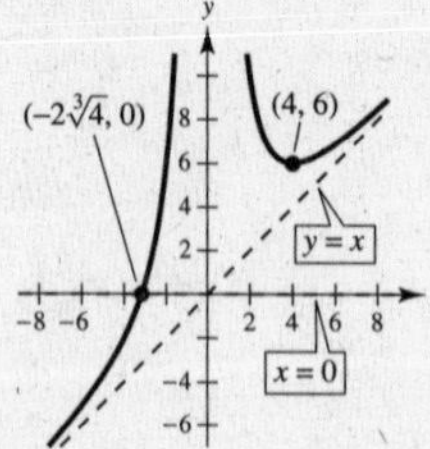


**13.** $f(x) = \dfrac{x^2+1}{x} = x + \dfrac{1}{x}$

$f'(x) = 1 - \dfrac{1}{x^2} = 0$ when $x = \pm 1$.

$f''(x) = \dfrac{2}{x^3} \neq 0$

Relative maximum: $(-1, -2)$

Relative minimum: $(1, 2)$

Vertical asymptote: $x = 0$

Slant asymptote: $y = x$

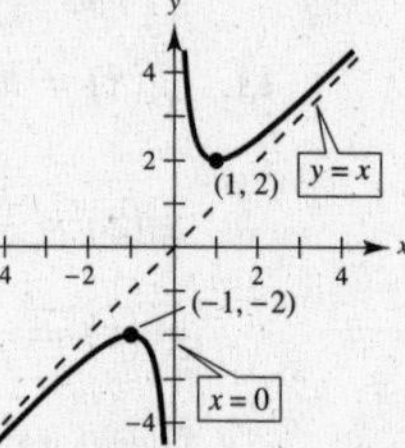


**14.** $f(x) = \dfrac{x^3}{x^2-9} = x + \dfrac{9x}{x^2-9}$

$f'(x) = \dfrac{x^2(x^2-27)}{(x^2-9)^2} = 0$ when $x = 0, \pm 3\sqrt{3}$

$f''(x) = \dfrac{18x(x^2+27)}{(x^2-9)^3} = 0$ when $x = 0$

Intercept: $(0, 0)$

Symmetry: origin

Relative maximum:

$\left(-3\sqrt{3}, -\dfrac{9\sqrt{3}}{2}\right) \approx (-5.196, 7.794)$

Relative minimum: $\left(3\sqrt{3}, \dfrac{9\sqrt{3}}{2}\right) \approx (5.196, 7.794)$

Vertical asymptotes: $x = \pm 3$

Slant asymptote: $y = x$

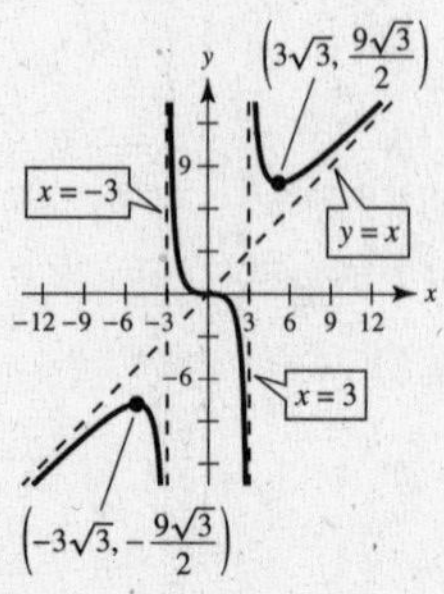


**15.** $y = \dfrac{x^2 - 6x + 12}{x-4} = x - 2 + \dfrac{4}{x-4}$

$y' = 1 - \dfrac{4}{(x-4)^2}$

$= \dfrac{(x-2)(x-6)}{(x-4)^2} = 0$ when $x = 2, 6$.

$y'' = \dfrac{8}{(x-4)^3}$

$y'' < 0$ when $x = 2$.

Therefore, $(2, -2)$ is a relative maximum.

$y'' > 0$ when $x = 6$.

Therefore, $(6, 6)$ is a relative minimum.

Vertical asymptote: $x = 4$

Slant asymptote: $y = x - 2$

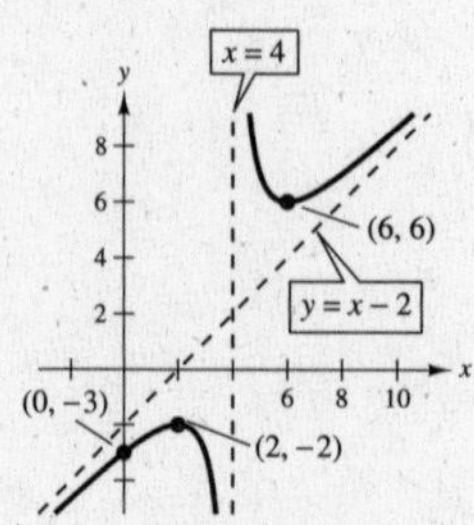

**16.** $y = \dfrac{2x^2 - 5x + 5}{x - 2} = 2x - 1 + \dfrac{3}{x - 2}$

$y' = 2 - \dfrac{3}{(x-2)^2} = \dfrac{2x^2 - 8x + 5}{(x-2)^2} = 0$ when $x = \dfrac{4 \pm \sqrt{6}}{2}$.

$y'' = \dfrac{6}{(x-2)^3} \neq 0$

Relative maximum: $\left(\dfrac{4 - \sqrt{6}}{2}, -1.8990\right)$

Relative minimum: $\left(\dfrac{4 + \sqrt{6}}{2}, 7.8990\right)$

Intercept: $(0, -5/2)$

Vertical asymptote: $x = 2$

Slant asymptote: $y = 2x - 1$

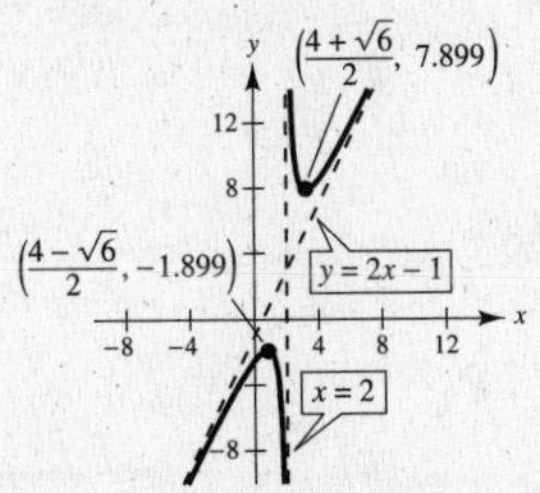


**17.** $y = x\sqrt{4 - x}$,

Domain: $(-\infty, 4]$

$y' = \dfrac{8 - 3x}{2\sqrt{4 - x}} = 0$ when $x = \dfrac{8}{3}$ and undefined when $x = 4$.

$y'' = \dfrac{3x - 16}{4(4 - x)^{3/2}} = 0$ when $x = \dfrac{16}{3}$ and undefined when $x = 4$.

**Note:** $x = \dfrac{16}{3}$ is not in the domain.

| | $y$ | $y'$ | $y''$ | Conclusion |
|---|---|---|---|---|
| $-\infty < x < \frac{8}{3}$ | | + | − | Increasing, concave down |
| $x = \frac{8}{3}$ | $\frac{16}{3\sqrt{3}}$ | 0 | − | Relative maximum |
| $\frac{8}{3} < x < 4$ | | − | − | Decreasing, concave down |
| $x = 4$ | 0 | Undefined | Undefined | Endpoint |

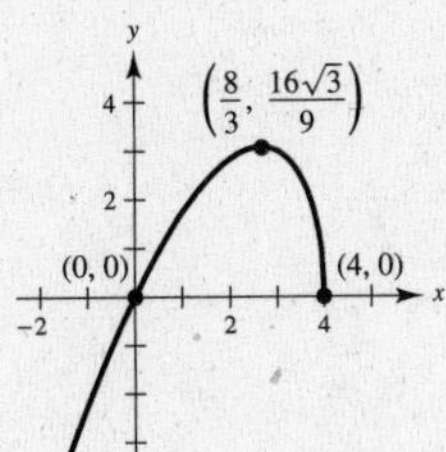

**18.** $g(x) = x\sqrt{9 - x}$ Domain: $x \le 9$

$$g'(x) = \frac{3(6 - x)}{2\sqrt{9 - x}} = 0 \text{ when } x = 6.$$

$$g''(x) = \frac{3(x - 12)}{4(9 - x)^{3/2}} < 0 \text{ when } x = 6.$$

Relative maximum: $\left(6, 6\sqrt{3}\right)$

Intercepts: $(0, 0), (9, 0)$

Concave downward on $(-\infty, 9)$

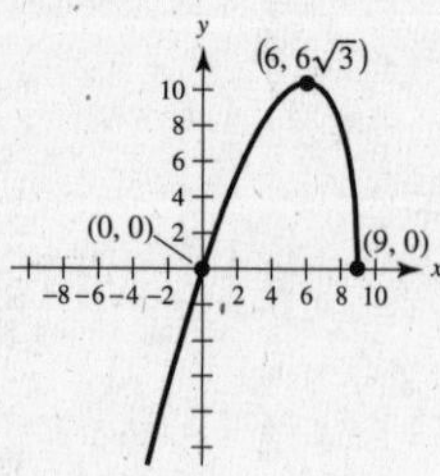


**19.** $h(x) = x\sqrt{4 - x^2}$

Domain. $-2 \le x \le 2$

$$h'(x) = \frac{4 - 2x^2}{\sqrt{4 - x^2}} = 0 \quad \text{when} \quad x = \pm\sqrt{2}$$

$$h''(x) = \frac{2x(x^2 - 6)}{\left(4 - x^2\right)^{3/2}} = 0 \quad \text{when} \quad x = 0$$

Relative maximum: $\left(\sqrt{2}, 2\right)$

Relative minimum: $\left(-\sqrt{2}, -2\right)$

Intercepts $(-2, 0), (0, 0), (2, 0)$

Symmetric with respect to origin.

Point of inflection: $(0, 0)$

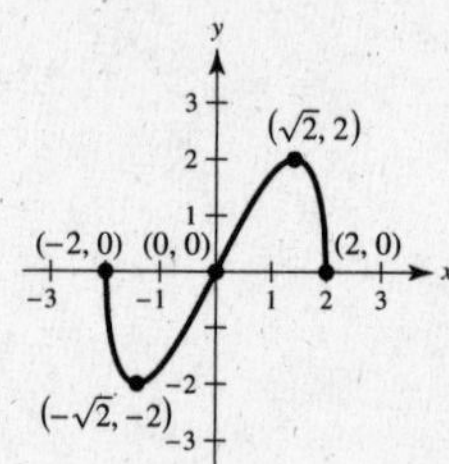


**20.** $h(x) = x\sqrt{9 - x^2}$ Domain: $-3 \le x \le 3$

$$h'(x) = \frac{9 - 2x^2}{\sqrt{9 - x^2}} = 0 \text{ when } x = \pm\frac{3}{\sqrt{2}} = \pm\frac{3\sqrt{2}}{2}.$$

$$h''(x) = \frac{x(2x^2 - 27)}{\left(9 - x^2\right)^{3/2}} = 0 \text{ when } x = 0.$$

Relative maximum: $\left(\frac{3\sqrt{2}}{2}, \frac{9}{2}\right)$

Relative minimum: $\left(-\frac{3\sqrt{2}}{2}, -\frac{9}{2}\right)$

Intercepts: $(0, 0), (\pm 3, 0)$

Symmetric with respect to the origin

Point of inflection: $(0, 0)$

**21.** $y = 3x^{2/3} - 2x$

$y' = 2x^{-1/3} - 2 = \dfrac{2(1 - x^{1/3})}{x^{1/3}}$

$= 0$ when $x = 1$ and undefined when $x = 0$.

$y'' = \dfrac{-2}{3x^{4/3}} < 0$ when $x \neq 0$.

| | $y$ | $y'$ | $y''$ | Conclusion |
|---|---|---|---|---|
| $-\infty < x < 0$ | | $-$ | $-$ | Decreasing, concave down |
| $x = 0$ | 0 | Undefined | Undefined | Relative minimum |
| $0 < x < 1$ | | $+$ | $-$ | Increasing, concave down |
| $x = 1$ | 1 | 0 | $-$ | Relative maximum |
| $1 < x < \infty$ | | $-$ | $-$ | Decreasing, concave down |

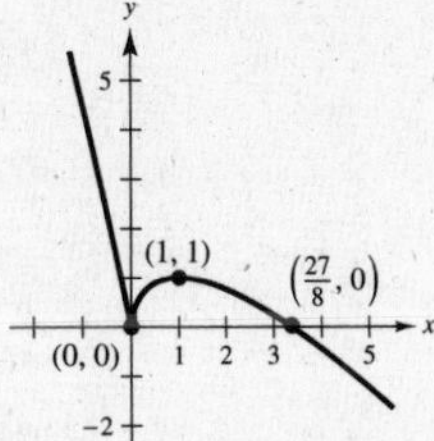


**22.** $y = 3(x - 1)^{2/3} - (x - 1)^2$

$y' = \dfrac{2}{(x - 1)^{1/3}} - 2(x - 1) = \dfrac{2 - 2(x - 1)^{4/3}}{(x - 1)^{1/3}} = 0$ when $x = 0, 2$

($y'$ undefined for $x = 1$).

$y'' = \dfrac{-2}{3(x - 1)^{4/3}} - 2 < 0$ for all $x \neq 1$.

Concave downward on $(-\infty, 1)$ and $(1, \infty)$

Relative maximum: $(0, 2), (2, 2)$

Relative minimum: $(1, 0)$

Intercepts: $(0, 2), (1, 0), (-1.280, 0), (3.280, 0)$

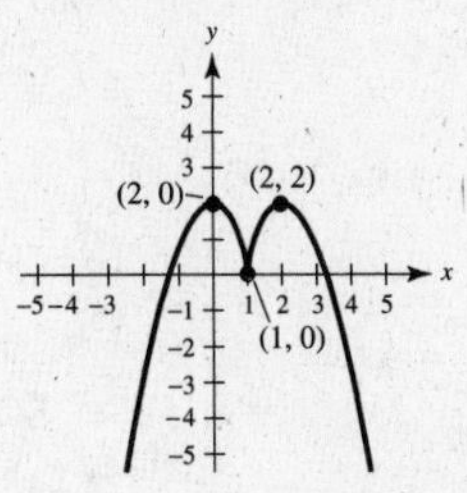

**23.** $y = x^3 - 3x^2 + 3$

$y' = 3x^2 - 6x = 3x(x - 2) = 0$ when $x = 0, x = 2$.

$y'' = 6x - 6 = 6(x - 1) = 0$ when $x = 1$.

| | $y$ | $y'$ | $y''$ | Conclusion |
|---|---|---|---|---|
| $-\infty < x < 0$ | | + | − | Increasing, concave down |
| $x = 0$ | 3 | 0 | − | Relative maximum |
| $0 < x < 1$ | | − | − | Decreasing, concave down |
| $x = 1$ | 1 | − | 0 | Point of inflection |
| $1 < x < 2$ | | − | + | Decreasing, concave up |
| $x = 2$ | −1 | 0 | + | Relative minimum |
| $2 < x < \infty$ | | + | + | Increasing, concave up |

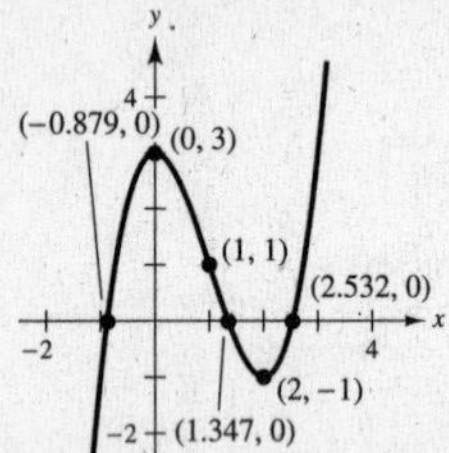


**24.** $y = -\frac{1}{3}(x^3 - 3x + 2)$

$y' = -x^2 + 1 = 0$ when $x = \pm 1$.

$y'' = -2x = 0$ when $x = 0$.

| | $y$ | $y'$ | $y''$ | Conclusion |
|---|---|---|---|---|
| $-\infty < x < -1$ | | − | + | Decreasing, concave up |
| $x = -1$ | $-\frac{4}{3}$ | 0 | + | Relative minimum |
| $-1 < x < 0$ | | + | + | Increasing, concave up |
| $x = 0$ | $-\frac{2}{3}$ | + | 0 | Point of inflection |
| $0 < x < 1$ | | + | − | Increasing, concave down |
| $x = 1$ | 0 | 0 | − | Relative maximum |
| $1 < x < \infty$ | | − | − | Decreasing, concave down |

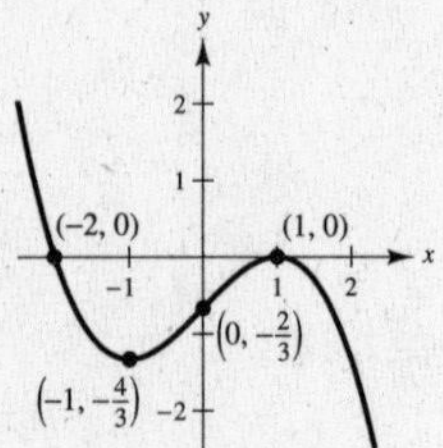

**25.** $y = 2 - x - x^3$

$y' = -1 - 3x^2$

No critical numbers

$y'' = -6x = 0$ when $x = 0$.

| | $y$ | $y'$ | $y''$ | Conclusion |
|---|---|---|---|---|
| $-\infty < x < 0$ | | $-$ | $+$ | Decreasing, concave up |
| $x = 0$ | 2 | $-$ | 0 | Point of inflection |
| $0 < x < \infty$ | | $-$ | $-$ | Decreasing, concave down |

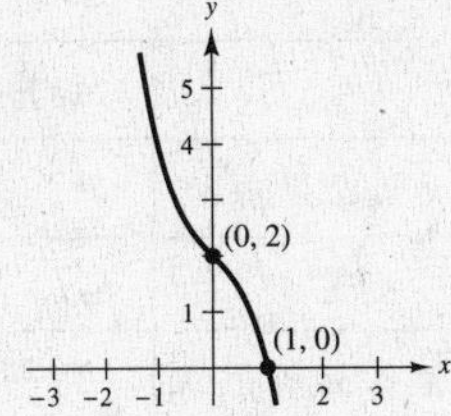


**26.** $f(x) = \frac{1}{3}(x - 1)^3 + 2$

$f'(x) = (x - 1)^2 = 0$ when $x = 1$.

$f''(x) = 2(x - 1) = 0$ when $x = 1$.

| | $f(x)$ | $f'(x)$ | $f''(x)$ | Conclusion |
|---|---|---|---|---|
| $-\infty < x < 1$ | | $+$ | $-$ | Increasing, concave down |
| $x = 1$ | 2 | 0 | 0 | Point of inflection |
| $1 < x < \infty$ | | $+$ | $+$ | Increasing, concave up |

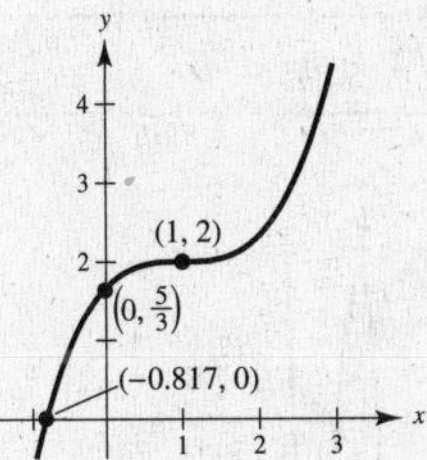


**27.** $f(x) = 3x^3 - 9x + 1$

$f'(x) = 9x^2 - 9 = 9(x^2 - 1) = 0$ when $x = \pm 1$.

$f''(x) = 18x = 0$ when $x = 0$.

| | $f(x)$ | $f'(x)$ | $f''(x)$ | Conclusion |
|---|---|---|---|---|
| $-\infty < x < -1$ | | $+$ | $-$ | Increasing, concave down |
| $x = -1$ | 7 | 0 | $-$ | Relative maximum |
| $-1 < x < 0$ | | $-$ | $-$ | Decreasing, concave down |
| $x = 0$ | 1 | $-$ | 0 | Point of inflection |
| $0 < x < 1$ | | $-$ | $+$ | Decreasing, concave up |
| $x = 1$ | $-5$ | 0 | $+$ | Relative minimum |
| $1 < x < \infty$ | | $+$ | $+$ | Increasing, concave up |

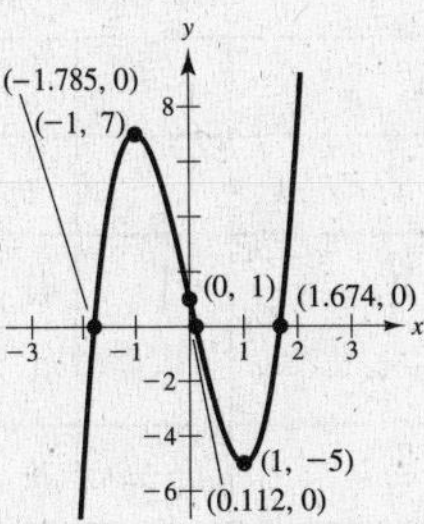

**28.** $f(x) = (x+1)(x-2)(x-5)$

$f'(x) = (x+1)(x-2) + (x+1)(x-5) + (x-2)(x-5)$

$= 3(x^2 - 4x + 1) = 0$ when $x = 2 \pm \sqrt{3}$.

$f''(x) = 6(x-2) = 0$ when $x = 2$.

| | $f(x)$ | $f'(x)$ | $f''(x)$ | Conclusion |
|---|---|---|---|---|
| $-\infty < x < 2-\sqrt{3}$ | | + | − | Increasing, concave down |
| $x = 2-\sqrt{3}$ | $6\sqrt{3}$ | 0 | − | Relative maximum |
| $2-\sqrt{3} < x < 2$ | | − | − | Decreasing, concave down |
| $x = 2$ | 0 | − | 0 | Point of inflection |
| $2 < x < 2+\sqrt{3}$ | | − | + | Decreasing, concave up |
| $x = 2+\sqrt{3}$ | $-6\sqrt{3}$ | 0 | + | Relative minimum |
| $2+\sqrt{3} < x < \infty$ | | + | + | Increasing, concave up |

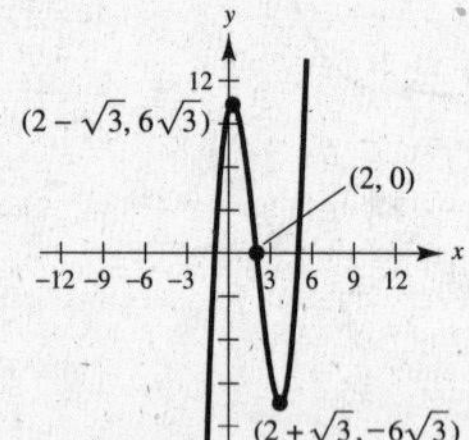


Intercepts: $(0, 10)$, $(-1, 0)$, $(2, 0)$, $(5, 0)$

**29.** $y = 3x^4 + 4x^3$

$y' = 12x^3 + 12x^2 = 12x^2(x+1) = 0$ when $x = 0, x = -1$.

$y'' = 36x^2 + 24x = 12x(3x+2) = 0$ when $x = 0, x = -\frac{2}{3}$.

| | $y$ | $y'$ | $y''$ | Conclusion |
|---|---|---|---|---|
| $-\infty < x < -1$ | | − | + | Decreasing, concave up |
| $x = -1$ | $-1$ | 0 | + | Relative minimum |
| $-1 < x < -\frac{2}{3}$ | | + | + | Increasing, concave up |
| $x = -\frac{2}{3}$ | $-\frac{16}{27}$ | + | 0 | Point of inflection |
| $-\frac{2}{3} < x < 0$ | | + | − | Increasing, concave down |
| $x = 0$ | 0 | 0 | 0 | Point of inflection |
| $0 < x < \infty$ | | + | + | Increasing, concave up |

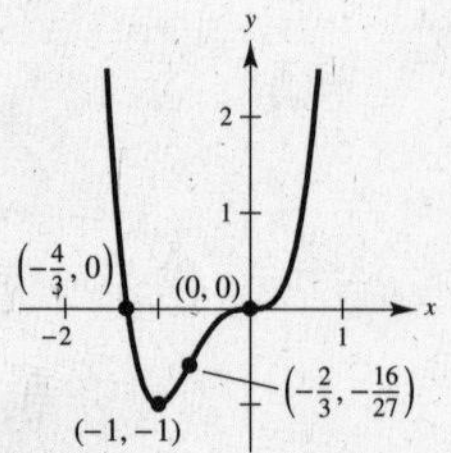

**30.** $y = 3x^4 - 6x^2 + \dfrac{5}{3}$

$y' = 12x^3 - 12x = 12x(x^2 - 1) = 0$ when $x = 0, x = \pm 1.$

$y'' = 36x^2 - 12 = 12(3x^2 - 1) = 0$ when $x = \pm\dfrac{\sqrt{3}}{3}.$

| | $y$ | $y'$ | $y''$ | Conclusion |
|---|---|---|---|---|
| $-\infty < x < -1$ | | $-$ | $+$ | Decreasing, concave up |
| $x = -1$ | $-4/3$ | 0 | $+$ | Relative minimum |
| $-1 < x < -\dfrac{\sqrt{3}}{3}$ | | $+$ | $+$ | Increasing, concave up |
| $x = -\dfrac{\sqrt{3}}{3}$ | 0 | $+$ | 0 | Point of inflection |
| $-\dfrac{\sqrt{3}}{3} < x < 0$ | | $+$ | $-$ | Increasing, concave down |
| $x = 0$ | $5/3$ | 0 | $-$ | Relative maximum |
| $0 < x < \dfrac{\sqrt{3}}{3}$ | | $-$ | $-$ | Decreasing, concave down |
| $x = \dfrac{\sqrt{3}}{3}$ | 0 | $-$ | 0 | Point of inflection |
| $\dfrac{\sqrt{3}}{3} < x < 1$ | | $-$ | $+$ | Decreasing, concave up |
| $x = 1$ | $-4/3$ | 0 | $+$ | Relative minimum |
| $1 < x < \infty$ | | $+$ | $+$ | Increasing, concave up |

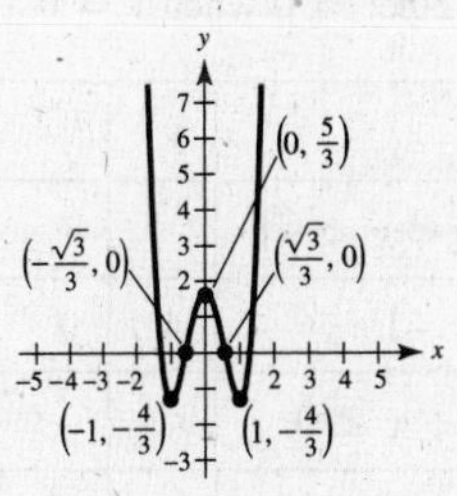


**31.** $f(x) = x^4 - 4x^3 + 16x$

$f'(x) = 4x^3 - 12x^2 + 16 = 4(x + 1)(x - 2)^2 = 0$ when $x = -1, x = 2.$

$f''(x) = 12x^2 - 24x = 12x(x - 2) = 0$ when $x = 0, x = 2.$

| | $f(x)$ | $f'(x)$ | $f''(x)$ | Conclusion |
|---|---|---|---|---|
| $-\infty < x < -1$ | | $-$ | $+$ | Decreasing, concave down |
| $x = -1$ | $-11$ | 0 | $+$ | Relative minimum |
| $-1 < x < 0$ | | $+$ | $+$ | Increasing, concave up |
| $x = 0$ | 0 | $+$ | 0 | Point of inflection |
| $0 < x < 2$ | | $+$ | $-$ | Increasing, concave down |
| $x = 2$ | 16 | 0 | 0 | Point of inflection |
| $2 < x < \infty$ | | $+$ | $+$ | Increasing, concave up |

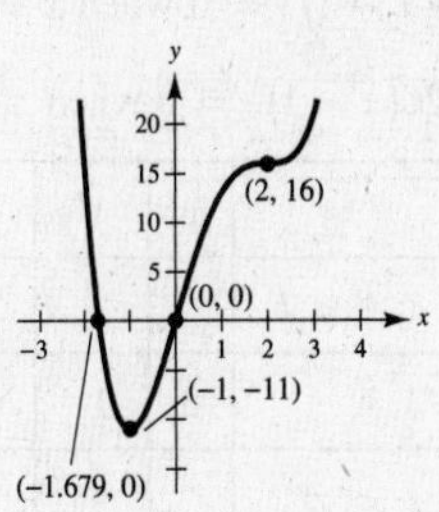

**32.** $f(x) = x^4 - 8x^3 - 16x + 5$

$f'(x) = 4x^3 - 24x^2 + 36x - 16 = 4(x - 4)(x - 1)^2 = 0$ when $x = 1, x = 4$.

$f''(x) = 12x^2 - 48x + 36 = 12x(x - 3)(x - 1) = 0$ when $x = 3, x = 1$.

| | $f(x)$ | $f'(x)$ | $f''(x)$ | Conclusion |
|---|---|---|---|---|
| $-\infty < x < 1$ | | $-$ | $+$ | Decreasing, concave up |
| $x = 1$ | 0 | 0 | 0 | Point of inflection |
| $1 < x < 3$ | | $-$ | $-$ | Decreasing, concave down |
| $x = 3$ | $-16$ | $-$ | 0 | Point of inflection |
| $3 < x < 4$ | | $-$ | $+$ | Decreasing, concave up |
| $x = 4$ | $-27$ | 0 | $+$ | Relative minimum |
| $4 < x < \infty$ | | $+$ | $+$ | Increasing, concave up |

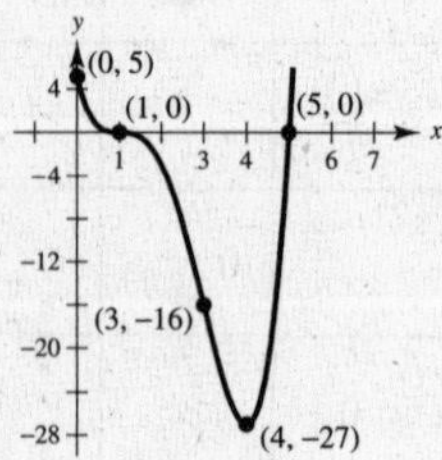


**33.** $y = x^5 - 5x$

$y' = 5x^4 - 5 = 5(x^4 - 1) = 0$ when $x = \pm 1$.

$y'' = 20x^3 = 0$ when $x = 0$.

| | $y$ | $y'$ | $y''$ | Conclusion |
|---|---|---|---|---|
| $-\infty < x < -1$ | | $+$ | $-$ | Increasing, concave down |
| $x = -1$ | 4 | 0 | $-$ | Relative maximum |
| $-1 < x < 0$ | | $-$ | $-$ | Decreasing, concave down |
| $x = 0$ | 0 | $-$ | 0 | Point of inflection |
| $0 < x < 1$ | | $-$ | $+$ | Decreasing, concave up |
| $x = 1$ | $-4$ | 0 | $+$ | Relative minimum |
| $1 < x < \infty$ | | $+$ | $+$ | Increasing, concave up |

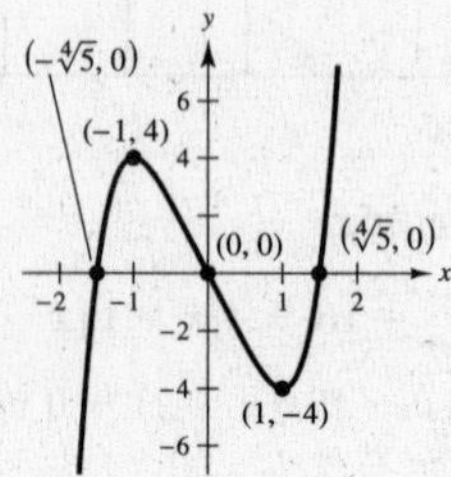


**34.** $y = (x - 1)^5$

$y' = 5(x - 1)^4 = 0$ when $x = 1$.

$y'' = 20(x - 1)^3 = 0$ when $x = 1$.

| | $y$ | $y'$ | $y''$ | Conclusion |
|---|---|---|---|---|
| $-\infty < x < 1$ | | $+$ | $-$ | Increasing, concave down |
| $x = 1$ | 0 | 0 | 0 | Point of inflection |
| $1 < x < \infty$ | | $+$ | $+$ | Increasing, concave up |

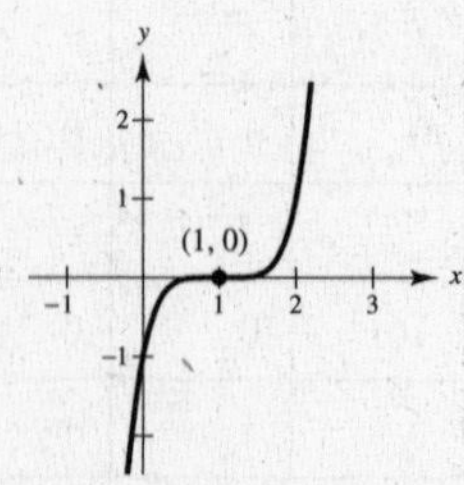

**35.** $y = |2x - 3|$

$y' = \dfrac{2(2x-3)}{|2x-3|}$ undefined at $x = \dfrac{3}{2}$.

$y'' = 0$

| | $y$ | $y'$ | Conclusion |
|---|---|---|---|
| $-\infty < x < \frac{3}{2}$ | | $-$ | Decreasing |
| $x = \frac{3}{2}$ | 0 | Undefined | Relative minimum |
| $\frac{3}{2} < x < \infty$ | | $+$ | Increasing |

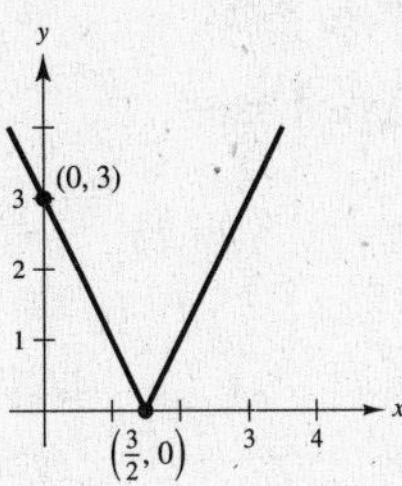


**36.** $y = |x^2 - 6x + 5|$

$y' = \dfrac{2(x-3)(x^2-6x+5)}{|x^2-6x+5|} = \dfrac{2(x-3)(x-5)(x-1)}{|(x-5)(x-1)|}$

$= 0$ when $x = 3$ and undefined when $x = 1, x = 5$.

$y'' = \dfrac{2(x^2-6x+5)}{|x^2-6x+5|} = \dfrac{2(x-5)(x-1)}{|(x-5)(x-1)|}$ undefined when $x = 1, x = 5$.

| | $y$ | $y'$ | $y''$ | Conclusion |
|---|---|---|---|---|
| $-\infty < x < 1$ | | $-$ | $+$ | Decreasing, concave up |
| $x = 1$ | 0 | Undefined | Undefined | Relative minimum, point of inflection |
| $1 < x < 3$ | | $+$ | $-$ | Increasing, concave down |
| $x = 3$ | 4 | 0 | $-$ | Relative maximum |
| $3 < x < 5$ | | $-$ | $-$ | Decreasing, concave down |
| $x = 5$ | 0 | Undefined | Undefined | Relative minimum, point of inflection |
| $5 < x < \infty$ | | $+$ | $+$ | Increasing, concave up |

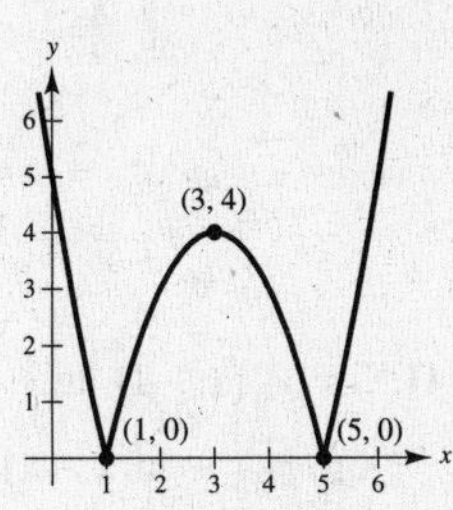


**37.** $f(x) = e^{3x}(2 - x)$

$f'(x) = -e^{3x} + 2(2 - x)e^{3x} = e^{3x}(5 - 3x)$

Critical point: $\left(\frac{5}{3}, 49.47\right)$

$f''(x) = -3e^{3x}(-4 + 3x) = 0$ when $x = \frac{4}{3}$.

Relative maximum: $\left(\frac{5}{3}, 49.47\right)$

Inflection point: $\left(\frac{4}{3}, 36.40\right)$

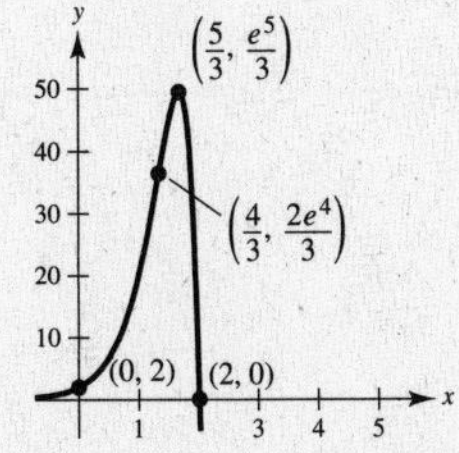


**38.** $f(x) = -2 + e^{3x}(4 - 2x)$

$f'(x) = -2e^{3x}(3x - 5)$

$f''(x) = -6e^{3x}(3x - 4)$

Horizontal asymptote (to left): $y = -2$

Critical point: $x = \frac{5}{3}$

Relative maximum: $\left(\frac{5}{3}, 96.9421\right)$

Inflection point: $\left(\frac{4}{3}, 70.7975\right)$

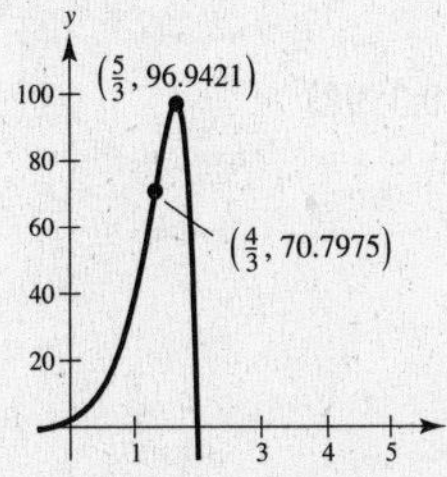

**39.** $g(t) = \dfrac{10}{1 + 4e^{-t}}$

$g'(t) = \dfrac{40e^{-t}}{\left(1 + 4e^{-t}\right)^2} > 0$ for all $t$.

$g''(t) = \dfrac{40e^{-t}\left(4e^{-t} - 1\right)}{\left(1 + 4e^{-t}\right)^3} = 0$ at $x \approx 1.386$.

$\lim\limits_{t\to\infty} g(t) = 10$

$\lim\limits_{t\to-\infty} g(t) = 0$

Point of inflection: $(1.386, 5)$

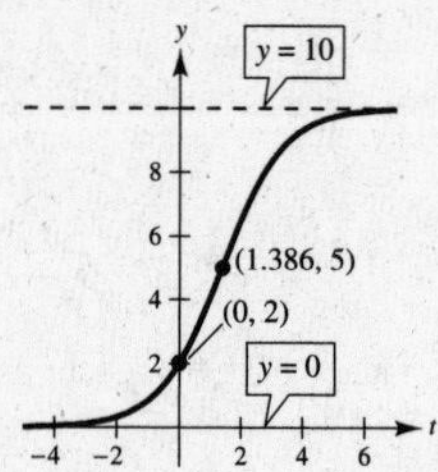


**40.** $h(x) = \dfrac{8}{2 + 3e^{-x/2}}$

$h'(x) = \dfrac{12e^{x/2}}{\left(2e^{x/2} + 3\right)^2}$

$h''(x) = \dfrac{6e^{x/2}\left(3 - 2e^{x/2}\right)}{\left(2e^{x/2} + 3\right)^3}$

$\lim\limits_{x\to\infty} h(x) = \dfrac{8}{2} = 4$

$\lim\limits_{x\to-\infty} h(x) = 0$

Horizontal asymptotes: $y = 4, y = 0$

No critical numbers, no relative extrema

$h''(x) = 0: 3 = 2e^{x/2} \Rightarrow e^{x/2} = \dfrac{3}{2} \Rightarrow x = 2\ln\left(\dfrac{3}{2}\right)$

Point of inflection: $\left(2\ln\left(\dfrac{3}{2}\right), 2\right)$

Intercept: $\left(0, \dfrac{8}{5}\right)$

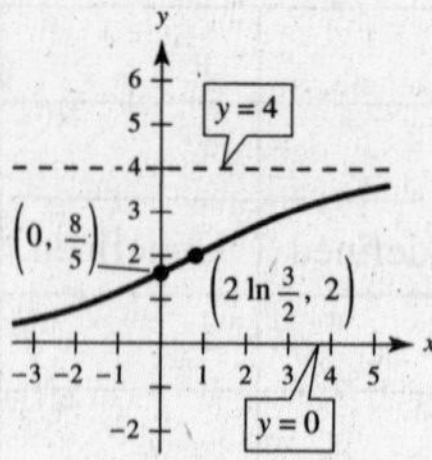


**41.** $y = (x - 1)\ln(x - 1)$, Domain: $x > 1$

$y' = 1 + \ln(x - 1)$

$y'' = \dfrac{1}{x - 1}$

Critical number: $\ln(x - 1) = -1 \Rightarrow (x - 1) = e^{-1} \Rightarrow x = 1 + e^{-1}$

Relative minimum: $(1.368, -0.368)$

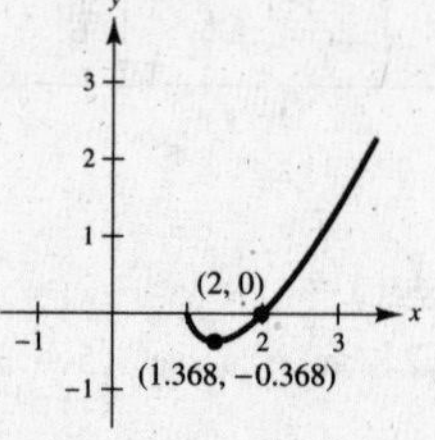


**42.** $y = \dfrac{1}{24}x^3 - \ln x$, Domain: $x > 0$

$y' = \dfrac{(x - 2)\left(x^2 + 2x + 4\right)}{8x}$

$y'' = \dfrac{x^3 + 4}{4x^2}$

Critical number: $x = 2$

Relative minimum: $(2, -0.3598)$

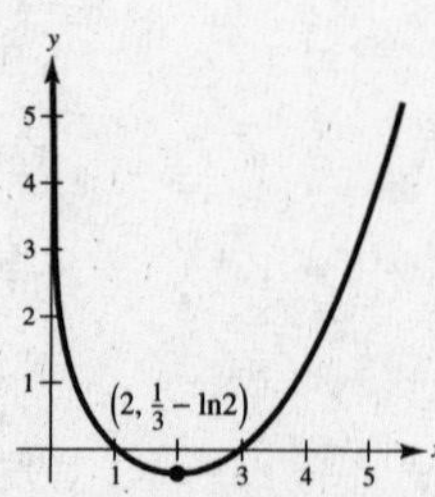

**43.** $g(x) = 6 \arcsin\left(\frac{x-2}{2}\right)^2$, Domain: $[0, 4]$

$$g'(x) = \frac{12(x-2)}{\sqrt{(4x - x^2)(x^2 - 4x + 8)}}$$

$$g''(x) = \frac{12(x^4 - 8x^3 + 24x^2 - 32x + 32)}{\left[(4x - x^2)(x^2 - 4x + 8)\right]^{3/2}}$$

Relative minimum: $(2, 0)$

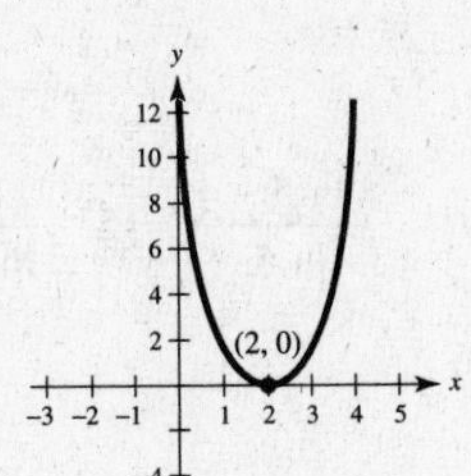


**44.** $h(x) = 7 \arctan(x + 1) - \ln(x^2 + 2x + 2)$

$$h'(x) = \frac{5 - 2x}{x^2 + 2x + 2}$$

$$h''(x) = \frac{2(x^2 - 5x - 7)}{(x^2 + 2x + 2)^2}$$

Relative maximum: $\left(\frac{5}{2}, 6.4635\right)$

Inflection points: $(6.1401, 6.0707), (-1.1401, -0.9935)$

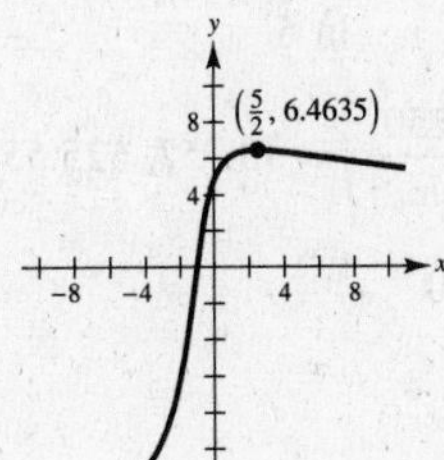


**45.** $f(x) = \frac{x}{3^{x-3}} = \frac{27x}{3^x}$

$$f'(x) = \frac{27(1 - x \ln 3)}{3^x}$$

$$f''(x) = \frac{27 \ln 3(x \ln 3 - 2)}{3^x}$$

$f'(x) = 0 \Rightarrow x = \frac{1}{\ln 3} \approx 0.910$ Critical number

Because $f'(x) > 0$ for $x < \frac{1}{\ln 3}$ and $f'(x) < 0$ for $x > \frac{1}{\ln 3}$, $\left(\frac{1}{\ln 3}, \frac{27}{e \ln 3}\right)$ is a relative maximum.

$f''(x) = 0 \Rightarrow x = \frac{2}{\ln 3} \approx 1.820$

Point of inflection: $\left(\frac{2}{\ln 3}, \frac{54}{e^2 \ln 3}\right)$

$\lim_{x \to \infty} f(x) = 0$, $\lim_{x \to -\infty} f(x) = -\infty$

Horizontal symptote: $y = 0$

Intercept: $(0, 0)$

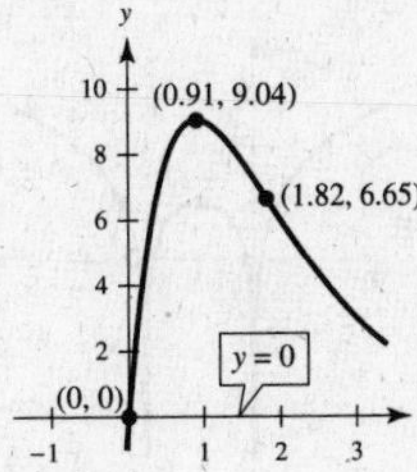

**46.** $g(t) = (5 - t)5^t$

$g'(t) = 5^t(5 \ln 5 - 1 - t \ln 5)$

$g''(t) = 5^t \ln 5(5 \ln 5 - 2 - t \ln 5)$

$$g'(t) = 0 \Rightarrow t \ln 5 = 5 \ln 5 - 1 \Rightarrow t = \frac{5 \ln 5 - 1}{\ln 5} = 5 - \frac{1}{\ln 5}$$

Critical number: $t = 5 - \dfrac{1}{\ln 5} \approx 4.379$

Because $g'(t) > 0$ for $t < 5 - \dfrac{1}{\ln 5}$ and $g'(t) < 0$ for $t > 5 - \dfrac{1}{\ln 5}$, $\left(5 - \dfrac{1}{\ln 5}, \dfrac{3125}{e \ln 5}\right) \approx (4.379, 714.301)$

is a relative maximum.

$$g''(t) = 0 \Rightarrow t = \frac{5 \ln 5 - 2}{\ln 5} = 5 - \frac{2}{\ln 5} \approx 3.757$$

Point of inflection: $\left(5 - \dfrac{2}{\ln 5}, \dfrac{6250}{e^2 \ln 5}\right) \approx (3.757, 525.553)$

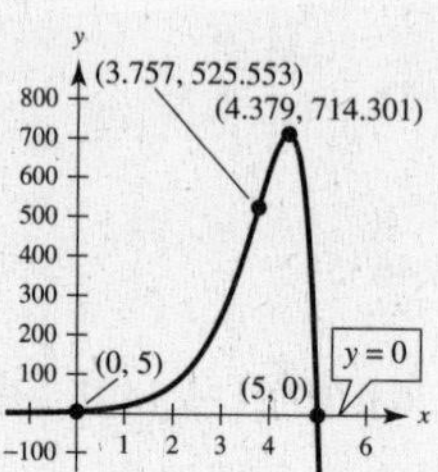


$\lim_{t \to \infty} g(t) = -\infty$ and $\lim_{t \to -\infty} g(t) = 0$

Horizontal asymptote: $y = 0$

Intercepts: $(5, 0)$, $(0, 5)$

**47.** $g(x) = \log_4(x - x^2) = \dfrac{\ln(x - x^2)}{\ln 4}$, Domain: $0 < x < 1$

$$g'(x) = \frac{2x - 1}{\ln 4 \cdot x(x - 1)}$$

$$g''(x) = \frac{-2x^2 + 2x - 1}{\ln 4 \cdot x^2(x - 1)^2}$$

Relative maximum: $\left(\dfrac{1}{2}, -1\right)$

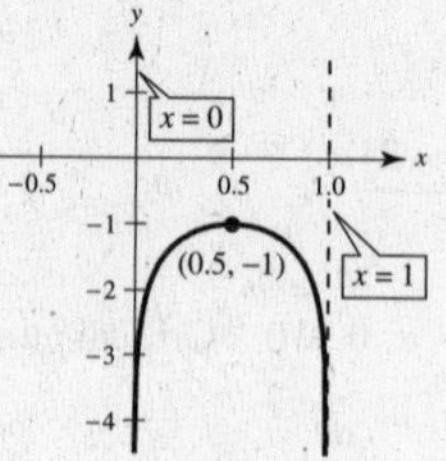


**48.** $f(x) = \log_2\left|x^2 - 4x\right| = \dfrac{\ln\left|x^2 - 4x\right|}{\ln 2}$

$$f'(x) = \frac{2(x - 2)}{x(x - 4) \ln 2}$$

$$f''(x) = \frac{-2(x^2 - 4x + 8)}{x^2(x - 4)^2 \ln 2}$$

Relative maximum: $(2, 2)$

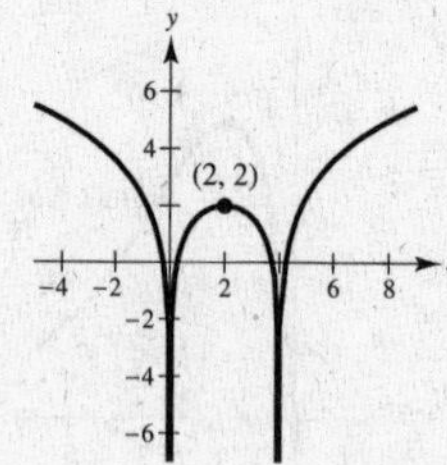

**49.** $f(x) = \dfrac{20x}{x^2+1} - \dfrac{1}{x} = \dfrac{19x^2-1}{x(x^2+1)}$

$f'(x) = \dfrac{-(19x^4 - 22x^2 - 1)}{x^2(x^2+1)^2} = 0$ for $x \approx \pm 1.10$

$f''(x) = \dfrac{2(19x^6 - 63x^9 - 3x^2 - 1)}{x^3(x^2+1)^3} = 0$ for $x \approx \pm 1.84$

Vertical asymptote: $x = 0$

Horizontal asymptote: $y = 0$

Minimum: $(-1.10, -9.05)$

Maximum: $(1.10, 9.05)$

Points of inflection: $(-1.84, -7.86), (1.84, 7.86)$

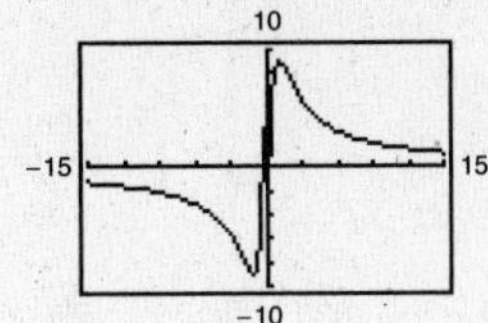


**50.** $f(x) = x + \dfrac{4}{x^2+1} = \dfrac{x^3+x+4}{x^2+1} = 0$ for $x \approx -1.379$

$f'(x) = \dfrac{x^4 + 2x^2 - 8x + 1}{(x^2+1)^2} = 0$ for $x \approx 1.608, x \approx 0.129$

$f''(x) = \dfrac{8(3x^2-1)}{(x^2+1)^3} = 0$ for $x = \pm\dfrac{1}{\sqrt{3}} \approx \pm 0.577$

Slant asymptote: $y = x$

Points of inflection: $(-0.577, 2.423), (0.577, 3.577)$

Relative maximum: $(0.129, 4.064)$

Relative minimum: $(1.608, 2.724)$

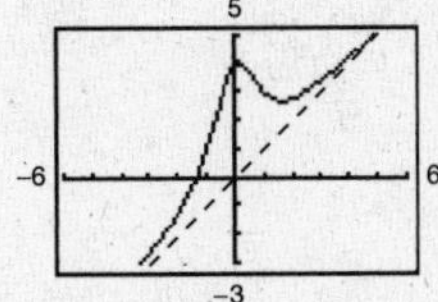


**51.** $f(x) = \dfrac{-2x}{\sqrt{x^2+7}}$

$f'(x) = \dfrac{-14}{(x^2+7)^{3/2}} < 0$

$f''(x) = \dfrac{42x}{(x^2+7)^{5/2}} = 0$ at $x = 0$

Horizontal asymptotes: $y = \pm 2$

Point of inflection: $(0, 0)$

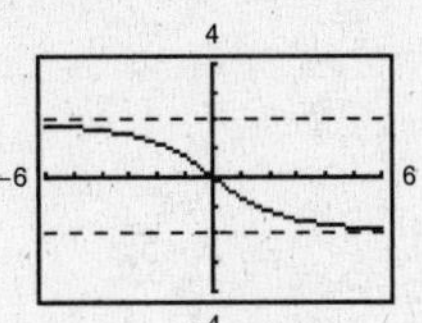


**52.** $f(x) = \dfrac{4x}{\sqrt{x^2+15}}$

$f'(x) = \dfrac{60}{(x^2+15)^{3/2}} > 0$

$f''(x) = \dfrac{-180x}{(x^2+15)^{5/2}} = 0$ at $x = 0$

Horizontal asymptotes: $y = \pm 4$

Point of inflection: $(0, 0)$

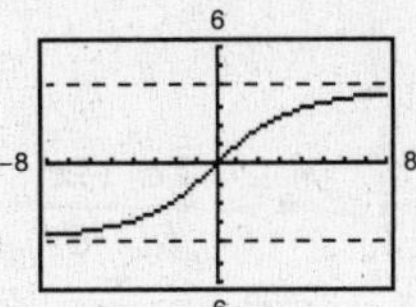


**53.** $y = \dfrac{x}{2} + \ln\left(\dfrac{x}{x+3}\right)$

$y' = \dfrac{1}{2} + \dfrac{3}{x(x+3)}$

$y'' = \dfrac{-3(2x+3)}{x^2(x+3)^2}$

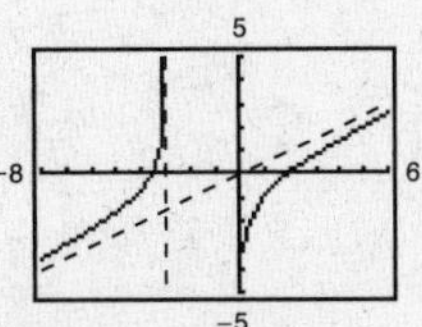


Vertical asymptotes: $x = -3, x = 0$

Slant asymptote: $y = \dfrac{x}{2}$

**54.** $y = \dfrac{3x}{2}\left(1 + 4e^{-x/3}\right)$

$y' = \dfrac{3e^{x/3} - 4(x - 3)}{2e^{x/3}}$

$y'' = \dfrac{2(x - 6)}{3e^{x/3}}$

Slant asymptote: $y = \dfrac{3}{2}x$

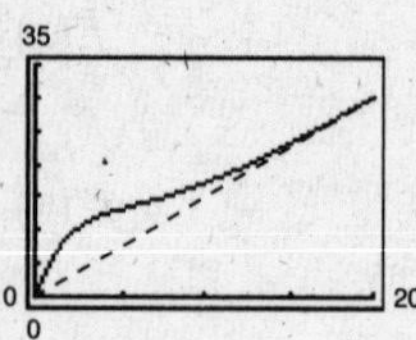


**55.** $f(x) = 2x - 4\sin x, 0 \le x \le 2\pi$

$f'(x) = 2 - 4\cos x$

$f''(x) = 4\sin x$

$f'(x) = 0 \Rightarrow \cos x = \dfrac{1}{2} \Rightarrow x = \dfrac{\pi}{3}, \dfrac{5\pi}{3}$

$f''(x) = 0 \Rightarrow x = 0, \pi, 2\pi$

Relative minimum: $\left(\dfrac{\pi}{3}, \dfrac{2\pi}{3} - 2\sqrt{3}\right)$

Relative maximum: $\left(\dfrac{5\pi}{3}, \dfrac{10\pi}{3} + 2\sqrt{3}\right)$

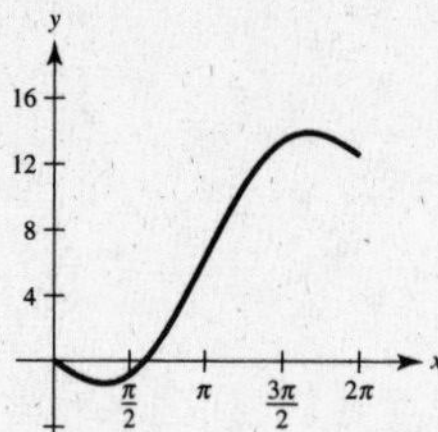


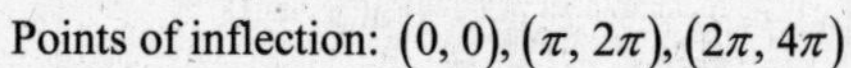
Points of inflection: $(0, 0), (\pi, 2\pi), (2\pi, 4\pi)$

**56.** $f(x) = -x + 2\cos x, 0 \le x \le 2\pi$

$f'(x) = -1 - 2\sin x$

$f''(x) = -2\cos x$

$f(x) = 0$ at $x \approx 1.030$

$f'(x) = 0 \Rightarrow \sin x = -\dfrac{1}{2} \Rightarrow x = \dfrac{7\pi}{6}, \dfrac{11\pi}{6}$

$f''(x) = 0 \Rightarrow x = \dfrac{\pi}{2}, \dfrac{3\pi}{2}$

Relative minimum: $\left(\dfrac{7\pi}{6}, -\sqrt{3} - \dfrac{7\pi}{6}\right) \approx (3.665, -5.397)$

Relative maximum: $\left(\dfrac{11\pi}{6}, \sqrt{3} - \dfrac{11\pi}{6}\right) \approx (5.760, -4.028)$

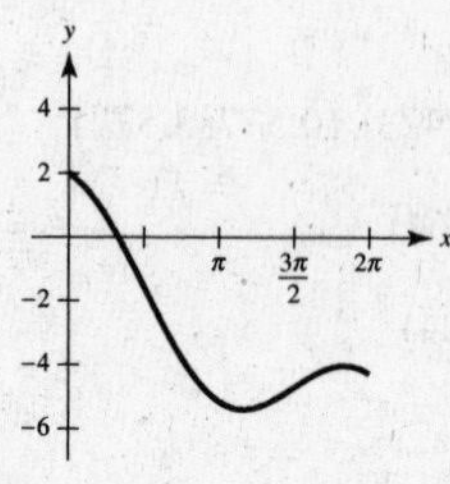

**57.** $y = \sin x - \frac{1}{18}\sin 3x, 0 \le x \le 2\pi$

$$y' = \cos x - \frac{1}{6}\cos 3x$$
$$= \cos x - \frac{1}{6}[\cos 2x \cos x - \sin 2x \sin x]$$
$$= \cos x - \frac{1}{6}\left[\left(1 - 2\sin^2 x\right)\cos x - 2\sin^2 x \cos x\right]$$
$$= \cos x\left[1 - \frac{1}{6}\left(1 - 2\sin^2 x - 2\sin^2 x\right)\right] = \cos x\left[\frac{5}{6} + \frac{2}{3}\sin^2 x\right]$$

$y' = 0$: $\quad \cos x = 0 \Rightarrow x = \pi/2, 3\pi/2$

$\frac{5}{6} + \frac{2}{3}\sin^2 x = 0 \Rightarrow \sin^2 x = -5/4$, impossible

$$y'' = -\sin x + \frac{1}{2}\sin 3x = 0 \Rightarrow 2\sin x = \sin 3x$$
$$= \sin 2x \cos x + \cos 2x \sin x$$
$$= 2\sin x \cos^2 x + \left(2\cos^2 x - 1\right)\sin x$$
$$= \sin x\left(2\cos^2 x + 2\cos^2 x - 1\right)$$
$$= \sin x\left(4\cos^2 x - 1\right)$$

$\sin x = 0 \Rightarrow x = 0, \pi, 2\pi$

$2 = 4\cos^2 x - 1 \Rightarrow \cos x = \pm\sqrt{3}/2 \Rightarrow x = \frac{\pi}{6}, \frac{5\pi}{6}, \frac{7\pi}{6}, \frac{11\pi}{6}$

Relative maximum: $\left(\frac{\pi}{2}, \frac{19}{18}\right)$

Relative minimum: $\left(\frac{3\pi}{2}, -\frac{19}{18}\right)$

Points of inflection: $\left(\frac{\pi}{6}, \frac{4}{9}\right), \left(\frac{5\pi}{6}, \frac{4}{9}\right), (\pi, 0), \left(\frac{7\pi}{6}, -\frac{4}{9}\right), \left(\frac{11\pi}{6}, -\frac{4}{9}\right)$

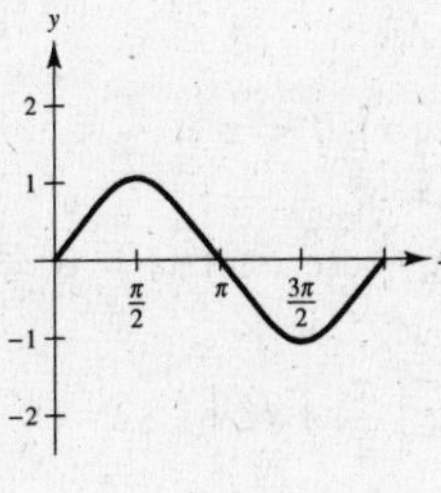


**58.** $y = \cos x - \frac{1}{4}\cos 2x, 0 \le x \le 2\pi$

$$y' = -\sin x + \frac{1}{2}\sin 2x = -\sin x + \sin x \cos x$$
$$= \sin x(\cos x - 1)$$

$y' = 0$: $\quad \sin x = 0 \Rightarrow x = 0, \pi, 2\pi$

$\cos x - 1 = 0 \Rightarrow x = 0, 2\pi$

$$y'' = -\cos x + \cos 2x$$
$$= -\cos x + 2\cos^2 x - 1$$
$$= (2\cos x + 1)(\cos x - 1)$$

$y'' = 0$: $2\cos x + 1 = 0 \Rightarrow x = \frac{2\pi}{3}, \frac{4\pi}{3}$

$\cos x - 1 = 0 \Rightarrow x = 0, 2\pi$

Relative minimum: $\left(\pi, -\frac{5}{4}\right)$

Points of inflection: $\left(\frac{2\pi}{3}, -\frac{3}{8}\right), \left(\frac{4\pi}{3}, -\frac{3}{8}\right)$

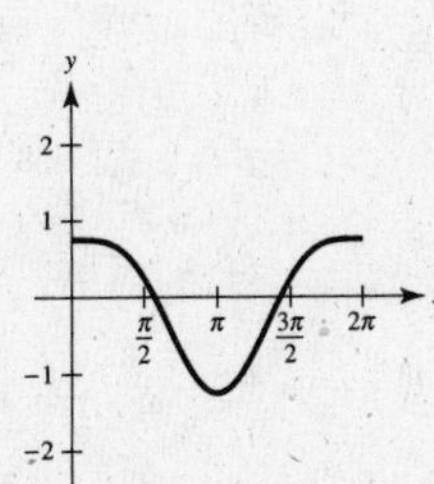

**59.** $y = 2x - \tan x, -\frac{\pi}{2} < x < \frac{\pi}{2}$

$y' = 2 - \sec^2 x = 0$ when $x = \pm\frac{\pi}{4}$.

$y'' = -2\sec^2 x \tan x = 0$ when $x = 0$.

Relative maximum: $\left(\frac{\pi}{4}, \frac{\pi}{2} - 1\right)$

Relative minimum: $\left(-\frac{\pi}{4}, 1 - \frac{\pi}{2}\right)$

Point of inflection: $(0, 0)$

Vertical asymptotes: $x = \pm\frac{\pi}{2}$

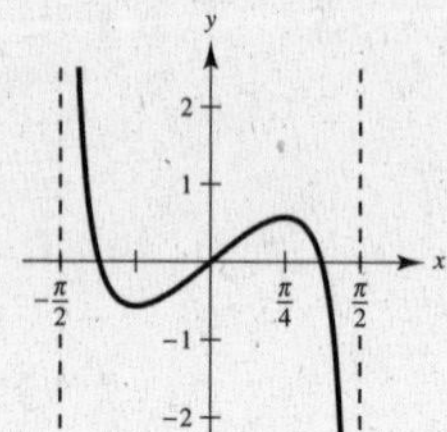

**60.** $y = 2(x - 2) + \cot x, 0 < x < \pi$

$y' = 2 - \csc^2 x = 0$ when $x = \frac{\pi}{4}, \frac{3\pi}{4}$.

$y'' = 2\csc^2 x \cot x = 0$ when $x = \frac{\pi}{2}$.

Relative maximum: $\left(\frac{3\pi}{4}, \frac{3\pi}{2} - 5\right)$

Relative minimum: $\left(\frac{\pi}{4}, \frac{\pi}{2} - 3\right)$

Point of inflection: $\left(\frac{\pi}{2}, \pi - 4\right)$

Vertical asymptotes: $x = 0, \pi$

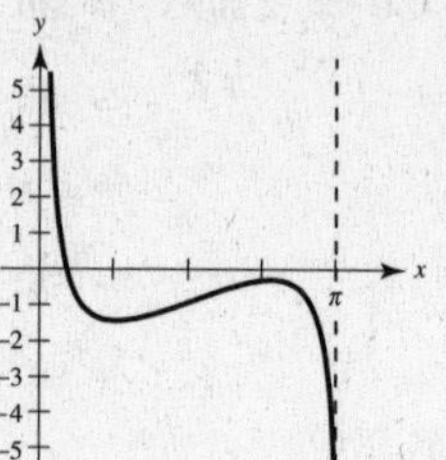

**61.** $y = 2(\csc x + \sec x), 0 < x < \frac{\pi}{2}$

$y' = 2(\sec x \tan x - \csc x \cot x) = 0 \Rightarrow x = \frac{\pi}{4}$

Relative minimum: $\left(\frac{\pi}{4}, 4\sqrt{2}\right)$

Vertical asymptotes: $x = 0, \frac{\pi}{2}$

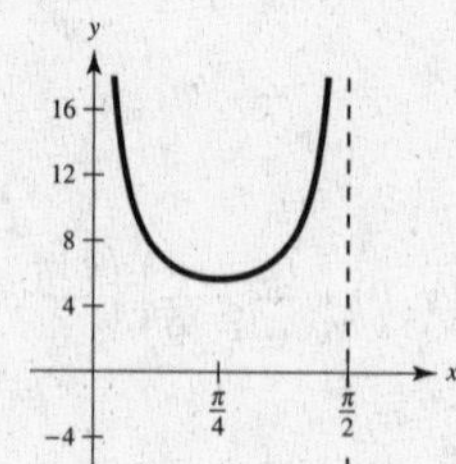

**62.** $y = \sec^2\left(\frac{\pi x}{8}\right) - 2\tan\left(\frac{\pi x}{8}\right) - 1, -3 < x < 3$

$y' = 2\sec^2\left(\frac{\pi x}{8}\right)\tan\left(\frac{\pi x}{8}\right)\left(\frac{\pi}{8}\right) - 2\sec^2\left(\frac{\pi x}{8}\right)\left(\frac{\pi}{8}\right) = 0 \Rightarrow x = 2$

Relative minimum: $(2, -1)$

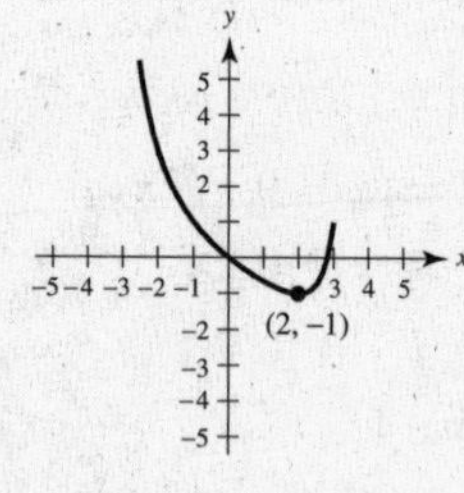

**63.** $g(x) = x \tan x, -\dfrac{3\pi}{2} < x < \dfrac{3\pi}{2}$

$g'(x) = \dfrac{x + \sin x \cos x}{\cos^2 x} = 0$ when $x = 0$.

$g''(x) = \dfrac{2(\cos x + x \sin x)}{\cos^3 x}$

Vertical asymptotes: $x = -\dfrac{3\pi}{2}, -\dfrac{\pi}{2}, \dfrac{\pi}{2}, \dfrac{3\pi}{2}$

Intercepts: $(-\pi, 0), (0, 0), (\pi, 0)$

Symmetric with respect to $y$-axis.

Increasing on $\left(0, \dfrac{\pi}{2}\right)$ and $\left(\dfrac{\pi}{2}, \dfrac{3\pi}{2}\right)$

Points of inflection: $(\pm 2.80, -1)$

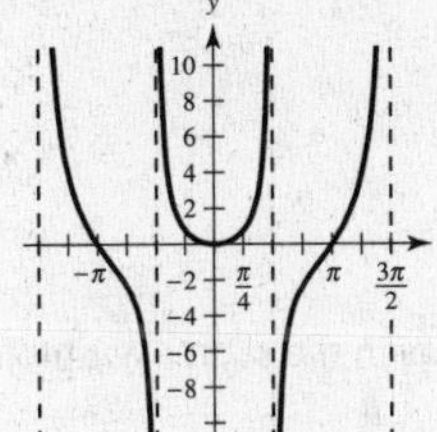

**64.** $g(x) = x \cot x, -2\pi < x < 2\pi$

$g'(x) = \dfrac{\sin x \cos x - x}{\sin^2 x}$

$g'(0)$ does not exist. But $\lim\limits_{x \to 0} x \cot x = \lim\limits_{x \to 0} \dfrac{x}{\tan x} = 1$.

Vertical asymptotes: $x = \pm 2\pi, \pm\pi$

Intercepts: $\left(-\dfrac{3\pi}{2}, 0\right), \left(-\dfrac{\pi}{2}, 0\right), \left(\dfrac{\pi}{2}, 0\right), \left(\dfrac{3\pi}{2}, 0\right)$

Symmetric with respect to $y$-axis.

Decreasing on $(0, \pi)$ and $(\pi, 2\pi)$

Points of inflection: $(\pm 4.49, 1)$

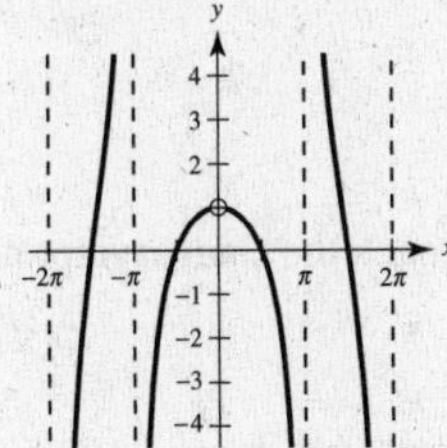

**65.** $f$ is cubic.

$f'$ is quadratic.

$f''$ is linear.

The zeros of $f'$ correspond to the points where the graph of $f$ has horizontal tangents. The zero of $f''$ corresponds to the point where the graph of $f'$ has a horizontal tangent.

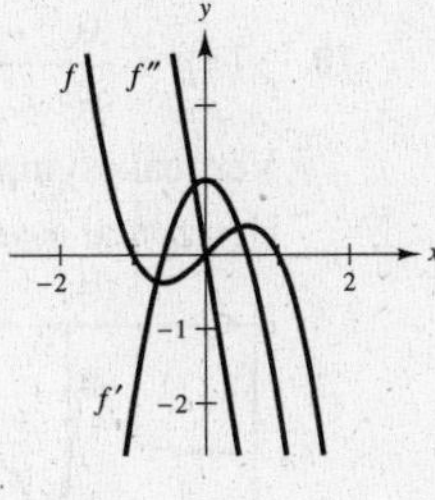

**66.** $f''$ is constant.

$f'$ is linear.

$f$ is quadratic.

The zero of $f'$ corresponds to the points where the graph of $f$ has a horizontal tangent. There are no zeros of $f''$, which means the graph of $f'$ has no horizontal tangent.

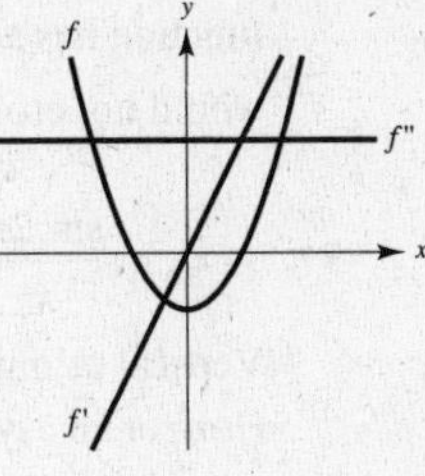

**67.** Because the slope is negative, the function is decreasing on $(2, 8)$, and so $f(3) > f(5)$.

**68.** If $f'(x) = 2$ in $[-5, 5]$, then $f(x) = 2x + 3$ and $f(2) = 7$ is the least possible value of $f(2)$. If $f'(x) = 4$ in $[-5, 5]$, then $f(x) = 4x + 3$ and $f(2) = 11$ is the greatest possible value of $f(2)$.

**69.** $f(x) = \dfrac{4(x - 1)^2}{x^2 - 4x + 5}$

Vertical asymptote: none

Horizontal asymptote: $y = 4$

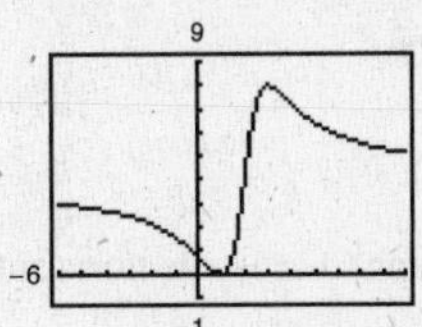

The graph crosses the horizontal asymptote $y = 4$. If a function has a vertical asymptote at $x = c$, the graph would not cross it because $f(c)$ is undefined.

**70.** $g(x) = \dfrac{3x^4 - 5x + 3}{x^4 + 1}$

Vertical asymptote: none
Horizontal asymptote: $y = 3$

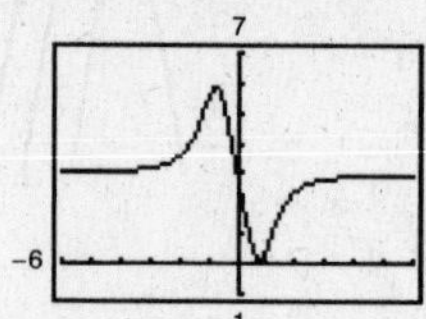

The graph crosses the horizontal asymptote $y = 3$. If a function has a vertical asymptote at $x = c$, the graph would not cross it because $f(c)$ is undefined.

**71.** $h(x) = \dfrac{\sin 2x}{x}$

Vertical asymptote: none
Horizontal asymptote: $y = 0$

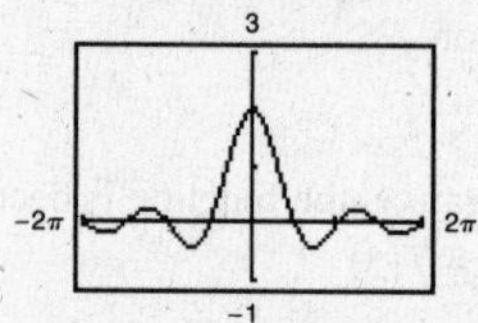

Yes, it is possible for a graph to cross its horizontal asymptote.
It is not possible to cross a vertical asymptote because the function is not continuous there.

**72.** $f(x) = \dfrac{\cos 3x}{4x}$

Vertical asymptote: $x = 0$
Horizontal asymptote: $y = 0$

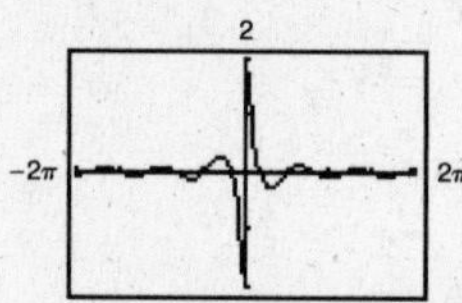

Yes, it is possible for a graph to cross its horizontal asymptote.
It is not possible to cross a vertical asymptote because the function is not continuous there.

**73.** $h(x) = \dfrac{6 - 2x}{3 - x}$

$$= \frac{2(3 - x)}{3 - x} = \begin{cases} 2, & \text{if } x \neq 3 \\ \text{Undefined}, & \text{if } x = 3 \end{cases}$$

The rational function is not reduced to lowest terms.

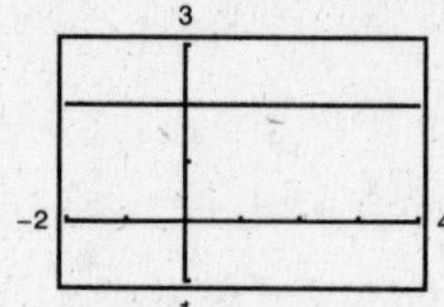

There is a hole at $(3, 2)$.

**74.** $g(x) = \dfrac{x^2 + x - 2}{x - 1}$

$$= \frac{(x + 2)(x - 1)}{x - 1} = \begin{cases} x + 2, & \text{if } x \neq 1 \\ \text{Undefined}, & \text{if } x = 1 \end{cases}$$

The rational function is not reduced to lowest terms.

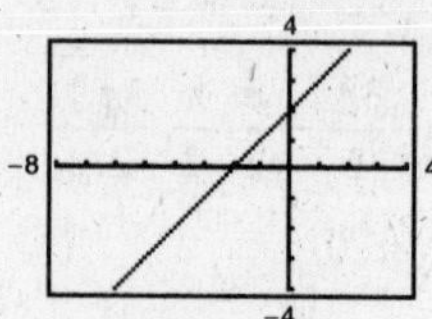

There is a hole at $(1, 3)$.

**75.** $f(x) = -\dfrac{x^2 - 3x - 1}{x - 2} = -x + 1 + \dfrac{3}{x - 2}$

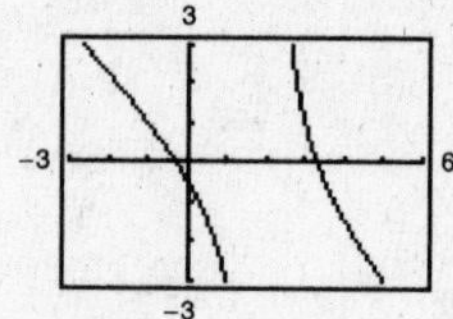

The graph appears to approach the slant asymptote $y = -x + 1$.

**76.** $g(x) = \dfrac{2x^2 - 8x - 15}{x - 5} = 2x + 2 - \dfrac{5}{x - 5}$

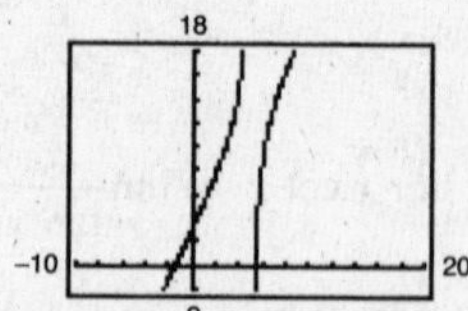

The graph appears to approach the slant asymptote $y = 2x + 2$.

**77.** $f(x) = \dfrac{x^3}{x^2 + 1} = x - \dfrac{x}{x^2 + 1}$

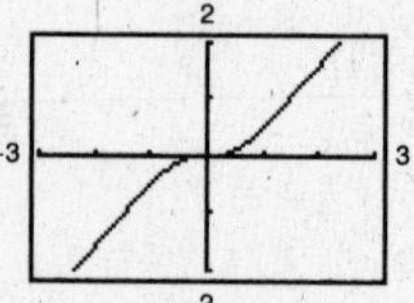

The graph appears to approach the slant asymptote $y = x$.

**78.** $h(x) = \dfrac{-x^3 + x^2 + 4}{x^2} = -x + 1 + \dfrac{4}{x^2}$

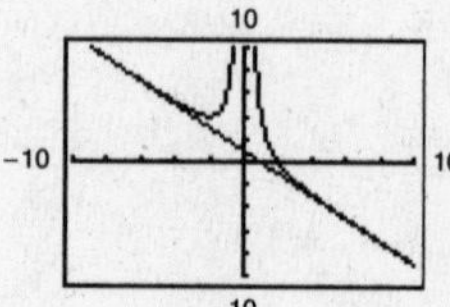

The graph appears to approach the slant asymptote $y = -x + 1$.

**79.**

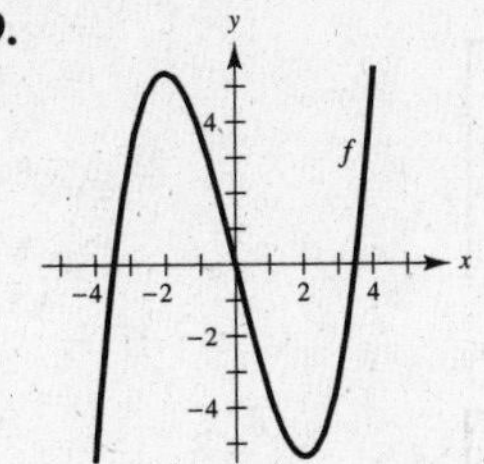

(or any vertical translation of $f$)

**80.**

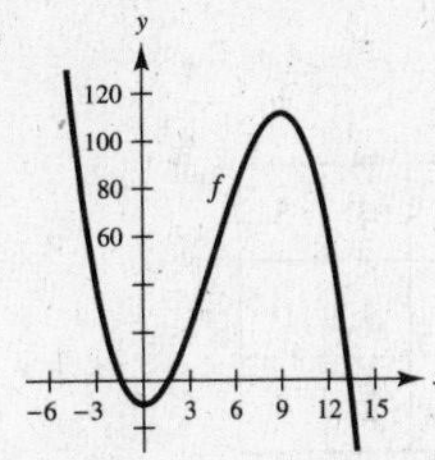

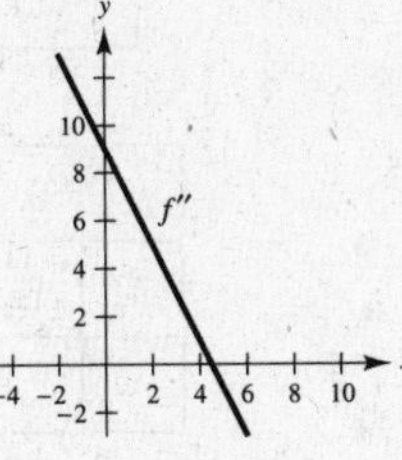

(or any vertical translation of $f$)

**81.**

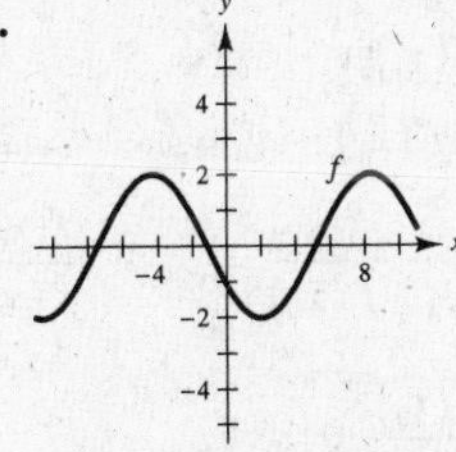

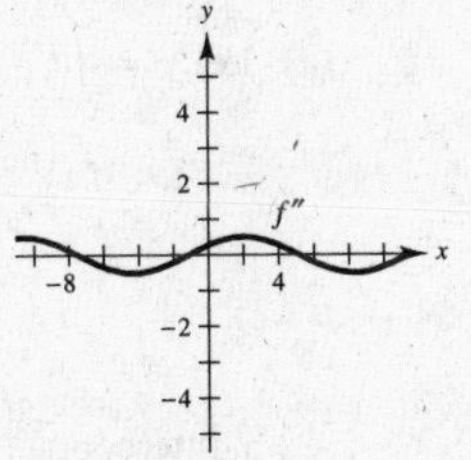

(or any vertical translation of $f$)

**82.**

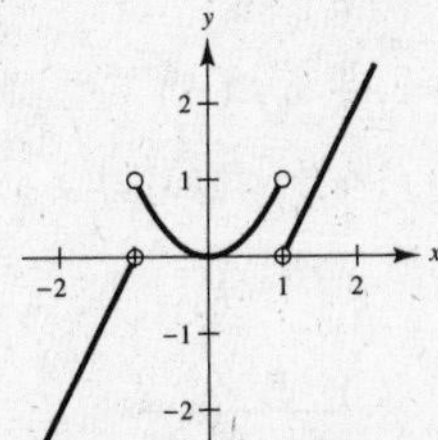

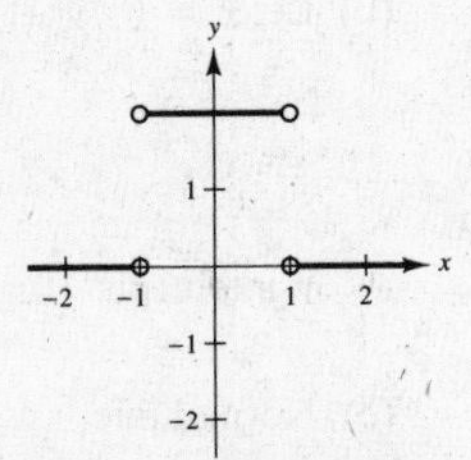

(or any vertical translation of the 3 segments of $f$)

**83.** $f(x) = \dfrac{\cos^2 \pi x}{\sqrt{x^2 + 1}}, (0, 4)$

(a)

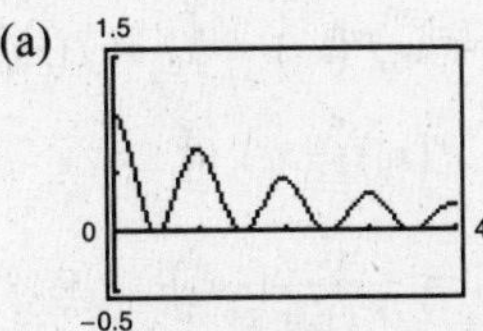

On $(0, 4)$ there seem to be 7 critical numbers: 0.5, 1.0, 1.5, 2.0, 2.5, 3.0, 3.5

(b) $f'(x) = \dfrac{-\cos \pi x\left(x \cos \pi x + 2\pi\left(x^2 + 1\right) \sin \pi x\right)}{\left(x^2 + 1\right)^{3/2}} = 0$

Critical numbers $\approx \dfrac{1}{2}, 0.97, \dfrac{3}{2}, 1.98, \dfrac{5}{2}, 2.98, \dfrac{7}{2}$.

The critical numbers where maxima occur appear to be integers in part (a), but approximating them using $f'$ shows that they are not integers.

**84.** $f(x) = \tan(\sin \pi x)$

(a)

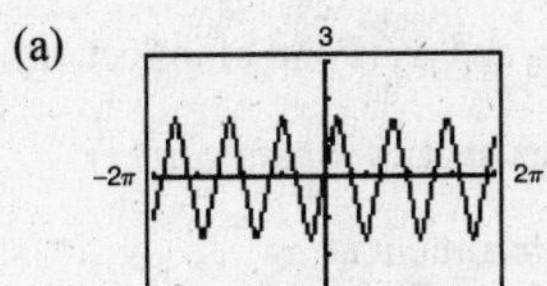

(b) $f(-x) = \tan(\sin(-\pi x)) = \tan(-\sin \pi x)$

$= -\tan(\sin \pi x) = -f(x)$

Symmetry with respect to the origin

(c) Periodic with period 2

(d) On $(-1, 1)$, there is a relative maximum at $\left(\frac{1}{2}, \tan 1\right)$ and a relative minimum at $\left(-\frac{1}{2}, -\tan 1\right)$.

(e) On $(0, 1)$, the graph of $f$ is concave downward.

**85.** Vertical asymptote: $x = 3$

Horizontal asymptote: $y = 0$

$$y = \frac{1}{x - 3}$$

**86.** Vertical asymptote: $x = -5$

Horizontal asymptote: none

$$y = \frac{x^2}{x + 5}$$

**87.** Vertical asymptote: $x = 3$

Slant asymptote: $y = 3x + 2$

$$y = 3x + 2 + \frac{1}{x - 3} = \frac{3x^2 - 7x - 5}{x - 3}$$

**88.** Vertical asymptote: $x = 2$

Slant asymptote: $y = -x$

$$y = -x + \frac{1}{x - 2} = \frac{-x^2 + 2x + 1}{x - 2}$$

**89.** (a) $f'(x) = 0$ for $x = -2$ and $x = 2$

$f'$ is negative for $-2 < x < 2$ (decreasing function).

$f'$ is positive for $x > 2$ and $x < -2$ (increasing function).

(b) $f''(x) = 0$ at $x = 0$ (Point of inflection).

$f''$ is positive for $x > 0$ (Concave upward).

$f''$ is negative for $x < 0$ (Concave downward).

(c) $f'$ is increasing on $(0, \infty)$. $(f'' > 0)$

(d) $f'(x)$ is minimum at $x = 0$. The rate of change of $f$ at $x = 0$ is less than the rate of change of $f$ for all other values of $x$.

**90.** (a) $f'(x) = 0$ at $x_0$, $x_2$ and $x_4$ (Horizontal tangent)

(b) $f''(x) = 0$ at $x_2$ and $x_3$ (Point of inflection)

(c) $f'(x)$ does not exist at $x_1$ (Sharp corner)

(d) $f$ has a relative maximum at $x_1$

(e) $f$ has a point of inflection at $x_2$ and $x_3$. (Change in concavity)

**91.** $f(x) = \dfrac{ax}{(x-b)^2}$

Answers will vary. *Sample answer*: The graph has a vertical asymptote at $x = b$. If $a$ and $b$ are both positive, or both negative, then the graph of $f$ approaches $\infty$ as $x$ approaches $b$, and the graph has a minimum at $x = -b$. If $a$ and $b$ have opposite signs, then the graph of $f$ approaches $-\infty$ as $x$ approaches $b$, and the graph has a maximum at $x = -b$.

**92.** $f(x) = \dfrac{1}{2}(ax)^2 - (ax) = \dfrac{1}{2}(ax)(ax - 2),\ a \neq 0$

$f'(x) = a^2x - a = a(ax - 1) = 0$ when $x = \dfrac{1}{a}$.

$f''(x) = a^2 > 0$ for all $x$.

(a) Intercepts: $(0, 0), \left(\dfrac{2}{a}, 0\right)$

Relative minimum: $\left(\dfrac{1}{a}, -\dfrac{1}{2}\right)$

Points of inflection: none

(b)

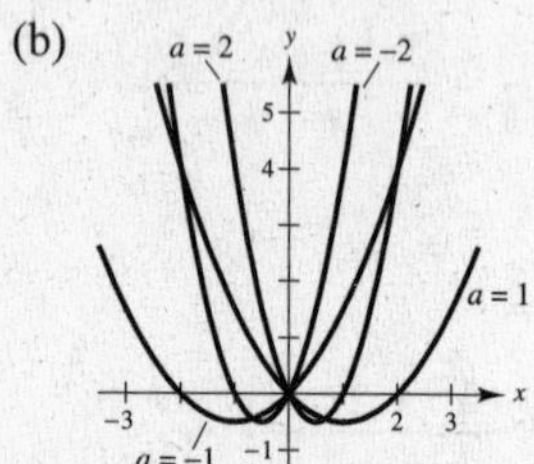


**93.** $f(x) = \dfrac{2x^n}{x^4 + 1}$

(a) For $n$ even, $f$ is symmetric about the $y$-axis. For $n$ odd, $f$ is symmetric about the origin.

(b) The $x$-axis will be the horizontal asymptote if the degree of the numerator is less than 4. That is, $n = 0, 1, 2, 3$.

(c) $n = 4$ gives $y = 2$ as the horizontal asymptote.

(d) There is a slant asymptote $y = 2x$ if

$n = 5$: $\dfrac{2x^5}{x^4 + 1} = 2x - \dfrac{2x}{x^4 + 1}$.

(e)

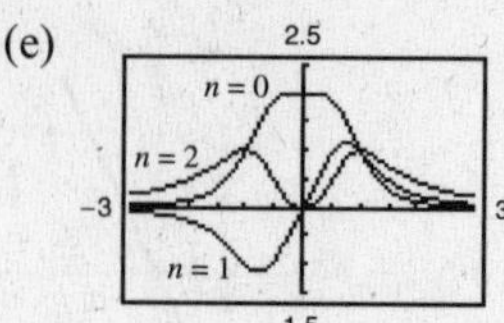


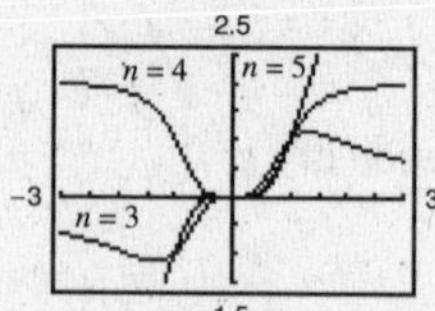


| $n$ | 0 | 1 | 2 | 3 | 4 | 5 |
|---|---|---|---|---|---|---|
| $M$ | 1 | 2 | 3 | 2 | 1 | 0 |
| $N$ | 2 | 3 | 4 | 5 | 2 | 3 |

**94.** Tangent line at $P$: $y - y_0 = f'(x_0)(x - x_0)$

(a) Let $y = 0$: $-y_0 = f'(x_0)(x - x_0)$

$$f'(x_0)x = x_0 f'(x_0) - y_0$$

$$x = x_0 - \frac{y_0}{f'(x_0)} = x_0 - \frac{f(x_0)}{f'(x_0)}$$

$x$-intercept: $\left(x_0 - \dfrac{f(x_0)}{f'(x_0)}, 0\right)$

(b) Let $x = 0$: $y - y_0 = f'(x_0)(-x_0)$

$$y = y_0 - x_0 f'(x_0)$$

$$y = f(x_0) - x_0 f'(x_0)$$

$y$-intercept: $(0, f(x_0) - x_0 f'(x_0))$

(c) Normal line: $y - y_0 = -\dfrac{1}{f'(x_0)}(x - x_0)$

Let $y = 0$: $-y_0 = -\dfrac{1}{f'(x_0)}(x - x_0)$

$$-y_0 f'(x_0) = -x + x_0$$

$$x = x_0 + y_0 f'(x_0) = x_0 + f(x_0)f'(x_0)$$

$x$-intercept: $(x_0 + f(x_0)f'(x_0), 0)$

(d) Let $x = 0$: $y - y_0 = \dfrac{-1}{f'(x_0)}(-x_0)$

$$y = y_0 + \frac{x_0}{f'(x_0)}$$

$y$-intercept: $\left(0, y_0 + \dfrac{x_0}{f'(x_0)}\right)$

(e) $|BC| = \left|x_0 - \dfrac{f(x_0)}{f'(x_0)} - x_0\right| = \left|\dfrac{f(x_0)}{f'(x_0)}\right|$

(f) $|PC|^2 = y_0^2 + \left(\frac{f(x_0)}{f'(x_0)}\right) = \frac{f(x_0)^2 f'(x_0)^2 + f(x_0)^2}{f'(x_0)^2}$

$|PC| = \left|\frac{f(x_0)\sqrt{1 + [f'(x_0)]^2}}{f'(x_0)}\right|$

(g) $|AB| = |x_0 - (x_0 + f(x_0)f'(x_0))| = |f(x_0)f'(x_0)|$

(h) $|AP|^2 = f(x_0)^2 f'(x_0)^2 + y_0^2$

$|AP| = |f(x_0)|\sqrt{1 + [f'(x_0)]^2}$

**95.**

| $h$ | 0 | 5 | 10 | 15 | 20 |
|---|---|---|---|---|---|
| $P$ | 10,332 | 5,583 | 2,376 | 1,240 | 517 |
| $\ln P$ | 9.243 | 8.627 | 7.773 | 7.123 | 6.248 |

(a)

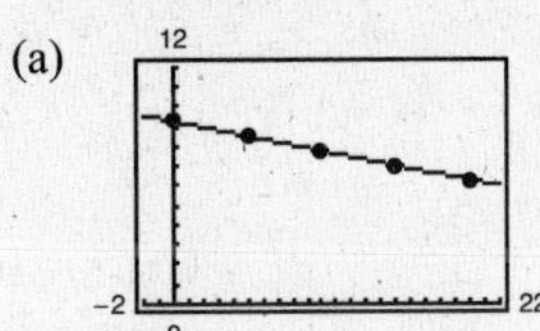


$y = -0.1499h + 9.3018$ is the regression line for data $(h, \ln P)$.

(b) $\ln P = ah + b$

$P = e^{ah+b} = e^b e^{ah}$

$P = Ce^{ah}, C = e^b$

For our data, $a = -0.1499$ and $C = e^{9.3018} = 10{,}957.7$.

$P = 10{,}957.7e^{-0.1499h}$

(c)

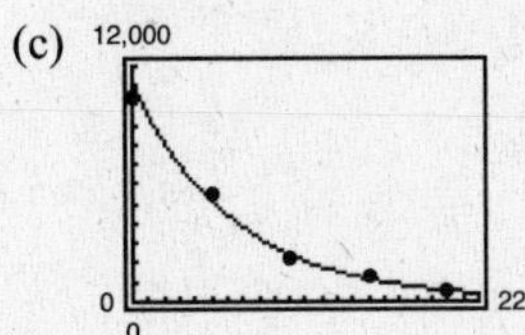


(d) $\frac{dP}{dh} = (10{,}957.71)(-0.1499)e^{-0.1499h}$

$= -1.642.56e^{-0.1499h}$

For $h = 5$, $\frac{dP}{dh} \approx -776.3$. For $h = 18$,

$\frac{dP}{dh} \approx -110.6$.

**96.** $g(x) = \ln f(x), f(x) > 0$

$g'(x) = \frac{f'(x)}{f(x)}$

(a) Yes. If the graph of $g$ is increasing, then $g'(x) > 0$. Because $f(x) > 0$, you know that $f'(x) = g'(x)f(x)$ and $f'(x) > 0$. So, the graph of $f$ is increasing.

(b) No. Let $f(x) = x^2 + 1$ (positive and concave up). $g(x) = \ln(x^2 + 1)$ is not concave up.

**97.** (a) $f(x) = \ln x, g(x) = \sqrt{x}$

$f'(x) = \frac{1}{x}, g'(x) = \frac{1}{2\sqrt{x}}$

For $x > 4$, $g'(x) > f'(x)$. $g$ is increasing at a higher rate than $f$ for "large" values of $x$.

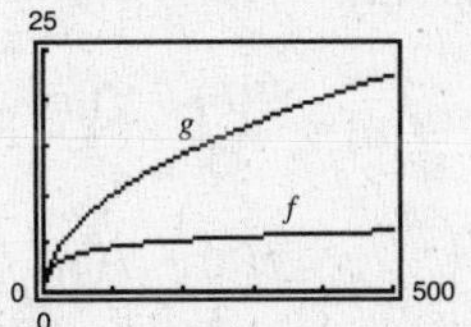


(b) $f(x) = \ln x, g(x) = \sqrt[4]{x}$

$f'(x) = \frac{1}{x}, g'(x) = \frac{1}{4\sqrt[4]{x^3}}$

For $x > 256$, $g'(x) > f'(x)$. $g$ is increasing at a higher rate than $f$ for "large" values of $x$. $f(x) = \ln x$ increases very slowly for "large" values of $x$.

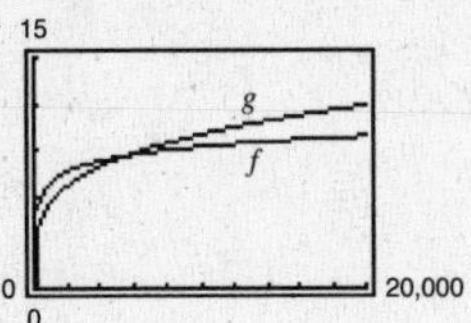


**98.** $y = \sqrt{4 + 16x^2}$

As $x \to \infty, y \to 4x$. As $x \to -\infty, y \to -4x$.

Slant asymptotes: $y = \pm 4x$

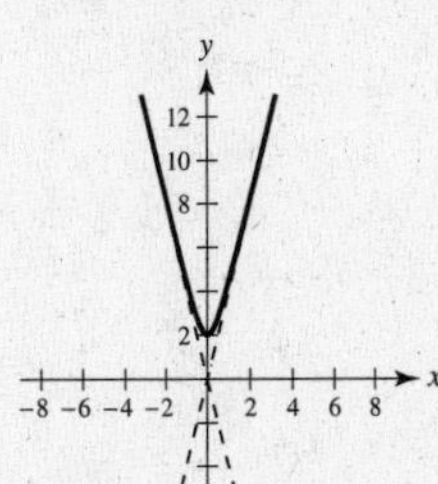

**99.** $y = \sqrt{x^2 + 6x} = \sqrt{(x + 3)^2 - 9}$

$y \to x + 3$ as $x \to \infty$, and $y \to -x - 3$ as $x \to -\infty$.

Slant asymptotes: $y = x + 3,\ y = -x - 3$

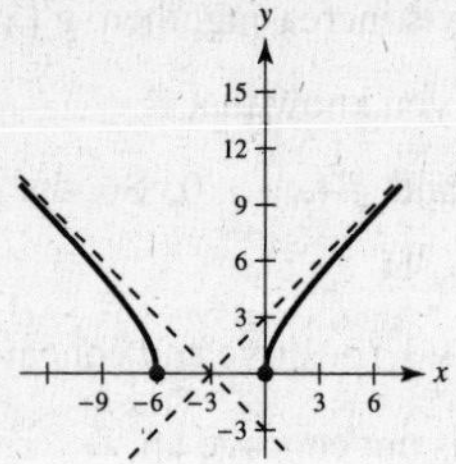


**100.** Let $\lambda = \dfrac{\dfrac{f(x) - f(a)}{x - a} - \dfrac{f(b) - f(a)}{b - a}}{x - b}$, $a < x < b$.

$$\lambda(x - b) = \frac{f(x) - f(a)}{x - a} - \frac{f(b) - f(a)}{b - a}$$

$$\lambda(x - b)(x - a) = f(x) - f(a) - \frac{f(b) - f(a)}{b - a}(x - a)$$

$$f(x) = f(a) + \frac{f(b) - f(a)}{b - a}(x - a) + \lambda(x - b)(x - a)$$

Let $h(t) = f(t) - \left\{f(a) + \dfrac{f(b) - f(a)}{b - a}(t - a) + \lambda(t - a)(t - b)\right\}$.

$h(a) = 0,\ h(b) = 0,\ h(x) = 0$

By Rolle's Theorem, there exist numbers $\alpha_1$ and $\alpha_2$ such that $a < \alpha_1 < x < \alpha_2 < b$ and $h'(\alpha_1) = h'(\alpha_2) = 0$. By Rolle's Theorem, there exists $\beta$ in $(a, b)$ such that $h''(\beta) = 0$. Finally,

$0 = h''(\beta) = f''(\beta) - \{2\lambda\} \Rightarrow \lambda = \frac{1}{2}f''(\beta)$.

## Section 4.7 Optimization Problems

**1.** (a)

| First Number, $x$ | Second Number | Product, $P$ |
|---|---|---|
| 10 | 110 – 10 | 10(110 – 10) = 1000 |
| 20 | 110 – 20 | 20(110 – 20) = 1800 |
| 30 | 110 – 30 | 30(110 – 30) = 2400 |
| 40 | 110 – 40 | 40(110 – 40) = 2800 |
| 50 | 110 – 50 | 50(110 – 50) = 3000 |
| 60 | 110 – 60 | 60(110 – 60) = 3000 |

(b)

| First Number, $x$ | Second Number | Product, $P$ |
|---|---|---|
| 10 | 110 – 10 | 10(110 – 10) = 1000 |
| 20 | 110 – 20 | 20(110 – 20) = 1800 |
| 30 | 110 – 30 | 30(110 – 30) = 2400 |
| 40 | 110 – 40 | 40(110 – 40) = 2800 |
| 50 | 110 – 50 | 50(110 – 50) = 3000 |
| 60 | 110 – 60 | 60(110 – 60) = 3000 |
| 70 | 110 – 70 | 70(110 – 70) = 2800 |
| 80 | 110 – 80 | 80(110 – 80) = 2400 |
| 90 | 110 – 90 | 90(110 – 90) = 1800 |
| 100 | 110 – 100 | 100(110 – 100) = 1000 |

The maximum is attained near $x = 50$ and 60.

(c) $P = x(110 - x) = 110x - x^2$

(d)

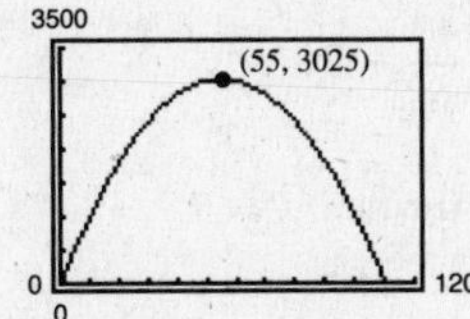


The solution appears to be $x = 55$.

(e) $\dfrac{dP}{dx} = 110 - 2x = 0$ when $x = 55$.

$$\frac{d^2P}{dx^2} = -2 < 0$$

$P$ is a maximum when $x = 110 - x = 55$. The two numbers are 55 and 55.

**2.** (a)

| Height, $x$ | Length & Width | Volume |
|---|---|---|
| 1 | $24 - 2(1)$ | $1[24 - 2(1)]^2 = 484$ |
| 2 | $24 - 2(2)$ | $2[24 - 2(2)]^2 = 800$ |
| 3 | $24 - 2(3)$ | $3[24 - 2(3)]^2 = 972$ |
| 4 | $24 - 2(4)$ | $4[24 - 2(4)]^2 = 1024$ |
| 5 | $24 - 2(5)$ | $5[24 - 2(5)]^2 = 980$ |
| 6 | $24 - 2(6)$ | $6[24 - 2(6)]^2 = 864$ |

The maximum is attained near $x = 4$.

(b) $V = x(24 - 2x)^2, 0 < x < 12$

(c) $\dfrac{dV}{dx} = 2x(24 - 2x)(-2) + (24 - 2x)^2 = (24 - 2x)(24 - 6x)$

$= 12(12 - x)(4 - x) = 0$ when $x = 12, 4$ (12 is not in the domain).

$\dfrac{d^2V}{dx^2} = 12(2x - 16)$

$\dfrac{d^2V}{dx^2} < 0$ when $x = 4$.

When $x = 4$, $V = 1024$ is maximum.

(d)

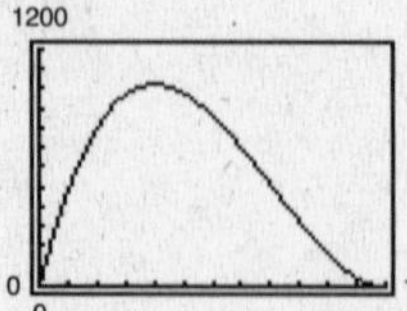


The maximum volume seems to be 1024.

**3.** Let $x$ and $y$ be two positive numbers such that $x + y = S$.

$P = xy = x(S - x) = Sx - x^2$

$\dfrac{dP}{dx} = S - 2x = 0$ when $x = \dfrac{S}{2}$.

$\dfrac{d^2P}{dx^2} = -2 < 0$ when $x = \dfrac{S}{2}$.

$P$ is a maximum when $x = y = S/2$.

**4.** Let $x$ and $y$ be two positive numbers such that $xy = 185$.

$S = x + y = x + \dfrac{185}{x}$

$\dfrac{dS}{dx} = 1 - \dfrac{185}{x^2} = 0$ when $x = \sqrt{185}$.

$\dfrac{d^2S}{dx^2} = \dfrac{370}{x^3} > 0$ when $x = \sqrt{185}$

$S$ is a minimum when $x = y = \sqrt{185}$.

**5.** Let $x$ and $y$ be two positive numbers such that $xy = 147$.

$S = x + 3y = \dfrac{147}{y} + 3y$

$\dfrac{dS}{dy} = 3 - \dfrac{147}{y^2} = 0$ when $y = 7$.

$\dfrac{d^2S}{dy^2} = \dfrac{294}{y^3} > 0$ when $y = 7$.

$S$ is minimum when $y = 7$ and $x = 21$.

**6.** Let $x$ be a positive number.

$S = x + \dfrac{1}{x}$

$\dfrac{dS}{dx} = 1 - \dfrac{1}{x^2} = 0$ when $x = 1$.

$\dfrac{d^2S}{dx^2} = \dfrac{2}{x^3} > 0$ when $x = 1$.

The sum is a minimum when $x = 1$ and $1/x = 1$.

**7.** Let $x$ and $y$ be two positive numbers such that $x + 2y = 108$.

$$P = xy = y(108 - 2y) = 108y - 2y^2$$

$$\frac{dP}{dy} = 108 - 4y = 0 \text{ when } y = 27.$$

$$\frac{d^2P}{dy^2} = -4 < 0 \text{ when } y = 27.$$

$P$ is a maximum when $x = 54$ and $y = 27$.

**8.** Let $x$ and $y$ be two positive numbers such that $x^2 + y = 54$.

$$P = xy = x(54 - x^2) = 54x - x^3$$

$$\frac{dP}{dx} = 54 - 3x^2 = 0 \text{ when } x = 3\sqrt{2}.$$

$$\frac{d^2P}{dx^2} = -6x < 0 \text{ when } x = 3\sqrt{2}.$$

The product is a maximum when $x = 3\sqrt{2}$ and $y = 36$.

**9.** Let $x$ be the length and $y$ the width of the rectangle.

$$2x + 2y = 80$$

$$y = 40 - x$$

$$A = xy = x(40 - x) = 40x - x^2$$

$$\frac{dA}{dx} = 40 - 2x = 0 \text{ when } x = 20.$$

$$\frac{d^2A}{dx^2} = -2 < 0 \text{ when } x = 20.$$

$A$ is maximum when $x = y = 20$ m.

**10.** Let $x$ be the length and $y$ the width of the rectangle.

$$2x + 2y = P$$

$$y = \frac{P - 2x}{2} = \frac{P}{2} - x$$

$$A = xy = x\left(\frac{P}{2} - x\right) = \frac{P}{2}x - x^2$$

$$\frac{dA}{dx} = \frac{P}{2} - 2x = 0 \text{ when } x = \frac{P}{4}.$$

$$\frac{d^2A}{dx^2} = -2 < 0 \text{ when } x = \frac{P}{4}.$$

$A$ is maximum when $x = y = P/4$ units. (A square!)

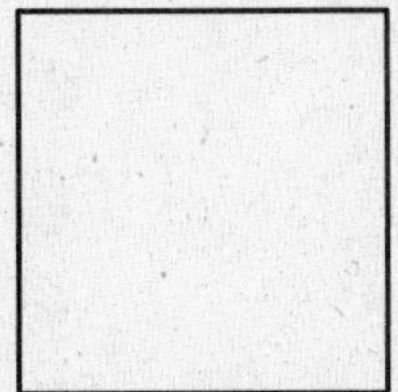


**11.** Let $x$ be the length and $y$ the width of the rectangle.

$$xy = 32$$

$$y = \frac{32}{x}$$

$$P = 2x + 2y = 2x + 2\left(\frac{32}{x}\right) = 2x + \frac{64}{x}$$

$$\frac{dP}{dx} = 2 - \frac{64}{x^2} = 0 \text{ when } x = 4\sqrt{2}.$$

$$\frac{d^2P}{dx^2} = \frac{128}{x^3} > 0 \text{ when } x = 4\sqrt{2}.$$

$P$ is minimum when $x = y = 4\sqrt{2}$ ft.

**12.** Let $x$ be the length and $y$ the width of the rectangle.

$$xy = A$$

$$y = \frac{A}{x}$$

$$P = 2x + 2y = 2x + 2\left(\frac{A}{x}\right) = 2x + \frac{2A}{x}$$

$$\frac{dP}{dx} = 2 - \frac{2A}{x^2} = 0 \text{ when } x = \sqrt{A}.$$

$$\frac{d^2P}{dx^2} = \frac{4A}{x^3} > 0 \text{ when } x = \sqrt{A}.$$

$P$ is minimum when $x = y = \sqrt{A}$ cm. (A square!)

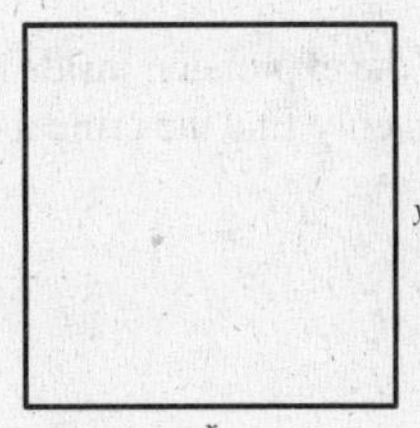


**13.** $f(x) = x^2, \left(2, \frac{1}{2}\right)$

$$d = \sqrt{(x - 2)^2 + \left[x^2 - (1/2)\right]^2}$$

$$= \sqrt{x^4 - 4x + (17/4)}$$

Because $d$ is smallest when the expression inside the radical is smallest, you need only find the critical numbers of

$$f(x) = x^4 - 4x + \tfrac{17}{4}.$$

$$f'(x) = 4x^3 - 4 = 0$$

$$x = 1$$

By the First Derivative Test, the point nearest to $\left(2, \frac{1}{2}\right)$ is $(1, 1)$.

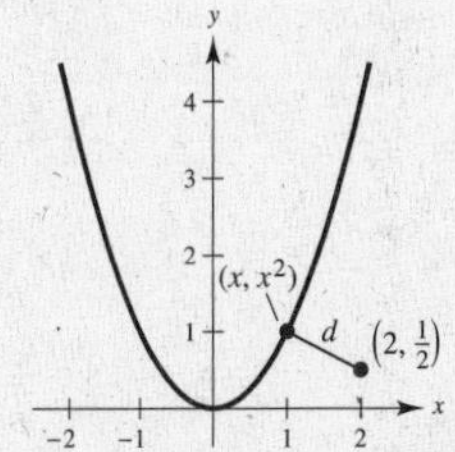

**14.** $f(x) = (x-1)^2, (-5, 3)$

$$d = \sqrt{(x+5)^2 + \left[(x-1)^2 - 3\right]^2}$$
$$= \sqrt{(x^2 + 10x + 25) + (x^2 - 2x - 2)^2}$$
$$= \sqrt{(x^2 + 10x + 25) + (x^4 - 4x^3 + 8x + 4)}$$
$$= \sqrt{x^4 - 4x^3 + x^2 + 18x + 29}$$

Because $d$ is smallest when the expression inside the radical is smallest, you need to find the critical numbers of

$$g(x) = x^4 - 4x^3 + x^2 + 18x + 29.$$
$$g'(x) = 4x^3 - 12x^2 + 2x + 18$$
$$= 2(x+1)(2x^2 - 8x + 9) = 0$$
$$x = -1$$

By the First Derivative Test, $x = -1$ yields a minimum. So, $(-1, 4)$ is closest to $(-5, 3)$.

**15.** $f(x) = \sqrt{x}, (4, 0)$

$$d = \sqrt{(x-4)^2 + (\sqrt{x} - 0)^2}$$
$$= \sqrt{x^2 - 7x + 16}$$

Because $d$ is smallest when the expression inside the radical is smallest, you need only find the critical numbers of

$$f(x) = x^2 - 7x + 16.$$
$$f'(x) = 2x - 7 = 0$$
$$x = \tfrac{7}{2}$$

By the First Derivative Test, the point nearest to $(4, 0)$ is $\left(7/2, \sqrt{7/2}\right)$.

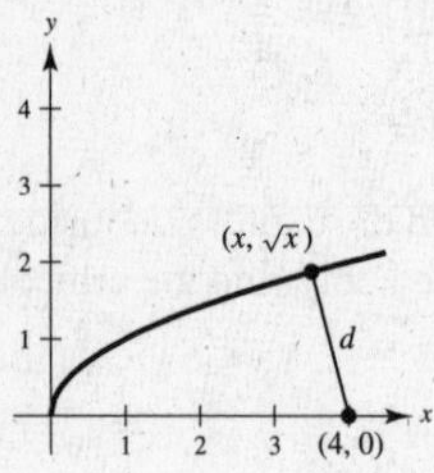


**16.** $f(x) = \sqrt{x-8}, (12, 0)$

$$d = \sqrt{(x-12)^2 + \left(\sqrt{x-8} - 0\right)^2}$$
$$= \sqrt{x^2 - 24x + 144 + x - 8}$$
$$= \sqrt{x^2 - 23x + 136}$$

Because $d$ is smallest when the expression inside the radical is smallest, you need to find the critical numbers of

$$g(x) = x^2 - 23x + 136.$$
$$g'(x) = 2x - 23 = 0$$
$$x = \frac{23}{2}$$

By the First Derivative Test, the point nearest to $(12, 0)$ is $\left(\dfrac{23}{2}, \dfrac{\sqrt{14}}{2}\right)$.

**17.** $xy = 30 \Rightarrow y = \dfrac{30}{x}$

$$A = (x+2)\left(\frac{30}{x} + 2\right) \text{ (see figure)}$$
$$\frac{dA}{dx} = (x+2)\left(\frac{-30}{x^2}\right) + \left(\frac{30}{x} + 2\right)$$
$$= \frac{2(x^2 - 30)}{x^2} = 0 \text{ when } x = \sqrt{30}.$$
$$y = \frac{30}{\sqrt{30}} = \sqrt{30}$$

By the First Derivative Test, the dimensions $(x+2)$ by $(y+2)$ are $\left(2 + \sqrt{30}\right)$ by $\left(2 + \sqrt{30}\right)$ (approximately 7.477 by 7.477). These dimensions yield a minimum area.

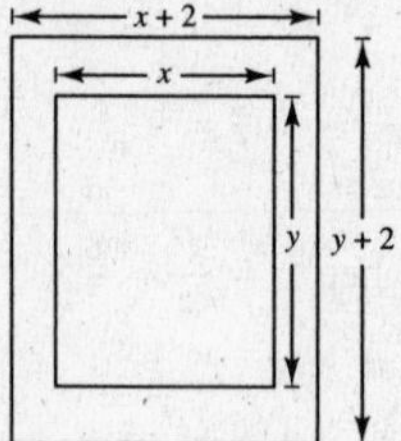

**18.** $xy = 36 \Rightarrow y = \dfrac{36}{x}$

$$A = (x+3)(y+3) = (x+3)\left(\frac{36}{x} + 3\right)$$

$$= 36 + \frac{108}{x} + 3x + 9$$

$$\frac{dA}{dx} = \frac{-108}{x^2} + 3 = 0 \Rightarrow 3x^2 = 108 \Rightarrow x = 6,\ y = 6$$

Dimensions: $9 \times 9$

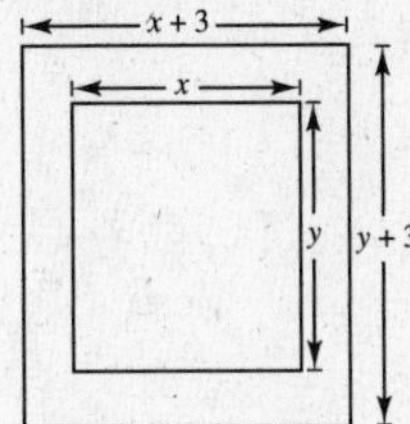


**19.** $\dfrac{dQ}{dx} = kx(Q_0 - x) = kQ_0x - kx^2$

$$\frac{d^2Q}{dx^2} = kQ_0 - 2kx$$

$$= k(Q_0 - 2x) = 0 \text{ when } x = \frac{Q_0}{2}.$$

$$\frac{d^3Q}{dx^3} = -2k < 0 \text{ when } x = \frac{Q_0}{2}.$$

$dQ/dx$ is maximum when $x = Q_0/2$.

**20.** $F = \dfrac{v}{22 + 0.02v^2}$

$$\frac{dF}{dv} = \frac{22 - 0.02v^2}{\left(22 + 0.02v^2\right)^2}$$

$$= 0 \text{ when } v = \sqrt{1100} \approx 33.166.$$

By the First Derivative Test, the flow rate on the road is maximized when $v \approx 33$ mi/h.

**21.** $xy = 245{,}000$ (see figure)

$S = x + 2y$

$= \left(x + \dfrac{490{,}000}{x}\right)$ where $S$ is the length of fence needed.

$$\frac{dS}{dx} = 1 - \frac{490{,}000}{x^2} = 0 \text{ when } x = 700.$$

$$\frac{d^2S}{dx^2} = \frac{980{,}000}{x^3} > 0 \text{ when } x = 700.$$

$S$ is a minimum when $x = 700$ m and $y = 350$ m.

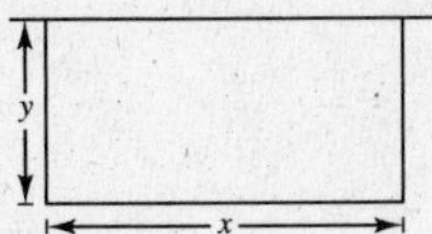


**22.** $4x + 3y = 400$ is the perimeter. (see figure)

$$A = 2xy = 2x\left(\frac{400 - 4x}{3}\right) = \frac{8}{3}\left(100x - x^2\right)$$

$$\frac{dA}{dx} = \frac{8}{3}(100 - 2x) = 0 \text{ when } x = 50.$$

$$\frac{d^2A}{dx^2} = -\frac{16}{3} < 0 \text{ when } x = 50.$$

$A$ is a maximum when $x = 50$ ft and $y = \dfrac{200}{3}$ ft.

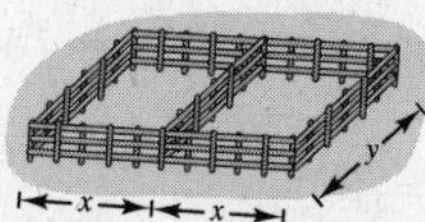


**23.** (a) $A = 4(\text{area of side}) + 2(\text{area of Top})$

(1) $A = 4(3)(11) + 2(3)(3) = 150 \text{ in}^2$.

(2) $A = 4(5)(5) + 2(5)(5) = 150 \text{ in}^2$.

(3) $A = 4(3.25)(6) + 2(6)(6) = 150 \text{ in}^2$.

(b) $V = (\text{length})(\text{width})(\text{height})$

(1) $V = (3)(3)(11) = 99 \text{ in}^3$.

(2) $V = (5)(5)(5) = 125 \text{ in}^3$.

(3) $V = (6)(6)(3.25) = 117 \text{ in}^3$.

(c) $S = 4xy + 2x^2 = 150 \Rightarrow y = \dfrac{150 - 2x^2}{4x}$

$$V = x^2y = x^2\left(\frac{150 - 2x^2}{4x}\right) = \frac{75}{2}x - \frac{1}{2}x^3$$

$$V' = \frac{75}{2} - \frac{3}{2}x^2 = 0 \Rightarrow x = \pm 5$$

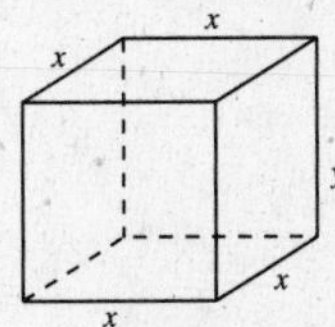


By the First Derivative Test, $x = 5$ yields the maximum volume. Dimensions: $5 \times 5 \times 5$ in. (A cube!)

**24.** $S = 2x^2 + 4xy = 337.5$

$$y = \frac{337.5 - 2x^2}{4x}$$

$$V = x^2y = x^2\left[\frac{337.5 - 2x^2}{4x}\right] = 84.375x - \frac{1}{2}x^3$$

$$\frac{dV}{dx} = 84.375 - \frac{3}{2}x^2 = 0 \Rightarrow x^2 = 56.25 \Rightarrow x = 7.5 \text{ and } y = 7.5.$$

$$\frac{d^2V}{dx^2} = -3x < 0 \text{ for } x = 7.5.$$

The maximum value occurs when $x = y = 7.5$ cm.

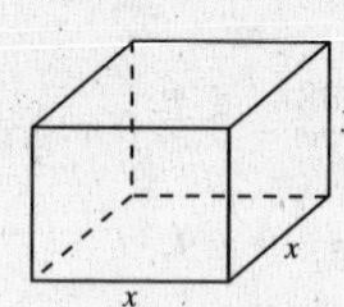


**25.** $16 = 2y + x + \pi\left(\frac{x}{2}\right)$

$$32 = 4y + 2x + \pi x$$

$$y = \frac{32 - 2x - \pi x}{4}$$

$$A = xy + \frac{\pi}{2}\left(\frac{x}{2}\right)^2 = \left(\frac{32 - 2x - \pi x}{4}\right)x + \frac{\pi x^2}{8} = 8x - \frac{1}{2}x^2 - \frac{\pi}{4}x^2 + \frac{\pi}{8}x^2$$

$$\frac{dA}{dx} = 8 - x - \frac{\pi}{2}x + \frac{\pi}{4}x = 8 - x\left(1 + \frac{\pi}{4}\right) = 0 \text{ when } x = \frac{8}{1 + (\pi/4)} = \frac{32}{4 + \pi}.$$

$$\frac{d^2A}{dx^2} = -\left(1 + \frac{\pi}{4}\right) < 0 \text{ when } x = \frac{32}{4 + \pi}.$$

$$y = \frac{32 - 2[32/(4 + \pi)] - \pi[32/(4 + \pi)]}{4} = \frac{16}{4 + \pi}$$

The area is maximum when $y = \frac{16}{4 + \pi}$ ft and $x = \frac{32}{4 + \pi}$ ft.

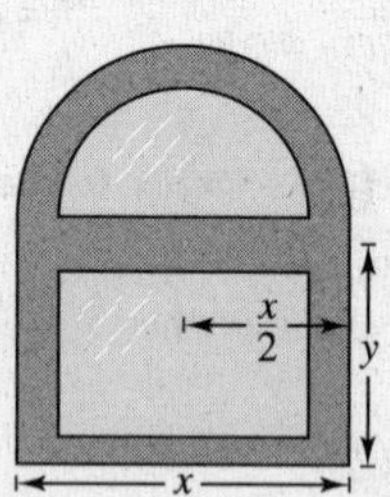


**26.** You can see from the figure that $A = xy$ and $y = \frac{6 - x}{2}$.

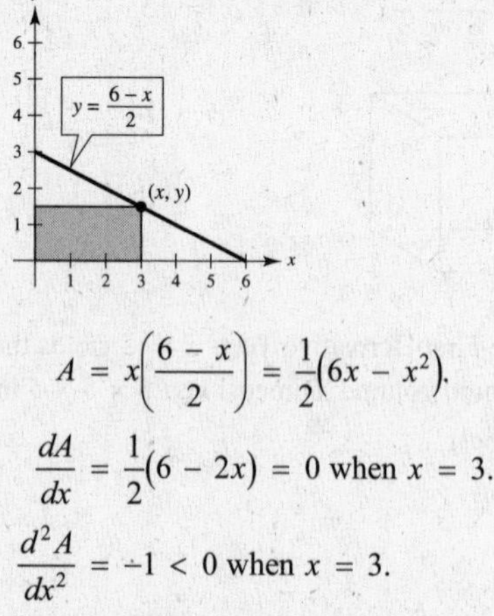


$$A = x\left(\frac{6 - x}{2}\right) = \frac{1}{2}(6x - x^2).$$

$$\frac{dA}{dx} = \frac{1}{2}(6 - 2x) = 0 \text{ when } x = 3.$$

$$\frac{d^2A}{dx^2} = -1 < 0 \text{ when } x = 3.$$

$A$ is a maximum when $x = 3$ and $y = 3/2$.

**27.** (a) $\dfrac{y-2}{0-1} = \dfrac{0-2}{x-1}$

$$y = 2 + \frac{2}{x-1}$$

$$L = \sqrt{x^2 + y^2} = \sqrt{x^2 + \left(2 + \frac{2}{x-1}\right)^2} = \sqrt{x^2 + 4 + \frac{8}{x-1} + \frac{4}{(x-1)^2}}, \quad x > 1$$

(b)

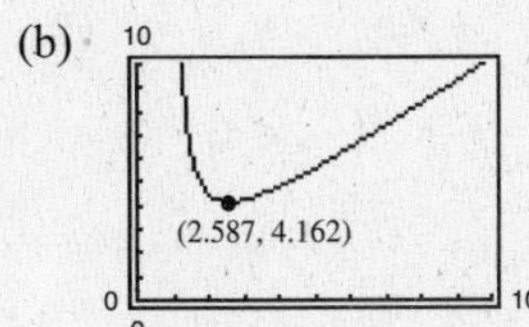


$L$ is minimum when $x \approx 2.587$ and $L \approx 4.162$.

(c) $\text{Area} = A(x) = \dfrac{1}{2}xy = \dfrac{1}{2}x\left(2 + \dfrac{2}{x-1}\right) = x + \dfrac{x}{x-1}$

$$A'(x) = 1 + \frac{(x-1) - x}{(x-1)^2} = 1 - \frac{1}{(x-1)^2} = 0$$

$$(x-1)^2 = 1$$

$$x - 1 = \pm 1$$

$$x = 0, 2 \text{ (select } x = 2)$$

Then $y = 4$ and $A = 4$.

Vertices: $(0, 0), (2, 0), (0, 4)$

**28.** (a) $A = \dfrac{1}{2}\text{base} \times \text{height} = \dfrac{1}{2}\left(2\sqrt{36 - h^2}\right)(6 + h) = \sqrt{36 - h^2}(6 + h)$

$$\frac{dA}{dh} = \frac{1}{2}\left(36 - h^2\right)^{-1/2}(-2h)(6 + h) + \left(36 - h^2\right)^{1/2}$$

$$= \left(36 - h^2\right)^{-1/2}\left[-h(6 + h) + \left(36 - h^2\right)\right] = \frac{-2\left(h^2 + 3h - 18\right)}{\sqrt{36 - h^2}} = \frac{-2(h + 6)(h - 3)}{\sqrt{36 - h^2}}$$

$\dfrac{dA}{dh} = 0$ when $h = 3$, which is a maximum by the First Derivative Test. So, the sides are $2\sqrt{36 - h^2} = 6\sqrt{3}$, an equilateral triangle. Area $= 27\sqrt{3}$ sq. units.

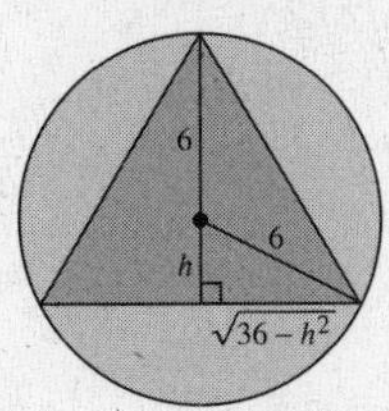

(b) $\cos\alpha = \dfrac{6+h}{2\sqrt{3}\sqrt{6+h}} = \dfrac{\sqrt{6+h}}{2\sqrt{3}}$

$\tan\alpha = \dfrac{\sqrt{36-h^2}}{6+h}$

$\text{Area} = 2\left(\frac{1}{2}\right)\left(\sqrt{36-h^2}\right)(6+h) = (6+h)^2\tan\alpha = 144\cos^4\alpha\tan\alpha$

$A'(\alpha) = 144\left[\cos^4\alpha\sec^2\alpha + 4\cos^3(-\sin\alpha)\tan\alpha\right] = 0$

$$\begin{aligned}\Rightarrow \cos^4\alpha\sec^2\alpha &= 4\cos^3\alpha\sin\alpha\tan\alpha\\ 1 &= 4\cos\alpha\sin\alpha\tan\alpha\\ \frac{1}{4} &= \sin^2\alpha\\ \sin\alpha &= \frac{1}{2} \Rightarrow \alpha = 30^\circ \text{ and } A = 27\sqrt{3}.\end{aligned}$$

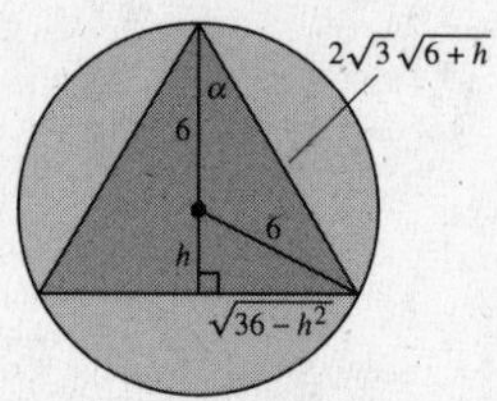


(c) Equilateral triangle

**29.** $A = 2xy = 2x\sqrt{25-x^2}$ (see figure)

$\dfrac{dA}{dx} = 2x\left(\frac{1}{2}\right)\left(\dfrac{-2x}{\sqrt{25-x^2}}\right) + 2\sqrt{25-x^2} = 2\left(\dfrac{25-2x^2}{\sqrt{25-x^2}}\right) = 0$ when $x = y = \dfrac{5\sqrt{2}}{2} \approx 3.54$.

By the First Derivative Test, the inscribed rectangle of maximum area has vertices

$\left(\pm\frac{5\sqrt{2}}{2}, 0\right), \left(\pm\frac{5\sqrt{2}}{2}, \frac{5\sqrt{2}}{2}\right)$.

Width: $\dfrac{5\sqrt{2}}{2}$; Length: $5\sqrt{2}$

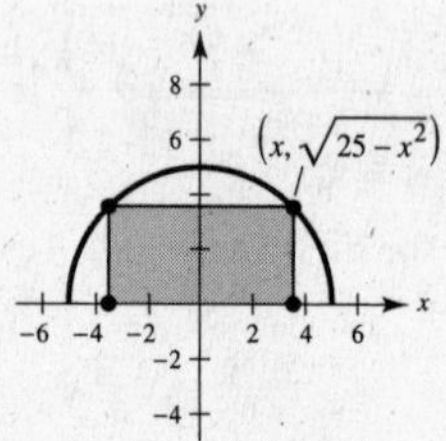


**30.** $A = 2xy = 2x\sqrt{r^2-x^2}$ (see figure)

$\dfrac{dA}{dx} = \dfrac{2(r^2-2x^2)}{\sqrt{r^2-x^2}} = 0$ when $x = \dfrac{\sqrt{2}r}{2}$.

By the First Derivative Test, $A$ is maximum when the rectangle has dimensions $\sqrt{2}r$ by $\left(\sqrt{2}r\right)/2$.

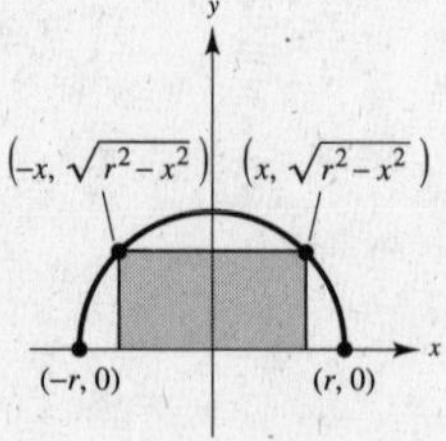

**31.** (a) $P = 2x + 2\pi r$

$$= 2x + 2\pi\left(\frac{y}{2}\right)$$

$$= 2x + \pi y = 200$$

$$\Rightarrow y = \frac{200 - 2x}{\pi} = \frac{2}{\pi}(100 - x)$$

(b)

| Length, $x$ | Width, $y$ | Area, $xy$ |
|---|---|---|
| 10 | $\frac{2}{\pi}(100 - 10)$ | $(10)\frac{2}{\pi}(100 - 10) \approx 573$ |
| 20 | $\frac{2}{\pi}(100 - 20)$ | $(20)\frac{2}{\pi}(100 - 20) \approx 1019$ |
| 30 | $\frac{2}{\pi}(100 - 30)$ | $(30)\frac{2}{\pi}(100 - 30) \approx 1337$ |
| 40 | $\frac{2}{\pi}(100 - 40)$ | $(40)\frac{2}{\pi}(100 - 40) \approx 1528$ |
| 50 | $\frac{2}{\pi}(100 - 50)$ | $(50)\frac{2}{\pi}(100 - 50) \approx 1592$ |
| 60 | $\frac{2}{\pi}(100 - 60)$ | $(60)\frac{2}{\pi}(100 - 60) \approx 1528$ |

The maximum area of the rectangle is approximately 1592 $m^2$.

(c) $A = xy = x\frac{2}{\pi}(100 - x) = \frac{2}{\pi}(100x - x^2)$

(d) $A' = \frac{2}{\pi}(100 - 2x)$. $A' = 0$ when $x = 50$.

Maximum value is approximately 1592 when length $= 50$ m and width $= \frac{100}{\pi}$.

(e)

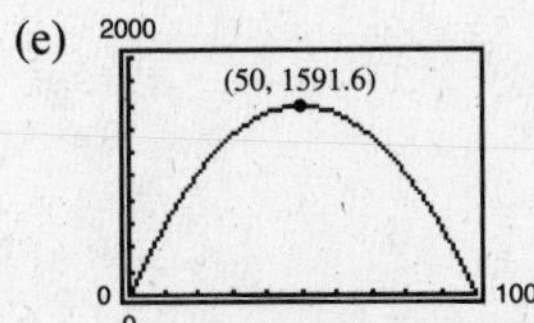


Maximum area is approximately $1591.55\ m^2\ (x = 50\ m)$.

**32.** $V = \pi r^2 h = 22$ cubic inches or $h = \dfrac{22}{\pi r^2}$

(a)

| Radius, $r$ | Height | Surface Area |
|---|---|---|
| 0.2 | $\dfrac{22}{\pi(0.2)^2}$ | $2\pi(0.2)\left[0.2 + \dfrac{22}{\pi(0.2)^2}\right] \approx 220.3$ |
| 0.4 | $\dfrac{22}{\pi(0.4)^2}$ | $2\pi(0.4)\left[0.4 + \dfrac{22}{\pi(0.4)^2}\right] \approx 111.0$ |
| 0.6 | $\dfrac{22}{\pi(0.6)^2}$ | $2\pi(0.6)\left[0.6 + \dfrac{22}{\pi(0.6)^2}\right] \approx 75.6$ |
| 0.8 | $\dfrac{22}{\pi(0.8)^2}$ | $2\pi(0.8)\left[0.8 + \dfrac{22}{\pi(0.8)^2}\right] \approx 59.0$ |

(b)

| Radius, $r$ | Height | Surface Area |
|---|---|---|
| 0.2 | $\dfrac{22}{\pi(0.2)^2}$ | $2\pi(0.2)\left[0.2 + \dfrac{22}{\pi(0.2)^2}\right] \approx 220.3$ |
| 0.4 | $\dfrac{22}{\pi(0.4)^2}$ | $2\pi(0.4)\left[0.4 + \dfrac{22}{\pi(0.4)^2}\right] \approx 111.0$ |
| 0.6 | $\dfrac{22}{\pi(0.6)^2}$ | $2\pi(0.6)\left[0.6 + \dfrac{22}{\pi(0.6)^2}\right] \approx 75.6$ |
| 0.8 | $\dfrac{22}{\pi(0.8)^2}$ | $2\pi(0.8)\left[0.8 + \dfrac{22}{\pi(0.8)^2}\right] \approx 59.0$ |
| 1.0 | $\dfrac{22}{\pi(1.0)^2}$ | $2\pi(1.0)\left[1.0 + \dfrac{22}{\pi(1.0)^2}\right] \approx 50.3$ |
| 1.2 | $\dfrac{22}{\pi(1.2)^2}$ | $2\pi(1.2)\left[1.2 + \dfrac{22}{\pi(1.2)^2}\right] \approx 45.7$ |
| 1.4 | $\dfrac{22}{\pi(1.4)^2}$ | $2\pi(1.4)\left[1.4 + \dfrac{22}{\pi(1.4)^2}\right] \approx 43.7$ |
| 1.6 | $\dfrac{22}{\pi(1.6)^2}$ | $2\pi(1.6)\left[1.6 + \dfrac{22}{\pi(1.6)^2}\right] \approx 43.6$ |
| 1.8 | $\dfrac{22}{\pi(1.8)^2}$ | $2\pi(1.8)\left[1.8 + \dfrac{22}{\pi(1.8)^2}\right] \approx 44.8$ |
| 2.0 | $\dfrac{22}{\pi(2.0)^2}$ | $2\pi(2.0)\left[2.0 + \dfrac{22}{\pi(2.0)^2}\right] \approx 47.1$ |

The minimum seems to the about 43.6 for $r = 1.6$.

(c) $S = 2\pi r^2 + 2\pi rh = 2\pi r(r + h) = 2\pi r\left[r + \dfrac{22}{\pi r^2}\right] = 2\pi r^2 + \dfrac{44}{r}$

(d)

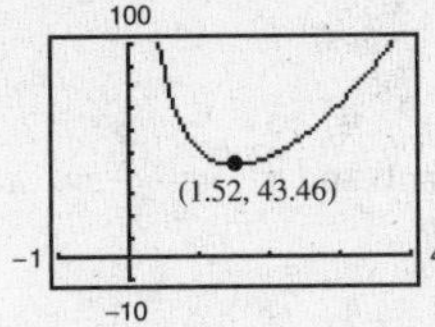


The minimum seems to be 43.46 for $r \approx 1.52$.

(e) $\dfrac{dS}{dr} = 4\pi r - \dfrac{44}{r^2} = 0$ when $r = \sqrt[3]{11/\pi} \approx 1.52$ in.

$h = \dfrac{22}{\pi r^2} \approx 3.04$ in.

**Note:** Notice that $h = \dfrac{22}{\pi r^2} = \dfrac{22}{\pi(11/\pi)^{2/3}} = 2\left(\dfrac{11^{1/3}}{\pi^{1/3}}\right) = 2r.$

**33.** Let $x$ be the sides of the square ends and $y$ the length of the package.

$P = 4x + y = 108 \Rightarrow y = 108 - 4x$

$V = x^2y = x^2(108 - 4x) = 108x^2 - 4x^3$

$\dfrac{dV}{dx} = 216x - 12x^2$

$= 12x(18 - x) = 0$ when $x = 18$.

$\dfrac{d^2V}{dx^2} = 216 - 24x = -216 < 0$ when $x = 18$.

The volume is maximum when $x = 18$ in. and $y = 108 - 4(18) = 36$ in.

**34.** $V = \pi r^2 x$

$x + 2\pi r = 108 \Rightarrow x = 108 - 2\pi r$ (see figure)

$V = \pi r^2(108 - 2\pi r) = \pi(108r^2 - 2\pi r^3)$

$\dfrac{dV}{dr} = \pi(216r - 6\pi r^2) = 6\pi r(36 - \pi r)$

$= 0$ when $r = \dfrac{36}{\pi}$ and $x = 36$.

$\dfrac{d^2V}{dr^2} = \pi(216 - 12\pi r) < 0$ when $r = \dfrac{36}{\pi}$.

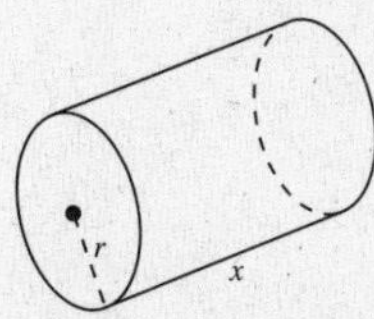


Volume is maximum when $x = 36$ in. and $r = 36/\pi \approx 11.459$ in.

**35.** $V = \dfrac{1}{3}\pi x^2 h = \dfrac{1}{3}\pi x^2\left(r + \sqrt{r^2 - x^2}\right)$ (see figure)

$\dfrac{dV}{dx} = \dfrac{1}{3}\pi\left[\dfrac{-x^3}{\sqrt{r^2 - x^2}} + 2x\left(r + \sqrt{r^2 - x^2}\right)\right]$

$= \dfrac{\pi x}{3\sqrt{r^2 - x^2}}\left(2r^2 + 2r\sqrt{r^2 - x^2} - 3x^2\right) = 0$

$2r^2 + 2r\sqrt{r^2 - x^2} - 3x^2 = 0$

$2r\sqrt{r^2 - x^2} = 3x^2 - 2r^2$

$4r^2(r^2 - x^2) = 9x^4 - 12x^2r^2 + 4r^4$

$0 = 9x^4 - 8x^2r^2 = x^2(9x^2 - 8r^2)$

$x = 0, \dfrac{2\sqrt{2}r}{3}$

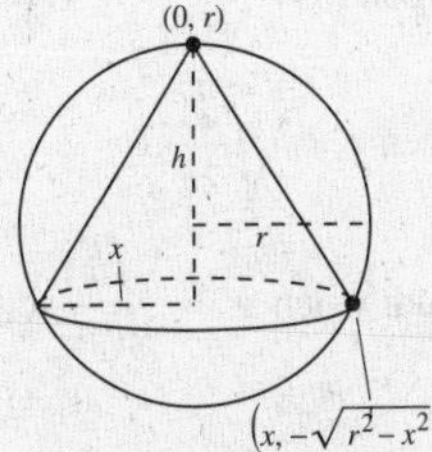


By the First Derivative Test, the volume is a maximum when

$x = \dfrac{2\sqrt{2}r}{3}$ and $h = r + \sqrt{r^2 - x^2} = \dfrac{4r}{3}$.

So, the maximum volume is

$V = \dfrac{1}{3}\pi\left(\dfrac{8r^2}{9}\right)\left(\dfrac{4r}{3}\right) = \dfrac{32\pi r^3}{81}$ cubic units.

**36.** $V = \pi x^2 h = \pi x^2\left(2\sqrt{r^2 - x^2}\right) = 2\pi x^2\sqrt{r^2 - x^2}$ (see figure)

$$\frac{dV}{dx} = 2\pi\left[x^2\left(\frac{1}{2}\right)\left(r^2 - x^2\right)^{-1/2}(-2x) + 2x\sqrt{r^2 - x^2}\right] = \frac{2\pi x}{\sqrt{r^2 - x^2}}\left(2r^2 - 3x^2\right) = 0 \text{ when } x = 0 \text{ and } x^2 = \frac{2r^2}{3} \Rightarrow x = \frac{\sqrt{6}r}{3}.$$

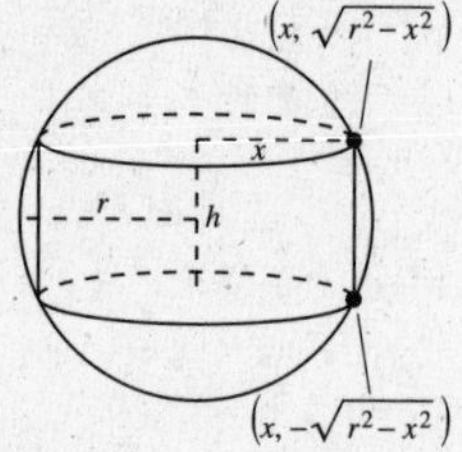


By the First Derivative Test, the volume is a maximum when $x = \dfrac{\sqrt{6}r}{3}$ and $h = \dfrac{2r}{\sqrt{3}}$.

So, the maximum volume is $V = \pi\left(\dfrac{2}{3}r^2\right)\left(\dfrac{2r}{\sqrt{3}}\right) = \dfrac{4\pi r^3}{3\sqrt{3}}$.

**37.** No. The volume will change because the shape of the container changes when squeezed.

**38.** No, there is no minimum area. If the sides are $x$ and $y$, then $2x + 2y = 20 \Rightarrow y = 10 - x$. The area is $A(x) = x(10 - x) = 10x - x^2$. This can be made arbitrarily small by selecting $x \approx 0$.

**39.** $V = 14 = \dfrac{4}{3}\pi r^3 + \pi r^2 h$

$$h = \frac{14 - (4/3)\pi r^3}{\pi r^2} = \frac{14}{\pi r^2} - \frac{4}{3}r$$

$$S = 4\pi r^2 + 2\pi r h = 4\pi r^2 + 2\pi r\left(\frac{14}{\pi r^2} - \frac{4}{3}r\right) = 4\pi r^2 + \frac{28}{r} - \frac{8}{3}\pi r^2 = \frac{4}{3}\pi r^2 + \frac{28}{r}$$

$$\frac{dS}{dr} = \frac{8}{3}\pi r - \frac{28}{r^2} = 0 \text{ when } r = \sqrt[3]{\frac{21}{2\pi}} \approx 1.495 \text{ cm.}$$

$$\frac{d^2S}{dr^2} = \frac{8}{3}\pi + \frac{56}{r^3} > 0 \text{ when } r = \sqrt[3]{\frac{21}{2\pi}}.$$

The surface area is minimum when $r = \sqrt[3]{\dfrac{21}{2\pi}}$ cm and $h = 0$. The resulting solid is a sphere of radius $r \approx 1.495$ cm.

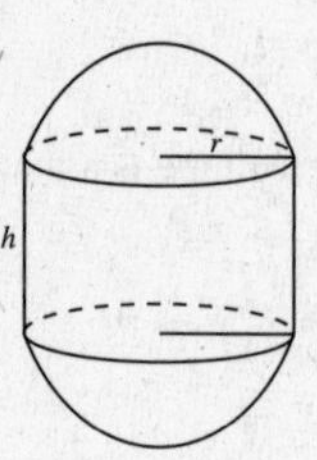

**40.** $V = 4000 = \frac{4}{3}\pi r^3 + \pi r^2 h$

$$h = \frac{4000}{\pi r^2} - \frac{4}{3}r$$

Let $k$ = cost per square foot of the surface area of the sides, then $2k$ = cost per square foot of the hemispherical ends.

$$C = 2k(4\pi r^2) + k(2\pi rh) = k\left[8\pi r^2 + 2\pi r\left(\frac{4000}{\pi r^2} - \frac{4}{3}r\right)\right] = k\left[\frac{16}{3}\pi r^2 + \frac{8000}{r}\right]$$

$$\frac{dC}{dr} = k\left[\frac{32}{3}\pi r - \frac{8000}{r^2}\right] = 0 \text{ when } r = \sqrt[3]{\frac{750}{\pi}} \approx 6.204 \text{ ft and } h \approx 24.814 \text{ ft.}$$

By the Second Derivative Test, you have $\frac{d^2C}{dr^2} = k\left[\frac{32}{3}\pi + \frac{12{,}000}{r^3}\right] > 0$ when $r = \sqrt[3]{\frac{750}{\pi}}$.

The cost is minimum when $r = \sqrt[3]{\frac{750}{\pi}}$ ft and $h \approx 24.814$ ft.

**41.** Let $x$ be the length of a side of the square and $y$ the length of a side of the triangle.

$$4x + 3y = 10$$

$$A = x^2 + \frac{1}{2}y\left(\frac{\sqrt{3}}{2}y\right)$$

$$= \frac{(10 - 3y)^2}{16} + \frac{\sqrt{3}}{4}y^2$$

$$\frac{dA}{dy} = \frac{1}{8}(10 - 3y)(-3) + \frac{\sqrt{3}}{2}y = 0$$

$$-30 + 9y + 4\sqrt{3}y = 0$$

$$y = \frac{30}{9 + 4\sqrt{3}}$$

$$\frac{d^2A}{dy^2} = \frac{9 + 4\sqrt{3}}{8} > 0$$

$A$ is minimum when $y = \frac{30}{9 + 4\sqrt{3}}$ and $x = \frac{10\sqrt{3}}{9 + 4\sqrt{3}}$.

**42.** (a) Let $x$ be the side of the triangle and $y$ the side of the square.

$$A = \frac{3}{4}\left(\cot\frac{\pi}{3}\right)x^2 + \frac{4}{4}\left(\cot\frac{\pi}{4}\right)y^2 \text{ where } 3x + 4y = 20$$

$$= \frac{\sqrt{3}}{4}x^2 + \left(5 - \frac{3}{4}x\right)^2, \; 0 \le x \le \frac{20}{3}.$$

$$A' = \frac{\sqrt{3}}{2}x + 2\left(5 - \frac{3}{4}x\right)\left(-\frac{3}{4}\right) = 0$$

$$x = \frac{60}{4\sqrt{3} + 9}$$

When $x = 0$, $A = 25$, when $x = 60/(4\sqrt{3} + 9)$, $A \approx 10.847$, and when $x = 20/3$, $A \approx 19.245$. Area is maximum when all 20 feet are used on the square.

(b) Let $x$ be the side of the square and $y$ the side of the pentagon.

$$A = \frac{4}{4}\left(\cot\frac{\pi}{4}\right)x^2 + \frac{5}{4}\left(\cot\frac{\pi}{5}\right)y^2 \text{ where } 4x + 5y = 20$$

$$= x^2 + 1.7204774\left(4 - \frac{4}{5}x\right)^2, 0 \le x \le 5.$$

$$A' = 2x - 2.75276384\left(4 - \frac{4}{5}x\right) = 0$$

$$x \approx 2.62$$

When $x = 0$, $A \approx 27.528$, when $x \approx 2.62$, $A \approx 13.102$, and when $x = 5$, $A \approx 25$. Area is maximum when all 20 feet are used on the pentagon.

(c) Let $x$ be the side of the pentagon and $y$ the side of the hexagon.

$$A = \frac{5}{4}\left(\cot\frac{\pi}{5}\right)x^2 + \frac{6}{4}\left(\cot\frac{\pi}{6}\right)y^2 \text{ where } 5x + 6y = 20$$

$$= \frac{5}{4}\left(\cot\frac{\pi}{5}\right)x^2 + \frac{3}{2}\left(\sqrt{3}\right)\left(\frac{20 - 5x}{6}\right)^2, 0 \le x \le 4.$$

$$A' = \frac{5}{2}\left(\cot\frac{\pi}{5}\right)x + 3\sqrt{3}\left(-\frac{5}{6}\right)\left(\frac{20 - 5x}{6}\right) = 0$$

$$x \approx 2.0475$$

When $x = 0$, $A \approx 28.868$, when $x \approx 2.0475$, $A \approx 14.091$, and when $x = 4$, $A \approx 27.528$. Area is maximum when all 20 feet are used on the hexagon.

(d) Let $x$ be the side of the hexagon and $r$ the radius of the circle.

$$A = \frac{6}{4}\left(\cot\frac{\pi}{6}\right)x^2 + \pi r^2 \text{ where } 6x + 2\pi r = 20$$

$$= \frac{3\sqrt{3}}{2}x^2 + \pi\left(\frac{10}{\pi} - \frac{3x}{\pi}\right)^2, 0 \le x \le \frac{10}{3}.$$

$$A' = 3\sqrt{3} - 6\left(\frac{10}{\pi} - \frac{3x}{\pi}\right) = 0$$

$$x \approx 1.748$$

When $x = 0$, $A \approx 31.831$, when $x \approx 1.748$, $A \approx 15.138$, and when $x = 10/3$, $A \approx 28.868$. Area is maximum when all 20 feet are used on the circle.

In general, using all of the wire for the figure with more sides will enclose the most area.

**43.** Let $S$ be the strength and $k$ the constant of proportionality. Given $h^2 + w^2 = 20^2$, $h^2 = 20^2 - w^2$,

$$S = kwh^2$$

$$S = kw\left(400 - w^2\right) = k\left(400w - w^3\right)$$

$$\frac{dS}{dw} = k\left(400 - 3w^2\right) = 0 \text{ when } w = \frac{20\sqrt{3}}{3} \text{ in. and } h = \frac{20\sqrt{6}}{3} \text{ in.}$$

$$\frac{d^2S}{dw^2} = -6kw < 0 \text{ when } w = \frac{20\sqrt{3}}{3}.$$

These values yield a maximum.

**44.** Let $A$ be the amount of the power line.

$$A = h - y + 2\sqrt{x^2 + y^2}$$

$$\frac{dA}{dy} = -1 + \frac{2y}{\sqrt{x^2 + y^2}} = 0 \text{ when } y = \frac{x}{\sqrt{3}}.$$

$$\frac{d^2A}{dy^2} = \frac{2x^2}{\left(x^2 + y^2\right)^{3/2}} > 0 \text{ for } y = \frac{x}{\sqrt{3}}.$$

The amount of power line is minimum when $y = x/\sqrt{3}$.

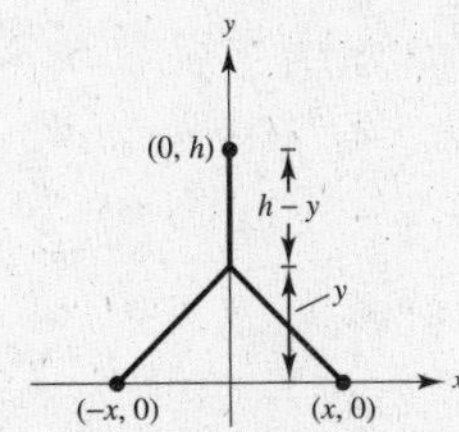


**45.** $R = \dfrac{v_0^2}{g}\sin 2\theta$

$$\frac{dR}{d\theta} = \frac{2v_0^2}{g}\cos 2\theta = 0 \text{ when } \theta = \frac{\pi}{4}, \frac{3\pi}{4}.$$

$$\frac{d^2R}{d\theta^2} = -\frac{4v_0^2}{g}\sin 2\theta < 0 \text{ when } \theta = \frac{\pi}{4}.$$

By the Second Derivative Test, $R$ is maximum when $\theta = \pi/4$.

**46.** $f(x) = \frac{1}{2}x^2 \qquad g(x) = \frac{1}{16}x^4 - \frac{1}{2}x^2$ on $[0, 4]$

(a)

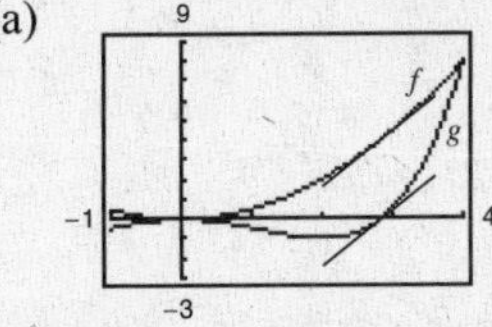


(b) $d(x) = f(x) - g(x) = \frac{1}{2}x^2 - \left(\frac{1}{16}x^4 - \frac{1}{2}x^2\right) = x^2 - \frac{1}{16}x^4$

$d'(x) = 2x - \frac{1}{4}x^3 = 0 \Rightarrow 8x = x^3$

$\Rightarrow x = 0, 2\sqrt{2}\left(\text{in } [0, 4]\right)$

The maximum distance is $d = 4$ when $x = 2\sqrt{2}$.

(c) $f'(x) = x$, Tangent line at $\left(2\sqrt{2}, 4\right)$ is

$$y - 4 = 2\sqrt{2}\left(x - 2\sqrt{2}\right)$$

$$y = 2\sqrt{2}x - 4.$$

$g'(x) = \frac{1}{4}x^3 - x$, Tangent line at $\left(2\sqrt{2}, 0\right)$ is

$$y - 0 = \left(\tfrac{1}{4}\left(2\sqrt{2}\right)^3 - 2\sqrt{2}\right)\left(x - 2\sqrt{2}\right)$$

$$y = 2\sqrt{2}x - 8.$$

The tangent lines are parallel and 4 vertical units apart.

(d) The tangent lines will be parallel. If $d(x) = f(x) - g(x)$, then $d'(x) = 0 = f'(x) - g'(x)$ implies that $f'(x) = g'(x)$ at the point $x$ where the distance is maximum.

**47.** $\sin \alpha = \frac{h}{s} \Rightarrow s = \frac{h}{\sin \alpha}, 0 < \alpha < \frac{\pi}{2}$

$$\tan \alpha = \frac{h}{2} \Rightarrow h = 2 \tan \alpha \Rightarrow s = \frac{2 \tan \alpha}{\sin \alpha} = 2 \sec \alpha$$

$$I = \frac{k \sin \alpha}{s^2} = \frac{k \sin \alpha}{4 \sec^2 \alpha} = \frac{k}{4} \sin \alpha \cos^2 \alpha$$

$$\frac{dI}{d\alpha} = \frac{k}{4}\left[\sin \alpha(-2 \sin \alpha \cos \alpha) + \cos^2 \alpha(\cos \alpha)\right]$$

$$= \frac{k}{4} \cos \alpha\left[\cos^2 \alpha - 2 \sin^2 \alpha\right]$$

$$= \frac{k}{4} \cos \alpha\left[1 - 3 \sin^2 \alpha\right]$$

$$= 0 \text{ when } \alpha = \frac{\pi}{2}, \frac{3\pi}{2}, \text{ or when } \sin \alpha = \pm\frac{1}{\sqrt{3}}.$$

Because $\alpha$ is acute, you have

$$\sin \alpha = \frac{1}{\sqrt{3}} \Rightarrow h = 2 \tan \alpha = 2\left(\frac{1}{\sqrt{2}}\right) = \sqrt{2} \text{ ft.}$$

Because $\left(d^2I\right)/\left(d\alpha^2\right) = (k/4) \sin \alpha\left(9 \sin^2 \alpha - 7\right) < 0$ when $\sin \alpha = 1/\sqrt{3}$, this yields a maximum.

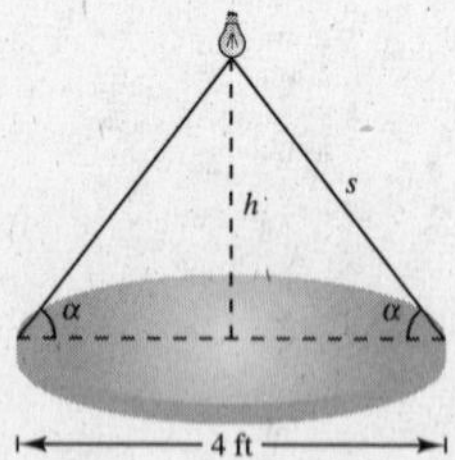


**48.** Let $F$ be the illumination at point $P$ which is $x$ units from source 1.

$$F = \frac{kI_1}{x^2} + \frac{kI_2}{(d - x)^2}$$

$$\frac{dF}{dx} = \frac{-2kI_1}{x^3} + \frac{2kI_2}{(d - x)^3} = 0 \text{ when } \frac{2kI_1}{x^3} = \frac{2kI_2}{(d - x)^3}.$$

$$\frac{\sqrt[3]{I_1}}{\sqrt[3]{I_2}} = \frac{x}{d - x}$$

$$(d - x)\sqrt[3]{I_1} = x\sqrt[3]{I_2}$$

$$d\sqrt[3]{I_1} = x\left(\sqrt[3]{I_1} + \sqrt[3]{I_2}\right)$$

$$x = \frac{d\sqrt[3]{I_1}}{\sqrt[3]{I_1} + \sqrt[3]{I_2}}$$

$$\frac{d^2F}{dx^2} = \frac{6kI_1}{x^4} + \frac{6kI_2}{(d - x)^4} > 0 \text{ when } x = \frac{d\sqrt[3]{I_1}}{\sqrt[3]{I_1} + \sqrt[3]{I_2}}.$$

This is the minimum point.

**49.**

$$S = \sqrt{x^2 + 4},\ L = \sqrt{1 + (3 - x)^2}$$

$$\text{Time} = T = \frac{\sqrt{x^2 + 4}}{2} + \frac{\sqrt{x^2 - 6x + 10}}{4}$$

$$\frac{dT}{dx} = \frac{x}{2\sqrt{x^2 + 4}} + \frac{x - 3}{4\sqrt{x^2 - 6x + 10}} = 0$$

$$\frac{x^2}{x^2 + 4} = \frac{9 - 6x + x^2}{4(x^2 - 6x + 10)}$$

$$x^4 - 6x^3 + 9x^2 + 8x - 12 = 0$$

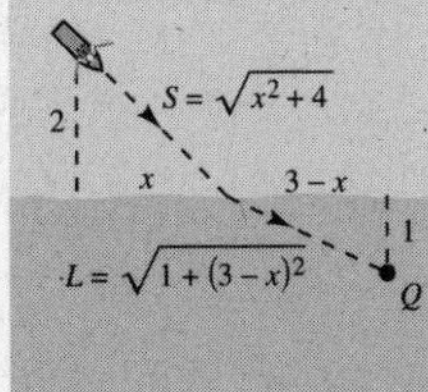


You need to find the roots of this equation in the interval $[0, 3]$. By using a computer or graphing utility you can determine that this equation has only one root in this interval $(x = 1)$. Testing at this value and at the endpoints, you see that $x = 1$ yields the minimum time. So, the man should row to a point 1 mile from the nearest point on the coast.

**50.** (a)

α
2sec α
2
3 − 2tan α
2tan α
Q

$$T = \frac{2\sec\alpha}{2} + \frac{3 - 2\tan\alpha}{4} = \sec\alpha + \frac{3 - 2\tan\alpha}{4}$$

(b) $$\frac{dT}{d\alpha} = \sec\alpha\tan\alpha - \frac{1}{2}\sec^2\alpha = 0$$

$$\tan\alpha = \frac{1}{2}\sec\alpha$$

$$\sin\alpha = \frac{1}{2}$$

$$\alpha = \frac{\pi}{6}$$

$$T\left(\frac{\pi}{6}\right) = \frac{\sqrt{3}}{2} + \frac{3}{4}$$

$$T(0) = \frac{7}{4} \qquad \text{Endpoint}$$

$$T\left(\arctan\left(\frac{3}{2}\right)\right) = \frac{\sqrt{13}}{2} \qquad \text{Endpoint}$$

Minimum time: $\frac{\sqrt{3}}{2} + \frac{3}{4} \approx 1.616$ hours

(c) $T = \dfrac{2 \sec \alpha}{v_1} + \dfrac{3 - 2 \tan \alpha}{v_2}$

$$\frac{dT}{d\alpha} = \frac{2}{v_1} \sec \alpha \tan \alpha - \frac{2}{v_2} \sec^2 \alpha = 0$$

$$\frac{\tan \alpha}{v_1} = \frac{\sec \alpha}{v_2}$$

$$\sin \alpha = \frac{v_1}{v_2}$$

$\alpha$ depends on $\dfrac{v_1}{v_2}$.

(d) $\text{Cost} = (2 \sec \alpha)c_1 + (3 - 2 \tan \alpha)c_2 = \dfrac{2 \sec \alpha}{\left(\dfrac{1}{c_1}\right)} + \dfrac{(3 - 2 \tan \alpha)}{\left(\dfrac{1}{c_2}\right)}$

From above part (c), minimum cost when $\sin \alpha = \dfrac{1/c_1}{1/c_2} = \dfrac{c_2}{c_1}$.

**51.** $T = \dfrac{\sqrt{x^2 + 4}}{v_1} + \dfrac{\sqrt{x^2 - 6x + 10}}{v_2}$

$$\frac{dT}{dx} = \frac{x}{v_1\sqrt{x^2 + 4}} + \frac{x - 3}{v_2\sqrt{x^2 - 6x + 10}} = 0$$

Because

$$\frac{x}{\sqrt{x^2 + 4}} = \sin \theta_1 \text{ and } \frac{x - 3}{\sqrt{x^2 - 6x + 10}} = -\sin \theta_2$$

you have

$$\frac{\sin \theta_1}{v_1} - \frac{\sin \theta_2}{v_2} = 0 \Rightarrow \frac{\sin \theta_1}{v_1} = \frac{\sin \theta_2}{v_2}.$$

Because

$$\frac{d^2T}{dx^2} = \frac{4}{v_1(x^2 + 4)^{3/2}} + \frac{1}{v_2(x^2 - 6x + 10)^{3/2}} > 0$$

this condition yields a minimum time.

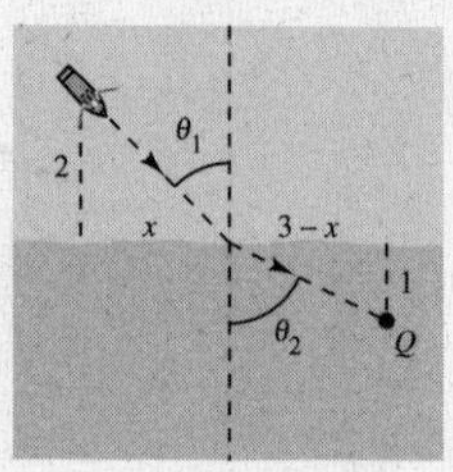


**52.** $T = \dfrac{\sqrt{x^2 + d_1^2}}{v_1} + \dfrac{\sqrt{d_2^2 + (a - x)^2}}{v_2}$

$$\frac{dT}{dx} = \frac{x}{v_1\sqrt{x^2 + d_1^2}} + \frac{x - a}{v_2\sqrt{d_2^2 + (a - x)^2}} = 0$$

Because

$$\frac{x}{\sqrt{x^2 + d_1^2}} = \sin \theta_1 \text{ and } \frac{x - a}{\sqrt{d_2^2 + (a - x)^2}} = -\sin \theta_2$$

you have

$$\frac{\sin \theta_1}{v_1} - \frac{\sin \theta_2}{v_2} = 0 \Rightarrow \frac{\sin \theta_1}{v_1} = \frac{\sin \theta_2}{v_2}.$$

Because

$$\frac{d^2T}{dx^2} = \frac{d_1^2}{v_1(x^2 + d_1^2)^{3/2}} + \frac{d_2^2}{v_2\left[d_2^2 + (a - x)^2\right]^{3/2}} > 0$$

this condition yields a minimum time.

**53.** $f(x) = 2 - 2\sin x$

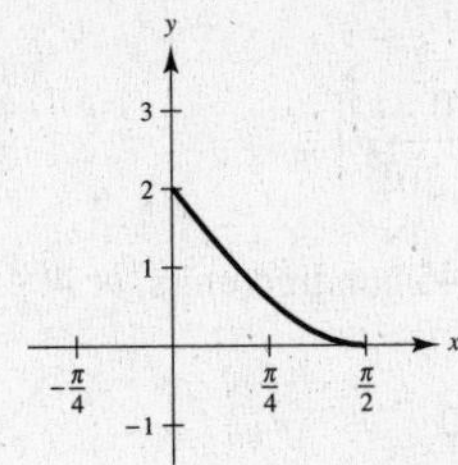


(a) Distance from origin to $y$-intercept is 2.

Distance from origin to $x$-intercept is $\pi/2 \approx 1.57$.

(b) $d = \sqrt{x^2 + y^2} = \sqrt{x^2 + (2 - 2\sin x)^2}$

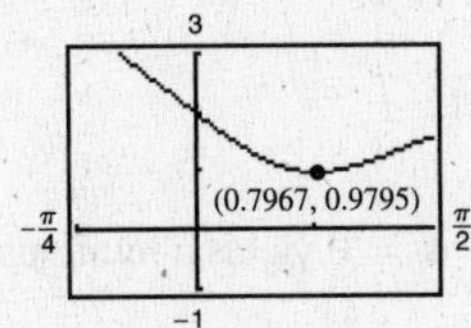


Minimum distance $= 0.9795$ at $x = 0.7967$.

(c) Let $f(x) = d^2(x) = x^2 + (2 - 2\sin x)^2$.

$f'(x) = 2x + 2(2 - 2\sin x)(-2\cos x)$

Setting $f'(x) = 0$, you obtain $x \approx 0.7967$, which corresponds to $d = 0.9795$.

**54.** $C(x) = 2k\sqrt{x^2 + 4} + k(4 - x)$

$$C'(x) = \frac{2xk}{\sqrt{x^2 + 4}} - k = 0$$

$$2x = \sqrt{x^2 + 4}$$

$$4x^2 = x^2 + 4$$

$$3x^2 = 4$$

$$x = \frac{2}{\sqrt{3}}$$

Or, use Exercise 50(d): $\sin\theta = \dfrac{C_2}{C_1} = \dfrac{1}{2} \Rightarrow \theta = 30°$.

So, $x = \dfrac{2}{\sqrt{3}}$.

**55.** $V = \dfrac{1}{3}\pi r^2 h = \dfrac{1}{3}\pi r^2\sqrt{144 - r^2}$

$$\frac{dV}{dr} = \frac{1}{3}\pi\left[r^2\left(\frac{1}{2}\right)\left(144 - r^2\right)^{-1/2}(-2r) + 2r\sqrt{144 - r^2}\right]$$

$$= \frac{1}{3}\pi\left[\frac{288r - 3r^3}{\sqrt{144 - r^2}}\right]$$

$$= \pi\left[\frac{r\left(96 - r^2\right)}{\sqrt{144 - r^2}}\right] = 0 \text{ when } r = 0, 4\sqrt{6}.$$

By the First Derivative Test, $V$ is maximum when $r = 4\sqrt{6}$ and $h = 4\sqrt{3}$.

Area of circle: $A = \pi(12)^2 = 144\pi$

Lateral surface area of cone:

$$S = \pi\left(4\sqrt{6}\right)\sqrt{\left(4\sqrt{6}\right)^2 + \left(4\sqrt{3}\right)^2} = 48\sqrt{6}\pi$$

Area of sector:

$$144\pi - 48\sqrt{6}\pi = \frac{1}{2}\theta r^2 = 72\theta$$

$$\theta = \frac{144\pi - 48\sqrt{6}\pi}{72}$$

$$= \frac{2\pi}{3}\left(3 - \sqrt{6}\right) \approx 1.153 \text{ radians or } 66°$$

**56.** (a)

| Base 1 | Base 2 | Altitude | Area |
|---|---|---|---|
| 8 | $8 + 16\cos 10°$ | $8\sin 10°$ | $\approx 22.1$ |
| 8 | $8 + 16\cos 20°$ | $8\sin 20°$ | $\approx 42.5$ |
| 8 | $8 + 16\cos 30°$ | $8\sin 30°$ | $\approx 59.7$ |
| 8 | $8 + 16\cos 40°$ | $8\sin 40°$ | $\approx 72.7$ |
| 8 | $8 + 16\cos 50°$ | $8\sin 50°$ | $\approx 80.5$ |
| 8 | $8 + 16\cos 60°$ | $8\sin 60°$ | $\approx 83.1$ |

(b)

| Base 1 | Base 2 | Altitude | Area |
|---|---|---|---|
| 8 | $8 + 16\cos 10°$ | $8\sin 10°$ | $\approx 22.1$ |
| 8 | $8 + 16\cos 20°$ | $8\sin 20°$ | $\approx 42.5$ |
| 8 | $8 + 16\cos 30°$ | $8\sin 30°$ | $\approx 59.7$ |
| 8 | $8 + 16\cos 40°$ | $8\sin 40°$ | $\approx 72.7$ |
| 8 | $8 + 16\cos 50°$ | $8\sin 50°$ | $\approx 80.5$ |
| 8 | $8 + 16\cos 60°$ | $8\sin 60°$ | $\approx 83.1$ |
| 8 | $8 + 16\cos 70°$ | $8\sin 70°$ | $\approx 80.7$ |
| 8 | $8 + 16\cos 80°$ | $8\sin 80°$ | $\approx 74.0$ |
| 8 | $8 + 16\cos 90°$ | $8\sin 90°$ | $\approx 64.0$ |

The maximum cross-sectional area is approximately 83.1 ft$^2$.

(c) $A = (a + b)\dfrac{h}{2}$

$= \left[8 + (8 + 16\cos\theta)\right]\dfrac{8\sin\theta}{2}$

$= 64(1 + \cos\theta)\sin\theta,\ 0° < \theta < 90°$

(d) $\dfrac{dA}{d\theta} = 64(1 + \cos\theta)\cos\theta + (-64\sin\theta)\sin\theta$

$= 64(\cos\theta + \cos^2\theta - \sin^2\theta)$

$= 64(2\cos^2\theta + \cos\theta - 1)$

$= 64(2\cos\theta - 1)(\cos\theta + 1)$

$= 0$ when $\theta = 60°, 180°, 300°$.

The maximum occurs when $\theta = 60°$.

(e)

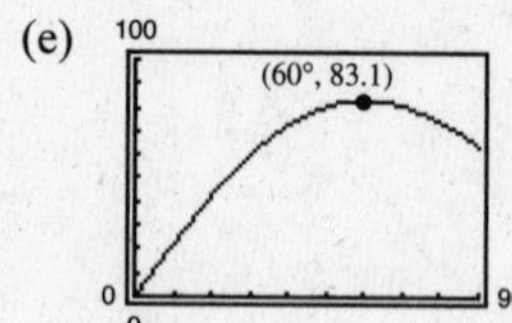


**57.** $C = 100\left(\dfrac{200}{x^2} + \dfrac{x}{x + 30}\right), 1 \le x$

$C' = 100\left(-\dfrac{400}{x^3} + \dfrac{30}{(x + 30)^2}\right)$

Approximation: $x \approx 40.45$ hundred units, or 4045 units

**58.** $P = -\dfrac{1}{10}s^3 + 6s^2 + 400$

(a) $\dfrac{dP}{ds} = -\dfrac{3}{10}s^2 + 12s$

$= -\dfrac{3}{10}s(s - 40)$

$= 0$ when $x = 0, s = 40$.

$\dfrac{d^2P}{ds^2} = -\dfrac{3}{5}s + 12$

$\dfrac{d^2P}{ds^2}(0) > 0 \Rightarrow s = 0$ yields a minimum.

$\dfrac{d^2P}{ds^2}(40) < 0 \Rightarrow s = 40$ yields a maximum.

The maximum profit occurs when $s = 40$, which corresponds to \$40,000 ($P$ = \$3,600,000).

(b) $\dfrac{d^2P}{ds^2} = -\dfrac{3}{5}s + 12 = 0$ when $s = 20$.

The point of diminishing returns occurs when $s = 20$, which corresponds to \$20,000 being spent on advertising.

**59.** $A = (\text{base})(\text{height}) = 2xe^{-x^2}$

$\dfrac{dA}{dx} = -4x^2e^{-x^2} + 2e^{-x^2}$

$= 2e^{-x^2}(1 - 2x^2) = 0$ when $x = \dfrac{\sqrt{2}}{2}$.

$A = \sqrt{2}e^{-1/2}$

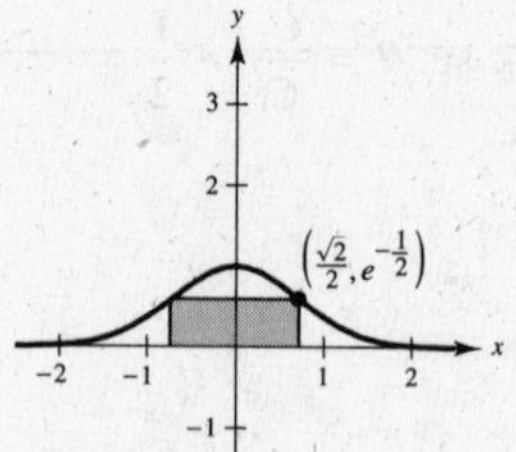


**60.** $p(t) = \dfrac{250}{1 + 4e^{-t/3}}$

$p'(t) = \dfrac{1000}{3}\dfrac{e^{-t/3}}{(1 + 4e^{-t/3})^2}$; $p'(2) \approx 18.35$ elk/month

$p''(t) = \dfrac{1000}{9}\dfrac{e^{-t/3}(4e^{-t/3} - 1)}{(1 + 4e^{-t/3})^3}$

$= 0$ when $t \approx 4.16$ months.

**61.** $y = \dfrac{L}{1 + ae^{-x/b}}, a > 0, b > 0, L > 0$

$$y' = \frac{-L\left(-\frac{a}{b}e^{-x/b}\right)}{\left(1 + ae^{-x/b}\right)^2} = \frac{\frac{aL}{b}e^{-x/b}}{\left(1 + ae^{-x/b}\right)^2}$$

$$y'' = \frac{\left(1 + ae^{-x/b}\right)^2\left(\frac{-aL}{b^2}e^{-x/b}\right) - \left(\frac{aL}{b}e^{-x/b}\right)2\left(1 + ae^{-x/b}\right)\left(\frac{-a}{b}e^{-x/b}\right)}{\left(1 + ae^{-x/b}\right)^4}$$

$$= \frac{\left(1 + ae^{-x/b}\right)\left(\frac{-aL}{b^2}e^{-x/b}\right) + 2\left(\frac{aL}{b}e^{-x/b}\right)\left(\frac{a}{b}e^{-x/b}\right)}{\left(1 + ae^{-x/b}\right)^3} = \frac{Lae^{-x/b}\left(ae^{-x/b} - 1\right)}{\left(1 + ae^{-x/b}\right)^3 b^2}$$

$$y'' = 0 \text{ if } ae^{-x/b} = 1 \Rightarrow \frac{-x}{b} = \ln\left(\frac{1}{a}\right) \Rightarrow x = b \ln a$$

$$y(b \ln a) = \frac{L}{1 + ae^{-(b \ln a)/b}} = \frac{L}{1 + a(1/a)} = \frac{L}{2}$$

Therefore, the $y$-coordinate of the inflection point is $L/2$.

**62.** (a)

$$f(c) = f(c + x)$$
$$10ce^{-c} = 10(c + x)e^{-(c+x)}$$
$$\frac{c}{e^c} = \frac{c + x}{e^{c+x}}$$
$$ce^{c+x} = (c + x)e^c$$
$$ce^x = c + x$$
$$ce^x - c = x$$
$$c = \frac{x}{e^x - 1}$$

(b) $A(x) = xf(c)$

$$= x\left[10\left(\frac{x}{e^x - 1}\right)e^{-x/(e^x-1)}\right]$$
$$= \frac{10x^2}{e^x - 1}e^{x/(1-e^x)}$$

(c) $A(x) = \dfrac{10x^2}{e^x - 1}e^{x/(1-e^x)}$

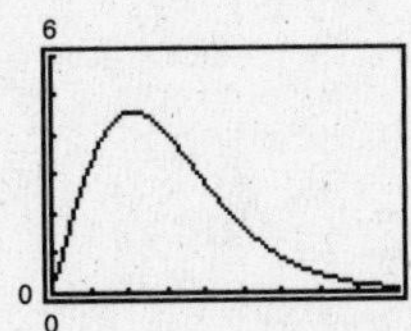


The maximum area is 4.591 for $x = 2.118$ and $f(x) = 2.547$.

(d) $c = \dfrac{x}{e^x - 1}$

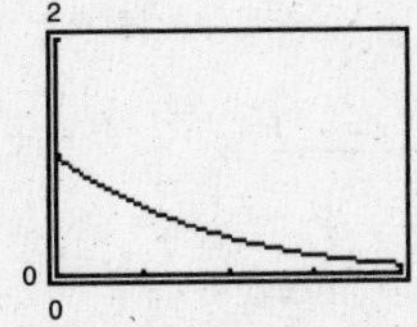


$$\lim_{x\to 0^+} c = 1$$
$$\lim_{x\to\infty} c = 0$$

**63.** $S_1 = (4m - 1)^2 + (5m - 6)^2 + (10m - 3)^2$

$$\frac{dS_1}{dm} = 2(4m - 1)(4) + 2(5m - 6)(5) + 2(10m - 3)(10)$$
$$= 282m - 128 = 0 \text{ when } m = \frac{64}{141}.$$

Line: $y = \dfrac{64}{141}x$

$$S_1 = \left|4\left(\frac{64}{141}\right) - 1\right| + \left|5\left(\frac{64}{141}\right) - 6\right| + \left|10\left(\frac{64}{141}\right) - 3\right|$$
$$= \left|\frac{256}{141} - 1\right| + \left|\frac{320}{141} - 6\right| + \left|\frac{640}{141} - 3\right| = \frac{858}{141} \approx 6.1 \text{ mi}$$

**64.** $S_2 = |4m - 1| + |5m - 6| + |10m - 3|$

Using a graphing utility, you can see that the minimum occurs when $m = 0.3$.

Line $y = 0.3x$

$S_2 = |4(0.3) - 1| + |5(0.3) - 6| + |10(0.3) - 3| = 4.7$ mi.

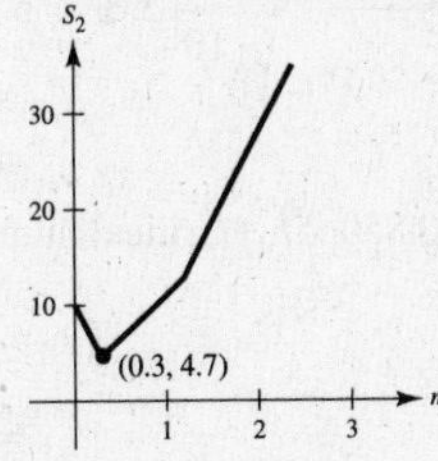

**65.** $S_3 = \dfrac{|4m - 1|}{\sqrt{m^2 + 1}} + \dfrac{|5m - 6|}{\sqrt{m^2 + 1}} + \dfrac{|10m - 3|}{\sqrt{m^2 + 1}}$

Using a graphing utility, you can see that the minimum occurs when $x \approx 0.3$.

Line: $y \approx 0.3x$

$$S_3 = \frac{|4(0.3) - 1| + |5(0.3) - 6| + |10(0.3) - 3|}{\sqrt{(0.3)^2 + 1}} \approx 4.5 \text{ mi.}$$

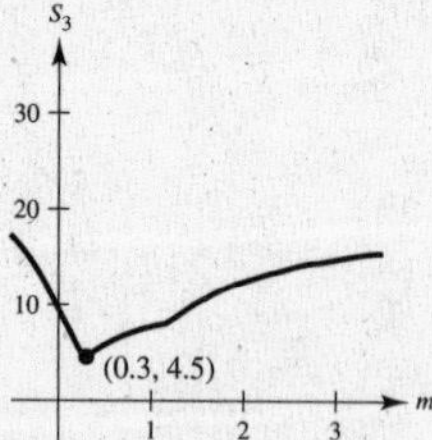


**66.** (a) Label the figure so that $r^2 = x^2 + h^2$. Then, the area $A$ is 8 times the area of the region given by $OPQR$:

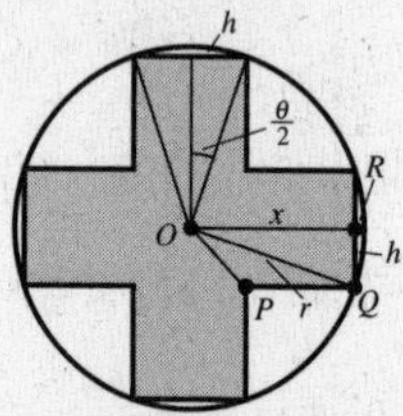


$$A = 8\left[\frac{1}{2}h^2 + (x - h)h\right] = 8\left[\frac{1}{2}(r^2 - x^2) + \left(x - \sqrt{r^2 - x^2}\right)\sqrt{r^2 - x^2}\right] = 8x\sqrt{r^2 - x^2} + 4x^2 - 4r^2$$

$$A'(x) = 8\sqrt{r^2 - x^2} - \frac{8x^2}{\sqrt{r^2 - x^2}} + 8x = 0$$

$$\frac{8x^2}{\sqrt{r^2 - x^2}} = 8x + 8\sqrt{r^2 - x^2}$$

$$x^2 = x\sqrt{r^2 - x^2} + (r^2 - x^2)$$

$$2x^2 - r^2 = x\sqrt{r^2 - x^2}$$

$$4x^4 - 4x^2r^2 + r^4 = x^2(r^2 - x^2)$$

$$5x^4 - 5x^2r^2 + r^4 = 0 \quad \text{Quadratic in } x^2.$$

$$x^2 = \frac{5r^2 \pm \sqrt{25r^4 - 20r^4}}{10} = \frac{r^2}{10}\left[5 \pm \sqrt{5}\right].$$

Take positive value.

$$x = r\sqrt{\frac{5 + \sqrt{5}}{10}} \approx 0.85065r \quad \text{Critical number}$$

(b) Note that $\sin\frac{\theta}{2} = \frac{h}{r}$ and $\cos\frac{\theta}{2} = \frac{x}{r}$. The area $A$ of the cross equals the sum of two large rectangles minus the common square in the middle.

$$A = 2(2x)(2h) - 4h^2 = 8xh - 4h^2 = 8r^2\sin\frac{\theta}{2}\cos\frac{\theta}{2} - 4r^2\sin^2\frac{\theta}{2} = 4r^2\left(\sin\theta - \sin^2\frac{\theta}{2}\right)$$

$$A'(\theta) = 4r^2\left(\cos\theta - \sin\frac{\theta}{2}\cos\frac{\theta}{2}\right) = 0$$

$$\cos\theta = \sin\frac{\theta}{2}\cos\frac{\theta}{2} = \frac{1}{2}\sin\theta$$

$$\tan\theta = 2$$

$$\theta = \arctan(2) \approx 1.10715 \quad \text{or} \quad 63.4°$$

(c) Note that $x^2 = \frac{r^2}{10}\left(5 + \sqrt{5}\right)$ and $r^2 - x^2 = \frac{r^2}{10}\left(5 - \sqrt{5}\right)$.

$$\begin{aligned}
A(x) &= 8x\sqrt{r^2 - x^2} + 4x^2 - 4r^2\\
&= 8\left[\frac{r^2}{10}\left(5 + \sqrt{5}\right)\frac{r^2}{10}\left(5 - \sqrt{5}\right)\right]^{1/2} + 4\frac{r^2}{10}\left(5 + \sqrt{5}\right) - 4r^2\\
&= 8\left[\frac{r^4}{10}(20)\right]^{1/2} + 2r^2 + \frac{2}{5}\sqrt{5}r^2 - 4r^2\\
&= \frac{8}{5}r^2\sqrt{5} - 2r^2 + \frac{2\sqrt{5}}{5}r^2\\
&= 2r^2\left[\frac{4}{5}\sqrt{5} - 1 + \frac{\sqrt{5}}{5}\right] = 2r^2\left(\sqrt{5} - 1\right)
\end{aligned}$$

Using the angle approach, note that $\tan\theta = 2$, $\sin\theta = \frac{2}{\sqrt{5}}$ and $\sin^2\left(\frac{\theta}{2}\right) = \frac{1}{2}(1 - \cos\theta) = \frac{1}{2}\left(1 - \frac{1}{\sqrt{5}}\right)$.

So, $A(\theta) = 4r^2\left(\sin\theta - \sin^2\frac{\theta}{2}\right) = 4r^2\left(\frac{2}{\sqrt{5}} - \frac{1}{2}\left(1 - \frac{1}{\sqrt{5}}\right)\right) = \frac{4r^2\left(\sqrt{5} - 1\right)}{2} = 2r^2\left(\sqrt{5} - 1\right)$

**67.** $f(x) = x^3 - 3x;\ x^4 + 36 \le 13x^2$

$$\begin{aligned}
x^4 - 13x^2 + 36 &= \left(x^2 - 9\right)\left(x^2 - 4\right)\\
&= (x - 3)(x - 2)(x + 2)(x + 3) \le 0
\end{aligned}$$

So, $-3 \le x \le -2$ or $2 \le x \le 3$.

$f'(x) = 3x^2 - 3 = 3(x + 1)(x - 1)$

$f$ is increasing on $(-\infty, -1)$ and $(1, \infty)$.

So, $f$ is increasing on $[-3, -2]$ and $[2, 3]$.

$f(-2) = -2$, $f(3) = 18$. The maximum value of $f$ is 18.

**68.** Let $a = \left(x + \frac{1}{x}\right)^3$ and $b = x^3 + \frac{1}{x^3}, x > 0.$

$$a^2 - b^2 = \left(x + \frac{1}{x}\right)^6 - \left(x^3 + \frac{1}{x^3}\right)^2 = \left(x + \frac{1}{x}\right)^6 - \left(x^6 + \frac{1}{x^6} + 2\right)$$

Let $f(x) = \dfrac{(x + 1/x)^6 - (x^6 + 1/x^6 + 2)}{(x + 1/x)^3 + (x^3 + 1/x^3)}$

$$= \frac{a^2 - b^2}{a + b} = a - b$$

$$= \left(x^3 + 3x + \frac{3}{x} + \frac{1}{x^3}\right) - \left(x^3 + \frac{1}{x^3}\right)$$

$$= 3x + \frac{3}{x} = 3\left(x + \frac{1}{x}\right).$$

Let $g(x) = x + \frac{1}{x}, g'(x) = 1 - \frac{1}{x^2} = 0 \Rightarrow x = 1.$

$g''(x) = \frac{2}{x^3}$ and $g''(1) = 2 > 0.$ So $g$ is a minimum at $x = 1$: $g(1) = 2.$

Finally, $f$ is a minimum of $3(2) = 6.$

## Section 4.8 Differentials

**1.** $f(x) = x^2$

$f'(x) = 2x$

Tangent line at (2, 4): $y - f(2) = f'(2)(x - 2)$

$$y - 4 = 4(x - 2)$$

$$y = 4x - 4$$

| $x$ | 1.9 | 1.99 | 2 | 2.01 | 2.1 |
|---|---|---|---|---|---|
| $f(x) = x^2$ | 3.6100 | 3.9601 | 4 | 4.0401 | 4.4100 |
| $T(x) = 4x - 4$ | 3.6000 | 3.9600 | 4 | 4.0400 | 4.4000 |

**2.** $f(x) = \frac{6}{x^2} = 6x^{-2}$

$f'(x) = -12x^{-3} = \frac{-12}{x^3}$

Tangent line at $\left(2, \frac{3}{2}\right)$:

$$y - \frac{3}{2} = \frac{-12}{8}(x - 2) = \frac{-3}{2}(x - 2)$$

$$y = -\frac{3}{2}x + \frac{9}{2}$$

| $x$ | 1.9 | 1.99 | 2 | 2.01 | 2.1 |
|---|---|---|---|---|---|
| $f(x) = \frac{6}{x^2}$ | 1.6620 | 1.5151 | 1.5 | 1.4851 | 1.3605 |
| $T(x) = -\frac{3}{2}x + \frac{9}{2}$ | 1.65 | 1.515 | 1.5 | 1.485 | 1.35 |

**3.** $f(x) = x^5$

$f'(x) = 5x^4$

Tangent line at $(2, 32)$:

$$y - f(2) = f'(2)(x - 2)$$
$$y - 32 = 80(x - 2)$$
$$y = 80x - 128$$

| $x$ | 1.9 | 1.99 | 2 | 2.01 | 2.1 |
|---|---|---|---|---|---|
| $f(x) = x^5$ | 24.7610 | 31.2080 | 32 | 32.8080 | 40.8410 |
| $T(x) = 80x - 128$ | 24.0000 | 31.2000 | 32 | 32.8000 | 40.0000 |

**4.** $f(x) = \sqrt{x}$

$f'(x) = \dfrac{1}{2\sqrt{x}}$

Tangent line at $\left(2, \sqrt{2}\right)$:

$$y - f(2) = f'(2)(x - 2)$$
$$y - \sqrt{2} = \frac{1}{2\sqrt{2}}(x - 2)$$
$$y = \frac{x}{2\sqrt{2}} + \frac{1}{\sqrt{2}}$$

| $x$ | 1.9 | 1.99 | 2 | 2.01 | 2.1 |
|---|---|---|---|---|---|
| $f(x) = \sqrt{x}$ | 1.3784 | 1.4107 | 1.4142 | 1.4177 | 1.4491 |
| $T(x) = \dfrac{x}{2\sqrt{2}} + \dfrac{1}{\sqrt{2}}$ | 1.3789 | 1.4107 | 1.4142 | 1.4177 | 1.4496 |

**5.** $f(x) = \sin x$

$f'(x) = \cos x$

Tangent line at $(2, \sin 2)$:

$$y - f(2) = f'(2)(x - 2)$$
$$y - \sin 2 = (\cos 2)(x - 2)$$
$$y = (\cos 2)(x - 2) + \sin 2$$

| $x$ | 1.9 | 1.99 | 2 | 2.01 | 2.1 |
|---|---|---|---|---|---|
| $f(x) = \sin x$ | 0.9463 | 0.9134 | 0.9093 | 0.9051 | 0.8632 |
| $T(x) = (\cos 2)(x - 2) + \sin 2$ | 0.9509 | 0.9135 | 0.9093 | 0.9051 | 0.8677 |

**6.** $f(x) = \log_2 x = \dfrac{\ln x}{\ln 2}, \quad (2, 1)$

$$f'(x) = \frac{1}{x \ln 2}$$

$$f'(2) = \frac{1}{2 \ln 2}$$

Tangent line at $(2, 1)$: $y - 1 = \dfrac{1}{2 \ln 2}(x - 2)$

$$y = \frac{1}{2 \ln 2}x + 1 - \frac{1}{\ln 2}$$

| $x$ | 1.9 | 1.99 | 2 | 2.01 | 2.1 |
|---|---|---|---|---|---|
| $f(x) = \log_2 x$ | 0.9260 | 0.9928 | 1 | 1.0072 | 1.0704 |
| $T(x) = \dfrac{1}{2 \ln 2}x + 1 - \dfrac{1}{\ln 2}$ | 0.9279 | 0.9928 | 1 | 1.0072 | 1.0721 |

**7.** $y = f(x) = x^3, f'(x) = 3x^2, x = 1, \Delta x = dx = 0.1$

$$\begin{aligned}\Delta y &= f(x + \Delta x) - f(x) \\ &= f(1.1) - f(1) \\ &= 0.331\end{aligned} \qquad \begin{aligned}dy &= f'(x)\,dx \\ &= f'(1)(0.1) \\ &= 3(0.1) \\ &= 0.3\end{aligned}$$

**8.** $y = f(x) = 1 - 2x^2, f'(x) = -4x, x = 0, \Delta x = dx = -0.1$

$$\begin{aligned}\Delta y &= f(x + \Delta x) - f(x) \\ &= f(-0.1) - f(0) \\ &= \left[1 - 2(-0.1)^2\right] - \left[1 - 2(0)^2\right] = -0.02\end{aligned} \qquad \begin{aligned}dy &= f'(x)\,dx \\ &= f'(0)(-0.1) \\ &= (0)(-0.1) = 0\end{aligned}$$

**9.** $y = f(x) = x^4 + 1, f'(x) = 4x^3, x = -1, \Delta x = dx = 0.01$

$$\begin{aligned}\Delta y &= f(x + \Delta x) - f(x) \\ &= f(-0.99) - f(-1) \\ &= \left[(-0.99)^4 + 1\right] - \left[(-1)^4 + 1\right] \approx -0.0394\end{aligned} \qquad \begin{aligned}dy &= f'(x)\,dx \\ &= f'(-1)(0.01) \\ &= (-4)(0.01) = -0.04\end{aligned}$$

**10.** $y = f(x) = 2 - x^4, f'(x) = -4x^3, x = 2, \Delta x = dx = 0.01$

$$\begin{aligned}\Delta y &= f(x + \Delta x) - f(x) \\ &= f(2.01) - f(2) \\ &\approx -14.3224 - (-14) = -0.3224\end{aligned} \qquad \begin{aligned}dy &= f'(x)\,dx \\ &= \left(-4x^3\right)dx \\ &= -4(2)^3(0.01) \\ &= -0.32\end{aligned}$$

**11.** $y = 3x^2 - 4$

$dy = 6x\,dx$

**12.** $y = 3x^{2/3}$

$dy = 2x^{-1/3}\,dx = \dfrac{2}{x^{1/3}}\,dx$

**13.** $y = \dfrac{x + 1}{2x - 1}$

$dy = -\dfrac{3}{(2x - 1)^2}\,dx$

**14.** $y = \sqrt{9 - x^2}$

$dy = \frac{1}{2}(9 - x^2)^{-1/2}(-2x)\,dx = \frac{-x}{\sqrt{9 - x^2}}\,dx$

**15.** $y = x\sqrt{1 - x^2}$

$dy = \left(x\frac{-x}{\sqrt{1 - x^2}} + \sqrt{1 - x^2}\right)dx = \frac{1 - 2x^2}{\sqrt{1 - x^2}}\,dx$

**16.** $y = \sqrt{x} + \frac{1}{\sqrt{x}}$

$dy = \left(\frac{1}{2\sqrt{x}} - \frac{1}{2x\sqrt{x}}\right)dx = \frac{x - 1}{2x\sqrt{x}}\,dx$

**17.** $y = \ln\sqrt{4 - x^2} = \frac{1}{2}\ln(4 - x^2)$

$dy = \frac{1}{2}\left(\frac{-2x}{4 - x^2}\right)dx = \frac{-x}{4 - x^2}\,dx$

**18.** $y = e^{-0.5x}\cos 4x$

$dy = \left[e^{-0.5x}(-4\sin 4x) + (-0.5)e^{-0.5x}\cos 4x\right]dx$

$= e^{-0.5x}\left[-4\sin 4x - 0.5\cos 4x\right]dx$

**19.** $y = 3x - \sin^2 x$

$dy = (3 - 2\sin x\cos x)\,dx = (3 - \sin 2x)\,dx$

**20.** $y = x\cos x$

$dy = (-x\sin x + \cos x)\,dx$

**21.** $y = \frac{1}{3}\cos\left(\frac{6\pi x - 1}{2}\right)$

$dy = -\pi\sin\left(\frac{6\pi x - 1}{2}\right)dx$

**22.** $y = \frac{\sec^2 x}{x^2 + 1}$

$dy = \left[\frac{(x^2 + 1)2\sec^2 x\tan x - \sec^2 x(2x)}{(x^2 + 1)^2}\right]dx$

$= \left[\frac{2\sec^2 x(x^2\tan x + \tan x - x)}{(x^2 + 1)^2}\right]dx$

**23.** $y = x\arcsin x$

$dy = \left(\frac{x}{\sqrt{1 - x^2}} + \arcsin x\right)dx$

**24.** $y = \arctan(x - 2)$

$dy = \frac{1}{1 + (x - 2)^2}\,dx$

**25.** (a) $f(1.9) = f(2 - 0.1) \approx f(2) + f'(2)(-0.1)$

$\approx 1 + (1)(-0.1) = 0.9$

(b) $f(2.04) = f(2 + 0.04) \approx f(2) + f'(2)(0.04)$

$\approx 1 + (1)(0.04) = 1.04$

**26.** (a) $f(1.9) = f(2 - 0.1) \approx f(2) + f'(2)(-0.1)$

$\approx 1 + (-1)(-0.1) = 1.1$

(b) $f(2.04) = f(2 + 0.04) \approx f(2) + f'(2)(0.04)$

$\approx 1 + (-1)(0.04) = 0.96$

**27.** (a) $f(1.9) = f(2 - 0.1) \approx f(2) + f'(2)(-0.1)$

$\approx 1 + \left(-\frac{1}{2}\right)(-0.1) = 1.05$

(b) $f(2.04) = f(2 + 0.04) \approx f(2) + f'(2)(0.04)$

$\approx 1 + \left(-\frac{1}{2}\right)(0.04) = 0.98$

**28.** (a) $f(1.9) = f(2 - 0.1) \approx f(2) + f'(2)(-0.1)$

$\approx 1 + 0(-0.1) = 1$

(b) $f(2.04) = f(2 + 0.04) \approx f(2) + f'(2)(0.04)$

$\approx 1 + 0(0.04) = 1$

**29.** (a) $g(2.93) = g(3 - 0.07) \approx g(3) + g'(3)(-0.07)$

$\approx 8 + \left(-\frac{1}{2}\right)(-0.07) = 8.035$

(b) $g(3.1) = g(3 + 0.1) \approx g(3) + g'(3)(0.1)$

$\approx 8 + \left(-\frac{1}{2}\right)(0.1) = 7.95$

**30.** (a) $g(2.93) = g(3 - 0.07) \approx g(3) + g'(3)(-0.07)$

$\approx 8 + (3)(-0.07) = 7.79$

(b) $g(3.1) = g(3 + 0.1) \approx g(3) + g'(3)(0.1)$

$\approx 8 + (3)(0.1) = 8.3$

**31.** $A = x^2$

$x = 10$

$\Delta x = dx = \pm\frac{1}{32}$

$dA = 2x\,dx$

$\Delta A \approx dA = 2(10)\left(\pm\frac{1}{32}\right)$

$= \pm\frac{5}{8}\text{ in.}^2$

**32.** $A = \frac{1}{2}bh,\ b = 36,\ h = 50$

$db = dh = \pm 0.25$

$dA = \frac{1}{2}b\,dh + \frac{1}{2}h\,db$

$\Delta A \approx dA = \frac{1}{2}(36)(\pm 0.25) + \frac{1}{2}(50)(\pm 0.25)$

$= \pm 10.75\text{ cm}^2$

**33.** $A = \pi r^2$

$r = 16$

$\Delta r = dr = \pm\frac{1}{4}$

$\Delta A \approx dA = 2\pi r\,dr = \pi(32)\left(\pm\frac{1}{4}\right)$

$= \pm 8\pi \text{ in.}^2$

**34.** $x = 15$ inches

$\Delta x = dx = \pm 0.03$ inch

(a) $V = x^3$

$dV = 3x^2\,dx = 3(15)^2(\pm 0.03)$

$= \pm 20.25 \text{ in.}^3$

(b) $S = 6x^2$

$dS = 12x\,dx = 12(15)(\pm 0.03)$

$= \pm 5.4 \text{ in.}^2$

**35.** (a) $x = 12$ cm

$\Delta x = dx = \pm 0.05$ cm

$A = x^2$

$\Delta A \approx dA = 2x\,dx = 2(12)(\pm 0.05)$

$= \pm 1.2 \text{ cm}^2$

Percentage error:

$$\frac{dA}{A} = \frac{1.2}{(12)^2} = 0.008\overline{33}\ldots = \frac{5}{6}\%$$

(b) $\dfrac{dA}{A} = \dfrac{2x\,dx}{x^2} = \dfrac{2\,dx}{x} \le 0.025$

$$\frac{dx}{x} \le \frac{0.025}{2} = 0.0125 = 1.25\%$$

**36.** (a) $C = 64$ cm

$\Delta C = dC = \pm 0.9$ cm

$C = 2\pi r \Rightarrow r = \dfrac{C}{2\pi}$

$A = \pi r^2 = \pi\left(\dfrac{C}{2\pi}\right)^2 = \dfrac{1}{4\pi}C^2$

$dA = \dfrac{1}{2\pi}C\,dC = \dfrac{1}{2\pi}(64)(\pm 0.9) = \dfrac{\pm 28.8}{\pi}$

$\dfrac{dA}{A} = \dfrac{28.8/\pi}{[1/(4\pi)](64)^2} \approx 0.028125 = 2.8\%$

(b) $\dfrac{dA}{A} = \dfrac{[1/(2\pi)]C\,dC}{[1/(4\pi)]C^2} = \dfrac{2\,dC}{C} \le 0.03$

$$\frac{dC}{C} \le \frac{0.03}{2} = 0.015 = 1.5\%$$

**37.** $r = 8$ in.

$\Delta r = dr = \pm 0.02$ in.

(a) $V = \frac{4}{3}\pi r^3$

$dV = 4\pi r^2 dr = 4\pi(8)^2(\pm 0.02) = \pm 5.12\pi \text{ in.}^3$

(b) $S = 4\pi r^2$

$dS = 8\pi r\,dr = 8\pi(8)(\pm 0.02) = \pm 1.28\pi \text{ in.}^2$

(c) Relative error: $\dfrac{dV}{V} = \dfrac{4\pi r^2 dr}{(4/3)\pi r^3} = \dfrac{3\,dr}{r} = \dfrac{3}{8}(0.02) = 0.0075 = 0.75\%$

Relative error: $\dfrac{dS}{S} = \dfrac{8\pi r\,dr}{4\pi r^2} = \dfrac{2\,dr}{r} = \dfrac{2(0.02)}{8} = 0.005 = \dfrac{1}{2}\%$

**38.** $T = 2.5x + 0.5x^2$, $\Delta x = dx = 26 - 25 = 1$, $x = 25$

$dT = (2.5 + x)dx = (2.5 + 25)(1) = 27.5$ mi

Percentage change $= \dfrac{dT}{T} = \dfrac{27.5}{375} \approx 7.3\%$

**39.** $P = 100xe^{-x/400}$, $x$ changes from 115 to 120.

$$dP = 100\left(e^{-x/400} - \frac{x}{400}e^{-x/400}\right)dx = e^{-115/400}\left(100 - \frac{115}{4}\right)(120 - 115) \approx 267.24$$

Approximate percentage change: $\frac{dP}{P}(100) = \frac{267.24}{8626.57}(100) \approx 3.1\%$

**40.** $dH = -\frac{401{,}493{,}267}{2{,}000{,}000}\frac{e^{369{,}444/(50t+19{,}793)}}{(50t + 19{,}793)^2}dt$

At $t = 72$ and $dt = 1$, $dH \approx -2.65$.

**41.** $V = \pi r^2 h = 40\pi r^2, r = 5$ cm, $h = 40$ cm, $dr = 0.2$ cm

$\Delta V \approx dV = 80\pi r\,dr = 80\pi(5)(0.2) = 80\pi$ cm$^3$

**42.** $V = \frac{4}{3}\pi r^3, r = 100$ cm, $dr = 0.2$ cm

$\Delta V \approx dV = 4\pi r^2 dr = 4\pi(100)^2(0.2) = 8000\pi$ cm$^3$

**43.** $\theta = 26°45' = 26.75°$

$d\theta = \pm 15' = \pm 0.25°$

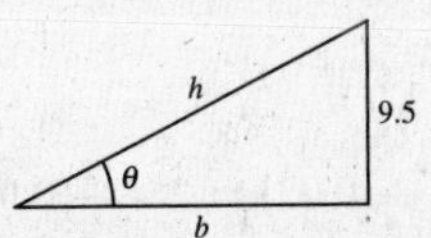


(a) $h = 9.5 \csc \theta$

$dh = -9.5 \csc \theta \cot \theta \, d\theta$

$\frac{dh}{h} = -\cot \theta \, d\theta$

$\left|\frac{dh}{h}\right| = (\cot 26.75°)(0.25°)$

Converting to radians,

$(\cot 0.4669)(0.0044) \approx 0.0087$

$= 0.87\%$ (in radians).

(b) $\left|\frac{dh}{h}\right| = \cot \theta \, d\theta \le 0.02$

$\frac{d\theta}{\theta} \le \frac{0.02}{\theta(\cot \theta)} = \frac{0.02 \tan \theta}{\theta}$

$\frac{d\theta}{\theta} \le \frac{0.02 \tan 26.75°}{26.75°} \approx \frac{0.02 \tan 0.4669}{0.4669}$

$\approx 0.0216$

$= 2.16\%$ (in radians)

**44.** $E = IR$

$R = \frac{E}{I}$

$dR = -\frac{E}{I^2}dI$

$\frac{dR}{R} = \frac{-(E/I^2)dI}{E/I} = -\frac{dI}{I}$

$\left|\frac{dR}{R}\right| = \left|-\frac{dI}{I}\right| = \left|\frac{dI}{I}\right|$

**45.** $R = \frac{v_0^2}{32}(\sin 2\theta)$

$v_0 = 2500$ ft/sec

$\theta$ changes from 10° to 11°.

$dR = \frac{v_0^2}{32}(2)(\cos 2\theta)d\theta = \frac{(2500)^2}{16}\cos 2\theta \, d\theta$

$\theta = 10\left(\frac{\pi}{180}\right)$

$d\theta = (11 - 10)\frac{\pi}{180}$

$\Delta R \approx dR$

$= \frac{(2500)^2}{16}\cos\left(\frac{20\pi}{180}\right)\left(\frac{\pi}{180}\right)$

$\approx 6407$ ft

**46.** $h = 50 \tan \theta$

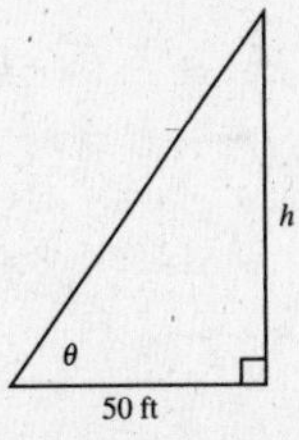


$\theta = 71.5° = 1.2479$ radians

$dh = 50 \sec^2\theta \cdot d\theta$

$\left|\frac{dh}{h}\right| = \left|\frac{50 \sec^2(1.2479)}{50 \tan(1.2479)}d\theta\right| \le 0.06$

$\left|\frac{9.9316}{2.9886}d\theta\right| \le 0.06$

$|d\theta| \le 0.018$

**47.** Let $f(x) = \sqrt{x}, x = 100, dx = -0.6.$

$$f(x + \Delta x) \approx f(x) + f'(x)\,dx = \sqrt{x} + \frac{1}{2\sqrt{x}}dx$$

$$f(x + \Delta x) = \sqrt{99.4}$$

$$\approx \sqrt{100} + \frac{1}{2\sqrt{100}}(-0.6) = 9.97$$

Using a calculator: $\sqrt{99.4} \approx 9.96995$

**48.** Let $f(x) = \sqrt[3]{x}, x = 27, dx = -1.$

$$f(x + \Delta x) \approx f(x) + f'(x)\,dx = \sqrt[3]{x} + \frac{1}{3\sqrt[3]{x^2}}dx$$

$$\sqrt[3]{26} \approx \sqrt[3]{27} + \frac{1}{3\sqrt[3]{27^2}}(-1) = 3 - \frac{1}{27} \approx 2.9630$$

Using a calculator, $\sqrt[3]{26} \approx 2.9625$

**49.** Let $f(x) = \sqrt[4]{x}, x = 625, dx = -1.$

$$f(x + \Delta x) \approx f(x) + f'(x)\,dx = \sqrt[4]{x} + \frac{1}{4\sqrt[4]{x^3}}dx$$

$$f(x + \Delta x) = \sqrt[4]{624} \approx \sqrt[4]{625} + \frac{1}{4\left(\sqrt[4]{625}\right)^3}(-1)$$

$$= 5 - \frac{1}{500} = 4.998$$

Using a calculator, $\sqrt[4]{624} \approx 4.9980.$

**50.** Let $f(x) = x^3, x = 3, dx = -0.01.$

$$f(x + \Delta x) \approx f(x) + f'(x)\,dx = x^3 + 3x^2dx$$

$$f(x + \Delta x) = (2.99)^3 \approx 3^3 + 3(3)^2(-0.01)$$

$$= 27 - 0.27 = 26.73$$

Using a calculator: $(2.99)^3 \approx 26.7309$

**51.** $f(x) = \sqrt{x + 4}$

$$f'(x) = \frac{1}{2\sqrt{x + 4}}$$

At $(0, 2)$, $f(0) = 2$, $f'(0) = \frac{1}{4}$

Tangent line: $y - 2 = \frac{1}{4}(x - 0)$

$$y = \frac{1}{4}x + 2$$

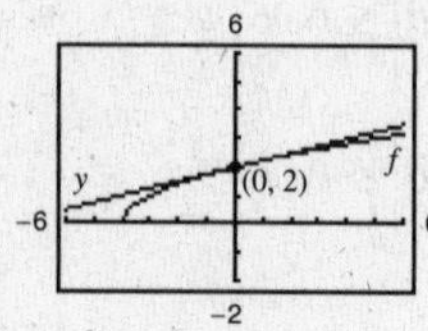


**52.** $f(x) = \tan x$

$f'(x) = \sec^2 x$

$f(0) = 0$

$f'(0) = 1$

Tangent line at $(0, 0)$: $y - 0 = (x - 0)$

$$y = x$$

**53.** In general, when $\Delta x \to 0$, $dy$ approaches $\Delta y$.

**54.** Propagated error $= f(x + \Delta x) - f(x)$,

relative error $= \left|\frac{dy}{y}\right|$, and the percent error

$= \left|\frac{dy}{y}\right| \times 100.$

**55.** (a) Let $f(x) = \sqrt{x}, x = 4, dx = 0.02,$

$f'(x) = 1/\left(2\sqrt{x}\right).$

Then

$$f(4.02) \approx f(4) + f'(4)\,dx$$

$$\sqrt{4.02} \approx \sqrt{4} + \frac{1}{2\sqrt{4}}(0.02) = 2 + \frac{1}{4}(0.02).$$

(b) Let $f(x) = \tan x, x = 0, dx = 0.05,$

$f'(x) = \sec^2 x.$

Then

$$f(0.05) \approx f(0) + f'(0)\,dx$$

$$\tan 0.05 \approx \tan 0 + \sec^2 0(0.05) = 0 + 1(0.05).$$

**56.** Yes. $y = x$ is the tangent line approximation to $f(x) = \sin x$ at $(0, 0)$.

$f'(x) = \cos x$

$f'(0) = 1$

Tangent line: $y - 0 = 1(x - 0)$

$$y = x$$

**57.** True

**58.** True, $\frac{\Delta y}{\Delta x} = \frac{dy}{dx} = a$

**59.** True

**60.** False

Let $f(x) = \sqrt{x}, x = 1$, and $\Delta x = dx = 3$. Then

$$\Delta y = f(x + \Delta x) - f(x) = f(4) - f(1) = 1$$

and $dy = f'(x)\,dx = \frac{1}{2\sqrt{1}}(3) = \frac{3}{2}.$

So, $dy > \Delta y$ in this example.

# Review Exercises for Chapter 4

1. A number $c$ in the domain of $f$ is a critical number if $f'(c) = 0$ or $f'$ is undefined at $c$.

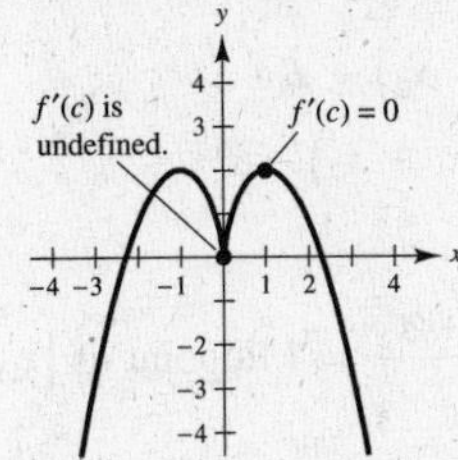


2. (a) $f(4) = -f(-4) = -3$

(b) $f(-3) = -f(3) = -(-4) = 4$

(c)

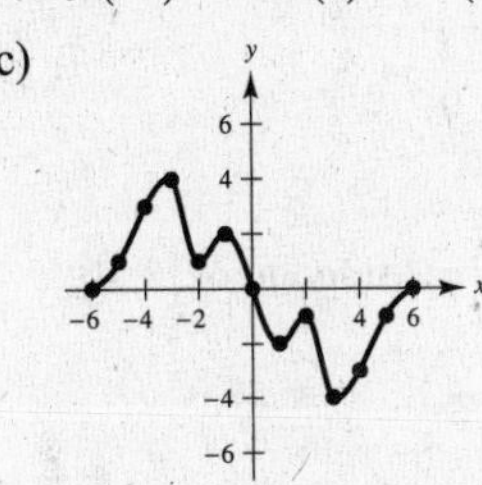

At least six critical numbers on $(-6, 6)$.

(d) Yes. Because $f(-2) = -f(2) = -(-1) = 1$ and $f(1) = -f(-1) = -2$, the Mean Value Theorem states that there exists at least one value $c$ in $(-2, 1)$ such that

$$f'(c) = \frac{f(1) - f(-2)}{1 - (-2)} = \frac{-2 - 1}{1 + 2} = -1.$$

(e) No, $\lim_{x \to 0} f(x)$ exists because $f$ is continuous at $(0, 0)$.

(f) Yes, $f$ is differentiable at $x = 2$.

3. $f(x) = x^2 + 5x, \quad [-4, 0]$

$f'(x) = 2x + 5 = 0$ when $x = -5/2$

Critical number: $x = -5/2$

Left endpoint: $(-4, -4)$

Critical number: $(-5/2, -25/4)$ Minimum

Right endpoint: $(0, 0)$ Maximum

4. $h(x) = 3\sqrt{x} - x, \quad [0, 9]$

$h'(x) = \dfrac{3}{2\sqrt{x}} - 1 = 0 \Rightarrow 2\sqrt{x} = 3 \Rightarrow x = 9/4$

Critical number: $x = 9/4$

Left endpoint: $(0, 0)$ Minimum

Critical number: $(9/4, 9/4)$ Maximum

Right endpoint: $(9, 0)$ Minimum

5. $g(x) = 2x + 5\cos x, [0, 2\pi]$

$g'(x) = 2 - 5\sin x = 0$ when $\sin x = \frac{2}{5}$.

Critical numbers: $x \approx 0.41, x \approx 2.73$

Left endpoint: $(0, 5)$

Critical number: $(0.41, 5.41)$

Critical number: $(2.73, 0.88)$ Minimum

Right endpoint: $(2\pi, 17.57)$ Maximum

6. $f(x) = \dfrac{x}{\sqrt{x^2 + 1}}, [0, 2]$

$$f'(x) = x\left[-\frac{1}{2}(x^2 + 1)^{-3/2}(2x)\right] + (x^2 + 1)^{-1/2}$$

$$= \frac{1}{(x^2 + 1)^{3/2}}$$

No Critical numbers

Left endpoint: $(0, 0)$ Minimum

Right endpoint: $(2, 2/\sqrt{5})$ Maximum

7. No, Rolle's Theorem cannot be applied.

$f(0) = -7 \neq 25 = f(4)$

8. Yes. $f(-3) = f(2) = 0$. $f$ is continuous on $[-3, 2]$, differentiable on $(-3, 2)$.

$f'(x) = (x + 3)(3x - 1) = 0$ for $x = \frac{1}{3}$.

$c = \frac{1}{3}$ satisfied $f'(c) = 0$.

9. No. $f(x) = \dfrac{x^2}{1 - x^2}$ is not continuous on $[-2, 2]$. $f(-1)$ is not defined.

10. No. $f$ is not differentiable at $x = 2$.

11. $f(x) = 3 - |x - 4|$

(a)

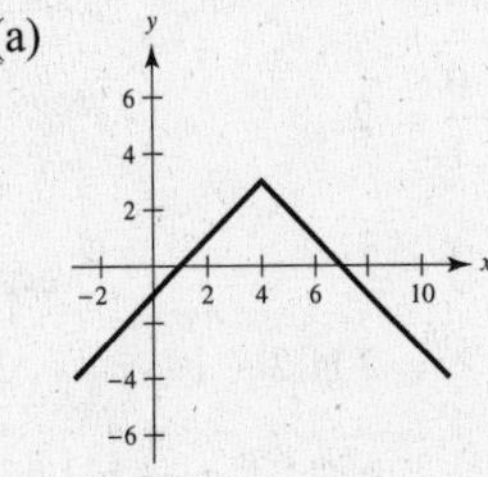

$f(1) = f(7) = 0$

(b) $f$ is not differentiable at $x = 4$.

**12.** No; the function is discontinuous at $x = 0$ which is in the interval $[-2, 1]$.

**13.** $f(x) = x^{2/3}, 1 \le x \le 8$

$f'(x) = \frac{2}{3}x^{-1/3}$

$\frac{f(b) - f(a)}{b - a} = \frac{4 - 1}{8 - 1} = \frac{3}{7}$

$f'(c) = \frac{2}{3}c^{-1/3} = \frac{3}{7}$

$c = \left(\frac{14}{9}\right)^3 = \frac{2744}{729} \approx 3.764$

**14.** $f(x) = \frac{1}{x}, 1 \le x \le 4$

$f'(x) = -\frac{1}{x^2}$

$\frac{f(b) - f(a)}{b - a} = \frac{(1/4) - 1}{4 - 1} = \frac{-3/4}{3} = -\frac{1}{4}$

$f'(c) = \frac{-1}{c^2} = -\frac{1}{4}$

$c = 2$

**15.** The Mean Value Theorem cannot be applied. $f$ is not differentiable at $x = 5$ in $[2, 6]$.

**16.** The Mean Value Theorem cannot be applied. $f$ is not defined for $x < 0$.

**17.** $f(x) = x - \cos x, -\frac{\pi}{2} \le x \le \frac{\pi}{2}$

$f'(x) = 1 + \sin x$

$\frac{f(b) - f(a)}{b - a} = \frac{(\pi/2) - (-\pi/2)}{(\pi/2) - (-\pi/2)} = 1$

$f'(c) = 1 + \sin c = 1$

$c = 0$

**18.** $f(x) = x \log_2 x = x \cdot \frac{\ln x}{\ln 2}, [1, 2]$

$f'(x) = \frac{1}{\ln 2}[\ln x + 1]$

$\frac{f(b) - f(a)}{b - a} = \frac{2 - 0}{2 - 1} = 2$

$f'(c) = \frac{1}{\ln 2}[\ln c + 1] = 2$

$\ln c = 2 \ln 2 - 1$

$c = e^{2 \ln 2 - 1} = \frac{4}{e} \approx 1.4715$

**19.** $f(x) = Ax^2 + Bx + C$

$f'(x) = 2Ax + B$

$\frac{f(x_2) - f(x_1)}{x_2 - x_1} = \frac{A(x_2^2 - x_1^2) + B(x_2 - x_1)}{x_2 - x_1}$

$= A(x_1 + x_2) + B$

$f'(c) = 2Ac + B = A(x_1 + x_2) + B$

$2Ac = A(x_1 + x_2)$

$c = \frac{x_1 + x_2}{2} = \text{Midpoint of } [x_1, x_2]$

**20.** $f(x) = 2x^2 - 3x + 1$

$f'(x) = 4x - 3$

$\frac{f(b) - f(a)}{b - a} = \frac{21 - 1}{4 - 0} = 5$

$f'(c) = 4c - 3 = 5$

$c = 2 = \text{Midpoint of } [0, 4]$

**21.** $f(x) = x^2 + 3x - 12$

$f'(x) = 2x + 3$

Critical number: $x = -\frac{3}{2}$

| Intervals: | $-\infty < x < -\frac{3}{2}$ | $-\frac{3}{2} < x < \infty$ |
|---|---|---|
| Sign of $f'(x)$: | $f'(x) < 0$ | $f'(x) > 0$ |
| Conclusion: | Decreasing | Increasing |

Increasing on: $\left(-\frac{3}{2}, \infty\right)$

Decreasing on: $\left(-\infty, -\frac{3}{2}\right)$

**22.** $h(x) = (x + 2)^{1/3} + 8$

$h'(x) = \frac{1}{3}(x + 2)^{-2/3} = \frac{1}{3(x + 2)^{2/3}}$

Critical number: $x = -2$

| Intervals: | $-\infty < x < -2$ | $-2 < x < \infty$ |
|---|---|---|
| Sign of $h'(x)$: | $h'(x) > 0$ | $h'(x) > 0$ |
| Conclusion: | Increasing | Increasing |

Increasing on: $(-\infty, \infty)$

**23.** $f(x) = (x - 1)^2(x - 3)$

$f'(x) = (x - 1)^2(1) + (x - 3)(2)(x - 1) = (x - 1)(3x - 7)$

Critical numbers: $x = 1$ and $x = \frac{7}{3}$

| Intervals: | $-\infty < x < 1$ | $1 < x < \frac{7}{3}$ | $\frac{7}{3} < x < \infty$ |
|---|---|---|---|
| Sign of $f'(x)$: | $f'(x) > 0$ | $f'(x) < 0$ | $f'(x) > 0$ |
| Conclusion: | Increasing | Decreasing | Increasing |

Increasing on: $(-\infty, 1), \left(\frac{7}{3}, \infty\right)$

Decreasing on: $\left(1, \frac{7}{3}\right)$

**24.** $g(x) = (x + 1)^3$

$g'(x) = 3(x + 1)^2$

Critical number: $x = -1$

Increasing on: $(-\infty, \infty)$

| Intervals: | $-\infty < x < -1$ | $-1 < x < \infty$ |
|---|---|---|
| Sign of $g'(x)$: | $g'(x) > 0$ | $g'(x) > 0$ |
| Conclusion: | Increasing | Increasing |

**25.** $h(x) = \sqrt{x}(x - 3) = x^{3/2} - 3x^{1/2}$

Domain: $(0, \infty)$

$h'(x) = \frac{3}{2}x^{3/2} - \frac{3}{2}x^{-1/2} = \frac{3}{2}x^{-1/2}(x - 1) = \frac{3(x - 1)}{2\sqrt{x}}$

Critical number: $x = 1$

Increasing on: $(1, \infty)$

Decreasing on: $(0, 1)$

| Intervals: | $0 < x < 1$ | $1 < x < \infty$ |
|---|---|---|
| Sign of $h'(x)$: | $h'(x) < 0$ | $h'(x) > 0$ |
| Conclusion: | Decreasing | Increasing |

**26.** $f(x) = \sin x + \cos x, \quad 0 \le x \le 2\pi$

$f'(x) = \cos x - \sin x$

Critical numbers: $x = \frac{\pi}{4}, \frac{5\pi}{4}$

Increasing on: $\left(0, \frac{\pi}{4}\right), \left(\frac{5\pi}{4}, 2\pi\right)$

Decreasing on: $\left(\frac{\pi}{4}, \frac{5\pi}{4}\right)$

| Intervals: | $0 < x < \frac{\pi}{4}$ | $\frac{\pi}{4} < x < \frac{5\pi}{4}$ | $\frac{5\pi}{4} < x < 2\pi$ |
|---|---|---|---|
| Sign of $f'(x)$: | $f'(x) > 0$ | $f'(x) < 0$ | $f'(x) > 0$ |
| Conclusion: | Increasing | Decreasing | Increasing |

**27.** $f(t) = (2 - t)2^t$

$f'(t) = (2 - t)2^t \ln 2 - 2^t = 2^t[(2 - t)\ln 2 - 1]$

$f'(t) = 0: (2 - t)\ln 2 = 1$

$2 - t = \frac{1}{\ln 2}$

$t = 2 - \frac{1}{\ln 2} \approx 0.5573$, Critical number

Increasing on: $\left(-\infty, 2 - \frac{1}{\ln 2}\right)$

Decreasing on: $\left(2 - \frac{1}{\ln 2}, \infty\right)$

| Intervals: | $-\infty < t < 2 - \frac{1}{\ln 2}$ | $2 - \frac{1}{\ln 2} < t < \infty$ |
|---|---|---|
| Sign of $f'(t)$: | $f'(t) > 0$ | $f'(t) < 0$ |
| Conclusion: | Increasing | Decreasing |

**28.** $g(x) = 2x \ln x$

$g'(x) = 2x\left(\frac{1}{x}\right) + 2x \ln x = 2 + 2x \ln x = 0$

$\ln x = -1$

Critical number: $x = \frac{1}{e}$

Increasing on: $\left(\frac{1}{e}, \infty\right)$

Decreasing on: $\left(0, \frac{1}{e}\right)$

| Intervals: | $0 < x < \frac{1}{e}$ | $\frac{1}{e} < x < \infty$ |
|---|---|---|
| Sign of $g'(x)$: | $g'(x) < 0$ | $g'(x) > 0$ |
| Conclusion: | Decreasing | Increasing |

**29.** $f(x) = 4x^3 - 5x$

$f'(x) = 12x^2 - 5 = 0$ when $x = \pm\sqrt{\frac{5}{12}} = \pm\frac{\sqrt{15}}{6}$

| Intervals: | $-\infty < x < \frac{\sqrt{15}}{6}$ | $-\frac{\sqrt{15}}{6} < x < \frac{\sqrt{15}}{6}$ | $\frac{\sqrt{15}}{6} < x < \infty$ |
|---|---|---|---|
| Sign of $f'(x)$: | $f'(x) > 0$ | $f'(x) < 0$ | $f'(x) > 0$ |
| Conclusion: | Increasing | Decreasing | Increasing |

Relative maximum: $\left(-\frac{\sqrt{15}}{6}, \frac{5\sqrt{15}}{9}\right)$

Relative minimum: $\left(\frac{\sqrt{15}}{6}, -\frac{5\sqrt{15}}{9}\right)$

**30.** $g(x) = \frac{1}{4}\left(x^3 - 8x\right)$

$g'(x) = \frac{3}{4}x^2 - 2 = 0 \Rightarrow x^2 = \frac{8}{3} \Rightarrow x = \pm\frac{2\sqrt{6}}{3}$

| Intervals: | $-\infty < x < -\frac{2\sqrt{6}}{3}$ | $-\frac{2\sqrt{6}}{3} < x < \frac{2\sqrt{6}}{3}$ | $\frac{2\sqrt{6}}{3} < x < \infty$ |
|---|---|---|---|
| Sign of $g'(x)$: | $g'(x) > 0$ | $g'(x) < 0$ | $g'(x) > 0$ |
| Conclusion: | Increasing | Decreasing | Increasing |

Relative maximum: $\left(-\frac{2\sqrt{6}}{3}, \frac{8\sqrt{6}}{9}\right)$

Relative minimum: $\left(\frac{2\sqrt{6}}{3}, -\frac{8\sqrt{6}}{9}\right)$

**31.** $h(t) = \frac{1}{4}t^4 - 8t$

$h'(t) = t^3 - 8 = 0$ when $t = 2$.

Relative minimum: $(2, -12)$

| Test Intervals: | $-\infty < t < 2$ | $2 < t < \infty$ |
|---|---|---|
| Sign of $h'(t)$: | $h'(t) < 0$ | $h'(t) > 0$ |
| Conclusion: | Decreasing | Increasing |

**32.** $g(x) = \frac{3}{2}\sin\left(\frac{\pi x}{2} - 1\right), \quad [0, 4]$

$g'(x) = \frac{3}{2}\left(\frac{\pi}{2}\right)\cos\left(\frac{\pi x}{2} - 1\right) = 0$ when $x = 1 + \frac{2}{\pi}, 3 + \frac{2}{\pi}$

Relative maximum: $\left(1 + \frac{2}{\pi}, \frac{3}{2}\right)$

Relative minimum: $\left(3 + \frac{2}{\pi}, -\frac{3}{2}\right)$

| Test Intervals: | $0 < x < 1 + \frac{2}{\pi}$ | $1 + \frac{2}{\pi} < x < 3 + \frac{2}{\pi}$ | $3 + \frac{2}{\pi} < x < 4$ |
|---|---|---|---|
| Sign of $g'(x)$: | $g'(x) > 0$ | $g'(x) < 0$ | $g'(x) > 0$ |
| Conclusion: | Increasing | Decreasing | Increasing |

**33.** $y = \frac{1}{3}\cos(12t) - \frac{1}{4}\sin(12t)$

$v = y' = -4\sin(12t) - 3\cos(12t)$

(a) When $t = \frac{\pi}{8}$, $y = \frac{1}{4}$ in. and $v = y' = 4$ in./sec.

(b) $y' = -4\sin(12t) - 3\cos(12t) = 0$ when $\frac{\sin(12t)}{\cos(12t)} = -\frac{3}{4} \Rightarrow \tan(12t) = -\frac{3}{4}$.

Therefore, $\sin(12t) = -\frac{3}{5}$ and $\cos(12t) = \frac{4}{5}$. The maximum displacement is

$$y = \left(\frac{1}{3}\right)\left(\frac{4}{5}\right) - \frac{1}{4}\left(-\frac{3}{5}\right) = \frac{5}{12} \text{ in.}$$

(c) Period: $\frac{2\pi}{12} = \frac{\pi}{6}$

Frequency: $\frac{1}{\pi/6} = \frac{6}{\pi}$

**34.** (a) $y = A\sin\left(\sqrt{k/m}\,t\right) + B\cos\left(\sqrt{k/m}\,t\right)$

$y' = A\sqrt{k/m}\cos\left(\sqrt{k/m}\,t\right) - B\sqrt{k/m}\sin\left(\sqrt{k/m}\,t\right) = 0$ when $\frac{\sin\sqrt{k/m}\,t}{\cos\sqrt{k/m}\,t} = \frac{A}{B} \Rightarrow \tan\left(\sqrt{k/m}\,t\right) = \frac{A}{B}$.

Therefore,

$$\sin\left(\sqrt{k/m}\,t\right) = \frac{A}{\sqrt{A^2 + B^2}}$$

$$\cos\left(\sqrt{k/m}\,t\right) = \frac{B}{\sqrt{A^2 + B^2}}.$$

When $v = y' = 0$,

$$y = A\left(\frac{A}{\sqrt{A^2 + B^2}}\right) + B\left(\frac{B}{\sqrt{A^2 + B^2}}\right) = \sqrt{A^2 + B^2}.$$

(b) Period: $\frac{2\pi}{\sqrt{k/m}}$

Frequency: $\frac{1}{2\pi/\sqrt{k/m}} = \frac{1}{2\pi}\sqrt{k/m}$

**35.** $f(x) = x^3 - 9x^2$

$f'(x) = 3x^2 - 18x$

$f''(x) = 6x - 18 = 0$ when $x = 3$

| Intervals: | $-\infty < x < 3$ | $3 < x < \infty$ |
|---|---|---|
| Sign of $f''(x)$: | $f''(x) < 0$ | $f''(x) > 0$ |
| Conclusion: | Concave downward | Concave upward |

Point of inflection: $(3, -54)$

**36.** $g(x) = x\sqrt{x+5}$ Domain: $x \ge -5$

$$g'(x) = x\left(\frac{1}{2}\right)(x+5)^{-1/2} + (x+5)^{1/2} = \frac{1}{2}(x+5)^{-1/2}(x + 2(x+5)) = \frac{3x+10}{2\sqrt{x+5}}$$

$$g''(x) = \frac{2\sqrt{x+5}(3) - (3x+10)(x+5)^{-1/2}}{4(x+5)} = \frac{6(x+5) - (3x+10)}{4(x+5)^{3/2}} = \frac{3x+20}{4(x+5)^{3/2}} > 0 \text{ on } (-5, \infty)$$

Concave upward: $(-5, \infty)$

No point of inflection

**37.** $f(x) = x + \cos x, 0 \le x \le 2\pi$

$f'(x) = 1 - \sin x$

$f''(x) = -\cos x = 0$ when $x = \dfrac{\pi}{2}, \dfrac{3\pi}{2}$.

Points of inflection: $\left(\dfrac{\pi}{2}, \dfrac{\pi}{2}\right), \left(\dfrac{3\pi}{2}, \dfrac{3\pi}{2}\right)$

| Test Intervals: | $0 < x < \frac{\pi}{2}$ | $\frac{\pi}{2} < x < \frac{3\pi}{2}$ | $\frac{3\pi}{2} < x < 2\pi$ |
|---|---|---|---|
| Sign of $f''(x)$: | $f''(x) < 0$ | $f''(x) > 0$ | $f''(x) < 0$ |
| Conclusion: | Concave downward | Concave upward | Concave downward |

**38.** $f(x) = (x+2)^2(x-4) = x^3 - 12x - 16$

$f'(x) = 3x^2 - 12$

$f''(x) = 6x = 0$ when $x = 0$.

Point of inflection: $(0, -16)$

| Test Intervals: | $-\infty < x < 0$ | $0 < x < \infty$ |
|---|---|---|
| Sign of $f''(x)$: | $f''(x) < 0$ | $f''(x) > 0$ |
| Conclusion: | Concave downward | Concave upward |

**39.** $f(x) = (x+9)^2$

$f'(x) = 2(x+9) = 0 \Rightarrow x = -9$

$f''(x) = 2 > 0 \Rightarrow (-9, 0)$ is a relative minimum.

**40.** $h(x) = x - 2\cos x, \quad [0, 4\pi]$

$h'(x) = 1 + 2\sin x = 0 \Rightarrow \sin x = -\dfrac{1}{2}$

Critical numbers: $x = \dfrac{7\pi}{6}, \dfrac{11\pi}{6}, \dfrac{19\pi}{6}, \dfrac{23\pi}{6}$

$h''(x) = 2\cos x$

$h''\left(\dfrac{7\pi}{6}\right) = -\sqrt{3} < 0 \Rightarrow \left(\dfrac{7\pi}{6}, \dfrac{7\pi}{6} + \sqrt{3}\right) \approx (3.665, 5.397)$ is a relative maximum.

$h''\left(\dfrac{11\pi}{6}\right) = \sqrt{3} > 0 \Rightarrow \left(\dfrac{11\pi}{6}, \dfrac{11\pi}{6} - \sqrt{3}\right) \approx (5.760, 4.028)$ is a relative minimum.

$h''\left(\dfrac{19\pi}{6}\right) = -\sqrt{3} < 0 \Rightarrow \left(\dfrac{19\pi}{6}, \dfrac{19\pi}{6} + \sqrt{3}\right) \approx (9.948, 11.680)$ is a relative maximum.

$h''\left(\dfrac{23\pi}{6}\right) = \sqrt{3} > 0 \Rightarrow \left(\dfrac{23\pi}{6}, \dfrac{23\pi}{6} - \sqrt{3}\right) \approx (12.043, 10.311)$ is a relative minimum.

**41.** $g(x) = 2x^2(1 - x^2)$

$g'(x) = -4x(2x^2 - 1) = 0 \Rightarrow x = 0, \pm\dfrac{1}{\sqrt{2}}$

$g''(x) = 4 - 24x^2$

$g''(0) = 4 > 0 \quad (0, 0)$ is a relative minimum.

$g''\left(\pm\dfrac{1}{\sqrt{2}}\right) = -8 < 0 \left(\pm\dfrac{1}{\sqrt{2}}, \dfrac{1}{2}\right)$ are relative maxima.

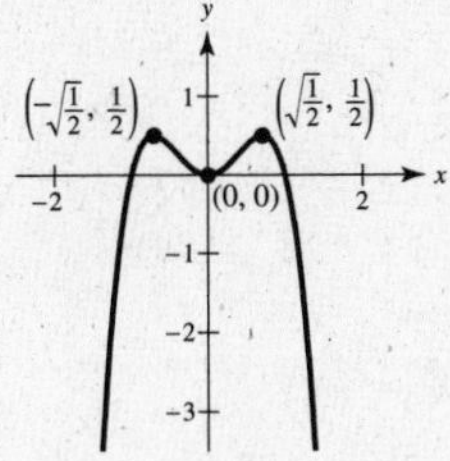


**42.** $h(t) = t - 4\sqrt{t + 1}$ Domain: $[-1, \infty]$

$h'(t) = 1 - \dfrac{2}{\sqrt{t + 1}} = 0 \Rightarrow t = 3$

$h''(t) = \dfrac{1}{(t + 1)^{3/2}}$

$h''(3) = \dfrac{1}{8} > 0 \quad (3, -5)$ is a relative minimum.

**43.**

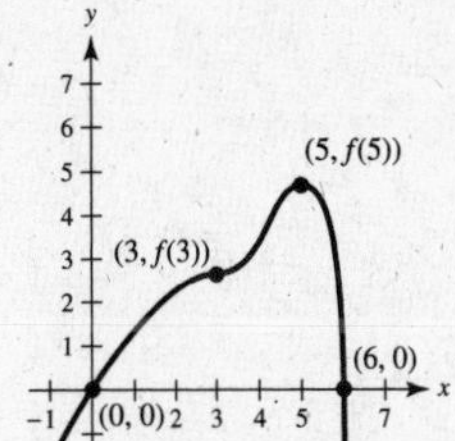

**44.**

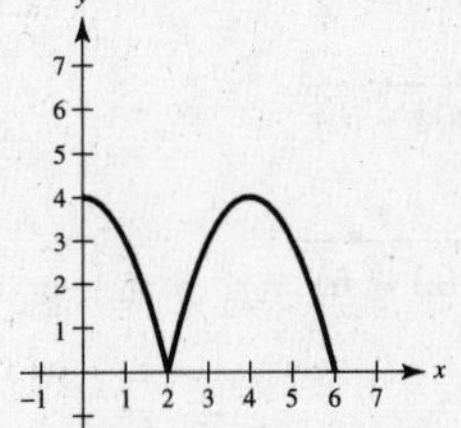

**45.** The first derivative is positive and the second derivative is negative. The graph is increasing and is concave down.

**46.** $C = \left(\dfrac{Q}{x}\right)s + \left(\dfrac{x}{2}\right)r$

$\dfrac{dC}{dx} = -\dfrac{Qs}{x^2} + \dfrac{r}{2} = 0$

$\dfrac{Qs}{x^2} = \dfrac{r}{2}$

$x^2 = \dfrac{2Qs}{r}$

$x = \sqrt{\dfrac{2Qs}{r}}$

**47.** (a) $D = 0.00430t^4 - 0.2856t^3 + 5.833t^2 - 26.85t + 87.1, \quad 0 \le t \le 35$

(b)

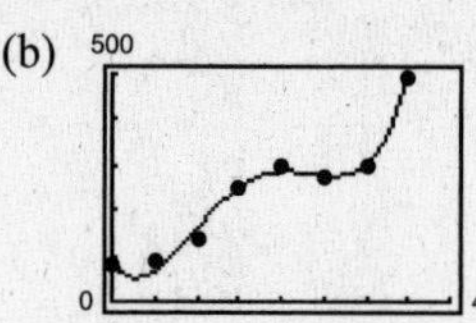


(c) Maximum occurs at $t = 35 \quad (2005)$

Minimum occurs at $t \approx 2.9 \quad (1972)$

(d) $D'(t)$ is greatest at $t = 35 \quad (2005)$

**48.** $t = 50 \log_{10}\left(\dfrac{18{,}000}{18{,}000 - h}\right)$

(a) Domain: $0 \le h < 18{,}000$

(b) Vertical asymptote: $h = 18{,}000$

(c) $t = 50 \log_{10} 18{,}000 - 50 \log_{10}(18{,}000 - h)$

$$\frac{dt}{dh} = \frac{50}{(\ln 10)(18{,}000 - h)}$$

$$\frac{d^2t}{dh^2} = \frac{50}{(\ln 10)(18{,}000 - h)^2}$$

No critical numbers

As $t$ increases, the rate of change of the altitude is increasing.

**49.** $\displaystyle\lim_{x\to\infty}\left(8 + \frac{1}{x}\right) = 8 + 0 = 8$

**50.** $\displaystyle\lim_{x\to\infty}\frac{3 - x}{2x + 5} = \lim_{x\to\infty}\frac{3/x - 1}{2 + 5/x} = -\frac{1}{2}$

**51.** $\displaystyle\lim_{x\to\infty}\frac{2x^2}{3x^2 + 5} = \lim_{x\to\infty}\frac{2}{3 + 5/x^2} = \frac{2}{3}$

**52.** $\displaystyle\lim_{x\to\infty}\frac{2x}{3x^2 + 5} = \lim_{x\to\infty}\frac{2/x}{3 + 5/x^2} = 0$

**53.** $\displaystyle\lim_{x\to-\infty}\frac{3x^2}{x + 5} = -\infty$

**54.** $\displaystyle\lim_{x\to-\infty}\frac{\sqrt{x^2 + x}}{-2x} = \frac{1}{2}$

**55.** $\displaystyle\lim_{x\to\infty}\frac{5 \cos x}{x} = 0$, because $|5 \cos x| \le 5$.

**56.** $\displaystyle\lim_{x\to\infty}\frac{3x}{\sqrt{x^2 + 4}} = \lim_{x\to\infty}\frac{3}{\sqrt{1 + 4/x^2}} = 3$

**57.** $\displaystyle\lim_{x\to-\infty}\frac{6x}{x + \cos x} = 6$

**58.** $\displaystyle\lim_{x\to-\infty}\frac{x}{2 \sin x}$ does not exist.

**59.** $f(x) = \dfrac{3}{x} - 2$

Discontinuity: $x = 0$

$\displaystyle\lim_{x\to\infty}\left(\frac{3}{x} - 2\right) = -2$

Vertical asymptote: $x = 0$

Horizontal asymptote: $y = -2$

**60.** $g(x) = \dfrac{5x^2}{x^2 + 2}$

$\lim\limits_{x\to\infty} \dfrac{5x^2}{x^2 + 2} = \lim\limits_{x\to\infty} \dfrac{5}{1 + (2/x^2)} = 5$

Horizontal asymptote: $y = 5$

**61.** $h(x) = \dfrac{2x + 3}{x - 4}$

Discontinuity: $x = 4$

$\lim\limits_{x\to\infty} \dfrac{2x + 3}{x - 4} = \lim\limits_{x\to\infty} \dfrac{2 + (3/x)}{1 - (4/x)} = 2$

Vertical asymptote: $x = 4$

Horizontal asymptote: $y = 2$

**62.** $f(x) = \dfrac{3x}{\sqrt{x^2 + 2}}$

$\lim\limits_{x\to\infty} \dfrac{3x}{\sqrt{x^2 + 2}} = \lim\limits_{x\to\infty} \dfrac{3x/x}{\sqrt{x^2 + 2}/\sqrt{x^2}}$

$= \lim\limits_{x\to\infty} \dfrac{3}{\sqrt{1 + (2/x^2)}} = 3$

$\lim\limits_{x\to-\infty} \dfrac{3x}{\sqrt{x^2 + 2}} = \lim\limits_{x\to-\infty} \dfrac{3x/x}{\sqrt{x^2 + 2}/\left(-\sqrt{x^2}\right)}$

$= \lim\limits_{x\to-\infty} \dfrac{3}{-\sqrt{1 + (2/x^2)}} = -3$

Horizontal asymptotes: $y = \pm 3$

**63.** $f(x) = \dfrac{5}{3 + 2e^{-x}}$

Horizontal asymptotes: $y = 0$ (to the left)

$y = \dfrac{5}{3}$ (to the right)

No vertical asymptotes

**64.** $g(x) = 30xe^{-2x}$

Horizontal asymptote: $y = 0$ (to the right)

No vertical asymptotes

**65.** $g(x) = 3\ln\left(1 + e^{-x/4}\right)$

Horizontal asymptote: $y = 0$ (to the right)

**66.** $h(x) = 10\ln\left(\dfrac{x}{x + 1}\right)$

Vertical asymptotes: $x = -1, x = 0$

Horizontal asymptote: $y = 0$

**67.** $f(x) = x^3 + \dfrac{243}{x}$

Relative minimum: $(3, 108)$

Relative maximum: $(-3, -108)$

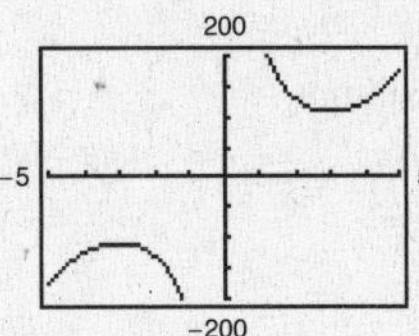


Vertical asymptote: $x = 0$

**68.** $f(x) = \left|x^3 - 3x^2 + 2x\right| = \left|x(x - 1)(x - 2)\right|$

Relative minima: $(0, 0), (1, 0), (2, 0)$

Relative maxima: $(1.577, 0.38), (0.423, 0.38)$

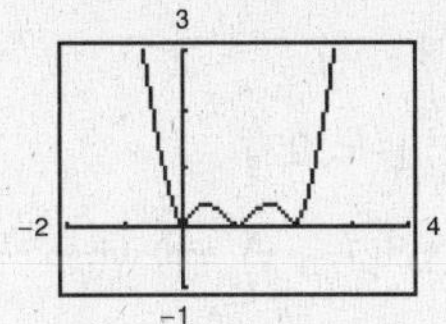


**69.** $f(x) = \dfrac{x - 1}{1 + 3x^2}$

Relative minimum: $(-0.155, -1.077)$

Relative maximum: $(2.155, 0.077)$

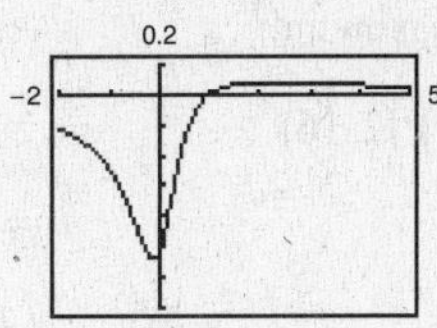


Horizontal asymptote: $y = 0$

**70.** $g(x) = \dfrac{\pi^2}{3} - 4\cos x + \cos 2x$

Relative minima: $(2\pi k, 0.29)$ where $k$ is any integer.

Relative maxima: $((2k - 1)\pi, 8.29)$ where $k$ is any integer.

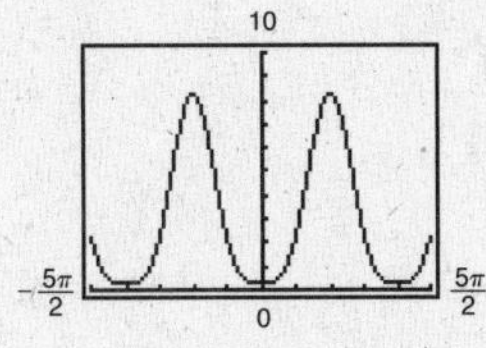

**71.** $f(x) = 4x - x^2 = x(4 - x)$

Domain: $(-\infty, \infty)$; Range: $(-\infty, 4]$

$f'(x) = 4 - 2x = 0$ when $x = 2$.

$f''(x) = -2$

So, $(2, 4)$ is a relative maximum.

Intercepts: $(0, 0), (4, 0)$

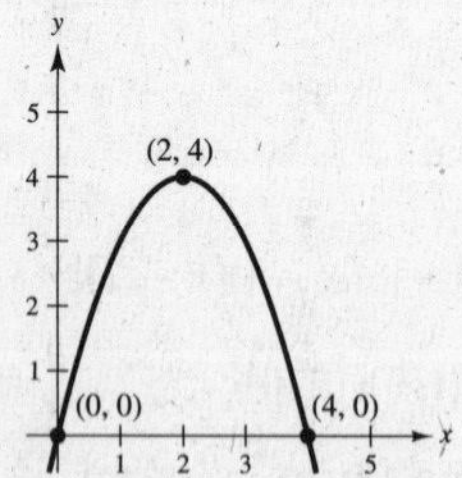


**72.** $f(x) = 4x^3 - x^4 = x^3(4 - x)$

Domain: $(-\infty, \infty)$; Range: $(-\infty, 27)$

$f'(x) = 12x^2 - 4x^3 = 4x^2(3 - x) = 0$ when $x = 0, 3$.

$f''(x) = 24x - 12x^2 = 12x(2 - x) = 0$ when $x = 0, 2$.

$f''(3) < 0$

So, $(3, 27)$ is a relative maximum.

Points of inflection: $(0, 0), (2, 16)$

Intercepts: $(0, 0), (4, 0)$

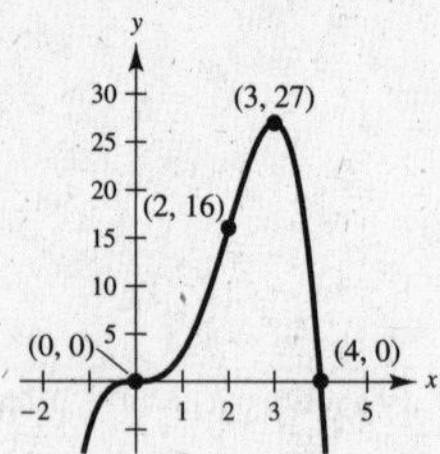


**73.** $f(x) = x\sqrt{16 - x^2}$

Domain: $[-4, 4]$; Range: $[-8, 8]$

$f'(x) = \dfrac{16 - 2x^2}{\sqrt{16 - x^2}} = 0$ when $x = \pm 2\sqrt{2}$ and undefined when $x = \pm 4$.

$f''(x) = \dfrac{2x(x^2 - 24)}{(16 - x^2)^{3/2}}$

$f''(-2\sqrt{2}) > 0$

So, $(-2\sqrt{2}, -8)$ is a relative minimum.

$f''(2\sqrt{2}) < 0$

So, $(2\sqrt{2}, 8)$ is a relative maximum.

Point of inflection: $(0, 0)$

Intercepts: $(-4, 0), (0, 0), (4, 0)$

Symmetry with respect to origin

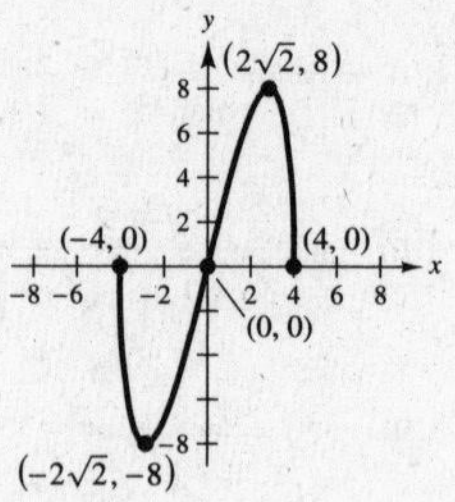


**74.** $f(x) = (x^2 - 4)^2$

Domain: $(-\infty, \infty)$; Range: $[0, \infty)$

$f'(x) = 4x(x^2 - 4) = 0$ when $x = 0, \pm 2$.

$f''(x) = 4(3x^2 - 4) = 0$ when $x = \pm\dfrac{2\sqrt{3}}{3}$.

$f''(0) < 0$

So, $(0, 16)$ is a relative maximum.

$f''(\pm 2) > 0$

So, $(\pm 2, 0)$ are relative minima.

Points of inflection: $(\pm 2\sqrt{3}/3, 64/9)$

Intercepts: $(-2, 0), (0, 16), (2, 0)$

Symmetry with respect to $y$-axis

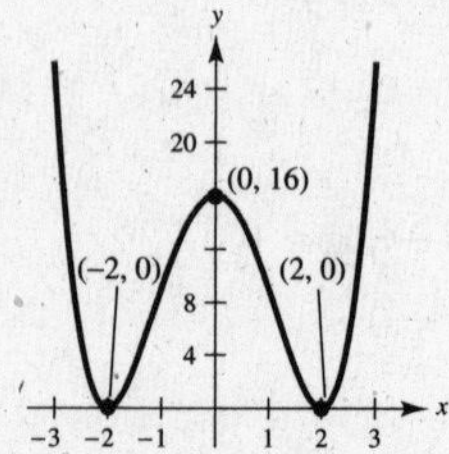

**75.** $f(x) = (x - 1)^3(x - 3)^2$

Domain: $(-\infty, \infty)$; Range: $(-\infty, \infty)$

$f'(x) = (x - 1)^2(x - 3)(5x - 11) = 0$ when $x = 1, \frac{11}{5}, 3.$

$f''(x) = 4(x - 1)(5x^2 - 22x + 23) = 0$ when

$x = 1, \frac{11 \pm \sqrt{6}}{5}.$

$f''(3) > 0$

So, $(3, 0)$ is a relative minimum.

$f''\left(\frac{11}{5}\right) < 0$

So, $\left(\frac{11}{5}, \frac{3456}{3125}\right)$ is a relative maximum.

Points of inflection:

$(1, 0), \left(\frac{11 - \sqrt{6}}{5}, 0.60\right), \left(\frac{11 + \sqrt{6}}{5}, 0.46\right)$

Intercepts: $(0, -9), (1, 0), (3, 0)$

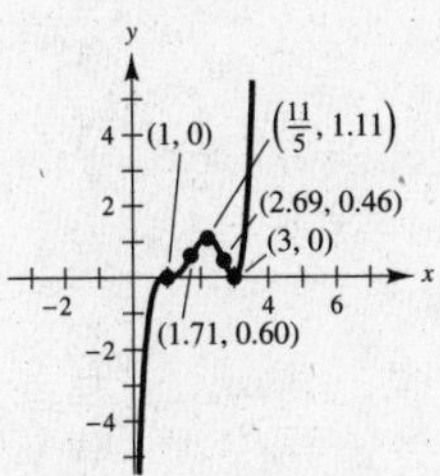


**76.** $f(x) = (x - 3)(x + 2)^3$

Domain: $(-\infty, \infty)$; Range: $\left[-\frac{16,875}{256}, \infty\right)$

$f'(x) = (x - 3)(3)(x + 2)^2 + (x + 2)^3$

$= (4x - 7)(x + 2)^2 = 0$ when $x = -2, \frac{7}{4}.$

$f''(x) = (4x - 7)(2)(x + 2) + (x + 2)^2(4)$

$= 6(2x - 1)(x + 2) = 0$ when $x = -2, \frac{1}{2}.$

$f''\left(\frac{7}{4}\right) > 0$

So, $\left(\frac{7}{4}, -\frac{16,875}{256}\right)$ is a relative minimum.

Points of inflection: $(-2, 0), \left(\frac{1}{2}, -\frac{625}{16}\right)$

Intercepts: $(-2, 0), (0, -24), (3, 0)$

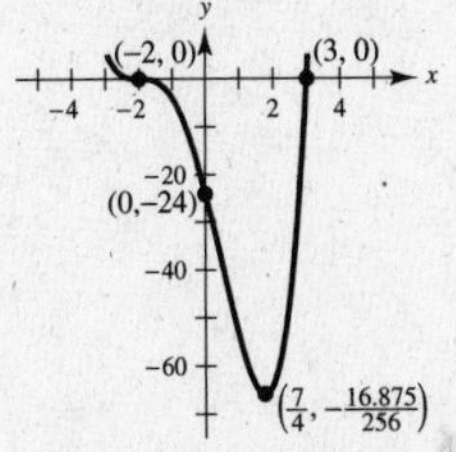


**77.** $f(x) = x^{1/3}(x + 3)^{2/3}$

Domain: $(-\infty, \infty)$; Range: $(-\infty, \infty)$

$f'(x) = \frac{x + 1}{(x + 3)^{1/3}x^{2/3}} = 0$ when $x = -1$ and

undefined when $x = -3, 0.$

$f''(x) = \frac{-2}{x^{5/3}(x + 3)^{4/3}}$ is undefined when $x = 0, -3.$

By the First Derivative Test $(-3, 0)$ is a relative maximum and $\left(-1, -\sqrt[3]{4}\right)$ is a relative minimum. $(0, 0)$ is a point of inflection.

Intercepts: $(-3, 0), (0, 0)$

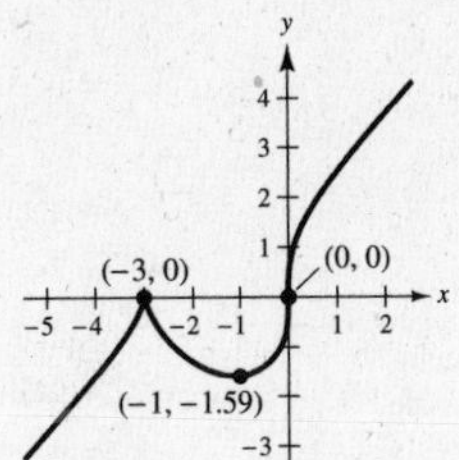


**78.** $f(x) = (x - 2)^{1/3}(x + 1)^{2/3}$

Graph of Exercise 77 translated 2 units to the right ($x$ replaced by $x - 2$).

$(-1, 0)$ is a relative maximum.

$\left(1, -\sqrt[3]{4}\right)$ is a relative minimum.

$(2, 0)$ is a point of inflection.

Intercepts: $(-1, 0), (2, 0), \left(0, -2^{1/3}\right)$

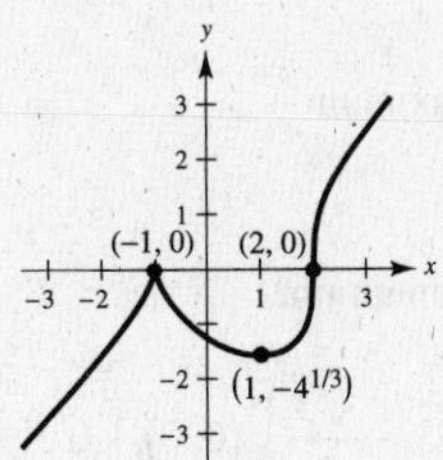

**79.** $f(x) = \dfrac{5 - 3x}{x - 2}$

$f'(x) = \dfrac{1}{(x - 2)^2} > 0$ for all $x \neq 2$

$f''(x) = \dfrac{-2}{(x - 2)^3}$

Concave upward on $(-\infty, 2)$

Concave downward on $(2, \infty)$

Vertical asymptote: $x = 2$

Horizontal asymptote: $y = -3$

Intercepts: $\left(\dfrac{5}{3}, 0\right), \left(0, -\dfrac{5}{2}\right)$

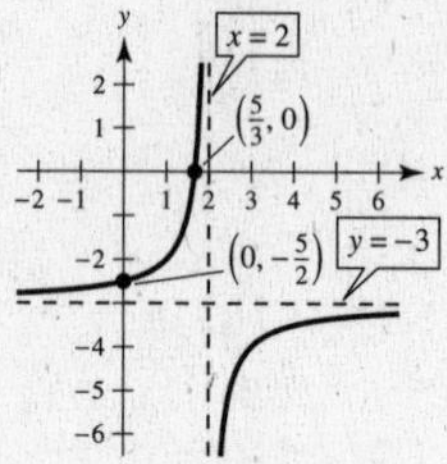


**80.** $f(x) = \dfrac{2x}{1 + x^2}$

Domain: $(-\infty, \infty)$; Range: $[-1, 1]$

$f'(x) = \dfrac{2(1 - x)(1 + x)}{(1 + x^2)^2} = 0$ when $x = \pm 1$.

$f''(x) = \dfrac{-4x(3 - x^2)}{(1 + x^2)^3} = 0$ when $x = 0, \pm\sqrt{3}$.

$f''(1) < 0$

So, $(1, 1)$ is a relative maximum.

$f''(-1) > 0$

So, $(-1, -1)$ is a relative minimum.

Points of inflection: $\left(-\sqrt{3}, -\dfrac{\sqrt{3}}{2}\right), (0, 0), \left(\sqrt{3}, \dfrac{\sqrt{3}}{2}\right)$

Intercept: $(0, 0)$

Symmetric with respect to the origin

Horizontal asymptote: $y = 0$

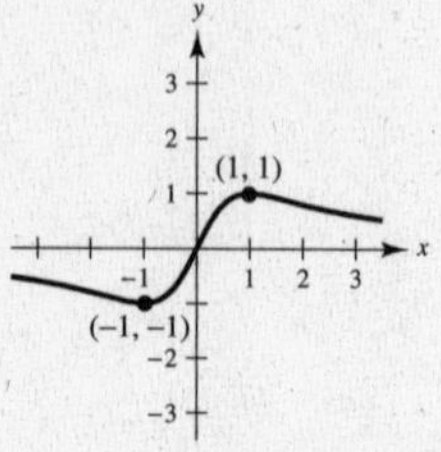


**81.** $f(x) = \dfrac{7}{1 + x^2}$

Domain: $(-\infty, \infty)$; Range: $(0, 7]$

$f'(x) = \dfrac{-14x}{(1 + x^2)^2} = 0$ when $x = 0$.

$f''(x) = \dfrac{14(3x^2 - 1)}{(x^2 + 1)^3} = 0$ when $x = \pm\dfrac{\sqrt{3}}{3}$.

$f''(0) < 0$

So, $(0, 7)$ is a relative maximum.

Points of inflection: $\left(\pm\dfrac{\sqrt{3}}{3}, \dfrac{21}{4}\right)$

Intercept: $(0, 7)$

Symmetric to $y$-axis

Horizontal asymptote: $y = 0$

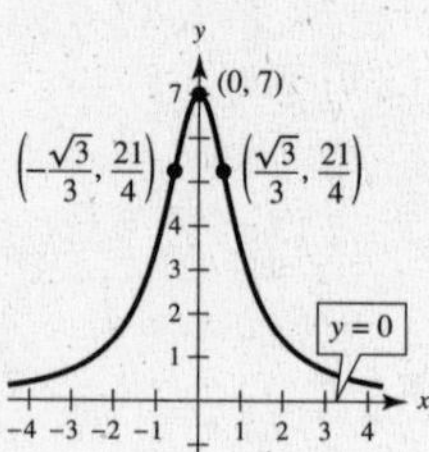

**82.** $f(x) = \dfrac{x^2}{1 + x^4}$

Domain: $(-\infty, \infty)$; Range: $\left[0, \dfrac{1}{2}\right]$

$$f'(x) = \frac{(1 + x^4)(2x) - x^2(4x^3)}{(1 + x^4)^2} = \frac{2x(1 - x)(1 + x)(1 + x^2)}{(1 + x^4)^2} = 0 \text{ when } x = 0, \pm 1.$$

$$f''(x) = \frac{(1 + x^4)^2(2 - 10x^4) - (2x - 2x^5)(2)(1 + x^4)(4x^3)}{(1 + x^4)^4} = \frac{2(1 - 12x^4 + 3x^8)}{(1 + x^4)^3} = 0 \text{ when } x = \pm\sqrt[4]{\frac{6 \pm \sqrt{33}}{3}}.$$

$f''(\pm 1) < 0$

So, $\left(\pm 1, \dfrac{1}{2}\right)$ are relative maxima.

$f''(0) > 0$

So, $(0, 0)$ is a relative minimum.

Points of inflection: $\left(\pm\sqrt[4]{\dfrac{6 - \sqrt{33}}{3}}, 0.29\right), \left(\pm\sqrt[4]{\dfrac{6 + \sqrt{33}}{3}}, 0.40\right)$

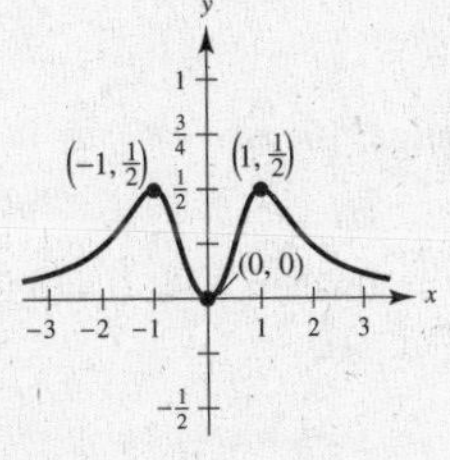


Intercept: $(0, 0)$
Symmetric to the $y$-axis
Horizontal asymptote: $y = 0$

**83.** $f(x) = x^3 + x + \dfrac{2}{x}$

Domain: all $x \neq 0$; Range: $(-\infty, -4], [4, \infty)$

$$f'(x) = 3x^2 + 1 - \frac{2}{x^2} = \frac{3x^4 + x^2 - 2}{x^2} = \frac{(x^2 + 1)(3x^2 - 2)}{x^2} = 0 \text{ when } x = \pm\sqrt{\frac{2}{3}}.$$

$$f''(x) = \frac{2(3x^4 + 4)}{x^3} \neq 0$$

$f''\left(-\sqrt{\dfrac{2}{3}}\right) < 0$

So, $\left(-\sqrt{\dfrac{2}{3}}, -3.8103\right)$ is a relative maximum.

$f''\left(\sqrt{\dfrac{2}{3}}\right) > 0$

So, $\left(\sqrt{\dfrac{2}{3}}, 3.8103\right)$ is a relative minimum.

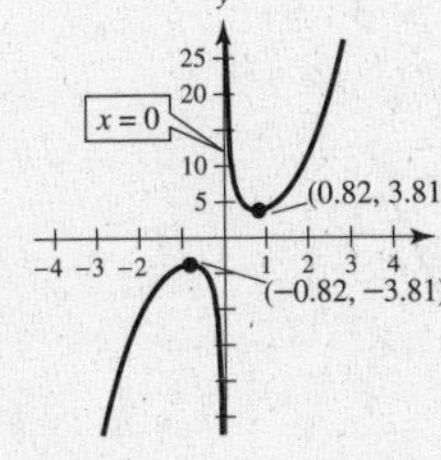


Vertical asymptote: $x = 0$
Symmetric with respect to the origin.
No intercepts

**84.** $f(x) = x^2 + \dfrac{8}{x} = \dfrac{x^3 + 8}{x}$

Domain: all $x \neq 0$

$f'(x) = \dfrac{2(x^3 - 4)}{x^2} = 0$ when $x = \sqrt[3]{4} \approx 1.5874.$

$f''(x) = \dfrac{2(x + 2)(x^2 - 2x + 4)}{x^3} = \dfrac{2(x^3 + 8)}{x^3} = 0$ when $x = -2.$

$f''\left(\sqrt[3]{4}\right) > 0$

So, $\left(\sqrt[3]{4}, 6\sqrt[3]{2}\right) \approx (1.5874, 7.5595)$ is a relative minimum.

Point of inflection: $(-2, 0)$

Intercept: $(-2, 0)$

Vertical asymptote: $x = 0$

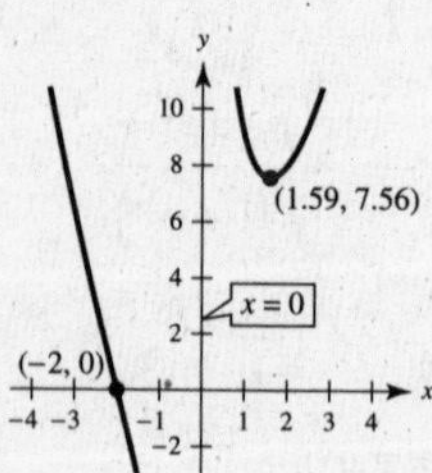


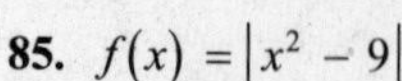

**85.** $f(x) = \left|x^2 - 9\right|$

Domain: $(-\infty, \infty)$; Range: $[0, \infty)$

$f'(x) = \dfrac{2x(x^2 - 9)}{\left|x^2 - 9\right|} = 0$ when $x = 0$ and is undefined when $x = \pm 3.$

$f''(x) = \dfrac{2(x^2 - 9)}{\left|x^2 - 9\right|}$ is undefined at $x = \pm 3.$

$f''(0) < 0$

So, $(0, 9)$ is a relative maximum.

Relative minima: $(\pm 3, 0)$

Intercepts: $(\pm 3, 0), (0, 9)$

Symmetric to the $y$-axis

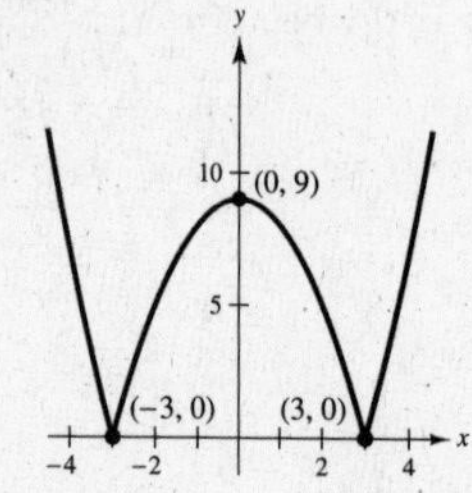


**86.** $f(x) = |x - 1| + |x - 3| = \begin{cases} -2x + 4, & x \leq 1 \\ 2, & 1 < x \leq 3 \\ 2x - 4, & x > 3 \end{cases}$

Domain: $(-\infty, \infty)$

Range: $[2, \infty)$

Intercept: $(0, 4)$

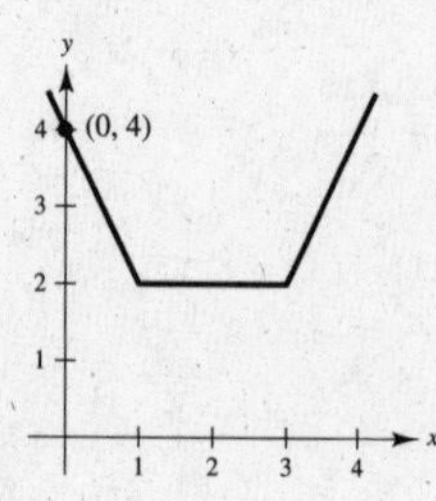


**87.** $h(x) = (1 - x)e^x$

$h'(x) = -xe^x$

$h''(x) = -(x + 1)e^x$

Horizontal asymptote: $y = 0$ (to the left)

Critical point: $(0, 1)$ (relative maximum)

Inflection point: $(1, 2/e) \approx (-1, 0.736)$

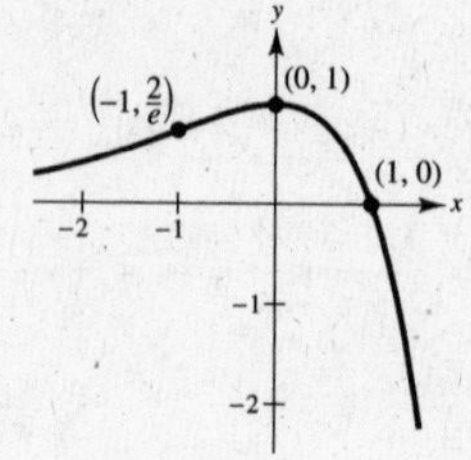

**88.** $g(x) = 5xe^{-x^2}$

$g'(x) = -5e^{-x^2}(2x^2 - 1)$

$g''(x) = 10xe^{-x^2}(2x^2 - 3)$

Horizontal asymptote: $y = 0$

Relative minimum: $\left(-\dfrac{1}{\sqrt{2}}, -2.144\right)$

Relative maximum: $\left(\dfrac{1}{\sqrt{2}}, -2.144\right)$

Inflection points: $(0, 0)$, $\left(\sqrt{\dfrac{3}{2}}, 1.366\right)$, $\left(-\sqrt{\dfrac{3}{2}}, -1.366\right)$

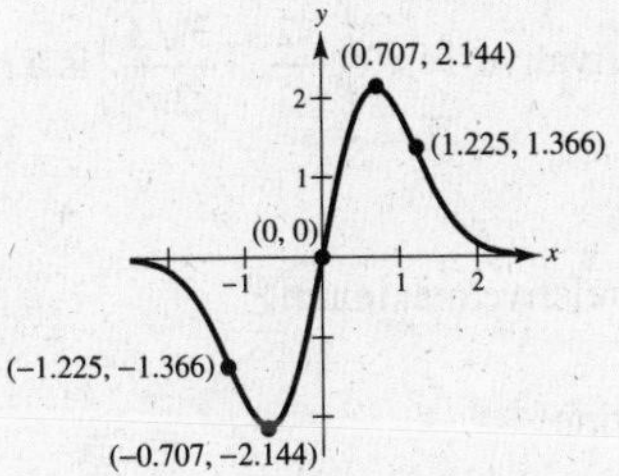


**89.** $g(x) = (x + 3)\ln(x + 3)$

$g'(x) = \ln(x + 3) + 1$

$g''(x) = \dfrac{1}{x + 3}$

Domain: $x > -3$

Relative minimum: $(-2.632, -0.368)$

Always concave upward

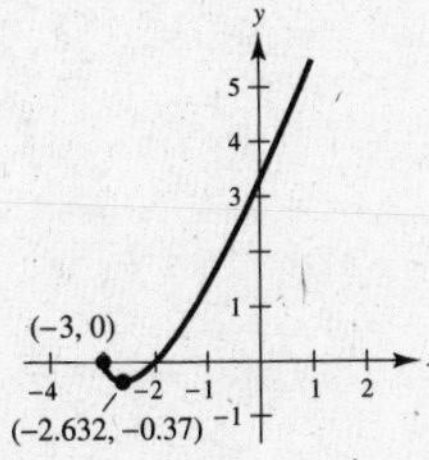


**90.** $h(t) = \dfrac{\ln t}{t^2}$

$h'(t) = \dfrac{1 - 2\ln t}{t^3}$

$h''(t) = \dfrac{6\ln t - 5}{t^4}$

Domain: $t > 0$

Relative maximum: $\left(e^{1/2}, \dfrac{1}{2e}\right) \approx (1.6487, 0.1839)$

Inflection point: $\left(e^{5/6}, \dfrac{5}{6e^{5/3}}\right) \approx (2.3010, 0.1573)$

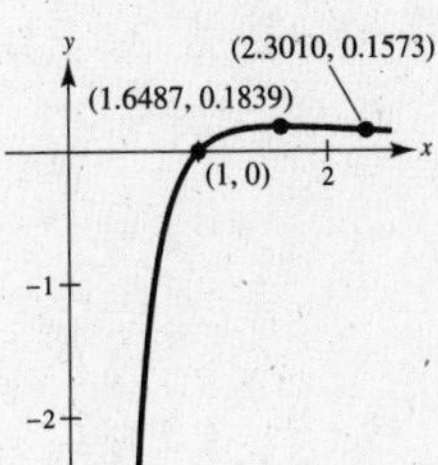


**91.** $f(x) = \dfrac{10\log_4 x}{x} = \dfrac{10\ln x}{x\ln 4}$

$f'(x) = \dfrac{10(1 - \ln x)}{x^2\ln 4}$

$f''(x) = \dfrac{10(2\ln x - 3)}{x^3\ln 4}$

Relative maximum: $\left(e, \dfrac{5}{e\ln 2}\right) \approx (2.7183, 2.6537)$

Inflection point: $(e^{3/2}, 2.4143)$

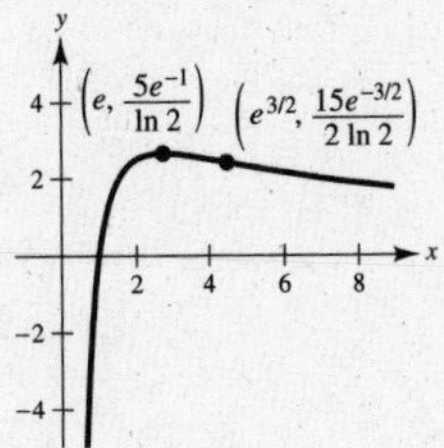

**92.** $g(x) = 100x(3^{-x})$

$g'(x) = 100(3^{-x})(1 - x \ln 3)$

$g''(x) = 100(3^{-x}) \ln 3(x \ln 3 - 2)$

Relative maximum: $\left(\frac{1}{\ln 3}, 33.4858\right)$

Inflection point: $\left(\frac{2}{\ln 3}, 24.6375\right)$

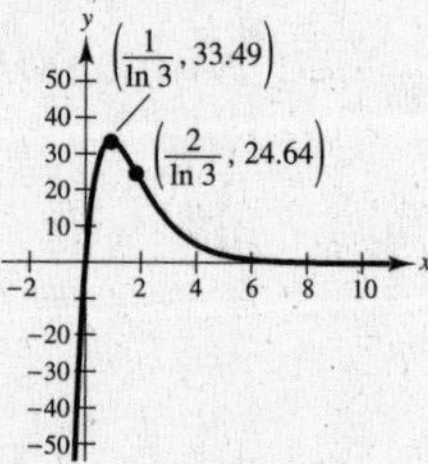


**93.** $f(x) = x + \cos x$

Domain: $[0, 2\pi]$; Range: $[1, 1 + 2\pi]$

$f'(x) = 1 - \sin x \geq 0$, $f$ is increasing.

$f''(x) = -\cos x = 0$ when $x = \frac{\pi}{2}, \frac{3\pi}{2}$.

Points of inflection: $\left(\frac{\pi}{2}, \frac{\pi}{2}\right), \left(\frac{3\pi}{2}, \frac{3\pi}{2}\right)$.

Intercept: $(0, 1)$

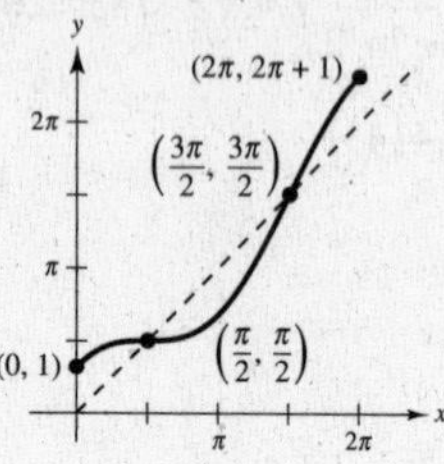


**94.** $f(x) = \frac{1}{\pi}(2 \sin \pi x - \sin 2\pi x)$

Domain: $[-1, 1]$; Range: $\left[\frac{-3\sqrt{3}}{2\pi}, \frac{3\sqrt{3}}{2\pi}\right]$

$f'(x) = 2(\cos \pi x - \cos 2\pi x)$

$= -2(2 \cos \pi x + 1)(\cos \pi x - 1) = 0$

Critical numbers: $x = \pm\frac{2}{3}, 0$

$f''(x) = 2\pi(-\sin \pi x + 2 \sin 2\pi x)$

$= 2\pi \sin \pi x(-1 + 4 \cos \pi x) = 0$

when $x = 0, \pm 1, \pm 0.420$.

By the First Derivative Test: $\left(-\frac{2}{3}, -\frac{3\sqrt{3}}{2\pi}\right)$ is a relative minimum.

$\left(\frac{2}{3}, \frac{3\sqrt{3}}{2\pi}\right)$ is a relative maximum.

Points of inflection:
$(-0.420, -0.462), (0.420, 0.462), (\pm 1, 0), (0, 0)$

Intercepts: $(-1, 0), (0, 0), (1, 0)$

Symmetric with respect to the origin

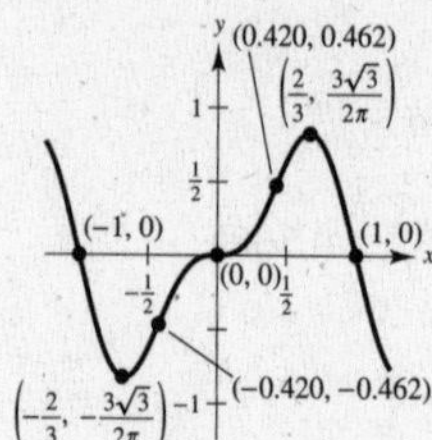


**95.** $y = 4x - 6 \arctan x$

$y' = 4 - \frac{6}{1 + x^2} = \frac{4x^2 - 2}{1 + x^2}$

$y'' = \frac{12x}{(1 + x^2)^2}$

Relative maximum: $\left(-\frac{\sqrt{2}}{2}, -2\sqrt{2} + 6 \arctan\frac{\sqrt{2}}{2}\right)$

Relative minimum: $\left(\frac{\sqrt{2}}{2}, 2\sqrt{2} - 6 \arctan\frac{\sqrt{2}}{2}\right)$

Inflection point: $(0, 0)$

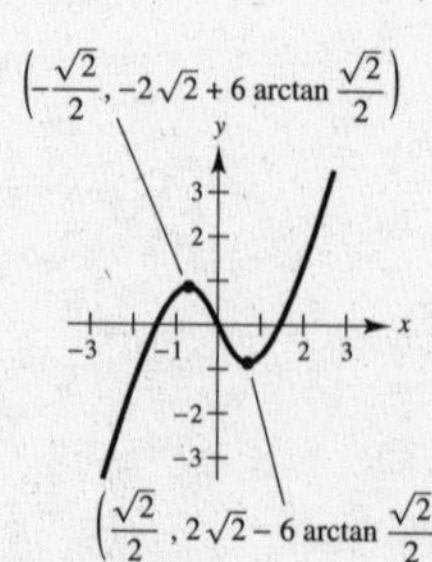

**96.** $y = \frac{1}{2}x^2 - \arcsin\frac{x}{2}$, Domain: $[-2, 2]$

$$y' = x - \frac{1}{\sqrt{4 - x^2}}$$

$$y'' = 1 - \frac{x}{\left(4 - x^2\right)^{3/2}}$$

$$y' = x - \frac{1}{\sqrt{4 - x^2}} = 0 \Rightarrow x^2 = \frac{1}{4 - x^2}$$

$$\Rightarrow 4x^2 - x^4 = 1 \Rightarrow x^4 - 4x^2 + 1 = 0$$

$$\Rightarrow x = \pm 1.9319 \text{ and } x = \pm 0.5176$$

Relative maximum: $(1.9319, 0.5570)$

Relative minimum: $(0.5176, -0.1278)$

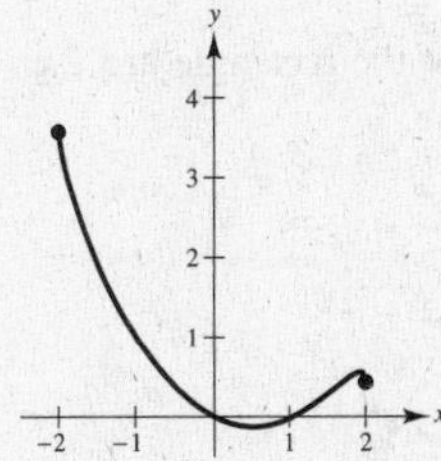

**97.** $x^2 + 4y^2 - 2x - 16y + 13 = 0$

(a) $\left(x^2 - 2x + 1\right) + 4\left(y^2 - 4y + 4\right) = -13 + 1 + 16$

$$(x - 1)^2 + 4(y - 2)^2 = 4$$

$$\frac{(x - 1)^2}{4} + \frac{(y - 2)^2}{1} = 1$$

The graph is an ellipse:

Maximum: $(1, 3)$

Minimum: $(1, 1)$

(b) $x^2 + 4y^2 - 2x - 16y + 13 = 0$

$$2x + 8y\frac{dy}{dx} - 2 - 16\frac{dy}{dx} = 0$$

$$\frac{dy}{dx}(8y - 16) = 2 - 2x$$

$$\frac{dy}{dx} = \frac{2 - 2x}{8y - 16} = \frac{1 - x}{4y - 8}$$

The critical numbers are $x = 1$ and $y = 2$. These correspond to the points $(1, 1)$, $(1, 3)$, $(2, -1)$, and $(2, 3)$. So, the maximum is $(1, 3)$ and the minimum is $(1, 1)$.

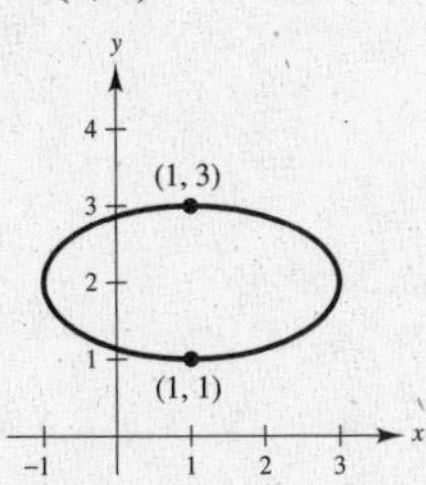


**98.** $f(x) = x^n$, $n$ is a positive integer.

(a) $f'(x) = nx^{n-1}$

The function has a relative minimum at $(0, 0)$ when $n$ is even.

(b) $f''(x) = n(n - 1)x^{n-2}$

The function has a point of inflection at $(0, 0)$ when $n$ is odd and $n \geq 3$.

**99.** Let $t = 0$ at noon.

$$L = d^2 = (100 - 12t)^2 + (-10t)^2$$

$$= 10{,}000 - 2400t + 244t^2$$

$$\frac{dL}{dt} = -2400 + 488t = 0 \text{ when } t = \frac{300}{61} \approx 4.92 \text{ h.}$$

Ship $A$ at $(40.98, 0)$; Ship $B$ at $(0, -49.18)$

$$d^2 = 10{,}000 - 2400t + 244t^2$$

$$\approx 4098.36 \text{ when } t \approx 4.92 \approx 4{:}55 \text{ P.M.}$$

$$d \approx 64 \text{ km}$$

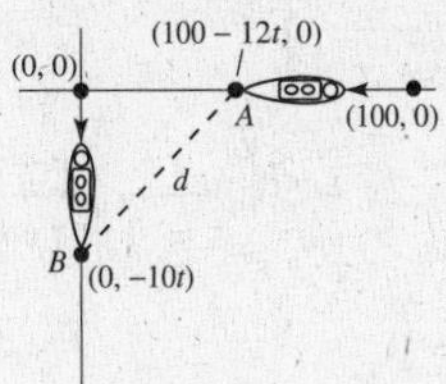

**100.** Ellipse: $\frac{x^2}{144} + \frac{y^2}{16} = 1$, $y = \frac{1}{3}\sqrt{144 - x^2}$

$$A = (2x)\left(\frac{2}{3}\sqrt{144 - x^2}\right) = \frac{4}{3}x\sqrt{144 - x^2}$$

$$\frac{dA}{dx} = \frac{4}{3}\left[\frac{-x^2}{\sqrt{144 - x^2}} + \sqrt{144 - x^2}\right] = \frac{4}{3}\left[\frac{144 - 2x^2}{\sqrt{144 - x^2}}\right] = 0 \text{ when } x = \sqrt{72} = 6\sqrt{2}.$$

The dimensions of the rectangle are $2x = 12\sqrt{2}$ by $y = \frac{2}{3}\sqrt{144 - 72} = 4\sqrt{2}$.

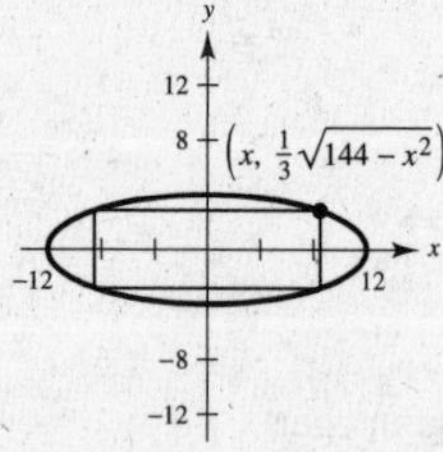


**101.** You have points $(0, y)$, $(x, 0)$, and $(1, 8)$. So,

$$m = \frac{y - 8}{0 - 1} = \frac{0 - 8}{x - 1} \text{ or } y = \frac{8x}{x - 1}.$$

Let $f(x) = L^2 = x^2 + \left(\frac{8x}{x - 1}\right)^2$.

$$f'(x) = 2x + 128\left(\frac{x}{x - 1}\right)\left[\frac{(x - 1) - x}{(x - 1)^2}\right] = 0$$

$$x - \frac{64x}{(x - 1)^3} = 0$$

$$x\left[(x - 1)^3 - 64\right] = 0 \text{ when } x = 0, 5 \text{ (minimum)}.$$

Vertices of triangle: $(0, 0)$, $(5, 0)$, $(0, 10)$

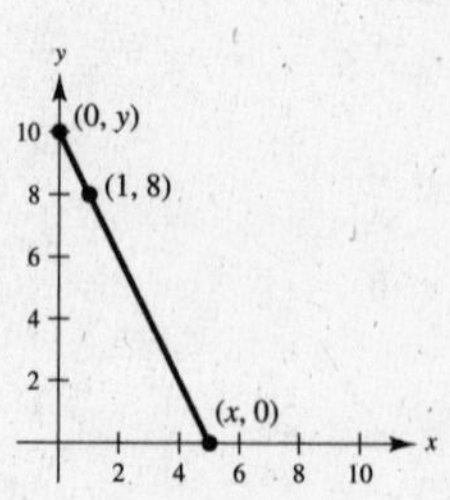


**102.** You have points $(0, y)$, $(x, 0)$, and $(4, 5)$. So,

$$m = \frac{y - 5}{0 - 4} = \frac{5 - 0}{4 - x} \text{ or } y = \frac{5x}{x - 4}.$$

Let $f(x) = L^2 = x^2 + \left(\frac{5x}{x - 4}\right)^2$

$$f'(x) = 2x + 50\left(\frac{x}{x - 4}\right)\left[\frac{x - 4 - x}{(x - 4)^2}\right] = 0$$

$$x - \frac{100x}{(x - 4)^3} = 0$$

$$x\left[(x - 4)^3 - 100\right] = 0 \text{ when } x = 0 \text{ or } x = 4 + \sqrt[3]{100}.$$

$$L = \sqrt{x^2 + \frac{25x^2}{(x - 4)^2}} = \frac{x}{x - 4}\sqrt{(x - 4)^2 + 25} = \frac{\sqrt[3]{100} + 4}{\sqrt[3]{100}}\sqrt{100^{2/3} + 25} \approx 12.7 \text{ ft}$$

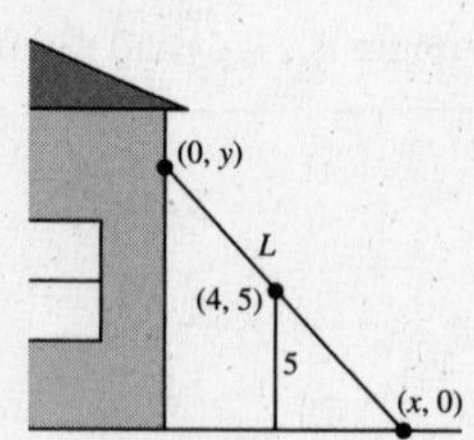

**103.** $A = (\text{Average of bases})(\text{Height}) = \left(\dfrac{x+s}{2}\right)\dfrac{\sqrt{3s^2 + 2sx - x^2}}{2}$ (see figure)

$$\frac{dA}{dx} = \frac{1}{4}\left[\frac{(s-x)(s+x)}{\sqrt{3s^2 + 2sx - x^2}} + \sqrt{3s^2 + 2sx - x^2}\right] = \frac{2(2s - x)(s + x)}{4\sqrt{3s^2 + 2sx - x^2}} = 0 \text{ when } x = 2s.$$

$A$ is a maximum when $x = 2s$.

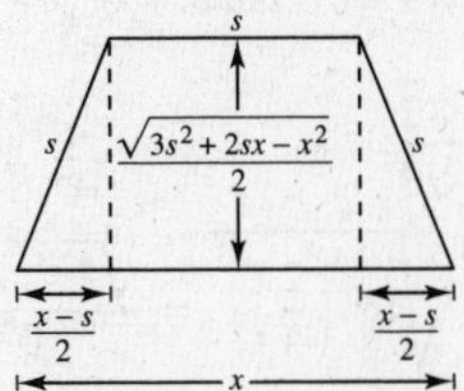


**104.** Label triangle with vertices $(0, 0)$, $(a, 0)$, and $(b, c)$. The equations of the sides of the triangle are $y = (c/b)x$ and $y = [c/(b-a)](x-a)$. Let $(x, 0)$ be a vertex of the inscribed rectangle. The coordinates of the upper left vertex are $(x, (c/b)x)$. The $y$-coordinate of the upper right vertex of the rectangle is $(c/b)x$. Solving for the $x$-coordinate $\overline{x}$ of the rectangle's upper right vertex, you get

$$\frac{c}{b}x = \frac{c}{b-a}(\overline{x} - a)$$

$$(b-a)x = b(\overline{x} - a)$$

$$\overline{x} = \frac{b-a}{b}x + a = a - \frac{a-b}{b}x.$$

Finally, the lower right vertex is $\left(a - \dfrac{a-b}{b}x, 0\right)$.

Width of rectangle: $a - \dfrac{a-b}{b}x - x$

Height of rectangle: $\dfrac{c}{b}x$ (see figure)

$$A = (\text{Width})(\text{Height}) = \left(a - \frac{a-b}{b}x - x\right)\left(\frac{c}{b}x\right) = \left(a - \frac{a}{b}x\right)\frac{c}{b}x$$

$$\frac{dA}{dx} = \left(a - \frac{a}{b}x\right)\frac{c}{b} + \left(\frac{c}{b}x\right)\left(-\frac{a}{b}\right) = \frac{ac}{b} - \frac{2ac}{b^2}x = 0 \text{ when } x = \frac{b}{2}.$$

$$A\left(\frac{b}{2}\right) = \left(a - \frac{a}{b}\frac{b}{2}\right)\left(\frac{c}{b}\frac{b}{2}\right) = \left(\frac{a}{2}\right)\left(\frac{c}{2}\right) = \frac{1}{4}ac = \frac{1}{2}\left(\frac{1}{2}ac\right) = \frac{1}{2}(\text{Area of triangle})$$

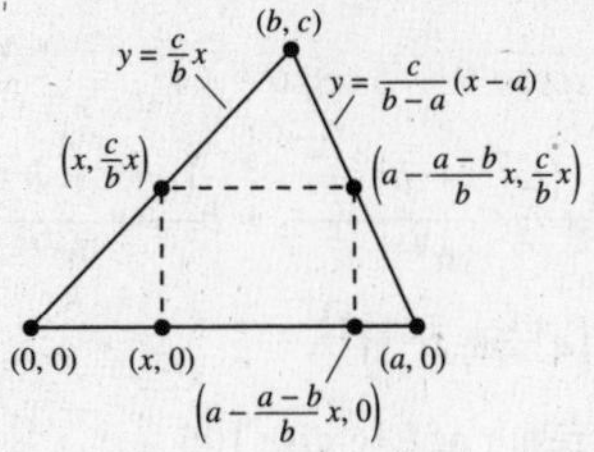

**105.** You can form a right triangle with vertices $(0, 0)$, $(x, 0)$ and $(0, y)$. Assume that the hypotenuse of length $L$ passes through $(4, 6)$.

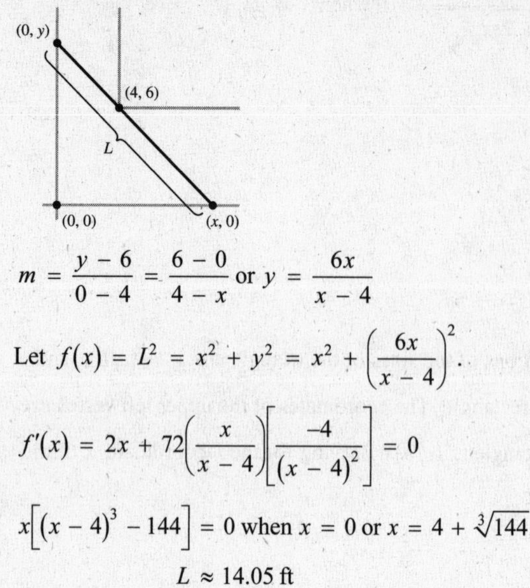


$$m = \frac{y-6}{0-4} = \frac{6-0}{4-x} \text{ or } y = \frac{6x}{x-4}$$

Let $f(x) = L^2 = x^2 + y^2 = x^2 + \left(\frac{6x}{x-4}\right)^2$.

$$f'(x) = 2x + 72\left(\frac{x}{x-4}\right)\left[\frac{-4}{(x-4)^2}\right] = 0$$

$x\left[(x-4)^3 - 144\right] = 0$ when $x = 0$ or $x = 4 + \sqrt[3]{144}$.

$$L \approx 14.05 \text{ ft}$$

**106.** You can form a right triangle with vertices $(0, y)$, $(0, 0)$, and $(x, 0)$. Choosing a point $(a, b)$ on the hypotenuse (assuming the triangle is in the first quadrant), the slope is

$$m = \frac{y-b}{0-a} = \frac{b-0}{a-x} \Rightarrow y = \frac{-bx}{a-x}.$$

Let $f(x) = L^2 = x^2 + y^2 = x^2 + \left(\frac{-bx}{a-x}\right)^2$.

$$f'(x) = 2x + 2\left(\frac{-bx}{a-x}\right)\left[\frac{-ab}{(a-x)^2}\right]$$

$$\frac{2x\left[(a-x)^3 + ab^2\right]}{(a-x)^3} = 0 \text{ when } x = 0, a + \sqrt[3]{ab^2}.$$

Choosing the nonzero value, you have $y = b + \sqrt[3]{a^2b}$.

$$L = \sqrt{\left(a + \sqrt[3]{ab^2}\right)^2 + \left(b + \sqrt[3]{a^2b}\right)^2}$$

$$= \left(a^2 + 3a^{4/3}b^{2/3} + 3a^{2/3}b^{4/3} + b^2\right)^{1/2}$$

$$= \left(a^{2/3} + b^{2/3}\right)^{3/2} \text{ m}$$

**107.** $\csc\theta = \dfrac{L_1}{6}$ or $L_1 = 6\csc\theta$ (see figure)

$\sec\theta = \dfrac{L_2}{9}$ or $L_2 = 9\sec\theta$

$$L = L_1 + L_2 = 6\csc\theta + 9\sec\theta$$

$$\frac{dL}{d\theta} = -6\csc\theta\cot\theta + 9\sec\theta\tan\theta = 0$$

$$\tan^3\theta = \frac{2}{3} \Rightarrow \tan\theta = \frac{\sqrt[3]{2}}{\sqrt[3]{3}}$$

$$\sec\theta = \sqrt{1+\tan^2\theta} = \sqrt{1+\left(\frac{2}{3}\right)^{2/3}} = \frac{\sqrt{3^{2/3}+2^{2/3}}}{3^{1/3}}$$

$$\csc\theta = \frac{\sec\theta}{\tan\theta} = \frac{\sqrt{3^{2/3}+2^{2/3}}}{2^{1/3}}$$

$$L = 6\frac{\left(3^{2/3}+2^{2/3}\right)^{1/2}}{2^{1/3}} + 9\frac{\left(3^{2/3}+2^{2/3}\right)^{1/2}}{3^{1/3}}$$

$$= 3\left(3^{2/3}+2^{2/3}\right)^{3/2} \text{ ft} \approx 21.07 \text{ ft}$$

(Compare to Exercise 106 using $a = 9$ and $b = 6$.)

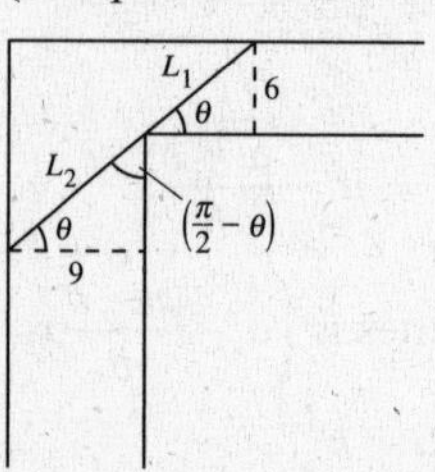


**108.** Using Exercise 107 as a guide you have $L_1 = a\csc\theta$ and $L_2 = b\sec\theta$. Then $dL/d\theta = -a\csc\theta\cot\theta + b\sec\theta\tan\theta = 0$ when

$$\tan\theta = \sqrt[3]{a/b}, \sec\theta = \frac{\sqrt{a^{2/3}+b^{2/3}}}{b^{1/3}},$$

$$\csc\theta = \frac{\sqrt{a^{2/3}+b^{2/3}}}{a^{1/3}}$$

and

$$L = L_1 + L_2 = a\csc\theta + b\sec\theta$$

$$= a\frac{\left(a^{2/3}+b^{2/3}\right)^{1/2}}{a^{1/3}} + b\frac{\left(a^{2/3}+b^{2/3}\right)^{1/2}}{b^{1/3}}$$

$$= \left(a^{2/3}+b^{2/3}\right)^{3/2}.$$

This matches the result of Exercise 106.

**109.** Total cost $=$ (Cost per hour)(Number of hours)

$$T = \left(\frac{v^2}{600} + 5\right)\left(\frac{110}{v}\right) = \frac{11v}{60} + \frac{550}{v}$$

$$\frac{dT}{dv} = \frac{11}{60} - \frac{550}{v^2} = \frac{11v^2 - 33{,}000}{60v^2}$$

$$= 0 \text{ when } v = \sqrt{3000} = 10\sqrt{30} \approx 54.77 \text{ mi/h}$$

$$\frac{d^2T}{dv^2} = \frac{1100}{v^3} > 0 \text{ when } v = 10\sqrt{30} \text{ so this value yields a minimum.}$$

**110.** Total cost $=$ (Cost per hour)(Number of hours)

$$T = \left(\frac{v^2}{500} + 7.50\right)\left(\frac{110}{v}\right) = \frac{11v}{50} + \frac{825}{v}$$

$$\frac{dT}{dv} = \frac{11}{50} - \frac{825}{v^2} = \frac{11v^2 - 41{,}250}{50v^2}$$

$$= 0 \text{ when } v = \sqrt{3750} = 25\sqrt{6} \approx 61.2 \text{ mi/h}$$

$$\frac{d^2T}{dv^2} = \frac{1650}{v^3} > 0 \text{ when } v = 25\sqrt{6} \text{ so this value yields a minimum.}$$

**111.** $y = x(1 - \cos x) = x - x\cos x$

$$\frac{dy}{dx} = 1 + x\sin x - \cos x$$

$$dy = (1 + x\sin x - \cos x)dx$$

**112.** $y = \sqrt{36 - x^2}$

$$\frac{dy}{dx} = \frac{1}{2}\left(36 - x^2\right)^{-1/2}(-2x) = \frac{-x}{\sqrt{36 - x^2}}$$

$$dy = \frac{-x}{\sqrt{36 - x^2}}dx$$

**113.** $S = 4\pi r^2,\ dr = \Delta r = \pm 0.025$

$$dS = 8\pi r\,dr = 8\pi(9)(\pm 0.025) = \pm 1.8\pi \text{ cm}^2$$

$$\frac{dS}{S}(100) = \frac{8\pi r\,dr}{4\pi r^2}(100) = \frac{2\,dr}{r}(100) = \frac{2(\pm 0.025)}{9}(100) \approx \pm 0.56\%$$

$$V = \frac{4}{3}\pi r^3$$

$$dV = 4\pi r^2\,dr = 4\pi(9)^2(\pm 0.025) = \pm 8.1\pi \text{ cm}^3$$

$$\frac{dV}{V}(100) = \frac{4\pi r^2\,dr}{(4/3)\pi r^3}(100) = \frac{3\,dr}{r}(100) = \frac{3(\pm 0.025)}{9}(100) \approx \pm 0.83\%$$

**114.** $p = 75 - \frac{1}{4}x$

$$\Delta p = p(8) - p(7) = \left(75 - \tfrac{8}{4}\right) - \left(75 - \tfrac{7}{4}\right) = -\tfrac{1}{4}$$

$$dp = -\tfrac{1}{4}dx = -\tfrac{1}{4}(1) = -\tfrac{1}{4}$$

[$\Delta p = dp$ because $p$ is linear]

# Problem Solving for Chapter 4

**1.** $p(x) = x^4 + ax^2 + 1$

(a) $p'(x) = 4x^3 + 2ax = 2x(2x^2 + a)$

$p''(x) = 12x^2 + 2a$

For $a \geq 0$, there is one relative minimum at $(0, 1)$.

(b) For $a < 0$, there is a relative maximum at $(0, 1)$.

(c) For $a < 0$, there are two relative minima at $x = \pm\sqrt{-\dfrac{a}{2}}$.

(d) If $a < 0$, there are three critical points; if $a > 0$, there is only one critical point.

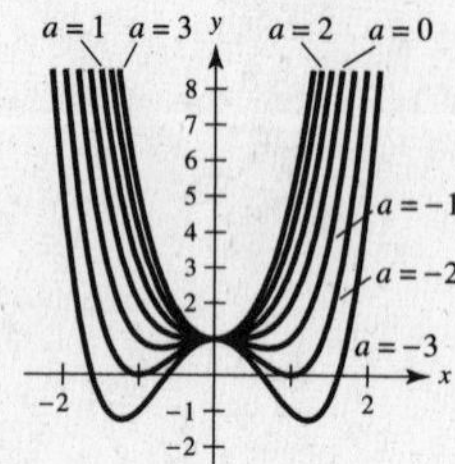


**2.** (a) For $a = -3, -2, -1, 0$, $p$ has a relative maximum at $(0, 0)$.

For $a = 1, 2, 3$, $p$ has a relative maximum at $(0, 0)$ and 2 relative minima.

(b) $p'(x) = 4ax^3 - 12x = 4x(ax^2 - 3) = 0 \Rightarrow x = 0, \pm\sqrt{\dfrac{3}{a}}$

$p''(x) = 12ax^2 - 12 = 12(ax^2 - 1)$

For $x = 0$, $p''(0) = -12 < 0 \Rightarrow p$ has a relative maximum at $(0, 0)$.

(c) If $a > 0$, $x = \pm\sqrt{\dfrac{3}{a}}$ are the remaining critical numbers.

$$p''\left(\pm\sqrt{\frac{3}{a}}\right) = 12a\left(\frac{3}{a}\right) - 12 = 24 > 0 \Rightarrow p \text{ has relative minima for } a > 0.$$

(d) $(0, 0)$ lies on $y = -3x^2$.

Let $x = \pm\sqrt{\dfrac{3}{a}}$. Then $p(x) = a\left(\dfrac{3}{a}\right)^2 - 6\left(\dfrac{3}{a}\right) = \dfrac{9}{a} - \dfrac{18}{a} = -\dfrac{9}{a}$.

So, $y = -\dfrac{9}{a} = -3\left(\pm\sqrt{\dfrac{3}{a}}\right)^2 = -3x^2$ is satisfied by all the relative extrema of $p$.

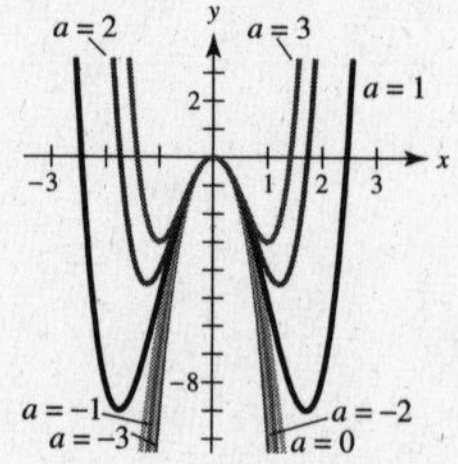

3. $f(x) = \frac{c}{x} + x^2$

$$f'(x) = -\frac{c}{x^2} + 2x = 0 \Rightarrow \frac{c}{x^2} = 2x \Rightarrow x^3 = \frac{c}{2} \Rightarrow x = \sqrt[3]{\frac{c}{2}}$$

$$f''(x) = \frac{2c}{x^3} + 2$$

If $c = 0$, $f(x) = x^2$ has a relative minimum, but no relative maximum.

If $c > 0$, $x = \sqrt[3]{\frac{c}{2}}$ is a relative minimum, because $f''\left(\sqrt[3]{\frac{c}{2}}\right) > 0$.

If $c < 0$, $x = \sqrt[3]{\frac{c}{2}}$ is a relative minimum, too.

Answer: All $c$.

4. (a) $f(x) = ax^2 + bx + c, a \neq 0$

$f'(x) = 2ax$

$f''(x) = 2a \neq 0$

No point of inflection

(b) $f(x) = ax^3 + bx^2 + cx + d, a \neq 0$

$f'(x) = 3ax^2 + 2bx + c$

$f''(x) = 6ax + 2b = 0 \Rightarrow x = \frac{-b}{3a}$

One point of inflection

(c) $y' = ky\left(1 - \frac{y}{L}\right) = ky - \frac{k}{L}y^2$

$y'' = ky' - \frac{2k}{L}yy' = ky'\left(1 - \frac{2}{L}y\right)$

$y''$: + + + + + + − − − − − ; $y = \frac{L}{2}$

If $y = \frac{L}{2}$, then $y'' = 0$, and this is a point of inflection because of the analysis above.

5. Assume $y_1 < d < y_2$. Let $g(x) = f(x) - d(x - a)$. $g$ is continuous on $[a, b]$ and therefore has a minimum $(c, g(c))$ on $[a, b]$. The point $c$ cannot be an endpoint of $[a, b]$ because

$g'(a) = f'(a) - d = y_1 - d < 0$

$g'(b) = f'(b) - d = y_2 - d > 0.$

So, $a < c < b$ and $g'(c) = 0 \Rightarrow f'(c) = d$.

6. Let $h(x) = g(x) - f(x)$, which is continuous on $[a, b]$ and differentiable on $(a, b)$. $h(a) = 0$ and $h(b) = g(b) - f(b)$.

By the Mean Value Theorem, there exists $c$ in $(a, b)$ such that

$$h'(c) = \frac{h(b) - h(a)}{b - a} = \frac{g(b) - f(b)}{b - a}.$$

Because $h'(c) = g'(c) - f'(c) > 0$ and $b - a > 0$, $g(b) - f(b) > 0 \Rightarrow g(b) > f(b)$.

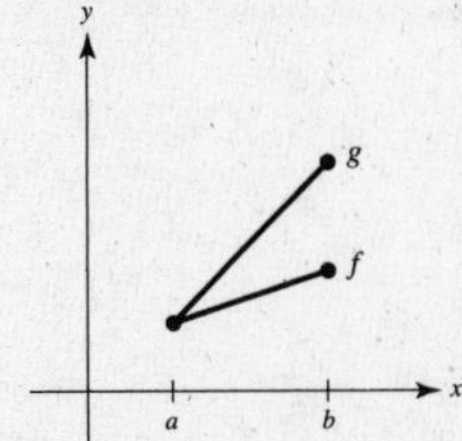

**7.** Set $\dfrac{f(b) - f(a) - f'(a)(b - a)}{(b - a)^2} = k.$

Define $F(x) = f(x) - f(a) - f'(a)(x - a) - k(x - a)^2.$

$F(a) = 0, F(b) = f(b) - f(a) - f'(a)(b - a) - k(b - a)^2 = 0$

$F$ is continuous on $[a, b]$ and differentiable on $(a, b)$.

There exists $c_1, a < c_1 < b$, satisfying $F'(c_1) = 0$.

$F'(x) = f'(x) - f'(a) - 2k(x - a)$ satisfies the hypothesis of Rolle's Theorem on $[a, c_1]$:

$F'(a) = 0, F'(c_1) = 0.$

There exists $c_2, a < c_2 < c_1$ satisfying $F''(c_2) = 0$.

Finally, $F''(x) = f''(x) - 2k$ and $F''(c_2) = 0$ implies that

$k = \dfrac{f''(c_2)}{2}.$

So, $k = \dfrac{f(b) - f(a) - f'(a)(b - a)}{(b - a)^2} = \dfrac{f''(c_2)}{2} \Rightarrow f(b) = f(a) + f'(a)(b - a) + \dfrac{1}{2}f''(c_2)(b - a)^2.$

**8.** (a) $dV = 3x^2dx = 3x^2\,\Delta x$

$\Delta V = (x + \Delta x)^3 - x^3 = 3x^2\,\Delta x + 3x(\Delta x)^2 + (\Delta x)^3$

$\Delta V - dV = 3x(\Delta x)^2 + (\Delta x)^3 = \underbrace{\left[3x\,\Delta x + (\Delta x)^2\right]}_{\varepsilon}\Delta x = \varepsilon\Delta x$, where $\varepsilon \to 0$ as $\Delta x \to 0$.

(b) Let $\varepsilon = \dfrac{\Delta y}{\Delta x} - f'(x)$. Then $\varepsilon \to 0$ as $\Delta x \to 0$.

Furthermore, $\Delta y - dy = \Delta y - f'(x)dx = \varepsilon\,\Delta x.$

**9.**

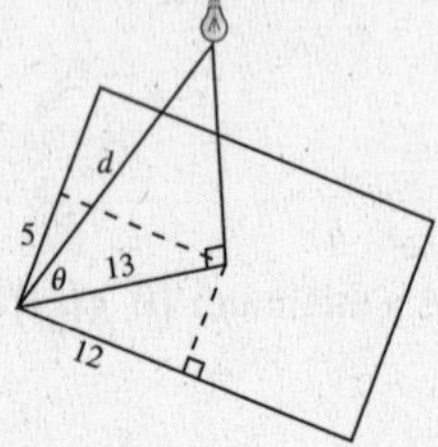


$d = \sqrt{13^2 + x^2}, \sin\theta = \dfrac{x}{d}.$

Let $A$ be the amount of illumination at one of the corners, as indicated in the figure. Then

$A = \dfrac{kI}{(13^2 + x^2)}\sin\theta = \dfrac{kIx}{(13^2 + x^2)^{3/2}}$

$A'(x) = kI\dfrac{(x^2 + 169)^{3/2}(1) - x\left(\frac{3}{2}\right)(x^2 + 169)^{1/2}(2x)}{(169 + x^2)^3} = 0$

$\Rightarrow (x^2 + 169)^{3/2} = 3x^2(x^2 + 169)^{1/2}$

$x^2 + 169 = 3x^2$

$2x^2 = 169$

$x = \dfrac{13}{\sqrt{2}} \approx 9.19$ ft

By the First Derivative Test, this is a maximum.

**10.** Distance $= \sqrt{4^2 + x^2} + \sqrt{(4 - x)^2 + 4^2} = f(x)$

$$f'(x) = \frac{x}{\sqrt{4^2 + x^2}} - \frac{4 - x}{\sqrt{(4 - x)^2 + 4^2}} = 0$$

$$x\sqrt{(4 - x)^2 + 4^2} = -(x - 4)\sqrt{4^2 + x^2}$$

$$x^2\left[16 - 8x + x^2 + 16\right] = \left(x^2 - 8x + 16\right)\left(16 + x^2\right)$$

$$32x^2 - 8x^3 + x^4 = x^4 - 8x^3 + 32x^2 - 128x + 256$$

$$128x = 256$$

$$x = 2$$

The bug should head towards the midpoint of the opposite side.

Without Calculus: Imagine opening up the cube:

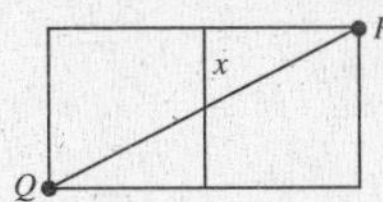


The shortest distance is the line $PQ$, passing through the midpoint.

**11.** Let $T$ be the intersection of $PQ$ and $RS$. Let $MN$ be the perpendicular to $SQ$ and $PR$ passing through $T$.

Let $TM = x$ and $TN = b - x$.

$$\frac{SN}{b - x} = \frac{MR}{x} \Rightarrow SN = \frac{b - x}{x}MR$$

$$\frac{NQ}{b - x} = \frac{PM}{x} \Rightarrow NQ = \frac{b - x}{x}PM$$

$$SQ = \frac{b - x}{x}(MR + PM) = \frac{b - x}{x}d$$

$$A(x) = \text{Area} = \frac{1}{2}dx + \frac{1}{2}\left(\frac{b - x}{x}d\right)(b - x) = \frac{1}{2}d\left[x + \frac{(b - x)^2}{x}\right] = \frac{1}{2}d\left[\frac{2x^2 - 2bx + b^2}{x}\right]$$

$$A'(x) = \frac{1}{2}d\left[\frac{x(4x - 2b) - \left(2x^2 - 2bx + b^2\right)}{x^2}\right]$$

$$A'(x) = 0 \Rightarrow 4x^2 - 2xb = 2x^2 - 2bx + b^2$$

$$2x^2 = b^2$$

$$x = \frac{b}{\sqrt{2}}$$

So, you have $SQ = \dfrac{b - x}{x}d = \dfrac{b - \left(b/\sqrt{2}\right)}{b/\sqrt{2}}d = \left(\sqrt{2} - 1\right)d.$

Using the Second Derivative Test, this is a minimum. There is no maximum.

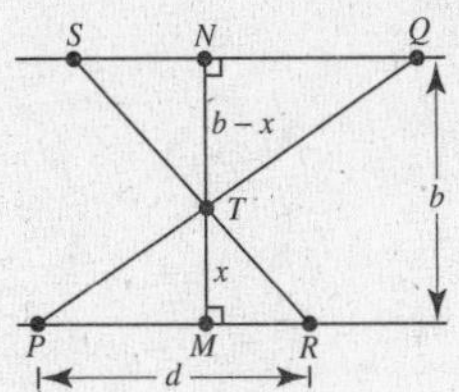

**12.** (a)

| $x$ | 0.1 | 0.2 | 0.3 | 0.4 | 0.5 | 1.0 |
|---|---|---|---|---|---|---|
| $\sin x$ | 0.09983 | 0.19867 | 0.29552 | 0.38942 | 0.47943 | 0.84147 |

$\sin x < x$

(b) Let $f(x) = \sin x$. For $x > 1$, $\sin x < x$ is obvious. So assume $0 < x \le 1$. Then $f'(x) = \cos x$ and on $[0, x]$ you have by the Mean Value Theorem,

$$f'(c) = \frac{f(x) - f(0)}{x - 0}, 0 < c < x$$

$$\cos(c) = \frac{\sin x}{x}$$

So, $\left|\frac{\sin x}{x}\right| = |\cos(c)| < 1 \Rightarrow |\sin x| < |x| \Rightarrow \sin x < x.$

**13.** (a)

| $x$ | 0 | 0.5 | 1 | 2 |
|---|---|---|---|---|
| $\sqrt{1 + x}$ | 1 | 1.2247 | 1.4142 | 1.7321 |
| $\frac{1}{2}x + 1$ | 1 | 1.25 | 1.5 | 2 |

(b) Let $f(x) = \sqrt{1 + x}$. Using the Mean Value Theorem on the interval $[0, x]$, there exists $c$, $0 < c < x$, satisfying

$$f'(c) = \frac{1}{2\sqrt{1 + c}} = \frac{f(x) - f(0)}{x - 0} = \frac{\sqrt{1 + x} - 1}{x}.$$

So $\sqrt{1 + x} = \frac{x}{2\sqrt{1 + c}} + 1 < \frac{x}{2} + 1 \left(\text{because } \sqrt{1 + c} > 1\right).$

**14.** The line has equation $\frac{x}{3} + \frac{y}{4} = 1$ or $y = -\frac{4}{3}x + 4$.

Rectangle:

$$\text{Area} = A = xy = x\left(-\frac{4}{3}x + 4\right) = -\frac{4}{3}x^2 + 4x.$$

$$A'(x) = -\frac{8}{3}x + 4 = 0 \Rightarrow \frac{8}{3}x = 4 \Rightarrow x = \frac{3}{2}$$

Dimensions: $\frac{3}{2} \times 2$ Calculus was helpful.

Circle: The distance from the center $(r, r)$ to the line $\frac{x}{3} + \frac{y}{4} - 1 = 0$ must be $r$:

$$r = \frac{\left|\frac{r}{3} + \frac{r}{4} - 1\right|}{\sqrt{\frac{1}{9} + \frac{1}{16}}} = \frac{12}{5}\left|\frac{7r - 12}{12}\right| = \frac{|7r - 12|}{5}$$

$5r = |7r - 12| \Rightarrow r = 1$ or $r = 6$.

Clearly, $r = 1$.

Semicircle: The center lies on the line $\frac{x}{3} + \frac{y}{4} = 1$ and satisfies $x = y = r$.

So $\frac{r}{3} + \frac{r}{4} = 1 \Rightarrow \frac{7}{12}r = 1 \Rightarrow r = \frac{12}{7}$. No calculus necessary.

**15.** (a) Let $M > 0$ be given. Take $N = \sqrt{M}$. Then whenever $x > N = \sqrt{M}$, you have $f(x) = x^2 > M$.

(b) Let $\varepsilon > 0$ be given. Let $M = \sqrt{\dfrac{1}{\varepsilon}}$. Then whenever $x > M = \sqrt{\dfrac{1}{\varepsilon}}$, you have $x^2 > \dfrac{1}{\varepsilon} \Rightarrow \dfrac{1}{x^2} < \varepsilon \Rightarrow \left|\dfrac{1}{x^2} - 0\right| < \varepsilon$.

(c) Let $\varepsilon > 0$ be given. There exists $N > 0$ such that $|f(x) - L| < \varepsilon$ whenever $x > N$.

Let $\delta = \dfrac{1}{N}$. Let $x = \dfrac{1}{y}$.

If $0 < y < \delta = \dfrac{1}{N}$, then $\dfrac{1}{x} < \dfrac{1}{N} \Rightarrow x > N$ and $|f(x) - L| = \left|f\left(\dfrac{1}{y}\right) - L\right| < \varepsilon$.

**16.** $y = \left(1 + x^2\right)^{-1}$

$$y' = \frac{-2x}{\left(1 + x^2\right)^2}$$

$$y'' = \frac{2\left(3x^2 - 1\right)}{\left(x^2 + 1\right)^3} = 0 \Rightarrow x = \pm\frac{1}{\sqrt{3}} = \pm\frac{\sqrt{3}}{3}$$

$y''$: +++ ---- ---- +++ at $-\frac{\sqrt{3}}{3}$, $0$, $\frac{\sqrt{3}}{3}$

The tangent line has greatest slope at $\left(-\dfrac{\sqrt{3}}{3}, \dfrac{3}{4}\right)$ and least slope at $\left(\dfrac{\sqrt{3}}{3}, \dfrac{3}{4}\right)$.

**17.** (a) $$s = \frac{v\dfrac{\text{km}}{\text{h}}\left(1000\dfrac{\text{m}}{\text{km}}\right)}{\left(3600\dfrac{\text{sec}}{\text{h}}\right)} = \frac{5}{18}v$$

| $v$ | 20 | 40 | 60 | 80 | 100 |
|---|---|---|---|---|---|
| $s$ | 5.56 | 11.11 | 16.67 | 22.22 | 27.78 |
| $d$ | 5.1 | 13.7 | 27.2 | 44.2 | 66.4 |

$d(s) = 0.071s^2 + 0.389s + 0.727$

(b) The distance between the back of the first vehicle and the front of the second vehicle is $d(s)$, the safe stopping distance. The first vehicle passes the given point in $5.5/s$ seconds, and the second vehicle takes $d(s)/s$ more seconds. So,

$$T = \frac{d(s)}{s} + \frac{5.5}{s}.$$

(c)

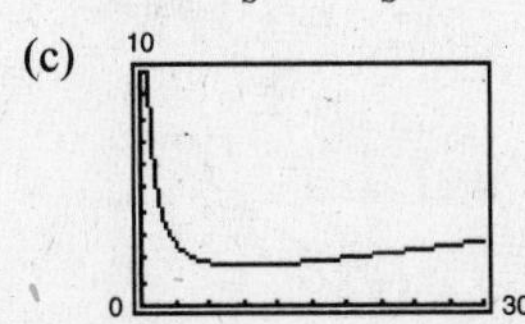


$$T = \frac{1}{s}\left(0.071s^2 + 0.389s + 0.727\right) + \frac{5.5}{s}$$

The minimum is attained when $s \approx 9.365$ m/sec.

(d) $T(s) = 0.071s + 0.389 + \dfrac{6.227}{s}$

$T'(s) = 0.071 - \dfrac{6.227}{s^2} \Rightarrow s^2 = \dfrac{6.227}{0.071} \Rightarrow s \approx 9.365$ m/sec

$T(9.365) \approx 1.719$ seconds

$9.365 \text{ m/sec} \cdot \dfrac{3600}{1000} = 33.7 \text{ km/h}$

(e) $d(9.365) = 10.597$ m

**18.** (a)

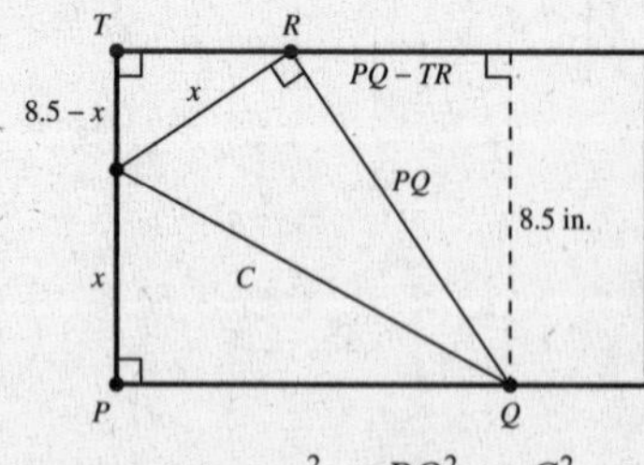


$$x^2 + PQ^2 = C^2 \Rightarrow PQ^2 = C^2 - x^2$$

$$TR^2 + (8.5 - x)^2 = x^2 \Rightarrow TR^2 = 17x - 8.5^2$$

$$(PQ - TR)^2 + 8.5^2 = PQ^2 \Rightarrow 2(PQ)(TR) = TR^2 + 8.5^2$$

So, $2(PQ)(TR) = 17x - 8.5^2 + 8.5^2$.

$$8.5x = (PQ)(TR) = \sqrt{C^2 - x^2}\sqrt{17x - 8.5^2}$$

$$\frac{(8.5x)^2}{17x - 8.5^2} = C^2 - x^2$$

$$C^2 = x^2 + \frac{(8.5x)^2}{17x - 8.5^2} = \frac{17x^3}{17x - 8.5^2}$$

$$C^2 = \frac{2x^3}{2x - 8.5}$$

(b) Domain: $4.25 < x < 8.5$

(c) To minimize $C$, minimize $f(x) = C^2$:

$$f'(x) = \frac{(2x - 8.5)(6x^2) - 2x^3(2)}{(2x - 8.5)^2} = \frac{8x^3 - 51x^2}{(2x - 8.5)^2} = 0$$

$x = \dfrac{51}{8} = 6.375$

By the First Derivative Test, $x = 6.375$ is a minimum.

(d) For $x = 6.375$, $C \approx 11.0418$ in.

**19.** $f(x) = \sin(\ln x)$

(a) Domain: $x > 0$ or $(0, \infty)$

(b) $f(x) = 1 = \sin(\ln x) \Rightarrow \ln x = \dfrac{\pi}{2} + 2k\pi.$

Two values are $x = e^{\pi/2}, e^{(\pi/2) + 2\pi}$.

(c) $f(x) = -1 = \sin(\ln x) \Rightarrow \ln x = \dfrac{3\pi}{2} + 2k\pi.$

Two values are $x = e^{-\pi/2}, e^{3\pi/2}$.

(d) Because the range of the sine function is $[-1, 1]$, parts (b) and (c) show that the range of $f$ is $[-1, 1]$.

(e) $f'(x) = \frac{1}{x}\cos(\ln x)$

$$f'(x) = 0 \Rightarrow \cos(\ln x) = 0 \Rightarrow \ln x = \frac{\pi}{2} + k\pi$$
$$\Rightarrow x = e^{\pi/2} \text{ on } [1, 10].$$

$$\left.\begin{array}{l} f(e^{\pi/2}) = 1 \\ f(1) = 0 \\ f(10) \approx 0.7440 \end{array}\right\} \text{Maximum is 1 at } x = e^{\pi/2} \approx 4.8105.$$

(f)

2

0 5

−2

$\lim_{x\to 0^+} f(x)$ seems to be $-\frac{1}{2}$. (This is incorrect.)

(g) For the points $x = e^{\pi/2}$, $x = e^{-3\pi/2}$, $x = e^{-7\pi/2}, \ldots$ you have $f(x) = 1$.

For the points $x = e^{-\pi/2}$, $x = e^{-5\pi/2}$, $x = e^{-9\pi/2}, \ldots$ you have $f(x) = -1$.

That is, as $x \to 0^+$, there is an infinite number of points where $f(x) = 1$, and an infinite number where $f(x) = -1$.

So, $\lim_{x\to 0^+} \sin(\ln x)$ does not exist.

You can verify this by graphing $f(x)$ on small intervals close to the origin.

**20.** $p(x) = ax^3 + bx^2 + cx + d$

$p'(x) = 3ax^2 + 2bx + c$

$p''(x) = 6ax + 2b$

$6ax + 2b = 0$

$x = -\frac{b}{3a}$

The sign of $p''(x)$ changes at $x = -b/3a$. Therefore, $(-b/3a, p(-b/3a))$ is a point of inflection.

$$p\left(-\frac{b}{3a}\right) = a\left(-\frac{b^3}{27a^3}\right) + b\left(\frac{b^2}{9a^2}\right) + c\left(-\frac{b}{3a}\right) + d = \frac{2b^3}{27a^2} - \frac{bc}{3a} + d$$

When $p(x) = x^3 - 3x^2 + 2$, $a = 1$, $b = -3$, $c = 0$, and $d = 2$.

$$x_0 = \frac{-(-3)}{3(1)} = 1$$

$$y_0 = \frac{2(-3)^3}{27(1)^2} - \frac{(-3)(0)}{3(1)} + 2 = -2 - 0 + 2 = 0$$

The point of inflection of $p(x) = x^3 - 3x^2 + 2$ is $(x_0, y_0) = (1, 0)$.

# CHAPTER 5
# Integration

# CHAPTER 5
# Integration

## Section 5.1 Antiderivatives and Indefinite Integration

1. $\frac{d}{dx}\left(\frac{2}{x^3} + C\right) = \frac{d}{dx}\left(2x^{-3} + C\right) = -6x^{-4} = \frac{-6}{x^4}$

2. $\frac{d}{dx}\left(2x^4 - \frac{1}{2x} + C\right) = \frac{d}{dx}\left(2x^4 - \frac{1}{2}x^{-1} + C\right)$

$= 8x^3 + \frac{1}{2}x^{-2} = 8x^3 + \frac{1}{2x^2}$

3. $\frac{d}{dx}\left(\frac{1}{3}x^3 - 16x + C\right) = x^2 - 16 = (x-4)(x+4)$

4. $\frac{d}{dx}\left(\frac{2(x^2+3)}{3\sqrt{x}} + C\right) = \frac{d}{dx}\left(\frac{2}{3}x^{3/2} + 2x^{-1/2} + C\right)$

$= x^{1/2} - x^{-3/2} = \frac{x^2 - 1}{x^{3/2}}$

5. $\frac{dy}{dt} = 9t^2$

$y = 3t^3 + C$

**Check:** $\frac{d}{dt}\left[3t^3 + C\right] = 9t^2$

6. $\frac{dr}{d\theta} = \pi$

$r = \pi\theta + C$

**Check:** $\frac{d}{d\theta}\left[\pi\theta + C\right] = \pi$

7. $\frac{dy}{dx} = x^{3/2}$

$y = \frac{2}{5}x^{5/2} + C$

**Check:** $\frac{d}{dx}\left[\frac{2}{5}x^{5/2} + C\right] = x^{3/2}$

8. $\frac{dy}{dx} = 2x^{-3}$

$y = \frac{2x^{-2}}{-2} + C = -\frac{1}{x^2} + C$

**Check:** $\frac{d}{dx}\left[-\frac{1}{x^2} + C\right] = 2x^{-3}$

| | *Given* | *Rewrite* | *Integrate* | *Simplify* |
|---|---|---|---|---|
| 9. | $\int \sqrt[3]{x}\,dx$ | $\int x^{1/3}\,dx$ | $\frac{x^{4/3}}{4/3} + C$ | $\frac{3}{4}x^{4/3} + C$ |
| 10. | $\int \frac{1}{4x^2}\,dx$ | $\frac{1}{4}\int x^{-2}\,dx$ | $\frac{1}{4}\left(\frac{x^{-1}}{-1}\right) + C$ | $-\frac{1}{4x} + C$ |
| 11. | $\int \frac{1}{x\sqrt{x}}\,dx$ | $\int x^{-3/2}\,dx$ | $\frac{x^{-1/2}}{-1/2} + C$ | $-\frac{2}{\sqrt{x}} + C$ |
| 12. | $\int x(x^3+1)\,dx$ | $\int (x^4 + x)\,dx$ | $\frac{x^5}{5} + \frac{x^2}{2} + C$ | $\frac{1}{5}x^5 + \frac{1}{2}x^2 + C$ |
| 13. | $\int \frac{1}{2x^3}\,dx$ | $\frac{1}{2}\int x^{-3}\,dx$ | $\frac{1}{2}\left(\frac{x^{-2}}{-2}\right) + C$ | $-\frac{1}{4x^2} + C$ |
| 14. | $\int \frac{1}{(3x)^2}\,dx$ | $\frac{1}{9}\int x^{-2}\,dx$ | $\frac{1}{9}\left(\frac{x^{-1}}{-1}\right) + C$ | $-\frac{1}{9x} + C$ |

15. $\int (x+7)\,dx = \frac{x^2}{2} + 7x + C$

**Check:** $\frac{d}{dx}\left[\frac{x^2}{2} + 7x + C\right] = x + 7$

16. $\int (13 - x)\,dx = 13x - \frac{x^2}{2} + C$

**Check:** $\frac{d}{dx}\left[13x - \frac{x^2}{2} + C\right] = 13 - x$

**17.** $\int\left(x^5 + 1\right) dx = \dfrac{x^6}{6} + x + C$

**Check:** $\dfrac{d}{dx}\left(\dfrac{x^6}{6} + x + C\right) = x^5 + 1$

**18.** $\int\left(8x^3 - 9x^2 + 4\right) dx = 2x^4 - 3x^3 + 4x + C$

**Check:** $\dfrac{d}{dx}\left(2x^4 - 3x^3 + 4x + C\right) = 8x^3 - 9x^2 + 4$

**19.** $\int\left(x^{3/2} + 2x + 1\right) dx = \dfrac{2}{5}x^{5/2} + x^2 + x + C$

**Check:** $\dfrac{d}{dx}\left(\dfrac{2}{5}x^{5/2} + x^2 + x + C\right) = x^{3/2} + 2x + 1$

**20.** $\int\left(\sqrt[4]{x^3} + 1\right) dx = \int\left(x^{3/4} + 1\right) dx = \dfrac{4}{7}x^{7/4} + x + C$

**Check:** $\dfrac{d}{dx}\left(\dfrac{4}{7}x^{7/4} + x + C\right) = x^{3/4} + 1 = \sqrt[4]{x^3} + 1$

**21.** $\int \dfrac{1}{x^5}\, dx = \int x^{-5}\, dx = \dfrac{x^{-4}}{-4} + C = -\dfrac{1}{4x^4} + C$

**Check:** $\dfrac{d}{dx}\left(-\dfrac{1}{4x^4} + C\right) = \dfrac{d}{dx}\left(-\dfrac{1}{4}x^{-4} + C\right)$

$= -\dfrac{1}{4}\left(-4x^{-5}\right) = \dfrac{1}{x^5}$

**22.** $\int \dfrac{1}{x^6}\, dx = \int x^{-6}\, dx = \dfrac{x^{-5}}{-5} + C = -\dfrac{1}{5x^5} + C$

**Check:** $\dfrac{d}{dx}\left(-\dfrac{1}{5x^5} + C\right) = \dfrac{d}{dx}\left(-\dfrac{1}{5}x^{-5} + C\right)$

$= -\dfrac{1}{5}\left(-5x^{-6}\right) = \dfrac{1}{x^6}$

**23.** $\int \dfrac{x + 6}{\sqrt{x}}\, dx = \int\left(x^{1/2} + 6x^{-1/2}\right) dx$

$= \dfrac{x^{3/2}}{3/2} + 6\dfrac{x^{1/2}}{1/2} + C$

$= \dfrac{2}{3}x^{3/2} + 12x^{1/2} + C$

$= \dfrac{2}{3}x^{1/2}(x + 18) + C$

**Check:** $\dfrac{d}{dx}\left(\dfrac{2}{3}x^{3/2} + 12x^{1/2} + C\right)$

$= \dfrac{2}{3}\left(\dfrac{3}{2}x^{1/2}\right) + 12\left(\dfrac{1}{2}x^{-1/2}\right)$

$= x^{1/2} + 6x^{-1/2} = \dfrac{x + 6}{\sqrt{x}}$

**24.** $\int \dfrac{x^2 + 2x - 3}{x^4}\, dx = \int\left(x^{-2} + 2x^{-3} - 3x^{-4}\right) dx = \dfrac{x^{-1}}{-1} + \dfrac{2x^{-2}}{-2} - \dfrac{3x^{-3}}{-3} + C = -\dfrac{1}{x} - \dfrac{1}{x^2} + \dfrac{1}{x^3} + C$

**Check:** $\dfrac{d}{dx}\left[-\dfrac{1}{x} - \dfrac{1}{x^2} + \dfrac{1}{x^3} + C\right] = x^{-2} + 2x^{-3} - 3x^{-4} = \dfrac{x^2 + 2x - 3}{x^4}$

**25.** $\int(x + 1)(3x - 2)\, dx = \int\left(3x^2 + x - 2\right) dx$

$= x^3 + \dfrac{1}{2}x^2 - 2x + C$

**Check:** $\dfrac{d}{dx}\left(x^3 + \dfrac{1}{2}x^2 - 2x + C\right) = 3x^2 + x - 2$

$= (x + 1)(3x - 2)$

**26.** $\int\left(2t^2 - 1\right)^2 dt = \int\left(4t^4 - 4t^2 + 1\right) dt$

$= \dfrac{4}{5}t^5 - \dfrac{4}{3}t^3 + t + C$

**Check:** $\dfrac{d}{dt}\left(\dfrac{4}{5}t^5 - \dfrac{4}{3}t^3 + t + C\right) = 4t^4 - 4t^2 + 1$

$= \left(2t^2 - 1\right)^2$

**27.** $\int y^2\sqrt{y}\, dy = \int y^{5/2}\, dy = \dfrac{2}{7}y^{7/2} + C$

**Check:** $\dfrac{d}{dy}\left(\dfrac{2}{7}y^{7/2} + C\right) = y^{5/2} = y^2\sqrt{y}$

**28.** $\int(1 + 3t)t^2\, dt = \int\left(t^2 + 3t^3\right) dt = \dfrac{1}{3}t^3 + \dfrac{3}{4}t^4 + C$

**Check:** $\dfrac{d}{dt}\left(\dfrac{1}{3}t^3 + \dfrac{3}{4}t^4 + C\right) = t^2 + 3t^3 = (1 + 3t)t^2$

**29.** $\int dx = \int 1\, dx = x + C$

**Check:** $\dfrac{d}{dx}(x + C) = 1$

**30.** $\int 14\, dt = 14t + C$

**Check:** $\dfrac{d}{dt}(14t + C) = 14$

**31.** $\int (5\cos x + 4\sin x)\,dx = 5\sin x - 4\cos x + C$

**Check:**

$$\frac{d}{dx}(5\sin x - 4\cos x + C) = 5\cos x + 4\sin x$$

**32.** $\int (t^2 - \cos t)\,dt = \frac{t^3}{3} - \sin t + C$

**Check:** $\frac{d}{dt}\left(\frac{t^3}{3} - \sin t + C\right) = t^2 - \cos t$

**33.** $\int (1 - \csc t \cot t)\,dt = t + \csc t + C$

**Check:** $\frac{d}{dt}(t + \csc t + C) = 1 - \csc t \cot t$

**34.** $\int (\theta^2 + \sec^2\theta)\,d\theta = \frac{1}{3}\theta^3 + \tan\theta + C$

**Check:** $\frac{d}{d\theta}\left(\frac{1}{3}\theta^3 + \tan\theta + C\right) = \theta^2 + \sec^2\theta$

**35.** $\int (2\sin x - 5e^x)\,dx = -2\cos x - 5e^x + C$

**Check:** $\frac{d}{dx}(-2\cos x - 5e^x + C) = 2\sin x - 5e^x$

**36.** $\int (3x^2 + 2e^x)\,dx = x^3 + 2e^x + C$

**Check:** $\frac{d}{dx}(x^3 + 2e^x + C) = 3x^2 + 2e^x$

**37.** $\int (\sec^2\theta - \sin\theta)\,d\theta = \tan\theta + \cos\theta + C$

**Check:** $\frac{d}{d\theta}(\tan\theta + \cos\theta + C) = \sec^2\theta - \sin\theta$

**38.** $\int \sec y(\tan y - \sec y)\,dy = \int (\sec y \tan y - \sec^2 y)\,dy$

$$= \sec y - \tan y + C$$

**Check:** $\frac{d}{dy}(\sec y - \tan y + C) = \sec y \tan y - \sec^2 y$

$$= \sec y(\tan y - \sec y)$$

**39.** $\int (\tan^2 y + 1)\,dy = \int \sec^2 y\,dy = \tan y + C$

**Check:** $\frac{d}{dy}(\tan y + C) = \sec^2 y = \tan^2 y + 1$

**40.** $\int \frac{\cos x}{1 - \cos^2 x}\,dx = \int \frac{\cos x}{\sin^2 x}\,dx = \int \left(\frac{1}{\sin x}\right)\left(\frac{\cos x}{\sin x}\right)dx$

$$= \int \csc x \cot x\,dx = -\csc x + C$$

**Check:** $\frac{d}{dx}[-\csc x + C] = \csc x \cot x = \frac{1}{\sin x}\cdot\frac{\cos x}{\sin x}$

$$= \frac{\cos x}{1 - \cos^2 x}$$

**41.** $\int (2x - 4^x)\,dx = x^2 - \frac{4^x}{\ln 4} + C$

**Check:** $\frac{d}{dx}\left(x^2 - \frac{4^x}{\ln 4} + C\right) = 2x - 4^x$

**42.** $\int (\cos x + 3^x)\,dx = \sin x + \frac{3^x}{\ln 3} + C$

**Check:** $\frac{d}{dx}\left(\sin x + \frac{3^x}{\ln 3} + C\right) = \cos x + 3^x$

**43.** $\int \left(x - \frac{5}{x}\right)dx = \frac{x^2}{2} - 5\ln|x| + C$

**Check:** $\frac{d}{dx}\left(\frac{x^2}{2} - 5\ln|x| + C\right) = x - \frac{5}{x}$

**44.** $\int \left(\frac{4}{x} + \sec^2 x\right)dx = 4\ln|x| + \tan x + C$

**Check:** $\frac{d}{dx}(4\ln|x| + \tan x + C) = \frac{4}{x} + \sec^2 x$

**45.** $f(x) = \cos x$

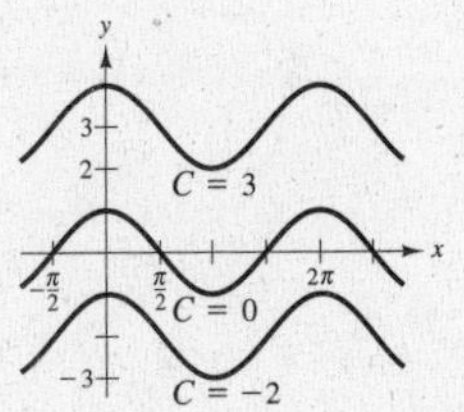


**46.** $f(x) = \sqrt{x}$ 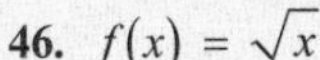

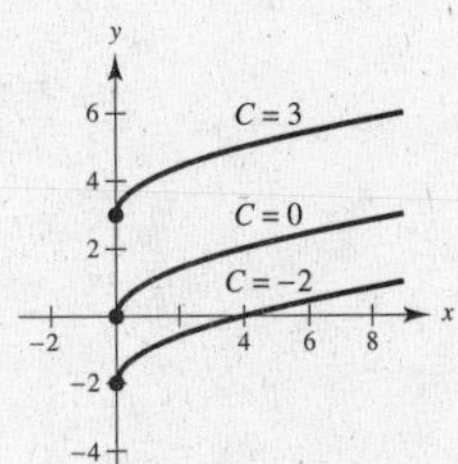


**47.** $f(x) = \ln x$

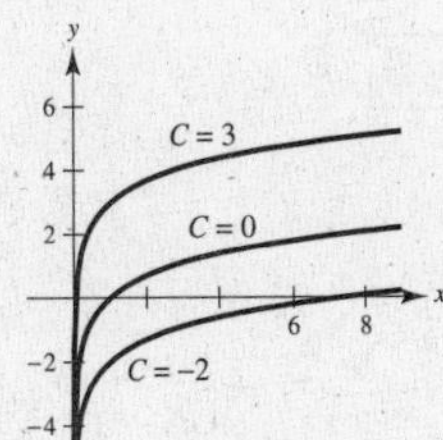

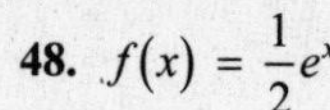

48. $f(x) = \frac{1}{2}e^x$

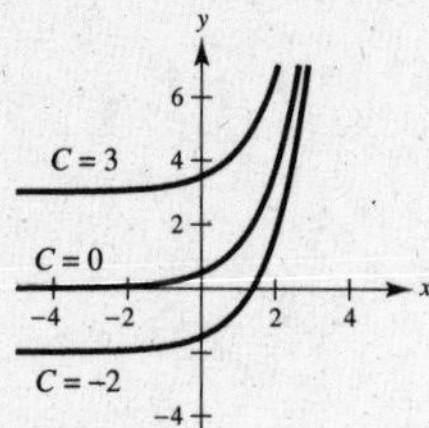


49. $f'(x) = 4$

$f(x) = 4x + C$

Answers will vary.

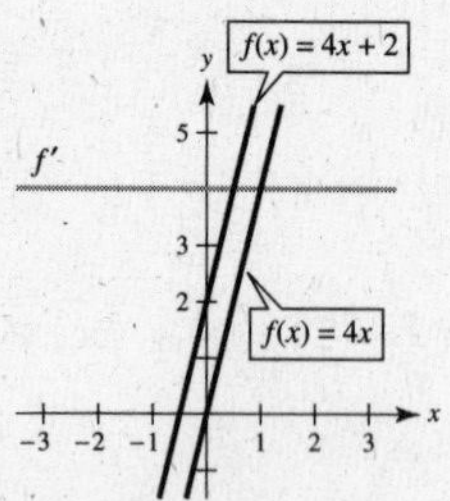


50. $f'(x) = x$

$f(x) = \frac{x^2}{2} + C$

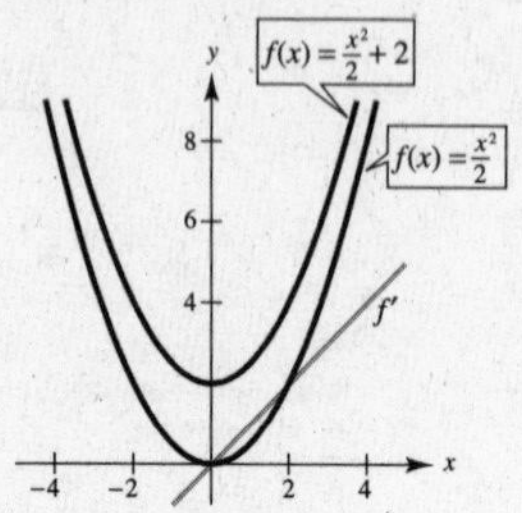


Answers will vary.

51. $f'(x) = 2 - x^2$

$f(x) = 2x - \frac{x^3}{3} + C$

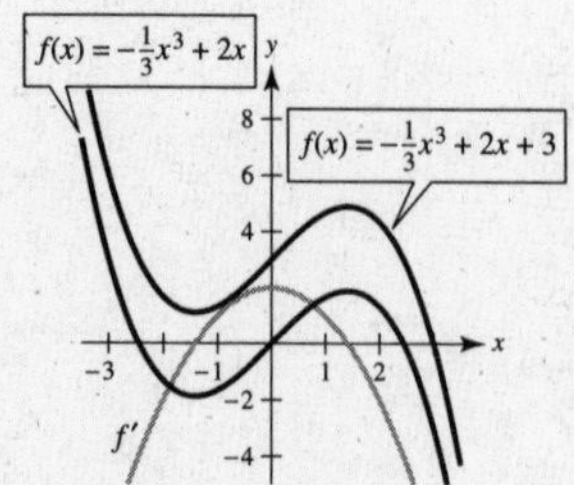


Answers will vary.

52. $f'(x) = \frac{1}{x^2}$

$f(x) = -\frac{1}{x} + C$

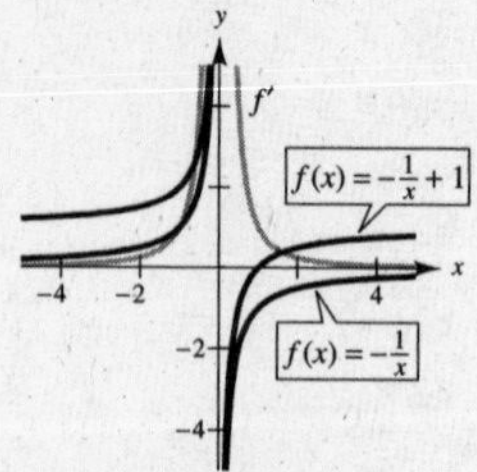


Answers will vary.

53. $\frac{dy}{dx} = 2x - 1, (1, 1)$

$y = \int (2x - 1)\,dx = x^2 - x + C$

$1 = (1)^2 - (1) + C \Rightarrow C = 1$

$y = x^2 - x + 1$

54. $\frac{dy}{dx} = 2(x - 1) = 2x - 2, (3, 2)$

$y = \int 2(x - 1)\,dx = x^2 - 2x + C$

$2 = (3)^2 - 2(3) + C \Rightarrow C = -1$

$y = x^2 - 2x - 1$

55. $\frac{dy}{dx} = \cos x, (0, 4)$

$y = \int \cos x\,dx = \sin x + C$

$4 = \sin 0 + C \Rightarrow C = 4$

$y = \sin x + 4$

56. $\frac{dy}{dx} = \frac{3}{x}, x > 0, (e, 3)$

$y = \int \frac{3}{x}\,dx = 3 \ln x + C$

$3 = 3 \ln e + C \Rightarrow C = 0$

$y = 3 \ln x$

**57.** (a) Answers will vary. *Sample answer.*

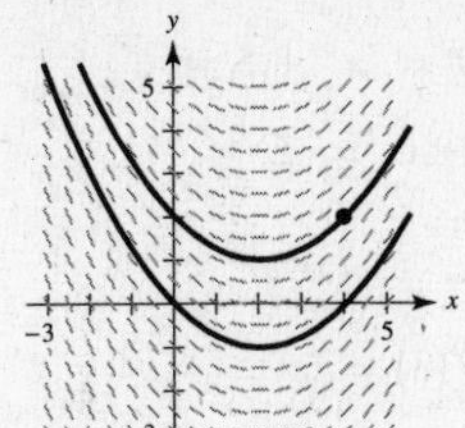

(b) $\frac{dy}{dx} = \frac{1}{2}x - 1, (4, 2)$

$$y = \frac{x^2}{4} - x + C$$

$$2 = \frac{4^2}{4} - 4 + C$$

$$2 = C$$

$$y = \frac{x^2}{4} - x + 2$$

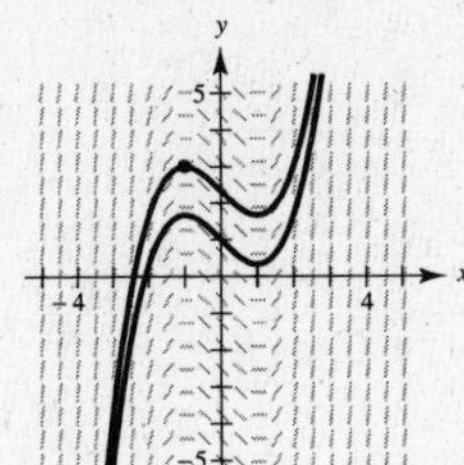

**58.** (a) Answers will vary. *Sample answer.*

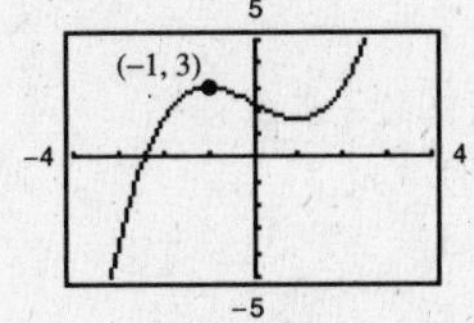

(b) $\frac{dy}{dx} = x^2 - 1, (-1, 3)$

$$y = \frac{x^3}{3} - x + C$$

$$3 = \frac{(-1)^3}{3} - (-1) + C$$

$$C = \frac{7}{3}$$

$$y = \frac{x^3}{3} - x + \frac{7}{3}$$

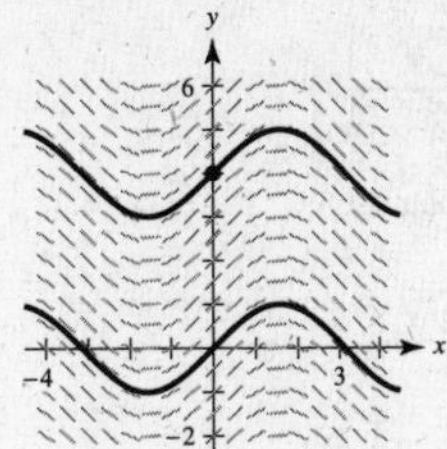

**59.** (a) Answers will vary. *Sample answer:*

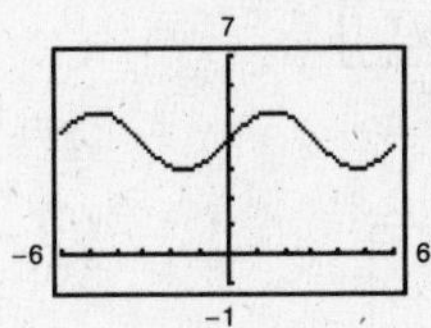

(b) $\frac{dy}{dx} = \cos x, (0, 4)$

$$y = \int \cos x \, dx = \sin x + C$$

$$4 = \sin(0) + C \Rightarrow C = 4$$

$$y = \sin x + 4$$

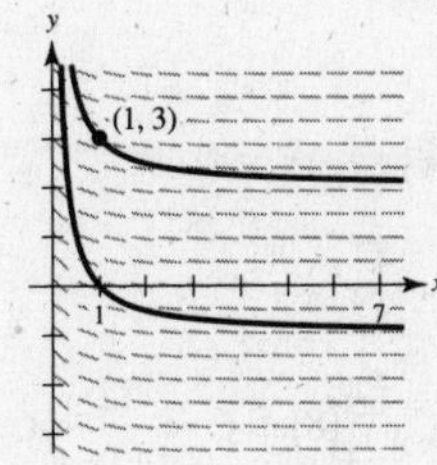

**60.** (a) Answers will vary. *Sample answer:*

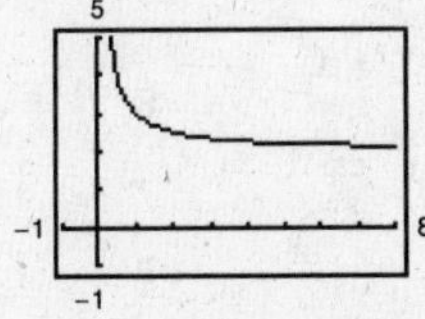

(b) $\frac{dy}{dx} = -\frac{1}{x^2}, x > 0, (1, 3)$

$$y = \int -\frac{1}{x^2} \, dx = \int -x^{-2} \, dx = \frac{-x^{-1}}{-1} + C = \frac{1}{x} + C$$

$$3 = \frac{1}{1} + C \Rightarrow C = 2$$

$$y = \frac{1}{x} + 2$$

**61.** (a)

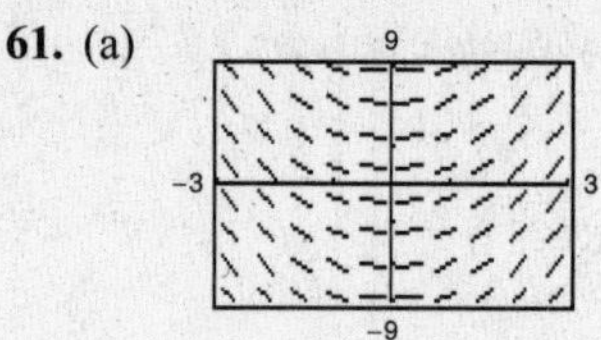


(b) $\dfrac{dy}{dx} = 2x, (-2, -2)$

$y = \int 2x\, dx = x^2 + C$

$-2 = (-2)^2 + C = 4 + C \Rightarrow C = -6$

$y = x^2 - 6$

(c)

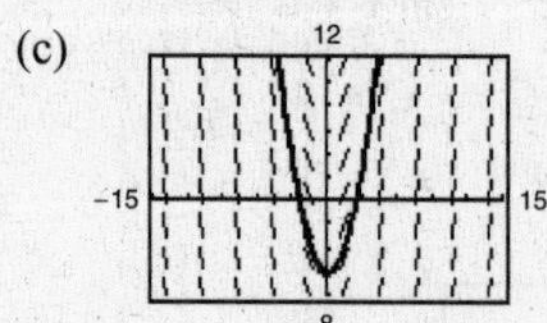


**62.** (a)

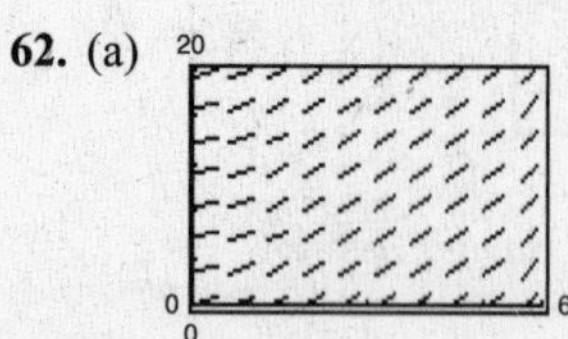


(b) $\dfrac{dy}{dx} = 2\sqrt{x}, (4, 12)$

$y = \int 2x^{1/2}\, dx = \dfrac{4}{3}x^{3/2} + C$

$12 = \dfrac{4}{3}(4)^{3/2} + C = \dfrac{4}{3}(8) + C = \dfrac{32}{3} + C \Rightarrow C = \dfrac{4}{3}$

$y = \dfrac{4}{3}x^{3/2} + \dfrac{4}{3}$

(c)

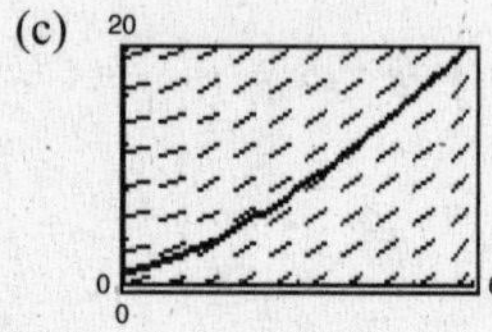


**63.** $f'(x) = 6x, f(0) = 8$

$f(x) = \int 6x\, dx = 3x^2 + C$

$f(0) = 8 = 3(0)^2 + C \Rightarrow C = 8$

$f(x) = 3x^2 + 8$

**64** $g'(x) = 6x^2, g(0) = -1$

$g(x) = \int 6x^2\, dx = 2x^3 + C$

$g(0) = -1 = 2(0)^3 + C \Rightarrow C = -1$

$g(x) = 2x^3 - 1$

**65.** $h'(t) = 8t^3 + 5, h(1) = -4$

$h(t) = \int (8t^3 + 5)\, dt = 2t^4 + 5t + C$

$h(1) = -4 = 2 + 5 + C \Rightarrow C = -11$

$h(t) = 2t^4 + 5t - 11$

**66.** $f'(s) = 10s - 12s^3, f(3) = 2$

$f(s) = \int (10s - 12s^3)\, ds = 5s^2 - 3s^4 + C$

$f(3) = 2 = 5(3)^2 - 3(3)^4 + C = 45 - 243 + C \Rightarrow C = 200$

$f(s) = 5s^2 - 3s^4 + 200$

**67.** $f''(x) = 2$

$f'(2) = 5$

$f(2) = 10$

$f'(x) = \int 2\, dx = 2x + C_1$

$f'(2) = 4 + C_1 = 5 \Rightarrow C_1 = 1$

$f'(x) = 2x + 1$

$f(x) = \int (2x + 1)\, dx = x^2 + x + C_2$

$f(2) = 6 + C_2 = 10 \Rightarrow C_2 = 4$

$f(x) = x^2 + x + 4$

**68.** $f''(x) = x^2$

$f'(0) = 8$

$f(0) = 4$

$f'(x) = \int x^2\, dx = \dfrac{1}{3}x^3 + C_1$

$f'(0) = 0 + C_1 = 8 \Rightarrow C_1 = 8$

$f'(x) = \dfrac{1}{3}x^3 + 8$

$f(x) = \int \left(\dfrac{1}{3}x^3 + 8\right) dx = \dfrac{1}{12}x^4 + 8x + C_2$

$f(0) = 0 + 0 + C_2 = 4 \Rightarrow C_2 = 4$

$f(x) = \dfrac{1}{12}x^4 + 8x + 4$

**69.** $f''(x) = x^{-3/2}$

$f'(4) = 2$

$f(0) = 0$

$f'(x) = \int x^{-3/2}\, dx = -2x^{-1/2} + C_1 = -\dfrac{2}{\sqrt{x}} + C_1$

$f'(4) = -\dfrac{2}{2} + C_1 = 2 \Rightarrow C_1 = 3$

$f'(x) = -\dfrac{2}{\sqrt{x}} + 3$

$f(x) = \int (-2x^{-1/2} + 3)\, dx = -4x^{1/2} + 3x + C_2$

$f(0) = 0 + 0 + C_2 = 0 \Rightarrow C_2 = 0$

$f(x) = -4x^{1/2} + 3x = -4\sqrt{x} + 3x$

**70.** $f''(x) = \sin x$

$f'(0) = 1$

$f(0) = 6$

$f'(x) = \int \sin x \, dx = -\cos x + C_1$

$f'(0) = -1 + C_1 = 1 \Rightarrow C_1 = 2$

$f'(x) = -\cos x + 2$

$f(x) = \int(-\cos x + 2) \, dx = -\sin x + 2x + C_2$

$f(0) = 0 + 0 + C_2 = 6 \Rightarrow C_2 = 6$

$f(x) = -\sin x + 2x + 6$

**71.** $f''(x) = e^x$

$f'(0) = 2$

$f(0) = 5$

$f'(x) = \int e^x \, dx = e^x + C_1$

$f'(0) = 2 = e^0 + C_1 \Rightarrow C_1 = 1$

$f'(x) = e^x + 1$

$f(x) = \int(e^x + 1) \, dx = e^x + x + C_2$

$f(0) = 5 = e^0 + 0 + C_2 \Rightarrow C_2 = 4$

$f(x) = e^x + x + 4$

**72.** $f''(x) = \dfrac{2}{x^2}$

$f'(1) = 4$

$f(1) = 3$

$f'(x) = \int \dfrac{2}{x^2} \, dx = \int 2x^{-2} \, dx = -\dfrac{2}{x} + C_1$

$f'(1) = 4 = -2 + C_1 \Rightarrow C_1 = 6$

$f'(x) = -\dfrac{2}{x} + 6$

$f(x) = \int\left(-\dfrac{2}{x} + 6\right) dx = -2 \ln|x| + 6x + C_2$

$f(1) = 3 = 6 + C_2 \Rightarrow C_2 = -3$

$f(x) = -2 \ln|x| + 6x - 3$

**73.** They are the same. In both cases you are finding a function $F(x)$ such that $F'(x) = f(x)$.

**74.** $f(x) = \tan^2 x \Rightarrow f'(x) = 2 \tan x \cdot \sec^2 x$

$g(x) = \sec^2 x \Rightarrow g'(x) = 2 \sec x \cdot \sec x \tan x = f'(x)$

The derivatives are the same, so $f$ and $g$ differ by a constant. In fact, $\tan^2 x + 1 = \sec^2 x$.

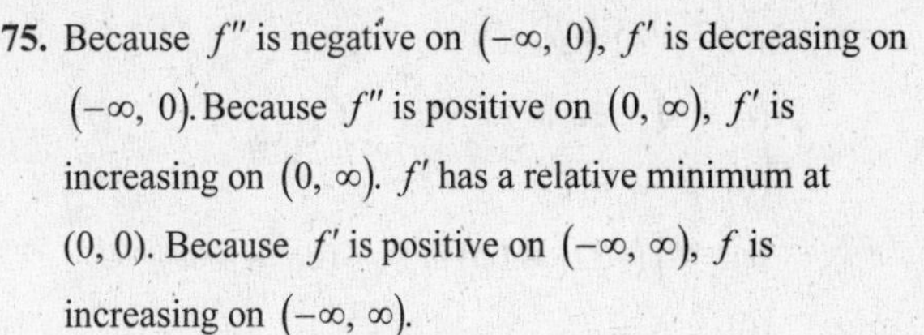

**75.** Because $f''$ is negative on $(-\infty, 0)$, $f'$ is decreasing on $(-\infty, 0)$. Because $f''$ is positive on $(0, \infty)$, $f'$ is increasing on $(0, \infty)$. $f'$ has a relative minimum at $(0, 0)$. Because $f'$ is positive on $(-\infty, \infty)$, $f$ is increasing on $(-\infty, \infty)$.

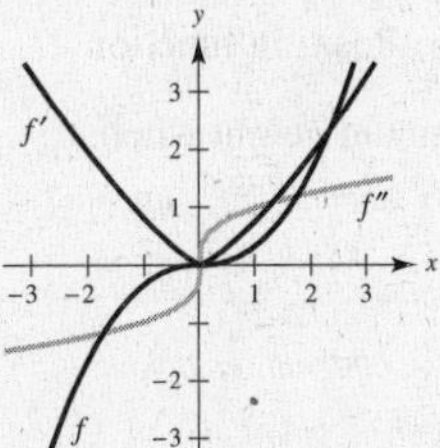


**76.** $f(0) = -4$. Graph of $f'$ is given.

(a) $f'(4) \approx -1.0$

(b) No. The slopes of the tangent lines are greater than 2 on $[0, 2]$. Therefore, $f$ must increase more than 4 units on $[0, 4]$.

(c) No, $f(5) < f(4)$ because $f$ is decreasing on $[4, 5]$.

(d) $f$ is a maximum at $x = 3.5$ because $f'(3.5) \approx 0$ and the First Derivative Test.

(e) $f$ is concave upward when $f'$ is increasing on $(-\infty, 1)$ and $(5, \infty)$. $f$ is concave downward on $(1, 5)$. Points of inflection at $x = 1, 5$.

(f) $f''$ is a minimum at $x = 3$.

(g)

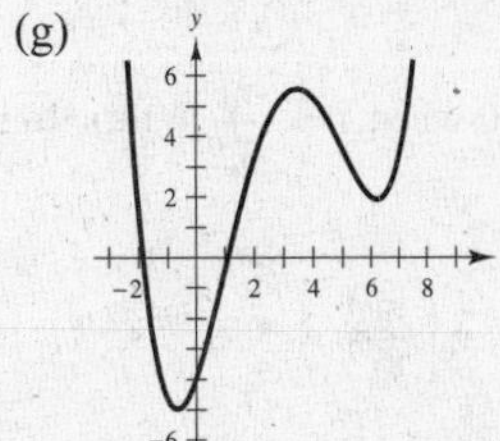

**77.** $a(t) = -32 \text{ ft/sec}^2$

$v(t) = \int -32\, dt = -32t + C_1$

$v(0) = 60 = C_1$

$s(t) = \int (-32t + 60)\, dt = -16t^2 + 60t + C_2$

$s(0) = 6 = C_2$

$s(t) = -16t^2 + 60t + 6$, Position function

The ball reaches its maximum height when

$v(t) = -32t + 60 = 0$

$32t = 60$

$t = \frac{15}{8}$ seconds.

$s\left(\frac{15}{8}\right) = -16\left(\frac{15}{8}\right)^2 + 60\left(\frac{15}{8}\right) + 6 = 62.25$ feet

**78.** $f''(t) = a(t) = -32 \text{ ft/sec}^2$

$f'(0) = v_0$

$f(0) = s_0$

$f'(t) = v(t) = \int -32\, dt = -32t + C_1$

$f'(0) = 0 + C_1 = v_0 \Rightarrow C_1 = v_0$

$f'(t) = -32t + v_0$

$f(t) = s(t) = \int (-32t + v_0)\, dt = -16t^2 + v_0 t + C_2$

$f(0) = 0 + 0 + C_2 = s_0 \Rightarrow C_2 = s_0$

$f(t) = -16t^2 + v_0 t + s_0$

**79.** From Exercise 78:

$s(t) = -16t^2 + v_0 t$

$s'(t) = -32t + v_0 = 0$ when $t = \frac{v_0}{32}$ = time to reach maximum height.

$$s\left(\frac{v_0}{32}\right) = -16\left(\frac{v_0}{32}\right)^2 + v_0\left(\frac{v_0}{32}\right) = 550$$

$$-\frac{v_0^2}{64} + \frac{v_0^2}{32} = 550$$

$$v_0^2 = 35{,}200$$

$$v_0 \approx 187.617 \text{ ft/sec}$$

**80.** $v_0 = 8$ ft/sec

$s_0 = 64$ ft

(a) $s(t) = -16t^2 + 8t + 64 = 0$

$-8(2t^2 - t - 8) = 0$

$$t = \frac{1 \pm \sqrt{65}}{4}$$

Choosing the positive value,

$$t = \frac{1 + \sqrt{65}}{4} \approx 2.266 \text{ seconds.}$$

(b) $v(t) = s'(t) = -32t + 8$

$$v\left(\frac{1 + \sqrt{65}}{4}\right) = -32\left(\frac{1 + \sqrt{65}}{4}\right) + 8$$

$$= -8\sqrt{65} \approx -64.498 \text{ ft/sec}$$

**81.** $a(t) = -9.8$

$v(t) = \int -9.8\, dt = -9.8t + C_1$

$v(0) = v_0 = C_1 \Rightarrow v(t) = -9.8t + v_0$

$f(t) = \int (-9.8t + v_0)\, dt = -4.9t^2 + v_0 t + C_2$

$f(0) = s_0 = C_2 \Rightarrow f(t) = -4.9t^2 + v_0 t + s_0$

**82.** From Exercise 81, $f(t) = -4.9t^2 + 1800$. (Using the canyon floor as position 0.)

$f(t) = 0 = -4.9t^2 + 1800$

$4.9t^2 = 1800$

$$t^2 = \frac{1800}{4.9} \Rightarrow t \approx 9.2 \text{ sec}$$

**83.** From Exercise 81, $f(t) = -4.9t^2 + 10t + 2$.

$v(t) = -9.8t + 10 = 0$ (Maximum height when $v = 0$.)

$9.8t = 10$

$$t = \frac{10}{9.8}$$

$$f\left(\frac{10}{9.8}\right) \approx 7.1 \text{ m}$$

**84.** From Exercise 81, $f(t) = -4.9t^2 + v_0 t + 2$. If

$f(t) = 200 = -4.9t^2 + v_0 t + 2$,

then $v(t) = -9.8t + v_0 = 0$

for this $t$ value. So, $t = v_0/9.8$ and you solve

$$-4.9\left(\frac{v_0}{9.8}\right)^2 + v_0\left(\frac{v_0}{9.8}\right) + 2 = 200$$

$$\frac{-4.9v_0^2}{(9.8)^2} + \frac{v_0^2}{9.8} = 198$$

$$-4.9v_0^2 + 9.8v_0^2 = (9.8)^2 198$$

$$4.9v_0^2 = (9.8)^2 198$$

$$v_0^2 = 3880.8$$

$$v_0 \approx 62.3 \text{ m/sec.}$$

**85.** $a = -1.6$

$v(t) = \int -1.6\,dt = -1.6t + v_0 = -1.6t$, because the stone was dropped, $v_0 = 0$.

$s(t) = \int(-1.6t)\,dt = -0.8t^2 + s_0$

$s(20) = 0 \Rightarrow -0.8(20)^2 + s_0 = 0$

$s_0 = 320$

So, the height of the cliff is 320 meters.

$v(t) = -1.6t$

$v(20) = -32$ m/sec

**86.** $\int v\,dv = -GM\int\frac{1}{y^2}\,dy$

$\frac{1}{2}v^2 = \frac{GM}{y} + C$

When $y = R$, $v = v_0$.

$\frac{1}{2}v_0^2 = \frac{GM}{R} + C$

$C = \frac{1}{2}v_0^2 - \frac{GM}{R}$

$\frac{1}{2}v^2 = \frac{GM}{y} + \frac{1}{2}v_0^2 - \frac{GM}{R}$

$v^2 = \frac{2GM}{y} + v_0^2 - \frac{2GM}{R}$

$v^2 = v_0^2 + 2GM\left(\frac{1}{y} - \frac{1}{R}\right)$

**87.** $x(t) = t^3 - 6t^2 + 9t - 2,\quad 0 \le t \le 5$

(a) $v(t) = x'(t) = 3t^2 - 12t + 9$

$= 3(t^2 - 4t + 3) = 3(t - 1)(t - 3)$

$a(t) = v'(t) = 6t - 12 = 6(t - 2)$

(b) $v(t) > 0$ when $0 < t < 1$ or $3 < t < 5$.

(c) $a(t) = 6(t - 2) = 0$ when $t = 2$.

$v(2) = 3(1)(-1) = -3$

**88.** $x(t) = (t - 1)(t - 3)^2,\quad 0 \le t \le 5$

$= t^3 - 7t^2 + 15t - 9$

(a) $v(t) = x'(t) = 3t^2 - 14t + 15 = (3t - 5)(t - 3)$

$a(t) = v'(t) = 6t - 14$

(b) $v(t) > 0$ when $0 < t < \frac{5}{3}$ and $3 < t < 5$.

(c) $a(t) = 6t - 14 = 0$ when $t = \frac{7}{3}$.

$v\left(\frac{7}{3}\right) = \left(3\left(\frac{7}{3}\right) - 5\right)\left(\frac{7}{3} - 3\right) = 2\left(-\frac{2}{3}\right) = -\frac{4}{3}$

**89.** $v(t) = \frac{1}{\sqrt{t}} = t^{-1/2},\quad t > 0$

$x(t) = \int v(t)dt = 2t^{1/2} + C$

$x(1) = 4 = 2(1) + C \Rightarrow C = 2$

Position function: $x(t) = 2t^{1/2} + 2 = 2\sqrt{t} + 2$

Acceleration function: $a(t) = v'(t) = -\frac{1}{2}t^{-3/2} = -\frac{1}{2t^{3/2}}$

**90.** (a) $a(t) = \cos t$

$v(t) = \int a(t)\,dt$

$= \int \cos t\,dt$

$= \sin t + C_1 = \sin t$ (because $v_0 = 0$)

$f(t) = \int v(t)\,dt = \int \sin t\,dt = -\cos t + C_2$

$f(0) = 3 = -\cos(0) + C_2 = -1 + C_2 \Rightarrow C_2 = 4$

$f(t) = -\cos t + 4$

(b) $v(t) = 0 = \sin t$ for $t = k\pi$, $k = 0, 1, 2, \ldots$

**91.** (a) $v(0) = 25$ km/h $= 25 \cdot \frac{1000}{3600} = \frac{250}{36}$ m/sec

$v(13) = 80$ km/h $= 80 \cdot \frac{1000}{3600} = \frac{800}{36}$ m/sec

$a(t) = a$ (constant acceleration)

$v(t) = at + C$

$v(0) = \frac{250}{36} \Rightarrow v(t) = at + \frac{250}{36}$

$v(13) = \frac{800}{36} = 13a + \frac{250}{36}$

$\frac{550}{36} = 13a$

$a = \frac{550}{468} = \frac{275}{234} \approx 1.175$ m/sec$^2$

(b) $s(t) = a\frac{t^2}{2} + \frac{250}{36}t \quad (s(0) = 0)$

$s(13) = \frac{275}{234}\frac{(13)^2}{2} + \frac{250}{36}(13) \approx 189.58$ m

**92.** $v(0) = 45 \text{ mi/h} = 66 \text{ ft/sec}$

$30 \text{ mi/h} = 44 \text{ ft/sec}$

$15 \text{ mi/h} = 22 \text{ ft/sec}$

$a(t) = -a$

$v(t) = -at + 66$

$s(t) = -\frac{a}{2}t^2 + 66t$ (Let $s(0) = 0$.)

$v(t) = 0$ after car moves 132 ft.

$-at + 66 = 0$ when $t = \frac{66}{a}$.

$s\left(\frac{66}{a}\right) = -\frac{a}{2}\left(\frac{66}{a}\right)^2 + 66\left(\frac{66}{a}\right)$

$= 132$ when $a = \frac{33}{2} = 16.5$.

$a(t) = -16.5$

$v(t) = -16.5t + 66$

$s(t) = -8.25t^2 + 66t$

(a) $-16.5t + 66 = 44$

$t = \frac{22}{16.5} \approx 1.333$

$s\left(\frac{22}{16.5}\right) \approx 73.33 \text{ ft}$

(b) $-16.5t + 66 = 22$

$t = \frac{44}{16.5} \approx 2.667$

$s\left(\frac{44}{16.5}\right) \approx 117.33 \text{ ft}$

(c)

45 mi/h = 66 ft/sec
30 mi/h = 44 ft/sec
15 mi/h = 22 ft/sec
0 mi/h
0
132
73.33 feet
117.33 feet

It takes 1.333 seconds to reduce the speed from 45 mi/h to 30 mi/h, 1.333 seconds to reduce the speed from 30 mi/h to 15 mi/h, and 1.333 seconds to reduce the speed from 15 mi/h to 0 mi/h. Each time, less distance is needed to reach the next speed reduction.

**93.** Truck: $v(t) = 30$

$s(t) = 30t$ (Let $s(0) = 0$.)

Automobile: $a(t) = 6$

$v(t) = 6t$ (Let $v(0) = 0$.)

$s(t) = 3t^2$ (Let $s(0) = 0$.)

At the point where the automobile overtakes the truck:

$30t = 3t^2$

$0 = 3t^2 - 30t$

$0 = 3t(t - 10)$ when $t = 10$ sec.

(a) $s(10) = 3(10)^2 = 300 \text{ ft}$

(b) $v(10) = 6(10) = 60 \text{ ft/sec} \approx 41 \text{ mi/h}$

**94.** $\frac{(1 \text{ mi/hr})(5280 \text{ ft/mi})}{(3600 \text{ sec/hr})} = \frac{22}{15} \text{ ft/sec}$

(a)

| $t$ | 0 | 5 | 10 | 15 | 20 | 25 | 30 |
|---|---|---|---|---|---|---|---|
| $v_1$(ft/sec) | 0 | 3.67 | 10.27 | 23.47 | 42.53 | 66 | 95.33 |
| $v_2$(ft/sec) | 0 | 30.8 | 55.73 | 74.8 | 88 | 93.87 | 95.33 |

(b) $v_1(t) = 0.1068t^2 - 0.0416t + 0.3679$

$v_2(t) = -0.1208t^2 + 6.7991t - 0.0707$

(c) $s_1(t) = \int v_1(t)\,dt = \frac{0.1068}{3}t^3 - \frac{0.0416}{2}t^2 + 0.3679t$

$s_2(t) = \int v_2(t)\,dt = -\frac{0.1208t^3}{3} + \frac{6.7991t^2}{2} - 0.0707t$

[In both cases, the constant of integration is 0 because $s_1(0) = s_2(0) = 0$.]

$s_1(30) \approx 953.5$ feet

$s_2(30) \approx 1970.3$ feet

The second car was going faster than the first until the end.

**95.** True

**96.** True

**97.** True

**98.** True

**99.** False. For example, $\int x \cdot x\,dx \neq \int x\,dx \cdot \int x\,dx$ because $\frac{x^3}{3} + C \neq \left(\frac{x^2}{2} + C_1\right)\left(\frac{x^2}{2} + C_2\right)$.

**100.** False. $f$ has an infinite number of antiderivatives, each differing by a constant.

**101.** $f''(x) = 2x$

$f'(x) = x^2 + C$

$f'(2) = 0 \Rightarrow 4 + C = 0 \Rightarrow C = -4$

$f(x) = \frac{x^3}{3} - 4x + C_1$

$f(2) = 0 \Rightarrow \frac{8}{3} - 8 + C_1 = 0 \Rightarrow C_1 = \frac{16}{3}$

$f(x) = \frac{x^3}{3} - 4x + \frac{16}{3}$

**102.** $f'(x) = \begin{cases} -1, & 0 \le x < 2 \\ 2, & 2 < x < 3 \\ 0, & 3 < x \le 4 \end{cases}$

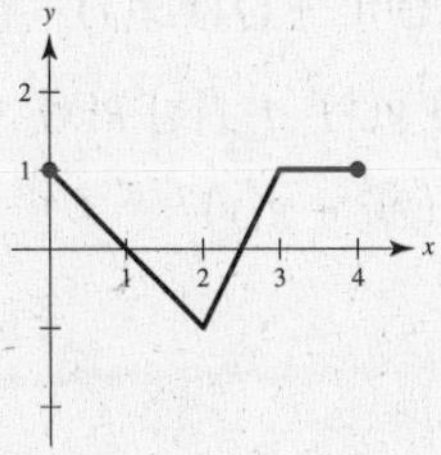

$f(x) = \begin{cases} -x + C_1, & 0 \le x < 2 \\ 2x + C_2, & 2 < x < 3 \\ C_3, & 3 < x \le 4 \end{cases}$

$f(0) = 1 \Rightarrow C_1 = 1$

$f$ continuous at $x = 2 \Rightarrow -2 + 1 = 4 + C_2 \Rightarrow C_2 = -5$

$f$ continuous at $x = 3 \Rightarrow 6 - 5 = C_3 = 1$

$f(x) = \begin{cases} -x + 1, & 0 \le x < 2 \\ 2x - 5, & 2 \le x < 3 \\ 1, & 3 \le x \le 4 \end{cases}$

**103.** $f'(x) = \begin{cases} 1, & 0 \le x < 2 \\ 3x, & 2 \le x \le 5 \end{cases}$

$f(x) = \begin{cases} x + C_1, & 0 \le x < 2 \\ \frac{3x^2}{2} + C_2, & 2 \le x \le 5 \end{cases}$

$f(1) = 3 \Rightarrow 1 + C_1 = 3 \Rightarrow C_1 = 2$

$f$ is continuous: Values must agree at $x = 2$:

$4 = 6 + C_2 \Rightarrow C_2 = -2$

$f(x) = \begin{cases} x + 2, & 0 \le x < 2 \\ \frac{3x^2}{2} - 2, & 2 \le x \le 5 \end{cases}$

The left and right hand derivatives at $x = 2$ do not agree. So $f$ is not differentiable at $x = 2$.

**104.** $\frac{d}{dx}\left[[s(x)]^2 + [c(x)]^2\right] = 2s(x)s'(x) + 2c(x)c'(x) = 2s(x)c(x) - 2c(x)s(x) = 0$

So, $[s(x)]^2 + [c(x)]^2 = k$ for some constant $k$.

Because, $s(0) = 0$ and $c(0) = 1$, $k = 1$.

Therefore, $[s(x)]^2 + [c(x)]^2 = 1$.

[Note that $s(x) = \sin x$ and $c(x) = \cos x$ satisfy these properties.]

**105.** $\frac{d}{dx}(\ln|Cx|) = \frac{d}{dx}(\ln|C| + \ln|x|) = 0 + \frac{1}{x} = \frac{1}{x}$

**106.** $\frac{d}{dx}(\ln|x| + C) = \frac{1}{x} + 0 = \frac{1}{x}$

**107.** $f(x + y) = f(x)f(y) - g(x)g(y)$

$g(x + y) = f(x)g(y) + g(x)f(y)$

$f'(0) = 0$

[Note: $f(x) = \cos x$ and $g(x) = \sin x$ satisfy these conditions]

$f'(x + y) = f(x)f'(y) - g(x)g'(y)$ (Differentiate with respect to $y$)

$g'(x + y) = f(x)g'(y) + g(x)f'(y)$ (Differentiate with respect to $y$)

Letting $y = 0$, $f'(x) = f(x)f'(0) - g(x)g'(0) = -g(x)g'(0)$

$g'(x) = f(x)g'(0) + g(x)f'(0) = f(x)g'(0)$

So, $2f(x)f'(x) = -2f(x)g(x)g'(0)$

$2g(x)g'(x) = 2g(x)f(x)g'(0)$.

Adding, $2f(x)f'(x) + 2g(x)g'(x) = 0$.

Integrating, $f(x)^2 + g(x)^2 = C$.

Clearly $C \neq 0$, for if $C = 0$, then $f(x)^2 = -g(x)^2 \Rightarrow f(x) = g(x) = 0$, which contradicts that $f$, $g$ are nonconstant.

$$\begin{aligned}\text{Now, } C = f(x + y)^2 + g(x + y)^2 &= \left(f(x)f(y) - g(x)g(y)\right)^2 + \left(f(x)g(y) + g(x)f(y)\right)^2\\ &= f(x)^2 f(y)^2 + g(x)^2 g(y)^2 + f(x)^2 g(y)^2 + g(x)^2 f(y)^2\\ &= \left[f(x)^2 + g(x)^2\right]\left[f(y)^2 + g(y)^2\right] = C^2\end{aligned}$$

So, $C = 1$ and you have $f(x)^2 + g(x)^2 = 1$.

## Section 5.2 Area

**1.** $\displaystyle\sum_{i=1}^{6}(3i + 2) = 3\sum_{i=1}^{6} i + \sum_{i=1}^{6} 2 = 3(1 + 2 + 3 + 4 + 5 + 6) + 12 = 75$

**2.** $\displaystyle\sum_{k=5}^{8} k(k - 4) = 5(1) + 6(2) + 7(3) + 8(4) = 70$

**3.** $\displaystyle\sum_{k=0}^{4}\frac{1}{k^2 + 1} = 1 + \frac{1}{2} + \frac{1}{5} + \frac{1}{10} + \frac{1}{17} = \frac{158}{85}$

**4.** $\displaystyle\sum_{j=4}^{7}\frac{2}{j} = \frac{2}{4} + \frac{2}{5} + \frac{2}{6} = \frac{319}{210}$

**5.** $\displaystyle\sum_{k=1}^{4} c = c + c + c + c = 4c$

**6.** $\displaystyle\sum_{i=1}^{4}\left[(i - 1)^2 + (i + 1)^3\right] = (0 + 8) + (1 + 27) + (4 + 64) + (9 + 125) = 238$

**7.** $\displaystyle\sum_{i=1}^{11}\frac{1}{5i}$

**8.** $\displaystyle\sum_{i=1}^{14}\frac{9}{1 + i}$

**9.** $\displaystyle\sum_{j=1}^{6}\left[7\left(\frac{j}{6}\right) + 5\right]$

**10.** $\displaystyle\sum_{j=1}^{4}\left[1 - \left(\frac{j}{4}\right)^2\right]$

11. $\dfrac{2}{n}\sum_{i=1}^{n}\left[\left(\dfrac{2i}{n}\right)^3 - \left(\dfrac{2i}{n}\right)\right]$

12. $\dfrac{2}{n}\sum_{i=1}^{n}\left[1 - \left(\dfrac{2i}{n} - 1\right)^2\right]$

13. $\dfrac{3}{n}\sum_{i=1}^{n}\left[2\left(1 + \dfrac{3i}{n}\right)^2\right]$

14. $\dfrac{1}{n}\sum_{i=0}^{n-1}\sqrt{1 - \left(\dfrac{i}{n}\right)^2}$

15. $\sum_{i=1}^{12} 7 = 7(12) = 84$

16. $\sum_{i=1}^{30}(-18) = (-18)(30) = -540$

17. $\sum_{i=1}^{24} 4i = 4\sum_{i=1}^{24} i = 4\left[\dfrac{24(25)}{2}\right] = 1200$

18. $\sum_{i=1}^{16}(5i - 4) = 5\sum_{i=1}^{16} i - 4(16) = 5\left[\dfrac{16(17)}{2}\right] - 64 = 616$

19. $\sum_{i=1}^{20}(i - 1)^2 = \sum_{i=1}^{19} i^2 = \left[\dfrac{19(20)(39)}{6}\right] = 2470$

20. $\sum_{i=1}^{10}(i^2 - 1) = \sum_{i=1}^{10} i^2 - \sum_{i=1}^{10} 1 = \left[\dfrac{10(11)(21)}{6}\right] - 10 = 375$

21. $\sum_{i=1}^{15} i(i - 1)^2 = \sum_{i=1}^{15} i^3 - 2\sum_{i=1}^{15} i^2 + \sum_{i=1}^{15} i$

$$= \frac{15^2(16)^2}{4} - 2\frac{15(16)(31)}{6} + \frac{15(16)}{2}$$

$$= 14{,}400 - 2480 + 120 = 12{,}040$$

22. $\sum_{i=1}^{10} i(i^2 + 1) = \sum_{i=1}^{10} i^3 + \sum_{i=1}^{10} i$

$$= \frac{10^2(11)^2}{4} + \left[\frac{10(11)}{2}\right] = 3080$$

23. $\sum_{i=1}^{20}(i^2 + 3) = \dfrac{20(20 + 1)(2(20) + 1)}{6} + 3(20)$

$$= \frac{(20)(21)(41)}{6} + 60 = 2930$$

24. $\sum_{i=1}^{15}(i^3 - 2i) = \dfrac{(15)^2(15 + 1)^2}{4} - 2\dfrac{15(15 + 1)}{2}$

$$= \frac{(15)^2(16)^2}{4} - 15(16) = 14{,}160$$

25. (a)

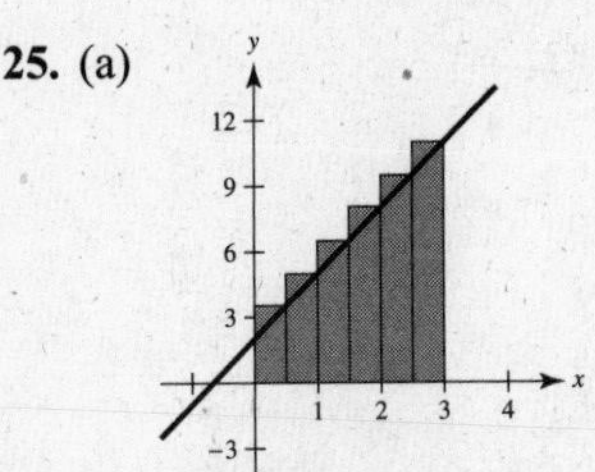


The width $\Delta x$ of each rectangle is $\frac{1}{2}$. The heights are given by the right endpoints.

$$\text{Area} \approx \tfrac{1}{2}\left[\left(3\left(\tfrac{1}{2}\right) + 2\right) + \left(3(1) + 2\right) + \left(3\left(\tfrac{3}{2}\right) + 2\right) + \left(3(2) + 2\right) + \left(3\left(\tfrac{5}{2}\right) + 2\right) + \left(3(3) + 2\right)\right] = \tfrac{87}{4} = 21.75$$

(b)

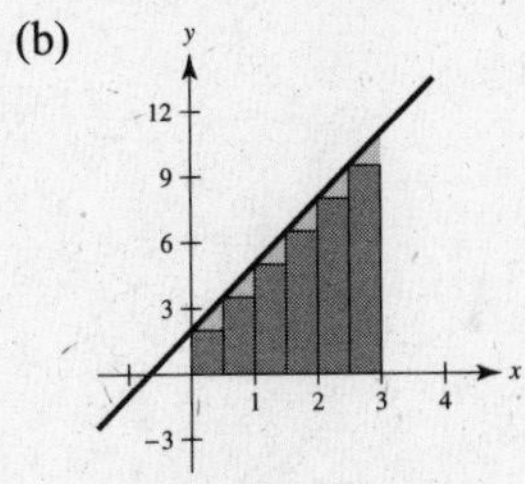


Using left endpoints,

$$\text{Area} \approx \tfrac{1}{2}\left[\left(3(0) + 2\right) + \left(3\left(\tfrac{1}{2}\right) + 2\right) + \left(3(1) + 2\right) + \left(3\left(\tfrac{3}{2}\right) + 2\right) + \left(3(2) + 2\right) + \left(3\left(\tfrac{5}{2}\right) + 2\right)\right] = \tfrac{69}{4} = 17.25$$

**26.** (a)

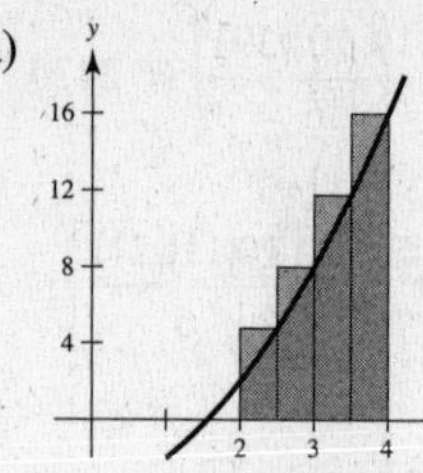

The width $\Delta x$ of each rectangle is $\frac{1}{2}$. The heights are given by the right endpoints

$$\text{Area} \approx \frac{1}{2}\left[\left(\left(\frac{5}{2}\right)^2 + \left(\frac{5}{2}\right) - 4\right) + \left(3^2 + 3 - 4\right) + \left(\left(\frac{7}{2}\right)^2 + \frac{7}{2} - 4\right) + \left(4^2 + 4 - 4\right)\right] = \frac{81}{4} = 20.25$$

(b)

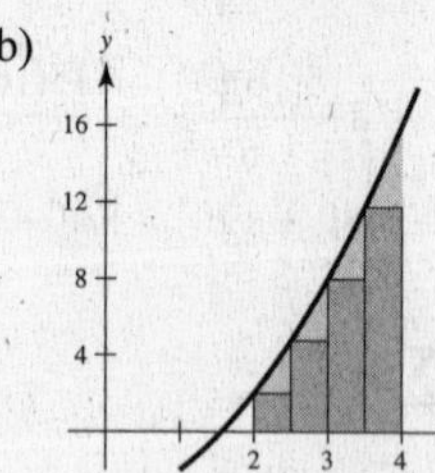

Using left endpoints,

$$\text{Area} \approx \frac{1}{2}\left[\left(2^2 + 2 - 4\right) + \left(\left(\frac{5}{2}\right)^2 + \frac{5}{2} - 4\right) + \left(3^2 + 3 - 4\right) + \left(\left(\frac{7}{2}\right)^2 + \frac{7}{2} - 4\right)\right] = \frac{53}{4} \approx 13.25$$

**27.**

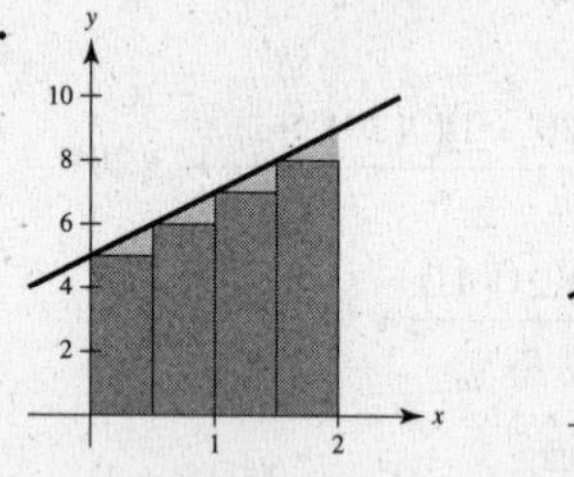

$$\Delta x = \frac{2-0}{4} = \frac{1}{2}$$

Left endpoints: Area $\approx \frac{1}{2}[5 + 6 + 7 + 8] = \frac{26}{2} = 13$

Right endpoints: Area $\approx \frac{1}{2}[6 + 7 + 8 + 9] = \frac{30}{2} = 15$

$13 < \text{Area} < 15$

**28.**

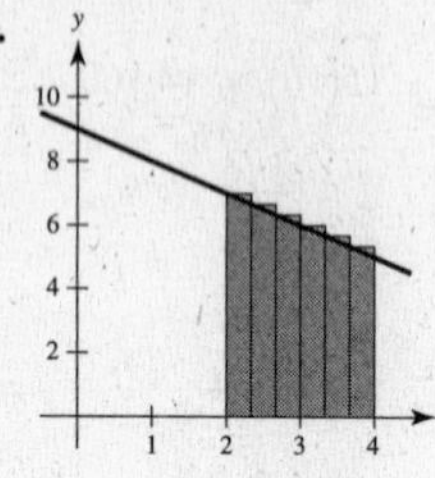

$$\Delta x = \frac{4-2}{6} = \frac{1}{3}$$

Left endpoints: Area $\approx \frac{1}{3}\left[7 + \frac{20}{3} + \frac{19}{3} + 6 + \frac{17}{3} + \frac{16}{3}\right] = \frac{37}{3} \approx 12.333$

Right endpoints: Area $\approx \frac{1}{3}\left[\frac{20}{3} + \frac{19}{3} + 6 + \frac{17}{3} + \frac{16}{3} + \frac{15}{3}\right] = \frac{35}{3} \approx 11.667$

$\frac{35}{3} < \text{Area} < \frac{37}{3}$

**29.**

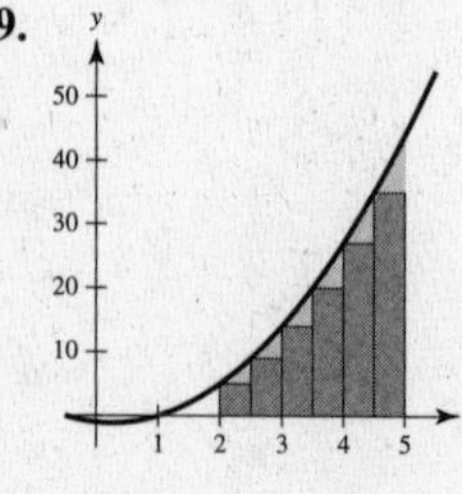

$$\Delta x = \frac{5-2}{6} = \frac{1}{2}$$

Left endpoints: Area $\approx \frac{1}{2}[5 + 9 + 14 + 20 + 27 + 35] = 55$

Right endpoints:

Area $\approx \frac{1}{2}[9 + 14 + 20 + 27 + 35 + 44] = \frac{149}{2} = 74.5$

$55 < \text{Area} < 74.5$

**30.**

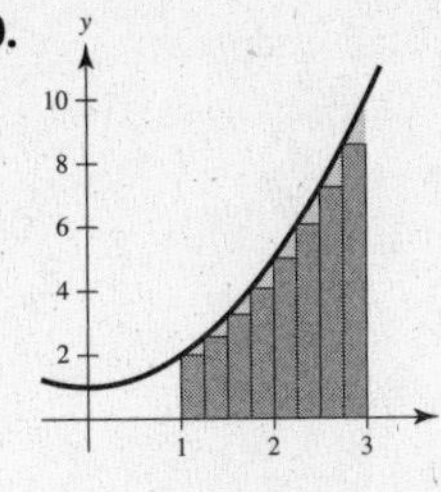

$$\Delta x = \frac{3-1}{8} = \frac{1}{4}$$

Left endpoints: Area $\approx \frac{1}{4}\left[2 + \frac{41}{16} + \frac{13}{4} + \frac{65}{16} + 5 + \frac{97}{16} + \frac{29}{4} + \frac{137}{16}\right] = \frac{155}{16} = 9.6875$

Right endpoint: Area $\approx \frac{1}{4}\left[\frac{41}{16} + \frac{13}{4} + \frac{65}{16} + 5 + \frac{97}{16} + \frac{29}{4} + \frac{137}{16} + 10\right] = 11.6875$

$9.6875 < \text{Area} < 11.6875$

**31.**

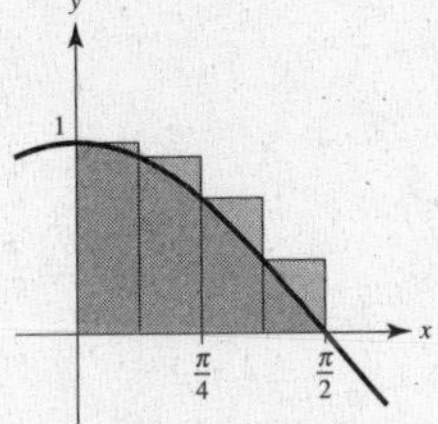

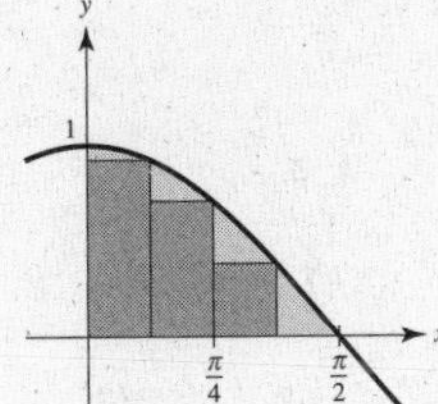

$$\Delta x = \frac{\frac{\pi}{2} - 0}{4} = \frac{\pi}{8}$$

Left endpoints: Area $\approx \frac{\pi}{8}\left[\cos(0) + \cos\left(\frac{\pi}{8}\right) + \cos\left(\frac{\pi}{4}\right) + \cos\left(\frac{3\pi}{8}\right)\right] \approx 1.1835$

Right endpoints: Area $\approx \frac{\pi}{8}\left[\cos\left(\frac{\pi}{8}\right) + \cos\left(\frac{\pi}{4}\right) + \cos\left(\frac{3\pi}{8}\right) + \cos\left(\frac{\pi}{2}\right)\right] \approx 0.7908$

$0.7908 < \text{Area} < 1.1835$

**32.**

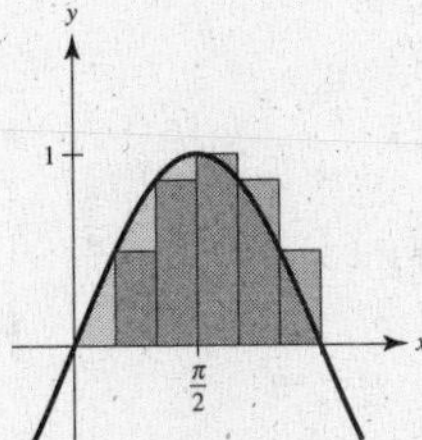

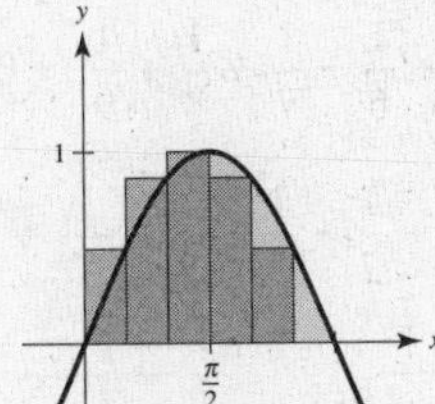

$$\Delta x = \frac{\pi - 0}{6} = \frac{\pi}{6}$$

Left endpoints: Area $\approx \frac{\pi}{6}\left[\sin 0 + \sin\frac{\pi}{6} + \sin\frac{\pi}{3} + \sin\frac{\pi}{2} + \sin\frac{2\pi}{3} + \sin\frac{5\pi}{6}\right] \approx 1.9541$

Right endpoints: Area $\approx \frac{\pi}{6}\left[\sin\frac{\pi}{6} + \sin\frac{\pi}{3} + \sin\frac{\pi}{2} + \sin\frac{2\pi}{3} + \sin\frac{5\pi}{6} + \sin\pi\right] \approx 1.9541$

By symmetry, the answers are the same. The exact area (2) is larger.

**33.** $S = \left[3 + 4 + \frac{9}{2} + 5\right](1) = \frac{33}{2} = 16.5$

$s = \left[1 + 3 + 4 + \frac{9}{2}\right](1) = \frac{25}{2} = 12.5$

**34.** $S = [5 + 5 + 4 + 2](1) = 16$

$s = [4 + 4 + 2 + 0](1) = 10$

**35.** $S = [3 + 3 + 5](1) = 11$

$s = [2 + 2 + 3](1) = 7$

**36.** $S = \left[4 + 2 + \frac{4}{3} + 1 + \frac{4}{5}\right](1) = \frac{137}{15} \approx 9.13$

$s = \left[2 + \frac{4}{3} + 1 + \frac{4}{5} + \frac{2}{3}\right](1) = \frac{29}{5} = 5.8$

**37.** $\lim_{n\to\infty}\left[\left(\frac{81}{n^4}\right)\frac{n^2(n+1)^2}{4}\right] = \frac{81}{4}\lim_{n\to\infty}\left[\frac{n^4 + 2n^3 + n^2}{n^4}\right] = \frac{81}{4}(1) = \frac{81}{4}$

**38.** $\lim_{n\to\infty}\left[\left(\frac{64}{n^3}\right)\frac{n(n+1)(2n+1)}{6}\right] = \frac{64}{6}\lim_{n\to\infty}\left[\frac{2n^3 + 3n^2 + n}{n^3}\right] = \frac{64}{6}(2) = \frac{64}{3}$

**39.** $\lim_{n\to\infty}\left[\left(\frac{18}{n^2}\right)\frac{n(n+1)}{2}\right] = \frac{18}{2}\lim_{n\to\infty}\left[\frac{n^2 + n}{n^2}\right] = \frac{18}{2}(1) = 9$

**40.** $\lim_{n\to\infty}\left[\left(\frac{1}{n^2}\right)\frac{n(n+1)}{2}\right] = \frac{1}{2}\lim_{n\to\infty}\left[\frac{n^2 + n}{n^2}\right] = \frac{1}{2}(1) = \frac{1}{2}$

**41.** $S(4) = \sqrt{\frac{1}{4}}\left(\frac{1}{4}\right) + \sqrt{\frac{1}{2}}\left(\frac{1}{4}\right) + \sqrt{\frac{3}{4}}\left(\frac{1}{4}\right) + \sqrt{1}\left(\frac{1}{4}\right) = \frac{1 + \sqrt{2} + \sqrt{3} + 2}{8} \approx 0.768$

$s(4) = 0\left(\frac{1}{4}\right) + \sqrt{\frac{1}{4}}\left(\frac{1}{4}\right) + \sqrt{\frac{1}{2}}\left(\frac{1}{4}\right) + \sqrt{\frac{3}{4}}\left(\frac{1}{4}\right) = \frac{1 + \sqrt{2} + \sqrt{3}}{8} \approx 0.518$

**42.** $S(4) = 4\left(e^{-0} + e^{-0.5} + e^{-1} + e^{-1.5}\right)\frac{1}{2} \approx 4.395$

$s(4) = 4\left(e^{-0.5} + e^{-1} + e^{-1.5} + e^{-2}\right)\frac{1}{2} \approx 2.666$

**43.** $S(5) = 1\left(\frac{1}{5}\right) + \frac{1}{6/5}\left(\frac{1}{5}\right) + \frac{1}{7/5}\left(\frac{1}{5}\right) + \frac{1}{8/5}\left(\frac{1}{5}\right) + \frac{1}{9/5}\left(\frac{1}{5}\right) = \frac{1}{5} + \frac{1}{6} + \frac{1}{7} + \frac{1}{8} + \frac{1}{9} \approx 0.746$

$s(5) = \frac{1}{6/5}\left(\frac{1}{5}\right) + \frac{1}{7/5}\left(\frac{1}{5}\right) + \frac{1}{8/5}\left(\frac{1}{5}\right) + \frac{1}{9/5}\left(\frac{1}{5}\right) + \frac{1}{2}\left(\frac{1}{5}\right) = \frac{1}{6} + \frac{1}{7} + \frac{1}{8} + \frac{1}{9} + \frac{1}{10} \approx 0.646$

**44.** $S(5) = 1\left(\frac{1}{5}\right) + \sqrt{1 - \left(\frac{1}{5}\right)^2}\left(\frac{1}{5}\right) + \sqrt{1 - \left(\frac{2}{5}\right)^2}\left(\frac{1}{5}\right) + \sqrt{1 - \left(\frac{3}{5}\right)^2}\left(\frac{1}{5}\right) + \sqrt{1 - \left(\frac{4}{5}\right)^2}\left(\frac{1}{5}\right)$

$= \frac{1}{5}\left[1 + \frac{\sqrt{24}}{5} + \frac{\sqrt{21}}{5} + \frac{\sqrt{16}}{5} + \frac{\sqrt{9}}{5}\right] \approx 0.859$

$s(5) = \sqrt{1 - \left(\frac{1}{5}\right)^2}\left(\frac{1}{5}\right) + \sqrt{1 - \left(\frac{2}{5}\right)^2}\left(\frac{1}{5}\right) + \sqrt{1 - \left(\frac{3}{5}\right)^2}\left(\frac{1}{5}\right) + \sqrt{1 - \left(\frac{4}{5}\right)^2}\left(\frac{1}{5}\right) + 0 \approx 0.659$

**45.** $\displaystyle\sum_{i=1}^{n}\frac{2i+1}{n^2} = \frac{1}{n^2}\sum_{i=1}^{n}(2i+1) = \frac{1}{n^2}\left[2\frac{n(n+1)}{2} + n\right] = \frac{n+2}{n} = 1 + \frac{2}{n} = S(n)$

$$S(10) = \frac{12}{10} = 1.2$$
$$S(100) = 1.02$$
$$S(1000) = 1.002$$
$$S(10{,}000) = 1.0002$$

**46.** $\displaystyle\sum_{j=1}^{n}\frac{4j+1}{n^2} = \frac{1}{n^2}\sum_{j=1}^{n}(4j+1) = \frac{1}{n^2}\left[\frac{4n(n+1)}{2} + n\right] = \frac{2n+3}{n} = S(n)$

$$S(10) = \frac{23}{10} = 2.3$$
$$S(100) = 2.03$$
$$S(1000) = 2.003$$
$$S(10{,}000) = 2.0003$$

**47.** $\displaystyle\sum_{k=1}^{n}\frac{6k(k-1)}{n^3} = \frac{6}{n^3}\sum_{k=1}^{n}(k^2 - k) = \frac{6}{n^3}\left[\frac{n(n+1)(2n+1)}{6} - \frac{n(n+1)}{2}\right]$

$$= \frac{6}{n^2}\left[\frac{2n^2 + 3n + 1 - 3n - 3}{6}\right] = \frac{1}{n^2}\left[2n^2 - 2\right] = 2 - \frac{2}{n^2} = S(n)$$

$$S(10) = 1.98$$
$$S(100) = 1.9998$$
$$S(1000) = 1.999998$$
$$S(10{,}000) = 1.99999998$$

**48.** $\displaystyle\sum_{i=1}^{n}\frac{4i^2(i-1)}{n^4} = \frac{4}{n^4}\sum_{i=1}^{n}(i^3 - i^2) = \frac{4}{n^4}\left[\frac{n^2(n+1)^2}{4} - \frac{n(n+1)(2n+1)}{6}\right]$

$$= \frac{4}{n^3}\left[\frac{n^3 + 2n^2 + n}{4} - \frac{2n^2 + 3n + 1}{6}\right]$$

$$= \frac{1}{3n^3}\left[3n^3 + 6n^2 + 3n - 4n^2 - 6n - 2\right]$$

$$= \frac{1}{3n^3}\left[3n^3 + 2n^2 - 3n - 2\right] = S(n)$$

$$S(10) = 1.056$$
$$S(100) = 1.006566$$
$$S(1000) = 1.00066567$$
$$S(10{,}000) = 1.000066657$$

**49.** $\displaystyle\lim_{n\to\infty}\sum_{i=1}^{n}\left(\frac{24i}{n^2}\right) = \lim_{n\to\infty}\frac{24}{n^2}\sum_{i=1}^{n} i = \lim_{n\to\infty}\frac{24}{n^2}\left(\frac{n(n+1)}{2}\right) = \lim_{n\to\infty}\left[12\left(\frac{n^2+n}{n^2}\right)\right] = 12\lim_{n\to\infty}\left(1 + \frac{1}{n}\right) = 12$

**50.** $\displaystyle\lim_{n\to\infty}\sum_{i=1}^{n}\left(\frac{2i}{n}\right)\left(\frac{2}{n}\right) = \lim_{n\to\infty}\frac{4}{n^2}\sum_{i=1}^{n} i = \lim_{n\to\infty}\frac{4}{n^2}\left(\frac{n(n+1)}{2}\right) = \lim_{n\to\infty}\frac{4}{2}\left(1 + \frac{1}{n}\right) = 2$

**51.** $\displaystyle \lim_{n\to\infty}\sum_{i=1}^{n}\frac{1}{n^3}(i-1)^2 = \lim_{n\to\infty}\frac{1}{n^3}\sum_{i=1}^{n-1}i^2 = \lim_{n\to\infty}\frac{1}{n^3}\left[\frac{(n-1)(n)(2n-1)}{6}\right]$

$$= \lim_{n\to\infty}\frac{1}{6}\left[\frac{2n^3-3n^2+n}{n^3}\right] = \lim_{n\to\infty}\left[\frac{1}{6}\left(2-\frac{3}{n}+\frac{1}{n^2}\right)\right] = \frac{1}{3}$$

**52.** $\displaystyle \lim_{n\to\infty}\sum_{i=1}^{n}\left(1+\frac{2i}{n}\right)^2\left(\frac{2}{n}\right) = \lim_{n\to\infty}\frac{2}{n^3}\sum_{i=1}^{n}(n+2i)^2$

$$= \lim_{n\to\infty}\frac{2}{n^3}\left[\sum_{i=1}^{n}n^2 + 4n\sum_{i=1}^{n}i + 4\sum_{i=1}^{n}i^2\right]$$

$$= \lim_{n\to\infty}\frac{2}{n^3}\left[n^3 + (4n)\left(\frac{n(n+1)}{2}\right) + \frac{4(n)(n+1)(2n+1)}{6}\right]$$

$$= 2\lim_{n\to\infty}\left[1+2+\frac{2}{n}+\frac{4}{3}+\frac{2}{n}+\frac{2}{3n^2}\right] = 2\left(1+2+\frac{4}{3}\right) = \frac{26}{3}$$

**53.** $\displaystyle \lim_{n\to\infty}\sum_{i=1}^{n}\left(1+\frac{i}{n}\right)\left(\frac{2}{n}\right) = 2\lim_{n\to\infty}\frac{1}{n}\left[\sum_{i=1}^{n}1+\frac{1}{n}\sum_{i=1}^{n}i\right] = 2\lim_{n\to\infty}\frac{1}{n}\left[n+\frac{1}{n}\left(\frac{n(n+1)}{2}\right)\right] = 2\lim_{n\to\infty}\left[1+\frac{1}{2}+\frac{1}{2n}\right] = 2\left(1+\frac{1}{2}\right) = 3$

**54.** $\displaystyle \lim_{n\to\infty}\sum_{i=1}^{n}\left(1+\frac{2i}{n}\right)^3\left(\frac{2}{n}\right) = 2\lim_{n\to\infty}\frac{1}{n^4}\sum_{i=1}^{n}(n+2i)^3$

$$= 2\lim_{n\to\infty}\frac{1}{n^4}\sum_{i=1}^{n}\left(n^3+6n^2i+12ni^2+8i^3\right)$$

$$= 2\lim_{n\to\infty}\frac{1}{n^4}\left[n^4+6n^2\left(\frac{n(n+1)}{2}\right)+12n\left(\frac{n(n+1)(2n+1)}{6}\right)+8\left(\frac{n^2(n+1)^2}{4}\right)\right]$$

$$= 2\lim_{n\to\infty}\left(1+3+\frac{3}{n}+4+\frac{6}{n}+\frac{2}{n^2}+2+\frac{4}{n}+\frac{2}{n^2}\right) = 2\lim_{n\to\infty}\left(10+\frac{13}{n}+\frac{4}{n^2}\right) = 20$$

**55.** (a)

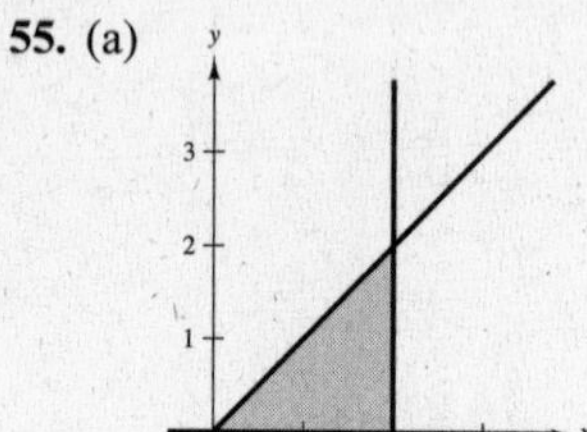


(b) $\Delta x = \dfrac{2-0}{n} = \dfrac{2}{n}$

Endpoints: $0 < 1\left(\frac{2}{n}\right) < 2\left(\frac{2}{n}\right) < \ldots < (n-1)\left(\frac{2}{n}\right) < n\left(\frac{2}{n}\right) = 2$

(c) Because $y = x$ is increasing, $f(m_i) = f(x_{i-1})$ on $[x_{i-1}, x_i]$.

$$s(n) = \sum_{i=1}^{n}f(x_{i-1})\Delta x = \sum_{i=1}^{n}f\left(\frac{2i-2}{n}\right)\left(\frac{2}{n}\right) = \sum_{i=1}^{n}\left[(i-1)\left(\frac{2}{n}\right)\right]\left(\frac{2}{n}\right)$$

(d) $f(M_i) = f(x_i)$ on $[x_{i-1}, x_i]$

$$S(n) = \sum_{i=1}^{n}f(x_i)\,\Delta x = \sum_{i=1}^{n}f\left(\frac{2i}{n}\right)\frac{2}{n} = \sum_{i=1}^{n}\left[i\left(\frac{2}{n}\right)\right]\left(\frac{2}{n}\right)$$

(e)

| $x$ | 5 | 10 | 50 | 100 |
|---|---|---|---|---|
| $s(n)$ | 1.6 | 1.8 | 1.96 | 1.98 |
| $S(n)$ | 2.4 | 2.2 | 2.04 | 2.02 |

(f) $\lim_{n\to\infty} \sum_{i=1}^{n} \left[(i-1)\left(\frac{2}{n}\right)\right]\left(\frac{2}{n}\right) = \lim_{n\to\infty} \frac{4}{n^2} \sum_{i=1}^{n} (i-1) = \lim_{n\to\infty} \frac{4}{n^2}\left[\frac{n(n+1)}{2} - n\right] = \lim_{n\to\infty}\left[\frac{2(n+1)}{n} - \frac{4}{n}\right] = 2$

$\lim_{n\to\infty} \sum_{i=1}^{n} \left[i\left(\frac{2}{n}\right)\right]\left(\frac{2}{n}\right) = \lim_{n\to\infty} \frac{4}{n^2} \sum_{i=1}^{n} i = \lim_{n\to\infty}\left(\frac{4}{n^2}\right)\frac{n(n+1)}{2} = \lim_{n\to\infty} \frac{2(n+1)}{n} = 2$

**56.** (a) 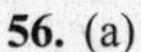

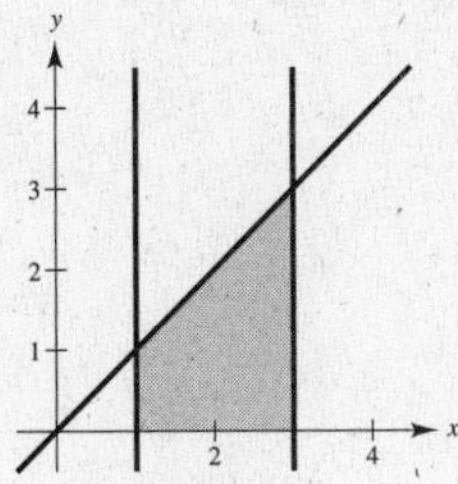

(b) $\Delta x = \frac{3-1}{n} = \frac{2}{n}$

Endpoints:

$$1 < 1 + \frac{2}{n} < 1 + \frac{4}{n} < \cdots < 1 + \frac{2n}{n} = 3$$

$$1 < 1 + 1\left(\frac{2}{n}\right) < 1 + 2\left(\frac{2}{n}\right) < \cdots < 1 + (n-1)\left(\frac{2}{n}\right) < 1 + n\left(\frac{2}{n}\right)$$

(c) Because $y = x$ is increasing, $f(m_i) = f(x_{i-1})$ on $[x_{i-1}, x_i]$.

$$s(n) = \sum_{i=1}^{n} f(x_{i-1})\,\Delta x = \sum_{i=1}^{n} f\left[1 + (i-1)\left(\frac{2}{n}\right)\right]\left(\frac{2}{n}\right) = \sum_{i=1}^{n}\left[1 + (i-1)\left(\frac{2}{n}\right)\right]\left(\frac{2}{n}\right)$$

(d) $f(M_i) = f(x_i)$ on $[x_{i-1}, x_i]$

$$S(n) = \sum_{i=1}^{n} f(x_i)\,\Delta x = \sum_{i=1}^{n} f\left[1 + i\left(\frac{2}{n}\right)\right]\left(\frac{2}{n}\right) = \sum_{i=1}^{n}\left[1 + i\left(\frac{2}{n}\right)\right]\left(\frac{2}{n}\right)$$

(e)

| $x$ | 5 | 10 | 50 | 100 |
|---|---|---|---|---|
| $s(n)$ | 3.6 | 3.8 | 3.96 | 3.98 |
| $S(n)$ | 4.4 | 4.2 | 4.04 | 4.02 |

(f) $\lim_{n\to\infty} \sum_{i=1}^{n}\left[1 + (i-1)\left(\frac{2}{n}\right)\right]\left(\frac{2}{n}\right) = \lim_{n\to\infty}\left(\frac{2}{n}\right)\left[n + \frac{2}{n}\left(\frac{n(n+1)}{2} - n\right)\right]$

$$= \lim_{n\to\infty}\left[2 + \frac{2n+2}{n} - \frac{4}{n}\right] = \lim_{n\to\infty}\left[4 - \frac{2}{n}\right] = 4$$

$\lim_{n\to\infty} \sum_{i=1}^{n}\left[1 + i\left(\frac{2}{n}\right)\right]\left(\frac{2}{n}\right) = \lim_{n\to\infty} \frac{2}{n}\left[n + \left(\frac{2}{n}\right)\frac{n(n+1)}{2}\right]$

$$= \lim_{n\to\infty}\left[2 + \frac{2(n+1)}{n}\right] = \lim_{n\to\infty}\left[4 + \frac{2}{n}\right] = 4$$

**57.** $y = -4x + 5$ on $[0, 1]$. $\left(\textbf{Note: } \Delta x = \dfrac{1}{n}\right)$

$$s(n) = \sum_{i=1}^{n} f\left(\frac{i}{n}\right)\left(\frac{1}{n}\right) = \sum_{i=1}^{n}\left[-4\left(\frac{i}{n}\right) + 5\right]\left(\frac{1}{n}\right)$$
$$= -\frac{4}{n^2}\sum_{i=1}^{n} i + 5$$
$$= -\frac{4}{n^2}\left(\frac{n(n+1)}{2}\right) + 5$$
$$= -2\left(1 + \frac{1}{n}\right) + 5$$

$$\text{Area} = \lim_{n\to\infty} s(n) = 3$$

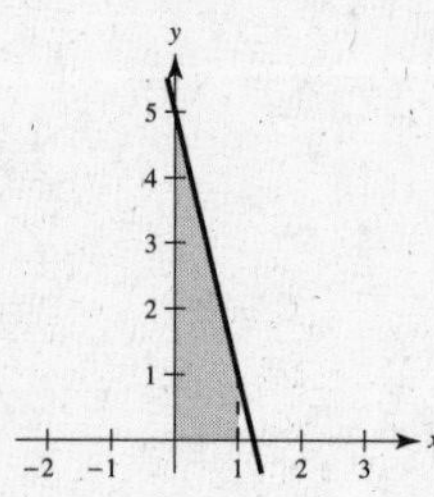

**58.** $y = 3x - 2$ on $[2, 5]$. $\left(\textbf{Note: } \Delta x = \dfrac{5-2}{n} = \dfrac{3}{n}\right)$

$$S(n) = \sum_{i=1}^{n} f\left(2 + \frac{3i}{n}\right)\left(\frac{3}{n}\right)$$
$$= \sum_{i=1}^{n}\left[3\left(2 + \frac{3i}{n}\right) - 2\right]\left(\frac{3}{n}\right)$$
$$= 18 + 3\left(\frac{3}{n}\right)^2\sum_{i=1}^{n} i - 6$$
$$= 12 + \frac{27}{n^2}\left(\frac{(n+1)n}{2}\right) = 12 + \frac{27}{2}\left(1 + \frac{1}{n}\right)$$

$$\text{Area} = \lim_{n\to\infty} S(n) = 12 + \frac{27}{2} = \frac{51}{2}$$

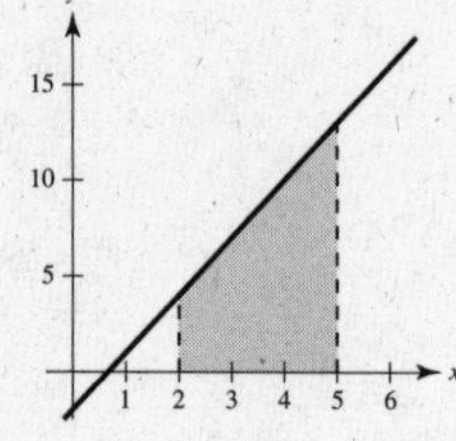

**59.** $y = x^2 + 2$ on $[0, 1]$. $\left(\textbf{Note: } \Delta x = \dfrac{1}{n}\right)$

$$S(n) = \sum_{i=1}^{n} f\left(\frac{i}{n}\right)\left(\frac{1}{n}\right)$$
$$= \sum_{i=1}^{n}\left[\left(\frac{i}{n}\right)^2 + 2\right]\left(\frac{1}{n}\right)$$
$$= \left[\frac{1}{n^3}\sum_{i=1}^{n} i^2\right] + 2$$
$$= \frac{n(n+1)(2n+1)}{6n^3} + 2 = \frac{1}{6}\left(2 + \frac{3}{n} + \frac{1}{n^2}\right) + 2$$

$$\text{Area} = \lim_{n\to\infty} S(n) = \frac{7}{3}$$

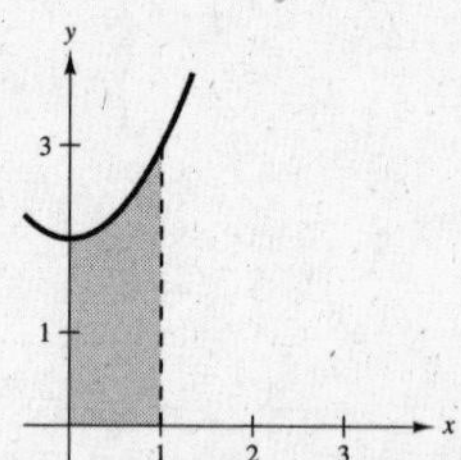

**60.** $y = x^2 + 1$ on $[0, 3]$. $\left(\textbf{Note: } \Delta x = \dfrac{3-0}{n} = \dfrac{3}{n}\right)$

$$S(n) = \sum_{i=1}^{n} f\left(\frac{3i}{n}\right)\left(\frac{3}{n}\right) = \sum_{i=1}^{n}\left[\left(\frac{3i}{n}\right)^2 + 1\right]\left(\frac{3}{n}\right)$$
$$= \frac{27}{n^3}\sum_{i=1}^{n} i^2 + \frac{3}{n}\sum_{i=1}^{n} 1$$
$$= \frac{27}{n^3}\left(\frac{n(n+1)(2n+1)}{6}\right) + \frac{3}{n}(n)$$
$$= \frac{9}{2}\left(\frac{2n^2 + 3n + 1}{n^2}\right) + 3$$

$$\text{Area} = \lim_{n\to\infty} S(n) = \frac{9}{2}(2) + 3 = 12$$

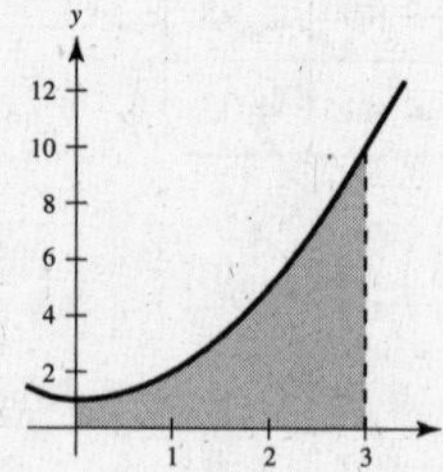

**61.** $y = 25 - x^2$ on $[1, 4]$. $\left(\textbf{Note: } \Delta x = \dfrac{3}{n}\right)$

$$s(n) = \sum_{i=1}^{n} f\left(1 + \frac{3i}{n}\right)\left(\frac{3}{n}\right) = \sum_{i=1}^{n}\left[25 - \left(1 + \frac{3i}{n}\right)^2\right]\left(\frac{3}{n}\right)$$

$$= \frac{3}{n}\sum_{i=1}^{n}\left[24 - \frac{9i^2}{n^2} - \frac{6i}{n}\right]$$

$$= \frac{3}{n}\left[24n - \frac{9}{n^2}\left(\frac{n(n+1)(2n+1)}{6}\right) - \frac{6}{n}\left(\frac{n(n+1)}{2}\right)\right]$$

$$= 72 - \frac{9}{2n^2}(n+1)(2n+1) - \frac{9}{n}(n+1)$$

$$\text{Area} = \lim_{n\to\infty} s(n) = 72 - 9 - 9 = 54$$

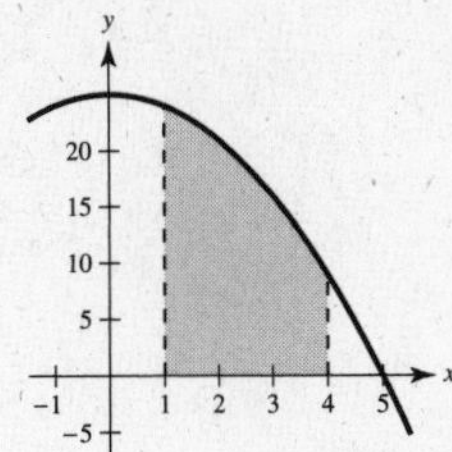


**62.** $y = 4 - x^2$ on $[-2, 2]$. Find area of region over the interval $[0, 2]$. $\left(\textbf{Note: } \Delta x = \dfrac{2}{n}\right)$

$$s(n) = \sum_{i=1}^{n} f\left(\frac{2i}{n}\right)\left(\frac{2}{n}\right)$$

$$= \sum_{i=1}^{n}\left[4 - \left(\frac{2i}{n}\right)^2\right]\left(\frac{2}{n}\right)$$

$$= 8 - \frac{8}{n^3}\sum_{i=1}^{n} i^2$$

$$= 8 - \frac{8n(n+1)(2n+1)}{6n^3} = 8 - \frac{4}{3}\left(2 + \frac{3}{n} + \frac{1}{n^2}\right)$$

$$\frac{1}{2}\text{Area} = \lim_{n\to\infty} s(n) = 8 - \frac{8}{3} = \frac{16}{3}$$

$$\text{Area} = \frac{32}{3}$$

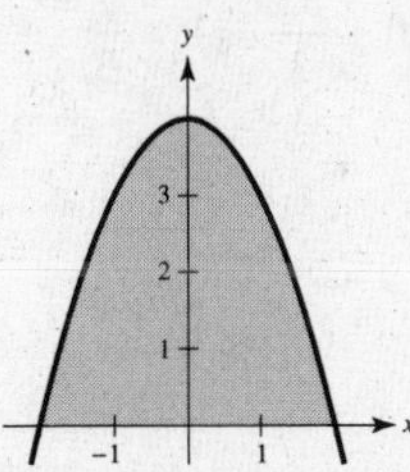


**63.** $y = 27 - x^3$ on $[1, 3]$. $\left(\textbf{Note: } \Delta x = \dfrac{3-1}{n} = \dfrac{2}{n}\right)$

$$s(n) = \sum_{i=1}^{n} f\left(1 + \frac{2i}{n}\right)\left(\frac{2}{n}\right) = \sum_{i=1}^{n}\left[27 - \left(1 + \frac{2i}{n}\right)^3\right]\left(\frac{2}{n}\right)$$

$$= \frac{2}{n}\sum_{i=1}^{n}\left[26 - \frac{8i^3}{n^3} - \frac{12i^2}{n^2} - \frac{6i}{n}\right]$$

$$= \frac{2}{n}\left[26n - \frac{8}{n^3}\left(\frac{n^2(n+1)^2}{4}\right) - \frac{12}{n^2}\left(\frac{n(n+1)(2n+1)}{6}\right) - \frac{6}{n}\left(\frac{n(n+1)}{2}\right)\right]$$

$$= 52 - \frac{4}{n^2}(n+1)^2 - \frac{4}{n^2}(n+1)(2n+1) - \frac{6n+1}{n}$$

$$\text{Area} = \lim_{n\to\infty} s(n) = 52 - 4 - 8 - 6 = 34$$

**64.** $y = 2x - x^3$ on $[0, 1]$. $\left(\textbf{Note: } \Delta x = \dfrac{1-0}{n} = \dfrac{1}{n}\right)$

Because $y$ both increases and decreases on $[0, 1]$, $T(n)$ is neither an upper nor lower sum.

$$T(n) = \sum_{i=1}^{n} f\left(\frac{i}{n}\right)\left(\frac{1}{n}\right) = \sum_{i=1}^{n}\left[2\left(\frac{i}{n}\right) - \left(\frac{i}{n}\right)^3\right]\left(\frac{1}{n}\right)$$

$$= \frac{2}{n^2}\sum_{i=1}^{n} i - \frac{1}{n^4}\sum_{i=1}^{n} i^3 = \frac{n(n+1)}{n^2} - \frac{1}{n^4}\left[\frac{n^2(n+1)^2}{4}\right] = 1 + \frac{1}{n} - \frac{1}{4} - \frac{2}{4n} - \frac{1}{4n^2}$$

$$\text{Area} = \lim_{n\to\infty} T(n) = 1 - \frac{1}{4} = \frac{3}{4}$$

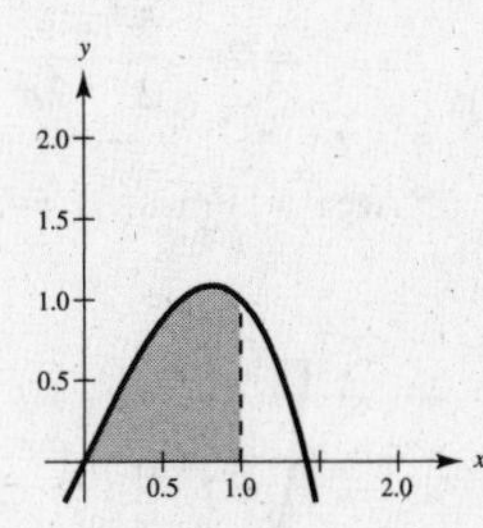

**65.** $y = x^2 - x^3$ on $[-1, 1]$. $\left(\textbf{Note: } \Delta x = \dfrac{1-(-1)}{n} = \dfrac{2}{n}\right)$

Because $y$ both increases and decreases on $[-1, 1]$, $T(n)$ is neither an upper nor a lower sum.

$$T(n) = \sum_{i=1}^{n} f\left(-1 + \frac{2i}{n}\right)\left(\frac{2}{n}\right) = \sum_{i=1}^{n}\left[\left(-1 + \frac{2i}{n}\right)^2 - \left(-1 + \frac{2i}{n}\right)^3\right]\left(\frac{2}{n}\right)$$

$$= \sum_{i=1}^{n}\left[\left(1 - \frac{4i}{n} + \frac{4i^2}{n^2}\right) - \left(-1 + \frac{6i}{n} - \frac{12i^2}{n^2} + \frac{8i^3}{n^3}\right)\right]\left(\frac{2}{n}\right)$$

$$= \sum_{i=1}^{n}\left[2 - \frac{10i}{n} + \frac{16i^2}{n^2} - \frac{8i^3}{n^3}\right]\left(\frac{2}{n}\right) = \frac{4}{n}\sum_{i=1}^{n} 1 - \frac{20}{n^2}\sum_{i=1}^{n} i + \frac{32}{n^3}\sum_{i=1}^{n} i^2 - \frac{16}{n^4}\sum_{i=1}^{n} i^3$$

$$= \frac{4}{n}(n) - \frac{20}{n^2}\cdot\frac{n(n+1)}{2} + \frac{32}{n^3}\cdot\frac{n(n+1)(2n+1)}{6} - \frac{16}{n^4}\cdot\frac{n^2(n+1)^2}{4}$$

$$= 4 - 10\left(1 + \frac{1}{n}\right) + \frac{16}{3}\left(2 + \frac{3}{n} + \frac{1}{n^2}\right) - 4\left(1 + \frac{2}{n} + \frac{1}{n^2}\right)$$

$$\text{Area} = \lim_{n\to\infty} T(n) = 4 - 10 + \frac{32}{3} - 4 = \frac{2}{3}$$

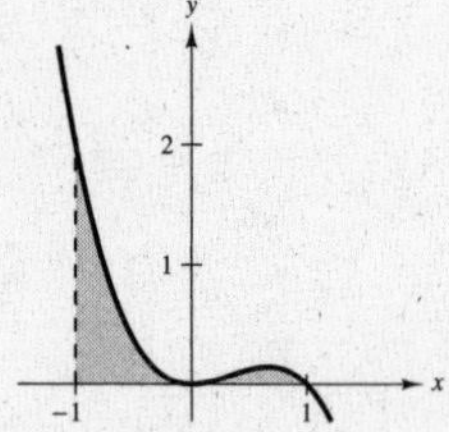

**66.** $y = x^2 - x^3$ on $[-1, 0]$.

$\left(\textbf{Note: } \Delta x = \dfrac{0-(-1)}{n} = \dfrac{1}{n}\right)$

$$s(n) = \sum_{i=1}^{n} f\left(-1 + \frac{i}{n}\right)\left(\frac{1}{n}\right)$$

$$= \sum_{i=1}^{n}\left[\left(-1 + \frac{i}{n}\right)^2 - \left(-1 + \frac{i}{n}\right)^3\right]\left(\frac{1}{n}\right)$$

$$= \sum_{i=1}^{n}\left[\left(2 - \frac{5i}{n} + \frac{4i^2}{n^2} - \frac{i^3}{n^3}\right)\right]\left(\frac{1}{n}\right)$$

$$= 2 - \frac{5}{n^2}\sum_{i=1}^{n} i + \frac{4}{n^3}\sum_{i=1}^{n} i^2 - \frac{1}{n^4}\sum_{i=1}^{n} i^3$$

$$= 2 - \frac{5}{2} - \frac{5}{2n} + \frac{4}{3} + \frac{2}{n} + \frac{2}{3n^3} - \frac{1}{4} - \frac{1}{2n} - \frac{1}{4n^2}$$

$$\text{Area} = \lim_{n\to\infty} s(n) = 2 - \frac{5}{2} + \frac{4}{3} - \frac{1}{4} = \frac{7}{12}$$

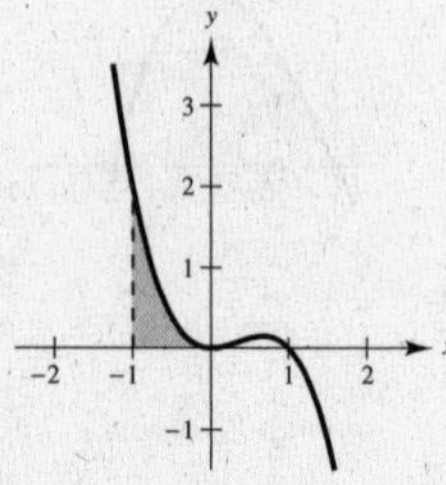

**67.** $f(y) = 4y,\ 0 \le y \le 2$ $\left(\textbf{Note: } \Delta y = \dfrac{2-0}{n} = \dfrac{2}{n}\right)$

$$S(n) = \sum_{i=1}^{n} f(m_i)\Delta y$$

$$= \sum_{i=1}^{n} f\left(\frac{2i}{n}\right)\left(\frac{2}{n}\right)$$

$$= \sum_{i=1}^{n} 4\left(\frac{2i}{n}\right)\left(\frac{2}{n}\right)$$

$$= \frac{16}{n^2}\sum_{i=1}^{n} i$$

$$= \left(\frac{16}{n^2}\right)\cdot\frac{n(n+1)}{2} = \frac{8(n+1)}{n} = 8 + \frac{8}{n}$$

$$\text{Area} = \lim_{n\to\infty} S(n) = \lim_{n\to\infty}\left(8 + \frac{8}{n}\right) = 8$$

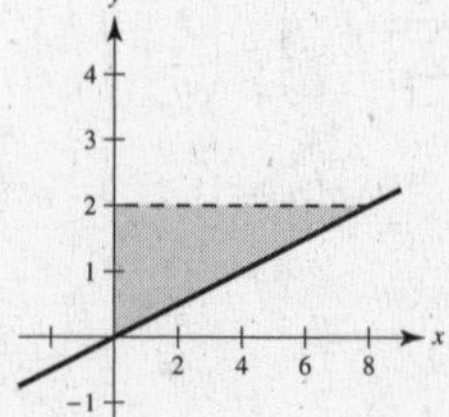

**68.** $g(y) = \frac{1}{2}y,\ 2 \le y \le 4.\ \left(\textbf{Note: } \Delta y = \frac{4-2}{n} = \frac{2}{n}\right)$

$$S(n) = \sum_{i=1}^{n} g\left(2 + \frac{2i}{n}\right)\left(\frac{2}{n}\right)$$
$$= \sum_{i=1}^{n} \frac{1}{2}\left(2 + \frac{2i}{n}\right)\left(\frac{2}{n}\right) = \frac{2}{n}\sum_{i=1}^{n}\left(1 + \frac{i}{n}\right)$$
$$= \frac{2}{n}\left[n + \frac{1}{n} \cdot \frac{n(n+1)}{2}\right] = 2 + \frac{n+1}{n}$$

$$\text{Area} = \lim_{n\to\infty} S(n) = 2 + 1 = 3$$

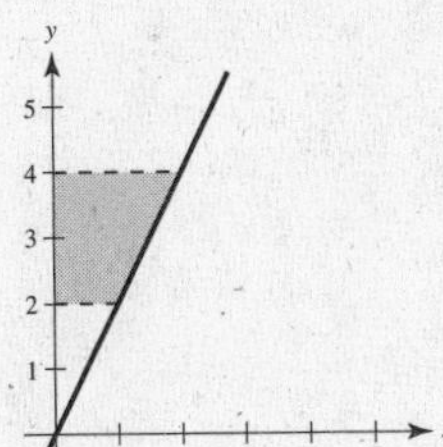

**69.** $f(y) = y^2,\ 0 \le y \le 5\ \left(\textbf{Note: } \Delta y = \frac{5-0}{n} = \frac{5}{n}\right)$

$$S(n) = \sum_{i=1}^{n} f\left(\frac{5i}{n}\right)\left(\frac{5}{n}\right)$$
$$= \sum_{i=1}^{n}\left(\frac{5i}{n}\right)^2\left(\frac{5}{n}\right)$$
$$= \frac{125}{n^3}\sum_{i=1}^{n} i^2$$
$$= \frac{125}{n^3} \cdot \frac{n(n+1)(2n+1)}{6}$$
$$= \frac{125}{n^2}\left(\frac{2n^2 + 3n + 1}{6}\right) = \frac{125}{3} + \frac{125}{2n} + \frac{125}{6n^2}$$

$$\text{Area} \lim_{n\to\infty} S(n) = \lim_{n\to\infty}\left(\frac{125}{3} + \frac{125}{2n} + \frac{125}{6n^2}\right) = \frac{125}{3}$$

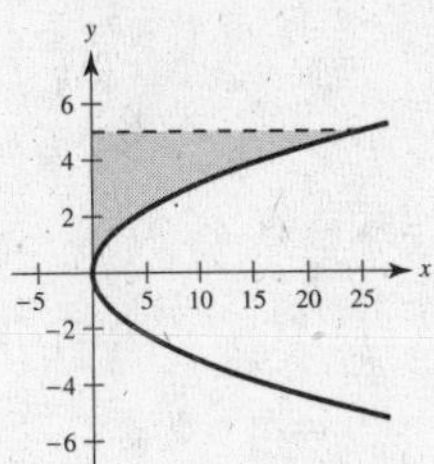

**70.** $f(y) = 4y - y^2,\ 1 \le y \le 2.\ \left(\textbf{Note: } \Delta y = \frac{2-1}{n} = \frac{1}{n}\right)$

$$S(n) = \sum_{i=1}^{n} f\left(1 + \frac{i}{n}\right)\left(\frac{1}{n}\right)$$
$$= \frac{1}{n}\sum_{i=1}^{n}\left[4\left(1 + \frac{i}{n}\right) - \left(1 + \frac{i}{n}\right)^2\right]$$
$$= \frac{1}{n}\sum_{i=1}^{n}\left(4 + \frac{4i}{n} - 1 - \frac{2i}{n} - \frac{i^2}{n^2}\right)$$
$$= \frac{1}{n}\sum_{i=1}^{n}\left(3 + \frac{2i}{n} - \frac{i^2}{n^2}\right)$$
$$= \frac{1}{n}\left[3n + \frac{2}{n} \cdot \frac{n(n+1)}{2} - \frac{1}{n^2} \cdot \frac{n(n+1)(2n+1)}{6}\right]$$
$$= 3 + \frac{n+1}{n} - \frac{(n+1)(2n+1)}{6}$$

$$\text{Area} = \lim_{n\to\infty} S(n) = 3 + 1 - \frac{1}{3} = \frac{11}{3}$$

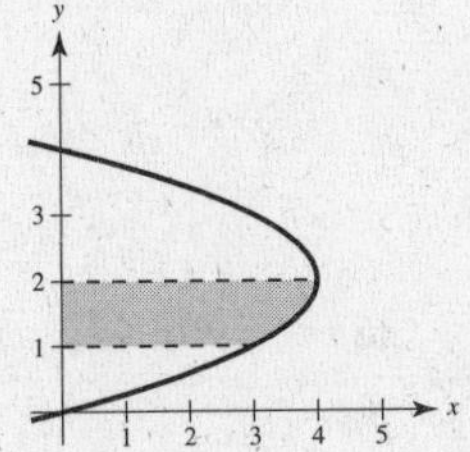

**71.** $g(y) = 4y^2 - y^3,\ 1 \le y \le 3.$ $\left(\textbf{Note: } \Delta y = \dfrac{3-1}{n} = \dfrac{2}{n}\right)$

$$S(n) = \sum_{i=1}^{n} g\left(1 + \frac{2i}{n}\right)\left(\frac{2}{n}\right)$$

$$= \sum_{i=1}^{n}\left[4\left(1 + \frac{2i}{n}\right)^2 - \left(1 + \frac{2i}{n}\right)^3\right]\frac{2}{n}$$

$$= \frac{2}{n}\sum_{i=1}^{n} 4\left[1 + \frac{4i}{n} + \frac{4i^2}{n^2}\right] - \left[1 + \frac{6i}{n} + \frac{12i^2}{n^2} + \frac{8i^3}{n^3}\right]$$

$$= \frac{2}{n}\sum_{i=1}^{n}\left[3 + \frac{10i}{n} + \frac{4i^2}{n^2} - \frac{8i^3}{n^3}\right]$$

$$= \frac{2}{n}\left[3n + \frac{10}{n}\cdot\frac{n(n+1)}{2} + \frac{4}{n^2}\cdot\frac{n(n+1)(2n+1)}{6} - \frac{8}{n^2}\cdot\frac{n^2(n+1)^2}{4}\right]$$

$$\text{Area} = \lim_{n\to\infty} S(n) = 6 + 10 + \frac{8}{3} - 4 = \frac{44}{3}$$

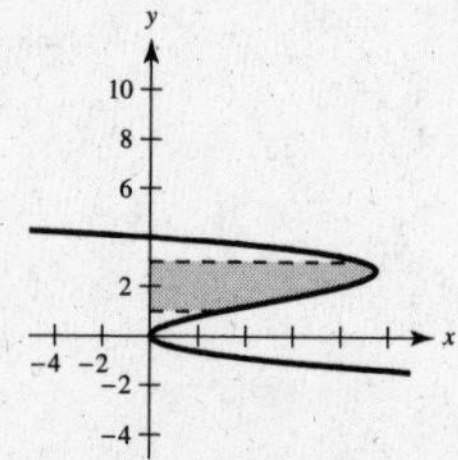

**72.** $h(y) = y^3 + 1,\ 1 \le y \le 2$ $\left(\textbf{Note: } \Delta y = \dfrac{1}{n}\right)$

$$S(n) = \sum_{i=1}^{n} h\left(1 + \frac{i}{n}\right)\left(\frac{1}{n}\right)$$

$$= \sum_{i=1}^{n}\left[\left(1 + \frac{i}{n}\right)^3 + 1\right]\frac{1}{n}$$

$$= \frac{1}{n}\sum_{i=1}^{n}\left(2 + \frac{i^3}{n^3} + \frac{3i^2}{n^2} + \frac{3i}{n}\right)$$

$$= \frac{1}{n}\left[2n + \frac{1}{n^3}\cdot\frac{n^2(n+1)^2}{4} + \frac{3}{n^2}\cdot\frac{n(n+1)(2n+1)}{6} + \frac{3}{n}\cdot\frac{3n(n+1)}{2n}\right]$$

$$= 2 + \frac{(n+1)^2}{4n^2} + \frac{(n+1)(2n+1)}{2n^2} + \frac{3(n+1)}{2n}$$

$$\text{Area} = \lim_{n\to\infty} S(n) = 2 + \frac{1}{4} + 1 + \frac{3}{2} = \frac{19}{4}$$

**73.** $f(x) = x^2 + 3,\ 0 \le x \le 2,\ n = 4$

Let $c_i = \dfrac{x_i + x_{i-1}}{2}$.

$$\Delta x = \frac{1}{2},\ c_1 = \frac{1}{4},\ c_2 = \frac{3}{4},\ c_3 = \frac{5}{4},\ c_4 = \frac{7}{4}$$

$$\text{Area} \approx \sum_{i=1}^{n} f(c_i)\Delta x = \sum_{i=1}^{4}\left[c_i^2 + 3\right]\left(\frac{1}{2}\right) = \frac{1}{2}\left[\left(\frac{1}{16} + 3\right) + \left(\frac{9}{16} + 3\right) + \left(\frac{25}{16} + 3\right) + \left(\frac{49}{16} + 3\right)\right] = \frac{69}{8}$$

**74.** $f(x) = x^2 + 4x,\ 0 \le x \le 4,\ n = 4$

Let $c_i = \dfrac{x_i + x_{i-1}}{2}$.

$\Delta x = 1,\ c_1 = \dfrac{1}{2},\ c_2 = \dfrac{3}{2},\ c_3 = \dfrac{5}{2},\ c_4 = \dfrac{7}{2}$

$$\text{Area} \approx \sum_{i=1}^{n} f(c_i)\,\Delta x = \sum_{i=1}^{4}\left[c_i^2 + 4c_i\right](1) = \left[\left(\frac{1}{4} + 2\right) + \left(\frac{9}{4} + 6\right) + \left(\frac{25}{4} + 10\right) + \left(\frac{49}{4} + 14\right)\right] = 53$$

**75.** $f(x) = \tan x,\ 0 \le x \le \dfrac{\pi}{4},\ n = 4$

Let $c_i = \dfrac{x_i + x_{i-1}}{2}$.

$\Delta x = \dfrac{\pi}{16},\ c_1 = \dfrac{\pi}{32},\ c_2 = \dfrac{3\pi}{32},\ c_3 = \dfrac{5\pi}{32},\ c_4 = \dfrac{7\pi}{32}$

$$\text{Area} \approx \sum_{i=1}^{n} f(c_i)\Delta x = \sum_{i=1}^{4}(\tan c_i)\left(\frac{\pi}{16}\right) = \frac{\pi}{16}\left(\tan\frac{\pi}{32} + \tan\frac{3\pi}{32} + \tan\frac{5\pi}{32} + \tan\frac{7\pi}{32}\right) \approx 0.345$$

**76.** $f(x) = \sin x,\ 0 \le x \le \dfrac{\pi}{2},\ n = 4$

Let $c_i = \dfrac{x_i + x_{i-1}}{2}$.

$\Delta x = \dfrac{\pi}{8},\ c_1 = \dfrac{\pi}{16},\ c_2 = \dfrac{3\pi}{16},\ c_3 = \dfrac{5\pi}{16},\ c_4 = \dfrac{7\pi}{16}$

$$\text{Area} \approx \sum_{i=1}^{n} f(c_i)\Delta x = \sum_{i=1}^{4}(\sin c_i)\left(\frac{\pi}{8}\right) = \frac{\pi}{8}\left(\sin\frac{\pi}{16} + \sin\frac{3\pi}{16} + \sin\frac{5\pi}{16} + \sin\frac{7\pi}{16}\right) \approx 1.006$$

**77.** $f(x) = \sqrt{x}$ on $[0, 4]$.

| $n$ | 4 | 8 | 12 | 16 | 20 |
|---|---|---|---|---|---|
| Approximate area | 5.3838 | 5.3523 | 5.3439 | 5.3403 | 5.3384 |

(Exact value is 16/3.)

**78.** $f(x) = \dfrac{8}{x^2 + 1}$ on $[2, 6]$.

| $n$ | 4 | 8 | 12 | 16 | 20 |
|---|---|---|---|---|---|
| Approximate area | 2.3397 | 2.3755 | 2.3824 | 2.3848 | 2.3860 |

**79.** $f(x) = \tan\left(\dfrac{\pi x}{8}\right)$ on $[1, 3]$.

| $n$ | 4 | 8 | 12 | 16 | 20 |
|---|---|---|---|---|---|
| Approximate area | 2.2223 | 2.2387 | 2.2418 | 2.2430 | 2.2435 |

**80.** $f(x) = \cos\sqrt{x}$ on $[0, 2]$.

| $n$ | 4 | 8 | 12 | 16 | 20 |
|---|---|---|---|---|---|
| Approximate area | 1.1041 | 1.1053 | 1.1055 | 1.1056 | 1.1056 |

**81.** $f(x) = \ln x$, $[1, 5]$

| $n$ | 4 | 8 | 12 | 16 | 20 |
|---|---|---|---|---|---|
| Approximate area | 4.0786 | 4.0554 | 4.0509 | 4.0493 | 4.0485 |

**82.** $f(x) = xe^x$, $[0, 2]$

| $n$ | 4 | 8 | 12 | 16 | 20 |
|---|---|---|---|---|---|
| Approximate area | 8.1711 | 8.3341 | 8.3646 | 8.3753 | 8.3802 |

**83.**

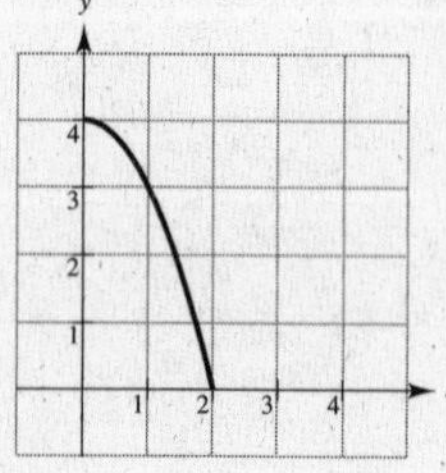

(b) $A \approx 6$ square units

**84.**

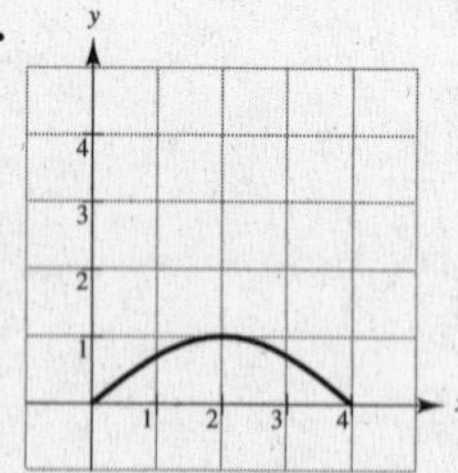

(a) $A \approx 3$ square units

**85.** You can use the line $y = x$ bounded by $x = a$ and $x = b$. The sum of the areas of these inscribed rectangles is the lower sum.

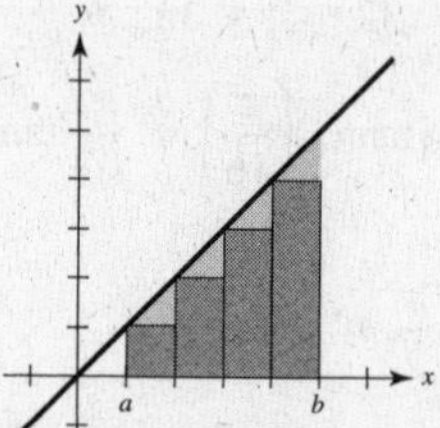

The sum of the areas of these circumscribed rectangles is the upper sum.

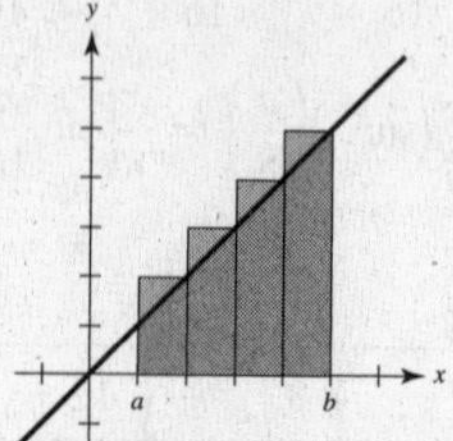

You can see that the rectangles do not contain all of the area in the first graph and the rectangles in the second graph cover more than the area of the region. The exact value of the area lies between these two sums.

**86.** See the definition of area, page 301.

**87.** (a)

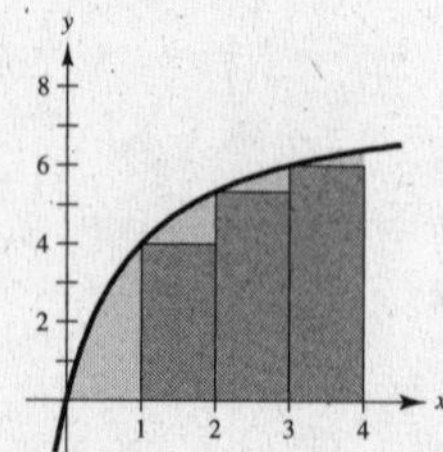

Lower sum: $s(4) = 0 + 4 + 5\frac{1}{3} + 6 = 15\frac{1}{3} = \frac{46}{3} \approx 15.333$

(b) 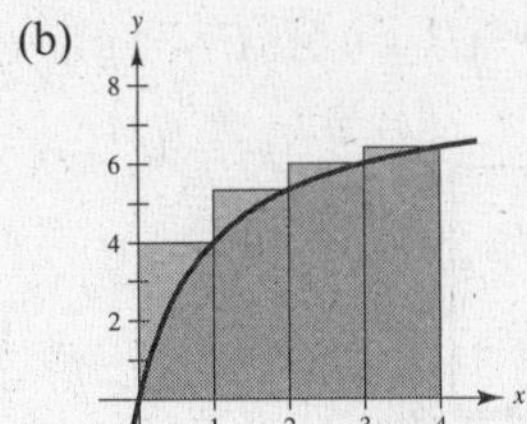

Upper sum: $S(4) = 4 + 5\frac{1}{3} + 6 + 6\frac{2}{5} = 21\frac{11}{15} = \frac{326}{15} \approx 21.733$

(c) 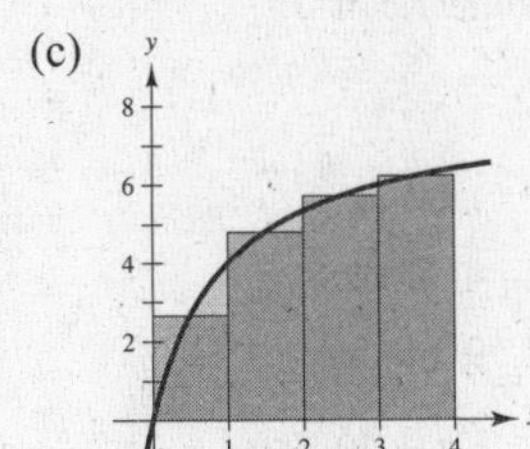

Midpoint Rule: $M(4) = 2\frac{2}{3} + 4\frac{4}{5} + 5\frac{5}{7} + 6\frac{2}{9} = \frac{6112}{315} \approx 19.403$

(d) In each case, $\Delta x = 4/n$. The lower sum uses left end-points, $(i - 1)(4/n)$. The upper sum uses right endpoints, $(i)(4/n)$. The Midpoint Rule uses midpoints, $\left(i - \frac{1}{2}\right)(4/n)$.

(e)

| $N$ | 4 | 8 | 20 | 100 | 200 |
|---|---|---|---|---|---|
| $s(n)$ | 15.333 | 17.368 | 18.459 | 18.995 | 19.06 |
| $S(n)$ | 21.733 | 20.568 | 19.739 | 19.251 | 19.188 |
| $M(n)$ | 19.403 | 19.201 | 19.137 | 19.125 | 19.125 |

(f) $s(n)$ increases because the lower sum approaches the exact value as $n$ increases. $S(n)$ decreases because the upper sum approaches the exact value as $n$ increases. Because of the shape of the graph, the lower sum is always smaller than the exact value, whereas the upper sum is always larger.

**88.** 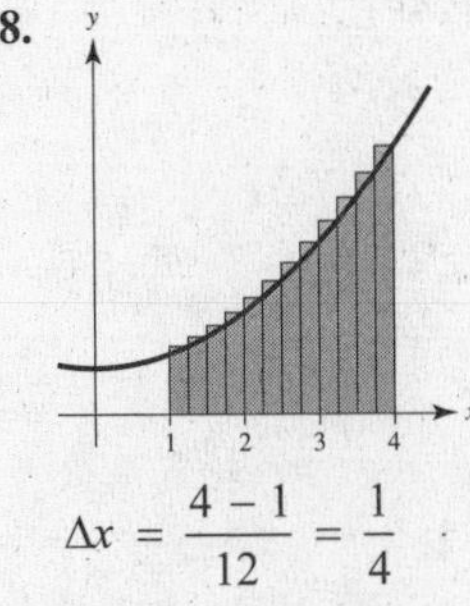

$$\Delta x = \frac{4 - 1}{12} = \frac{1}{4}$$

(a) The left endpoint of the first subinterval is 1, and the left endpoint of the last subinterval is $4 - \frac{1}{4} = \frac{15}{4}$.

(b) The right end points of the first two subintervals are $1 + \frac{1}{4} = \frac{5}{4}$ and $1 + 2\left(\frac{1}{4}\right) = \frac{3}{2}$.

(c) When using right endpoints, the rectangles will be above the curve.

(d) For a constant function, the heights of the rectangles are the same.

**89.** True. (Theorem 5.2 (2))

**90.** True. (Theorem 5.3)

**91.** Suppose there are $n$ rows and $n + 1$ columns in the figure. The stars on the left total $1 + 2 + \cdots + n$, as do the stars on the right. There are $n(n + 1)$ stars in total, so

$$2[1 + 2 + \cdots + n] = n(n + 1)$$

$$1 + 2 + \cdots + n = \frac{1}{2}(n)(n + 1).$$

**92.** (a) $\theta = \dfrac{2\pi}{n}$

(b) $\sin \theta = \dfrac{h}{r}$

$h = r \sin \theta$

$A = \dfrac{1}{2}bh = \dfrac{1}{2}r(r \sin \theta) = \dfrac{1}{2}r^2 \sin \theta$

(c) $A_n = n\left(\dfrac{1}{2}r^2 \sin \dfrac{2\pi}{n}\right)$

$= \dfrac{r^2 n}{2} \sin \dfrac{2\pi}{n} = \pi r^2 \left(\dfrac{\sin(2\pi/n)}{2\pi/n}\right)$

Let $x = 2\pi/n$. As $n \to \infty$, $x \to 0$.

$\lim_{n\to\infty} A_n = \lim_{x\to 0} \pi r^2 \left(\dfrac{\sin x}{x}\right) = \pi r^2(1) = \pi r^2$

**93.** (a) $y = (-4.09 \times 10^{-5})x^3 + 0.016x^2 - 2.67x + 452.9$

(b)

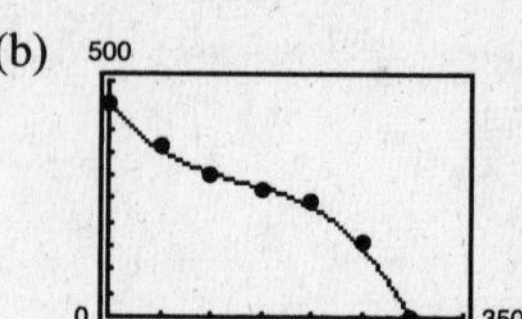


(c) Using the integration capability of a graphing utility, you obtain $A \approx 76{,}897.5 \text{ ft}^2$.

**94.** For $n$ odd,

$n = 1$, 1 row, 1 block

$n = 3$, 2 rows, 4 blocks

$n = 5$, 3 rows, 9 blocks

$n$, $\dfrac{n+1}{2}$ rows, $\left(\dfrac{n+1}{2}\right)^2$ blocks,

For $n$ even,

$n = 2$, 1 row, 2 block

$n = 4$, 2 rows, 6 blocks

$n = 6$, 3 rows, 12 blocks

$n$, $\dfrac{n}{2}$ rows, $\dfrac{n^2 + 2n}{4}$ blocks,

**95.** (a) $\displaystyle\sum_{i=1}^{n} 2i = n(n + 1)$

The formula is true for $n = 1$: $2 = 1(1 + 1) = 2$.

Assume that the formula is true for $n = k$: $\displaystyle\sum_{i=1}^{k} 2i = k(k + 1)$.

Then you have $\displaystyle\sum_{i=1}^{k+1} 2i = \sum_{i=1}^{k} 2i + 2(k + 1) = k(k + 1) + 2(k + 1) = (k + 1)(k + 2)$

which shows that the formula is true for $n = k + 1$.

(b) $\displaystyle\sum_{i=1}^{n} i^3 = \frac{n^2(n + 1)^2}{4}$

The formula is true for $n = 1$ because $1^3 = \dfrac{1^2(1 + 1)^2}{4} = \dfrac{4}{4} = 1$.

Assume that the formula is true for $n = k$: $\displaystyle\sum_{i=1}^{k} i^3 = \frac{k^2(k + 1)^2}{4}$.

Then you have $\displaystyle\sum_{i=1}^{k+1} i^3 = \sum_{i=1}^{k} i^3 + (k + 1)^3 = \frac{k^2(k + 1)^2}{4} + (k + 1)^3 = \frac{(k + 1)^2}{4}\left[k^2 + 4(k + 1)\right] = \frac{(k + 1)^2}{4}(k + 2)^2$

which shows that the formula is true for $n = k + 1$.

**96.** Assume that the dartboard has corners at $(\pm 1, \pm 1)$.

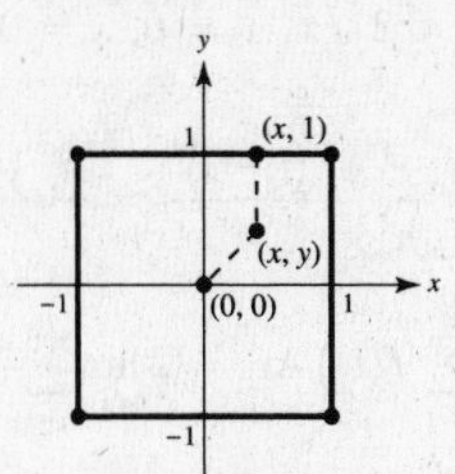


A point $(x, y)$ in the square is closer to the center than the top edge if

$$\sqrt{x^2 + y^2} \le 1 - y$$
$$x^2 + y^2 \le 1 - 2y + y^2$$
$$y \le \tfrac{1}{2}\left(1 - x^2\right).$$

By symmetry, a point $(x, y)$ in the square is closer to the center than the right edge if

$x \le \tfrac{1}{2}\left(1 - y^2\right)$.

In the first quadrant, the parabolas $y = \tfrac{1}{2}\left(1 - x^2\right)$ and $x = \tfrac{1}{2}\left(1 - y^2\right)$ intersect at $\left(\sqrt{2} - 1, \sqrt{2} - 1\right)$. There are 8 equal regions that make up the total region, as indicated in the figure.

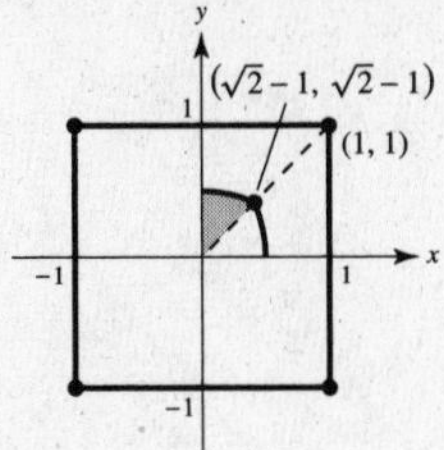


Area of shaded region $S = \int_0^{\sqrt{2}-1} \left[\frac{1}{2}\left(1 - x^2\right) - x\right] dx = \frac{2\sqrt{2}}{3} - \frac{5}{6}$

Probability $= \dfrac{8S}{\text{Area square}} = 2\left[\frac{2\sqrt{2}}{3} - \frac{5}{6}\right] = \frac{4\sqrt{2}}{3} - \frac{5}{3}$

# Section 5.3 Riemann Sums and Definite Integrals

**1.** $f(x) = \sqrt{x},\ y = 0,\ x = 0,\ x = 3,\ c_i = \dfrac{3i^2}{n^2}$

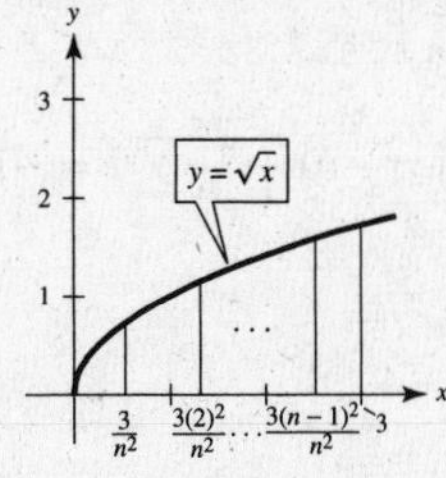


$$\Delta x_i = \frac{3i^2}{n^2} - \frac{3(i-1)^2}{n^2} = \frac{3}{n^2}(2i - 1)$$

$$\lim_{n\to\infty} \sum_{i=1}^{n} f(c_i)\Delta x_i = \lim_{n\to\infty} \sum_{i=1}^{n} \sqrt{\frac{3i^2}{n^2}}\,\frac{3}{n^2}(2i - 1)$$
$$= \lim_{n\to\infty} \frac{3\sqrt{3}}{n^3} \sum_{i=1}^{n} \left(2i^2 - i\right)$$
$$= \lim_{n\to\infty} \frac{3\sqrt{3}}{n^3}\left[2\frac{n(n+1)(2n+1)}{6} - \frac{n(n+1)}{2}\right]$$
$$= \lim_{n\to\infty} 3\sqrt{3}\left[\frac{(n+1)(2n+1)}{3n^2} - \frac{n+1}{2n^2}\right]$$
$$= 3\sqrt{3}\left[\frac{2}{3} - 0\right] = 2\sqrt{3} \approx 3.464$$

**2.** $f(x) = 2\sqrt[3]{x},\ y = 0,\ x = 0,\ x = 1,\ c_i = \dfrac{i^3}{n^3}$

$$\Delta x_i = \frac{i^3}{n^3} - \frac{(i-1)^3}{n^3} = \frac{3i^2 - 3i + 1}{n^3}$$

$$\lim_{n\to\infty}\sum_{i=1}^{n} f(c_i)\,\Delta x_i = 2\lim_{n\to\infty}\sum_{i=1}^{n}\sqrt[3]{\frac{i^3}{n^3}}\left[\frac{3i^2 - 3i + 1}{n^3}\right]$$

$$= 2\lim_{n\to\infty}\frac{1}{n^4}\sum_{i=1}^{n}\left(3i^3 - 3i^2 + i\right)$$

$$= 2\lim_{n\to\infty}\frac{1}{n^4}\left[3\left(\frac{n^2(n+1)^2}{4}\right) - 3\left(\frac{n(n+1)(2n+1)}{6}\right) + \frac{n(n+1)}{2}\right]$$

$$= 2\lim_{n\to\infty}\frac{1}{n^4}\left[\frac{3n^4 + 6n^3 + 3n^2}{4} - \frac{2n^3 + 3n^2 + n}{2} + \frac{n^2 + n}{2}\right]$$

$$= 2\lim_{n\to\infty}\frac{1}{n^4}\left[\frac{3n^4}{4} + \frac{n^3}{2} - \frac{n^2}{4}\right] = 2\lim_{n\to\infty}\left[\frac{3}{4} + \frac{1}{2n} - \frac{1}{4n^2}\right] = \frac{3}{2}$$

**3.** $y = 8$ on $[2, 6]$. $\left(\textbf{Note: } \Delta x = \dfrac{6-2}{n} = \dfrac{4}{n},\ \|\Delta\| \to 0 \text{ as } n \to \infty\right)$

$$\sum_{i=1}^{n} f(c_i)\,\Delta x_i = \sum_{i=1}^{n} f\left(2 + \frac{4i}{n}\right)\left(\frac{4}{n}\right) = \sum_{i=1}^{n} 8\left(\frac{4}{n}\right) = \sum_{i=1}^{n}\frac{32}{n} = \frac{1}{n}\sum_{i=1}^{n} 32 = \frac{1}{n}(32n) = 32$$

$$\int_2^6 8\,dx = \lim_{n\to\infty} 32 = 32$$

**4.** $y = x$ on $[-2, 3]$. $\left(\textbf{Note: } \Delta x = \dfrac{3-(-2)}{n} = \dfrac{5}{n},\ \|\Delta\| \to 0 \text{ as } n \to \infty\right)$

$$\sum_{i=1}^{n} f(c_i)\,\Delta x_i = \sum_{i=1}^{n} f\left(-2 + \frac{5i}{n}\right)\left(\frac{5}{n}\right)$$

$$= \sum_{i=1}^{n}\left(-2 + \frac{5i}{n}\right)\left(\frac{5}{n}\right) = -10 + \frac{25}{n^2}\sum_{i=1}^{n} i = -10 + \left(\frac{25}{n^2}\right)\frac{n(n+1)}{2} = -10 + \frac{25}{2}\left(1 + \frac{1}{n}\right) = \frac{5}{2} + \frac{25}{2n}$$

$$\int_{-2}^{3} x\,dx = \lim_{n\to\infty}\left(\frac{5}{2} + \frac{25}{2n}\right) = \frac{5}{2}$$

**5.** $y = x^3$ on $[-1, 1]$. $\left(\textbf{Note: } \Delta x = \dfrac{1-(-1)}{n} = \dfrac{2}{n},\ \|\Delta\| \to 0 \text{ as } n \to \infty\right)$

$$\sum_{i=1}^{n} f(c_i)\Delta x_i = \sum_{i=1}^{n} f\left(-1 + \frac{2i}{n}\right)\left(\frac{2}{n}\right)$$

$$= \sum_{i=1}^{n}\left(-1 + \frac{2i}{n}\right)^3\left(\frac{2}{n}\right)$$

$$= \sum_{i=1}^{n}\left[-1 + \frac{6i}{n} - \frac{12i^2}{n^2} + \frac{8i^3}{n^3}\right]\left(\frac{2}{n}\right)$$

$$= -2 + \frac{12}{n^2}\sum_{i=1}^{n} i - \frac{24}{n^3}\sum_{i=1}^{n} i^2 + \frac{16}{n^4}\sum_{i=1}^{n} i^3$$

$$= -2 + 6\left(1 + \frac{1}{n}\right) - 4\left(2 + \frac{3}{n} + \frac{1}{n^2}\right) + 4\left(1 + \frac{2}{n} + \frac{1}{n^2}\right) = \frac{2}{n}$$

$$\int_{-1}^{1} x^3\,dx = \lim_{n\to\infty}\frac{2}{n} = 0$$

**6.** $y = 4x^2$ on $[1, 4]$. $\left(\textbf{Note: } \Delta x = \dfrac{4-1}{n} = \dfrac{3}{n}, \|\Delta\| \to 0 \text{ as } n \to \infty\right)$

$$\begin{aligned}
\sum_{i=1}^{n} f(c_i)\Delta x_i &= \sum_{i=1}^{n} f\left(1 + \frac{3i}{n}\right)\left(\frac{3}{n}\right) \\
&= \sum_{i=1}^{n} 4\left(1 + \frac{3i}{n}\right)^2\left(\frac{3}{n}\right) \\
&= \frac{12}{n}\sum_{i=1}^{n}\left(1 + \frac{6i}{n} + \frac{9i^2}{n^2}\right) \\
&= \frac{12}{n}\left[n + \frac{6}{n}\frac{n(n+1)}{2} + \frac{9}{n^2}\frac{n(n+1)(2n+1)}{6}\right] \\
&= 12 + 36\frac{n+1}{n} + 18\frac{(n+1)(2n+1)}{n^2} \\
\int_1^4 4x^2\,dx &= \lim_{n\to\infty}\left[12 + \frac{36(n+1)}{n} + \frac{18(n+1)(2n+1)}{n^2}\right] \\
&= 12 + 36 + 36 = 84
\end{aligned}$$

**7.** $y = x^2 + 1$ on $[1, 2]$. $\left(\textbf{Note: } \Delta x = \dfrac{2-1}{n} = \dfrac{1}{n}, \|\Delta\| \to 0 \text{ as } n \to \infty\right)$

$$\begin{aligned}
\sum_{i=1}^{n} f(c_i)\,\Delta x_i &= \sum_{i=1}^{n} f\left(1 + \frac{i}{n}\right)\left(\frac{1}{n}\right) \\
&= \sum_{i=1}^{n}\left[\left(1 + \frac{i}{n}\right)^2 + 1\right]\left(\frac{1}{n}\right) \\
&= \sum_{i=1}^{n}\left[1 + \frac{2i}{n} + \frac{i^2}{n^2} + 1\right]\left(\frac{1}{n}\right) \\
&= 2 + \frac{2}{n^2}\sum_{i=1}^{n} i + \frac{1}{n^3}\sum_{i=1}^{n} i^2 = 2 + \left(1 + \frac{1}{n}\right) + \frac{1}{6}\left(2 + \frac{3}{n} + \frac{1}{n^2}\right) = \frac{10}{3} + \frac{3}{2n} + \frac{1}{6n^2} \\
\int_1^2 \left(x^2 + 1\right)dx &= \lim_{n\to\infty}\left(\frac{10}{3} + \frac{3}{2n} + \frac{1}{6n^2}\right) = \frac{10}{3}
\end{aligned}$$

**8.** $y = 2x^2 + 3$ on $[-2, 1]$. $\left(\textbf{Note: } \Delta x = \dfrac{1-(-2)}{n} = \dfrac{3}{n}, \|\Delta\| \to 0 \text{ as } n \to \infty\right)$

$$\begin{aligned}
\sum_{i=1}^{n} f(c_i)\Delta x_i &= \sum_{i=1}^{n} f\left(-2 + \frac{3i}{n}\right)\left(\frac{3}{n}\right) \\
&= \sum_{i=1}^{n}\left[2\left(-2 + \frac{3i}{n}\right)^2 + 3\right]\left(\frac{3}{n}\right) \\
&= \frac{3}{n}\sum_{i=1}^{n}\left[2\left(4 - \frac{12i}{n} + \frac{9i^2}{n^2}\right) + 3\right] \\
&= \frac{3}{n}\sum_{i=1}^{n}\left[11 - \frac{24i}{n} + \frac{18i^2}{n^2}\right] \\
&= \frac{3}{n}\left[11n - \frac{24}{n}\frac{n(n+1)}{2} + \frac{18}{n^2}\frac{n(n+1)(2n+1)}{6}\right] = 33 - 36\frac{n+1}{n} + 9\frac{(n+1)(2n+1)}{n^2}
\end{aligned}$$

$$\int_{-2}^{1}\left(2x^2 + 3\right)dx = \lim_{n\to\infty}\left[33 - 36\frac{n+1}{n} + 9\frac{(n+1)(2n+1)}{n^2}\right] = 33 - 36 + 18 = 15$$

**9.** $\lim_{\|\Delta\|\to 0} \sum_{i=1}^{n} (3c_i + 10)\,\Delta x_i = \int_{-1}^{5} (3x + 10)\,dx$

on the interval $[-1, 5]$.

**10.** $\lim_{\|\Delta\|\to 0} \sum_{i=1}^{n} 6c_i(4 - c_i)^2\,\Delta x_i = \int_{0}^{4} 6x(4 - x)^2\,dx$

on the interval [0, 4].

**11.** $\lim_{\|\Delta\|\to 0} \sum_{i=1}^{n} \sqrt{c_i^2 + 4}\,\Delta x_i = \int_{0}^{3} \sqrt{x^2 + 4}\,dx$

on the interval [0, 3].

**12.** $\lim_{\|\Delta\|\to 0} \sum_{i=1}^{n} \left(\frac{3}{c_i^2}\right)\Delta x_i = \int_{1}^{3} \frac{3}{x^2}\,dx$

on the interval [1, 3].

**13.** $\lim_{\|\Delta\|\to 0} \sum_{i=1}^{n} \left(1 + \frac{3}{c_i}\right)\Delta x_i = \int_{1}^{5} \left(1 + \frac{3}{x}\right)dx$

on the interval [1, 5].

**14.** $\lim_{\|\Delta\|\to 0} \sum_{i=1}^{n} \left(2^{-c_i} \sin c_i\right)\Delta x_i = \int_{0}^{\pi} 2^{-x} \sin x\,dx$

on the interval $[0, \pi]$.

**15.** $\int_{0}^{4} 5\,dx$

**16.** $\int_{0}^{2} x^2\,dx$

**17.** $\int_{1}^{4} \frac{2}{x}\,dx$

**18.** $\int_{0}^{2} 2e^{-x}\,dx$

**19.** $\int_{0}^{\pi/2} \cos x\,dx$

**20.** $\int_{0}^{\pi/4} \tan x\,dx$

**21.** $\int_{0}^{2} y^3\,dy$

**22.** $\int_{0}^{2} (y - 2)^2\,dy$

**23.** Rectangle

$A = bh = 3(4)$

$A = \int_{0}^{3} 4\,dx = 12$

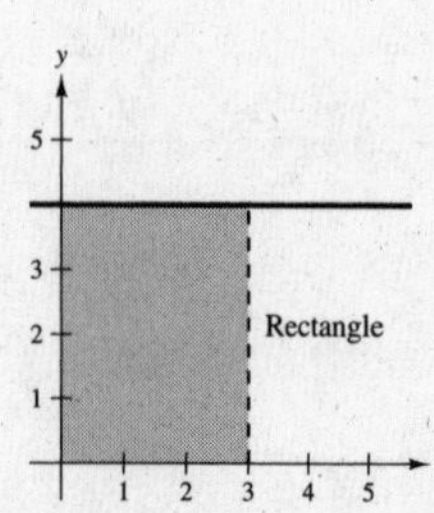


**24.** Rectangle

$A = bh = 2(4)(a) = 8a$

$A = \int_{-a}^{a} 4\,dx = 8a$

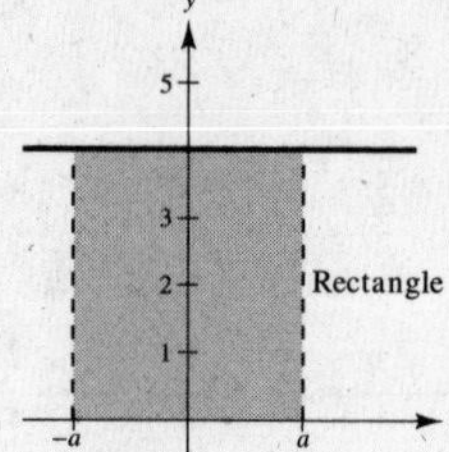


**25.** Triangle

$A = \frac{1}{2}bh = \frac{1}{2}(4)(4) = 8$

$A = \int_{0}^{4} x\,dx = 8$

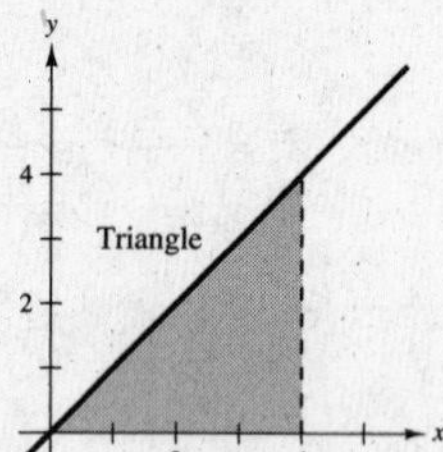


**26.** Triangle

$A = \frac{1}{2}bh = \frac{1}{2}(4)(2) = 4$

$A = \int_{0}^{4} \frac{x}{2}\,dx = 4$

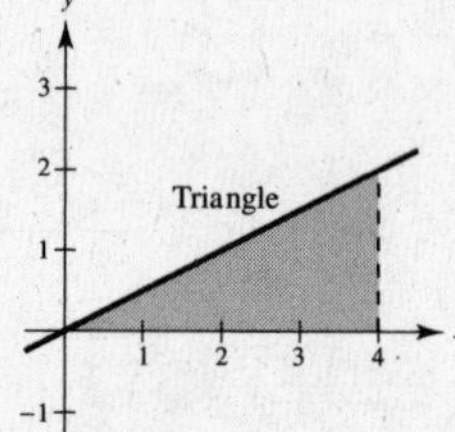


**27.** Trapezoid

$A = \frac{b_1 + b_2}{2}h = \left(\frac{4 + 10}{2}\right)2 = 14$

$A = \int_{0}^{2} (3x + 4)\,dx = 14$

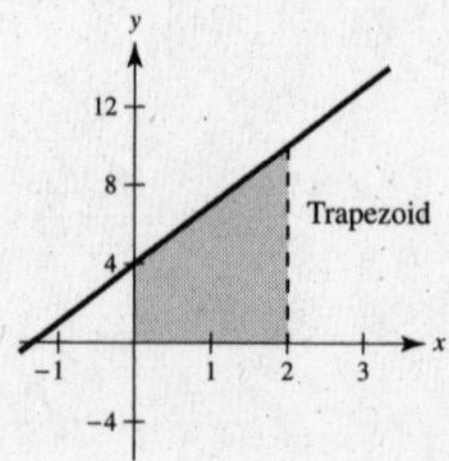

**28.** Triangle

$A = \frac{1}{2}bh = \frac{1}{2}(6)(6) = 18$

$A = \int_0^8 (6 - x)\, dx = 18$

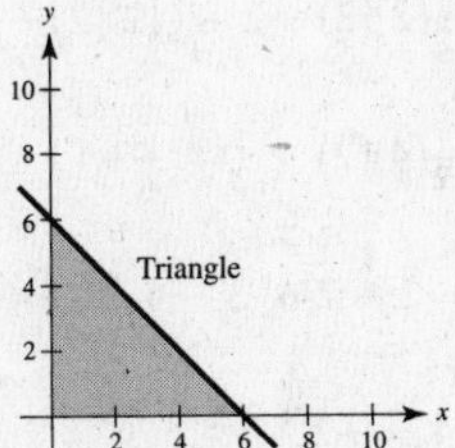


**29.** Triangle

$A = \frac{1}{2}bh = \frac{1}{2}(2)(1) = 1$

$A = \int_{-1}^1 (1 - |x|)\, dx = 1$

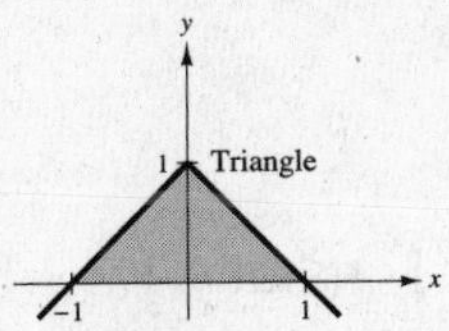


**30.** Triangle

$A = \frac{1}{2}bh = \frac{1}{2}(2a)\, a = a^2$

$A = \int_{-a}^a (a - |x|)\, dx = a^2$

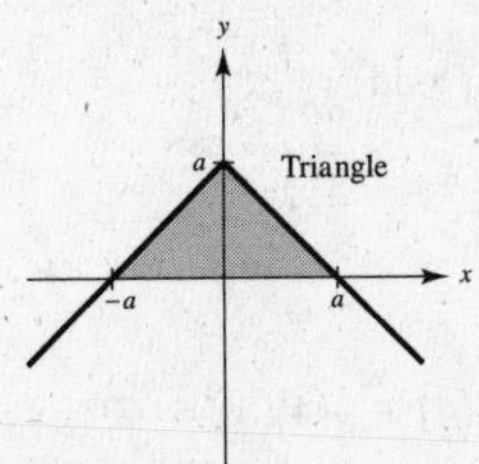


**31.** Semicircle

$A = \frac{1}{2}\pi r^2 = \frac{1}{2}\pi(7)^2 = \frac{49\pi}{2}$

$A = \int_{-7}^7 \sqrt{49 - x^2}\, dx = \frac{49\pi}{2}$

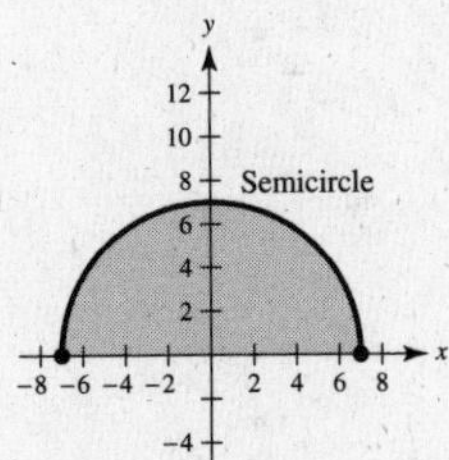


**32.** Semicircle

$A = \frac{1}{2}\pi r^2$

$A = \int_{-r}^r \sqrt{r^2 - x^2}\, dx = \frac{1}{2}\pi r^2$

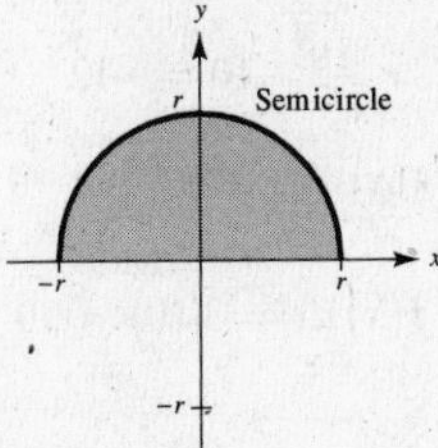


**In Exercises 33–40, $\int_2^4 x^3\, dx = 60$, $\int_2^4 x\, dx = 6$, $\int_2^4 dx = 2$**

**33.** $\int_4^2 x\, dx = -\int_2^4 x\, dx = -6$

**34.** $\int_2^2 x^3\, dx = 0$

**35.** $\int_2^4 8x\, dx = 8\int_2^4 x\, dx = 8(6) = 48$

**36.** $\int_2^4 25\, dx = 25\int_2^4 dx = 25(2) = 50$

**37.** $\int_2^4 (x - 9)\, dx = \int_2^4 x\, dx - 9\int_2^4 dx = 6 - 9(2) = -12$

**38.** $\int_2^4 (x^3 + 4)\, dx = \int_2^4 x^3\, dx + 4\int_2^4 dx = 60 + 4(2) = 68$

**39.** $\int_2^4 \left(\frac{1}{2}x^3 - 3x + 2\right) dx = \frac{1}{2}\int_2^4 x^3\, dx - 3\int_2^4 x\, dx + 2\int_2^4 dx$

$= \frac{1}{2}(60) - 3(6) + 2(2) = 16$

**40.** $\int_2^4 (10 + 4x - 3x^3)\, dx = 10\int_2^4 dx + 4\int_2^4 x\, dx - 3\int_2^4 x^3\, dx$

$= 10(2) + 4(6) - 3(60) = -136$

**41.** (a) $\int_0^7 f(x)\, dx = \int_0^5 f(x)\, dx + \int_5^7 f(x)\, dx = 10 + 3 = 13$

(b) $\int_5^0 f(x)\, dx = -\int_0^5 f(x)\, dx = -10$

(c) $\int_5^5 f(x)\, dx = 0$

(d) $\int_0^5 3f(x)\, dx = 3\int_0^5 f(x)\, dx = 3(10) = 30$

**42.** (a) $\int_0^6 f(x)\, dx = \int_0^3 f(x)\, dx + \int_3^6 f(x)\, dx = 4 + (-1) = 3$

(b) $\int_6^3 f(x)\, dx = -\int_3^6 f(x)\, dx = -(-1) = 1$

(c) $\int_3^3 f(x)\, dx = 0$

(d) $\int_3^6 -5f(x)\, dx = -5\int_3^6 f(x)\, dx = -5(-1) = 5$

**43.** (a) $\int_2^6 [f(x) + g(x)]\,dx = \int_2^6 f(x)\,dx + \int_2^6 g(x)\,dx$
$= 10 + (-2) = 8$

(b) $\int_2^6 [g(x) - f(x)]\,dx = \int_2^6 g(x)\,dx - \int_2^6 f(x)\,dx$
$= -2 - 10 = -12$

(c) $\int_2^6 2g(x)\,dx = 2\int_2^6 g(x)\,dx = 2(-2) = -4$

(d) $\int_2^6 3f(x)\,dx = 3\int_2^6 f(x)\,dx = 3(10) = 30$

**44.** (a) $\int_{-1}^0 f(x)\,dx = \int_{-1}^1 f(x)\,dx - \int_0^1 f(x)\,dx$
$= 0 - 5 = -5$

(b) $\int_0^1 f(x)\,dx - \int_1^0 f(x)\,dx = 5 - (-5) = 10$

(c) $\int_{-1}^1 3f(x)\,dx = 3\int_{-1}^1 f(x)\,dx = 3(0) = 0$

(d) $\int_0^1 3f(x)\,dx = 3\int_0^1 f(x)\,dx = 3(5) = 15$

**45.** Lower estimate: $[24 + 12 - 4 - 20 - 36](2) = -48$

Upper estimate: $[32 + 24 + 12 - 4 - 20](2) = 88$

**46.** (a) $[-6 + 8 + 30](2) = 64$ left endpoint estimate

(b) $[8 + 30 + 80](2) = 236$ right endpoint estimate

(c) $[0 + 18 + 50](2) = 136$ midpoint estimate

If $f$ is increasing, then (a) is below the actual value and (b) is above.

**47.** (a) Quarter circle below $x$-axis:
$-\frac{1}{4}\pi r^2 = -\frac{1}{4}\pi(2)^2 = -\pi$

(b) Triangle: $\frac{1}{2}bh = \frac{1}{2}(4)(2) = 4$

(c) Triangle + Semicircle below $x$-axis:
$-\frac{1}{2}(2)(1) - \frac{1}{2}\pi(2)^2 = -(1 + 2\pi)$

(d) Sum of parts (b) and (c): $4 - (1 + 2\pi) = 3 - 2\pi$

(e) Sum of absolute values of (b) and (c):
$4 + (1 + 2\pi) = 5 + 2\pi$

(f) Answers to (d) plus
$2(10) = 20$: $(3 - 2\pi) + 20 = 23 - 2\pi$

**48.** (a) $\int_0^1 -f(x)\,dx = -\int_0^1 f(x)\,dx = \frac{1}{2}$

(b) $\int_3^4 3f(x)\,dx = 3(2) = 6$

(c) $\int_0^7 f(x)\,dx = -\frac{1}{2} + \frac{1}{2}(2)(2) + 2 + \frac{1}{2}(2)(2) - \frac{1}{2} = 5$

(d) $\int_5^{11} f(x)\,dx = \frac{1}{2} - \frac{1}{2}(4)(2) + \frac{1}{2} = -3$

(e) $\int_0^{11} f(x)\,dx = -\frac{1}{2} + 2 + 2 + 2 - 4 + \frac{1}{2} = 2$

(f) $\int_4^{10} f(x)\,dx = 2 - 4 = -2$

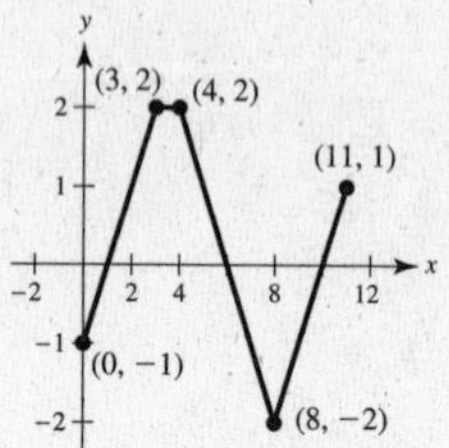


**49.** (a) $\int_0^5 [f(x) + 2]\,dx = \int_0^5 f(x)\,dx + \int_0^5 2\,dx$
$= 4 + 10 = 14$

(b) $\int_{-2}^3 f(x + 2)\,dx = \int_0^5 f(x)\,dx = 4$ (Let $u = x + 2$.)

(c) $\int_{-5}^5 f(x)\,dx = 2\int_0^5 f(x)\,dx = 2(4) = 8$ ($f$ even)

(d) $\int_{-5}^5 f(x)\,dx = 0$ ($f$ odd)

**50.** $f(x) = \begin{cases} 4, & x < 4 \\ x, & x \geq 4 \end{cases}$

$\int_0^8 f(x)\,dx = 4(4) + 4(4) + \frac{1}{2}(4)(4) = 40$

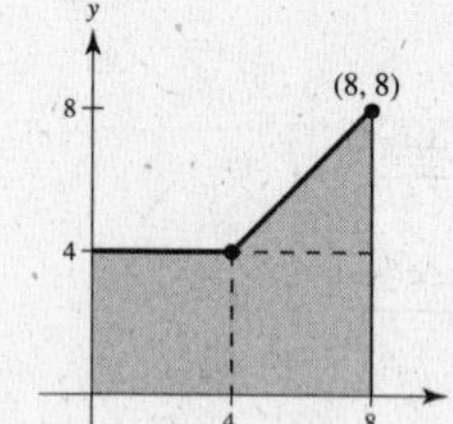

**51.** $f(x) = \begin{cases} 6, & x > 6 \\ -\frac{1}{2}x + 9, & x \le 6 \end{cases}$

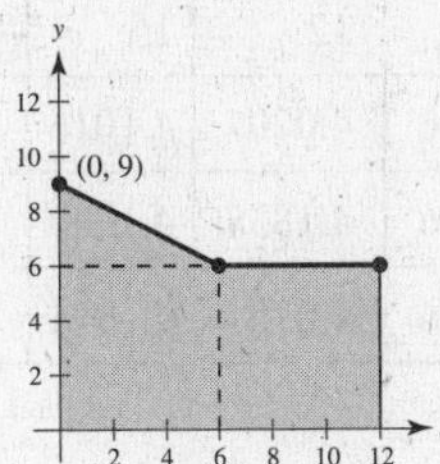


$\int_0^{12} f(x)\,dx = 6(6) + \frac{1}{2}6(3) + 6(6) = 36 + 9 + 36 = 81$

**52.** (a) $\int_{-2}^{1} f(x)\,dx + \int_1^5 f(x)\,dx = \int_{-2}^{5} f(x)\,dx$

$a = -2,\ b = 5$

(b) $\int_{-3}^{3} f(x)\,dx + \int_3^6 f(x)\,dx - \int_a^b f(x)\,dx = \int_{-1}^{6} f(x)\,dx$

$\int_{-3}^{6} f(x)\,dx + \int_b^a f(x)\,dx = \int_{-1}^{6} f(x)\,dx$

$a = -3,\ b = -1$

(c) Answers will vary. *Sample answer:* $a = \pi,\ b = 2\pi$

$\int_\pi^{2\pi} \sin x\,dx < 0$

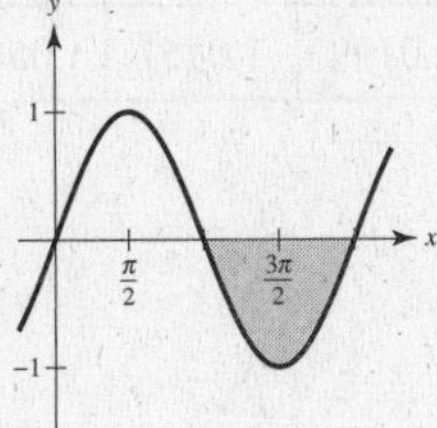

(d) Answers will vary. *Sample answer:* $a = 0,\ b = \pi$

$\int_0^\pi \cos x\,dx = 0$

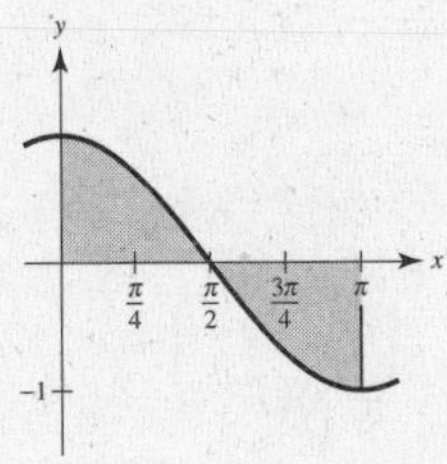

**53.** The left endpoint approximation will be greater than the actual area so,

$\sum_{i=1}^{n} f(x_i)\Delta x > \int_1^5 f(x)\,dx.$

**54.** The right endpoint approximation will be less than the actual area so,

$\sum_{i=1}^{n} f(x_i)\Delta x < \int_1^5 f(x)\,dx.$

**55.** $f(x) = \dfrac{1}{x - 4}$

is not integrable on the interval $[3, 5]$ because $f$ has a discontinuity at $x = 4$.

**56.** $f(x) = |x|/x$ is integrable on $[-1, 1]$, but is not continuous on $[-1, 1]$. There is discontinuity at $x = 0$. To see that

$\int_{-1}^{1} \frac{|x|}{x}\,dx$

is integrable, sketch a graph of the region bounded by $f(x) = |x|/x$ and the $x$-axis for $-1 \le x \le 1$. You see that the integral equals 0.

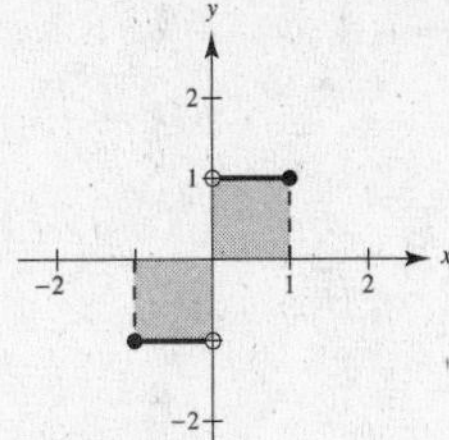

**57.**

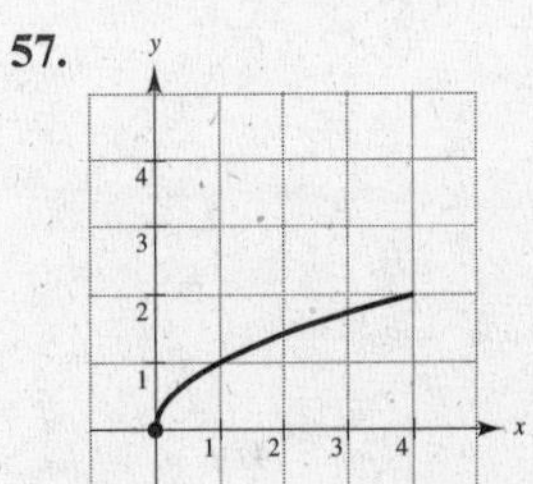

(a) $A \approx 5$ square units

**58.**

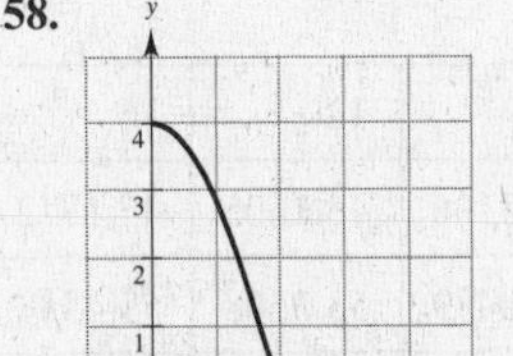

(b) $A \approx \frac{4}{3}$ square units

**59.**

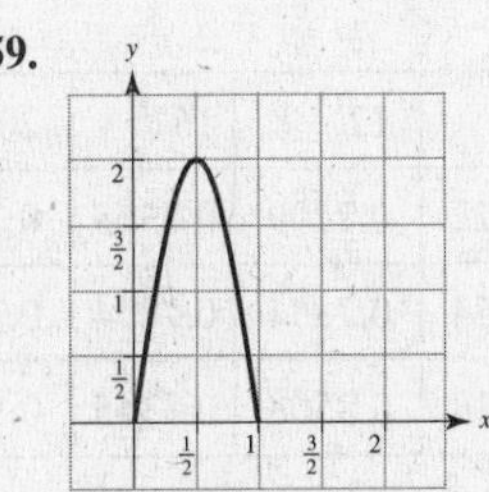

(d) $\int_0^1 2 \sin \pi x\,dx \approx \frac{1}{2}(1)(2) \approx 1$

**60.** 

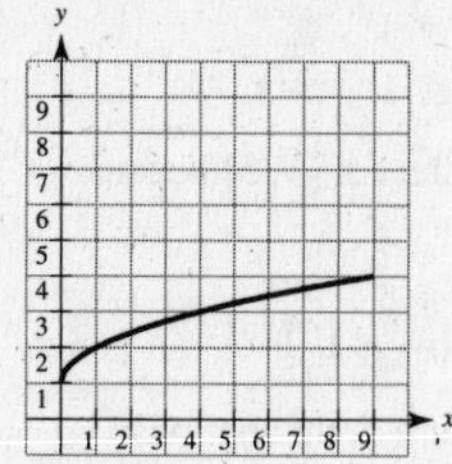

(c) Area ≈ 27

**61.**

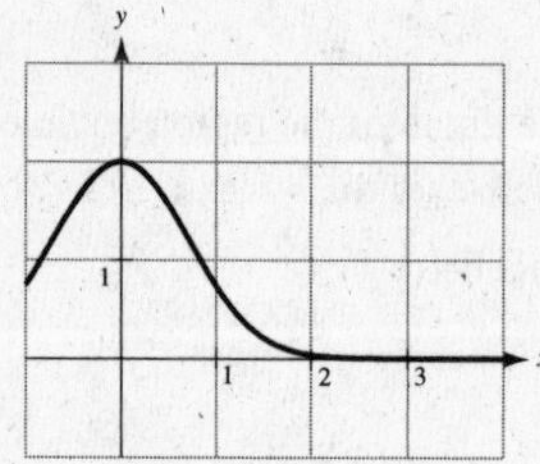

(c) $\int_0^2 2e^{-x^2}\,dx \approx \frac{1}{2}(2)(2) = 2$

**62.** $\int_1^2 \ln x\,dx$

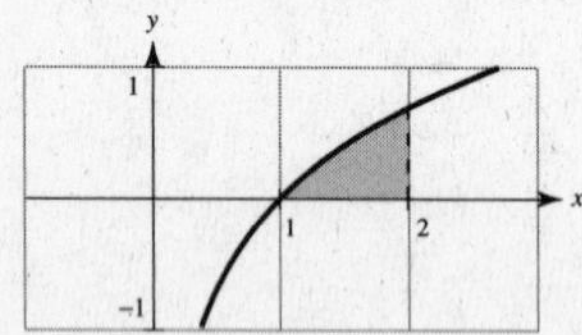

(a) Area $\approx \frac{1}{3}$

**63.** $\int_0^3 x\sqrt{3 - x}\,dx$

| $N$ | 4 | 8 | 12 | 16 | 20 |
|---|---|---|---|---|---|
| $L(n)$ | 3.6830 | 3.9956 | 4.0707 | 4.1016 | 4.1177 |
| $M(n)$ | 4.3082 | 4.2076 | 4.1838 | 4.1740 | 4.1690 |
| $R(n)$ | 3.6830 | 3.9956 | 4.0707 | 4.1016 | 4.1177 |

**64.** $\int_0^3 \frac{5}{x^2 + 1}\,dx$

| $N$ | 4 | 8 | 12 | 16 | 20 |
|---|---|---|---|---|---|
| $L(n)$ | 7.9224 | 7.0855 | 6.8062 | 6.6662 | 6.5822 |
| $M(n)$ | 6.2485 | 6.2470 | 6.2460 | 6.2457 | 6.2455 |
| $R(n)$ | 4.5474 | 5.3980 | 5.6812 | 5.8225 | 5.9072 |

**65.** $\int_1^3 \frac{1}{x}\,dx$

| $N$ | 4 | 8 | 12 | 16 | 20 |
|---|---|---|---|---|---|
| $L(n)$ | 1.2833 | 1.1865 | 1.1562 | 1.1414 | 1.1327 |
| $M(n)$ | 1.0898 | 1.0963 | 1.0976 | 1.0980 | 1.0982 |
| $R(n)$ | 0.9500 | 1.0199 | 1.0451 | 1.0581 | 1.0660 |

**66.** $\int_0^4 e^x\,dx$

| $n$ | 4 | 8 | 12 | 16 | 20 |
|---|---|---|---|---|---|
| $L(n)$ | 31.1929 | 41.3106 | 45.1605 | 47.1772 | 48.4169 |
| $M(n)$ | 51.4284 | 53.0439 | 53.3508 | 53.4588 | 53.5089 |
| $R(n)$ | 84.7910 | 68.1097 | 63.0265 | 60.5768 | 59.1365 |

**67.** $\int_0^{\pi/2} \sin^2 x\,dx$

| $n$ | 4 | 8 | 12 | 16 | 20 |
|---|---|---|---|---|---|
| $L(n)$ | 0.5890 | 0.6872 | 0.7199 | 0.7363 | 0.7461 |
| $M(n)$ | 0.7854 | 0.7854 | 0.7854 | 0.7854 | 0.7854 |
| $R(n)$ | 0.9817 | 0.8836 | 0.8508 | 0.8345 | 0.8247 |

**68.** $\int_0^3 x \sin x\,dx$

| $n$ | 4 | 8 | 12 | 16 | 20 |
|---|---|---|---|---|---|
| $L(n)$ | 2.8186 | 2.9985 | 3.0434 | 3.0631 | 3.0740 |
| $M(n)$ | 3.1784 | 3.1277 | 3.1185 | 3.1152 | 3.1138 |
| $R(n)$ | 3.1361 | 3.1573 | 3.1493 | 3.1425 | 3.1375 |

**69.** True

**70.** False

$$\int_0^1 x\sqrt{x}\,dx \neq \left(\int_0^1 x\,dx\right)\left(\int_0^1 \sqrt{x}\,dx\right)$$

**71.** True

**72.** True

**73.** False

$$\int_0^2 (-x)\,dx = -2$$

**74.** True. The limits of integration are the same.

**75.** $f(x) = x^2 + 3x, [0, 8]$

$x_0 = 0,\ x_1 = 1,\ x_2 = 3,\ x_3 = 7,\ x_4 = 8$

$\Delta x_1 = 1,\ \Delta x_2 = 2,\ \Delta x_3 = 4,\ \Delta x_4 = 1$

$c_1 = 1, c_2 = 2,\ c_3 = 5,\ c_4 = 8$

$$\begin{aligned}\sum_{i=1}^{4} f(c_i)\Delta x &= f(1)\Delta x_1 + f(2)\Delta x_2 + f(5)\Delta x_3 + f(8)\Delta x_4\\ &= (4)(1) + (10)(2) + (40)(4) + (88)(1) = 272\end{aligned}$$

**76.** $f(x) = \sin x, [0, 2\pi]$

$x_0 = 0,\ x_1 = \dfrac{\pi}{4},\ x_2 = \dfrac{\pi}{3},\ x_3 = \pi,\ x_4 = 2\pi$

$\Delta x_1 = \dfrac{\pi}{4},\ \Delta x_2 = \dfrac{\pi}{12},\ \Delta x_3 = \dfrac{2\pi}{3},\ \Delta x_4 = \pi$

$c_1 = \dfrac{\pi}{6},\ c_2 = \dfrac{\pi}{3},\ c_3 = \dfrac{2\pi}{3},\ c_4 = \dfrac{3\pi}{2}$

$$\begin{aligned}\sum_{i=1}^{4} f(c_i)\,\Delta x_i &= f\left(\frac{\pi}{6}\right)\Delta x_1 + f\left(\frac{\pi}{3}\right)\Delta x_2 + f\left(\frac{2\pi}{3}\right)\Delta x_3 + f\left(\frac{3\pi}{2}\right)\Delta x_4\\ &= \left(\frac{1}{2}\right)\left(\frac{\pi}{4}\right) + \left(\frac{\sqrt{3}}{2}\right)\left(\frac{\pi}{12}\right) + \left(\frac{\sqrt{3}}{2}\right)\left(\frac{2\pi}{3}\right) + (-1)(\pi) \approx -0.708\end{aligned}$$

**77.** $\Delta x = \dfrac{b-a}{n},\ c_i = a + i(\Delta x) = a + i\left(\dfrac{b-a}{n}\right)$

$$\begin{aligned}\int_0^b x\,dx &= \lim_{\|\Delta\|\to 0} \sum_{i=1}^{n} f(c_i)\Delta x\\ &= \lim_{n\to\infty} \sum_{i=1}^{n}\left[a + i\left(\frac{b-a}{n}\right)\right]\left(\frac{b-a}{n}\right)\\ &= \lim_{n\to\infty}\left[\left(\frac{b-a}{n}\right)\sum_{i=1}^{n} a + \left(\frac{b-a}{n}\right)^2\sum_{i=1}^{n} i\right]\\ &= \lim_{n\to\infty}\left[\frac{b-a}{n}(an) + \left(\frac{b-a}{n}\right)^2\frac{n(n+1)}{2}\right]\\ &= \lim_{n\to\infty}\left[a(b-a) + \frac{(b-a)^2}{n}\frac{n+1}{2}\right]\\ &= a(b-a) + \frac{(b-a)^2}{2}\\ &= (b-a)\left[a + \frac{b-a}{2}\right]\\ &= \frac{(b-a)(a+b)}{2} = \frac{b^2-a^2}{2}\end{aligned}$$

**78.** $\Delta x = \dfrac{b-a}{n},\ c_i = a + i(\Delta x) = a + i\left(\dfrac{b-a}{n}\right)$

$$\begin{aligned}
\int_a^b x^2\,dx &= \lim_{\|\Delta\|\to 0}\sum_{i=1}^{n} f(c_i)\Delta x \\
&= \lim_{n\to\infty}\sum_{i=1}^{n}\left[a + i\left(\frac{b-a}{n}\right)\right]^2\left(\frac{b-a}{n}\right) \\
&= \lim_{n\to\infty}\left[\left(\frac{b-a}{n}\right)\sum_{i=1}^{n}\left(a^2 + \frac{2ai(b-a)}{n} + i^2\left(\frac{b-a}{n}\right)^2\right)\right] \\
&= \lim_{n\to\infty}\left(\frac{b-a}{n}\right)\left[na^2 + \frac{2a(b-a)}{n}\frac{n(n+1)}{2} + \left(\frac{b-a}{n}\right)^2\frac{n(n+1)(2n+1)}{6}\right] \\
&= \lim_{n\to\infty}\left[a^2(b-a) + \frac{a(b-a)^2(n+1)}{n} + \frac{(b-a)^3}{6}\frac{(n+1)(2n+1)}{n^2}\right] \\
&= a^2(b-a) + a(b-a)^2 + \frac{1}{3}(b-a)^3 = \frac{1}{3}\left(b^3 - a^3\right)
\end{aligned}$$

**79.** $f(x) = \begin{cases} 1, & x \text{ is rational} \\ 0, & x \text{ is irrational}\end{cases}$

is not integrable on the interval $[0, 1]$. As $\|\Delta\| \to 0$, $f(c_i) = 1$ or $f(c_i) = 0$ in each subinterval because there are an infinite number of both rational and irrational numbers in any interval, no matter how small.

**80.** $f(x) = \begin{cases} 0, & x = 0 \\ \dfrac{1}{x}, & 0 < x \le 1\end{cases}$

The limit

$$\lim_{\|\Delta\|\to 0}\sum_{i=1}^{n} f(c_i)\Delta x_i$$

does not exist. This does not contradict Theorem 5.4 because $f$ is not continuous on [0, 1].

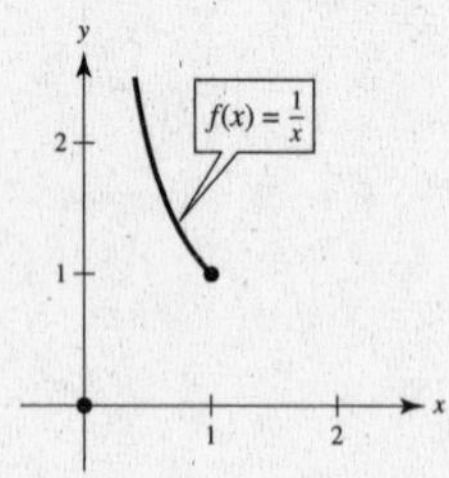


**81.** The function $f$ is nonnegative between $x = -1$ and $x = 1$.

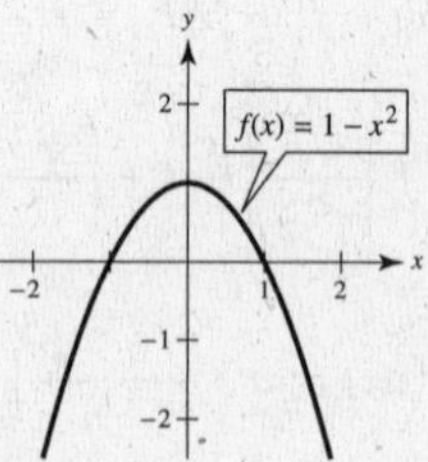


So,

$$\int_a^b \left(1 - x^2\right)dx$$

is a maximum for $a = -1$ and $b = 1$.

**82.** To find $\int_0^2 [\![x]\!]\,dx$, use a geometric approach.

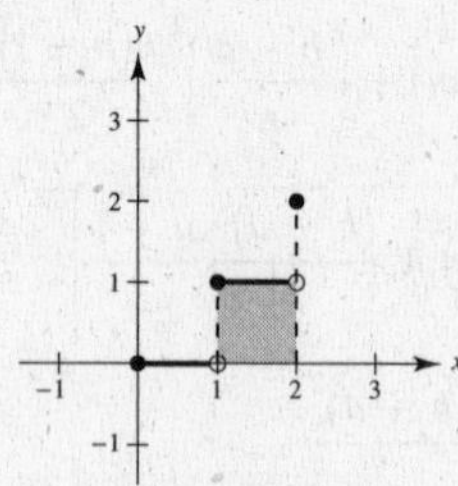

So, $\int_0^2 [\![x]\!]\,dx = 1(2 - 1) = 1$.

**83.** Let $f(x) = x^2$, $0 \le x \le 1$, and $\Delta x_i = 1/n$. The appropriate Riemann Sum is

$$\sum_{i=1}^{n} f(c_i)\Delta x_i = \sum_{i=1}^{n}\left(\frac{i}{n}\right)^2\frac{1}{n} = \frac{1}{n^3}\sum_{i=1}^{n} i^2.$$

$$\lim_{n\to\infty}\frac{1}{n^3}\left[1^2 + 2^2 + 3^2 + \cdots + n^2\right] = \lim_{n\to\infty}\frac{1}{n^3}\cdot\frac{n(2n+1)(n+1)}{6} = \lim_{n\to\infty}\frac{2n^2 + 3n + 1}{6n^2} = \lim_{n\to\infty}\left(\frac{1}{3} + \frac{1}{2n} + \frac{1}{6n^2}\right) = \frac{1}{3}$$

**84.** $I(f) - J(f) = \int_0^1 x^2 f(x)\,dx - \int_0^1 x f(x)^2\,dx.$

Observe that

$$\frac{x^3}{4} - x\left(f(x) - \frac{x}{2}\right)^2 = \frac{x^3}{4} - x\left(f(x)^2 - xf(x) + \frac{x^2}{4}\right) = \frac{x^3}{4} - xf(x)^2 + x^2 f(x) - \frac{x^3}{4} = x^2 f(x) - xf(x)^2$$

So, $I(f) - J(f) = \int_0^1 \left[x^2 f(x) - xf(x)^2\right] dx = \int_0^1 \left[\frac{x^3}{4} - x\left(f(x) - \frac{x}{2}\right)^2\right] dx \le \int_0^1 \frac{x^3}{4}\,dx = \frac{1}{16}$

Furthermore, $6 + f(x) = \frac{x}{2}$. Then $I(f) = \int_0^1 x^2\left(\frac{x}{2}\right) dx = \frac{1}{8}$ and $J(f) = \int_0^1 x\left(\frac{x^2}{4}\right) = \frac{1}{16}$

So $I(f) - J(f) = \frac{1}{8} - \frac{1}{16} = \frac{1}{16}$

The maximum value is $\frac{1}{16}$.

## Section 5.4 The Fundamental Theorem of Calculus

**1.** $f(x) = \dfrac{4}{x^2 + 1}$

$\int_0^{\pi} \dfrac{4}{x^2 + 1}\,dx$ is positive.

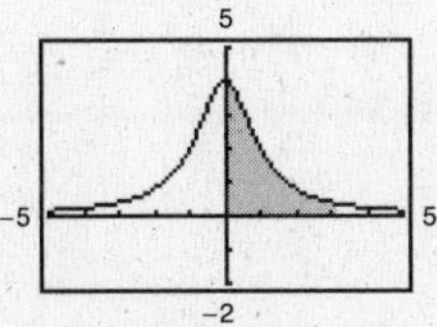


**2.** $f(x) = \cos x$

$\int_0^{\pi} \cos x\,dx = 0$

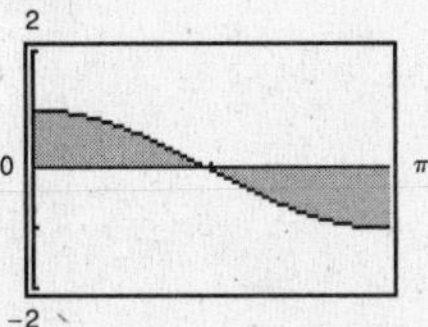


**3.** $f(x) = x\sqrt{x^2 + 1}$

$\int_{-2}^{2} x\sqrt{x^2 + 1}\,dx = 0$

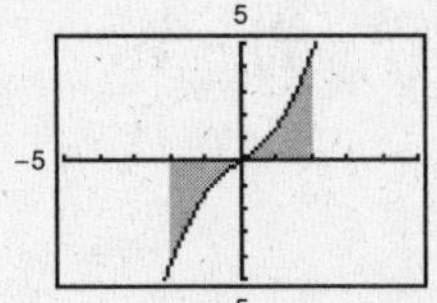


**4.** $f(x) = x\sqrt{2 - x}$

$\int_{-2}^{2} x\sqrt{2 - x}\,dx$ is negative.

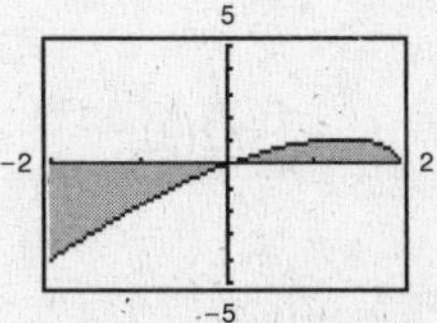


**5.** $\int_0^2 6x\,dx = \left[3x^2\right]_0^2 = 12 - 0 = 12$

**6.** $\int_4^9 5\,dv = \left[5v\right]_4^9 = 5(9) - 5(4) = 25$

**7.** $\int_{-1}^{0} (2x - 1)\,dx = \left[x^2 - x\right]_{-1}^{0}$

$= 0 - \left((-1)^2 - (-1)\right) = -(1 + 1) = -2$

**8.** $\int_2^5 (-3v + 4)\,dv = \left[-\frac{3}{2}v^2 + 4v\right]_2^5$

$= \left(-\frac{75}{2} + 20\right) - (-6 + 8) = -\frac{39}{2}$

**9.** $\int_{-1}^{1} \left(t^2 - 2\right) dt = \left[\frac{t^3}{3} - 2t\right]_{-1}^{1}$

$= \left(\frac{1}{3} - 2\right) - \left(-\frac{1}{3} + 2\right) = -\frac{10}{3}$

10. $\int_1^7 \left(6x^2 + 2x - 3\right) dx = \left[2x^3 + x^2 - 3x\right]_1^7 = \left[2(7)^3 + (7)^2 - 3(7)\right] - [2 + 1 - 3] = 714 - 0 = 714$

11. $\int_0^1 (2t - 1)^2\, dt = \int_0^1 \left(4t^2 - 4t + 1\right) dt = \left[\frac{4}{3}t^3 - 2t^2 + t\right]_0^1 = \frac{4}{3} - 2 + 1 = \frac{1}{3}$

12. $\int_{-1}^1 \left(t^3 - 9t\right) dt = \left[\frac{1}{4}t^4 - \frac{9}{2}t^2\right]_{-1}^1 = \left(\frac{1}{4} - \frac{9}{2}\right) - \left(\frac{1}{4} - \frac{9}{2}\right) = 0$

13. $\int_1^2 \left(\frac{3}{x^2} - 1\right) dx = \left[-\frac{3}{x} - x\right]_1^2 = \left(-\frac{3}{2} - 2\right) - (-3 - 1) = \frac{1}{2}$

14. $\int_{-2}^{-1} \left(u - \frac{1}{u^2}\right) du = \left[\frac{u^2}{2} + \frac{1}{u}\right]_{-2}^{-1} = \left(\frac{1}{2} - 1\right) - \left(2 - \frac{1}{2}\right) = -2$

15. $\int_1^4 \frac{u - 2}{\sqrt{u}}\, du = \int_1^4 \left(u^{1/2} - 2u^{-1/2}\right) du = \left[\frac{2}{3}u^{3/2} - 4u^{1/2}\right]_1^4 = \left[\frac{2}{3}\left(\sqrt{4}\right)^3 - 4\sqrt{4}\right] - \left[\frac{2}{3} - 4\right] = \frac{2}{3}$

16. $\int_{-3}^3 v^{1/3}\, dv = \left[\frac{3}{4}v^{4/3}\right]_{-3}^3 = \frac{3}{4}\left[\left(\sqrt[3]{-3}\right)^4\right] - \left(\sqrt[3]{-3}\right)^4\right] = 0$

17. $\int_{-1}^1 \left(\sqrt[3]{t} - 2\right) dt = \left[\frac{3}{4}t^{4/3} - 2t\right]_{-1}^1 = \left(\frac{3}{4} - 2\right) - \left(\frac{3}{4} + 2\right) = -4$

18. $\int_1^8 \sqrt{\frac{2}{x}}\, dx = \sqrt{2}\int_1^8 x^{-1/2}\, dx = \left[\sqrt{2}(2)x^{1/2}\right]_1^8 = \left[2\sqrt{2x}\right]_1^8 = 8 - 2\sqrt{2}$

19. $\int_0^1 \frac{x - \sqrt{x}}{3}\, dx = \frac{1}{3}\int_0^1 \left(x - x^{1/2}\right) dx = \frac{1}{3}\left[\frac{x^2}{2} - \frac{2}{3}x^{3/2}\right]_0^1 = \frac{1}{3}\left(\frac{1}{2} - \frac{2}{3}\right) = -\frac{1}{18}$

20. $\int_0^2 (2 - t)\sqrt{t}\, dt = \int_0^2 \left(2t^{1/2} - t^{3/2}\right) dt = \left[\frac{4}{3}t^{3/2} - \frac{2}{5}t^{5/2}\right]_0^2 = \left[\frac{t\sqrt{t}}{15}(20 - 6t)\right]_0^2 = \frac{2\sqrt{2}}{15}(20 - 12) = \frac{16\sqrt{2}}{15}$

21. $\int_{-1}^0 \left(t^{1/3} - t^{2/3}\right) dt = \left[\frac{3}{4}t^{4/3} - \frac{3}{5}t^{5/3}\right]_{-1}^0 = 0 - \left(\frac{3}{4} + \frac{3}{5}\right) = -\frac{27}{20}$

22. $\int_{-8}^{-1} \frac{x - x^2}{2\sqrt[3]{x}}\, dx = \frac{1}{2}\int_{-8}^{-1} \left(x^{2/3} - x^{5/3}\right) dx$

$= \frac{1}{2}\left[\frac{3}{5}x^{5/3} - \frac{3}{8}x^{8/3}\right]_{-8}^{-1} = \left[\frac{x^{5/3}}{80}(24 - 15x)\right]_{-8}^{-1} = -\frac{1}{80}(39) + \frac{32}{80}(144) = \frac{4569}{80}$

23. $\int_0^5 |2x - 5|\, dx = \int_0^{5/2} (5 - 2x)\, dx + \int_{5/2}^5 (2x - 5)\, dx$ (split up the integral at the zero $x = \frac{5}{2}$)

$= \left[5x - x^2\right]_0^{5/2} + \left[x^2 - 5x\right]_{5/2}^5 = \left(\frac{25}{2} - \frac{25}{4}\right) - 0 + (25 - 25) - \left(\frac{25}{4} - \frac{25}{2}\right) = 2\left(\frac{25}{2} - \frac{25}{4}\right) = \frac{25}{2}$

**Note:** By Symmetry, $\int_0^5 |2x - 5|\, dx = 2\int_{5/2}^5 (2x - 5)\, dx$.

**24.** $\int_2^5 (3 - |x - 4|)\,dx = \int_2^4 [3 + (x - 4)]\,dx + \int_4^5 [3 - (x - 4)]\,dx$

$= \int_2^4 (x - 1)\,dx + \int_4^5 (7 - x)\,dx$

$= \left[\frac{x^2}{2} - x\right]_2^4 + \left[7x - \frac{x^2}{2}\right]_4^5$

$= (4 - 0) + \left[\left(35 - \frac{25}{2}\right) - (28 - 8)\right]$

$= \frac{13}{2}$

**25.** $\int_0^4 |x^2 - 9|\,dx = \int_0^3 (9 - x^2)\,dx + \int_3^4 (x^2 - 9)\,dx$ (split up integral at the zero $x = 3$)

$= \left[9x - \frac{x^3}{3}\right]_0^3 + \left[\frac{x^3}{3} - 9x\right]_3^4 = (27 - 9) + \left(\frac{64}{3} - 36\right) - (9 - 27) = \frac{64}{3}$

**26.** $\int_0^4 |x^2 - 4x + 3|\,dx = \int_0^1 (x^2 - 4x + 3)\,dx - \int_1^3 (x^2 - 4x + 3)\,dx + \int_3^4 (x^2 - 4x + 3)\,dx$ (split up the integral at the zeros $x = 1, 3$)

$= \left[\frac{x^3}{3} - 2x^2 + 3x\right]_0^1 - \left[\frac{x^3}{3} - 2x^2 + 3x\right]_1^3 + \left[\frac{x^3}{3} - 2x^2 + 3x\right]_3^4$

$= \left(\frac{1}{3} - 2 + 3\right) - (9 - 18 + 9) + \left(\frac{1}{3} - 2 + 3\right) + \left(\frac{64}{3} - 32 + 12\right) - (9 - 18 + 9)$

$= \frac{4}{3} - 0 + \frac{4}{3} + \frac{4}{3} - 0 = 4$

**27.** $\int_0^\pi (1 + \sin x)\,dx = [x - \cos x]_0^\pi = (\pi + 1) - (0 - 1) = 2 + \pi$

**28.** $\int_0^{\pi/4} \frac{1 - \sin^2\theta}{\cos^2\theta}\,d\theta = \int_0^{\pi/4} d\theta = [\theta]_0^{\pi/4} = \frac{\pi}{4}$

**29.** $\int_{-\pi/6}^{\pi/6} \sec^2 x\,dx = [\tan x]_{-\pi/6}^{\pi/6} = \frac{\sqrt{3}}{3} - \left(-\frac{\sqrt{3}}{3}\right) = \frac{2\sqrt{3}}{3}$

**30.** $\int_{\pi/4}^{\pi/2} (2 - \csc^2 x)\,dx = [2x + \cot x]_{\pi/4}^{\pi/2} = (\pi + 0) - \left(\frac{\pi}{2} + 1\right) = \frac{\pi}{2} - 1 = \frac{\pi - 2}{2}$

**31.** $\int_1^e \left(2x - \frac{1}{x}\right)dx = [x^2 - \ln x]_1^e = (e^2 - 1) - (1 - 0) = e^2 - 2$

**32.** $\int_1^5 \frac{x + 1}{x}\,dx = \int_1^5 \left(1 + \frac{1}{x}\right)dx = [x + \ln x]_1^5 = (5 + \ln 5) - (1 + \ln 1) = 4 + \ln 5$

**33.** $\int_{-\pi/3}^{\pi/3} 4\sec\theta\tan\theta\,d\theta = [4\sec\theta]_{-\pi/3}^{\pi/3} = 4(2) - 4(2) = 0$

**34.** $\int_{-\pi/2}^{\pi/2} (2t + \cos t)\,dt = [t^2 + \sin t]_{-\pi/2}^{\pi/2} = \left(\frac{\pi^2}{4} + 1\right) - \left(\frac{\pi^2}{4} - 1\right) = 2$

**35.** $\int_0^2 (2^x + 6)\,dx = \left[\frac{2^x}{\ln 2} + 6x\right]_0^2 = \left(\frac{4}{\ln 2} + 12\right) - \left(\frac{1}{\ln 2} + 0\right) = \frac{3}{\ln 2} + 12$

**36.** $\int_0^3 (t - 5^t)\,dt = \left[\frac{t^2}{2} - \frac{5^t}{\ln 5}\right]_0^3 = \left(\frac{9}{2} - \frac{125}{\ln 5}\right) - \left(0 - \frac{1}{\ln 5}\right) = \frac{9}{2} - \frac{124}{\ln 5} \approx -72.546$

**37.** $\int_{-1}^1 (e^\theta + \sin\theta)\,d\theta = \left[e^\theta - \cos\theta\right]_{-1}^1 = (e - \cos 1) - \left[e^{-1} - \cos(-1)\right] = e - \frac{1}{e}$

**38.** $\int_e^{2e} \left(\cos x - \frac{1}{x}\right) dx = \left[\sin x - \ln x\right]_e^{2e} = \left[\sin(2e) - \ln(2e)\right] - \left[\sin(e) - \ln(e)\right] = \sin(2e) - \sin(e) - \ln 2$

**39.** $A = \int_0^1 (x - x^2)\,dx = \left[\frac{x^2}{2} - \frac{x^3}{3}\right]_0^1 = \frac{1}{6}$

**40.** $A = \int_1^2 \frac{1}{x^2}\,dx = \left[-\frac{1}{x}\right]_1^2 = \frac{1}{2}$

**41.** $A = \int_0^{\pi/2} \cos x\,dx = \left[\sin x\right]_0^{\pi/2} = 1$

**42.** $A = \int_0^\pi (x + \sin x)\,dx = \left[\frac{x^2}{2} - \cos x\right]_0^\pi = \frac{\pi^2}{2} + 2 = \frac{\pi^2 + 4}{2}$

**43.** Because $y > 0$ on $[0, 2]$,

Area $= \int_0^2 (5x^2 + 2)\,dx = \left[\frac{5}{3}x^3 + 2x\right]_0^2 = \frac{40}{3} + 4 = \frac{52}{3}.$

**44.** Because $y > 0$ on $[0, 2]$,

Area $= \int_0^2 (x^3 + x)\,dx = \left[\frac{x^4}{4} + \frac{x^2}{2}\right]_0^2 = 4 + 2 = 6.$

**45.** Because $y > 0$ on $[0, 8]$,

Area $= \int_0^8 (1 + x^{1/3})\,dx = \left[x + \frac{3}{4}x^{4/3}\right]_0^8 = 8 + \frac{3}{4}(16) = 20.$

**46.** Because $y > 0$ on $[0, 3]$,

Area $= \int_0^3 (3 - x)\sqrt{x}\,dx = \int_0^3 (3x^{1/2} - x^{3/2})\,dx = \left[\frac{3x^{3/2}}{3/2} - \frac{x^{5/2}}{5/2}\right]_0^3 = \left[2x^{3/2} - \frac{2}{5}x^{5/2}\right]_0^3 = 2 \cdot 3 \cdot \sqrt{3} - \frac{2}{5}9\sqrt{3} = \frac{12}{5}\sqrt{3}.$

**47.** Because $y > 0$ on $[0, 4]$,

Area $= \int_0^4 (-x^2 + 4x)\,dx = \left[-\frac{x^3}{3} + 2x^2\right]_0^4 = -\frac{64}{3} + 32 = \frac{32}{3}.$

**48.** Because $y > 0$ on $[-1, 1]$,

Area $= \int_{-1}^1 (1 - x^4)\,dx$

$= 2\int_0^1 (1 - x^4)\,dx$

$= 2\left[x - \frac{x^5}{5}\right]_0^1 = 2\left(1 - \frac{1}{5}\right) = \frac{8}{5}.$

**49.** $\int_1^e \frac{4}{x}\,dx = \left[4\ln x\right]_1^e = 4\ln e - 4\ln 1 = 4$

**50.** $\int_0^2 e^x\,dx = \left[e^x\right]_0^2 = e^2 - e^0 = e^2 - 1$

**51.** $\int_0^3 x^3\,dx = \left[\frac{x^4}{4}\right]_0^3 = \frac{81}{4}$

$$f(c)(3-0) = \frac{81}{4}$$
$$f(c) = \frac{27}{4}$$
$$c^3 = \frac{27}{4}$$
$$c = \frac{3}{\sqrt[3]{4}} = \frac{3}{2}\sqrt[3]{2} \approx 1.8899$$

**52.** $\int_1^3 \frac{9}{x^3}\,dx = \left[-\frac{9}{2x^2}\right]_1^3 = -\frac{1}{2} + \frac{9}{2} = 4$

$$f(c)(3-1) = 4$$
$$\frac{9}{c^3} = 2$$
$$c^3 = \frac{9}{2}$$
$$c = \sqrt[3]{\frac{9}{2}} \approx 1.6510$$

**53.** $\int_4^9 \sqrt{x}\,dx = \left[\frac{2}{3}x^{3/2}\right]_4^9 = \frac{2}{3}(27-8) = \frac{38}{3}$

$$f(c)(9-4) = \frac{38}{3}$$
$$f(c) = \frac{38}{15}$$
$$\sqrt{c} = \frac{38}{15}$$
$$c = \frac{1444}{225} \approx 6.4178$$

**54.** $\int_0^2 \left(x - 2\sqrt{x}\right)dx = \left[\frac{x^2}{2} - \frac{4x^{3/2}}{3}\right]_0^2 = 2 - \frac{8\sqrt{2}}{3}$

$$f(c)(2-0) = \frac{6-8\sqrt{2}}{3}$$
$$c - 2\sqrt{c} = \frac{3-4\sqrt{2}}{3}$$
$$c - 2\sqrt{c} + 1 = \frac{3-4\sqrt{2}}{3} + 1$$
$$\left(\sqrt{c}-1\right)^2 = \frac{6-4\sqrt{2}}{3}$$
$$\sqrt{c} - 1 = \pm\sqrt{\frac{6-4\sqrt{2}}{3}}$$
$$c = \left[1 \pm \sqrt{\frac{6-4\sqrt{2}}{3}}\right]^2$$
$$c \approx 0.4380 \text{ or } c \approx 1.7908$$

**55.** $\int_{-\pi/4}^{\pi/4} 2\sec^2 x\,dx = \left[2\tan x\right]_{-\pi/4}^{\pi/4} = 2(1) - 2(-1) = 4$

$$f(c)\left[\frac{\pi}{4} - \left(-\frac{\pi}{4}\right)\right] = 4$$
$$2\sec^2 c = \frac{8}{\pi}$$
$$\sec^2 c = \frac{4}{\pi}$$
$$\sec c = \pm\frac{2}{\sqrt{\pi}}$$
$$c = \pm\operatorname{arcsec}\left(\frac{2}{\sqrt{\pi}}\right)$$
$$= \pm\arccos\frac{\sqrt{\pi}}{2} \approx \pm 0.4817$$

**56.** $\int_{-\pi/3}^{\pi/3} \cos x\,dx = \left[\sin x\right]_{-\pi/3}^{\pi/3} = \sqrt{3}$

$$f(c)\left[\frac{\pi}{3} - \left(-\frac{\pi}{3}\right)\right] = \sqrt{3}$$
$$\cos c = \frac{3\sqrt{3}}{2\pi}$$
$$c \approx \pm 0.5971$$

**57.** $\int_1^4 \left(5 - \frac{1}{x}\right)dx = \left[5x - \ln x\right]_1^4$

$$= (20 - \ln 4) - (5 - 0) = 15 - \ln 4$$
$$f(c)(4-1) = 15 - \ln 4$$
$$\left(5 - \frac{1}{c}\right)(3) = 15 - \ln 4$$
$$15 - \frac{3}{c} = 15 - \ln 4$$
$$\frac{3}{c} = \ln 4$$
$$c = \frac{3}{\ln 4} \approx 2.1640$$

**58.** $\int_0^3 \left(10 - 2^x\right) dx = \left[10x - \frac{2^x}{\ln 2}\right]_0^3$

$$= \left(30 - \frac{8}{\ln 2}\right) - \left(0 - \frac{1}{\ln 2}\right) = 30 - \frac{7}{\ln 2}$$

$$f(c)(3 - 0) = 30 - \frac{7}{\ln 2}$$

$$\left(10 - 2^c\right)(3) = 30 - \frac{7}{\ln 2}$$

$$3\left(2^c\right) = \frac{7}{\ln 2}$$

$$2^c = \frac{7}{3 \ln 2}$$

$$c = \log_2\left(\frac{7}{3 \ln 2}\right) \approx 1.7512$$

**59.** $\frac{1}{3 - (-3)} \int_{-3}^3 \left(9 - x^2\right) dx = \frac{1}{6}\left[9x - \frac{1}{3}x^3\right]_{-3}^3$

$$= \frac{1}{6}\left[(27 - 9) - (-27 + 9)\right]$$

$$= 6$$

Average value = 6

$9 - x^2 = 6$

$x^2 = 3$

$x = \pm\sqrt{3} \approx \pm 1.7321.$

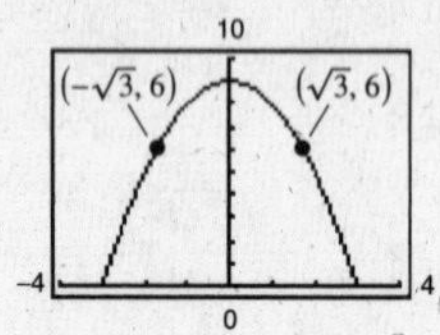


**60.** $\frac{1}{3 - 1} \int_1^3 \frac{4\left(x^2 + 1\right)}{x^2} dx = 2\int_1^3 \left(1 + x^{-2}\right) dx$

$$= 2\left[x - \frac{1}{x}\right]_1^3$$

$$= 2\left(3 - \frac{1}{3}\right) = \frac{16}{3}$$

Average value $= \frac{16}{3}$

$\frac{4\left(x^2 + 1\right)}{x^2} = \frac{16}{3} \Rightarrow x = \sqrt{3}$ (on $[1, 3]$)

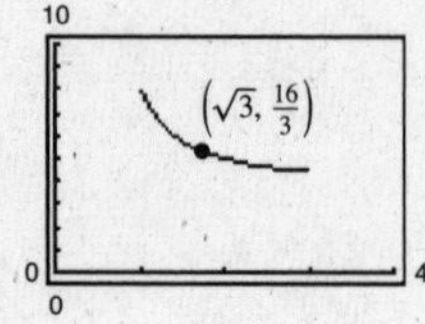


**61.** $\frac{1}{1 - 0} \int_0^1 x^3\, dx = \left[\frac{x^4}{4}\right]_0^1 = \frac{1}{4}$

Average value $= \frac{1}{4}$

$x^3 = \frac{1}{4}$

$x = \sqrt[3]{\frac{1}{4}} = \frac{\sqrt[3]{2}}{2} \approx 0.6300$

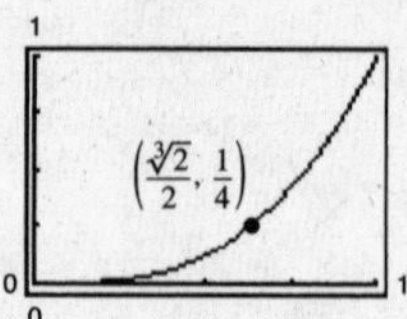


**62.** $\frac{1}{1 - 0} \int_0^1 \left(4x^3 - 3x^2\right) dx = \int_0^1 \left(4x^3 - 3x^2\right) dx$

$$= \left[x^4 - x^3\right]_0^1 = 0$$

Average value = 0

$4x^3 - 3x^2 = 0$

$x^2(4x - 3) = 0 \Rightarrow x = 0, 0.75$

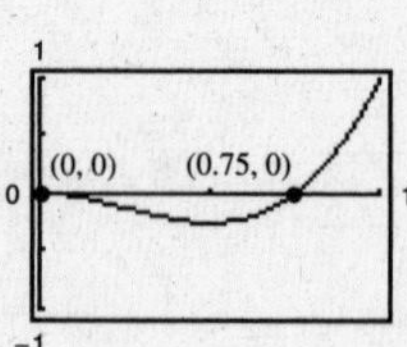

**63.** $\frac{1}{1-(-1)}\int_{-1}^{1} 2e^x\,dx = \int_{-1}^{1} e^x\,dx$

$= \left[e^x\right]_{-1}^{1} = e - e^{-1} \approx 2.3504$

Average value $= e - e^{-1} \approx 2.3504$

$2e^x = e - e^{-1}$

$e^x = \frac{1}{2}\left(e - e^{-1}\right)$

$x = \ln\left(\frac{e - e^{-1}}{2}\right) \approx 0.1614$

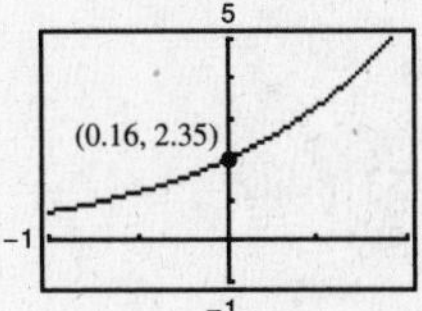


**64.** $\frac{1}{4-1}\int_{1}^{4} \frac{1}{2x}\,dx = \left[\frac{1}{6}\ln x\right]_{1}^{4} = \frac{1}{6}\ln 4 \approx 0.2310$

Average value $= \frac{1}{6}\ln 4 \approx 0.2310$

$\frac{1}{2x} = \frac{1}{6}\ln 4$

$2x = \frac{6}{\ln 4}$

$x = \frac{3}{\ln 4} \approx 2.1640$

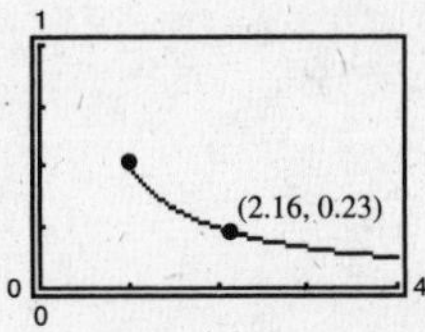


**65.** $\frac{1}{\pi - 0}\int_{0}^{\pi} \sin x\,dx = \left[-\frac{1}{\pi}\cos x\right]_{0}^{\pi} = \frac{2}{\pi}$

Average value $= \frac{2}{\pi}$

$\sin x = \frac{2}{\pi}$

$x \approx 0.690, 2.451$

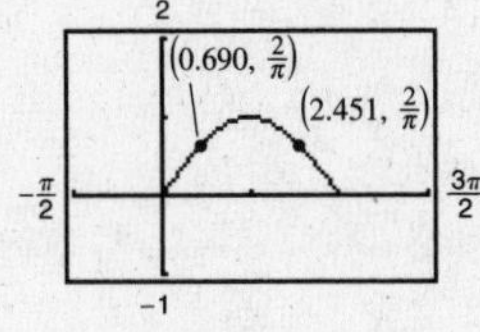


**66.** $\frac{1}{(\pi/2) - 0}\int_{0}^{\pi/2} \cos x\,dx = \left[\frac{2}{\pi}\sin x\right]_{0}^{\pi/2} = \frac{2}{\pi}$

Average value $= \frac{2}{\pi}$

$\cos x = \frac{2}{\pi}$

$x \approx 0.881$

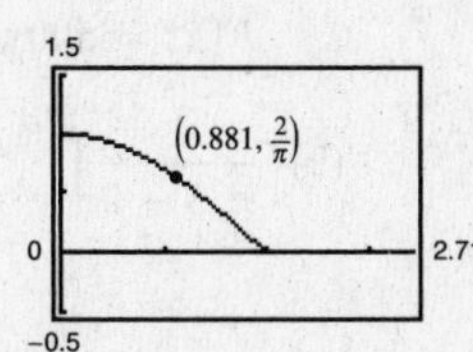


**67.** The distance traveled is $\int_{0}^{8} v(t)\,dt$. The area under the curve from $0 \le t \le 8$ is approximately (18 squares) $(30) \approx 540$ ft.

**68.** The distance traveled is $\int_{0}^{5} v(t)\,dt$. The area under the curve from $0 \le t \le 5$ is approximately (29 squares) $(5) = 145$ ft.

**69.** (a) $\int_{1}^{7} f(x)\,dx = $ Sum of the areas

$= A_1 + A_2 + A_3 + A_4$

$= \frac{1}{2}(3+1) + \frac{1}{2}(1+2) + \frac{1}{2}(2+1) + (3)(1)$

$= 8$

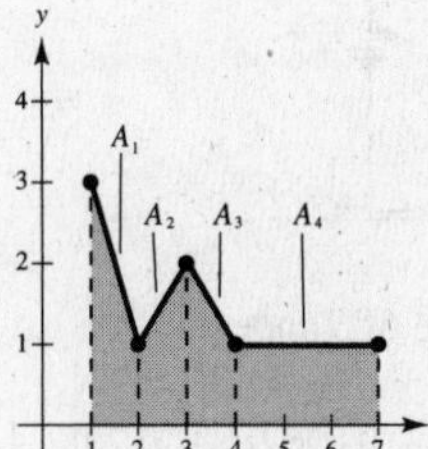


(b) Average value $= \frac{\int_{1}^{7} f(x)\,dx}{7-1} = \frac{8}{6} = \frac{4}{3}$

(c) $A = 8 + (6)(2) = 20$

Average value $= \frac{20}{6} = \frac{10}{3}$

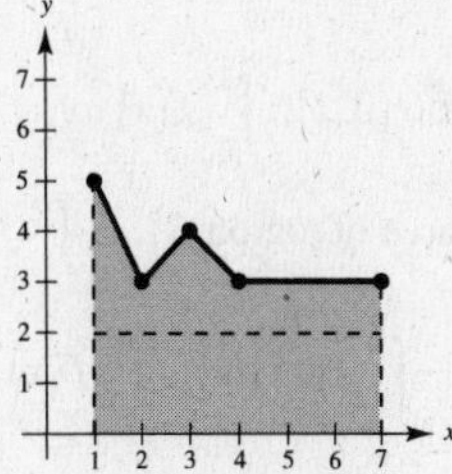


**70.** $r(t)$ represents the weight in pounds of the dog at time $t$.

$\int_{2}^{6} r'(t)\,dt$ represents the net change in the weight of the dog from year 2 to year 6.

**71.** (a) $F(x) = k\sec^2 x$

$F(0) = k = 500$

$F(x) = 500\sec^2 x$

(b) $\displaystyle \frac{1}{\pi/3 - 0}\int_0^{\pi/3} 500\sec^2 x\,dx = \frac{1500}{\pi}\Big[\tan x\Big]_0^{\pi/3}$

$\displaystyle = \frac{1500}{\pi}\left(\sqrt{3} - 0\right)$

$\approx 827$ newtons

**72.** $\displaystyle \frac{1}{R - 0}\int_0^R k\left(R^2 - r^2\right)dr = \frac{k}{R}\left[R^2 r - \frac{r^3}{3}\right]_0^R = \frac{2kR^2}{3}$

**73.** $\displaystyle \frac{1}{5 - 0}\int_0^5 \left(0.1729t + 0.1522t^2 - 0.0374t^3\right)dt \approx \frac{1}{5}\Big[0.08645t^2 + 0.05073t^3 - 0.00935t^4\Big]_0^5 \approx 0.5318$ liter

**74.** (a)

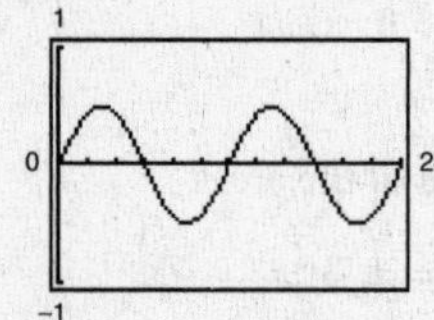


The area above the $x$-axis equals the area below the $x$-axis. So, the average value is zero.

(b)

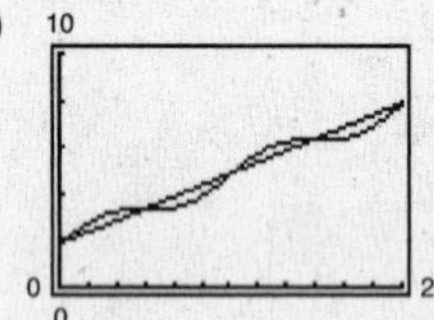


The average value of $S$ appears to be $g$.

**75.** (a) $v = -0.00086t^3 + 0.0782t^2 - 0.208t + 0.10$

(b)

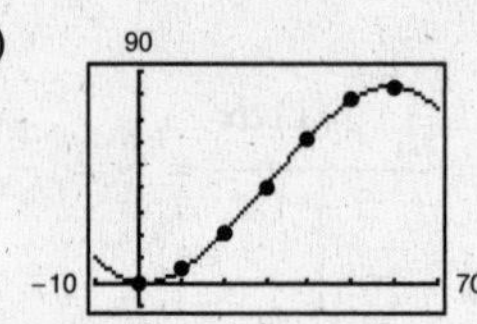


(c) $\displaystyle \int_0^{60} v(t)\,dt = \left[\frac{-0.00086t^4}{4} + \frac{0.0782t^3}{3} - \frac{0.208t^2}{2} + 0.10t\right]_0^{60} \approx 2476$ meters

**76.** (a) Because $y < 0$ on $[0, 2]$, $\int_0^2 f(x)\,dx = -(\text{area of region } A) = -1.5.$

(b) $\int_2^6 f(x)\,dx = (\text{area of region } B) = \int_0^6 f(x)\,dx - \int_0^2 f(x)\,dx = 3.5 - (-1.5) = 5.0$

(c) $\int_0^6 |f(x)|\,dx = -\int_0^2 f(x)\,dx + \int_2^6 f(x)\,dx = 1.5 + 5.0 = 6.5$

(d) $\int_0^2 -2f(x)\,dx = -2\int_0^2 f(x)\,dx = -2(-1.5) = 3.0$

(e) $\int_0^6 \left[2 + f(x)\right]dx = \int_0^6 2\,dx + \int_0^6 f(x)\,dx = 12 + 3.5 = 15.5$

(f) Average value $= \frac{1}{6}\int_0^6 f(x)\,dx = \frac{1}{6}(3.5) \approx 0.5833$

**77.** $F(x) = \int_0^x (4t - 7)\,dt = \left[2t^2 - 7t\right]_0^x = 2x^2 - 7x$

$F(2) = 2(2^2) - 7(2) = -6$

$F(5) = 2(5^2) - 7(5) = 15$

$F(8) = 2(8^2) - 7(8) = 72$

**78.** $F(x) = \int_2^x (t^3 + 2t - 2)\,dt = \left[\frac{t^4}{4} + t^2 - 2t\right]_2^x = \left(\frac{x^4}{4} + x^2 - 2x\right) - (4 + 4 - 4) = \frac{x^4}{4} + x^2 - 2x - 4$

$F(2) = 4 + 4 - 4 - 4 = 0$ $\left[\textbf{Note: } F(2) = \int_2^2 (t^3 + 2t - 2)\,dt = 0\right]$

$F(5) = \frac{625}{4} + 25 - 10 - 4 = 167.25$

$F(8) = \frac{8^4}{4} + 64 - 16 - 4 = 1068$

**79.** $F(x) = \int_1^x \frac{20}{v^2}\,dv = \int_1^x 20v^{-2}\,dv = -\frac{20}{v}\Big]_1^x$

$= -\frac{20}{x} + 20 = 20\left(1 - \frac{1}{x}\right)$

$F(2) = 20\left(\frac{1}{2}\right) = 10$

$F(5) = 20\left(\frac{4}{5}\right) = 16$

$F(8) = 20\left(\frac{7}{8}\right) = \frac{35}{2}$

**80.** $F(x) = \int_2^x -\frac{2}{t^3}\,dt = -\int_2^x 2t^{-3}\,dt = \frac{1}{t^2}\Big]_2^x = \frac{1}{x^2} - \frac{1}{4}$

$F(2) = \frac{1}{4} - \frac{1}{4} = 0$

$F(5) = \frac{1}{25} - \frac{1}{4} = -\frac{21}{100} = -0.21$

$F(8) = \frac{1}{64} - \frac{1}{4} = -\frac{15}{64}$

**81.** $F(x) = \int_1^x \cos\theta\,d\theta = \sin\theta\Big]_1^x = \sin x - \sin 1$

$F(2) = \sin 2 - \sin 1 \approx 0.0678$

$F(5) = \sin 5 - \sin 1 \approx -1.8004$

$F(8) = \sin 8 - \sin 1 \approx 0.1479$

**82.** $F(x) = \int_0^x \sin\theta\,d\theta = -\cos\theta\Big]_0^x$

$= -\cos x + \cos 0$

$= 1 - \cos x$

$F(2) = 1 - \cos 2 \approx 1.4161$

$F(5) = 1 - \cos 5 \approx 0.7163$

$F(8) = 1 - \cos 8 \approx 1.1455$

**83.** $g(x) = \int_0^x f(t)\,dt$

(a) $g(0) = \int_0^0 f(t)\,dt = 0$

$g(2) = \int_0^2 f(t)\,dt \approx 4 + 2 + 1 = 7$

$g(4) = \int_0^4 f(t)\,dt \approx 7 + 2 = 9$

$g(6) = \int_0^6 f(t)\,dt \approx 9 + (-1) = 8$

$g(8) = \int_0^8 f(t)\,dt \approx 8 - 3 = 5$

(b) $g$ increasing on $(0, 4)$ and decreasing on $(4, 8)$

(c) $g$ is a maximum of 9 at $x = 4$.

(d)

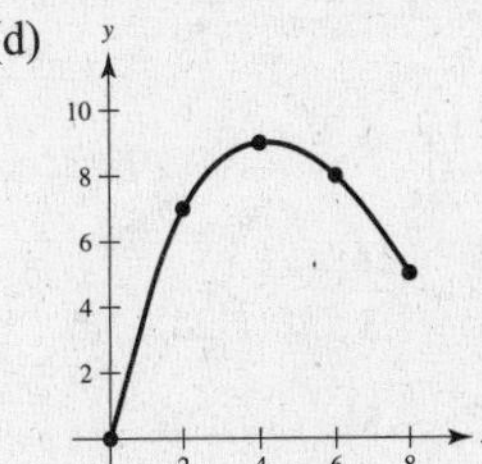

**84.** $g(x) = \int_0^x f(t)\,dt$

(a) $g(0) = \int_0^0 f(t)\,dt = 0$

$g(2) = \int_0^2 f(t)\,dt = -\frac{1}{2}(2)(4) = -4$

$g(4) = \int_0^4 f(t)\,dt = -\frac{1}{2}(4)(4) = -8$

$g(6) = \int_0^6 f(t)\,dt = -8 + 2 + 4 = -2$

$g(8) = \int_0^8 f(t)\,dt = -2 + 6 = 4$

(b) $g$ decreasing on $(0, 4)$ and increasing on $(4, 8)$

(c) $g$ is a minimum of $-8$ at $x = 4$.

(d)

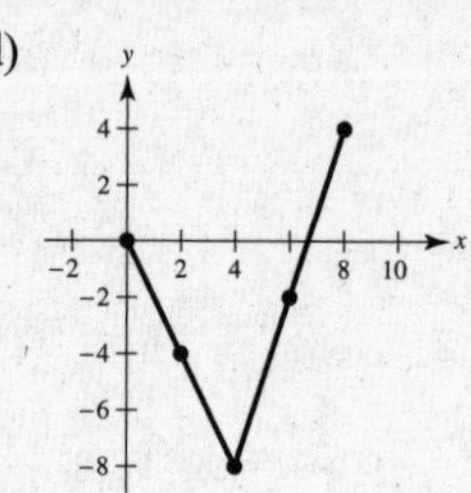

**85.** (a) $\int_0^x (t + 2)\,dt = \left[\frac{t^2}{2} + 2t\right]_0^x = \frac{1}{2}x^2 + 2x$

(b) $\frac{d}{dx}\left[\frac{1}{2}x^2 + 2x\right] = x + 2$

**86.** (a) $\int_0^x t(t^2 + 1)dt = \int_0^x (t^3 + t)\,dt$

$= \left[\frac{1}{4}t^4 + \frac{1}{2}t^2\right]_0^x$

$= \frac{1}{4}x^4 + \frac{1}{2}x^2 = \frac{x^2}{4}(x^2 + 2)$

(b) $\frac{d}{dx}\left[\frac{1}{4}x^4 + \frac{1}{2}x^2\right] = x^3 + x = x(x^2 + 1)$

**87.** (a) $\int_8^x \sqrt[3]{t}\,dt = \left[\frac{3}{4}t^{4/3}\right]_8^x = \frac{3}{4}(x^{4/3} - 16) = \frac{3}{4}x^{4/3} - 12$

(b) $\frac{d}{dx}\left[\frac{3}{4}x^{4/3} - 12\right] = x^{1/3} = \sqrt[3]{x}$

**88.** (a) $\int_4^x \sqrt{t}\,dt = \left[\frac{2}{3}t^{3/2}\right]_4^x$

$= \frac{2}{3}x^{3/2} - \frac{16}{3}$

$= \frac{2}{3}(x^{3/2} - 8)$

(b) $\frac{d}{dx}\left[\frac{2}{3}x^{3/2} - \frac{16}{3}\right] = x^{1/2} = \sqrt{x}$

**89.** (a) $\int_{\pi/4}^x \sec^2 t\,dt = [\tan t]_{\pi/4}^x = \tan x - 1$

(b) $\frac{d}{dx}[\tan x - 1] = \sec^2 x$

**90.** (a) $\int_{\pi/3}^x \sec t \tan t\,dt = [\sec t]_{\pi/3}^x = \sec x - 2$

(b) $\frac{d}{dx}[\sec x - 2] = \sec x \tan x$

**91.** (a) $F(x) = \int_{-1}^x e^t\,dt = e^t\Big]_{-1}^x = e^x - e^{-1}$

(b) $\frac{d}{dx}(e^x - e^{-1}) = e^x$

**92.** (a) $F(x) = \int_1^x \frac{1}{t}dt = \ln t\Big]_1^x = \ln x$

(b) $\frac{d}{dx}(\ln x) = \frac{1}{x}$

**93.** $F(x) = \int_{-2}^x (t^2 - 2t)\,dt$

$F'(x) = x^2 - 2x$

**94.** $F(x) = \int_1^x \frac{t^2}{t^2 + 1}\,dt$

$F'(x) = \frac{x^2}{x^2 + 1}$

**95.** $F(x) = \int_{-1}^x \sqrt{t^4 + 1}\,dt$

$F'(x) = \sqrt{x^4 + 1}$

**96.** $F(x) = \int_1^x \sqrt[4]{t}\,dt$

$F'(x) = \sqrt[4]{x}$

**97.** $F(x) = \int_0^x t \cos t\,dt$

$F'(x) = x \cos x$

**98.** $F(x) = \int_0^x \sec^3 t\,dt$

$F'(x) = \sec^3 x$

**99.** $F(x) = \int_x^{x+2} (4t + 1)\,dt$

$= \left[2t^2 + t\right]_x^{x+2}$

$= \left[2(x+2)^2 + (x+2)\right] - \left[2x^2 + x\right]$

$= 8x + 10$

$F'(x) = 8$

**Alternate solution:**

$F(x) = \int_x^{x+2} (4t + 1)\,dt$

$= \int_x^0 (4t + 1)\,dt + \int_0^{x+2} (4t + 1)\,dt$

$= -\int_0^x (4t + 1)\,dt + \int_0^{x+2} (4t + 1)\,dt$

$F'(x) = -(4x + 1) + 4(x + 2) + 1 = 8$

**100.** $F(x) = \int_{-x}^{x} t^3\,dt = \left[\dfrac{t^4}{4}\right]_{-x}^{x} = 0$

$F'(x) = 0$

**Alternate solution:**

$F(x) = \int_{-x}^{x} t^3\,dt$

$= \int_{-x}^{0} t^3\,dt + \int_0^x t^3\,dt$

$= -\int_0^{-x} t^3\,dt + \int_0^x t^3\,dt$

$F'(x) = -(-x)^3(-1) + (x^3) = 0$

**101.** $F(x) = \int_0^{\sin x} \sqrt{t}\,dt = \left[\frac{2}{3}t^{3/2}\right]_0^{\sin x} = \frac{2}{3}(\sin x)^{3/2}$

$F'(x) = (\sin x)^{1/2}\cos x = \cos x\sqrt{\sin x}$

**Alternate solution:**

$F(x) = \int_0^{\sin x} \sqrt{t}\,dt$

$F'(x) = \sqrt{\sin x}\dfrac{d}{dx}(\sin x) = \sqrt{\sin x}(\cos x)$

**102.** $F(x) = \int_2^{x^2} t^{-3}\,dt = \left[\dfrac{t^{-2}}{-2}\right]_2^{x^2} = \left[-\dfrac{1}{2t^2}\right]_2^{x^2} = -\dfrac{1}{2x^4} + \dfrac{1}{8}$

$F'(x) = 2x^{-5}$

**Alternate solution:**

$F(x) = \int_2^{x^2} t^{-3}\,dt$

$F'(x) = (x^2)^{-3}(2x) = 2x^{-5}$

**103.** $F(x) = \int_0^{x^3} \sin t^2\,dt$

$F'(x) = \sin(x^3)^2 \cdot 3x^2 = 3x^2 \sin x^6$

**104.** $F(x) = \int_0^{x^2} \sin \theta^2\,d\theta$

$F'(x) = \sin(x^2)^2(2x) = 2x \sin x^4$

**105.** $g(x) = \int_0^x f(t)\,dt$

$g(0) = 0, g(1) \approx \frac{1}{2}, g(2) \approx 1, g(3) \approx \frac{1}{2}, g(4) = 0$

$g$ has a relative maximum at $x = 2$.

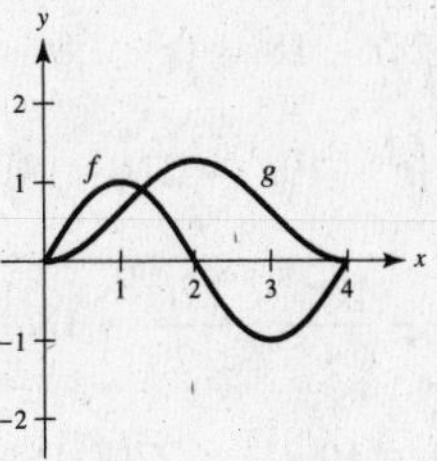


**106.** (a) $g(t) = 4 - \dfrac{4}{t^2}$

$\lim_{t\to\infty} g(t) = 4$

Horizontal asymptote: $y = 4$

(b) $A(x) = \int_1^x \left(4 - \dfrac{4}{t^2}\right)dt = \left[4t + \dfrac{4}{t}\right]_1^x = 4x + \dfrac{4}{x} - 8 = \dfrac{4x^2 - 8x + 4}{x} = \dfrac{4(x-1)^2}{x}$

$\lim_{x\to\infty} A(x) = \lim_{x\to\infty}\left(4x + \dfrac{4}{x} - 8\right) = \infty + 0 - 8 = \infty$

The graph of $A(x)$ does not have a horizontal asymptote.

**107.** (a) $v(t) = 5t - 7,\ 0 \le t \le 3$

Displacement $= \int_0^3 (5t - 7)\,dt = \left[\frac{5t^2}{2} - 7t\right]_0^3 = \frac{45}{2} - 21 = \frac{3}{2}$ ft to the right

(b) Total distance traveled $= \int_0^3 |5t - 7|\,dt$

$$= \int_0^{7/5} (7 - 5t)\,dt + \int_{7/5}^3 (5t - 7)\,dt$$

$$= \left[7t - \frac{5t^2}{2}\right]_0^{7/5} + \left[\frac{5t^2}{2} - 7t\right]_{7/5}^3$$

$$= 7\left(\frac{7}{5}\right) - \frac{5}{2}\left(\frac{7}{2}\right)^2 + \left(\frac{5}{2}(9) - 21\right) - \left(\frac{5}{2}\left(\frac{7}{5}\right)^2 - 7\left(\frac{7}{5}\right)\right)$$

$$= \frac{49}{5} - \frac{49}{10} + \frac{45}{2} - 21 - \frac{49}{10} + \frac{49}{5} = \frac{113}{10} \text{ ft}$$

**108.** (a) $v(t) = t^2 - t - 12 = (t - 4)(t + 3),\ 1 \le t \le 5$

Displacement $= \int_1^5 (t^2 - t - 12)\,dt$

$$= \left[\frac{t^3}{3} - \frac{t^2}{2} - 12t\right]_1^5 = \left(\frac{125}{3} - \frac{25}{2} - 60\right) - \left(\frac{1}{3} - \frac{1}{2} - 12\right) = -\frac{56}{3}\ \left(\frac{56}{3} \text{ ft to the left}\right)$$

(b) Total distance traveled $= \int_1^4 (-t^2 + t + 12)\,dt + \int_4^5 (t^2 - t - 12)\,dt$

$$= \left[-\frac{t^3}{3} + \frac{t^2}{2} + 12t\right]_1^4 + \left[\frac{t^3}{3} - \frac{t^2}{2} - 12t\right]_4^5$$

$$= \left(-\frac{64}{3} + 8 + 48\right) - \left(-\frac{1}{3} + \frac{1}{2} + 12\right) + \left(\frac{125}{3} - \frac{25}{2} - 60\right) - \left(\frac{64}{3} - 8 - 48\right)$$

$$= \frac{104}{3} - \frac{73}{6} + \left(-\frac{185}{6}\right) - \left(-\frac{104}{3}\right) = \frac{79}{3} \text{ ft}$$

**109.** (a) $v(t) = t^3 - 10t^2 + 27t - 18 = (t - 1)(t - 3)(t - 6),\ 1 \le t \le 7$

Displacement $= \int_1^7 (t^3 - 10t^2 + 27t - 18)\,dt$

$$= \left[\frac{t^4}{4} - \frac{10t^3}{3} + \frac{27t^2}{2} - 18t\right]_1^7$$

$$= \left[\frac{7^4}{4} - \frac{10(7^3)}{3} + \frac{27(7^2)}{2} - 18(7)\right] - \left[\frac{1}{4} - \frac{10}{3} + \frac{27}{2} - 18\right]$$

$$= -\frac{91}{12} - \left(-\frac{91}{12}\right) = 0$$

(b) Total distance traveled $= \int_1^7 |v(t)|\,dt$

$$= \int_1^3 (t^3 - 10t^2 + 27t - 18)\,dt - \int_3^6 (t^3 - 10t^2 + 27t - 18)\,dt + \int_6^7 (t^3 - 10t^2 + 27t - 18)\,dt$$

Evaluating each of these integrals, you obtain

Total distance $= \frac{16}{3} - \left(-\frac{63}{4}\right) + \frac{125}{12} = \frac{63}{2}$ ft

**110.** (a) $v(t) = t^3 - 8t^2 + 15t = t(t-3)(t-5),\ 0 \le t \le 5$

$$\text{Displacement} = \int_0^5 \left(t^3 - 8t^2 + 15t\right) dt$$

$$= \left[\frac{t^4}{4} - \frac{8t^3}{3} + \frac{15t^2}{2}\right]_0^5$$

$$= \frac{625}{4} - \frac{8(125)}{3} + \frac{375}{2} = \frac{125}{12} \text{ ft to the right}$$

(b) $$\text{Total distance traveled} = \int_0^5 |v(t)|\, dt$$

$$= \int_0^3 \left(t^3 - 8t^2 + 15t\right) dt - \int_3^5 \left(t^3 - 8t^2 + 15t\right) dt$$

Evaluating each of these integrals, you obtain

$$\text{Total distance} = \frac{63}{4} - \left(-\frac{16}{3}\right) = \frac{253}{12} \approx 21.08 \text{ ft}$$

**111.** (a) $v(t) = \dfrac{1}{\sqrt{t}},\ 1 \le t \le 4$

Because $v(t) > 0$,

Displacement = Total Distance

$$\text{Displacement} = \int_1^4 t^{-1/2}\, dt = \left[2t^{1/2}\right]_1^4 = 4 - 2 = 2 \text{ ft to the right}$$

(b) Total distance = 2 ft

**112.** (a) $v(t) = \cos t,\ 0 \le t \le 3\pi$

$$\text{Displacement} = \int_0^{3\pi} \cos t\, dt = \left[\sin t\right]_0^{3\pi} = 0 \text{ ft}$$

(b) $$\text{Total distance} = \int_0^{\pi/2} \cos t\, dt - \int_{\pi/2}^{3\pi/2} \cos t\, dt + \int_{3\pi/2}^{5\pi/2} \cos t\, dt - \int_{5\pi/2}^{3\pi} \cos t\, dt$$

$$= \left[\sin t\right]_0^{\pi/2} - \left[\sin t\right]_{\pi/2}^{3\pi/2} + \left[\sin t\right]_{3\pi/2}^{5\pi/2} - \left[\sin t\right]_{5\pi/2}^{3\pi} = 1 - (-2) + 2 - (-1) = 6$$

**113.** $x(t) = t^3 - 6t^2 + 9t - 2$

$x'(t) = 3t^2 - 12t + 9 = 3\left(t^2 - 4t + 3\right) = 3(t-3)(t-1)$

$$\text{Total distance} = \int_0^5 |x'(t)|\, dt$$

$$= \int_0^5 3\left|(t-3)(t-1)\right| dt$$

$$= 3\int_0^1 \left(t^2 - 4t + 3\right) dt - 3\int_1^3 \left(t^2 - 4t + 3\right) dt + 3\int_3^5 \left(t^2 - 4t + 3\right) dt = 4 + 4 + 20 = 28 \text{ units}$$

**114.** $x(t) = (t-1)(t-3)^2 = t^3 - 7t^2 + 15t - 9$

$x'(t) = 3t^2 - 14t + 15$

Using a graphing utility,

$$\text{Total distance} = \int_0^5 |x'(t)|\, dt \approx 27.37 \text{ units.}$$

**115.** Let $c(t)$ be the amount of water that is flowing out of the tank. Then $c'(t) = 500 - 5t$ L/min is the rate of flow.

$$\int_0^{18} c'(t)dt = \int_0^{18} (500 - 5t)\,dt = \left[500t - \frac{5t^2}{2}\right]_0^{18} = 9000 - 810 = 8190 \text{ L}$$

**116.** Let $c(t)$ be the amount of oil leaking and $t = 0$ represent 1 P.M. Then $c'(t) = 4 + 0.75t$ gal/min is the rate of flow.

(a) From 1 P.M. to 4 P.M. (3 hours):

$$\int_0^3 (4 + 0.75t)\,dt = \left[4t + \frac{0.75}{2}t^2\right]_0^3 = \frac{123}{8} = 15.375 \text{ gal}$$

(b) From 4 P.M. to 7 P.M. (3 hours):

$$\int_3^6 (4 + 0.75t)\,dt = \left[4t + \frac{0.75}{2}t^2\right]_3^6 = 22.125 \text{ gal}$$

(c) The second answer is larger because the rate of flow is increasing.

**117.** The function $f(x) = x^{-2}$ is not continuous on $[-1, 1]$.

$$\int_{-1}^1 x^{-2}\,dx = \int_{-1}^0 x^{-2}\,dx + \int_0^1 x^{-2}\,dx$$

Each of these integrals is infinite. $f(x) = x^{-2}$ has a nonremovable discontinuity at $x = 0$.

**118.** The function $f(x) = \dfrac{2}{x^3}$ is not continuous on $[-2, 1]$.

$$\int_{-2}^1 \frac{2}{x^3}\,dx = \int_{-2}^0 \frac{2}{x^3}\,dx + \int_0^1 \frac{2}{x^3}\,dx$$

Each of these integrals is infinite. $f(x) = \dfrac{2}{x^3}$ has a nonremovable discontinuity at $x = 0$.

**119.** The function $f(x) = \sec^2 x$ is not continuous on $\left[\dfrac{\pi}{4}, \dfrac{3\pi}{4}\right]$.

$$\int_{\pi/4}^{3\pi/4} \sec^2 x\,dx = \int_{\pi/4}^{\pi/2} \sec^2 x\,dx + \int_{\pi/2}^{3\pi/4} \sec^2 x\,dx$$

Each of these integrals is infinite. $f(x) = \sec^2 x$ has a nonremovable discontinuity at $x = \dfrac{\pi}{2}$.

**120.** The function $f(x) = \csc x \cot x$ is not continuous on $\left[\dfrac{\pi}{2}, \dfrac{3\pi}{2}\right]$.

$$\int_{\pi/2}^{3\pi/2} \csc x \cot x\,dx = \int_{\pi/2}^{\pi} \csc x \cot x\,dx + \int_{\pi}^{3\pi/2} \csc x \cot x\,dx$$

Each of these integrals is infinite $f(x) = \csc x \cot x$ has a nonremovable discontinuity at $x = \pi$.

**121.** $P = \dfrac{2}{\pi}\displaystyle\int_0^{\pi/2} \sin\theta\,d\theta = \left[-\frac{2}{\pi}\cos\theta\right]_0^{\pi/2} = -\frac{2}{\pi}(0 - 1) = \frac{2}{\pi} \approx 63.7\%$

**122.** Let $F(t)$ be an antiderivative of $f(t)$. Then,

$$\int_{u(x)}^{v(x)} f(t)\,dt = \left[F(t)\right]_{u(x)}^{v(x)} = F(v(x)) - F(u(x))$$

$$\frac{d}{dx}\left[\int_{u(x)}^{v(x)} f(t)\,dt\right] = \frac{d}{dx}\left[F(v(x)) - F(u(x))\right] = F'(v(x))v'(x) - F'(u(x))u'(x) = f(v(x))v'(x) - f(u(x))u'(x).$$

**123.** True

**124.** True

**125.** $f(x) = \int_0^{1/x} \frac{1}{t^2+1}\,dt + \int_0^x \frac{1}{t^2+1}\,dt$

By the Second Fundamental Theorem of Calculus, you have $f'(x) = \frac{1}{(1/x)^2+1}\left(-\frac{1}{x^2}\right) + \frac{1}{x^2+1} = -\frac{1}{1+x^2} + \frac{1}{x^2+1} = 0.$

Because $f'(x) = 0$, $f(x)$ must be constant.

**126.** $\int_c^x f(t)\,dt = x^2 + x - 2$

Let $f(t) = 2t + 1$. Then

$$\begin{aligned}\int_c^x f(t)dt = \int_c^x (2t+1)dt = \left[t^2 + t\right]_c^x = x^2 + x - c^2 - c &= x^2 + x - 2\\ -c^2 - c &= -2\\ c^2 + c - 2 &= 0\\ (c+2)(c-1) &= 0 \Rightarrow c = 1, -2.\end{aligned}$$

So, $f(x) = 2x + 1$, and $c = 1$ or $c = -2$.

**127.** $G(x) = \int_0^x \left[s\int_0^s f(t)\,dt\right] ds$

(a) $G(0) = \int_0^0 \left[s\int_0^s f(t)\,dt\right] ds = 0$

(b) Let $F(s) = s\int_0^s f(t)\,dt$.

$G(x) = \int_0^x F(s)\,ds$

$G'(x) = F(x) = x\int_0^x f(t)\,dt$

$G'(0) = 0\int_0^0 f(t)\,dt = 0$

(c) $G''(x) = x \cdot f(x) + \int_0^x f(t)\,dt$

(d) $G''(0) = 0 \cdot f(0) + \int_0^0 f(t)\,dt = 0$

## Section 5.5 Integration by Substitution

| | $\int f(g(x))g'(x)\,dx$ | $u = g(x)$ | $du = g'(x)\,dx$ |
|---|---|---|---|
| **1.** | $\int (8x^2+1)^2(16x)dx$ | $8x^2 + 1$ | $16x\,dx$ |
| **2.** | $\int x^2\sqrt{x^3+1}\,dx$ | $x^3 + 1$ | $3x^2\,dx$ |
| **3.** | $\int \frac{x}{\sqrt{x^2+1}}\,dx$ | $x^2 + 1$ | $2x\,dx$ |
| **4.** | $\int \sec 2x \tan 2x\,dx$ | $2x$ | $2\,dx$ |
| **5.** | $\int \tan^2 x \sec^2 x\,dx$ | $\tan x$ | $\sec^2 x\,dx$ |
| **6.** | $\int \frac{\cos x}{\sin^3 x}\,dx$ | $\sin x$ | $\cos x\,dx$ |

**7.** $\int \sqrt{x}(6 - x)\,dx = \int \left(6x^{1/2} - x^{3/2}\right)dx$

Substitution not needed

**8.** $\int x\sqrt{x + 4}\,dx$

Substitution is necessary $(u = x + 4)$

**9.** $\int x\sqrt[3]{1 + x^2}\,dx = \int \left(1 + x^2\right)^{1/3} x\,dx$

Substitution is necessary $\left(u = 1 + x^2\right)$

**10.** $\int x \cos x^2\,dx$

Substitution is necessary $\left(u = x^2\right)$

**11.** $\int (1 + 6x)^4(6)\,dx = \dfrac{(1 + 6x)^5}{5} + C$

**Check:** $\dfrac{d}{dx}\left[\dfrac{(1 + 6x)^5}{5} + C\right] = 6(1 + 6x)^4$

**12.** $\int \left(x^2 - 9\right)^3(2x)\,dx = \dfrac{\left(x^2 - 9\right)^4}{4} + C$

**Check:** $\dfrac{d}{dx}\left[\dfrac{\left(x^2 - 9\right)^4}{4} + C\right] = \dfrac{4\left(x^2 - 9\right)^3}{4}(2x) = \left(x^2 - 9\right)^3(2x)$

**13.** $\int \sqrt{25 - x^2}(-2x)\,dx = \dfrac{\left(25 - x^2\right)^{3/2}}{3/2} + C = \dfrac{2}{3}\left(25 - x^2\right)^{3/2} + C$

**Check:** $\dfrac{d}{dx}\left[\dfrac{2}{3}\left(25 - x^2\right)^{3/2} + C\right] = \dfrac{2}{3}\left(\dfrac{3}{2}\right)\left(25 - x^2\right)^{1/2}(-2x) = \sqrt{25 - x^2}(-2x)$

**14.** $\int \sqrt[3]{3 - 4x^2}(-8x)\,dx = \int \left(3 - 4x^2\right)^{1/3}(-8x)\,dx = \dfrac{\left(3 - 4x^2\right)^{4/3}}{4/3} + C = \dfrac{3}{4}\left(3 - 4x^2\right)^{4/3} + C$

**Check:** $\dfrac{d}{dx}\left[\dfrac{3}{4}\left(3 - 4x^2\right)^{4/3} + C\right] = \dfrac{3}{4}\left(\dfrac{4}{3}\right)\left(3 - 4x^2\right)^{1/3}(-8x) = \left(3 - 4x^2\right)^{1/3}(-8x)$

**15.** $\int x^3\left(x^4 + 3\right)^2 dx = \dfrac{1}{4}\int \left(x^4 + 3\right)^2\left(4x^3\right)dx = \dfrac{1}{4}\dfrac{\left(x^4 + 3\right)^3}{3} + C = \dfrac{\left(x^4 + 3\right)^3}{12} + C$

**Check:** $\dfrac{d}{dx}\left[\dfrac{\left(x^4 + 3\right)^3}{12} + C\right] = \dfrac{3\left(x^4 + 3\right)^2}{12}\left(4x^3\right) = \left(x^4 + 3\right)^2\left(x^3\right)$

**16.** $\int x^2\left(x^3 + 5\right)^4 dx = \dfrac{1}{3}\int \left(x^3 + 5\right)^4\left(3x^2\right)dx = \dfrac{1}{3}\dfrac{\left(x^3 + 5\right)^5}{5} + C = \dfrac{\left(x^3 + 5\right)^5}{15} + C$

**Check:** $\dfrac{d}{dx}\left[\dfrac{\left(x^3 + 5\right)^5}{15} + C\right] = \dfrac{5\left(x^3 + 5\right)^4\left(3x^2\right)}{15} = \left(x^3 + 5\right)^4 x^2$

**17.** $\int x^2\left(x^3 - 1\right)^4 dx = \dfrac{1}{3}\int \left(x^3 - 1\right)^4\left(3x^2\right)dx = \dfrac{1}{3}\left[\dfrac{\left(x^3 - 1\right)^5}{5}\right] + C = \dfrac{\left(x^3 - 1\right)^5}{15} + C$

**Check:** $\dfrac{d}{dx}\left[\dfrac{\left(x^3 - 1\right)^5}{15} + C\right] = \dfrac{5\left(x^3 - 1\right)^4\left(3x^2\right)}{15} = x^2\left(x^3 - 1\right)^4$

**18.** $\int x\left(5x^2 + 4\right)^3 dx = \dfrac{1}{10}\int \left(5x^2 + 4\right)^3(10x)\,dx = \dfrac{1}{10}\left[\dfrac{\left(5x^2 + 4\right)^4}{4}\right] + C = \dfrac{\left(5x^2 + 4\right)^4}{40} + C$

**Check:** $\dfrac{d}{dx}\left[\dfrac{\left(5x^2 + 4\right)^4}{40} + C\right] = \dfrac{4\left(5x^2 + 4\right)^3(10x)}{40} = x\left(5x^2 + 4\right)^3$

**19.** $\int t\sqrt{t^2+2}\,dt = \frac{1}{2}\int (t^2+2)^{1/2}(2t)\,dt = \frac{1}{2}\frac{(t^2+2)^{3/2}}{3/2} + C = \frac{(t^2+2)^{3/2}}{3} + C$

**Check:** $\frac{d}{dt}\left[\frac{(t^2+2)^{3/2}}{3} + C\right] = \frac{3/2(t^2+2)^{1/2}(2t)}{3} = (t^2+2)^{1/2}t$

**20.** $\int t^3\sqrt{t^4+5}\,dt = \frac{1}{4}\int (t^4+5)^{1/2}(4t^3)\,dt = \frac{1}{4}\frac{(t^4+5)^{3/2}}{3/2} + C = \frac{1}{6}(t^4+5)^{3/2} + C$

**Check:** $\frac{d}{dt}\left[\frac{1}{6}(t^4+5)^{3/2} + C\right] = \frac{1}{6}\cdot\frac{3}{2}(t^4+5)^{1/2}(4t^3) = (t^4+5)^{1/2}(t^3)$

**21.** $\int 5x(1-x^2)^{1/3}\,dx = -\frac{5}{2}\int (1-x^2)^{1/3}(-2x)\,dx = -\frac{5}{2}\cdot\frac{(1-x^2)^{4/3}}{4/3} + C = -\frac{15}{8}(1-x^2)^{4/3} + C$

**Check:** $\frac{d}{dx}\left[-\frac{15}{8}(1-x^2)^{4/3} + C\right] = -\frac{15}{8}\cdot\frac{4}{3}(1-x^2)^{1/3}(-2x) = 5x(1-x^2)^{1/3} = 5x\sqrt[3]{1-x^2}$

**22.** $\int u^2\sqrt{u^3+2}\,du = \frac{1}{3}\int (u^3+2)^{1/2}(3u^2)\,du = \frac{1}{3}\frac{(u^3+2)^{3/2}}{3/2} + C = \frac{2(u^3+2)^{3/2}}{9} + C$

**Check:** $\frac{d}{du}\left[\frac{2(u^3+2)^{3/2}}{9} + C\right] = \frac{2}{9}\cdot\frac{3}{2}(u^3+2)^{1/2}(3u^2) = (u^3+2)^{1/2}(u^2)$

**23.** $\int \frac{x}{(1-x^2)^3}\,dx = -\frac{1}{2}\int (1-x^2)^{-3}(-2x)\,dx = -\frac{1}{2}\frac{(1-x^2)^{-2}}{-2} + C = \frac{1}{4(1-x^2)^2} + C$

**Check:** $\frac{d}{dx}\left[\frac{1}{4(1-x^2)^2} + C\right] = \frac{1}{4}(-2)(1-x^2)^{-3}(-2x) = \frac{x}{(1-x^2)^3}$

**24.** $\int \frac{x^3}{(1+x^4)^2}\,dx = \frac{1}{4}\int (1+x^4)^{-2}(4x^3)\,dx = -\frac{1}{4}(1+x^4)^{-1} + C = \frac{-1}{4(1+x^4)} + C$

**Check:** $\frac{d}{dx}\left[\frac{-1}{4(1+x^4)} + C\right] = \frac{1}{4}(1+x^4)^{-2}(4x^3) = \frac{x^3}{(1+x^4)^2}$

**25.** $\int \frac{x^2}{(1+x^3)^2}\,dx = \frac{1}{3}\int (1+x^3)^{-2}(3x^2)\,dx = \frac{1}{3}\left[\frac{(1+x^3)^{-1}}{-1}\right] + C = -\frac{1}{3(1+x^3)} + C$

**Check:** $\frac{d}{dx}\left[-\frac{1}{3(1+x^3)} + C\right] = -\frac{1}{3}(-1)(1+x^3)^{-2}(3x^2) = \frac{x^2}{(1+x^3)^2}$

**26.** $\int \frac{x^2}{(16-x^3)^2}\,dx = -\frac{1}{3}\int (16-x^3)^{-2}(-3x^2)\,dx = -\frac{1}{3}\left[\frac{(16-x^3)^{-1}}{-1}\right] + C = \frac{1}{3(16-x^3)} + C$

**Check:** $\frac{d}{dx}\left[\frac{1}{3(16-x^3)} + C\right] = \frac{1}{3}(-1)(16-x^3)^{-2}(3x^2) = \frac{x^2}{(16-x^3)^2}$

27. $\int \frac{x}{\sqrt{1-x^2}}\,dx = -\frac{1}{2}\int\left(1-x^2\right)^{-1/2}(-2x)\,dx = -\frac{1}{2}\frac{\left(1-x^2\right)^{1/2}}{1/2} + C = -\sqrt{1-x^2} + C$

**Check:** $\frac{d}{dx}\left[-\left(1-x^2\right)^{1/2} + C\right] = -\frac{1}{2}\left(1-x^2\right)^{-1/2}(-2x) = \frac{x}{\sqrt{1-x^2}}$

28. $\int \frac{x^3}{\sqrt{1+x^4}}\,dx = \frac{1}{4}\int\left(1+x^4\right)^{-1/2}\left(4x^3\right)dx = \frac{1}{4}\frac{\left(1+x^4\right)^{1/2}}{1/2} + C = \frac{\sqrt{1+x^4}}{2} + C$

**Check:** $\frac{d}{dx}\left[\frac{\sqrt{1+x^4}}{2} + C\right] = \frac{1}{2}\cdot\frac{1}{2}\left(1+x^4\right)^{-1/2}\left(4x^3\right) = \frac{x^3}{\sqrt{1+x^4}}$

29. $\int\left(1+\frac{1}{t}\right)^3\left(\frac{1}{t^2}\right)dt = -\int\left(1+\frac{1}{t}\right)^3\left(-\frac{1}{t^2}\right)dt = -\frac{\left[1+\left(\frac{1}{t}\right)\right]^4}{4} + C$

**Check:** $\frac{d}{dt}\left[-\frac{\left[1+(1/t)\right]^4}{4} + C\right] = -\frac{1}{4}(4)\left(1+\frac{1}{t}\right)^3\left(-\frac{1}{t^2}\right) = \frac{1}{t^2}\left(1+\frac{1}{t}\right)^3$

30. $\int\left[x^2 + \frac{1}{(3x)^2}\right]dx = \int\left(x^2 + \frac{1}{9}x^{-2}\right)dx = \frac{x^3}{3} + \frac{1}{9}\left(\frac{x^{-1}}{-1}\right) + C = \frac{x^3}{3} - \frac{1}{9x} + C = \frac{3x^4-1}{9x} + C$

**Check:** $\frac{d}{dx}\left[\frac{1}{3}x^3 - \frac{1}{9}x^{-1} + C\right] = x^2 + \frac{1}{9}x^{-2} = x^2 + \frac{1}{(3x)^2}$

31. $\int \frac{1}{\sqrt{2x}}\,dx = \frac{1}{2}\int(2x)^{-1/2}2\,dx = \frac{1}{2}\left[\frac{(2x)^{1/2}}{1/2}\right] + C = \sqrt{2x} + C$

**Alternate Solution:** $\int \frac{1}{\sqrt{2x}}\,dx = \frac{1}{\sqrt{2}}\int x^{-1/2}\,dx = \frac{1}{\sqrt{2}}\frac{x^{1/2}}{(1/2)} + C = \sqrt{2x} + C$

**Check:** $\frac{d}{dx}\left[\sqrt{2x} + C\right] = \frac{1}{2}(2x)^{-1/2}(2) = \frac{1}{\sqrt{2x}}$

32. $\int \frac{1}{2\sqrt{x}}\,dx = \frac{1}{2}\int x^{-1/2}\,dx = \frac{1}{2}\left(\frac{x^{1/2}}{1/2}\right) + C = \sqrt{x} + C$

**Check:** $\frac{d}{dx}\left[\sqrt{x} + C\right] = \frac{1}{2\sqrt{x}}$

33. $\int \frac{x^2+5x-8}{\sqrt{x}}\,dx = \int\left(x^{3/2} + 5x^{1/2} - 8x^{-1/2}\right)dx = \frac{2}{5}x^{5/2} + \frac{10}{3}x^{3/2} - 16x^{1/2} + C = \frac{1}{15}\sqrt{x}\left[6x^2 + 50x - 240\right] + C$

**Check:** $\frac{d}{dx}\left[\frac{2}{5}x^{5/2} + \frac{10}{3}x^{3/2} - 16x^{1/2} + C\right] = x^{3/2} + 5x^{1/2} - 8x^{-1/2} = \frac{x^2+5x-8}{\sqrt{x}}$

34. $\int \frac{t-9t^2}{\sqrt{t}}\,dt = \int\left(t^{1/2} - 9t^{3/2}\right)dt = \frac{2}{3}t^{3/2} - \frac{18}{5}t^{5/2} + C = \frac{2}{15}t^{3/2}(5-27t) + C$

**Check:** $\frac{d}{dt}\left[\frac{2}{3}t^{3/2} - \frac{18}{5}t^{5/2} + C\right] = t^{1/2} - 9t^{3/2} = \frac{t-9t^2}{\sqrt{t}}$

**35.** $\int t^2\left(t - \frac{8}{t}\right) dt = \int\left(t^3 - 8t\right) dt = \frac{t^4}{4} - 4t^2 + C$

**Check:** $\frac{d}{dt}\left[\frac{t^4}{4} - 4t^2 + C\right] = t^3 - 8t = t^2\left(t - \frac{8}{t}\right)$

**36.** $\int\left(\frac{t^3}{3} + \frac{1}{4t^2}\right) dt = \int\left(\frac{1}{3}t^3 + \frac{1}{4}t^{-2}\right) dt = \frac{1}{3}\left(\frac{t^4}{4}\right) + \frac{1}{4}\left(\frac{t^{-1}}{-1}\right) + C = \frac{1}{12}t^4 - \frac{1}{4t} + C$

**Check:** $\frac{d}{dt}\left[\frac{1}{12}t^4 - \frac{1}{4t} + C\right] = \frac{1}{3}t^3 + \frac{1}{4t^2}$

**37.** $\int(9 - y)\sqrt{y}\, dy = \int\left(9y^{1/2} - y^{3/2}\right) dy = 9\left(\frac{2}{3}y^{3/2}\right) - \frac{2}{5}y^{5/2} + C = \frac{2}{5}y^{3/2}(15 - y) + C$

**Check:** $\frac{d}{dy}\left[\frac{2}{5}y^{3/2}(15 - y) + C\right] = \frac{d}{dy}\left[6y^{3/2} - \frac{2}{5}y^{5/2} + C\right] = 9y^{1/2} - y^{3/2} = (9 - y)\sqrt{y}$

**38.** $\int 4\pi y\left(6 + y^{3/2}\right) dy = \int\left(24\pi y + 4\pi y^{5/2}\right) dy = 12\pi y^2 + \frac{8\pi}{7}y^{7/2} + C$

**Check:** $\frac{d}{dy}\left[12\pi y^2 + \frac{8\pi}{7}y^{7/2} + C\right] = 24\pi y + 4\pi y^{5/2} = 4\pi y\left[6 + y^{3/2}\right]$

**39.** $y = \int\left[4x + \frac{4x}{\sqrt{16 - x^2}}\right] dx = 4\int x\, dx - 2\int\left(16 - x^2\right)^{-1/2}(-2x)\, dx = 4\left(\frac{x^2}{2}\right) - 2\left[\frac{\left(16 - x^2\right)^{1/2}}{1/2}\right] + C = 2x^2 - 4\sqrt{16 - x^2} + C$

**40.** $y = \int\frac{10x^2}{\sqrt{1 + x^3}}\, dx$

$= \frac{10}{3}\int\left(1 + x^3\right)^{-1/2}\left(3x^2\right) dx$

$= \frac{10}{3}\left[\frac{\left(1 + x^3\right)^{1/2}}{1/2}\right] + C$

$= \frac{20}{3}\sqrt{1 + x^3} + C$

**41.** $y = \int\frac{x + 1}{\left(x^2 + 2x - 3\right)^2}\, dx$

$= \frac{1}{2}\int\left(x^2 + 2x - 3\right)^{-2}(2x + 2)\, dx$

$= \frac{1}{2}\left[\frac{\left(x^2 + 2x - 3\right)^{-1}}{-1}\right] + C$

$= -\frac{1}{2\left(x^2 + 2x - 3\right)} + C$

**42.** $y = \int\frac{x - 4}{\sqrt{x^2 - 8x + 1}}\, dx$

$= \frac{1}{2}\int\left(x^2 - 8x + 1\right)^{-1/2}(2x - 8)\, dx$

$= \frac{1}{2}\left[\frac{\left(x^2 - 8x + 1\right)^{1/2}}{1/2}\right] + C = \sqrt{x^2 - 8x + 1} + C$

**43.** (a) Answers will vary. *Sample answer:*

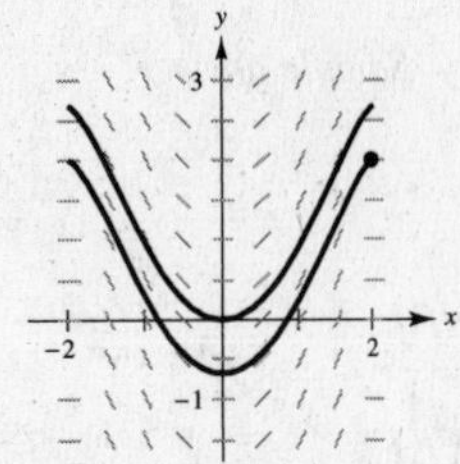

(b) $\frac{dy}{dx} = x\sqrt{4 - x^2}$, $(2, 2)$

$y = \int x\sqrt{4 - x^2}\, dx = -\frac{1}{2}\int\left(4 - x^2\right)^{1/2}(-2x\, dx)$

$= -\frac{1}{2}\cdot\frac{2}{3}\left(4 - x^2\right)^{3/2} + C = -\frac{1}{3}\left(4 - x^2\right)^{3/2} + C$

$(2, 2)$: $2 = -\frac{1}{3}\left(4 - 2^2\right)^{3/2} + C \Rightarrow C = 2$

$y = -\frac{1}{3}\left(4 - x^2\right)^{3/2} + 2$

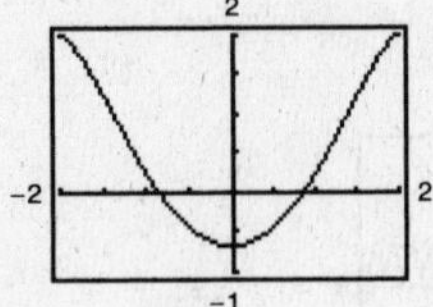

**44.** (a) Answers will vary: *Sample answer:*

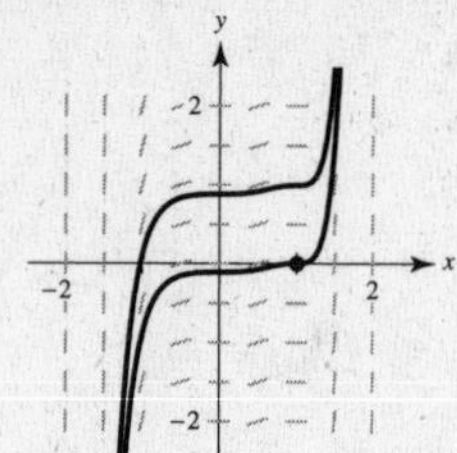

(b) $\dfrac{dy}{dx} = x^2(x^3 - 1)^2, (1, 0)$

$$y = \int x^2(x^3 - 1)^2\,dx$$
$$= \frac{1}{3}\int (x^3 - 1)^2(3x^2\,dx)$$
$$= \frac{1}{3}\frac{(x^3 - 1)^3}{3} + C = \frac{1}{9}(x^3 - 1)^3 + C$$

$(0, 1)$: $1 = \frac{1}{9}(1 - 1)^3 + C \Rightarrow C = 0$

$y = \frac{1}{9}(x^3 - 1)^3$

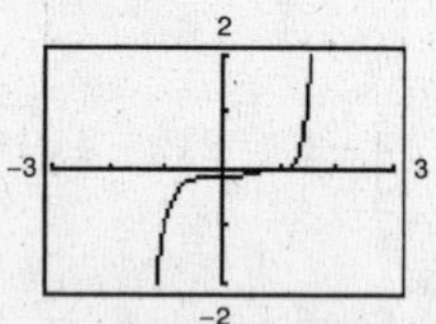

**45.** (a) Answers will vary. *Sample answer:*

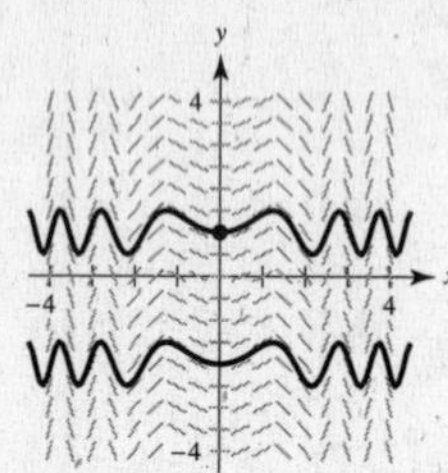

(b) $\dfrac{dy}{dx} = x\cos x^2, (0,1)$

$$y = \int x\cos x^2\,dx = \frac{1}{2}\int \cos(x^2)2x\,dx$$
$$= \frac{1}{2}\sin(x^2) + C$$

$(0, 1)$: $1 = \frac{1}{2}\sin(0) + C \Rightarrow C = 1$

$y = \frac{1}{2}\sin(x^2) + 1$

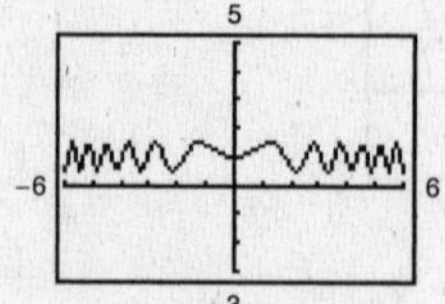

**46.** (a) Answers will vary. *Sample answer:*

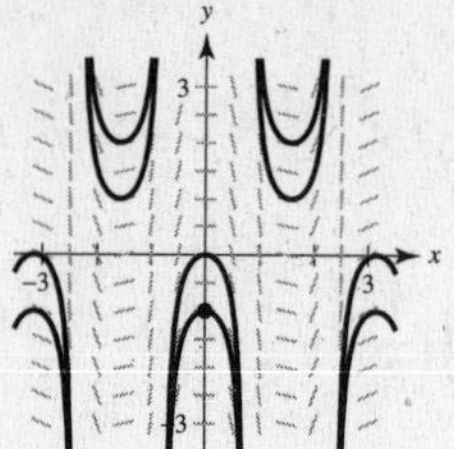

(b) $\dfrac{dy}{dx} = -2\sec(2x)\tan(2x), (0, -1)$

$$y = \int -2\sec(2x)\tan(2x)\,dx$$
$$= -\sec(2x) + C$$

$(0, 1)$: $-1 = -\sec(0) + C \Rightarrow C = 0$

$y = -\sec(2x)$

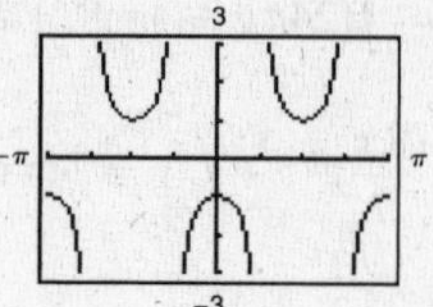

**47.** (a) Answers will vary. *Sample answer:*

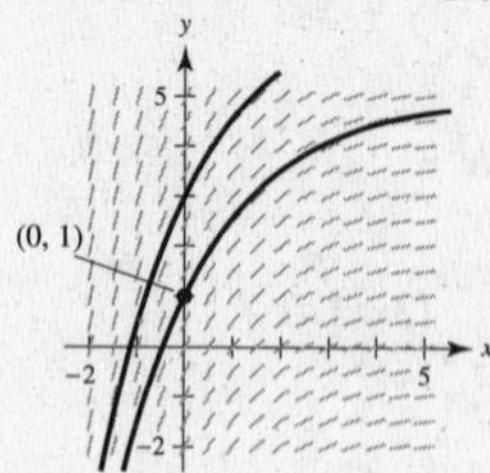

(b) $\dfrac{dy}{dx} = 2e^{-x/2}, (0, 1)$

$$y = \int 2e^{-x/2}\,dx = -4\int e^{-x/2}\left(-\frac{1}{2}\,dx\right)$$
$$= -4e^{-x/2} + C$$

$(0, 1)$: $1 = -4e^0 + C = -4 + C \Rightarrow C = 5$

$y = -4e^{-x/2} + 5$

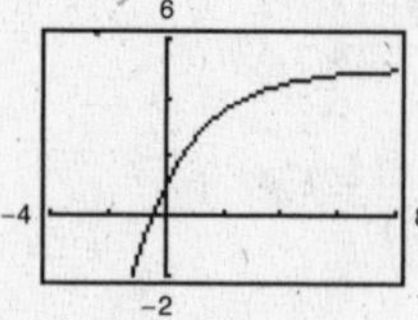

**48.** (a) Answers will vary. *Sample answer:*

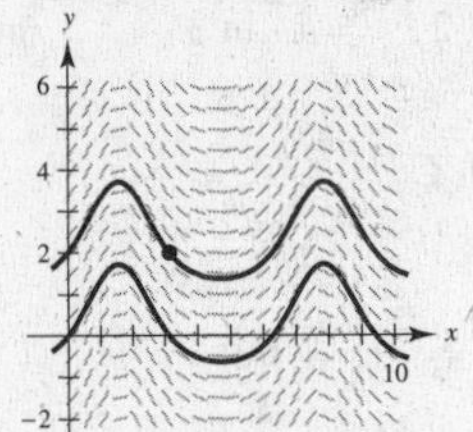

(b) $\frac{dy}{dx} = e^{\sin x} \cos x, (\pi, 2)$

$y = \int e^{\sin x} \cos x \, dx = e^{\sin x} + C$

$(\pi, 2): 2 = e^{\sin \pi} + C = 1 + C \Rightarrow C = 1$

$y = e^{\sin x} + 1$

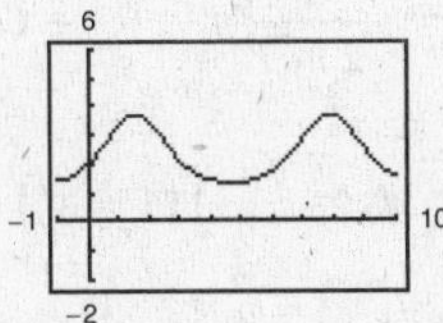

**49.** $\int \pi \sin \pi x \, dx = -\cos \pi x + C$

**50.** $\int 4x^3 \sin x^4 \, dx = \int \sin x^4 (4x^3) \, dx = -\cos x^4 + C$

**51.** $\int \sin 4x \, dx = \frac{1}{4}\int (\sin 4x)(4) \, dx = -\frac{1}{4}\cos 4x + C$

**52.** $\int \cos 8x \, dx = \frac{1}{8}\int (\cos 8x)(8) \, dx = \frac{1}{8}\sin 8x + C$

**53.** $\int \frac{1}{\theta^2}\cos\frac{1}{\theta} \, d\theta = -\int \cos\frac{1}{\theta}\left(-\frac{1}{\theta^2}\right) d\theta = -\sin\frac{1}{\theta} + C$

**54.** $\int x \sin x^2 \, dx = \frac{1}{2}\int (\sin x^2)(2x) \, dx = -\frac{1}{2}\cos x^2 + C$

**55.** $\int e^{7x}(7) \, dx = e^{7x} + C$

**56.** $\int e^{x/3}\left(\frac{1}{3}\right) dx = e^{x/3} + C$

**57.** $\int e^{x^2}(2x) \, dx = e^{x^2} + C$

**58.** $\int e^{-x^3}\left(-3x^2\right) dx = e^{-x^3} + C$

**59.** $\int x^2 e^{-x^3} \, dx = -\frac{1}{3}\int e^{-x^3}\left(-3x^2\right) dx$

$= -\frac{1}{3}e^{-x^3} + C$

**60.** $\int (x + 1)e^{x^2+2x} \, dx = \frac{1}{2}\int e^{x^2+2x}(2x + 2) \, dx = \frac{1}{2}e^{x^2+2x} + C$

**61.** $\int \sin 2x \cos 2x \, dx = \frac{1}{2}\int (\sin 2x)(2\cos 2x) \, dx = \frac{1}{2}\frac{(\sin 2x)^2}{2} + C = \frac{1}{4}\sin^2 2x + C$ OR

$\int \sin 2x \cos 2x \, dx = -\frac{1}{2}\int (\cos 2x)(-2\sin 2x) \, dx = -\frac{1}{2}\frac{(\cos 2x)^2}{2} + C_1 = -\frac{1}{4}\cos^2 2x + C_1$ OR

$\int \sin 2x \cos 2x \, dx = \frac{1}{2}\int 2\sin 2x \cos 2x \, dx = \frac{1}{2}\int \sin 4x \, dx = -\frac{1}{8}\cos 4x + C_2$

**62.** $\int \sec(2 - x)\tan(2 - x) \, dx = -\int [\sec(2 - x)\tan(2 - x)](-1) \, dx = -\sec(2 - x) + C$

**63.** $\int \tan^4 x \sec^2 x \, dx = \frac{\tan^5 x}{5} + C = \frac{1}{5}\tan^5 x + C$

**64.** $\int \sqrt{\tan x}\sec^2 x \, dx = \frac{(\tan x)^{3/2}}{3/2} + C = \frac{2}{3}(\tan x)^{3/2} + C$

**65.** $\int \frac{\csc^2 x}{\cot^3 x} \, dx = -\int (\cot x)^{-3}(-\csc^2 x) \, dx$

$= -\frac{(\cot x)^{-2}}{-2} + C = \frac{1}{2\cot^2 x} + C = \frac{1}{2}\tan^2 x + C = \frac{1}{2}(\sec^2 x - 1) + C = \frac{1}{2}\sec^2 x + C_1$

**66.** $\int \frac{\sin x}{\cos^3 x} \, dx = -\int (\cos x)^{-3}(-\sin x) \, dx$

$= -\frac{(\cos x)^{-2}}{-2} + C = \frac{1}{2\cos^2 x} + C = \frac{1}{2}\sec^2 x + C$

**67.** $\int \cot^2 x\,dx = \int(\csc^2 x - 1)\,dx = -\cot x - x + C$

**68.** $\int \csc^2\left(\frac{x}{2}\right)dx = 2\int \csc^2\left(\frac{x}{2}\right)\left(\frac{1}{2}\right)dx = -2\cot\left(\frac{x}{2}\right) + C$

**69.** $\int e^x(e^x + 1)^2\,dx = \frac{(e^x + 1)^3}{3} + C$

**70.** $\int e^x(1 - 3e^x)\,dx = -\frac{1}{3}\int(1 - 3e^x)(-3e^x)\,dx$

$= -\frac{(1 - 3e^x)^2}{6}$

**71.** Let $u = 1 - e^x$, $du = -e^x\,dx$.

$\int e^x\sqrt{1 - e^x}\,dx = -\int(1 - e^x)^{1/2}(-e^x)\,dx$

$= -\frac{2}{3}(1 - e^x)^{3/2} + C$

**72.** Let $u = e^x + e^{-x}$, $du = (e^x - e^{-x})dx$.

$\int \frac{2e^x - 2e^{-x}}{(e^x + e^{-x})^2}dx = 2\int(e^x + e^{-x})^{-2}(e^x - e^{-x})\,dx$

$= \frac{-2}{e^x + e^{-x}} + C$

**73.** $\int \frac{5 - e^x}{e^{2x}}dx = \int 5e^{-2x}\,dx - \int e^{-x}\,dx$

$= -\frac{5}{2}e^{-2x} + e^{-x} + C$

**74.** $\int \frac{e^{2x} + 2e^x + 1}{e^x}dx = \int(e^x + 2 + e^{-x})\,dx$

$= e^x + 2x - e^{-x} + C$

**75.** $\int e^{\sin \pi x}\cos \pi x\,dx = \frac{1}{\pi}\int e^{\sin \pi x}(\pi \cos \pi x)\,dx$

$= \frac{1}{\pi}e^{\sin \pi x} + C$

**76.** $\int e^{\tan 2x}\sec^2 2x\,dx = \frac{1}{2}\int e^{\tan 2x}(2\sec^2 2x)\,dx$

$= \frac{1}{2}e^{\tan 2x} + C$

**77.** $\int e^{-x}\sec^2(e^{-x})\,dx = -\int \sec^2(e^{-x})(-e^{-x})\,dx$

$= -\tan(e^{-x}) + C$

**78.** $\int \ln(e^{2x-1})\,dx = \int(2x - 1)\,dx$

$= x^2 - x + C$

**79.** $\int 3^{x/2}\,dx = 2\int 3^{x/2}\left(\frac{1}{2}\right)dx = 2\frac{3^{x/2}}{\ln 3} + C = \frac{2}{\ln 3}3^{x/2} + C$

**80.** $\int 4^{-x}\,dx = -\frac{4^{-x}}{\ln 4} + C$

**81.** $\int x5^{-x^2}\,dx = -\frac{1}{2}\int 5^{-x^2}(-2x)\,dx$

$= -\left(\frac{1}{2}\right)\frac{5^{-x^2}}{\ln 5} + C$

$= -\frac{1}{2\ln 5}\left(5^{-x^2}\right) + C$

**82.** $\int(3 - x)7^{(3-x)^2}\,dx = -\frac{1}{2}\int -2(3 - x)7^{(3-x)^2}\,dx$

$= -\frac{1}{2\ln 7}\left[7^{(3-x)^2}\right] + C$

**83.** $f(x) = \int x\sqrt{4 - x^2}\,dx = -\frac{1}{2}\int(4 - x^2)^{1/2}(-2x)\,dx$

$= -\frac{1}{2}(4 - x^2)^{3/2}\left(\frac{2}{3}\right) + C = -\frac{1}{3}(4 - x^2)^{3/2} + C$

$f(2) = 2 = -\frac{1}{3}(0) + C \Rightarrow C = 2$

$f(x) = -\frac{1}{3}(4 - x^2)^{3/2} + 2$

**84.** $f(x) = \int 0.4^{x/3}\,dx = 3\int 0.4^{x/3}\left(\frac{1}{3}\right)dx$

$= \frac{3}{\ln 0.4}0.4^{x/3} + C$

$f(0) = \frac{3}{\ln 0.4} + C = \frac{1}{2} \Rightarrow C = \frac{1}{2} - \frac{3}{\ln 0.4}$

$f(x) = \frac{3}{\ln 0.4}0.4^{x/3} + \frac{1}{2} - \frac{3}{\ln 0.4}$

**85.** $f(x) = \int -\sin\frac{x}{2}\,dx = 2\cos\frac{x}{2} + C$

$f(0) = 6 = 2\cos\left(\frac{0}{2}\right) + C \Rightarrow C = 4$

$f(x) = 2\cos\frac{x}{2} + 4$

**86.** $f(x) = \int \pi \sec \pi x \tan \pi x\,dx = \sec \pi x + C$

$f(1/3) = 1 = \sec(\pi/3) + C \Rightarrow C = -1$

$f(x) = \sec \pi x - 1$

**87.** $f(x) = \int 2e^{-x/4}\,dx = -8\int e^{-x/4}\left(-\frac{1}{4}\right)dx$

$= -8e^{-x/4} + C$

$f(0) = 1 = -8 + C \Rightarrow C = 9$

$f(x) = -8e^{-x/4} + 9$

**88.** $f(x) = \int x^2 e^{-0.2x^3}\,dx$

$$= \frac{1}{-0.6}\int e^{-0.2x^3}\left(-0.6x^2\right)dx$$

$$= -\frac{5}{3}e^{-0.2x^3} + C$$

$$f(0) = \frac{3}{2} = -\frac{5}{3} + C \Rightarrow C = \frac{19}{6}$$

$$f(x) = -\frac{5}{3}e^{-0.2x^3} + \frac{19}{6}$$

**89.** $f'(x) = \int \frac{1}{2}\left(e^x + e^{-x}\right)dx = \frac{1}{2}\left(e^x - e^{-x}\right) + C_1$

$$f'(0) = C_1 = 0$$

$$f(x) = \int \frac{1}{2}\left(e^x - e^{-x}\right)dx = \frac{1}{2}\left(e^x + e^{-x}\right) + C_2$$

$$f(0) = 1 + C_2 = 1 \Rightarrow C_2 = 0$$

$$f(x) = \frac{1}{2}\left(e^x + e^{-x}\right)$$

**90.** $f'(x) = \int\left(\sin x + e^{2x}\right)dx = -\cos x + \frac{1}{2}e^{2x} + C_1$

$$f'(0) = -1 + \frac{1}{2} + C_1 = \frac{1}{2} \Rightarrow C_1 = 1$$

$$f'(x) = -\cos x + \frac{1}{2}e^{2x} + 1$$

$$f(x) = \int\left(-\cos x + \frac{1}{2}e^{2x} + 1\right)dx$$

$$= -\sin x + \frac{1}{4}e^{2x} + x + C_2$$

$$f(0) = \frac{1}{4} + C_2 = \frac{1}{4} \Rightarrow C_2 = 0$$

$$f(x) = x - \sin x + \frac{1}{4}e^{2x}$$

**91.** $u = x + 6,\ x = u - 6,\ dx = du$

$$\int x\sqrt{x+6}\,dx = \int (u-6)\sqrt{u}\,du$$

$$= \int\left(u^{3/2} - 6u^{1/2}\right)du$$

$$= \frac{2}{5}u^{5/2} - 4u^{3/2} + C$$

$$= \frac{2u^{3/2}}{5}(u - 10) + C$$

$$= \frac{2}{5}(x+6)^{3/2}\left[(x+6) - 10\right] + C$$

$$= \frac{2}{5}(x+6)^{3/2}(x-4) + C$$

**92.** $u = 4x + 1,\ x = \frac{1}{4}(u - 1),\ dx = \frac{1}{4}\,du$

$$\int x\sqrt{4x+1}\,dx = \int \frac{1}{4}(u-1)\sqrt{u}\,\frac{1}{4}\,du$$

$$= \frac{1}{16}\int\left(u^{3/2} - u^{1/2}\right)du$$

$$= \frac{1}{16}\left(\frac{2}{5}u^{5/2} - \frac{2}{3}u^{3/2}\right) + C$$

$$= \frac{u^{3/2}}{120}(3u - 5) + C$$

$$= \frac{1}{120}(4x+1)^{3/2}\left[3(4x+1) - 5\right] + C$$

$$= \frac{1}{120}(4x+1)^{3/2}(12x - 2) + C$$

$$= \frac{1}{60}(4x+1)^{3/2}(6x - 1) + C$$

**93.** $u = 1 - x,\ x = 1 - u,\ dx = -du$

$$\int x^2\sqrt{1-x}\,dx = -\int (1-u)^2\sqrt{u}\,du$$

$$= -\int\left(u^{1/2} - 2u^{3/2} + u^{5/2}\right)du$$

$$= -\left(\frac{2}{3}u^{3/2} - \frac{4}{5}u^{5/2} + \frac{2}{7}u^{7/2}\right) + C$$

$$= -\frac{2u^{3/2}}{105}\left(35 - 42u + 15u^2\right) + C$$

$$= -\frac{2}{105}(1-x)^{3/2}\left[35 - 42(1-x) + 15(1-x)^2\right] + C$$

$$= -\frac{2}{105}(1-x)^{3/2}\left(15x^2 + 12x + 8\right) + C$$

**94.** $u = 2 - x,\ x = 2 - u,\ dx = -du$

$$\begin{aligned}\int (x + 1)\sqrt{2 - x}\,dx &= -\int (3 - u)\sqrt{u}\,du\\ &= -\int\left(3u^{1/2} - u^{3/2}\right)du\\ &= -\left(2u^{3/2} - \frac{2}{5}u^{5/2}\right) + C\\ &= -\frac{2u^{3/2}}{5}(5 - u) + C\\ &= -\frac{2}{5}(2 - x)^{3/2}\left[5 - (2 - x)\right] + C\\ &= -\frac{2}{5}(2 - x)^{3/2}(x + 3) + C\end{aligned}$$

**95.** $u = 2x - 1,\ x = \frac{1}{2}(u + 1),\ dx = \frac{1}{2}\,du$

$$\begin{aligned}\int \frac{x^2 - 1}{\sqrt{2x - 1}}\,dx &= \frac{1}{2}\int \frac{\left[(1/2)(u + 1)\right]^2 - 1}{\sqrt{u}}\,du\\ &= \frac{1}{8}\int u^{-1/2}\left[\left(u^2 + 2u + 1\right) - 4\right]du\\ &= \frac{1}{8}\int\left(u^{3/2} + 2u^{1/2} - 3u^{-1/2}\right)du\\ &= \frac{1}{8}\left(\frac{2}{5}u^{5/2} + \frac{4}{3}u^{3/2} - 6u^{1/2}\right) + C\\ &= \frac{u^{1/2}}{60}\left(3u^2 + 10u - 45\right) + C\\ &= \frac{\sqrt{2x - 1}}{60}\left[3(2x - 1)^2 + 10(2x - 1) - 45\right] + C\\ &= \frac{1}{60}\sqrt{2x - 1}\left(12x^2 + 8x - 52\right) + C\\ &= \frac{1}{15}\sqrt{2x - 1}\left(3x^2 + 2x - 13\right) + C\end{aligned}$$

**96.** Let $u = x + 4,\ x = u - 4,\ du = dx.$

$$\begin{aligned}\int \frac{2x + 1}{\sqrt{x + 4}}\,dx &= \int \frac{2(u - 4) + 1}{\sqrt{u}}\,du\\ &= \int\left(2u^{1/2} - 7u^{-1/2}\right)du\\ &= \frac{4}{3}u^{3/2} - 14u^{1/2} + C\\ &= \frac{2}{3}u^{1/2}(2u - 21) + C\\ &= \frac{2}{3}\sqrt{x + 4}\left[2(x + 4) - 21\right] + C\\ &= \frac{2}{3}\sqrt{x + 4}(2x - 13) + C\end{aligned}$$

**97.** $u = x + 1,\ x = u - 1,\ dx = du$

$$\begin{aligned}\int \frac{-x}{(x + 1) - \sqrt{x + 1}}\,dx &= \int \frac{-(u - 1)}{u - \sqrt{u}}\,du\\ &= -\int \frac{\left(\sqrt{u} + 1\right)\left(\sqrt{u} - 1\right)}{\sqrt{u}\left(\sqrt{u} - 1\right)}\,du\\ &= -\int\left(1 + u^{-1/2}\right)du\\ &= -\left(u + 2u^{1/2}\right) + C\\ &= -u - 2\sqrt{u} + C\\ &= -(x + 1) - 2\sqrt{x + 1} + C\\ &= -x - 2\sqrt{x + 1} - 1 + C\\ &= -\left(x + 2\sqrt{x + 1}\right) + C_1\end{aligned}$$

where $C_1 = -1 + C$.

**98.** $u = t + 10,\ t = u - 10,\ du = dt$

$$\begin{aligned}\int t(t+10)^{1/3}\,dt &= \int (u-10)u^{1/3}\,du\\ &= \int\left(u^{4/3} - 10u^{1/3}\right)du\\ &= \frac{3}{7}u^{7/3} - \frac{15}{2}u^{4/3} + C\\ &= \frac{3}{14}u^{4/3}(2u - 35) + C\\ &= \frac{3}{14}(t+10)^{4/3}\left[2(t+10) - 35\right] + C\\ &= \frac{3}{14}(t+10)^{4/3}(2t - 15) + C\end{aligned}$$

**99.** Let $u = x^2 + 1,\ du = 2x\,dx.$

$$\int_{-1}^{1} x\left(x^2+1\right)^3 dx = \tfrac{1}{2}\int_{-1}^{1}\left(x^2+1\right)^3(2x)\,dx = \left[\tfrac{1}{8}\left(x^2+1\right)^4\right]_{-1}^{1} = 0$$

**100.** Let $u = x^3 + 8,\ du = 3x^2\,dx.$

$$\int_{-2}^{4} x^2\left(x^3+8\right)^2 dx = \frac{1}{3}\int_{-2}^{4}\left(x^3+8\right)^2\left(3x^2\right)dx = \left[\frac{1}{3}\frac{\left(x^3+8\right)^3}{3}\right]_{-2}^{4} = \frac{1}{9}\left[(64+8)^3 - (-8+8)^3\right] = 41{,}472$$

**101.** Let $u = x^3 + 1,\ du = 3x^2\,dx.$

$$\int_1^2 2x^2\sqrt{x^3+1}\,dx = 2\cdot\frac{1}{3}\int_1^2\left(x^3+1\right)^{1/2}\left(3x^2\right)dx = \left[\frac{\left(x^3+1\right)^{3/2}}{3/2}\right]_1^2 = \frac{4}{9}\left[\left(x^3+1\right)^{3/2}\right]_1^2 = \frac{4}{9}\left[27 - 2\sqrt{2}\right] = 12 - \frac{8}{9}\sqrt{2}$$

**102.** Let $u = 4 - x^2,\ du = -2x\,dx.$

$$\int_0^2 x\sqrt{4-x^2}\,dx = -\frac{1}{2}\int_0^2\left(4-x^2\right)^{1/2}(-2x)\,dx = \left[-\frac{1}{3}\left(4-x^2\right)^{3/2}\right]_0^2 = 0 + \frac{8}{3} = \frac{8}{3}$$

**103.** Let $u = 2x + 1,\ du = 2\,dx.$

$$\int_0^4 \frac{1}{\sqrt{2x+1}}\,dx = \frac{1}{2}\int_0^4 (2x+1)^{-1/2}(2)\,dx = \left[\sqrt{2x+1}\right]_0^4 = \sqrt{9} - \sqrt{1} = 2$$

**104.** Let $u = 1 + 2x^2,\ du = 4x\,dx.$

$$\int_0^2 \frac{x}{\sqrt{1+2x^2}}\,dx = \frac{1}{4}\int_0^2\left(1+2x^2\right)^{-1/2}(4x)\,dx = \left[\frac{1}{2}\sqrt{1+2x^2}\right]_0^2 = \frac{3}{2} - \frac{1}{2} = 1$$

**105.** $$\int_0^1 e^{-2x}\,dx = -\frac{1}{2}\int_0^1 e^{-2x}(-2)\,dx = \left[-\frac{1}{2}e^{-2x}\right]_0^1 = -\frac{1}{2}e^{-2} + \frac{1}{2}$$

**106.** $$\int_1^2 e^{1-x}\,dx = -\int_1^2 e^{1-x}(-1)\,dx = \left[-e^{1-x}\right]_1^2 = -e^{-1} + 1$$

**107.** $$\int_1^3 \frac{e^{3/x}}{x^2}\,dx = -\frac{1}{3}\int_1^3 e^{3/x}\left(-\frac{3}{x^2}\right)dx = \left[-\frac{1}{3}e^{3/x}\right]_1^3 = -\frac{1}{3}\left(e - e^3\right) = \frac{e}{3}\left(e^2 - 1\right)$$

**108.** Let $u = \dfrac{-x^2}{2},\ du = -x\,dx.$

$$\int_0^{\sqrt{2}} xe^{-x^2/2}\,dx = -\int_0^{\sqrt{2}} e^{-x^2/2}(-x)\,dx = \left[-e^{-x^2/2}\right]_0^{\sqrt{2}} = 1 - e^{-1} = \frac{e-1}{e}$$

**109.** Let $u = 1 + \sqrt{x}, du = \dfrac{1}{2\sqrt{x}}\,dx.$

$$\int_1^9 \frac{1}{\sqrt{x}\left(1+\sqrt{x}\right)^2}\,dx = 2\int_1^9 \left(1+\sqrt{x}\right)^{-2}\left(\frac{1}{2\sqrt{x}}\right)dx = \left[-\frac{2}{1+\sqrt{x}}\right]_1^9 = -\frac{1}{2} + 1 = \frac{1}{2}$$

**110.** Let $u = 4 + x^2, du = 2x\,dx.$

$$\int_0^2 x\sqrt[3]{4+x^2}\,dx = \frac{1}{2}\int_0^2 \left(4+x^2\right)^{1/3}(2x)\,dx = \left[\frac{3}{8}\left(4+x^2\right)^{4/3}\right]_0^2 = \frac{3}{8}\left(8^{4/3} - 4^{4/3}\right) = 6 - \frac{3}{2}\sqrt[3]{4} \approx 3.619$$

**111.** $u = 2 - x, x = 2 - u, dx = -du$

When $x = 1, u = 1$. When $x = 2, u = 0$.

$$\int_1^2 (x-1)\sqrt{2-x}\,dx = \int_1^0 -\left[(2-u)-1\right]\sqrt{u}\,du = \int_1^0 \left(u^{3/2} - u^{1/2}\right)du = \left[\frac{2}{5}u^{5/2} - \frac{2}{3}u^{3/2}\right]_1^0 = -\left[\frac{2}{5} - \frac{2}{3}\right] = \frac{4}{15}$$

**112.** Let $u = 2x - 1, du = 2\,dx, x = \dfrac{1}{2}(u+1).$

When $x = 1, u = 1$. When $x = 5, u = 9$.

$$\int_1^5 \frac{x}{\sqrt{2x-1}}\,dx = \int_1^9 \frac{1/2(u+1)}{\sqrt{u}}\frac{1}{2}\,du = \frac{1}{4}\int_1^9 \left(u^{1/2} + u^{-1/2}\right)du$$

$$= \frac{1}{4}\left[\frac{2}{3}u^{3/2} + 2u^{1/2}\right]_1^9$$

$$= \frac{1}{4}\left[\left(\frac{2}{3}(27) + 2(3)\right) - \left(\frac{2}{3} + 2\right)\right]$$

$$= \frac{16}{3}$$

**113.** $\displaystyle\int_0^{\pi/2} \cos\left(\frac{2}{3}x\right)dx = \left[\frac{3}{2}\sin\left(\frac{2}{3}x\right)\right]_0^{\pi/2} = \frac{3}{2}\left(\frac{\sqrt{3}}{2}\right) = \frac{3\sqrt{3}}{4}$

**114.** $\displaystyle\int_{\pi/3}^{\pi/2} (x + \cos x)\,dx = \left[\frac{x^2}{2} + \sin x\right]_{\pi/3}^{\pi/2} = \left(\frac{\pi^2}{8} + 1\right) - \left(\frac{\pi^2}{18} + \frac{\sqrt{3}}{2}\right) = \frac{5\pi^2}{72} + \frac{2-\sqrt{3}}{2}$

**115.** $\displaystyle\int_{-1}^2 2^x\,dx = \left[\frac{2^x}{\ln 2}\right]_{-1}^2 = \frac{1}{\ln 2}\left[4 - \frac{1}{2}\right] = \frac{7}{2\ln 2} = \frac{7}{\ln 4}$

**116.** $\displaystyle\int_{-2}^0 \left(3^3 - 5^2\right)dx = \int_{-2}^0 (27 - 25)\,dx$

$$= \int_{-2}^0 2\,dx = \left[2x\right]_{-2}^0 = 4$$

**117.** $\dfrac{dy}{dx} = 18x^2\left(2x^3+1\right)^2, (0, 4)$

$y = 3\int\left(2x^3+1\right)^2\left(6x^2\right)dx \quad \left(u = 2x^3+1\right)$

$y = 3\dfrac{\left(2x^3+1\right)^3}{3} + C = \left(2x^3+1\right)^3 + C$

$4 = 1^3 + C \Rightarrow C = 3$

$y = \left(2x^3+1\right)^3 + 3$

**118.** $\dfrac{dy}{dx} = \dfrac{-48}{(3x+5)^3}, (-1, 3)$

$y = -48\int(3x+5)^{-3}\,dx$

$= (-48)\dfrac{1}{3}\int(3x+5)^{-3}3\,dx$

$= \dfrac{-16(3x+5)^{-2}}{-2} + C$

$= \dfrac{8}{(3x+5)^2} + C$

$3 = \dfrac{8}{(3(-1)+5)^2} + C = \dfrac{8}{4} + C \Rightarrow C = 1$

$y = \dfrac{8}{(3x+5)^2} + 1$

**119.** $\dfrac{dy}{dx} = \dfrac{2x}{\sqrt{2x^2 - 1}}, (5, 4)$

$y = \dfrac{1}{2}\int (2x^2 - 1)^{-1/2}(4x\,dx) \quad (u = 2x^2 - 1)$

$y = \dfrac{1}{2}\dfrac{(2x^2 - 1)^{1/2}}{1/2} + C = \sqrt{2x^2 - 1} + C$

$4 = \sqrt{49} + C = 7 + C \Rightarrow C = -3$

$y = \sqrt{2x^2 - 1} - 3$

**120.** $\dfrac{dy}{dx} = 4x + \dfrac{9x^2}{(3x^3 + 1)^{3/2}}, (0, 2)$

$y = \int \left(4x + (3x^3 + 1)^{-3/2} 9x^2\right) dx$

$= 2x^2 + \dfrac{(3x^3 + 1)^{-1/2}}{(-1/2)} + C$

$= 2x^2 - \dfrac{2}{\sqrt{3x^3 + 1}} + C$

$2 = 0 - \dfrac{2}{1} + C \Rightarrow C = 4$

$y = 2x^2 - \dfrac{2}{\sqrt{3x^3 + 1}} + 4$

**121.** $u = x + 1, x = u - 1, dx = du$

When $x = 0, u = 1$. When $x = 7, u = 8$.

$\text{Area} = \int_0^7 x\sqrt[3]{x + 1}\,dx = \int_1^8 (u - 1)\sqrt[3]{u}\,du$

$= \int_1^8 \left(u^{4/3} - u^{1/3}\right) du$

$= \left[\dfrac{3}{7}u^{7/3} - \dfrac{3}{4}u^{4/3}\right]_1^8$

$= \left(\dfrac{384}{7} - 12\right) - \left(\dfrac{3}{7} - \dfrac{3}{4}\right)$

$= \dfrac{1209}{28}$

**122.** $u = x + 2, x = u - 2, dx = du$

When $x = -2, u = 0$. When $x = 6, u = 8$.

$\text{Area} = \int_{-2}^6 x^2\sqrt[3]{x + 2}\,dx$

$= \int_0^8 (u - 2)^2\sqrt[3]{u}\,du$

$= \int_0^8 \left(u^{7/3} - 4u^{4/3} + 4u^{1/3}\right) du$

$= \left[\dfrac{3}{10}u^{10/3} - \dfrac{12}{7}u^{7/3} + 3u^{4/3}\right]_0^8 = \dfrac{4752}{35}$

**123.** $\text{Area} = \int_0^\pi (2\sin x + \sin 2x)\,dx$

$= -\left[2\cos x + \dfrac{1}{2}\cos 2x\right]_0^\pi = 4$

**124.** $\text{Area} = \int_0^\pi (\sin x + \cos 2x)\,dx$

$= \left[-\cos x + \tfrac{1}{2}\sin 2x\right]_0^\pi = 2$

**125.** $\text{Area} = \int_{\pi/2}^{2\pi/3} \sec^2\left(\dfrac{x}{2}\right) dx$

$= 2\int_{\pi/2}^{2\pi/3} \sec^2\left(\dfrac{x}{2}\right)\left(\dfrac{1}{2}\right) dx$

$= \left[2\tan\left(\dfrac{x}{2}\right)\right]_{\pi/2}^{2\pi/3} = 2\left(\sqrt{3} - 1\right)$

**126.** Let $u = 2x, du = 2\,dx$.

$\text{Area} = \int_{\pi/12}^{\pi/4} \csc 2x \cot 2x\,dx$

$= \tfrac{1}{2}\int_{\pi/12}^{\pi/4} \csc 2x \cot 2x(2)\,dx$

$= \left[-\tfrac{1}{2}\csc 2x\right]_{\pi/12}^{\pi/4} = \tfrac{1}{2}$

**127.** $\int_0^5 e^x\,dx = \left[e^x\right]_0^5 = e^5 - 1 \approx 147.413$

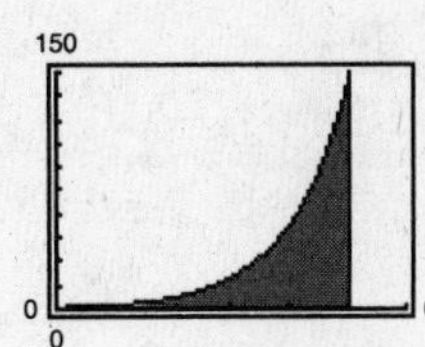


**128.** $\int_a^b e^{-x}\,dx = \left[-e^{-x}\right]_a^b = e^{-a} - e^{-b}$

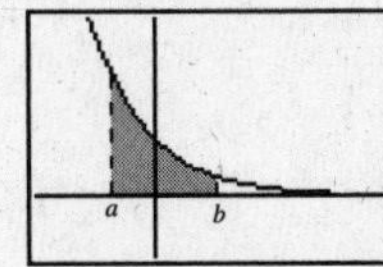


**129.** $\int_0^{\sqrt{6}} xe^{-x^2/4}\,dx = \left[-2e^{-x^2/4}\right]_0^{\sqrt{6}}$

$= -2e^{-3/2} + 2 \approx 1.554$

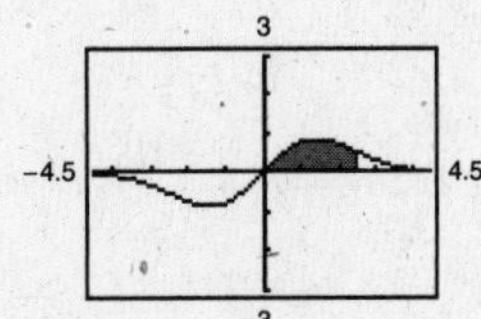

**130.** $\int_0^2 \left(e^{-2x} + 2\right) dx = \left[-\frac{1}{2}e^{-2x} + 2x\right]_0^2$

$= -\frac{1}{2}e^{-4} + 4 + \frac{1}{2} \approx 4.491$

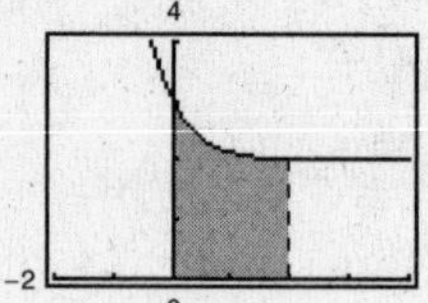

**131.** $\int_0^6 \frac{x}{\sqrt{4x+1}} dx \approx 4.667 = \frac{14}{3}$

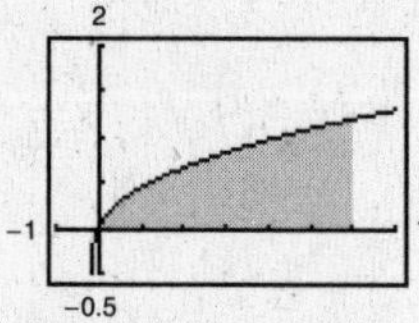

**132.** $\int_0^2 x^3\sqrt{2x+3}\, dx \approx 9.9451$

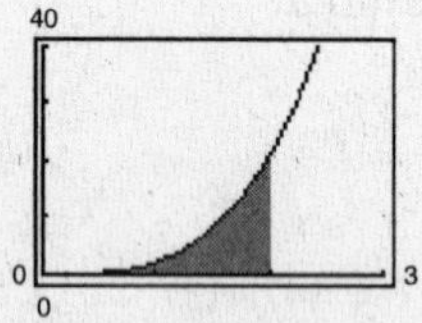

**133.** $\int_3^7 x\sqrt{x-3}\, dx \approx 28.8 = \frac{144}{5}$

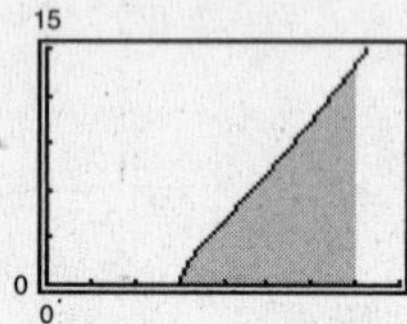

**134.** $\int_1^5 x^2\sqrt{x-1}\, dx \approx 67.505$

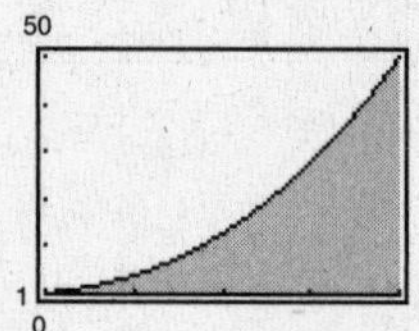

**135.** $\int_1^4 \left(\theta + \sin\left(\frac{\theta}{4}\right)\right) d\theta \approx 9.2144$

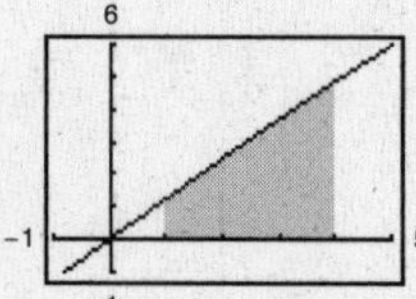

**136.** $\int_0^{\pi/6} \cos 3x\, dx = \frac{1}{3} \approx 0.3333$

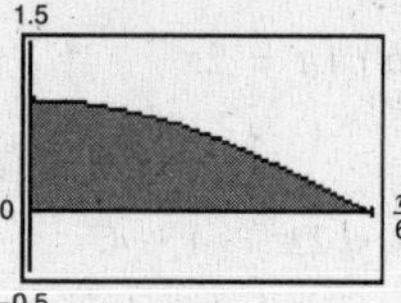

**137.** $\int_0^{\sqrt{2}} xe^{-x^2/2}\, dx = \left[-e^{-(x^2/2)}\right]_0^{\sqrt{2}}$

$= -e^{-1} + 1 \approx 0.632$

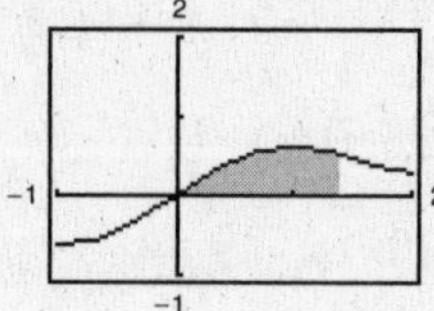

**138.** $\int_0^2 \left(e^{-2x} + 2\right) dx = \left[-\frac{1}{2}e^{-2x} + 2x\right]_0^2$

$= -\frac{1}{2}e^{-4} + 4 + \frac{1}{2} \approx 4.491$

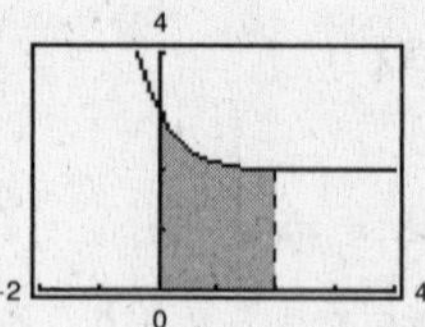

**139.** $f(x) = x^2(x^2+1)$ is even.

$\int_{-2}^2 x^2(x^2+1)\, dx = 2\int_0^2 \left(x^4 + x^2\right) dx = 2\left[\frac{x^5}{5} + \frac{x^3}{3}\right]_0^2$

$= 2\left[\frac{32}{5} + \frac{8}{3}\right] = \frac{272}{15}$

**140.** $f(x) = \sin^2 x \cos x$ is even.

$\int_{-\pi/2}^{\pi/2} \sin^2 x \cos x\, dx = 2\int_0^{\pi/2} \sin^2 x(\cos x)\, dx$

$= 2\left[\frac{\sin^3 x}{3}\right]_0^{\pi/2}$

$= \frac{2}{3}$

**141.** $f(x) = x(x^2+1)^3$ is odd.

$\int_{-2}^2 x(x^2+1)^3\, dx = 0$

**142.** $f(x) = \sin x \cos x$ is odd.

$\int_{-\pi/4}^{\pi/4} \sin x \cos x\, dx = 0$

**143.** $\int_0^4 x^2\,dx = \left[\frac{x^3}{3}\right]_0^4 = \frac{64}{3}$; the function $x^2$ is an even function.

(a) $\int_{-4}^0 x^2\,dx = \int_0^4 x^2\,dx = \frac{64}{3}$

(b) $\int_{-4}^4 x^2\,dx = 2\int_0^4 x^2\,dx = \frac{128}{3}$

(c) $\int_0^4 \left(-x^2\right) dx = -\int_0^4 x^2\,dx = -\frac{64}{3}$

(d) $\int_{-4}^0 3x^2\,dx = 3\int_0^4 x^2\,dx = 64$

**144.** (a) $\int_{-\pi/4}^{\pi/4} \sin x\,dx = 0$ because $\sin x$ is symmetric to the origin.

(b) $\int_{-\pi/4}^{\pi/4} \cos x\,dx = 2\int_0^{\pi/4} \cos x\,dx = \left[2\sin x\right]_0^{\pi/4} = \sqrt{2}$ because $\cos x$ is symmetric to the $y$-axis.

(c) $\int_{-\pi/2}^{\pi/2} \cos x\,dx = 2\int_0^{\pi/2} \cos x\,dx = \left[2\sin x\right]_0^{\pi/2} = 2$

(d) $\int_{-\pi/2}^{\pi/2} \sin x \cos x\,dx = 0$ because $\sin(-x)\cos(-x) = -\sin x \cos x$ and so, is symmetric to the origin.

**145.** $\int_{-3}^3 \left(x^3 + 4x^2 - 3x - 6\right) dx = \int_{-3}^3 \left(x^3 - 3x\right) dx + \int_{-3}^3 \left(4x^2 - 6\right) dx = 0 + 2\int_0^3 \left(4x^2 - 6\right) dx = 2\left[\frac{4}{3}x^3 - 6x\right]_0^3 = 36$

**146.** $\int_{-\pi/2}^{\pi/2} \left(\sin 4x + \cos 4x\right) dx = \int_{-\pi/2}^{\pi/2} \sin 4x\,dx + \int_{-\pi/2}^{\pi/2} \cos 4x\,dx = 0 + 2\int_0^{\pi/2} \cos 4x\,dx = \left[\frac{2}{4}\sin 4x\right]_0^{\pi/2} = 0$

**147.** If $u = 5 - x^2$, then $du = -2x\,dx$ and $\int x\left(5 - x^2\right)^3 dx = -\frac{1}{2}\int \left(5 - x^2\right)^3(-2x)\,dx = -\frac{1}{2}\int u^3\,du$.

**148.** $f(x) = x\left(x^2 + 1\right)^2$ is odd. So, $\int_{-2}^2 x\left(x^2 + 1\right)^2 dx = 0$.

**149.** Let $u = 2x$, $du = 2\,dx$.

When $x = 0$, $u = 0$, and when $x = 4$, $u = 8$. So, $\int_0^4 f(2x)\,dx = \int_0^8 f(u)\frac{1}{2}\,du = \frac{1}{2}\int_0^8 f(u)\,du = \frac{1}{2}(32) = 16$.

**150.** (a) $\int (2x - 1)^2\,dx = \frac{1}{2}\int (2x - 1)^2 2\,dx = \frac{1}{6}(2x - 1)^3 + C_1 = \frac{4}{3}x^3 - 2x^2 + x - \frac{1}{6} + C_1$

$\int (2x - 1)^2\,dx = \int \left(4x^2 - 4x + 1\right) dx = \frac{4}{3}x^3 - 2x^2 + x + C_2$

They differ by a constant: $C_2 = C_1 - \frac{1}{6}$.

(b) $\int \sin x \cos x\,dx = \int (\sin x)^1(\cos x\,dx) = \frac{\sin^2 x}{2} + C_1$

$\int \sin x \cos x\,dx = -\int (\cos x)^1(-\sin x\,dx) = -\frac{\cos^2 x}{2} + C_2$

$-\frac{\cos^2 x}{2} + C_2 = -\frac{\left(1 - \sin^2 x\right)}{2} + C_2 = \frac{\sin^2 x}{2} - \frac{1}{2} + C_2$

They differ by a constant: $C_2 = C_1 + \frac{1}{2}$.

(c) $\int \tan x \sec^2 x\,dx = \frac{\tan^2 x}{2} + C_1$

$\int \tan x \sec^2 x\,dx = \int \sec x(\sec x \tan x)\,dx = \frac{\sec^2 x}{2} + C_2$

The answers differ by a constant because

$\frac{\tan^2 x}{2} + C_1 = \frac{\sec^2 x}{2} - \frac{1}{2} + C_1$.

**151.** $\dfrac{dQ}{dt} = k(100 - t)^2$

$Q(t) = \int k(100 - t)^2\,dt = -\dfrac{k}{3}(100 - t)^3 + C$

$Q(100) = C = 0$

$Q(t) = -\dfrac{k}{3}(100 - t)^3$

$Q(0) = -\dfrac{k}{3}(100)^3 = 4{,}000{,}000 \Rightarrow k = -12$

So, $Q(t) = 4(100 - t)^3$.

When $t = 50$, $Q(50) = \$500{,}000$.

**152.** $\dfrac{dV}{dt} = \dfrac{k}{(t + 1)^2}$

$V(t) = \int \dfrac{k}{(t + 1)^2}\,dt = -\dfrac{k}{t + 1} + C$

$V(0) = -k + C = 500{,}000$

$V(1) = -\dfrac{1}{2}k + C = 400{,}000$

Solving this system yields $k = -200{,}000$ and $C = 300{,}000$. So, $V(t) = \dfrac{200{,}000}{t + 1} + 300{,}000$.

When $t = 4$, $V(4) = \$340{,}000$.

**153.** (a) $R(t) = 2.876 + 2.202\sin(0.576t + 0.847)$

$R'(t) = 2.202\cos(0.576t + 0.847)(0.576) = 1.268352\cos(0.576t + 0.847)$

$R'(t) = 0$ when $0.576t + 0.847 = \dfrac{\pi}{2}, \dfrac{3\pi}{2}, \dfrac{5\pi}{2}, \dfrac{7\pi}{2}, \ldots$

So, $t = 1.257, 6.711$ (others are outside $[0, 12]$).

By the First Derivative Test,
(6.7, 0.7) is a relative minimum (July) and
(1.3, 5.1) is a relative maximum (February).

(b) $\int_0^{12} R(t)\,dt \approx 36.68$ inches

(c) $\frac{1}{3}\int_9^{12} R(t)\,dt \approx 3.99$ inches

**154.** $\dfrac{1}{b - a}\int_a^b \left[74.50 + 43.75\sin\dfrac{\pi t}{6}\right]dt = \dfrac{1}{b - a}\left[74.50t - \dfrac{262.5}{\pi}\cos\dfrac{\pi t}{6}\right]_a^b$

(a) $\dfrac{1}{3}\left[74.50t - \dfrac{262.5}{\pi}\cos\dfrac{\pi t}{6}\right]_0^3 = \dfrac{1}{3}\left(223.5 + \dfrac{262.5}{\pi}\right) \approx 102.352$ thousand units

(b) $\dfrac{1}{3}\left[74.50t - \dfrac{262.5}{\pi}\cos\dfrac{\pi t}{6}\right]_3^6 = \dfrac{1}{3}\left(447 + \dfrac{262.5}{\pi} - 223.5\right) \approx 102.352$ thousand units

(c) $\dfrac{1}{12}\left[74.50t - \dfrac{262.5}{\pi}\cos\dfrac{\pi t}{6}\right]_0^{12} = \dfrac{1}{12}\left(894 - \dfrac{262.5}{\pi} + \dfrac{262.5}{\pi}\right) = 74.5$ thousand units

**155.** (a)

Maximum flow: $R \approx 61.713$ at $t = 9.36$.
[(18.861, 61.178) is a relative maximum.]

(b) Volume $= \int_0^{24} R(t)\,dt \approx 1272$ thousand gallons

**156.** $\dfrac{1}{b-a}\displaystyle\int_a^b \left[2\sin(60\pi t) + \cos(120\pi t)\right] dt = \dfrac{1}{b-a}\left[-\dfrac{1}{30\pi}\cos(60\pi t) + \dfrac{1}{120\pi}\sin(120\pi t)\right]_a^b$

(a) $\dfrac{1}{(1/60)-0}\left[-\dfrac{1}{30\pi}\cos(60\pi t) + \dfrac{1}{120\pi}\sin(120\pi t)\right]_0^{1/60} = 60\left[\left(\dfrac{1}{30\pi}+0\right) - \left(-\dfrac{1}{30\pi}\right)\right] = \dfrac{4}{\pi} \approx 1.273$ amps

(b) $\dfrac{1}{(1/240)-0}\left[-\dfrac{1}{30\pi}\cos(60\pi t) + \dfrac{1}{120\pi}\sin(120\pi t)\right]_0^{1/240} = 240\left[\left(-\dfrac{1}{30\sqrt{2}\pi} + \dfrac{1}{120\pi}\right) - \left(-\dfrac{1}{30\pi}\right)\right]$

$= \dfrac{2}{\pi}\left(5 - 2\sqrt{2}\right) \approx 1.382$ amps

(c) $\dfrac{1}{(1/30)-0}\left[-\dfrac{1}{30\pi}\cos(60\pi t) + \dfrac{1}{120\pi}\sin(120\pi t)\right]_0^{1/30} = 30\left[\left(-\dfrac{1}{30\pi}\right) - \left(-\dfrac{1}{30\pi}\right)\right] = 0$ amp

**157.** $u = 1 - x,\ x = 1 - u,\ dx = -du$

When $x = a,\ u = 1 - a$. When $x = b,\ u = 1 - b$.

$P_{a,b} = \displaystyle\int_a^b \frac{15}{4}x\sqrt{1-x}\,dx = \frac{15}{4}\int_{1-a}^{1-b} -(1-u)\sqrt{u}\,du$

$= \dfrac{15}{4}\displaystyle\int_{1-a}^{1-b}\left(u^{3/2} - u^{1/2}\right)du = \frac{15}{4}\left[\frac{2}{5}u^{5/2} - \frac{2}{3}u^{3/2}\right]_{1-a}^{1-b} = \frac{15}{4}\left[\frac{2u^{3/2}}{15}(3u-5)\right]_{1-a}^{1-b} = \left[-\frac{(1-x)^{3/2}}{2}(3x+2)\right]_a^b$

(a) $P_{0.50,\,0.75} = \left[-\dfrac{(1-x)^{3/2}}{2}(3x+2)\right]_{0.50}^{0.75} = 0.353 = 35.3\%$

(b) $P_{0,b} = \left[-\dfrac{(1-x)^{3/2}}{2}(3x+2)\right]_0^b = -\dfrac{(1-b)^{3/2}}{2}(3b+2) + 1 = 0.5$

$(1-b)^{3/2}(3b+2) = 1$

$b \approx 0.586 = 58.6\%$

**158.** $u = 1 - x,\ x = 1 - u,\ dx = -du$

When $x = a,\ u = 1 - a$. When $x = b,\ u = 1 - b$.

$P_{a,b} = \displaystyle\int_a^b \frac{1155}{32}x^3(1-x)^{3/2}\,dx = \frac{1155}{32}\int_{1-a}^{1-b} -(1-u)^3u^{3/2}\,du$

$= \dfrac{1155}{32}\displaystyle\int_{1-a}^{1-b}\left(u^{9/2} - 3u^{7/2} + 3u^{5/2} - u^{3/2}\right)du = \frac{1155}{32}\left[\frac{2}{11}u^{11/2} - \frac{2}{3}u^{9/2} + \frac{6}{7}u^{7/2} - \frac{2}{5}u^{5/2}\right]_{1-a}^{1-b}$

$= \dfrac{1155}{32}\left[\dfrac{2u^{5/2}}{1155}\left(105u^3 - 385u^2 + 495u - 231\right)\right]_{1-a}^{1-b} = \left[\dfrac{u^{5/2}}{16}\left(105u^3 - 385u^2 + 495u - 231\right)\right]_{1-a}^{1-b}$

(a) $P_{0,\,0.25} = \left[\dfrac{u^{5/2}}{16}\left(105u^3 - 385u^2 + 495u - 231\right)\right]_1^{0.75} \approx 0.025 = 2.5\%$

(b) $P_{0.5,\,1} = \left[\dfrac{u^{5/2}}{16}\left(105u^3 - 385u^2 + 495u - 231\right)\right]_{0.5}^{0} \approx 0.736 = 73.6\%$

**159.** $0.0665\displaystyle\int_{48}^{60} e^{-0.0139(t-48)^2}\,dt$

Graphing utility: $0.4772 = 47.72\%$

**160.** $\displaystyle\int_0^x e^t\,dt \ge \int_0^x 1\,dt$

$\left[e^t\right]_0^x \ge \left[t\right]_0^x$

$e^x - 1 \ge x \Rightarrow e^x \ge 1 + x$ for $x \ge 0$

**161.** (a)

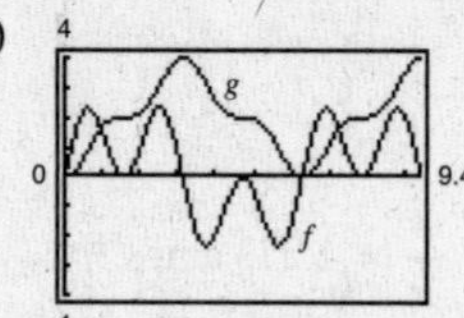


(b) $g$ is nonnegative because the graph of $f$ is positive at the beginning, and generally has more positive sections than negative ones.

(c) The points on $g$ that correspond to the extrema of $f$ are points of inflection of $g$.

(d) No, some zeros of $f$, like $x = \pi/2$, do not correspond to an extrema of $g$. The graph of $g$ continues to increase after $x = \pi/2$ because $f$ remains above the $x$-axis.

(e) The graph of $h$ is that of $g$ shifted 2 units downward.

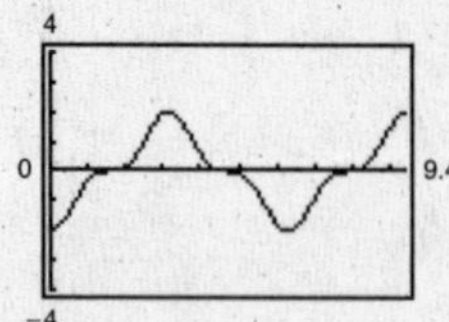


$$g(t) = \int_0^t f(x)\,dx = \int_0^{\pi/2} f(x)\,dx + \int_{\pi/2}^t f(x)\,dx = 2 + h(t).$$

**162.** Let $f(x) = \sin \pi x,\ 0 \le x \le 1$.

Let $\Delta x = \dfrac{1}{n}$ and use righthand endpoints

$c_i = \dfrac{i}{n},\ i = 1, 2, \ldots, n.$

$$\lim_{n\to\infty} \sum_{i=1}^{n} \frac{\sin(i\pi/n)}{n} = \lim_{\|\Delta x\|\to 0} \sum_{i=1}^{n} f(c_i)\,\Delta x$$
$$= \int_0^1 \sin \pi x\,dx$$
$$= -\frac{1}{\pi}\cos \pi x\Big]_0^1$$
$$= -\frac{1}{\pi}(-1 - 1) = \frac{2}{\pi}$$

**163.** (a) Let $u = 1 - x,\ du = -dx,\ x = 1 - u$

$x = 0 \Rightarrow u = 1,\ x = 1 \Rightarrow u = 0$

$$\int_0^1 x^2(1 - x)^5\,dx = \int_1^0 (1 - u)^2 u^5(-du)$$
$$= \int_0^1 u^5(1 - u)^2\,du$$
$$= \int_0^1 x^5(1 - x)^2\,dx$$

(b) Let $u = 1 - x,\ du = -dx,\ x = 1 - u$

$x = 0 \Rightarrow u = 1,\ x = 1 \Rightarrow u = 0$

$$\int_0^1 x^a(1 - x)^b\,dx = \int_1^0 (1 - u)^a u^b(-du)$$
$$= \int_0^1 u^b(1 - u)^a\,du$$
$$= \int_0^1 x^b(1 - x)^a\,dx$$

**164.** (a) $\sin x = \cos\left(\dfrac{\pi}{2} - x\right)$ and $\cos x = \sin\left(\dfrac{\pi}{2} - x\right)$

Let $u = \dfrac{\pi}{2} - x,\ du = -dx,\ x = \dfrac{\pi}{2} - u$:

$$\int_0^{\pi/2} \sin^2 x\,dx = \int_0^{\pi/2} \cos^2\left(\frac{\pi}{2} - x\right)dx$$
$$= \int_{\pi/2}^0 \cos^2 u(-du)$$
$$= \int_0^{\pi/2} \cos^2 u\,du = \int_0^{\pi/2} \cos^2 x\,dx$$

(b) Let $u = \dfrac{\pi}{2} - x$ as in part (a):

$$\int_0^{\pi/2} \sin^n x\,dx = \int_0^{\pi/2} \cos^n\left(\frac{\pi}{2} - x\right)dx$$
$$= \int_{\pi/2}^0 \cos^n u(-du)$$
$$= \int_0^{\pi/2} \cos^n u\,du = \int_0^{\pi/2} \cos^n x\,dx$$

**165.** False

$$\int (2x + 1)^2\,dx = \tfrac{1}{2}\int (2x + 1)^2 2\,dx = \tfrac{1}{6}(2x + 1)^3 + C$$

**166.** False

$$\int x(x^2 + 1)\,dx = \tfrac{1}{2}\int (x^2 + 1)(2x)\,dx$$
$$= \tfrac{1}{4}(x^2 + 1)^2 + C$$

**167.** True

$$\int_{-10}^{10}\left(ax^3 + bx^2 + cx + d\right) dx = \underbrace{\int_{-10}^{10}\left(ax^3 + cx\right) dx}_{\text{Odd}} + \underbrace{\int_{-10}^{10}\left(bx^2 + d\right) dx}_{\text{Even}} = 0 + 2\int_{0}^{10}\left(bx^2 + d\right) dx$$

**168.** True

$$\int_a^b \sin x\, dx = \left[-\cos x\right]_a^b = -\cos b + \cos a = -\cos(b + 2\pi) + \cos a = \int_a^{b+2\pi} \sin x\, dx$$

**169.** True

$$4\int \sin x \cos x\, dx = 2\int \sin 2x\, dx = -\cos 2x + C$$

**170.** False

$$\int \sin^2 2x \cos 2x\, dx = \frac{1}{2}\int (\sin 2x)^2 (2\cos 2x)\, dx$$
$$= \frac{1}{2}\frac{(\sin 2x)^3}{3} + C$$
$$= \frac{1}{6}\sin^3 2x + C$$

**171.** Let $u = cx$, $du = c\, dx$:

$$c\int_a^b f(cx)\, dx = c\int_{ca}^{cb} f(u)\frac{du}{c}$$
$$= \int_{ca}^{cb} f(u)\, du$$
$$= \int_{ca}^{cb} f(x)\, dx$$

**172.** (a) $\dfrac{d}{du}\left[\sin u - u\cos u + C\right] = \cos u - \cos u + u\sin u$

$$= u \sin u$$

So, $\int u \sin u\, du = \sin u - u\cos u + C$.

(b) Let $u = \sqrt{x}$, $u^2 = x$, $2u\, du = dx$.

$$\int_0^{\pi^2} \sin\sqrt{x}\, dx = \int_0^{\pi} \sin u(2u\, du)$$
$$= 2\int_0^{\pi} u \sin u\, du$$
$$= 2\left[\sin u - u\cos u\right]_0^{\pi} \quad \text{(part (a))}$$
$$= 2\left[-\pi\cos(\pi)\right]$$
$$= 2\pi$$

**173.** Because $f$ is odd, $f(-x) = -f(x)$. Then

$$\int_{-a}^{a} f(x)\, dx = \int_{-a}^{0} f(x)\, dx + \int_0^a f(x)\, dx$$
$$= -\int_0^{-a} f(x)\, dx + \int_0^a f(x)\, dx.$$

Let $x = -u$, $dx = -du$ in the first integral.

When $x = 0$, $u = 0$. When $x = -a$, $u = a$.

$$\int_{-a}^{1} f(x)\, dx = -\int_0^a f(-u)(-du) + \int_0^a f(x)\, dx$$
$$= -\int_0^a f(u)\, du + \int_0^a f(x)\, dx = 0$$

**174.** Let $u = x + h$, then $du = dx$.

When $x = a$, $u = a + h$.

When $x = b$, $u = b + h$. So,

$$\int_a^b f(x + h)\, dx = \int_{a+h}^{b+h} f(u)\, du = \int_{a+h}^{b+h} f(x)\, dx.$$

**175.** Let $f(x) = a_0 + a_1x + a_2x^2 + \cdots + a_nx^n$.

$$\int_0^1 f(x)\, dx = \left[a_0x + a_1\frac{x^2}{2} + a_2\frac{x^3}{3} + \cdots + a_n\frac{x^{n+1}}{n+1}\right]_0^1$$
$$= a_0 + \frac{a_1}{2} + \frac{a_2}{3} + \cdots + \frac{a_n}{n+1} = 0 \text{ (Given)}$$

By the Mean Value Theorem for Integrals, there exists $c$ in $[0, 1]$ such that

$$\int_0^1 f(x)\, dx = f(c)(1 - 0)$$
$$0 = f(c).$$

So the equation has at least one real zero.

**176.** $\alpha^2\int_0^1 f(x)\, dx = \alpha^2(1) = \alpha^2$

$$-2\alpha\int_0^1 f(x)x\, dx = -2\alpha(\alpha) = -2\alpha^2$$

$$\int_0^1 f(x)x^2\, dx = \alpha^2$$

Adding,

$$\int_0^1 \left[\alpha^2 f(x) - 2\alpha x f(x) + x^2 f(x)\right] dx = 0$$

$$\int_0^1 f(x)(\alpha - x)^2\, dx = 0.$$

Because $(\alpha - x)^2 \geq 0$, $f = 0$. So, there are no such functions.

## Section 5.6 Numerical Integration

**1.** Exact: $\int_0^2 x^2\,dx = \left[\frac{1}{3}x^3\right]_0^2 = \frac{8}{3} \approx 2.6667$

Trapezoidal: $\int_0^2 x^2\,dx \approx \frac{1}{4}\left[0 + 2\left(\frac{1}{2}\right)^2 + 2(1)^2 + 2\left(\frac{3}{2}\right)^2 + (2)^2\right] = \frac{11}{4} = 2.7500$

Simpson's: $\int_0^2 x^2\,dx \approx \frac{1}{6}\left[0 + 4\left(\frac{1}{2}\right)^2 + 2(1)^2 + 4\left(\frac{3}{2}\right)^2 + (2)^2\right] = \frac{8}{3} \approx 2.6667$

**2.** Exact: $\int_1^2 \left(\frac{x^2}{4} + 1\right)dx = \left[\frac{x^3}{12} + x\right]_1^2 = \frac{19}{12} \approx 1.5833$

Trapezoidal: $\int_1^2 \left(\frac{x^2}{4} + 1\right)dx \approx \frac{1}{8}\left[\left(\frac{1^2}{4} + 1\right) + 2\left(\frac{(5/4)^2}{4} + 1\right) + 2\left(\frac{(3/2)^2}{4} + 1\right) + 2\left(\frac{(7/4)^2}{4} + 1\right) + \left(\frac{2^2}{4} + 1\right)\right] = \frac{203}{128} \approx 1.5859$

Simpson's: $\int_0^1 \left(\frac{x^2}{4} + 1\right)dx \approx \frac{1}{12}\left[\left(\frac{1^2}{4} + 1\right) + 4\left(\frac{(5/4)^2}{4} + 1\right) + 2\left(\frac{(3/2)^2}{4} + 1\right) + 4\left(\frac{(7/4)^2}{4} + 1\right) + \left(\frac{2^2}{4} + 1\right)\right] = \frac{19}{12} \approx 1.5833$

**3.** Exact: $\int_0^2 x^3\,dx = \left[\frac{x^4}{4}\right]_0^2 = 4.0000$

Trapezoidal: $\int_0^2 x^3\,dx \approx \frac{1}{4}\left[0 + 2\left(\frac{1}{2}\right)^3 + 2(1)^3 + 2\left(\frac{3}{2}\right)^3 + (2)^3\right] = \frac{17}{4} = 4.2500$

Simpson's: $\int_0^2 x^3\,dx \approx \frac{1}{6}\left[0 + 4\left(\frac{1}{2}\right)^3 + 2(1)^3 + 4\left(\frac{3}{2}\right)^3 + (2)^3\right] = \frac{24}{6} = 4.0000$

**4.** Exact: $\int_2^3 \frac{2}{x^2}\,dx = \left[-\frac{2}{x}\right]_2^3 = -\frac{2}{3} + \frac{2}{2} = \frac{1}{3}$

Trapezoidal: $\int_2^3 \frac{2}{x^2}\,dx \approx \frac{1}{8}\left[\frac{2}{2^2} + 2\left(\frac{2}{(9/4)^2}\right) + 2\left(\frac{2}{(10/4)^2}\right) + 2\left(\frac{2}{(11/4)^2}\right) + \frac{2}{3^2}\right] \approx 0.3352$

Simpson's: $\int_2^3 \frac{2}{x^2}\,dx \approx \frac{1}{12}\left[\frac{2}{2^2} + 4\left(\frac{2}{(9/4)^2}\right) + 2\left(\frac{2}{(10/4)^2}\right) + 4\left(\frac{2}{(11/4)^2}\right) + \frac{2}{3^2}\right] \approx 0.3334$

**5.** Exact: $\int_1^3 x^3\,dx = \left[\frac{x^4}{4}\right]_1^3 = \frac{81}{4} - \frac{1}{4} = 20$

Trapezoidal: $\int_1^3 x^3\,dx \approx \frac{1}{6}\left[1 + 2\left(\frac{4}{3}\right)^3 + 2\left(\frac{5}{3}\right)^3 + 2(2)^3 + 2\left(\frac{7}{3}\right)^3 + 2\left(\frac{8}{3}\right)^3 + 27\right] \approx 20.2222$

Simpson's: $\int_1^3 x^3\,dx \approx \frac{1}{9}\left[1 + 4\left(\frac{4}{3}\right)^3 + 2\left(\frac{5}{3}\right)^3 + 4(2)^3 + 2\left(\frac{7}{3}\right)^3 + 4\left(\frac{8}{3}\right)^3 + 27\right] = 20.0000$

**6.** Exact: $\int_0^8 \sqrt[3]{x}\,dx = \left[\frac{3}{4}x^{4/3}\right]_0^8 = 12.0000$

Trapezoidal: $\int_0^8 \sqrt[3]{x}\,dx \approx \frac{1}{2}\left[0 + 2 + 2\sqrt[3]{2} + 2\sqrt[3]{3} + 2\sqrt[3]{4} + 2\sqrt[3]{5} + 2\sqrt[3]{6} + 2\sqrt[3]{7} + 2\right] \approx 11.7296$

Simpson's: $\int_0^8 \sqrt[3]{x}\,dx \approx \frac{1}{3}\left[0 + 4 + 2\sqrt[3]{2} + 4\sqrt[3]{3} + 2\sqrt[3]{4} + 4\sqrt[3]{5} + 2\sqrt[3]{6} + 4\sqrt[3]{7} + 2\right] \approx 11.8632$

**7.** Exact: $\int_4^9 \sqrt{x}\,dx = \left[\frac{2}{3}x^{3/2}\right]_4^9 = 18 - \frac{16}{3} = \frac{38}{3} \approx 12.6667$

Trapezoidal: $\int_4^9 \sqrt{x}\,dx \approx \frac{5}{16}\left[2 + 2\sqrt{\frac{37}{8}} + 2\sqrt{\frac{21}{4}} + 2\sqrt{\frac{47}{8}} + 2\sqrt{\frac{26}{4}} + 2\sqrt{\frac{57}{8}} + 2\sqrt{\frac{31}{4}} + 2\sqrt{\frac{67}{8}} + 3\right] \approx 12.6640$

Simpson's: $\int_4^9 \sqrt{x}\,dx \approx \frac{5}{24}\left[2 + 4\sqrt{\frac{37}{8}} + \sqrt{21} + 4\sqrt{\frac{47}{8}} + \sqrt{26} + 4\sqrt{\frac{57}{8}} + \sqrt{31} + 4\sqrt{\frac{67}{8}} + 3\right] \approx 12.6667$

**8.** Exact: $\int_1^4 \left(4 - x^2\right) dx = \left[4x - \frac{x^3}{3}\right]_1^4 = -\frac{16}{3} - \frac{11}{3} = -9$

Trapezoidal: $\int_1^4 \left(4 - x^2\right) dx \approx \frac{1}{4}\left\{3 + 2\left[4 - \left(\frac{3}{2}\right)^2\right] + 2(0) + 2\left[4 - \left(\frac{5}{2}\right)^2\right] + 2(-5) + 2\left[4 - \left(\frac{7}{2}\right)^2\right] - 12\right\} \approx -9.1250$

Simpson's: $\int_1^4 \left(4 - x^2\right) dx \approx \frac{1}{6}\left[3 + 4\left(4 - \frac{9}{4}\right) + 0 + 4\left(4 - \frac{25}{4}\right) - 10 + 4\left(4 - \frac{49}{4}\right) - 12\right] = -9$

**9.** Exact: $\int_0^1 \frac{2}{(x+2)^2}\,dx = \left[\frac{-2}{(x+2)}\right]_0^1 = \frac{-2}{3} + \frac{2}{2} = \frac{1}{3}$

Trapezoidal: $\int_0^1 \frac{2}{(x+2)^2}\,dx \approx \frac{1}{8}\left[\frac{1}{2} + 2\left(\frac{2}{((1/4)+2)^2}\right) + 2\left(\frac{2}{((1/2)+2)^2}\right) + 2\left(\frac{2}{((3/4)+2)^2}\right) + \frac{2}{9}\right]$

$= \frac{1}{8}\left[\frac{1}{2} + 2\left(\frac{32}{81}\right) + 2\left(\frac{8}{25}\right) + 2\left(\frac{32}{121}\right) + \frac{2}{9}\right] \approx 0.3352$

Simpson's: $\int_0^1 \frac{2}{(x+2)^2}\,dx \approx \frac{1}{12}\left[\frac{1}{2} + 4\left(\frac{2}{((1/4)+2)^2}\right) + 2\left(\frac{2}{((1/2)+2)^2}\right) + 4\left(\frac{2}{((3/4)+2)^2}\right) + \frac{2}{9}\right]$

$= \frac{1}{12}\left[\frac{1}{2} + 4\left(\frac{32}{81}\right) + 2\left(\frac{8}{25}\right) + 4\left(\frac{32}{121}\right) + \frac{2}{9}\right] \approx 0.3334$

**10.** Exact: $\int_0^2 x\sqrt{x^2+1}\,dx = \frac{1}{3}\left[\left(x^2+1\right)^{3/2}\right]_0^2 = \frac{1}{3}\left(5^{3/2} - 1\right) \approx 3.393$

Trapezoidal: $\int_0^2 x\sqrt{x^2+1}\,dx \approx \frac{1}{4}\left[0 + 2\left(\frac{1}{2}\right)\sqrt{\left(\frac{1}{2}\right)^2 + 1} + 2(1)\sqrt{1^2+1} + 2\left(\frac{3}{2}\right)\sqrt{\left(\frac{3}{2}\right)^2 + 1} + 2\sqrt{2^2+1}\right] \approx 3.457$

Simpson's: $\int_0^2 x\sqrt{x^2+1}\,dx \approx \frac{1}{6}\left[0 + 4\left(\frac{1}{2}\right)\sqrt{\left(\frac{1}{2}\right)^2 + 1} + 2(1)\sqrt{1^2+1} + 4\left(\frac{3}{2}\right)\sqrt{\left(\frac{3}{2}\right)^2 + 1} + 2\sqrt{2^2+1}\right] \approx 3.392$

**11.** Trapezoidal: $\int_0^2 \sqrt{1+x^3}\,dx \approx \frac{1}{4}\left[1 + 2\sqrt{1 + \left(\frac{1}{8}\right)} + 2\sqrt{2} + 2\sqrt{1 + \left(\frac{27}{8}\right)} + 3\right] \approx 3.283$

Simpson's: $\int_0^2 \sqrt{1+x^3}\,dx \approx \frac{1}{6}\left[1 + 4\sqrt{1 + \left(\frac{1}{8}\right)} + 2\sqrt{2} + 4\sqrt{1 + \left(\frac{27}{8}\right)} + 3\right] \approx 3.240$

Graphing utility: 3.241

**12.** Trapezoidal: $\int_0^2 \frac{1}{\sqrt{1+x^3}}\,dx \approx \frac{1}{4}\left[1 + 2\left(\frac{1}{\sqrt{1+(1/2)^3}}\right) + 2\left(\frac{1}{\sqrt{1+1^3}}\right) + 2\left(\frac{1}{\sqrt{1+(3/2)^3}}\right) + \frac{1}{3}\right] \approx 1.397$

Simpson's: $\int_0^2 \frac{1}{\sqrt{1+x^3}}\,dx \approx \frac{1}{6}\left[1 + 4\left(\frac{1}{\sqrt{1+(1/2)^3}}\right) + 2\left(\frac{1}{\sqrt{1+1^3}}\right) + 4\left(\frac{1}{\sqrt{1+(3/2)^3}}\right) + \frac{1}{3}\right] \approx 1.405$

Graphing utility: 1.402

**13.** $\int_0^1 \sqrt{x}\sqrt{1-x}\,dx = \int_0^1 \sqrt{x(1-x)}\,dx$

Trapezoidal: $\int_0^1 \sqrt{x(1-x)}\,dx \approx \frac{1}{8}\left[0 + 2\sqrt{\frac{1}{4}\left(1-\frac{1}{4}\right)} + 2\sqrt{\frac{1}{2}\left(1-\frac{1}{2}\right)} + 2\sqrt{\frac{3}{4}\left(1-\frac{3}{4}\right)}\right] \approx 0.342$

Simpson's: $\int_0^1 \sqrt{x(1-x)}\,dx \approx \frac{1}{12}\left[0 + 4\sqrt{\frac{1}{4}\left(1-\frac{1}{4}\right)} + 2\sqrt{\frac{1}{2}\left(1-\frac{1}{2}\right)} + 4\sqrt{\frac{3}{4}\left(1-\frac{3}{4}\right)}\right] \approx 0.372$

Graphing utility: 0.393

**14.** Trapezoidal: $\int_{\pi/2}^{\pi} \sqrt{x}\sin x\,dx \approx \frac{\pi}{16}\left[\sqrt{\frac{\pi}{2}}(1) + 2\sqrt{\frac{5\pi}{8}}\sin\left(\frac{5\pi}{8}\right) + 2\sqrt{\frac{3\pi}{4}}\sin\left(\frac{3\pi}{4}\right) + 2\sqrt{\frac{7\pi}{8}}\sin\left(\frac{7\pi}{8}\right) + 0\right] \approx 1.430$

Simpson's: $\int_{\pi/2}^{\pi} \sqrt{x}\sin x\,dx \approx \frac{\pi}{24}\left[\sqrt{\frac{\pi}{2}} + 4\sqrt{\frac{5\pi}{8}}\sin\left(\frac{5\pi}{8}\right) + 2\sqrt{\frac{3\pi}{4}}\sin\left(\frac{3\pi}{4}\right) + 4\sqrt{\frac{7\pi}{8}}\sin\left(\frac{7\pi}{8}\right) + 0\right] \approx 1.458$

Graphing utility: 1.458

**15.** Trapezoidal: $\int_0^{\sqrt{\pi/2}} \sin\left(x^2\right)dx \approx \frac{\sqrt{\pi/2}}{8}\left[\sin 0 + 2\sin\left(\frac{\sqrt{\pi/2}}{4}\right)^2 + 2\sin\left(\frac{\sqrt{\pi/2}}{2}\right)^2 + 2\sin\left(\frac{3\sqrt{\pi/2}}{4}\right)^2 + \sin\left(\sqrt{\frac{\pi}{2}}\right)^2\right] \approx 0.550$

Simpson's: $\int_0^{\sqrt{\pi/2}} \sin\left(x^2\right)dx \approx \frac{\sqrt{\pi/2}}{12}\left[\sin 0 + 4\sin\left(\frac{\sqrt{\pi/2}}{4}\right)^2 + 2\sin\left(\frac{\sqrt{\pi/2}}{2}\right)^2 + 4\sin\left(\frac{3\sqrt{\pi/2}}{4}\right)^2 + \sin\left(\sqrt{\frac{\pi}{2}}\right)^2\right] \approx 0.548$

Graphing utility: 0.549

**16.** Trapezoidal: $\int_0^{\sqrt{\pi/4}} \tan\left(x^2\right)dx \approx \frac{\sqrt{\pi/4}}{8}\left[\tan 0 + 2\tan\left(\frac{\sqrt{\pi/4}}{4}\right)^2 + 2\tan\left(\frac{\sqrt{\pi/4}}{2}\right)^2 + 2\tan\left(\frac{3\sqrt{\pi/4}}{4}\right)^2 + \tan\left(\sqrt{\frac{\pi}{4}}\right)^2\right] \approx 0.271$

Simpson's: $\int_0^{\sqrt{\pi/4}} \tan\left(x^2\right)dx \approx \frac{\sqrt{\pi/4}}{12}\left[\tan 0 + 4\tan\left(\frac{\sqrt{\pi/4}}{4}\right)^2 + 2\tan\left(\frac{\sqrt{\pi/4}}{2}\right)^2 + 4\tan\left(\frac{3\sqrt{\pi/4}}{4}\right)^2 + \tan\left(\sqrt{\frac{\pi}{4}}\right)^2\right] \approx 0.257$

Graphing utility: 0.256

**17.** Trapezoidal: $\int_3^{3.1} \cos x^2\,dx \approx \frac{0.1}{8}\left[\cos(3)^2 + 2\cos(3.025)^2 + 2\cos(3.05)^2 + 2\cos(3.075)^2 + \cos(3.1)^2\right] \approx -0.098$

Simpson's: $\int_3^{3.1} \cos x^2\,dx \approx \frac{0.1}{12}\left[\cos(3)^2 + 4\cos(3.025)^2 + 2\cos(3.05)^2 + 4\cos(3.075)^2 + \cos(3.1)^2\right] \approx -0.098$

Graphing utility: −0.098

**18.** Trapezoidal: $\int_0^{\pi/2} \sqrt{1+\sin^2 x}\,dx \approx \frac{\pi}{16}\left[1 + 2\sqrt{1+\sin^2\left(\frac{\pi}{8}\right)} + 2\sqrt{1+\sin^2\left(\frac{\pi}{4}\right)} + 2\sqrt{1+\sin^2\left(\frac{3\pi}{8}\right)} + \sqrt{2}\right] \approx 1.910$

Simpson's: $\int_0^{\pi/2} \sqrt{1+\sin^2 x}\,dx \approx \frac{\pi}{24}\left[1 + 4\sqrt{1+\sin^2\left(\frac{\pi}{8}\right)} + 2\sqrt{1+\sin^2\left(\frac{\pi}{4}\right)} + 4\sqrt{1+\sin^2\left(\frac{3\pi}{8}\right)} + \sqrt{2}\right] \approx 1.910$

Graphing utility: 1.910

**19.** Trapezoidal: $\int_0^2 x\ln(x+1)\,dx \approx \frac{1}{4}\left[0 + 2(0.5)\ln(1.5) + 2\ln(2) + 2(1.5)\ln(2.5) + 2\ln(3)\right] \approx 1.684$

Simpson's: $\int_0^2 x\ln(x+1)\,dx \approx \frac{1}{6}\left[0 + 4(0.5)\ln(1.5) + 2\ln(2) + 4(1.5)\ln(2.5) + 2\ln(3)\right] \approx 1.649$

Graphing utility: 1.648

**20.** Trapezoidal: $\int_1^3 \ln x\,dx \approx \frac{1}{4}\left[0 + 2\ln(1.5) + 2\ln 2 + 2\ln(2.5) + \ln 3\right] \approx \frac{5.1284}{4} \approx 1.282$

Simpson's: $\int_1^3 \ln x\,dx \approx \frac{1}{6}\left[0 + 4\ln(1.5) + 2\ln 2 + 4\ln(2.5) + \ln 3\right] \approx \frac{7.7719}{6} \approx 1.295$

Graphing utility: 1.296

**21.** Trapezoidal: $\int_0^{\pi/4} x\tan x\,dx \approx \frac{\pi}{32}\left[0 + 2\left(\frac{\pi}{16}\right)\tan\left(\frac{\pi}{16}\right) + 2\left(\frac{2\pi}{16}\right)\tan\left(\frac{2\pi}{16}\right) + 2\left(\frac{3\pi}{16}\right)\tan\left(\frac{3\pi}{16}\right) + \frac{\pi}{4}\right] \approx 0.194$

Simpson's: $\int_0^{\pi/4} x\tan x\,dx \approx \frac{\pi}{48}\left[0 + 4\left(\frac{\pi}{16}\right)\tan\left(\frac{\pi}{16}\right) + 2\left(\frac{2\pi}{16}\right)\tan\left(\frac{2\pi}{16}\right) + 4\left(\frac{3\pi}{16}\right)\tan\left(\frac{3\pi}{16}\right) + \frac{\pi}{4}\right] \approx 0.186$

Graphing utility: 0.186

**22.** Trapezoidal: $\int_0^{\pi} \frac{\sin x}{x}\,dx \approx \frac{\pi}{8}\left[1 + \frac{2\sin(\pi/4)}{\pi/4} + \frac{2\sin(\pi/2)}{\pi/2} + \frac{2\sin(3\pi/4)}{3\pi/4} + 0\right] \approx 1.836$

Simpson's: $\int_0^{\pi} \frac{\sin x}{x}\,dx \approx \frac{\pi}{12}\left[1 + \frac{4\sin(\pi/4)}{\pi/4} + \frac{2\sin(\pi/2)}{\pi/2} + \frac{4\sin(3\pi/4)}{3\pi/4} + 0\right] \approx 1.852$

Graphing utility: 1.852

**23.** Trapezoidal: $\int_0^4 \sqrt{x}e^x\,dx \approx \frac{1}{2}\left[0 + 2e^1 + 2\sqrt{2}e^2 + 2\sqrt{3}e^3 + 2e^4\right] \approx 102.555$

Simpson's: $\int_0^4 \sqrt{x}e^x\,dx \approx \frac{1}{3}\left[0 + 4e^1 + 2\sqrt{2}e^2 + 4\sqrt{3}e^3 + 2e^4\right] \approx 93.375$

Graphing utility: 92.744

**24.** Trapezoidal: $\int_0^2 xe^{-x}\,dx \approx \frac{1}{4}\left[0 + e^{-1/2} + 2e^{-1} + 3e^{-3/2} + 2e^{-2}\right] \approx \frac{2.2824}{4} \approx 0.5706$

Simpson's: $\int_0^2 2xe^{-x}\,dx \approx \frac{1}{6}\left[0 + 2e^{-1/2} + 2e^{-1} + 6e^{-3/2} + 2e^{-2}\right] \approx \frac{3.5583}{6} \approx 0.5930$

Graphing utility: 0.594

**25.** Trapezoidal: Linear polynomials
Simpson's: Quadratic polynomials

**26.** For a linear function, the Trapezoidal Rule is exact. The error formula says that $E \le \frac{(b-a)^3}{12n^2}\left[\max\left|f''(x)\right|\right]$ and $f''(x) = 0$ for a linear function. Geometrically, a linear function is approximated exactly by trapezoids:

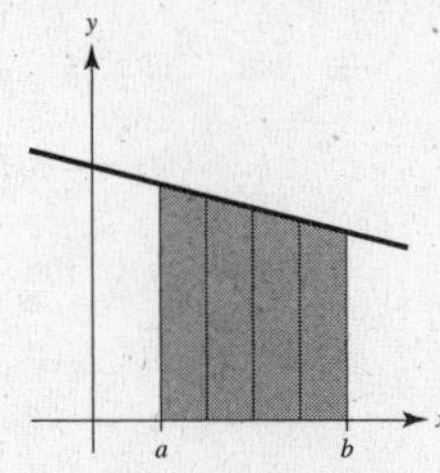

**27.** $f(x) = 2x^3$

$f'(x) = 6x^2$

$f''(x) = 12x$

$f'''(x) = 12$

$f^{(4)}(x) = 0$

(a) Trapezoidal: Error $\leq \dfrac{(3-1)^3}{12(4^2)}(36) = 1.5$ because

$|f''(x)|$ is maximum in [1, 3] when $x = 3$.

(b) Simpson's: Error $\leq \dfrac{(3-1)^5}{180(4^4)}(0) = 0$ because

$f^{(4)}(x) = 0$.

**28.** $f(x) = 5x + 2$

$f'(x) = 5$

$f''(x) = 0$

The error is 0 for both rules.

**29.** $f(x) = \cos x$

$f'(x) = -\sin x$

$f''(x) = -\cos x$

$f'''(x) = \sin x$

$f^{(4)}(x) = \cos x$

(a) Trapezoidal: Error $\leq \dfrac{(\pi - 0)^3}{12(4^2)}(1) = \dfrac{\pi^3}{192} \approx 0.1615$

because $|f''(x)|$ is at most 1 on $[0, \pi]$.

(b) Simpson's:

Error $\leq \dfrac{(\pi - 0)^5}{180(4^4)}(1) = \dfrac{\pi^5}{46{,}080} \approx 0.006641$

because $|f^{(4)}(x)|$ is at most 1 on $[0, \pi]$.

**30.** $f(x) = \sin(\pi x)$

$f'(x) = \pi\cos(\pi x)$

$f''(x) = -\pi^2\sin(\pi x)$

$f'''(x) = -\pi^3\cos(\pi x)$

$f^{(4)}(x) = \pi^4\sin(\pi x)$

(a) Trapezoidal:

Error $\leq \dfrac{(1-0)^3}{12(4^2)}\pi^2 = \dfrac{\pi^2}{192} \approx 0.0514$,

because $|f''(x)| \leq \pi^2$ on [0, 1].

(b) Simpson's:

Error $\leq \dfrac{(1-0)^5}{180(4^4)}\pi^4 = \dfrac{\pi^4}{46{,}080} \approx 0.0021$,

because $|f^{(4)}(x)| \leq \pi^4$ on [0, 1].

**31.** $f(x) = (x+2)^{1/2},\quad 0 \leq x \leq 2$

$f'(x) = \dfrac{1}{2}(x+2)^{-1/2}$

$f''(x) = -\dfrac{1}{4}(x+2)^{-3/2}$

$f'''(x) = \dfrac{3}{8}(x+2)^{-5/2}$

$f^{(4)}(x) = -\dfrac{15}{16}(x+2)^{-7/2}$

(a) Maximum of $|f''(x)| = \left|\dfrac{-1}{4(x+2)^{3/2}}\right|$ is

$\dfrac{\sqrt{2}}{16} \approx 0.0884$.

Trapezoidal:

Error $\leq \dfrac{(2-0)^3}{12n^2}\left(\dfrac{\sqrt{2}}{16}\right) \leq 0.00001$

$n^2 \geq \dfrac{8\sqrt{2}}{12(16)}10^5 = \dfrac{\sqrt{2}}{24}10^5$

$n \geq 76.8$. Let $n = 77$.

(b) Maximum of $|f^{(4)}(x)| = \left|\dfrac{-15}{16(x+2)^{7/2}}\right|$ is

$\dfrac{15\sqrt{2}}{256} \approx 0.0829$.

Simpson's:

Error $\leq \dfrac{2^5}{180n^4}\left(\dfrac{15\sqrt{2}}{256}\right) \leq 0.00001$

$n^4 \geq \dfrac{32(15)\sqrt{2}}{180(256)}10^5$

$= \dfrac{\sqrt{2}}{96}10^5$

$n \geq 6.2$. Let $n = 8$ (even).

**32.** $f(x) = x^{-1/2}, \quad 1 \le x \le 3$

$$f'(x) = -\frac{1}{2}x^{-3/2}$$

$$f''(x) = \frac{3}{4}x^{-5/2}$$

$$f'''(x) = -\frac{15}{8}x^{-7/2}$$

$$f^{(4)}(x) = \frac{105}{16}x^{-9/2}$$

(a) Maximum of $\left|f''(x)\right| = \left|\frac{3}{4x^{5/2}}\right|$ is $\frac{3}{4}$ on [1, 3].

Trapezoidal:

$$\text{Error} \le \frac{(3-1)^3}{12n^2}\left(\frac{3}{4}\right) \le 0.00001$$

$$n^2 \ge \frac{1}{2}10^5$$

$$n \ge 223.6. \text{ Let } n = 224.$$

(b) Maximum of $\left|f^{(4)}(x)\right| = \left|\frac{105}{16x^{9/2}}\right|$ is $\frac{105}{16}$ on [1, 3].

$$\text{Simpson's: Error} \le \frac{2^5}{180n^4}\left(\frac{105}{16}\right) \le 0.00001$$

$$n^4 \ge \frac{7}{6}10^5$$

$$n \ge 18.5.$$

Let $n = 20$ (even).

**33.** $f(x) = \cos(\pi x), \quad 0 \le x \le 1$

$$f'(x) = -\pi\sin(\pi x)$$

$$f''(x) = -\pi^2\cos(\pi x)$$

$$f'''(x) = \pi^3\sin(\pi x)$$

$$f^{(4)}(x) = \pi^4\cos(\pi x)$$

(a) Maximum of $\left|f''(x)\right| = \left|-\pi^2\cos(\pi x)\right|$ is $\pi^2$.

Trapezoidal:

$$\text{Error} \le \frac{(1-0)^3}{12n^2}\pi^2 \le 0.00001$$

$$n^2 \ge \frac{\pi^2}{12}10^5$$

$$n \ge 286.8. \text{ Let } n = 287.$$

(b) Maximum of $\left|f^{(4)}(x)\right| = \left|\pi^4\cos(\pi x)\right|$ is $\pi^4$.

$$\text{Simpson's: Error} \le \frac{1}{180n^4}\pi^4 \le 0.00001$$

$$n^4 \ge \frac{\pi^4}{180}10^5$$

$$n \ge 15.3. \text{ Let } n = 16.$$

**34.** $f(x) = \sin x, \quad 0 \le x \le \frac{\pi}{2}$

$$f'(x) = \cos x$$

$$f''(x) = -\sin x$$

$$f'''(x) = -\cos x$$

$$f^{(4)}(x) = \sin x$$

All derivatives are bounded by 1.

(a) Trapezoidal:

$$\text{Error} \le \frac{(\pi/2)^3}{12n^2}(1) \le 0.00001$$

$$n^2 \ge \frac{\pi^3}{96}10^5$$

$$n \ge 179.7. \text{ Let } n = 180.$$

(b) Simpson's:

$$\text{Error} \le \frac{(\pi/2)^5}{180n^4}(1) \le 0.00001$$

$$n^4 \ge \frac{\pi^5}{5760}10^5$$

$$n \ge 8.5. \text{ Let } n = 10 \text{ (even)}.$$

**35.** $f(x) = \sqrt{1+x}$

(a) $f''(x) = -\frac{1}{4(1+x)^{3/2}}$ in [0, 2].

$\left|f''(x)\right|$ is maximum when $x = 0$ and $\left|f''(0)\right| = \frac{1}{4}$.

Trapezoidal: Error $\le \frac{8}{12n^2}\left(\frac{1}{4}\right) \le 0.00001$,

$n^2 \ge 16{,}666.67$, $n \ge 129.10$; let $n = 130$.

(b) $f^{(4)}(x) = -\frac{15}{16(1+x)^{7/2}}$ in [0, 2]

$\left|f^{(4)}(x)\right|$ is maximum when $x = 0$ and

$\left|f^{(4)}(0)\right| = \frac{15}{16}$.

Simpson's: Error $\le \frac{32}{180n^4}\left(\frac{15}{16}\right) \le 0.00001$,

$n^4 \ge 16{,}666.67$, $n \ge 11.36$; let $n = 12$.

**36.** $f(x) = (x + 1)^{2/3}$

(a) $f''(x) = -\dfrac{2}{9(x + 1)^{4/3}}$ in $[0, 2]$.

$|f''(x)|$ is maximum when $x = 0$ and $|f''(0)| = \dfrac{2}{9}$.

Trapezoidal: Error $\le \dfrac{8}{12n^4}\left(\dfrac{2}{9}\right) \le 0.00001$,

$n^2 \ge 14{,}814.81$, $n \ge 121.72$; let $n = 122$.

(b) $f^{(4)}(x) = -\dfrac{56}{81(x + 1)^{10/3}}$ in $[0, 2]$.

$\left|f^{(4)}(x)\right|$ is maximum when $x = 0$ and $\left|f^{(4)}(0)\right| = \dfrac{56}{81}$.

Simpson's: Error $\le \dfrac{32}{180n^4}\left(\dfrac{56}{81}\right) \le 0.00001$,

$n^4 \ge 12{,}290.81$, $n \ge 10.53$; let $n = 12$. (In Simpson's Rule, $n$ must be even.)

**37.** $f(x) = \tan(x^2)$

(a) $f''(x) = 2\sec^2(x^2)\left[1 + 4x^2\tan(x^2)\right]$ in $[0, 1]$.

$|f''(x)|$ is maximum when $x = 1$ and $|f''(1)| \approx 49.5305$.

Trapezoidal: Error $\le \dfrac{(1 - 0)^3}{12n^2}(49.5305) \le 0.00001$, $n^2 \ge 412{,}754.17$, $n \ge 642.46$; let $n = 643$.

(b) $f^{(4)}(x) = 8\sec^2(x^2)\left[12x^2 + (3 + 32x^4)\tan(x^2) + 36x^2\tan^2(x^2) + 48x^4\tan^3(x^2)\right]$ in $[0, 1]$.

$\left|f^{(4)}(x)\right|$ is maximum when $x = 1$ and $\left|f^{(4)}(1)\right| \approx 9184.4734$.

Simpson's: Error $\le \dfrac{(1 - 0)^5}{180n^4}(9184.4734) \le 0.00001$, $n^4 \ge 5{,}102{,}485.22$, $n \ge 47.53$; let $n = 48$.

**38.** $f(x) = \sin(x^2)$

(a) $f''(x) = 2\left[-2x^2\sin(x^2) + \cos(x^2)\right]$ in $[0, 1]$. $|f''(x)|$ is maximum when $x = 1$ and $|f''(1)| \approx 2.2853$.

Trapezoidal: Error $\le \dfrac{(1 - 0)^3}{12n^2}(2.2853) \le 0.00001$, $n^2 \ge 19{,}044.17$, $n \ge 138.00$; let $n = 139$.

(b) $f^{(4)}(x) = (16x^4 - 12)\sin(x^2) - 48x^2\cos(x^2)$ in $[0, 1]$.

$\left|f^{(4)}(x)\right|$ is maximum when $x \approx 0.852$ and $\left|f^{(4)}(0.852)\right| \approx 28.4285$.

Simpson's: Error $\le \dfrac{(1, - 0)^5}{180n^4}(28.4285) \le 0.00001$, $n^4 \ge 15{,}793.61$, $n \ge 11.21$; Let $n = 12$.

**39.** $n = 4$, $b - a = 4 - 0 = 4$

(a) $\int_0^4 f(x)\,dx \approx \frac{4}{8}\left[3 + 2(7) + 2(9) + 2(7) + 0\right] = \frac{1}{2}(49) = \frac{49}{2} = 24.5$

(b) $\int_0^4 f(x)\,dx \approx \frac{4}{12}\left[3 + 4(7) + 2(9) + 4(7) + 0\right] = \frac{77}{3} \approx 25.67$

**40.** $n = 8, b - a = 8 - 0 = 8$

(a) $\int_0^8 f(x)\,dx \approx \frac{8}{16}\left[0 + 2(1.5) + 2(3) + 2(5.5) + 2(9) + 2(10) + 2(9) + 2(6) + 0\right] = \frac{1}{2}(88) = 44$

(b) $\int_0^8 f(x)\,dx \approx \frac{8}{24}\left[0 + 4(1.5) + 2(3) + 4(5.5) + 2(9) + 4(10) + 2(9) + 4(6) + 0\right] = \frac{1}{3}(134) = \frac{134}{3}$

**41.** The program will vary depending upon the computer or programmable calculator that you use.

**42.** $f(x) = \sqrt{2 + 3x^2}$ on $[0, 4]$.

| $n$ | $L(n)$ | $M(n)$ | $R(n)$ | $T(n)$ | $S(n)$ |
|---|---|---|---|---|---|
| 4 | 12.7771 | 15.3965 | 18.4340 | 15.6055 | 15.4845 |
| 8 | 14.0868 | 15.4480 | 16.9152 | 15.5010 | 15.4662 |
| 10 | 14.3569 | 15.4544 | 16.6197 | 15.4883 | 15.4658 |
| 12 | 14.5386 | 15.4578 | 16.4242 | 15.4814 | 15.4657 |
| 16 | 14.7674 | 15.4613 | 16.1816 | 15.4745 | 15.4657 |
| 20 | 14.9056 | 15.4628 | 16.0370 | 15.4713 | 15.4657 |

**43.** $f(x) = \sqrt{1 - x^2}$ on $[0, 1]$.

| $n$ | $L(n)$ | $M(n)$ | $R(n)$ | $T(n)$ | $S(n)$ |
|---|---|---|---|---|---|
| 4 | 0.8739 | 0.7960 | 0.6239 | 0.7489 | 0.7709 |
| 8 | 0.8350 | 0.7892 | 0.7100 | 0.7725 | 0.7803 |
| 10 | 0.8261 | 0.7881 | 0.7261 | 0.7761 | 0.7818 |
| 12 | 0.8200 | 0.7875 | 0.7367 | 0.7783 | 0.7826 |
| 16 | 0.8121 | 0.7867 | 0.7496 | 0.7808 | 0.7836 |
| 20 | 0.8071 | 0.7864 | 0.7571 | 0.7821 | 0.7841 |

**44.** $f(x) = \sin\sqrt{x}$ on $[0, 4]$.

| $n$ | $L(n)$ | $M(n)$ | $R(n)$ | $T(n)$ | $S(n)$ |
|---|---|---|---|---|---|
| 4 | 2.8163 | 3.5456 | 3.7256 | 3.2709 | 3.3996 |
| 8 | 3.1809 | 3.5053 | 3.6356 | 3.4083 | 3.4541 |
| 10 | 3.2478 | 3.4990 | 3.6115 | 3.4296 | 3.4624 |
| 12 | 3.2909 | 3.4952 | 3.5940 | 3.4425 | 3.4674 |
| 16 | 3.3431 | 3.4910 | 3.5704 | 3.4568 | 3.4730 |
| 20 | 3.3734 | 3.4888 | 3.5552 | 3.4643 | 3.4759 |

**45.** $f(x) = \dfrac{\sin x}{x}$ on $[1, 2]$.

| $n$ | $L(n)$ | $M(n)$ | $R(n)$ | $T(n)$ | $S(n)$ |
|---|---|---|---|---|---|
| 4 | 0.7070 | 0.6597 | 0.6103 | 0.6586 | 0.6593 |
| 8 | 0.6833 | 0.6594 | 0.6350 | 0.6592 | 0.6593 |
| 10 | 0.6786 | 0.6594 | 0.6399 | 0.6592 | 0.6593 |
| 12 | 0.6754 | 0.6594 | 0.6431 | 0.6593 | 0.6593 |
| 16 | 0.6714 | 0.6594 | 0.6472 | 0.6593 | 0.6593 |
| 20 | 0.6690 | 0.6593 | 0.6496 | 0.6593 | 0.6593 |

**46.** $f(x) = 6e^{-x^2/2}$ on $[0, 2]$.

| $n$ | $L(n)$ | $M(n)$ | $R(n)$ | $T(n)$ | $S(n)$ |
|---|---|---|---|---|---|
| 4 | 8.4410 | 7.1945 | 5.8470 | 7.1440 | 7.1770 |
| 8 | 7.8178 | 7.1820 | 6.5208 | 7.1693 | 7.1777 |
| 10 | 7.6911 | 7.1804 | 6.6535 | 7.1723 | 7.1777 |
| 12 | 7.6093 | 7.1796 | 6.7416 | 7.1740 | 7.1777 |
| 16 | 7.4999 | 7.1788 | 6.8514 | 7.1756 | 7.1777 |
| 20 | 7.4358 | 7.1784 | 6.9170 | 7.1764 | 7.1777 |

**47.** $f(x) = \sqrt{x}\ln(x + 1)$ on $[0, 3]$.

| $n$ | $L(n)$ | $M(n)$ | $R(n)$ | $T(n)$ | $S(n)$ |
|---|---|---|---|---|---|
| 4 | 2.5311 | 3.3953 | 4.3320 | 3.4316 | 3.4140 |
| 8 | 2.9632 | 3.4026 | 3.8637 | 3.4135 | 3.4074 |
| 10 | 3.0508 | 3.4037 | 3.7711 | 3.4109 | 3.4068 |
| 12 | 3.1094 | 3.4044 | 3.7097 | 3.4095 | 3.4065 |
| 16 | 3.1829 | 3.4050 | 3.6331 | 3.4050 | 3.4062 |
| 20 | 3.2273 | 3.4054 | 3.5874 | 3.4073 | 3.4061 |

**48.** $f$ is concave upward on $[0, 2]$.

$g$ is concave downward on $[0, 2]$.

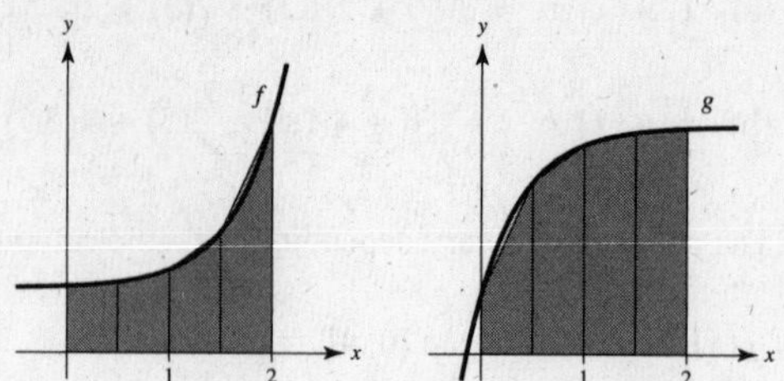


(a) The integral $\int_0^2 f(x)\,dx$ would be overestimated, and the integral $\int_0^2 g(x)\,dx$ would be underestimated.

(b) Simpson's Rule would give a more accurate approximation because it takes into account the curvature of the graph.

**49.** $A = \int_0^{\pi/2} \sqrt{x}\cos x\,dx$

Simpson's Rule: $n = 14$

$$\int_0^{\pi/2} \sqrt{x}\cos x\,dx \approx \frac{\pi}{84}\left[\sqrt{0}\cos 0 + 4\sqrt{\frac{\pi}{28}}\cos\frac{\pi}{28} + 2\sqrt{\frac{\pi}{14}}\cos\frac{\pi}{14} + 4\sqrt{\frac{3\pi}{28}}\cos\frac{3\pi}{28} + \cdots + \sqrt{\frac{\pi}{2}}\cos\frac{\pi}{2}\right] \approx 0.701$$

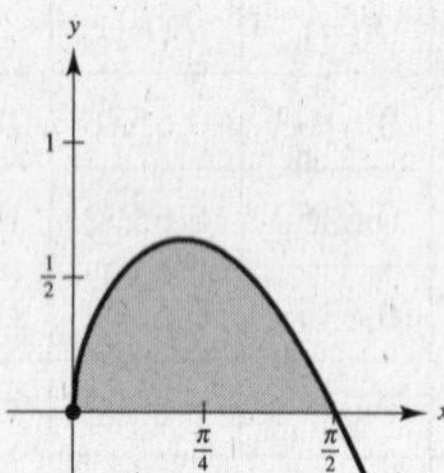


**50.** (a) Trapezoidal:

$$\int_0^2 f(x)\,dx \approx \frac{2}{2(8)}\left[4.32 + 2(4.36) + 2(4.58) + 2(5.79) + 2(6.14) + 2(7.25) + 2(7.64) + 2(8.08) + 8.14\right] \approx 12.518$$

Simpson's:

$$\int_0^2 f(x)\,dx \approx \frac{2}{3(8)}\left[4.32 + 4(4.36) + 2(4.58) + 4(5.79) + 2(6.14) + 4(7.25) + 2(7.64) + 4(8.08) + 8.14\right] \approx 12.592$$

(b) Using a graphing utility,

$y = -1.37266x^3 + 4.0092x^2 - 0.620x + 4.28$. Integrating, $\int_0^2 y\,dx \approx 12.521$.

**51.** $\int_0^{1/2} \frac{6}{\sqrt{1 - x^2}}\,dx$ Simpson's Rule, $n = 6$

$$\pi \approx \frac{\left(\frac{1}{2} - 0\right)}{3(6)}\left[6 + 4(6.0209) + 2(6.0851) + 4(6.1968) + 2(6.3640) + 4(6.6002) + 6.9282\right] \approx \frac{1}{36}[113.098] \approx 3.1416$$

**52.** Simpson's Rule: $n = 6$

$$\pi = 4\int_0^1 \frac{1}{1 + x^2}\,dx \approx \frac{4}{3(6)}\left[1 + \frac{4}{1 + (1/6)^2} + \frac{2}{1 + (2/6)^2} + \frac{4}{1 + (3/6)^2} + \frac{2}{1 + (4/6)^2} + \frac{4}{1 + (5/6)^2} + \frac{1}{2}\right] \approx 3.14159$$

**53.** Area $\approx \frac{1000}{2(10)}\left[125 + 2(125) + 2(120) + 2(112) + 2(90) + 2(90) + 2(95) + 2(88) + 2(75) + 2(35)\right] = 89{,}250 \text{ m}^2$

**54.** Area $\approx \frac{120}{2(12)}\left[75 + 2(81) + 2(84) + 2(76) + 2(67) + 2(68) + 2(69) + 2(72) + 2(68) + 2(56) + 2(42) + 2(23) + 0\right]$

$= 7435 \text{ m}^2$

**55.** Let $f(x) = Ax^3 + Bx^2 + Cx + D$. Then $f^{(4)}(x) = 0$.

Simpson's: Error $\le \frac{(b-a)^5}{180n^4}(0) = 0$

So, Simpson's Rule is exact when approximating the integral of a cubic polynomial.

Example: $\int_0^1 x^3\,dx = \frac{1}{6}\left[0 + 4\left(\frac{1}{2}\right)^3 + 1\right] = \frac{1}{4}$

This is the exact value of the integral.

**56.** $\int_0^t \sin\sqrt{x}\,dx = 2,\ n = 10$

By trial and error, you obtain $t \approx 2.477$.

**57.** The quadratic polynomial

$$p(x) = \frac{(x-x_2)(x-x_3)}{(x_1-x_2)(x_1-x_3)}y_1 + \frac{(x-x_1)(x-x_3)}{(x_2-x_1)(x_2-x_3)}y_2 + \frac{(x-x_1)(x-x_2)}{(x_3-x_1)(x_3-x_2)}y_3$$

passes through the three points.

## Section 5.7 The Natural Logarithmic Function: Integration

**1.** $\int \frac{5}{x}\,dx = 5\int \frac{1}{x}\,dx = 5\ln|x| + C$

**2.** $\int \frac{10}{x}\,dx = 10\int \frac{1}{x}\,dx = 10\ln|x| + C$

**3.** $u = x + 1,\ du = dx$

$\int \frac{1}{x+1}\,dx = \ln|x+1| + C$

**4.** $u = x - 5,\ du = dx$

$\int \frac{1}{x-5}\,dx = \ln|x-5| + C$

**5.** $u = 2x + 5,\ du = 2\,dx$

$\int \frac{1}{2x+5}\,dx = \frac{1}{2}\int \frac{1}{2x+5}(2)\,dx$

$= \frac{1}{2}\ln|2x+5| + C$

**6.** $u = 4 - 3x,\ du = -3\,dx$

$\int \frac{1}{4-3x}\,dx = -\frac{1}{3}\int \frac{1}{4-3x}(-3)\,dx$

$= -\frac{1}{3}\ln|4-3x| + C$

**7.** $u = x^2 - 3,\ du = 2x\,dx$

$\int \frac{x}{x^2-3}\,dx = \frac{1}{2}\int \frac{1}{x^2-3}(2x)\,dx$

$= \frac{1}{2}\ln|x^2-3| + C$

**8.** $u = 5 - x^3,\ du = -3x^2\,dx$

$\int \frac{x^2}{5-x^3}\,dx = -\frac{1}{3}\int \frac{1}{5-x^3}(-3x^2)\,dx$

$= -\frac{1}{3}\ln|5-x^3| + C$

**9.** $u = x^4 + 3x,\ du = (4x^3 + 3)\,dx$

$\int \frac{4x^3+3}{x^4+3x}\,dx = \int \frac{1}{x^4+3x}(4x^3+3)\,dx$

$= \ln|x^4+3x| + C$

**10.** $u = x^3 - 3x^2,\ du = (3x^2 - 6x)\,dx = 3(x^2 - 2x)\,dx$

$\int \frac{x^2-2x}{x^3-3x^2}\,dx = \frac{1}{3}\int \frac{1}{x^3-3x^2}(3x^2-6x)\,dx$

$= \frac{1}{3}\ln|x^3-3x^2| + C$

11. $\int \frac{x^2 - 4}{x}\,dx = \int\left(x - \frac{4}{x}\right)dx$

$= \frac{x^2}{2} - 4\ln|x| + C$

$= \frac{x^2}{2} - \ln(x^4) + C$

12. $u = 9 - x^2,\ du = -2x\,dx$

$\int \frac{x}{\sqrt{9 - x^2}}\,dx = -\frac{1}{2}\int(9 - x^2)^{-1/2}(-2x)\,dx$

$= -\sqrt{9 - x^2} + C$

13. $u = x^3 + 3x^2 + 9x,\ du = 3(x^2 + 2x + 3)\,dx$

$\int \frac{x^2 + 2x + 3}{x^3 + 3x^2 + 9x}\,dx = \frac{1}{3}\int \frac{3(x^2 + 2x + 3)}{x^3 + 3x^2 + 9x}\,dx$

$= \frac{1}{3}\ln|x^3 + 3x^2 + 9x| + C$

14. $u = x^3 + 3x^2 - 4,\ du = (3x^2 + 6x)\,dx$

$\int \frac{x(x + 2)}{x^3 + 3x^2 - 4}\,dx = \frac{1}{3}\int \frac{3x^2 + 6x}{x^3 + 3x^2 - 4}\,dx$

$= \frac{1}{3}\ln|x^3 + 3x^2 - 4| + C$

15. $\int \frac{x^2 - 3x + 2}{x + 1}\,dx = \int\left(x - 4 + \frac{6}{x + 1}\right)dx$

$= \frac{x^2}{2} - 4x + 6\ln|x + 1| + C$

16. $\int \frac{2x^2 + 7x - 3}{x - 2}\,dx = \int\left(2x + 11 + \frac{19}{x - 2}\right)dx$

$= x^2 + 11x + 19\ln|x - 2| + C$

17. $\int \frac{x^3 - 3x^2 + 5}{x - 3}\,dx = \int\left(x^2 + \frac{5}{x - 3}\right)dx$

$= \frac{x^3}{3} + 5\ln|x - 3| + C$

18. $\int \frac{x^3 - 6x - 20}{x + 5}\,dx = \int\left(x^2 - 5x + 19 - \frac{115}{x + 5}\right)dx$

$= \frac{x^3}{3} - \frac{5x^2}{2} + 19x - 115\ln|x + 5| + C$

19. $\int \frac{x^4 + x - 4}{x^2 + 2}\,dx = \int\left(x^2 - 2 + \frac{x}{x^2 + 2}\right)dx$

$= \frac{x^3}{3} - 2x + \frac{1}{2}\ln(x^2 + 2) + C$

$= \frac{x^3}{3} - 2x + \ln\sqrt{x^2 + 2} + C$

20. $\int \frac{x^3 - 3x^2 + 4x - 9}{x^2 + 3}\,dx = \int\left(x - 3 + \frac{x}{x^2 + 3}\right)dx$

$= \frac{x^2}{2} - 3x + \frac{1}{2}\ln(x^2 + 3) + C$

21. $u = \ln x,\ du = \frac{1}{x}dx$

$\int \frac{(\ln x)^2}{x}\,dx = \frac{1}{3}(\ln x)^3 + C$

22. $\int \frac{1}{x\ln(x^3)}\,dx = \frac{1}{3}\int \frac{1}{\ln x}\cdot\frac{1}{x}\,dx$

$= \frac{1}{3}\ln|\ln|x|| + C$

23. $u = x + 1,\ du = dx$

$\int \frac{1}{\sqrt{x + 1}}\,dx = \int(x + 1)^{-1/2}\,dx$

$= 2(x + 1)^{1/2} + C$

$= 2\sqrt{x + 1} + C$

24. $u = 1 + x^{1/3},\ du = \frac{1}{3x^{2/3}}\,dx$

$\int \frac{1}{x^{2/3}(1 + x^{1/3})}\,dx = 3\int \frac{1}{1 + x^{1/3}}\left(\frac{1}{3x^{2/3}}\right)dx$

$= 3\ln|1 + x^{1/3}| + C$

25. $\int \frac{2x}{(x - 1)^2}\,dx = \int \frac{2x - 2 + 2}{(x - 1)^2}\,dx$

$= \int \frac{2(x - 1)}{(x - 1)^2}\,dx + 2\int \frac{1}{(x - 1)^2}\,dx$

$= 2\int \frac{1}{x - 1}\,dx + 2\int \frac{1}{(x - 1)^2}\,dx$

$= 2\ln|x - 1| - \frac{2}{(x - 1)} + C$

26. $\int \frac{x(x - 2)}{(x - 1)^3}\,dx = \int \frac{x^2 - 2x + 1 - 1}{(x - 1)^3}\,dx$

$= \int \frac{(x - 1)^2}{(x - 1)^3}\,dx - \int \frac{1}{(x - 1)^3}\,dx$

$= \int \frac{1}{x - 1}\,dx - \int \frac{1}{(x - 1)^3}\,dx$

$= \ln|x - 1| + \frac{1}{2(x - 1)^2} + C$

**27.** $u = 1 + \sqrt{2x},\ du = \dfrac{1}{\sqrt{2x}}\,dx \Rightarrow (u - 1)\,du = dx$

$$\int \frac{1}{1 + \sqrt{2x}}\,dx = \int \frac{(u-1)}{u}\,du = \int \left(1 - \frac{1}{u}\right)du$$
$$= u - \ln|u| + C_1$$
$$= \left(1 + \sqrt{2x}\right) - \ln\left|1 + \sqrt{2x}\right| + C_1$$
$$= \sqrt{2x} - \ln\left(1 + \sqrt{2x}\right) + C$$

where $C = C_1 + 1$.

**28.** $u = 1 + \sqrt{3x},\ du = \dfrac{3}{2\sqrt{3x}}\,dx \Rightarrow dx = \dfrac{2}{3}(u - 1)\,du$

$$\int \frac{1}{1 + \sqrt{3x}}\,dx = \int \frac{1}{u}\frac{2}{3}(u - 1)\,du$$
$$= \frac{2}{3}\int\left(1 - \frac{1}{u}\right)du$$
$$= \frac{2}{3}\left[u - \ln|u|\right] + C$$
$$= \frac{2}{3}\left[1 + \sqrt{3x} - \ln\left(1 + \sqrt{3x}\right)\right] + C_1$$
$$= \frac{2}{3}\sqrt{3x} - \frac{2}{3}\ln\left(1 + \sqrt{3x}\right) + C$$

where $C = C_1 + \dfrac{2}{3}$.

**29.** $u = \sqrt{x} - 3,\ du = \dfrac{1}{2\sqrt{x}}\,dx \Rightarrow 2(u + 3)du = dx$

$$\int \frac{\sqrt{x}}{\sqrt{x} - 3}\,dx = 2\int \frac{(u + 3)^2}{u}\,du$$
$$= 2\int \frac{u^2 + 6u + 9}{u}\,du = 2\int\left(u + 6 + \frac{9}{u}\right)du$$
$$= 2\left[\frac{u^2}{2} + 6u + 9\ln|u|\right] + C_1$$
$$= u^2 + 12u + 18\ln|u| + C_1$$
$$= \left(\sqrt{x} - 3\right)^2 + 12\left(\sqrt{x} - 3\right) + 18\ln\left|\sqrt{x} - 3\right| + C_1$$
$$= x + 6\sqrt{x} + 18\ln\left|\sqrt{x} - 3\right| + C$$

where $C = C_1 - 27$.

**30.** $u = x^{1/3} - 1,\ du = \dfrac{1}{3x^{2/3}}\,dx \Rightarrow dx = 3(u + 1)^2\,du$

$$\int \frac{\sqrt[3]{x}}{\sqrt[3]{x} - 1}\,dx = \int \frac{u + 1}{u}3(u + 1)^2\,du$$
$$= 3\int \frac{u + 1}{u}\left(u^2 + 2u + 1\right)du$$
$$= 3\int\left(u^2 + 3u + 3 + \frac{1}{u}\right)du$$
$$= 3\left[\frac{u^3}{3} + \frac{3u^2}{2} + 3u + \ln|u|\right] + C$$
$$= 3\left[\frac{\left(x^{1/3} - 1\right)^3}{3} + \frac{3\left(x^{1/3} - 1\right)^2}{2} + 3\left(x^{1/3} - 1\right) + \ln\left|x^{1/3} - 1\right|\right] + C_1$$
$$= 3\ln\left|x^{1/3} - 1\right| + \frac{3x^{2/3}}{2} + 3x^{1/3} + x + C$$

where $C = C_1 - \dfrac{11}{2}$.

31. $\int \cot\left(\frac{\theta}{3}\right) d\theta = 3\int \cot\left(\frac{\theta}{3}\right)\left(\frac{1}{3}\right) d\theta$

$= 3 \ln\left|\sin \frac{\theta}{3}\right| + C$

32. $\int \tan 5\theta \, d\theta = \frac{1}{5}\int \frac{5 \sin 5\theta}{\cos 5\theta} d\theta$

$= -\frac{1}{5} \ln|\cos 5\theta| + C$

33. $\int \csc 2x \, dx = \frac{1}{2}\int (\csc 2x)(2) \, dx$

$= -\frac{1}{2} \ln|\csc 2x + \cot 2x| + C$

34. $\int \sec \frac{x}{2} dx = 2\int \sec \frac{x}{2}\left(\frac{1}{2}\right) dx = 2 \ln\left|\sec \frac{x}{2} + \tan \frac{x}{2}\right| + C$

35. $\int (\cos 3\theta - 1) \, d\theta = \frac{1}{3}\int \cos 3\theta(3) \, d\theta - \int d\theta$

$= \frac{1}{3} \sin 3\theta - \theta + C$

36. $\int \left(2 - \tan \frac{\theta}{4}\right) d\theta = \int 2 d\theta - 4\int \tan \frac{\theta}{4}\left(\frac{1}{4}\right) d\theta$

$= 2\theta + 4 \ln\left|\cos \frac{\theta}{4}\right| + C$

37. $u = 1 + \sin t, \; du = \cos t \, dt$

$\int \frac{\cos t}{1 + \sin t} dt = \ln|1 + \sin t| + C$

38. $u = \cot t, \; du = -\csc^2 t \, dt$

$\int \frac{\csc^2 t}{\cot t} dt = -\ln|\cot t| + C$

39. $u = \sec x - 1, \; du = \sec x \tan x \, dx$

$\int \frac{\sec x \tan x}{\sec x - 1} dx = \ln|\sec x - 1| + C$

40. $\int (\sec 2x + \tan 2x) \, dx = \frac{1}{2}\int (\sec 2x + \tan 2x)(2) \, dx = \frac{1}{2} \ln|\sec 2x + \tan 2x| - \ln|\cos 2x| + C$

41. $\int e^{-x} \tan(e^{-x}) \, dx = -\int \tan(e^{-x})(-e^{-x}) \, dx$

$= -\left(-\ln\left|\cos\left(e^{-x}\right)\right|\right) + C$

$= \ln\left|\cos\left(e^{-x}\right)\right| + C$

42. $\int \sec t(\sec t + \tan t) \, dt = \int \sec^2 t \, dt + \int \sec t \tan t \, dt$

$= \tan t + \sec t + C$

43. $y = \int \frac{4}{x} dx = 4 \ln|x| + C$

$(1, 2)$: $2 = 4 \ln|1| + C \Rightarrow C = 2$

$y = 4 \ln|x| + 2$

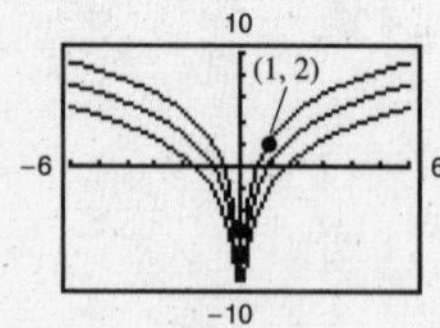


44. $y = \int \frac{x - 2}{x} dx = \int \left(1 - \frac{2}{x}\right) dx = x - 2 \ln|x| + C$

$(-1, 0)$: $0 = -1 - 2 \ln|-1| + C = -1 + C \Rightarrow C = 1$

$y = x - 2 \ln|x| + 1$

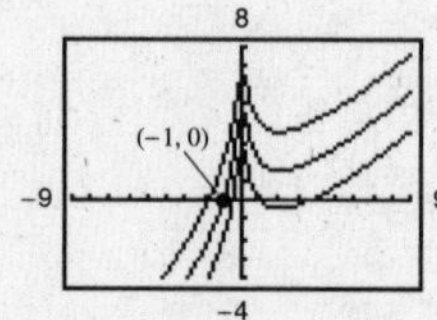


45. $y = \int \frac{3}{2 - x} dx$

$= -3\int \frac{1}{x - 2} dx$

$= -3 \ln|x - 2| + C$

$(1, 0)$: $0 = -3 \ln|1 - 2| + C \Rightarrow C = 0$

$y = -3 \ln|x - 2|$

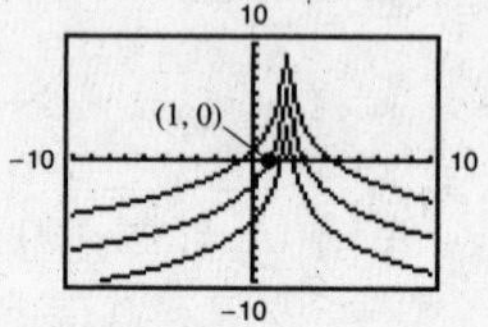


46. $y = \int \frac{2x}{x^2 - 9} dx$

$= \ln|x^2 - 9| + C$

$(0, 4)$: $4 = \ln|0 - 9| + C \Rightarrow C = 4 - \ln 9$

$y = \ln|x^2 - 9| + 4 - \ln 9$

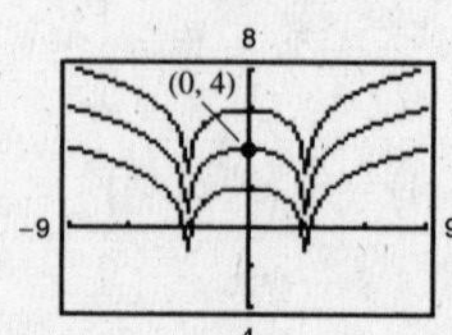

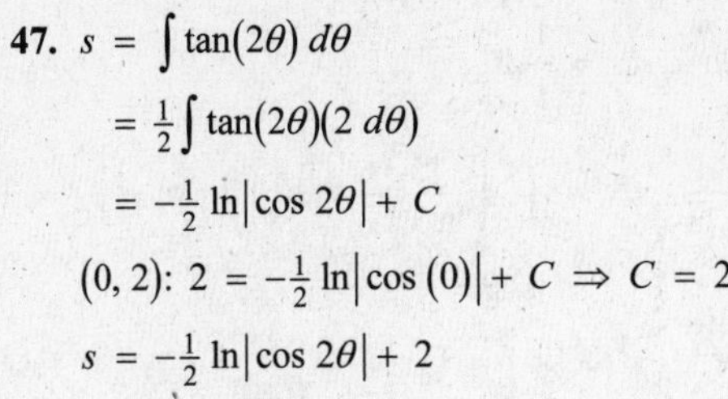

**47.** $s = \int \tan(2\theta)\,d\theta$

$= \frac{1}{2}\int \tan(2\theta)(2\,d\theta)$

$= -\frac{1}{2}\ln\left|\cos 2\theta\right| + C$

$(0, 2)$: $2 = -\frac{1}{2}\ln\left|\cos(0)\right| + C \Rightarrow C = 2$

$s = -\frac{1}{2}\ln\left|\cos 2\theta\right| + 2$

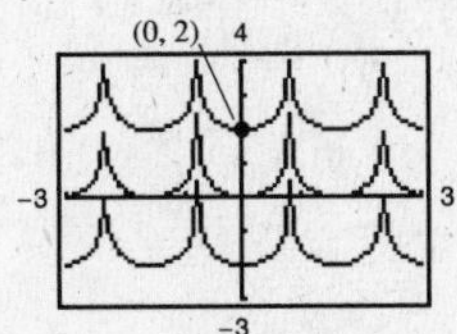


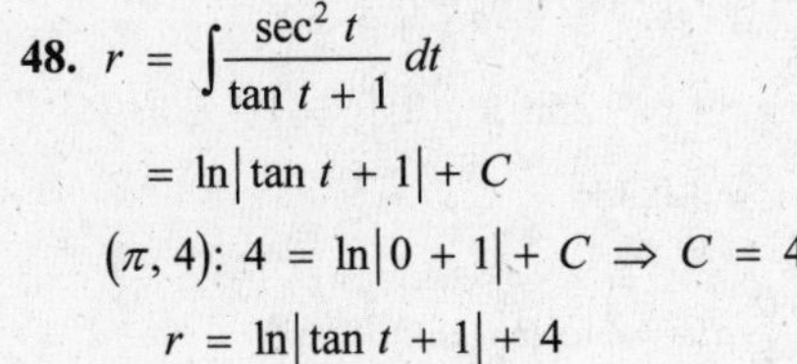

**48.** $r = \int \frac{\sec^2 t}{\tan t + 1}\,dt$

$= \ln\left|\tan t + 1\right| + C$

$(\pi, 4)$: $4 = \ln\left|0 + 1\right| + C \Rightarrow C = 4$

$r = \ln\left|\tan t + 1\right| + 4$

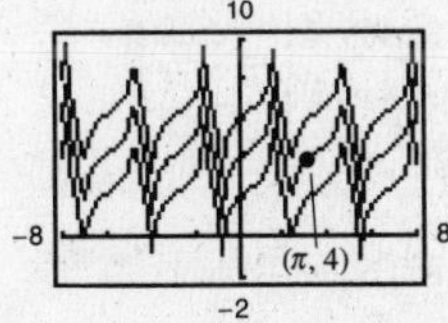


**49.** $f''(x) = \frac{2}{x^2} = 2x^{-2}, \quad x > 0$

$f'(x) = -\frac{2}{x} + C$

$f'(1) = 1 = -2 + C \Rightarrow C = 3$

$f'(x) = -\frac{2}{x} + 3$

$f(x) = -2\ln x + 3x + C_1$

$f(1) = 1 = -2(0) + 3 + C_1 \Rightarrow C_1 = -2$

$f(x) = -2\ln x + 3x - 2$

**50.** $f''(x) = -\frac{4}{(x-1)^2} - 2 = -4(x-1)^{-2} - 2, \; x > 1$

$f'(x) = \frac{4}{(x-1)} - 2x + C$

$f'(2) = 0 = 4 - 4 + C \Rightarrow C = 0$

$f'(x) = \frac{4}{x-1} - 2x$

$f(x) = 4\ln(x-1) - x^2 + C_1$

$f(2) = 3 = 4(0) - 4 + C_1 \Rightarrow C_1 = 7$

$f(x) = 4\ln(x-1) - x^2 + 7$

**51.** $\frac{dy}{dx} = \frac{1}{x+2}, (0, 1)$

(a)

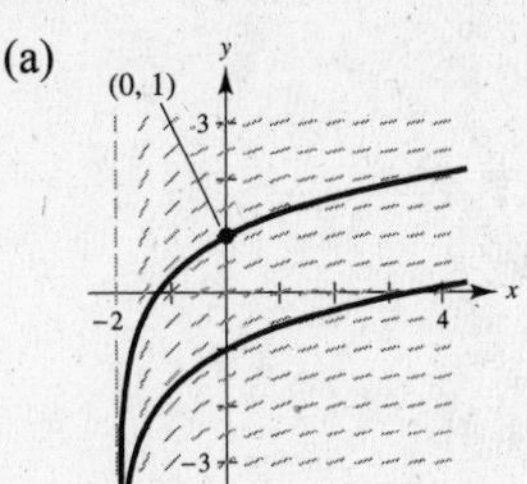


(b) $y = \int \frac{1}{x+2}\,dx = \ln\left|x+2\right| + C$

$y(0) = 1 \Rightarrow 1 = \ln 2 + C \Rightarrow C = 1 - \ln 2$

So, $y = \ln\left|x+2\right| + 1 - \ln 2 = \ln\left(\frac{x+2}{2}\right) + 1.$

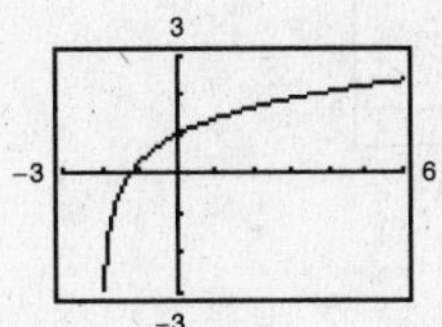


**52.** $\frac{dy}{dx} = \frac{\ln x}{x}, (1, -2)$

(a)

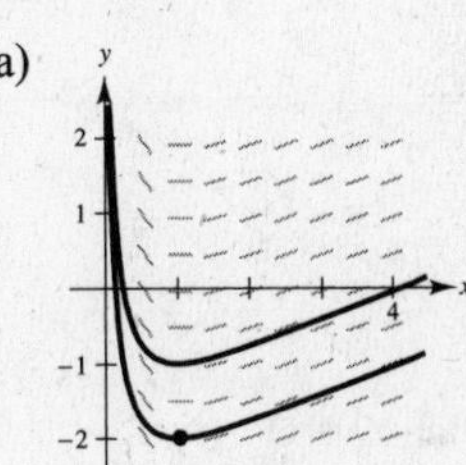


(b) $y = \int \frac{\ln x}{x}\,dx = \frac{(\ln x)^2}{2} + C$

$y(1) = -2 \Rightarrow -2 = \frac{(\ln 1)^2}{2} + C \Rightarrow C = -2$

So, $y = \frac{(\ln x)^2}{2} - 2.$

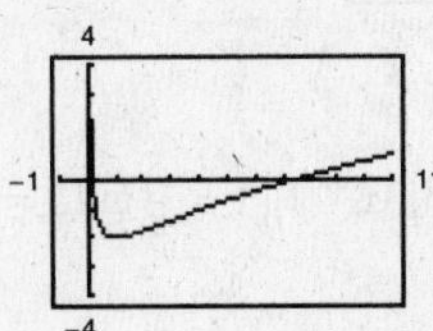

**53.** (a)

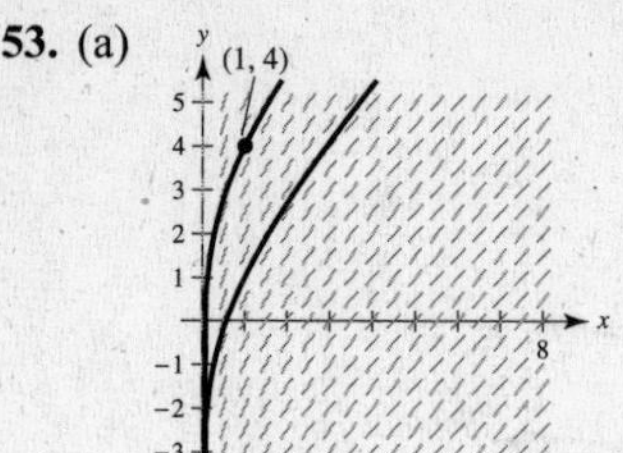


(b) $\dfrac{dy}{dx} = 1 + \dfrac{1}{x}, \quad (1, 4)$

$y = x + \ln x + C$

$4 = 1 + 0 + C \Rightarrow C = 3$

$y = x + \ln x + 3$

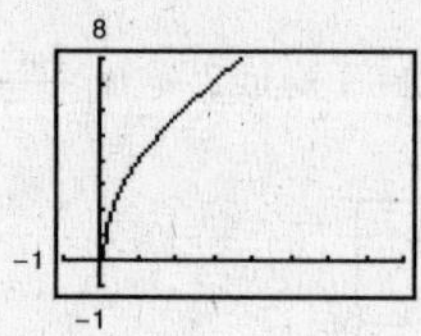


**54.** (a)

(b) $\dfrac{dy}{dx} = \sec x, \ (0, 1)$

$y = \ln|\sec x + \tan x| + C$

$1 = \ln|1 + 0| + C \Rightarrow C = 1$

$y = \ln|\sec x + \tan x| + 1$

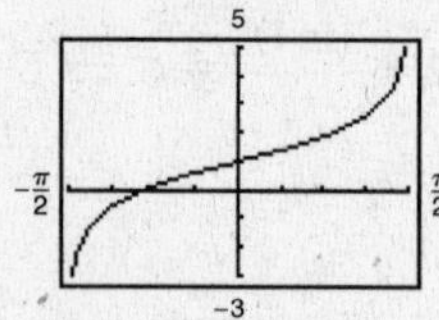


**55.** $\displaystyle\int_0^4 \frac{5}{3x+1}\,dx = \left[\frac{5}{3}\ln|3x+1|\right]_0^4 = \frac{5}{3}\ln 13 \approx 4.275$

**56.** $\displaystyle\int_{-1}^1 \frac{1}{2x+3}\,dx = \frac{1}{2}\Big[\ln|2x+3|\Big]_{-1}^1$

$\displaystyle = \frac{1}{2}\big[\ln 5 - \ln 1\big] = \frac{1}{2}\ln 5 \approx 0.805$

**57.** $u = 1 + \ln x,\ du = \dfrac{1}{x}\,dx$

$\displaystyle\int_1^e \frac{(1+\ln x)^2}{x}\,dx = \left[\frac{1}{3}(1+\ln x)^3\right]_1^e = \frac{7}{3}$

**58.** $u = \ln x,\ du = \dfrac{1}{x}dx$

$\displaystyle\int_e^{e^2} \frac{1}{x\ln x}\,dx = \int_e^{e^2}\left(\frac{1}{\ln x}\right)\frac{1}{x}\,dx = \Big[\ln|\ln|x||\Big]_e^{e^2} = \ln 2$

$\approx 0.693$

**59.** $\displaystyle\int_0^2 \frac{x^2-2}{x+1}\,dx = \int_0^2\left(x - 1 - \frac{1}{x+1}\right)dx$

$\displaystyle = \left[\frac{1}{2}x^2 - x - \ln|x+1|\right]_0^2 = -\ln 3$

$\approx -1.099$

**60.** $\displaystyle\int_0^1 \frac{x-1}{x+1}\,dx = \int_0^1 1\,dx + \int_0^1 \frac{-2}{x+1}\,dx$

$\displaystyle = \Big[x - 2\ln|x+1|\Big]_0^1 = 1 - 2\ln 2$

$\approx -0.386$

**61.** $\displaystyle\int_1^2 \frac{1-\cos\theta}{\theta - \sin\theta}\,d\theta = \Big[\ln|\theta - \sin\theta|\Big]_1^2$

$\displaystyle = \ln\left|\frac{2-\sin 2}{1-\sin 1}\right| \approx 1.929$

**62.** $\displaystyle\int_{0.1}^{0.2}(\csc 2\theta - \cot 2\theta)^2\,d\theta$

$\displaystyle = \int_{0.1}^{0.2}\left(\csc^2 2\theta - 2\csc 2\theta\cot 2\theta + \cot^2 2\theta\right)d\theta$

$\displaystyle = \int_{0.1}^{0.2}\left(2\csc^2 2\theta - 2\csc 2\theta\cot 2\theta - 1\right)d\theta$

$\displaystyle = \big[-\cot 2\theta + \csc 2\theta - \theta\big]_{0.1}^{0.2} \approx 0.0024$

**63.** $\displaystyle\int \frac{1}{1+\sqrt{x}}\,dx = 2\sqrt{x} - 2\ln\left(1+\sqrt{x}\right) + C$

**64.** $\displaystyle\int \frac{1-\sqrt{x}}{1+\sqrt{x}}\,dx = 4\sqrt{x} - x - 4\ln\left(1+\sqrt{x}\right) + C$

**65.** $\displaystyle\int \frac{\sqrt{x}}{x-1}\,dx = \ln\left(\frac{\sqrt{x}-1}{\sqrt{x}+1}\right) + 2\sqrt{x} + C$

**66.** $\displaystyle\int \frac{x^2}{x-1}\,dx = \ln|x-1| + \frac{x^2}{2} + x + C$

**67.** $\displaystyle\int_{\pi/4}^{\pi/2}(\csc x - \sin x)\,dx = \ln\left(\sqrt{2}+1\right) - \frac{\sqrt{2}}{2} \approx 0.174$

**68.** $\displaystyle\int_{-\pi/4}^{\pi/4}\frac{\sin^2 x - \cos^2 x}{\cos x}\,dx = \ln\left(\frac{\sqrt{2}+1}{\sqrt{2}-1}\right) - 2\sqrt{2}$

$\approx -1.066$

**Note: In Exercises 69–72, you can use the Second Fundamental Theorem of Calculus or integrate the function.**

**69.** $F(x) = \int_1^x \frac{1}{t}\,dt$

$F'(x) = \frac{1}{x}$

**70.** $F(x) = \int_0^x \tan t\,dt$

$F'(x) = \tan x$

**71.** $F(x) = \int_1^{3x} \frac{1}{t}\,dt$

$F'(x) = \frac{1}{3x}(3) = \frac{1}{x}$

(by Second Fundamental Theorem of Calculus)

**Alternate Solution:**

$F(x) = \int_1^{3x} \frac{1}{t}\,dt = \Big[\ln|t|\Big]_1^{3x} = \ln|3x|$

$F'(x) = \frac{1}{3x}(3) = \frac{1}{x}$

**72.** $F(x) = \int_1^{x^2} \frac{1}{t}\,dt$

$F'(x) = \frac{2x}{x^2} = \frac{2}{x}$

**73.**

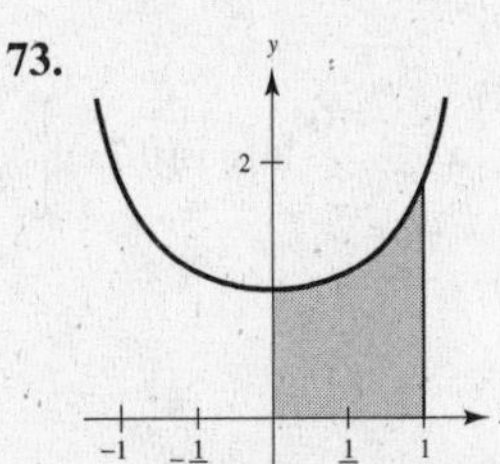

$A \approx 1.25$; Matches (d)

**74.**

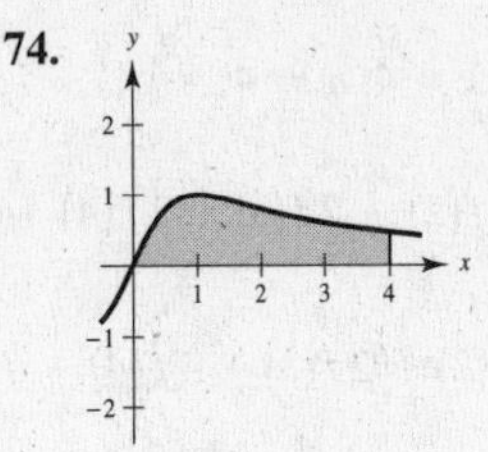

$A \approx 3$; Matches (a)

**75.** $A = \int_1^3 \frac{6}{x}\,dx = \Big[6\ln|x|\Big]_1^3 = 6\ln 3$

**76.** $A = \int_2^4 \frac{2}{x\ln x}\,dx = 2\int_2^4 \frac{1}{\ln x}\frac{1}{x}\,dx = 2\ln|\ln x|\Big]_2^4 = 2\big[\ln(\ln 4) - \ln(\ln 2)\big] = 2\ln\left(\frac{2\ln 2}{\ln 2}\right) = 2\ln 2$

**77.** $A = \int_0^{\pi/4} \tan x\,dx = -\ln|\cos x|\Big]_0^{\pi/4} = -\ln\frac{\sqrt{2}}{2} + 0 = \ln\sqrt{2} = \frac{\ln 2}{2}$

**78.** $A = \int_{\pi/4}^{3\pi/4} \frac{\sin x}{1+\cos x}\,dx = -\ln|1+\cos x|\Big]_{\pi/4}^{3\pi/4} = -\ln\left(1 - \frac{\sqrt{2}}{2}\right) + \ln\left(1 + \frac{\sqrt{2}}{2}\right) = \ln\left(\frac{2+\sqrt{2}}{2-\sqrt{2}}\right) = \ln\left(3 + 2\sqrt{2}\right)$

**79.** $A = \int_1^4 \frac{x^2+4}{x}\,dx = \int_1^4 \left(x + \frac{4}{x}\right)dx = \left[\frac{x^2}{2} + 4\ln x\right]_1^4 = (8 + 4\ln 4) - \frac{1}{2} = \frac{15}{2} + 8\ln 2 \approx 13.045$

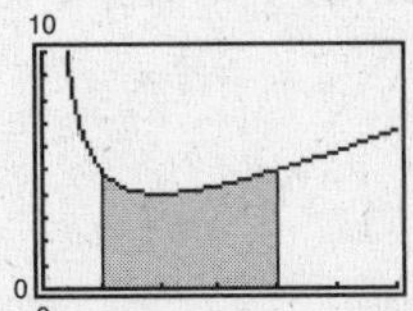

**80.** $A = \int_1^5 \frac{x+6}{x}\,dx = \int_1^5 \left(1 + \frac{6}{x}\right)dx = \big[x + 6\ln x\big]_1^5 = 5 + 6\ln 5 - 1 = 4 + 6\ln 5 \approx 13.6566$

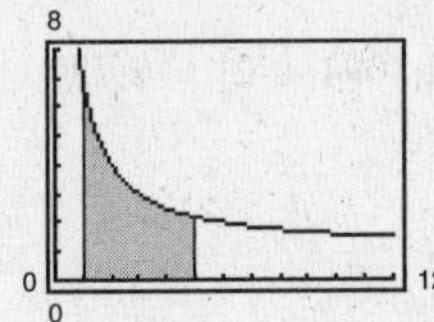

**81.** $\int_0^2 2\sec\frac{\pi x}{6}\,dx = \frac{12}{\pi}\int_0^2 \sec\left(\frac{\pi x}{6}\right)\frac{\pi}{6}\,dx = \frac{12}{\pi}\left[\ln\left|\sec\frac{\pi x}{6} + \tan\frac{\pi x}{6}\right|\right]_0^2$

$= \frac{12}{\pi}\left(\ln\left|\sec\frac{\pi}{3} + \tan\frac{\pi}{3}\right| - \ln|1 + 0|\right) = \frac{12}{\pi}\ln\left(2 + \sqrt{3}\right) \approx 5.03041$

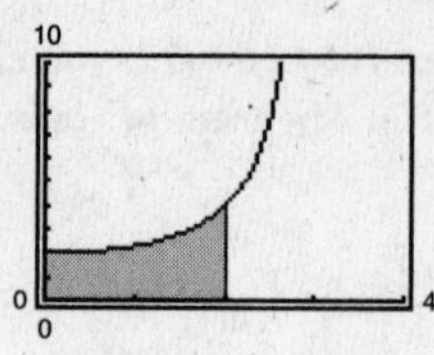


**82.** $\int_1^4 \left(2x - \tan(0.3x)\right)dx = \left[x^2 + \frac{10}{3}\ln\left|\cos(0.3x)\right|\right]_1^4 = \left[16 + \frac{10}{3}\ln\cos(1.2)\right] - \left[1 + \frac{10}{3}\ln\cos(0.3)\right] \approx 11.7686$

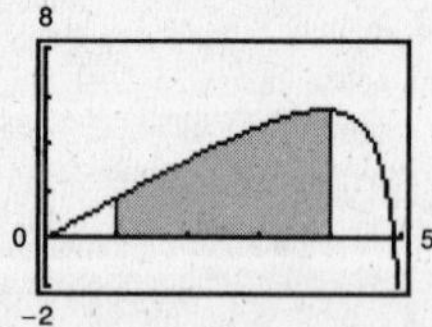


**83.** $f(x) = \frac{12}{x}, b - a = 5 - 1 = 4, n = 4$

Trapezoid: $\frac{4}{2(4)}\left[f(1) + 2f(2) + 2f(3) + 2f(4) + f(5)\right] = \frac{1}{2}[12 + 12 + 8 + 6 + 2.4] = 20.2$

Simpson: $\frac{4}{3(4)}\left[f(1) + 4f(2) + 2f(3) + 4f(4) + f(5)\right] = \frac{1}{3}[12 + 24 + 8 + 12 + 2.4] \approx 19.4667$

Calculator: $\int_1^5 \frac{12}{x}\,dx \approx 19.3133$

Exact: $12\ln 5$

**84.** $f(x) = \frac{8x}{x^2 + 4}, b - a = 4 - 0 = 4, n = 4$

Trapezoid: $\frac{4}{2(4)}\left[f(0) + 2f(1) + 2f(2) + 2f(3) + f(4)\right] = \frac{1}{2}[0 + 3.2 + 4 + 3.6923 + 1.6] \approx 6.2462$

Simpson: $\frac{4}{3(4)}\left[f(0) + 4f(1) + 2f(2) + 4f(3) + f(4)\right] \approx 6.4615$

Calculator: $\int_0^4 \frac{8x}{x^2 + 4}\,dx \approx 6.438$

Exact: $4\ln 5$

**85.** $f(x) = \ln x, b - a = 6 - 2 = 4, n = 4$

Trapezoid: $\frac{4}{2(4)}\left[f(2) + 2f(3) + 2f(4) + 2f(5) + f(6)\right] = \frac{1}{2}[0.6931 + 2.1972 + 2.7726 + 3.2189 + 1.7918] \approx 5.3368$

Simpson: $\frac{4}{3(4)}\left[f(2) + 4f(3) + 2f(4) + 4f(5) + f(6)\right] \approx 5.3632$

Calculator: $\int_2^6 \ln x\,dx \approx 5.3643$

**86.** $f(x) = \sec x, b - a = \frac{\pi}{3} - \left(-\frac{\pi}{3}\right) = \frac{2\pi}{3}, n = 4$

Trapezoid: $\frac{2\pi/3}{2(4)}\left[f\left(-\frac{\pi}{3}\right) + 2f\left(-\frac{\pi}{6}\right) + 2f(0) + 2f\left(\frac{\pi}{6}\right) + f\left(\frac{\pi}{3}\right)\right] \approx \frac{\pi}{12}\left[2 + 2.3094 + 2 + 2.3094 + 2\right] \approx 2.780$

Simpson: $\frac{2\pi/3}{3(4)}\left[f\left(-\frac{\pi}{3}\right) + 4f\left(-\frac{\pi}{6}\right) + 2f(0) + 4f\left(\frac{\pi}{6}\right) + f\left(\frac{\pi}{3}\right)\right] \approx 2.6595$

Calculator: $\int_{-\pi/3}^{\pi/3} \sec x\,dx \approx 2.6339$

**87.** Power Rule

**88.** Substitution: $(u = x^2 + 4)$ and Power Rule

**89.** Substitution: $(u = x^2 + 4)$ and Log Rule

**90.** Substitution: $(u = \tan x)$ and Log Rule

**91.** $\int_1^x \frac{3}{t}\,dt = \int_{1/4}^x \frac{1}{t}\,dt$

$$\Big[3\ln|t|\Big]_1^x = \Big[\ln|t|\Big]_{1/4}^x$$

$$3\ln x = \ln x - \ln\left(\frac{1}{4}\right)$$

$$2\ln x = -\ln\left(\frac{1}{4}\right) = \ln 4$$

$$\ln x = \frac{1}{2}\ln 4 = \ln 2$$

$$x = 2$$

**92.** $\int_1^x \frac{1}{t}\,dt = \Big[\ln|t|\Big]_1^x = \ln x \quad (\text{assume } x > 0)$

(a) $\ln x = \ln 5 \Rightarrow x = 5$

(b) $\ln x = 1 \Rightarrow x = e$

**93.** $\int \cot u\,du = \int \frac{\cos u}{\sin u}\,du = \ln|\sin u| + C$

**Alternate solution:**

$$\frac{d}{du}\Big[\ln|\sin u| + C\Big] = \frac{1}{\sin u}\cos u + C = \cot u + C$$

**94.** $\int \csc u\,du = \int \csc u\left(\frac{\csc u + \cot u}{\csc u + \cot u}\right)du = -\int \frac{1}{\csc u + \cot u}\left(-\csc u\cot u - \csc^2 u\right)du = -\ln|\csc u + \cot u| + C$

**Alternate solution:**

$$\frac{d}{du}\Big[-\ln|\csc u + \cot u| + C\Big] = -\frac{1}{\csc u + \cot u}\left(-\csc u\cot u - \csc^2 u\right) = \frac{\csc u(\cot u + \csc u)}{\csc u + \cot u} = \csc u$$

**95.** $-\ln|\cos x| + C = \ln\left|\frac{1}{\cos x}\right| + C = \ln|\sec x| + C$

**96.** $\ln|\sin x| + C = \ln\left|\frac{1}{\csc x}\right| + C = -\ln|\csc x| + C$

**97.** $\ln|\sec x + \tan x| + C = \ln\left|\frac{(\sec x + \tan x)(\sec x - \tan x)}{(\sec x - \tan x)}\right| + C$

$$= \ln\left|\frac{\sec^2 x - \tan^2 x}{\sec x - \tan x}\right| + C$$

$$= \ln\left|\frac{1}{\sec x - \tan x}\right| + C = -\ln|\sec x - \tan x| + C$$

**98.** $-\ln|\csc x + \cot x| + C = -\ln\left|\frac{(\csc x + \cot x)(\csc x - \cot x)}{(\csc x - \cot x)}\right| + C$

$$= -\ln\left|\frac{\csc^2 x - \cot^2 x}{\csc x - \cot x}\right| + C$$

$$= -\ln\left|\frac{1}{\csc x - \cot x}\right| + C = \ln|\csc x - \cot x| + C$$

**99.** Average value $= \frac{1}{4-2}\int_2^4 \frac{8}{x^2}\,dx$

$= 4\int_2^4 x^{-2}\,dx$

$= \left[-4\frac{1}{x}\right]_2^4$

$= -4\left(\frac{1}{4} - \frac{1}{2}\right) = 1$

**100.** Average value $= \frac{1}{4-2}\int_2^4 \frac{4(x+1)}{x^2}\,dx$

$= 2\int_2^4\left(\frac{1}{x} + \frac{1}{x^2}\right)dx$

$= 2\left[\ln x - \frac{1}{x}\right]_2^4$

$= 2\left[\ln 4 - \frac{1}{4} - \ln 2 + \frac{1}{2}\right]$

$= 2\left[\ln 2 + \frac{1}{4}\right] = \ln 4 + \frac{1}{2} \approx 1.8863$

**101.** Average value $= \frac{1}{e-1}\int_1^e \frac{2\ln x}{x}\,dx$

$= \frac{2}{e-1}\left[\frac{(\ln x)^2}{2}\right]_1^e$

$= \frac{1}{e-1}(1-0)$

$= \frac{1}{e-1} \approx 0.582$

**102.** Average value $= \frac{1}{2-0}\int_0^2 \sec\frac{\pi x}{6}\,dx$

$= \left[\frac{1}{2}\left(\frac{6}{\pi}\right)\ln\left|\sec\frac{\pi x}{6} + \tan\frac{\pi x}{6}\right|\right]_0^2$

$= \frac{3}{\pi}\left[\ln\left(2+\sqrt{3}\right) - \ln(1+0)\right]$

$= \frac{3}{\pi}\ln\left(2+\sqrt{3}\right)$

**103.** $P(t) = \int \frac{3000}{1+0.25t}\,dt = (3000)(4)\int\frac{0.25}{1+0.25t}\,dt$

$= 12{,}000\ln|1+0.25t| + C$

$P(0) = 12{,}000\ln|1+0.25(0)| + C = 1000$

$C = 1000$

$P(t) = 12{,}000\ln|1+0.25t| + 1000$

$= 1000\left[12\ln|1+0.25t| + 1\right]$

$P(3) = 1000\left[12(\ln 1.75) + 1\right] \approx 7715$

**104.** $t = \frac{10}{\ln 2}\int_{250}^{300}\frac{1}{T-100}\,dT$

$= \frac{10}{\ln 2}\left[\ln(T-100)\right]_{250}^{300} = \frac{10}{\ln 2}\left[\ln 200 - \ln 150\right]$

$= \frac{10}{\ln 2}\left[\ln\left(\frac{4}{3}\right)\right] \approx 4.1504$ min

**105.** $\frac{1}{50-40}\int_{40}^{50}\frac{90{,}000}{400+3x}\,dx = \left[3000\ln|400+3x|\right]_{40}^{50}$

$\approx \$168.27$

**106.** $\frac{dS}{dt} = \frac{k}{t}$

$S(t) = \int\frac{k}{t}\,dt = k\ln|t| + C = k\ln t + C$ because $t > 1$.

$S(2) = k\ln 2 + C = 200$

$S(4) = k\ln 4 + C = 300$

Solving this system yields $k = 100/\ln 2$ and $C = 100$. So,

$S(t) = \frac{100\ln t}{\ln 2} + 100 = 100\left[\frac{\ln t}{\ln 2} + 1\right].$

**107.** False

$\frac{1}{2}(\ln x) = \ln\left(x^{1/2}\right) \neq (\ln x)^{1/2}$

**108.** False

$\frac{d}{dx}[\ln x] = \frac{1}{x}$

**109.** True

$\int\frac{1}{x}\,dx = \ln|x| + C_1 = \ln|x| + \ln|C| = \ln|Cx|,\ C \neq 0$

**110.** False; the integrand has a nonremovable discontinuity at $x = 0$.

**111.** (a) $2x^2 - y^2 = 8$

$y^2 = 2x^2 - 8$

$y_1 = \sqrt{2x^2 - 8}$

$y_2 = -\sqrt{2x^2 - 8}$

(b) $y^2 = e^{-\int(1/x)\,dx} = e^{-\ln x + C} = e^{\ln(1/x)}\left(e^C\right) = \dfrac{1}{x}k$

Let $k = 4$ and graph

$y^2 = \dfrac{4}{x}.\quad \left(y_1 = \dfrac{2}{\sqrt{x}},\ y_2 = -\dfrac{2}{\sqrt{x}}\right)$

(c) In part (a): $2x^2 - y^2 = 8$

$4x - 2yy' = 0$

$y' = \dfrac{2x}{y}$

In part (b): $y^2 = \dfrac{4}{x} = 4x^{-1}$

$2yy' = \dfrac{-4}{x^2}$

$y' = \dfrac{-2}{yx^2} = \dfrac{-2y}{y^2x^2} = \dfrac{-2y}{4x} = \dfrac{-y}{2x}$

Using a graphing utility the graphs intersect at $(2.214, 1.344)$. The slopes are 3.295 and $-0.304 = (-1)/3.295$, respectively.

**112.** $f(x) = \dfrac{x}{1 + x^2}$

(a) $y = \dfrac{1}{2}x$ intersects $f(x) = \dfrac{x}{1 + x^2}$:

$\dfrac{1}{2}x = \dfrac{x}{1 + x^2}$

$1 + x^2 = 2$

$x = 1$

$A = \displaystyle\int_0^1 \left(\left[\frac{x}{1 + x^2}\right] - \frac{1}{2}x\right) dx$

$= \left[\dfrac{1}{2}\ln\left(x^2 + 1\right) - \dfrac{x^2}{4}\right]_0^1$

$= \dfrac{1}{2}\ln 2 - \dfrac{1}{4}$

(b) $f'(x) = \dfrac{\left(1 + x^2\right) - x(2x)}{\left(1 + x^2\right)^2} = \dfrac{1 - x^2}{\left(1 + x^2\right)^2}$

$f'(0) = 1$

So, for $0 < m < 1$, the graphs of $f$ and $y = mx$ enclose a finite region.

(c)

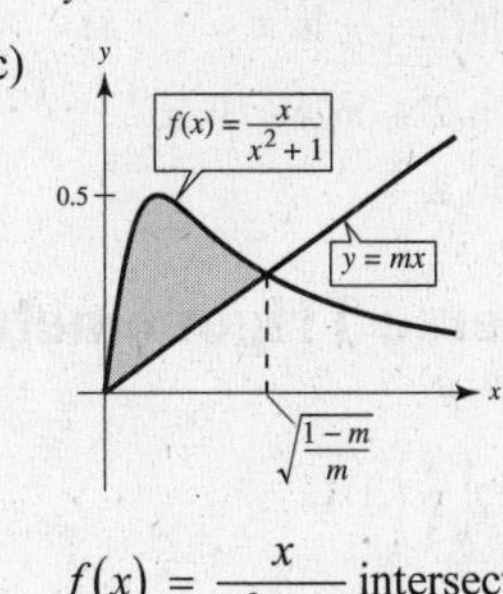


$f(x) = \dfrac{x}{x^2 + 1}$ intersects $y = mx$:

$\dfrac{x}{1 + x^2} = mx$

$1 = m + mx^2$

$x^2 = \dfrac{1 - m}{m}$

$x = \sqrt{\dfrac{1 - m}{m}}$

$A = \displaystyle\int_0^{\sqrt{(1-m)/m}} \left(\frac{x}{1 + x^2} - mx\right) dx, \quad 0 < m < 1$

$= \left[\dfrac{1}{2}\ln\left(1 + x^2\right) - \dfrac{mx^2}{2}\right]_0^{\sqrt{(1-m)/m}}$

$= \dfrac{1}{2}\ln\left(1 + \dfrac{1 - m}{m}\right) - \dfrac{1}{2}m\left(\dfrac{1 - m}{m}\right)$

$= \dfrac{1}{2}\ln\left(\dfrac{1}{m}\right) - \dfrac{1}{2}(1 - m)$

$= \dfrac{1}{2}\left[m - \ln(m) - 1\right]$

**113.** Let $f(t) = \ln t$ on $[x, y]$, $\quad 0 < x < y$.

By the Mean Value Theorem,

$\dfrac{f(y) - f(x)}{y - x} = f'(c), \quad x < c < y,$

$\dfrac{\ln y - \ln x}{y - x} = \dfrac{1}{c}.$

Because $0 < x < c < y$, $\dfrac{1}{x} > \dfrac{1}{c} > \dfrac{1}{y}$. So,

$\dfrac{1}{y} < \dfrac{\ln y - \ln x}{y - x} < \dfrac{1}{x}.$

**114.** $F(x) = \int_x^{2x} \frac{1}{t}\,dt, \quad x > 0$

$F'(x) = \frac{1}{2x}(2) - \frac{1}{x} = 0 \Rightarrow F$ is constant on $(0, \infty)$.

**Alternate Solution:**

$$F(x) = \left[\ln t\right]_x^{2x} = \ln(2x) - \ln x$$
$$= \ln 2 + \ln x - \ln x$$
$$= \ln 2$$

**115.** $\frac{d}{dx}\ln|x| = \frac{1}{x}$ implies that

$$\int \frac{1}{x}\,dx = \ln|x| + C.$$

The second formula follows by the Chain Rule.

## Section 5.8 Inverse Trigonometric Functions: Integration

**1.** $\int \frac{dx}{\sqrt{9 - x^2}} = \arcsin\left(\frac{x}{3}\right) + C$

**2.** $\int \frac{dx}{\sqrt{1 - 4x^2}} = \frac{1}{2}\int \frac{2}{\sqrt{1 - 4x^2}}\,dx = \frac{1}{2}\arcsin(2x) + C$

**3.** $\int \frac{11}{36 + x^2}\,dx = 11\int \frac{1}{36 + x^2}\,dx$

$$= 11\left(\frac{1}{6}\right)\arctan\frac{x}{6} + C$$
$$= \frac{11}{6}\arctan\left(\frac{x}{6}\right) + C$$

**4.** $\int \frac{12}{1 + 9x^2}\,dx = 4\int \frac{3}{1 + 9x^2}\,dx = 4\arctan(3x) + C$

**5.** $\int \frac{1}{x\sqrt{4x^2 - 1}}\,dx = \int \frac{2}{2x\sqrt{(2x)^2 - 1}}\,dx = \operatorname{arcsec}|2x| + C$

**6.** $\int \frac{1}{4 + (x - 3)^2}\,dx = \frac{1}{2}\arctan\left(\frac{x - 3}{2}\right) + C$

**7.** $\int \frac{1}{\sqrt{1 - (x + 1)^2}}\,dx = \arcsin(x + 1) + C$

**8.** Let $u = t^2$, $du = 2t\,dt$.

$$\int \frac{t}{t^4 + 16}\,dt = \frac{1}{2}\int \frac{1}{(4)^2 + (t^2)^2}(2t)\,dt = \frac{1}{8}\arctan\frac{t^2}{4} + C$$

**9.** Let $u = t^2$, $du = 2t\,dt$.

$$\int \frac{t}{\sqrt{1 - t^4}}\,dt = \frac{1}{2}\int \frac{1}{\sqrt{1 - (t^2)^2}}(2t)\,dt = \frac{1}{2}\arcsin t^2 + C$$

**10.** Let $u = x^2$, $du = 2x\,dx$.

$$\int \frac{1}{x\sqrt{x^4 - 4}}\,dx = \frac{1}{2}\int \frac{1}{x^2\sqrt{(x^2)^2 - 2^2}}(2x)\,dx$$
$$= \frac{1}{4}\operatorname{arcsec}\frac{x^2}{2} + C$$

**11.** $\int \frac{t}{t^4 + 25}\,dt = \frac{1}{2}\int \frac{1}{(t^2)^2 + 5^2}(2)\,dt$

$$= \frac{1}{10}\arctan\left(\frac{t^2}{5}\right) + C$$

**12.** $\int \frac{1}{x\sqrt{1 - (\ln x)^2}}\,dx = \int \frac{1}{\sqrt{1 - (\ln x)^2}} \cdot \frac{1}{x}\,dx$

$$= \arcsin(\ln x) + C$$

**13.** Let $u = e^{2x}$, $du = 2e^{2x}\,dx$.

$$\int \frac{e^{2x}}{4 + e^{4x}}\,dx = \frac{1}{2}\int \frac{2e^{2x}}{4 + (e^{2x})^2}\,dx = \frac{1}{4}\arctan\frac{e^{2x}}{2} + C$$

**14.** $\int \frac{1}{3 + (x - 2)^2}\,dx = \int \frac{1}{(\sqrt{3})^2 + (x - 2)^2}\,dx$

$$= \frac{1}{\sqrt{3}}\arctan\left(\frac{x - 2}{\sqrt{3}}\right) + C$$
$$= \frac{\sqrt{3}}{3}\arctan\left(\frac{\sqrt{3}(x - 2)}{3}\right) + C$$

**15.** $\int \frac{\sec^2 x}{\sqrt{25 - \tan^2 x}}\,dx = \int \frac{\sec^2 x}{\sqrt{5^2 - (\tan x)^2}}\,dx$

$$= \arcsin\left(\frac{\tan x}{5}\right) + C$$

**16.** $\int \frac{\sin x}{7 + \cos^2 x}\,dx = \int \frac{-1}{\left(\sqrt{7}\right)^2 + \cos^2 x}(-\sin x)\,dx = -\frac{1}{\sqrt{7}}\arctan\left(\frac{\cos x}{\sqrt{7}}\right) + C = -\frac{\sqrt{7}}{7}\arctan\left(\frac{\sqrt{7}\cos x}{7}\right) + C$

**17.** $\int \frac{x^3}{x^2+1}\,dx = \int \left[x - \frac{x}{x^2+1}\right]dx = \int x\,dx - \frac{1}{2}\int \frac{2x}{x^2+1}\,dx = \frac{1}{2}x^2 - \frac{1}{2}\ln\left(x^2+1\right) + C$ (Use long division.)

**18.** $\int \frac{x^4-1}{x^2+1}\,dx = \int \left(x^2-1\right)dx = \frac{1}{3}x^3 - x + C$

**19.** $\int \frac{1}{\sqrt{x}\sqrt{1-x}}\,dx, u = \sqrt{x}, x = u^2, dx = 2u\,du$

$\int \frac{1}{u\sqrt{1-u^2}}(2u\,du) = 2\int \frac{du}{\sqrt{1-u^2}} = 2\arcsin u + C = 2\arcsin\sqrt{x} + C$

**20.** $\int \frac{3}{2\sqrt{x}(1+x)}\,dx, u = \sqrt{x}, du = \frac{1}{2\sqrt{x}}\,dx, dx = 2u\,du$

$\frac{3}{2}\int \frac{2u\,du}{u\left(1+u^2\right)} = 3\int \frac{du}{1+u^2} = 3\arctan u + C = 3\arctan\sqrt{x} + C$

**21.** $\int \frac{x-3}{x^2+1}\,dx = \frac{1}{2}\int \frac{2x}{x^2+1}\,dx - 3\int \frac{1}{x^2+1}\,dx = \frac{1}{2}\ln\left(x^2+1\right) - 3\arctan x + C$

**22.** $\int \frac{4x+3}{\sqrt{1-x^2}}\,dx = (-2)\int \frac{-2x}{\sqrt{1-x^2}}\,dx + 3\int \frac{1}{\sqrt{1-x^2}}\,dx = -4\sqrt{1-x^2} + 3\arcsin x + C$

**23.** $\int \frac{x+5}{\sqrt{9-(x-3)^2}}\,dx = \int \frac{x-3}{\sqrt{9-(x-3)^2}}\,dx + \int \frac{8}{\sqrt{9-(x-3)^2}}\,dx$

$= -\sqrt{9-(x-3)^2} + 8\arcsin\left(\frac{x-3}{3}\right) + C = -\sqrt{6x-x^2} + 8\arcsin\left(\frac{x}{3} - 1\right) + C$

**24.** $\int \frac{x-2}{(x+1)^2+4}\,dx = \frac{1}{2}\int \frac{2x+2}{(x+1)^2+4}\,dx - \int \frac{3}{(x+1)^2+4}\,dx$

$= \frac{1}{2}\ln\left(x^2+2x+5\right) - \frac{3}{2}\arctan\left(\frac{x+1}{2}\right) + C$

**25.** Let $u = 3x, du = 3\,dx$.

$\int_0^{1/6} \frac{3}{\sqrt{1-9x^2}}\,dx = \int_0^{1/6} \frac{1}{\sqrt{1-(3x)^2}}(3)\,dx$

$= \left[\arcsin(3x)\right]_0^{1/6} = \frac{\pi}{6}$

**26.** $\int_0^1 \frac{1}{\sqrt{4-x^2}}\,dx = \left[\arcsin\frac{x}{2}\right]_0^1 = \frac{\pi}{6}$

**27.** Let $u = 2x, du = 2\,dx$.

$\int_0^{\sqrt{3}/2} \frac{1}{1+4x^2}\,dx = \frac{1}{2}\int_0^{\sqrt{3}/2} \frac{2}{1+(2x)^2}\,dx$

$= \left[\frac{1}{2}\arctan(2x)\right]_0^{\sqrt{3}/2} = \frac{\pi}{6}$

**28.** $\int_{\sqrt{3}}^3 \frac{6}{9+x^2}\,dx = \left[6\left(\frac{1}{3}\right)\arctan\frac{x}{3}\right]_{\sqrt{3}}^3 = \frac{\pi}{6}$

**29.** Let $u = 1-x^2, du = -2x\,dx$.

$\int_{-1/2}^0 \frac{x}{\sqrt{1-x^2}}\,dx = -\frac{1}{2}\int_{-1/2}^0 \left(1-x^2\right)^{-1/2}(-2x)\,dx$

$= \left[-\sqrt{1-x^2}\right]_{-1/2}^0 = \frac{\sqrt{3}-2}{2}$

$\approx -0.134$

**30.** Let $u = 1 + x^2$, $du = 2x\,dx$.

$$\int_{-\sqrt{3}}^{0} \frac{x}{1+x^2}\,dx = \frac{1}{2}\int_{-\sqrt{3}}^{0} \frac{1}{1+x^2}(2x)\,dx$$

$$= \left[\frac{1}{2}\ln\left(1+x^2\right)\right]_{-\sqrt{3}}^{0} = -\ln 2$$

**31.** $\displaystyle\int_3^6 \frac{1}{25+(x-3)^2}\,dx = \left[\frac{1}{5}\arctan\left(\frac{x-3}{5}\right)\right]_3^6$

$$= \frac{1}{5}\arctan\left(\frac{3}{5}\right)$$

$$\approx 0.108$$

**32.** $\displaystyle\int_1^4 \frac{1}{x\sqrt{16x^2-5}}\,dx = \int_1^4 \frac{4\,dx}{(4x)\sqrt{(4x)^2-\left(\sqrt{5}\right)^2}}$

$$= \left[\left(\frac{1}{\sqrt{5}}\right)\operatorname{arcsec}\frac{|4x|}{\sqrt{5}}\right]_1^4 = \frac{1}{\sqrt{5}}\operatorname{arcsec}\frac{16}{\sqrt{5}} - \frac{1}{\sqrt{5}}\operatorname{arcsec}\left(\frac{4}{\sqrt{5}}\right) \approx 0.091$$

**33.** Let $u = e^x$, $du = e^x\,dx$.

$$\int_0^{\ln 5} \frac{e^x}{1+e^{2x}}\,dx = \left[\arctan\left(e^x\right)\right]_0^{\ln 5} = \arctan 5 - \frac{\pi}{4} \approx 0.588$$

**34.** Let $u = e^{-x}$, $du = -e^{-x}\,dx$.

$$\int_{\ln 2}^{\ln 4} \frac{e^{-x}}{\sqrt{1-e^{-2x}}}\,dx = \left[-\arcsin\left(e^{-x}\right)\right]_{\ln 2}^{\ln 4} = -\arcsin\left(\frac{1}{4}\right) + \arcsin\left(\frac{1}{2}\right) = \frac{\pi}{6} - \arcsin\left(\frac{1}{4}\right) \approx 0.271$$

**35.** Let $u = \cos x$, $du = -\sin x\,dx$.

$$\int_{\pi/2}^{\pi} \frac{\sin x}{1+\cos^2 x}\,dx = -\int_{\pi/2}^{\pi} \frac{-\sin x}{1+\cos^2 x}\,dx = \left[-\arctan(\cos x)\right]_{\pi/2}^{\pi} = \frac{\pi}{4}$$

**36.** $\displaystyle\int_0^{\pi/2} \frac{\cos x}{1+\sin^2 x}\,dx = \left[\arctan(\sin x)\right]_0^{\pi/2} = \frac{\pi}{4}$

**37.** Let $u = \arcsin x$, $du = \dfrac{1}{\sqrt{1-x^2}}\,dx$.

$$\int_0^{1/\sqrt{2}} \frac{\arcsin x}{\sqrt{1-x^2}}\,dx = \left[\frac{1}{2}\arcsin^2 x\right]_0^{1/\sqrt{2}} = \frac{\pi^2}{32} \approx 0.308$$

**38.** Let $u = \arccos x$, $du = -\dfrac{1}{\sqrt{1-x^2}}\,dx$.

$$\int_0^{1/\sqrt{2}} \frac{\arccos x}{\sqrt{1-x^2}}\,dx = -\int_0^{1/\sqrt{2}} \frac{-\arccos x}{\sqrt{1-x^2}}\,dx = \left[-\frac{1}{2}\arccos^2 x\right]_0^{1/\sqrt{2}} = \frac{3\pi^2}{32} \approx 0.925$$

**39.** $\displaystyle\int_0^2 \frac{dx}{x^2-2x+2} = \int_0^2 \frac{1}{1+(x-1)^2}\,dx = \left[\arctan(x-1)\right]_0^2 = \frac{\pi}{2}$

**40.** $\displaystyle\int_{-2}^2 \frac{dx}{x^2+4x+13} = \int_{-2}^2 \frac{dx}{(x+2)^2+9} = \left[\frac{1}{3}\arctan\left(\frac{x+2}{3}\right)\right]_{-2}^2 = \frac{1}{3}\arctan\left(\frac{4}{3}\right)$

**41.** $\displaystyle\int \frac{2x}{x^2+6x+13}\,dx = \int \frac{2x+6}{x^2+6x+13}\,dx - 6\int \frac{1}{x^2+6x+13}\,dx$

$$= \int \frac{2x+6}{x^2+6x+13}\,dx - 6\int \frac{1}{4+(x+3)^2}\,dx = \ln\left|x^2+6x+13\right| - 3\arctan\left(\frac{x+3}{2}\right) + C$$

**42.** $\displaystyle\int \frac{2x - 5}{x^2 + 2x + 2}\,dx = \int \frac{2x + 2}{x^2 + 2x + 2}\,dx - 7\int \frac{1}{1 + (x + 1)^2}\,dx = \ln\left|x^2 + 2x + 2\right| - 7\arctan(x + 1) + C$

**43.** $\displaystyle\int \frac{1}{\sqrt{-x^2 - 4x}}\,dx = \int \frac{1}{\sqrt{4 - (x + 2)^2}}\,dx = \arcsin\left(\frac{x + 2}{2}\right) + C$

**44.** $\displaystyle\int \frac{2}{\sqrt{-x^2 + 4x}}\,dx = \int \frac{2}{\sqrt{4 - (x^2 - 4x + 4)}}\,dx = \int \frac{2}{\sqrt{4 - (x - 2)^2}}\,dx = 2\arcsin\left(\frac{x - 2}{2}\right) + C$

**45.** Let $u = -x^2 - 4x$, $du = (-2x - 4)\,dx$.

$$\int \frac{x + 2}{\sqrt{-x^2 - 4x}}\,dx = -\frac{1}{2}\int \left(-x^2 - 4x\right)^{-1/2}(-2x - 4)\,dx = -\sqrt{-x^2 - 4x} + C$$

**46.** Let $u = x^2 - 2x$, $du = (2x - 2)\,dx$.

$$\int \frac{x - 1}{\sqrt{x^2 - 2x}}\,dx = \frac{1}{2}\int \left(x^2 - 2x\right)^{-1/2}(2x - 2)\,dx = \sqrt{x^2 - 2x} + C$$

**47.** 
$$\begin{aligned}\int_2^3 \frac{2x - 3}{\sqrt{4x - x^2}}\,dx &= \int_2^3 \frac{2x - 4}{\sqrt{4x - x^2}}\,dx + \int_2^3 \frac{1}{\sqrt{4x - x^2}}\,dx \\ &= -\int_2^3 \left(4x - x^2\right)^{-1/2}(4 - 2x)\,dx + \int_2^3 \frac{1}{\sqrt{4 - (x - 2)^2}}\,dx \\ &= \left[-2\sqrt{4x - x^2} + \arcsin\left(\frac{x - 2}{2}\right)\right]_2^3 = 4 - 2\sqrt{3} + \frac{\pi}{6} \approx 1.059\end{aligned}$$

**48.** $\displaystyle\int \frac{1}{(x - 1)\sqrt{x^2 - 2x}}\,dx = \int \frac{1}{(x - 1)\sqrt{(x - 1)^2 - 1}}\,dx = \operatorname{arcsec}\left|x - 1\right| + C$

**49.** Let $u = x^2 + 1$, $du = 2x\,dx$.

$$\int \frac{x}{x^4 + 2x^2 + 2}\,dx = \frac{1}{2}\int \frac{2x}{\left(x^2 + 1\right)^2 + 1}\,dx = \frac{1}{2}\arctan\left(x^2 + 1\right) + C$$

**50.** Let $u = x^2 - 4$, $du = 2x\,dx$.

$$\int \frac{x}{\sqrt{9 + 8x^2 - x^4}}\,dx = \frac{1}{2}\int \frac{2x}{\sqrt{25 - \left(x^2 - 4\right)^2}}\,dx = \frac{1}{2}\arcsin\left(\frac{x^2 - 4}{5}\right) + C$$

**51.** Let $u = \sqrt{e^t - 3}$. Then $u^2 + 3 = e^t$, $2u\,du = e^t\,dt$, and $\dfrac{2u\,du}{u^2 + 3} = dt$.

$$\begin{aligned}\int \sqrt{e^t - 3}\,dt &= \int \frac{2u^2}{u^2 + 3}\,du = \int 2\,du - \int 6\frac{1}{u^2 + 3}\,du \\ &= 2u - 2\sqrt{3}\arctan\frac{u}{\sqrt{3}} + C = 2\sqrt{e^t - 3} - 2\sqrt{3}\arctan\sqrt{\frac{e^t - 3}{3}} + C\end{aligned}$$

**52.** Let $u = \sqrt{x - 2}, u^2 + 2 = x, 2u\,du = dx$.

$$\int \frac{\sqrt{x-2}}{x+1}\,dx = \int \frac{2u^2}{u^2+3}\,du = \int \frac{2u^2+6-6}{u^2+3}\,du = 2\int du - 6\int \frac{1}{u^2+3}\,du$$

$$= 2u - \frac{6}{\sqrt{3}}\arctan\frac{u}{\sqrt{3}} + C = 2\sqrt{x-2} - 2\sqrt{3}\arctan\sqrt{\frac{x-2}{3}} + C$$

**53.** $\int_1^3 \frac{dx}{\sqrt{x}(1+x)}$

Let $u = \sqrt{x}, u^2 = x, 2u\,du = dx, 1 + x = 1 + u^2$.

$$\int_1^{\sqrt{3}} \frac{2u\,du}{u(1+u^2)} = \int_1^{\sqrt{3}} \frac{2}{1+u^2}\,du$$

$$= \left[2\arctan(u)\right]_1^{\sqrt{3}}$$

$$= 2\left(\frac{\pi}{3} - \frac{\pi}{4}\right) = \frac{\pi}{6}$$

**54.** $\int_0^1 \frac{dx}{2\sqrt{3-x}\sqrt{x+1}}$

Let $u = \sqrt{x+1}, u^2 = x + 1, 2u\,du = dx$,

$\sqrt{3-x} = \sqrt{4-u^2}$.

$$\int_1^{\sqrt{2}} \frac{2u\,du}{2\sqrt{4-u^2}u} = \int_1^{\sqrt{2}} \frac{du}{\sqrt{4-u^2}}$$

$$= \arcsin\left(\frac{u}{2}\right)\Big]_1^{\sqrt{2}}$$

$$= \arcsin\left(\frac{\sqrt{2}}{2}\right) - \arcsin\left(\frac{1}{2}\right)$$

$$= \frac{\pi}{4} - \frac{\pi}{6} = \frac{\pi}{12}$$

**55.** (a) $\int \frac{1}{\sqrt{1-x^2}}\,dx = \arcsin x + C, \quad u = x$

(b) $\int \frac{x}{\sqrt{1-x^2}}\,dx = -\sqrt{1-x^2} + C, \quad u = 1 - x^2$

(c) $\int \frac{1}{x\sqrt{1-x^2}}\,dx$ cannot be evaluated using the basic integration rules.

**56.** (a) $\int e^{x^2}\,dx$ cannot be evaluated using the basic integration rules.

(b) $\int xe^{x^2}\,dx = \frac{1}{2}e^{x^2} + C, \quad u = x^2$

(c) $\int \frac{1}{x^2}e^{1/x}\,dx = -e^{1/x} + C, \quad u = \frac{1}{x}$

**57.** (a) $\int \sqrt{x-1}\,dx = \frac{2}{3}(x-1)^{3/2} + C, \quad u = x - 1$

(b) Let $u = \sqrt{x-1}$. Then $x = u^2 + 1$ and $dx = 2u\,du$.

$$\int x\sqrt{x-1}\,dx = \int (u^2+1)(u)(2u)\,du$$

$$= 2\int (u^4 + u^2)\,du$$

$$= 2\left(\frac{u^5}{5} + \frac{u^3}{3}\right) + C$$

$$= \frac{2}{15}u^3(3u^2 + 5) + C$$

$$= \frac{2}{15}(x-1)^{3/2}\left[3(x-1) + 5\right] + C$$

$$= \frac{2}{15}(x-1)^{3/2}(3x+2) + C$$

(c) Let $u = \sqrt{x-1}$. Then $x = u^2 + 1$ and $dx = 2u\,du$.

$$\int \frac{x}{\sqrt{x-1}}\,dx = \int \frac{u^2+1}{u}(2u)\,du$$

$$= 2\int (u^2+1)\,du$$

$$= 2\left(\frac{u^3}{3} + u\right) + C$$

$$= \frac{2}{3}u(u^2+3) + C$$

$$= \frac{2}{3}\sqrt{x-1}(x+2) + C$$

**Note:** In (b) and (c), substitution was necessary *before* the basic integration rules could be used.

**58.** Area $\approx (1)(1) = 1$

Matches (c)

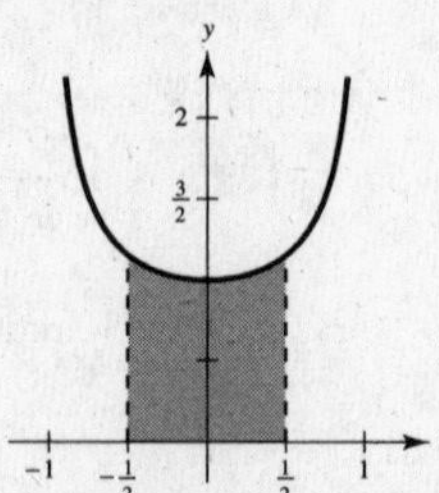


**59.** No. This integral does not correspond to any of the basic differentiation rules.

**60.** (a) $\int \frac{1}{1+x^4}\,dx$ cannot be evaluated using the basic integration rules.

(b) $$\int \frac{x}{1+x^4}\,dx = \frac{1}{2}\int \frac{2x}{1+\left(x^2\right)^2}\,dx$$
$$= \frac{1}{2}\arctan\left(x^2\right) + C,\quad u = x^2$$

(c) $$\int \frac{x^3}{1+x^4}\,dx = \frac{1}{4}\int \frac{4x^3}{1+x^4}\,dx$$
$$= \frac{1}{4}\ln\left(1+x^4\right) + C,\quad u = 1 + x^4$$

**61.** $y' = \frac{1}{\sqrt{4-x^2}},\quad (0, \pi)$

$$y = \int \frac{1}{\sqrt{4-x^2}}\,dx = \arcsin\left(\frac{x}{2}\right) + C$$

When $x = 0, y = \pi \Rightarrow C = \pi$

$$y = \arcsin\left(\frac{x}{2}\right) + \pi$$

**62.** $y' = \frac{1}{4+x^2},\quad (2, \pi)$

$$y = \int \frac{1}{4+x^2}\,dx = \frac{1}{2}\arctan\frac{x}{2} + C$$

When $x = 2, y = \pi$:

$$\pi = \frac{1}{2}\arctan\left(\frac{2}{2}\right) + C$$

$$\pi = \frac{\pi}{8} + C \Rightarrow C = \frac{7\pi}{8}$$

$$y = \frac{1}{2}\arctan\left(\frac{x}{2}\right) + \frac{7\pi}{8}$$

**63.** (a)

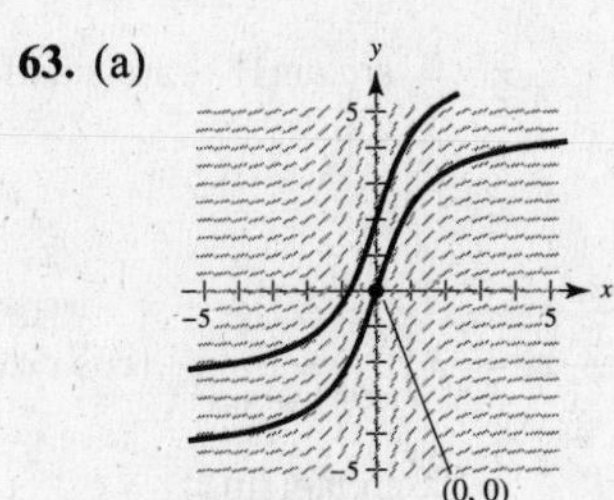


(b) $\frac{dy}{dx} = \frac{3}{1+x^2},\quad (0, 0)$

$$y = 3\int \frac{dx}{1+x^2} = 3\arctan x + C$$

$(0, 0)$: $0 = 3\arctan(0) + C \Rightarrow C = 0$

$y = 3\arctan x$

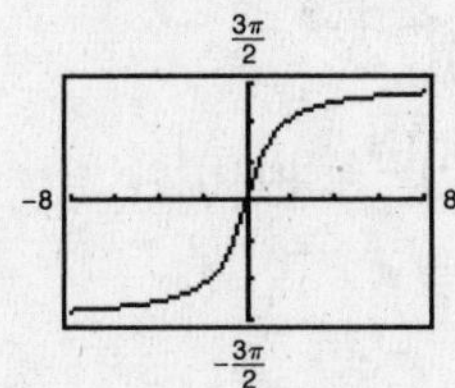

**64.** (a)

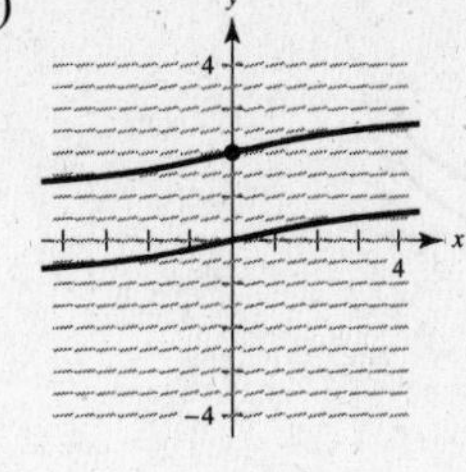

(b) $y' = \frac{2}{9+x^2},\quad (0, 2)$

$$y = \int \frac{2}{9+x^2}\,dx = \frac{2}{3}\arctan\left(\frac{x}{3}\right) + C$$

$2 = C$

$$y = \frac{2}{3}\arctan\left(\frac{x}{3}\right) + 2$$

**65.** (a)

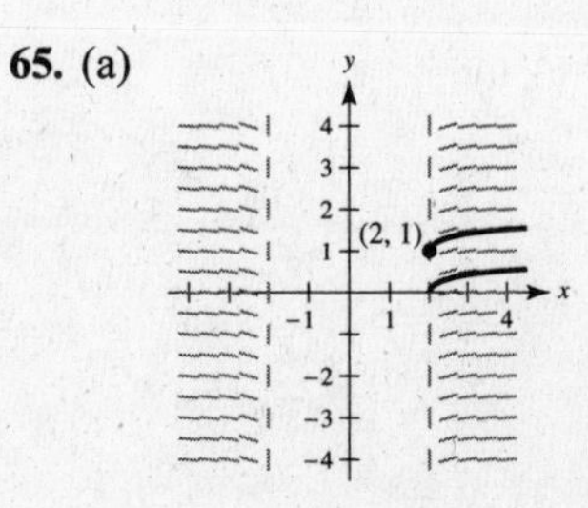


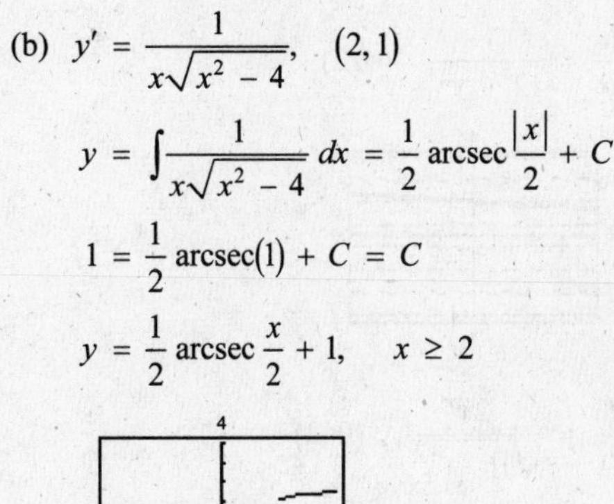

(b) $y' = \frac{1}{x\sqrt{x^2-4}},\quad (2, 1)$

$$y = \int \frac{1}{x\sqrt{x^2-4}}\,dx = \frac{1}{2}\operatorname{arcsec}\frac{|x|}{2} + C$$

$$1 = \frac{1}{2}\operatorname{arcsec}(1) + C = C$$

$$y = \frac{1}{2}\operatorname{arcsec}\frac{x}{2} + 1,\quad x \ge 2$$

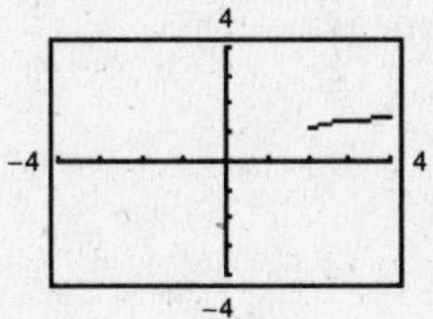

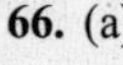

**66.** (a)

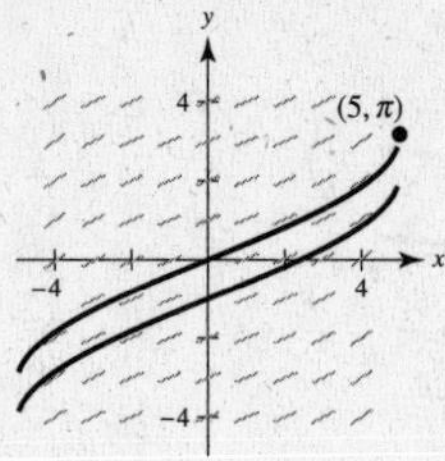


(b) $y' = \dfrac{2}{\sqrt{25 - x^2}}, \quad (5, \pi)$

$$y = \int \frac{2}{\sqrt{25 - x^2}}\,dx = 2\arcsin\left(\frac{x}{5}\right) + C$$

$$\pi = 2\arcsin(1) + C \Rightarrow C = 0$$

$$y = 2\arcsin\left(\frac{x}{5}\right)$$

**67.** $\dfrac{dy}{dx} = \dfrac{10}{x\sqrt{x^2 - 1}}, \quad (3, 0)$

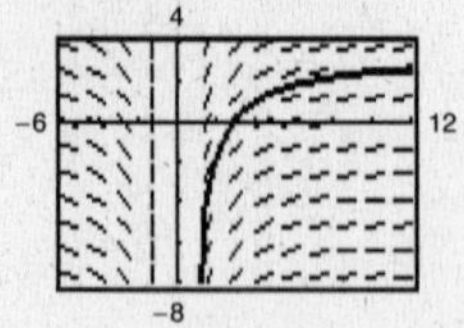


**68.** $\dfrac{dy}{dx} = \dfrac{1}{12 + x^2}, \quad (4, 2)$

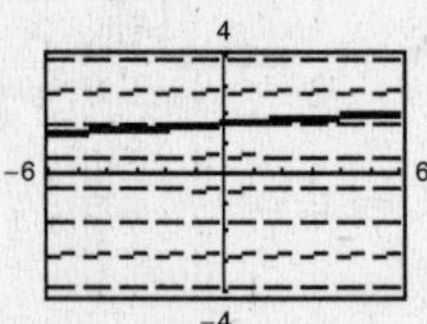


**69.** $\dfrac{dy}{dx} = \dfrac{2y}{\sqrt{16 - x^2}}, \quad (0, 2)$

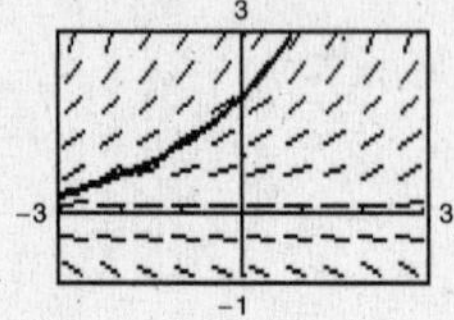


**70.** $\dfrac{dy}{dx} = \dfrac{\sqrt{y}}{1 + x^2}, \quad (0, 4)$

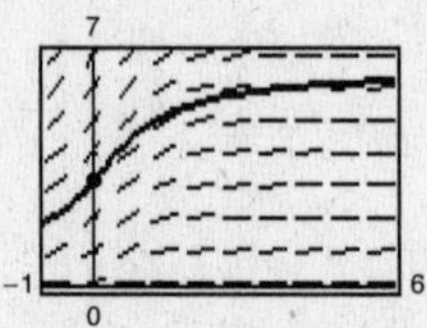


**71.** $\text{Area} = \displaystyle\int_0^1 \frac{2}{\sqrt{4 - x^2}}\,dx$

$$= \left[2\arcsin\left(\frac{x}{2}\right)\right]_0^1$$

$$= 2\arcsin\left(\frac{1}{2}\right) - 2\arcsin(0)$$

$$= 2\left(\frac{\pi}{6}\right) = \frac{\pi}{3}$$

**72.** $\text{Area} = \displaystyle\int_{2/\sqrt{2}}^2 \frac{1}{x\sqrt{x^2 - 1}}\,dx$

$$= \left[\operatorname{arcsec} x\right]_{2/\sqrt{2}}^2$$

$$= \operatorname{arcsec}(2) - \operatorname{arcsec}\left(\frac{2}{\sqrt{2}}\right)$$

$$= \frac{\pi}{3} - \frac{\pi}{4} = \frac{\pi}{12}$$

**73.** $\text{Area} = \displaystyle\int_1^3 \frac{1}{x^2 - 2x + 5}\,dx = \int_1^3 \frac{1}{(x - 1)^2 + 4}\,dx$

$$= \left[\frac{1}{2}\arctan\left(\frac{x - 1}{2}\right)\right]_1^3$$

$$= \frac{1}{2}\arctan(1) - \frac{1}{2}\arctan(0)$$

$$= \frac{\pi}{8}$$

**74.** $\text{Area} = \displaystyle\int_{-2}^0 \frac{2}{x^2 + 4x + 8}\,dx = \int_{-2}^0 \frac{2}{(x + 2)^2 + 4}\,dx$

$$= \left[\arctan\left(\frac{x + 2}{2}\right)\right]_{-2}^0$$

$$= \arctan(1) - \arctan(0)$$

$$= \frac{\pi}{4}$$

**75.** $\text{Area} = \displaystyle\int_{-\pi/2}^{\pi/2} \frac{3\cos x}{1 + \sin^2 x}\,dx = 3\int_{-\pi/2}^{\pi/2} \frac{1}{1 + \sin^2 x}(\cos x\,dx)$

$$= \left[3\arctan(\sin x)\right]_{-\pi/2}^{\pi/2}$$

$$= 3\arctan(1) - 3\arctan(-1)$$

$$= \frac{3\pi}{4} + \frac{3\pi}{4} = \frac{3\pi}{2}$$

**76.** $\text{Area} = \displaystyle\int_0^{\ln\sqrt{3}} \frac{4e^x}{1 + e^{2x}}\,dx, \quad (u = e^x)$

$$= 4\left[\arctan(e^x)\right]_0^{\ln\sqrt{3}}$$

$$= 4\left[\arctan(\sqrt{3}) - \arctan(1)\right]$$

$$= 4\left(\frac{\pi}{3} - \frac{\pi}{4}\right) = \frac{\pi}{3}$$

**77.** (a) $\dfrac{d}{dx}\left[\ln x - \dfrac{1}{2}\ln\left(1 + x^2\right) - \dfrac{\arctan x}{x} + C\right] = \dfrac{1}{x} - \dfrac{x}{1 + x^2} - \left(\dfrac{x\left[1/\left(1 + x^2\right)\right] - \arctan x}{x^2}\right)$

$$= \frac{1 + x^2 - x^2}{x\left(1 + x^2\right)} - \frac{1}{x\left(1 + x^2\right)} + \frac{\arctan x}{x^2} = \frac{\arctan x}{x^2}$$

So, $\displaystyle\int \frac{\arctan x}{x^2}\,dx = \ln x - \frac{1}{2}\ln\left(1 + x^2\right) - \frac{\arctan x}{x} + C.$

(b) $A = \displaystyle\int_1^{\sqrt{3}} \frac{\arctan x}{x^2}\,dx$

$$= \left[\ln x - \frac{1}{2}\ln\left(1 + x^2\right) - \frac{\arctan x}{x}\right]_1^{\sqrt{3}}$$

$$= \left(\ln\sqrt{3} - \frac{1}{2}\ln(4) - \frac{\arctan\sqrt{3}}{\sqrt{3}}\right) - \left(-\frac{1}{2}\ln 2 - \arctan(1)\right)$$

$$= \frac{1}{2}\ln 3 - \frac{1}{2}\ln 2 - \frac{\pi\sqrt{3}}{9} + \frac{\pi}{4} = \ln\frac{\sqrt{6}}{2} + \frac{9\pi - 4\pi\sqrt{3}}{36} \approx 0.3835$$

**78.** (a) $\dfrac{d}{dx}\left[x(\arcsin x)^2 - 2x + 2\sqrt{1 - x^2}\arcsin x + C\right]$

$$= (\arcsin x)^2 + 2x(\arcsin x)\frac{1}{\sqrt{1 - x^2}} - 2 - \frac{2x}{\sqrt{1 - x^2}}\arcsin x + 2\sqrt{1 - x^2}\frac{1}{\sqrt{1 - x^2}} = (\arcsin x)^2$$

(b) $A = \displaystyle\int_0^1 (\arcsin x)^2\,dx = \left[x(\arcsin x)^2 - 2x + 2\sqrt{1 - x^2}\arcsin x\right]_0^1 = \left(\left(\frac{\pi}{2}\right)^2 - 2\right) - (0) = \frac{\pi^4}{4} - 2 \approx 0.4674$

**79.** (a)

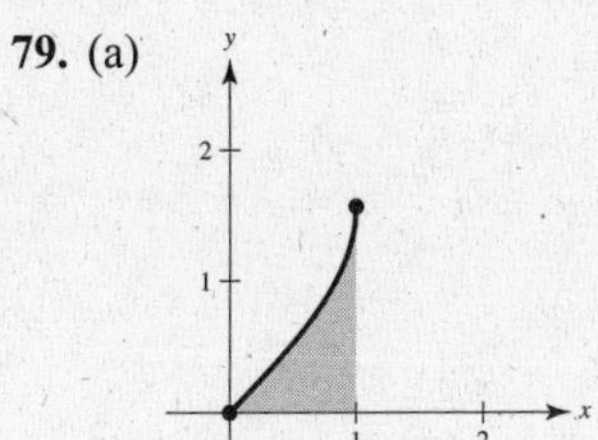


Shaded area is given by $\displaystyle\int_0^1 \arcsin x\,dx$.

(b) $\displaystyle\int_0^1 \arcsin x\,dx \approx 0.5708$

(c) Divide the rectangle into two regions.

Area rectangle $= (\text{base})(\text{height}) = 1\left(\dfrac{\pi}{2}\right) = \dfrac{\pi}{2}$

Area rectangle $= \displaystyle\int_0^1 \arcsin x\,dx + \int_0^{\pi/2} \sin y\,dy$

$$\frac{\pi}{2} = \int_0^1 \arcsin x\,dx + \left[(-\cos y)\right]_0^{\pi/2} = \int_0^1 \arcsin x\,dx + 1$$

So, $\displaystyle\int_0^1 \arcsin x\,dx = \frac{\pi}{2} - 1 \approx 0.5708.$

**80.** (a) $\displaystyle\int_0^1 \frac{4}{1 + x^2}\,dx = \left[4\arctan x\right]_0^1 = 4\arctan 1 - 4\arctan 0 = 4\left(\frac{\pi}{4}\right) - 4(0) = \pi$

(b) Let $n = 6$.

$$4\int_0^1 \frac{1}{1 + x^2}\,dx \approx 4\left(\frac{1}{18}\right)\left[1 + \frac{4}{1 + (1/36)} + \frac{2}{1 + (1/9)} + \frac{4}{1 + (1/4)} + \frac{2}{1 + (4/9)} + \frac{4}{1 + (25/36)} + \frac{1}{2}\right] \approx 3.1415918$$

(c) 3.1415927

**81.** $F(x) = \frac{1}{2}\int_x^{x+2} \frac{2}{t^2+1}\,dt$

(a) $F(x)$ represents the average value of $f(x)$ over the interval $[x, x+2]$. Maximum at $x = -1$, because the graph is greatest on $[-1, 1]$.

(b) $F(x) = \left[\arctan t\right]_x^{x+2} = \arctan(x+2) - \arctan x$

$$F'(x) = \frac{1}{1+(x+2)^2} - \frac{1}{1+x^2} = \frac{(1+x^2) - (x^2+4x+5)}{(x^2+1)(x^2+4x+5)} = \frac{-4(x+1)}{(x^2+1)(x^2+4x+5)} = 0 \text{ when } x = -1.$$

**82.** $\int \frac{1}{\sqrt{6x - x^2}}\,dx$

(a) $6x - x^2 = 9 - (x^2 - 6x + 9) = 9 - (x-3)^2$

$$\int \frac{1}{\sqrt{6x-x^2}}\,dx = \int \frac{dx}{\sqrt{9-(x-3)^2}} = \arcsin\left(\frac{x-3}{3}\right) + C$$

(b) $u = \sqrt{x}, u^2 = x, 2u\,du = dx$

$$\int \frac{1}{\sqrt{6u^2 - u^4}}(2u\,du) = \int \frac{2}{\sqrt{6-u^2}}\,du = 2\arcsin\left(\frac{u}{\sqrt{6}}\right) + C = 2\arcsin\left(\frac{\sqrt{x}}{\sqrt{6}}\right) + C$$

(c)

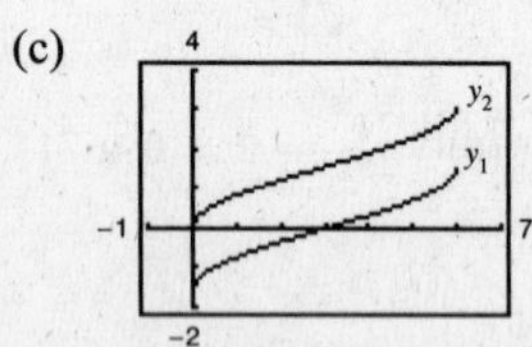


The antiderivatives differ by a constant, $\pi/2$.

Domain: $[0, 6]$

**83.** False, $\int \frac{dx}{3x\sqrt{9x^2-16}} = \frac{1}{12}\operatorname{arcsec}\frac{|3x|}{4} + C$

**84.** False, $\int \frac{dx}{25+x^2}\,dx = \frac{1}{5}\arctan\frac{x}{5} + C$

**85.** True

$$\frac{d}{dx}\left[-\arccos\frac{x}{2} + C\right] = \frac{1/2}{\sqrt{1-(x/2)^2}} = \frac{1}{\sqrt{4-x^2}}$$

**86.** False. Use substitution: $u = 9 - e^{2x}, du = -2e^{2x}dx$

**87.** $\frac{d}{dx}\left[\arcsin\left(\frac{u}{a}\right) + C\right] = \frac{1}{\sqrt{1-(u^2/a^2)}}\left(\frac{u'}{a}\right) = \frac{u'}{\sqrt{a^2-u^2}}$

So, $\int \frac{du}{\sqrt{a^2-u^2}} = \arcsin\left(\frac{u}{a}\right) + C.$

**88.** $\frac{d}{dx}\left[\frac{1}{a}\arctan\frac{u}{a} + C\right] = \frac{1}{a}\left[\frac{u'/a}{1 + (u/a)^2}\right]$

$$= \frac{1}{a^2}\left[\frac{u'}{(a^2 + u^2)/a^2}\right] = \frac{u'}{a^2 + u^2}$$

So, $\int \frac{du}{a^2 + u^2} = \int \frac{u'}{a^2 + u^2}\,dx = \frac{1}{a}\arctan\frac{u}{a} + C.$

**89.** Assume $u > 0$.

$$\frac{d}{dx}\left[\frac{1}{a}\operatorname{arcsec}\frac{u}{a} + C\right] = \frac{1}{a}\left[\frac{u'/a}{(u/a)\sqrt{(u/a)^2 - 1}}\right] = \frac{1}{a}\left[\frac{u'}{u\sqrt{(u^2 - a^2)/a^2}}\right] = \frac{u'}{u\sqrt{u^2 - a^2}}.$$

The case $u < 0$ is handled in a similar manner.

So, $\int \frac{du}{u\sqrt{u^2 - a^2}} = \int \frac{u'}{u\sqrt{u^2 - a^2}}\,dx = \frac{1}{a}\operatorname{arcsec}\frac{|u|}{a} + C.$

**90.** (a) Area $= \int_0^1 \frac{1}{1 + x^2}\,dx$

(b) Trapezoidal Rule: $n = 8, b - a = 1 - 0 = 1$

Area $\approx 0.7847$

(c) Because

$$\int_0^1 \frac{1}{1 + x^2}\,dx = \left[\arctan x\right]_0^1 = \frac{\pi}{4},$$

you can use the Trapezoidal Rule to approximate $\pi/4$, and therefore, $\pi$. For example, using $n = 200$, you obtain $\pi \approx 4(0.785397) = 3.141588$.

**91.** (a) $v(t) = -32t + 500$

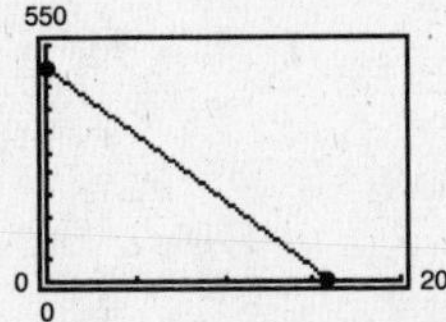


(b) $s(t) = \int v(t)\,dt = \int(-32t + 500)\,dt$

$$= -16t^2 + 500t + C$$

$s(0) = -16(0) + 500(0) + C = 0 \Rightarrow C = 0$

$s(t) = -16t^2 + 500t$

When the object reaches its maximum height, $v(t) = 0$.

$$v(t) = -32t + 500 = 0$$
$$-32t = -500$$
$$t = 15.625$$

$$s(15.625) = -16(15.625)^2 + 500(15.625)$$
$$= 3906.25 \text{ ft (Maximum height)}$$

(c) $$\int \frac{1}{32 + kv^2}\,dv = -\int dt$$

$$\frac{1}{\sqrt{32k}}\arctan\left(\sqrt{\frac{k}{32}}v\right) = -t + C_1$$

$$\arctan\left(\sqrt{\frac{k}{32}}v\right) = -\sqrt{32k}t + C$$

$$\sqrt{\frac{k}{32}}v = \tan\left(C - \sqrt{32k}t\right)$$

$$v = \sqrt{\frac{32}{k}}\tan\left(C - \sqrt{32k}t\right)$$

When $t = 0$, $v = 500$, $C = \arctan\left(500\sqrt{k/32}\right)$, and you have

$$v(t) = \sqrt{\frac{32}{k}}\tan\left[\arctan\left(500\sqrt{\frac{k}{32}}\right) - \sqrt{32k}t\right].$$

(d) When $k = 0.001$:

$$v(t) = \sqrt{32{,}000}\tan\left[\arctan\left(500\sqrt{0.00003125}\right) - \sqrt{0.032}t\right]$$

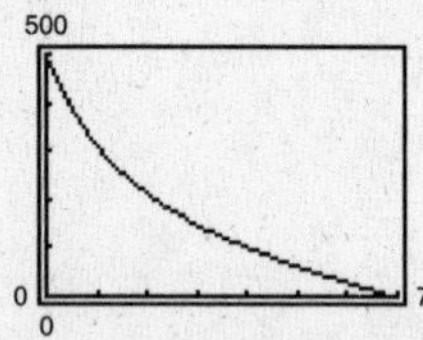


$v(t) = 0$ when $t_0 \approx 6.86$ sec.

(e) $h = \int_0^{6.86} \sqrt{32{,}000}\tan\left[\arctan\left(500\sqrt{0.00003125}\right) - \sqrt{0.032}\,t\right] dt$

Simpson's Rule: $n = 10$; $h \approx 1088$ feet

(f) Air resistance lowers the maximum height.

**92.** Let $f(x) = \arctan x - \dfrac{x}{1 + x^2}$

$$f'(x) = \frac{1}{1 + x^2} - \frac{1 - x^2}{\left(1 + x^2\right)^2} = \frac{2x^2}{\left(1 + x^2\right)} > 0 \text{ for } x > 0.$$

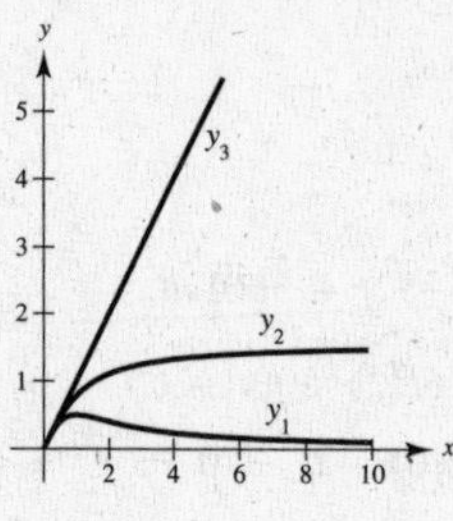


Because $f(0) = 0$ and $f$ is increasing for $x > 0$,

$\arctan x - \dfrac{x}{1 + x^2} > 0$ for $x > 0$. So, $\arctan x > \dfrac{x}{1 + x^2}$.

Let $g(x) = x - \arctan x$

$$g'(x) = 1 - \frac{1}{1 + x^2} = \frac{x^2}{1 + x^2} > 0 \text{ for } x > 0.$$

Because $g(0) = 0$ and $g$ is increasing for $x > 0$, $x - \arctan x > 0$ for $x > 0$. So, $x > \arctan x$. Therefore,

$$\frac{x}{1 + x^2} < \arctan x < x.$$

## Section 5.9 Hyperbolic Functions

**1.** (a) $\sinh 3 = \dfrac{e^3 - e^{-3}}{2} \approx 10.018$

(b) $\tanh(-2) = \dfrac{\sinh(-2)}{\cosh(-2)} = \dfrac{e^{-2} - e^2}{e^{-2} + e^2} \approx -0.964$

**2.** (a) $\cosh 0 = \dfrac{e^0 + e^0}{2} = 1$

(b) $\operatorname{sech} 1 = \dfrac{2}{e + e^{-1}} \approx 0.648$

**3.** (a) $\operatorname{csch}(\ln 2) = \dfrac{2}{e^{\ln 2} - e^{-\ln 2}} = \dfrac{2}{2 - (1/2)} = \dfrac{4}{3}$

(b) $\coth(\ln 5) = \dfrac{\cosh(\ln 5)}{\sinh(\ln 5)} = \dfrac{e^{\ln 5} + e^{-\ln 5}}{e^{\ln 5} - e^{-\ln 5}}$

$= \dfrac{5 + (1/5)}{5 - (1/5)} = \dfrac{13}{12}$

**4.** (a) $\sinh^{-1} 0 = 0$

(b) $\tanh^{-1} 0 = 0$

**5.** (a) $\cosh^{-1} 2 = \ln\left(2 + \sqrt{3}\right) \approx 1.317$

(b) $\operatorname{sech}^{-1} \dfrac{2}{3} = \ln\left(\dfrac{1 + \sqrt{1 - (4/9)}}{2/3}\right) \approx 0.962$

**6.** (a) $\operatorname{csch}^{-1} 2 = \ln\left(\dfrac{1 + \sqrt{5}}{2}\right) \approx 0.481$

(b) $\coth^{-1} 3 = \dfrac{1}{2}\ln\left(\dfrac{4}{2}\right) \approx 0.347$

**7.** $\sinh x + \cosh x = \dfrac{e^x - e^{-x}}{2} + \dfrac{e^x + e^{-x}}{2} = e^x$

**8.** $\sinh 2x + \cosh 2x = \dfrac{e^{2x} - e^{-2x}}{2} + \dfrac{e^{2x} + e^{-2x}}{2} = e^{2x}$

**9.** $\tanh^2 x + \operatorname{sech}^2 x = \left(\dfrac{e^x - e^{-x}}{e^x + e^{-x}}\right)^2 + \left(\dfrac{2}{e^x + e^{-x}}\right)^2$

$= \dfrac{e^{2x} - 2 + e^{-2x} + 4}{\left(e^x + e^{-x}\right)^2}$

$= \dfrac{e^{2x} + 2 + e^{-2x}}{e^{2x} + 2 + e^{-2x}} = 1$

**10.** $\coth^2 x - \operatorname{csch}^2 x = \dfrac{\cosh^2 x}{\sinh^2 x} - \dfrac{1}{\sinh^2 x}$

$= \dfrac{\cosh^2 x - 1}{\sinh^2 x}$

$= \dfrac{\sinh^2 x}{\sinh^2 x} = 1$

**11.** $\dfrac{1 + \cosh 2x}{2} = \dfrac{1 + \left(e^{2x} + e^{-2x}\right)/2}{2}$

$= \dfrac{e^{2x} + 2 + e^{-2x}}{4}$

$= \left(\dfrac{e^x + e^{-x}}{2}\right)^2 = \cosh^2 x$

**12.** $\sinh^2 x = \left(\dfrac{e^x - e^{-x}}{2}\right)^2 = \dfrac{e^{2x} - 2 + e^{-2x}}{4}$

$\dfrac{-1 + \cosh 2x}{2} = \dfrac{-1 + \left(\dfrac{e^{2x} + e^{-2x}}{2}\right)}{2} = \dfrac{-2 + e^{2x} + e^{-2x}}{4}$

So, $\sinh^2 x = \dfrac{-1 + \cosh 2x}{2}$.

**13.** $\sinh x \cosh y + \cosh x \sinh y = \left(\dfrac{e^x - e^{-x}}{2}\right)\left(\dfrac{e^y + e^{-y}}{2}\right) + \left(\dfrac{e^x + e^{-x}}{2}\right)\left(\dfrac{e^y - e^{-y}}{2}\right)$

$= \dfrac{1}{4}\left[e^{x+y} - e^{-x+y} + e^{x-y} - e^{-(x+y)} + e^{x+y} + e^{-x+y} - e^{x-y} - e^{-(x+y)}\right]$

$= \dfrac{1}{4}\left[2\left(e^{x+y} - e^{-(x+y)}\right)\right] = \dfrac{e^{(x+y)} - e^{-(x+y)}}{2} = \sinh(x + y)$

**14.** $2 \sinh x \cosh x = 2\left(\dfrac{e^x - e^{-x}}{2}\right)\left(\dfrac{e^x + e^{-x}}{2}\right) = \dfrac{e^{2x} - e^{-2x}}{2} = \sinh 2x$

**15.** $3\sinh x + 4\sinh^3 x = \sinh x\left(3 + 4\sinh^2 x\right) = \left(\dfrac{e^x - e^{-x}}{2}\right)\left[3 + 4\left(\dfrac{e^x - e^{-x}}{2}\right)^2\right]$

$$= \left(\frac{e^x - e^{-x}}{2}\right)\left[3 + e^{2x} - 2 + e^{-2x}\right] = \frac{1}{2}\left(e^x - e^{-x}\right)\left(e^{2x} + e^{-2x} + 1\right)$$

$$= \frac{1}{2}\left[e^{3x} + e^{-x} + e^x - e^x - e^{-3x} - e^{-x}\right] = \frac{e^{3x} - e^{-3x}}{2} = \sinh(3x)$$

**16.** $2\cosh\dfrac{x+y}{2}\cosh\dfrac{x-y}{2} = 2\left[\dfrac{e^{(x+y)/2} + e^{-(x+y)/2}}{2}\right]\left[\dfrac{e^{(x-y)/2} + e^{-(x-y)/2}}{2}\right]$

$$= 2\left[\frac{e^x + e^y + e^{-y} + e^{-x}}{4}\right] = \frac{e^x + e^{-x}}{2} + \frac{e^y + e^{-y}}{2}$$

$$= \cosh x + \cosh y$$

**17.** $\sinh x = \dfrac{3}{2}$

$\cosh^2 x - \left(\dfrac{3}{2}\right)^2 = 1 \Rightarrow \cosh^2 x = \dfrac{13}{4} \Rightarrow \cosh x = \dfrac{\sqrt{13}}{2}$

$\tanh x = \dfrac{3/2}{\sqrt{13}/2} = \dfrac{3\sqrt{13}}{13}$

$\operatorname{csch} x = \dfrac{1}{3/2} = \dfrac{2}{3}$

$\operatorname{sech} x = \dfrac{1}{\sqrt{13}/2} = \dfrac{2\sqrt{13}}{13}$

$\coth x = \dfrac{1}{3/\sqrt{13}} = \dfrac{\sqrt{13}}{3}$

**18.** $\tanh x = \dfrac{1}{2}$

$\left(\dfrac{1}{2}\right)^2 + \operatorname{sech}^2 x = 1 \Rightarrow \operatorname{sech}^2 x = \dfrac{3}{4} \Rightarrow \operatorname{sech} x = \dfrac{\sqrt{3}}{2}$

$\cosh x = \dfrac{1}{\sqrt{3}/2} = \dfrac{2\sqrt{3}}{3}$

$\coth x = \dfrac{1}{1/2} = 2$

$\sinh x = \tanh x \cosh x = \left(\dfrac{1}{2}\right)\left(\dfrac{2\sqrt{3}}{3}\right) = \dfrac{\sqrt{3}}{3}$

$\operatorname{csch} x = \dfrac{1}{\sqrt{3}/3} = \sqrt{3}$

Putting these in order:

$\sinh x = \dfrac{\sqrt{3}}{3}$ $\qquad \operatorname{csch} x = \sqrt{3}$

$\cosh x = \dfrac{2\sqrt{3}}{3}$ $\qquad \operatorname{sech} x = \dfrac{\sqrt{3}}{2}$

$\tanh x = \dfrac{1}{2}$ $\qquad \coth x = 2$

**19.** $f(x) = \sinh(3x)$

$f'(x) = 3\cosh(3x)$

**20.** $f(x) = \cosh(x - 2)$

$f'(x) = \sinh(x - 2)$

**21.** $y = \operatorname{sech}\left(5x^2\right)$

$y' = -\operatorname{sech}\left(5x^2\right)\tanh\left(5x^2\right)(10x)$

$= -10x\operatorname{sech}\left(5x^2\right)\tanh\left(5x^2\right)$

**22.** $y = \tanh\left(3x^2 - 1\right)$

$y' = \operatorname{sech}^2\left(3x^2 - 1\right)(6x)$

$= 6x\operatorname{sech}^2\left(3x^2 - 1\right)$

**23.** $f(x) = \ln(\sinh x)$

$f'(x) = \dfrac{1}{\sinh x}(\cosh x) = \coth x$

**24.** $g(x) = \ln(\cosh x)$

$g'(x) = \dfrac{1}{\cosh x}(\sinh x) = \tanh x$

**25.** $y = \ln\left(\tanh\frac{x}{2}\right)$

$$y' = \frac{1/2}{\tanh(x/2)}\operatorname{sech}^2\left(\frac{x}{2}\right)$$

$$= \frac{1}{2\sinh(x/2)\cosh(x/2)}$$

$$= \frac{1}{\sinh x} = \operatorname{csch} x$$

**26.** $y = x\cosh x - \sinh x$

$y' = x\sinh x + \cosh x - \cosh x$

$= x\sinh x$

**27.** $h(x) = \frac{1}{4}\sinh 2x - \frac{x}{2}$

$$h'(x) = \frac{1}{2}\cosh(2x) - \frac{1}{2} = \frac{\cosh(2x) - 1}{2} = \sinh^2 x$$

**28.** $h(t) = t - \coth t$

$h'(t) = 1 + \operatorname{csch}^2 t = \coth^2 t$

**29.** $f(t) = \arctan(\sinh t)$

$$f'(t) = \frac{1}{1 + \sinh^2 t}(\cosh t) = \frac{\cosh t}{\cosh^2 t} = \operatorname{sech} t$$

**30.** $g(x) = \operatorname{sech}^2 3x$

$g'(x) = -2\operatorname{sech}(3x)\operatorname{sech}(3x)\tanh(3x)(3)$

$= -6\operatorname{sech}^2 3x \tanh 3x$

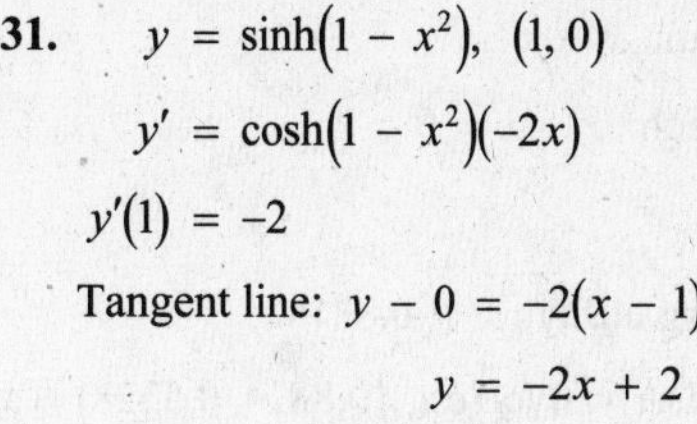

**31.** $y = \sinh(1 - x^2),\ (1, 0)$

$y' = \cosh(1 - x^2)(-2x)$

$y'(1) = -2$

Tangent line: $y - 0 = -2(x - 1)$

$y = -2x + 2$

**32.** $y = x^{\cosh x},\ (1, 1)$

$\ln y = \cosh x \ln x$

$$\frac{y'}{y} = \frac{\cosh x}{x} + \sinh x \ln x$$

At $(1, 1)$, $y' = \cosh(1)$.

Tangent line: $y - 1 = \cosh(1)(x - 1)$

$y = \cosh(1)x - \cosh(1) + 1$

**Note:** $\cosh(1) \approx 1.5431$

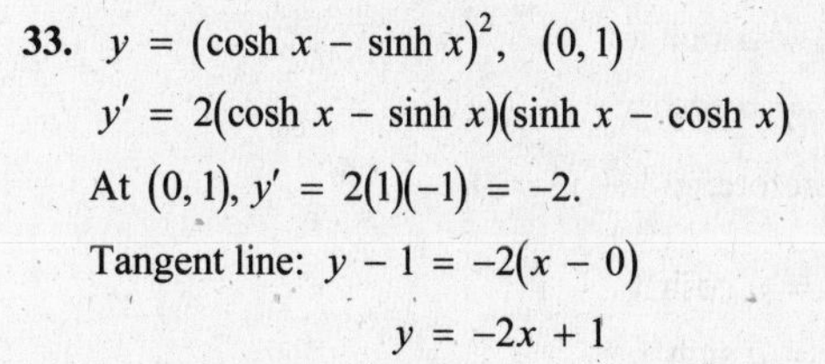

**33.** $y = (\cosh x - \sinh x)^2,\ (0, 1)$

$y' = 2(\cosh x - \sinh x)(\sinh x - \cosh x)$

At $(0, 1)$, $y' = 2(1)(-1) = -2$.

Tangent line: $y - 1 = -2(x - 0)$

$y = -2x + 1$

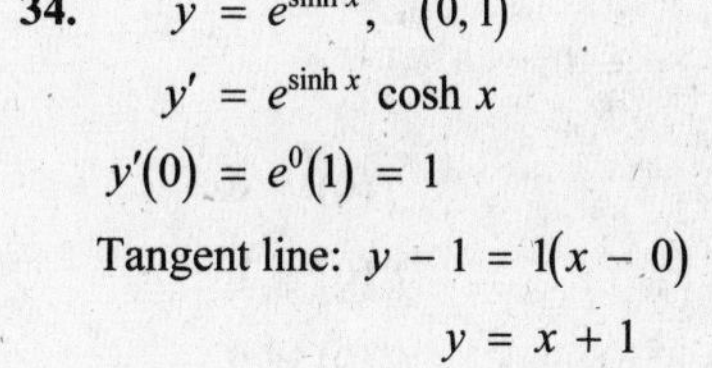

**34.** $y = e^{\sinh x},\ (0, 1)$

$y' = e^{\sinh x}\cosh x$

$y'(0) = e^0(1) = 1$

Tangent line: $y - 1 = 1(x - 0)$

$y = x + 1$

**35.** $f(x) = \sin x \sinh x - \cos x \cosh x, \quad -4 \le x \le 4$

$f'(x) = \sin x \cosh x + \cos x \sinh x - \cos x \sinh x + \sin x \cosh x$

$= 2\sin x \cosh x = 0$ when $x = 0, \pm\pi$.

Relative maxima: $(\pm\pi, \cosh\pi)$

Relative minimum: $(0, -1)$

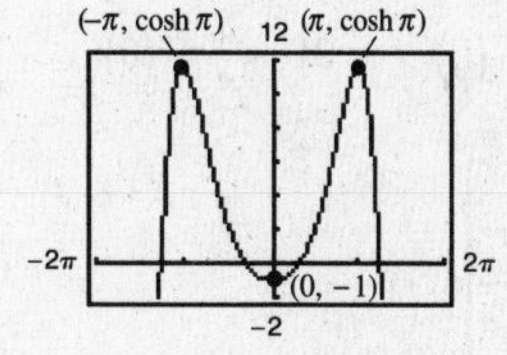


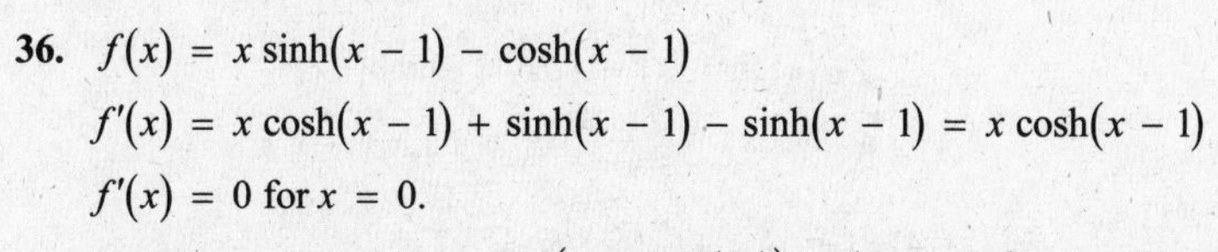

**36.** $f(x) = x\sinh(x - 1) - \cosh(x - 1)$

$f'(x) = x\cosh(x - 1) + \sinh(x - 1) - \sinh(x - 1) = x\cosh(x - 1)$

$f'(x) = 0$ for $x = 0$.

By the First Derivative Test, $(0, -\cosh(-1)) \approx (0, -1.543)$ is a relative minimum.

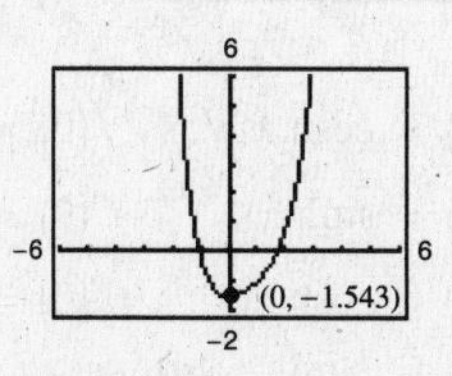

**37.** $g(x) = x\operatorname{sech} x$

$g'(x) = \operatorname{sech} x - x\operatorname{sech} x \tanh x = \operatorname{sech} x(1 - x\tanh x) = 0$

$x\tanh x = 1$

Using a graphing utility, $x \approx \pm 1.1997$.

By the First Derivative Test, $(1.1997, 0.6627)$ is a relative maximum and $(-1.1997, -0.6627)$ is a relative minimum.

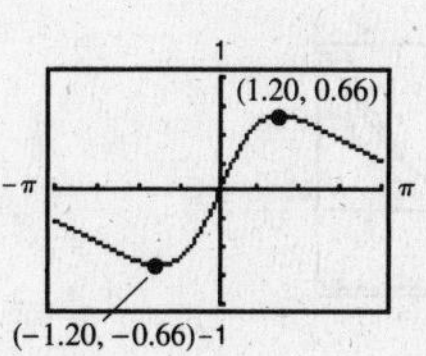

**38.** $h(x) = 2\tanh x - x$

$h'(x) = 2\,\text{sech}^2 x - 1 = 0$

$\text{sech}^2 x = \frac{1}{2}$

Using a graphing utility, $x \approx 0.8814$.

From the First Derivative Test, $(0.8814, 0.5328)$ is a relative maximum and $(-0.8814, -0.5328)$ is a relative minimum.

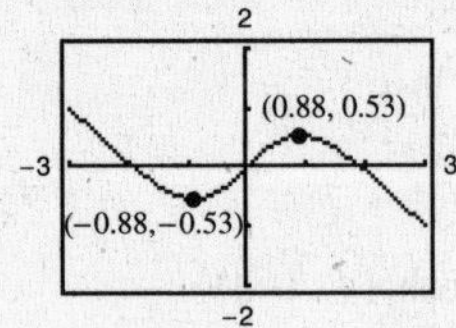


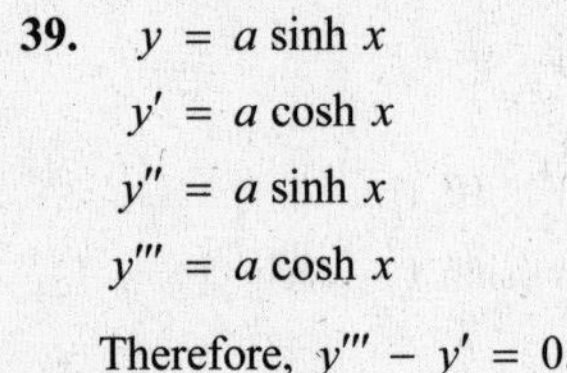

**39.** $y = a\sinh x$

$y' = a\cosh x$

$y'' = a\sinh x$

$y''' = a\cosh x$

Therefore, $y''' - y' = 0$.

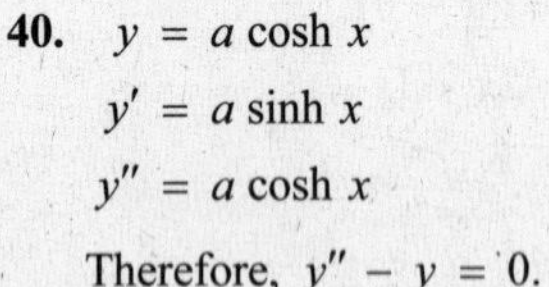

**40.** $y = a\cosh x$

$y' = a\sinh x$

$y'' = a\cosh x$

Therefore, $y'' - y = 0$.

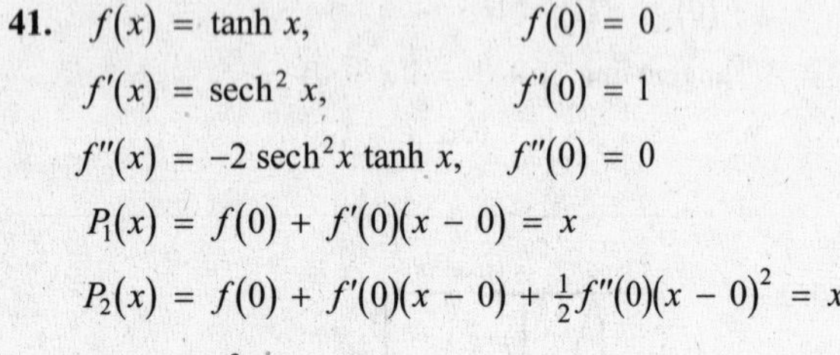

**41.** $f(x) = \tanh x, \qquad f(0) = 0$

$f'(x) = \text{sech}^2 x, \qquad f'(0) = 1$

$f''(x) = -2\,\text{sech}^2 x \tanh x, \qquad f''(0) = 0$

$P_1(x) = f(0) + f'(0)(x - 0) = x$

$P_2(x) = f(0) + f'(0)(x - 0) + \frac{1}{2}f''(0)(x - 0)^2 = x$

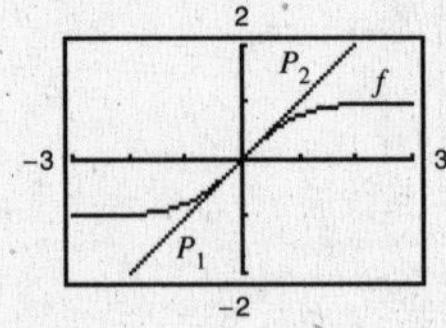


**42.** $f(x) = \cosh x \qquad f(0) = \cosh(0) \approx 1$

$f'(x) = \sinh x \qquad f'(0) = \sinh(0) \approx 0$

$f''(x) = \cosh x \qquad f''(0) = \cosh(0) \approx 1$

$P_1(x) = f(0) + f'(0)(x - 0) = 1$

$P_2(x) = 1 + \frac{1}{2}x^2$

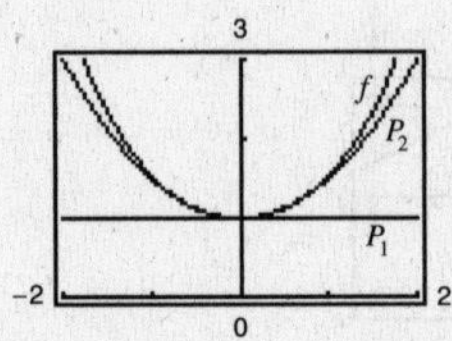


**43.** (a) $y = 10 + 15\cosh\dfrac{x}{15}, \quad -15 \le x \le 15$

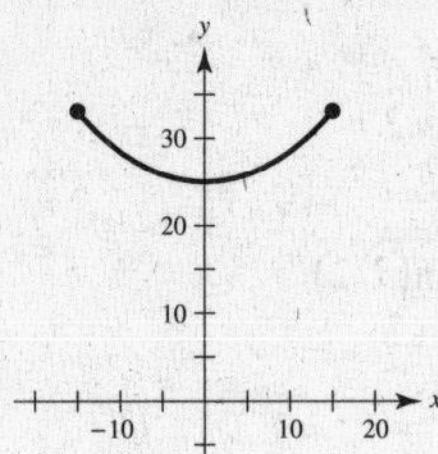


(b) At $x = \pm 15$, $y = 10 + 15\cosh(1) \approx 33.146$.

At $x = 0$, $y = 10 + 15\cosh(0) = 25$.

(c) $y' = \sinh\dfrac{x}{15}$. At $x = 15$, $y' = \sinh(1) \approx 1.175$.

**44.** (a) $y = 18 + 25\cosh\dfrac{x}{25}, \qquad -25 \le x \le 25$

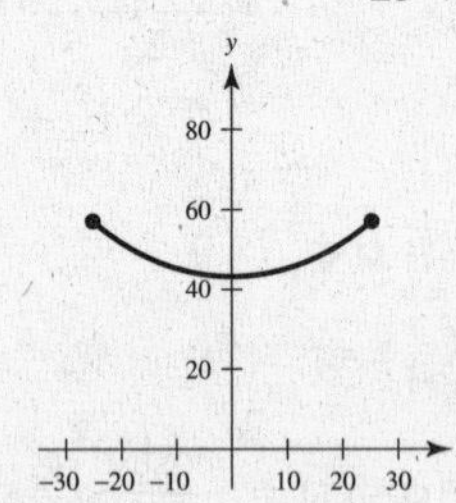


(b) At $x = \pm 25$, $y = 18 + 25\cosh(1) \approx 56.577$.

At $x = 0$, $y = 18 + 25 = 43$.

(c) $y' = \sinh\dfrac{x}{25}$. At $x = 25$, $y' = \sinh(1) \approx 1.175$.

**45.** $\displaystyle\int \cosh 2x\,dx = \frac{1}{2}\int \cosh(2x)(2)\,dx$

$= \frac{1}{2}\sinh 2x + C$

**46.** $\displaystyle\int \text{sech}^2(-x)\,dx = \int \text{sech}^2 x\,dx = \tanh x + C$

(**Note:** $f(x) = \text{sech}(x)$ is an even function.)

**Alternate Solution:**

$-\displaystyle\int \text{sech}^2(-x)(-1)\,dx = -\tanh(-x) + C$

$= \tanh x + C$

**47.** Let $u = 1 - 2x$, $du = -2\,dx$.

$\displaystyle\int \sinh(1 - 2x)\,dx = -\frac{1}{2}\int \sinh(1 - 2x)(-2)\,dx$

$= -\frac{1}{2}\cosh(1 - 2x) + C$

**48.** Let $u = \sqrt{x}$, $du = \dfrac{1}{2\sqrt{x}}\,dx$.

$$\int \frac{\cosh\sqrt{x}}{\sqrt{x}}\,dx = 2\int \cosh\sqrt{x}\left(\frac{1}{2\sqrt{x}}\right)dx$$
$$= 2\sinh\sqrt{x} + C$$

**49.** Let $u = \cosh(x-1)$, $du = \sinh(x-1)\,dx$.

$$\int \cosh^2(x-1)\sinh(x-1)\,dx = \tfrac{1}{3}\cosh^3(x-1) + C$$

**50.** Let $u = \cosh x$, $du = \sinh x\,dx$.

$$\int \frac{\sinh}{1+\sinh^2 x}\,dx = \int \frac{\sinh x}{\cosh^2 x}\,dx = \frac{-1}{\cosh x} + C$$
$$= -\text{sech}\,x + C$$

**51.** Let $u = \sinh x$, $du = \cosh x\,dx$.

$$\int \frac{\cosh x}{\sinh x}\,dx = \ln|\sinh x| + C$$

**52.** Let $u = 2x - 1$, $du = 2\,dx$.

$$\int \text{sech}^2(2x-1)\,dx = \tfrac{1}{2}\int \text{sech}^2(2x-1)(2)\,dx$$
$$= \tfrac{1}{2}\tanh(2x-1) + C$$

**53.** Let $u = \dfrac{x^2}{2}$, $du = x\,dx$.

$$\int x\,\text{csch}^2\frac{x^2}{2}\,dx = \int\left(\text{csch}^2\frac{x^2}{2}\right)x\,dx = -\coth\frac{x^2}{2} + C$$

**54.** Let $u = \text{sech}\,x$, $du = -\text{sech}\,x\tanh x\,dx$.

$$\int \text{sech}^3 x\tanh x\,dx = -\int \text{sech}^2 x(-\text{sech}\,x\tanh x)\,dx$$
$$= -\tfrac{1}{3}\text{sech}^3 x + C$$

**55.** Let $u = \dfrac{1}{x}$, $du = -\dfrac{1}{x^2}\,dx$.

$$\int \frac{\text{csch}(1/x)\coth(1/x)}{x^2}\,dx = -\int \text{csch}\frac{1}{x}\coth\frac{1}{x}\left(-\frac{1}{x^2}\right)dx$$
$$= \text{csch}\frac{1}{x} + C$$

**56.** Let $u = \sinh x$, $du = \cosh x\,dx$.

$$\int \frac{\cosh x}{\sqrt{9-\sinh^2 x}}\,dx = \arcsin\left(\frac{\sinh x}{3}\right) + C$$
$$= \arcsin\left(\frac{e^x - e^{-x}}{6}\right) + C$$

**57.** Let $u = x^2$, $du = 2x\,dx$.

$$\int \frac{x}{x^4+1}\,dx = \frac{1}{2}\int \frac{2x}{(x^2)^2+1}\,dx = \frac{1}{2}\arctan(x^2) + C$$

**58.** $$\int \frac{2}{x\sqrt{1+4x^2}}\,dx = 2\int \frac{1}{(2x)\sqrt{1+(2x)^2}}(2)\,dx$$
$$= 2\ln\left(\frac{-1+\sqrt{1+4x^2}}{|2x|}\right) + C$$

**59.** $$\int_0^{\ln 2}\tanh x\,dx = \int_0^{\ln 2}\frac{\sinh x}{\cosh x}\,dx,\ (u = \cosh x)$$
$$= \Big[\ln(\cosh x)\Big]_0^{\ln 2}$$
$$= \ln(\cosh(\ln 2)) - \ln(\cosh(0))$$
$$= \ln\left(\frac{5}{4}\right) - 0 = \ln\left(\frac{5}{4}\right)$$

**Note:** $\cosh(\ln 2) = \dfrac{e^{\ln 2} + e^{-\ln 2}}{2} = \dfrac{2 + (1/2)}{2} = \dfrac{5}{4}$

**60.** $$\int_0^1 \cosh^2 x\,dx = \int_0^1 \frac{1+\cosh(2x)}{2}\,dx$$
$$= \frac{1}{2}\left[x + \frac{1}{2}\sinh(2x)\right]_0^1$$
$$= \frac{1}{2}\left[1 + \frac{1}{2}\sinh(2)\right]$$
$$= \frac{1}{2} + \frac{1}{2}\sinh(1)\cosh(1)$$

**61.** $$\int_0^4 \frac{1}{25-x^2}\,dx = \frac{1}{10}\int_0^4 \frac{1}{5-x}\,dx + \frac{1}{10}\int_0^4 \frac{1}{5+x}\,dx$$
$$= \left[\frac{1}{10}\ln\left|\frac{5+x}{5-x}\right|\right]_0^4 = \frac{1}{10}\ln 9 = \frac{1}{5}\ln 3$$

**62.** $$\int_0^4 \frac{1}{\sqrt{25-x^2}}\,dx = \left[\arcsin\frac{x}{5}\right]_0^4 = \arcsin\frac{4}{5}$$

**63.** Let $u = 2x$, $du = 2\,dx$.

$$\int_0^{\sqrt{2}/4}\frac{2}{\sqrt{1-4x^2}}\,dx = \int_0^{\sqrt{2}/4}\frac{1}{\sqrt{1-(2x)^2}}(2)\,dx$$
$$= \Big[\arcsin(2x)\Big]_0^{\sqrt{2}/4} = \frac{\pi}{4}$$

**64.** $2e^{-x}\cosh x = 2e^{-x}\left[\dfrac{e^x + e^{-x}}{2}\right] = 1 + e^{-2x}$

$$\int_0^{\ln 2} 2e^{-x}\cosh x\,dx = \int_0^{\ln 2}\left(1 + e^{-2x}\right)dx$$
$$= \left[x - \frac{1}{2}e^{-2x}\right]_0^{\ln 2}$$
$$= \left[\ln 2 - \frac{1}{2}\left(\frac{1}{4}\right)\right] - \left[0 - \frac{1}{2}\right]$$
$$= \frac{3}{8} + \ln 2$$

**65.** $y = \cosh^{-1}(3x)$

$$y' = \frac{3}{\sqrt{9x^2 - 1}}$$

**66.** $y = \tanh^{-1}\dfrac{x}{2}$

$$y' = \frac{1}{1 - (x/2)^2}\left(\frac{1}{2}\right) = \frac{2}{4 - x^2}$$

**67.** $y = \tanh^{-1}\sqrt{x}$

$$y' = \frac{1}{1 - \left(\sqrt{x}\right)^2}\left(\frac{1}{2}x^{-1/2}\right)$$
$$= \frac{1}{2\sqrt{x}(1 - x)}$$

**68.** $f(x) = \coth^{-1}(x^2)$

$$f'(x) = \frac{1}{1 - \left(x^2\right)^2}(2x) = \frac{2x}{1 - x^4}$$

**69.** $y = \sinh^{-1}(\tan x)$

$$y' = \frac{1}{\sqrt{\tan^2 x + 1}}\left(\sec^2 x\right) = |\sec x|$$

**70.** $y = \tanh^{-1}(\sin 2x)$

$$y' = \frac{1}{1 - \sin^2 2x}(2\cos 2x) = 2\sec 2x$$

**71.** $y = \left(\operatorname{csch}^{-1} x\right)^2$

$$y' = 2\operatorname{csch}^{-1}x\left(\frac{-1}{|x|\sqrt{1 + x^2}}\right) = \frac{-2\operatorname{csch}^{-1} x}{|x|\sqrt{1 + x^2}}$$

**72.** $y = \operatorname{sech}^{-1}(\cos 2x), \quad 0 < x < \dfrac{\pi}{4}$

$$y' = \frac{-1}{\cos 2x\sqrt{1 - \cos^2 2x}}(-2\sin 2x)$$
$$= \frac{2\sin 2x}{\cos 2x|\sin 2x|} = \frac{2}{\cos 2x} = 2\sec 2x,$$

because $\sin 2x \ge 0$ for $0 < x < \pi/4$.

**73.** $y = 2x\sinh^{-1}(2x) - \sqrt{1 + 4x^2}$

$$y' = 2x\left(\frac{2}{\sqrt{1 + 4x^2}}\right) + 2\sinh^{-1}(2x) - \frac{4x}{\sqrt{1 + 4x^2}}$$
$$= 2\sinh^{-1}(2x)$$

**74.** $y = x\tanh^{-1}x + \ln\sqrt{1 - x^2}$

$$= x\tanh^{-1}x + \frac{1}{2}\ln\left(1 - x^2\right)$$
$$y' = x\left(\frac{1}{1 - x^2}\right) + \tanh^{-1}x + \frac{-x}{1 - x^2} = \tanh^{-1}x$$

**75.** Answers will vary.

**76.** See the definitions and graphs in the textbook.

**77.** The derivatives of $f(x) = \cosh x$ and $f(x) = \operatorname{sech} x$ differ by a minus sign.

**78.** $f(x) = \cosh x$ and $f(x) = \operatorname{sech} x$ take on only positive values. $f(x) = \sinh x$ and $f(x) = \tanh x$ are increasing functions.

**79.** $\lim_{x\to\infty} \sinh x = \infty$

**80.** $\lim_{x\to-\infty} \sinh x = \lim_{x\to-\infty} \dfrac{e^x - e^{-x}}{2} = -\infty$

**81.** $\lim_{x\to\infty} \tanh x = 1$

**82.** $\lim_{x\to-\infty} \tanh x = \lim_{x\to-\infty} \dfrac{e^x - e^{-x}}{e^x + e^{-x}} = -1$

**83.** $\lim_{x\to\infty} \operatorname{sech} x = 0$

**84.** $\lim_{x\to-\infty} \operatorname{csch} x = 0$

**85.** $\lim_{x\to 0} \dfrac{\sinh x}{x} = \lim_{x\to 0} \dfrac{e^x - e^{-x}}{2x} = 1$

**86.** $\lim_{x\to 0} \coth x$ does not exist.

$\left(\coth x \to \infty \text{ for } x \to 0^+, \coth x \to -\infty \text{ for } x \to 0^-\right)$

**87.** $$\int \frac{1}{3-9x^2}\,dx = \frac{1}{3}\int \frac{1}{3-(3x)^2}(3)\,dx = \frac{1}{3}\left(\frac{1}{2\sqrt{3}}\right)\ln\left|\frac{\sqrt{3}+3x}{\sqrt{3}-3x}\right| + C = \frac{\sqrt{3}}{18}\ln\left|\frac{1+\sqrt{3}x}{1-\sqrt{3}x}\right| + C$$

**88.** $$\int \frac{1}{2x\sqrt{1-4x^2}}\,dx = \frac{1}{2}\int \frac{1}{2x\sqrt{1-(2x)^2}}(2)\,dx = -\frac{1}{2}\ln\left[\frac{1+\sqrt{1-4x^2}}{|2x|}\right] + C$$

**89.** $$\int \frac{1}{\sqrt{1+e^{2x}}}\,dx = \int \frac{e^x}{e^x\sqrt{1+(e^x)^2}}\,dx = -\operatorname{csch}^{-1}(e^x) + C = -\ln\left(\frac{1+\sqrt{1+e^{2x}}}{e^x}\right) + C = \ln\left(\frac{e^x}{1+\sqrt{1+e^{2x}}}\right) + C = \ln\left(\frac{-e^x+e^x\sqrt{1+e^{2x}}}{e^{2x}}\right) + C = \ln\left(\sqrt{1+e^{2x}}-1\right) - x + C$$

**90.** $$\int \frac{x}{9-x^4}\,dx = -\frac{1}{2}\int \frac{-2x}{9-(x^2)^2}\,dx = -\frac{1}{2}\left(\frac{1}{6}\right)\ln\left|\frac{3-x^2}{3+x^2}\right| + C = -\frac{1}{12}\ln\left|\frac{3-x^2}{3+x^2}\right| + C$$

**91.** Let $u = \sqrt{x}$, $du = \dfrac{1}{2\sqrt{x}}\,dx$.

$$\int \frac{1}{\sqrt{x}\sqrt{1+x}}\,dx = 2\int \frac{1}{\sqrt{1+(\sqrt{x})^2}}\left(\frac{1}{2\sqrt{x}}\right)dx = 2\sinh^{-1}\sqrt{x} + C = 2\ln\left(\sqrt{x}+\sqrt{1+x}\right) + C$$

**92.** Let $u = x^{3/2}$, $du = \dfrac{3}{2}\sqrt{x}\,dx$.

$$\int \frac{\sqrt{x}}{\sqrt{1+x^3}}\,dx = \frac{2}{3}\int \frac{1}{\sqrt{1+(x^{3/2})^2}}\left(\frac{3}{2}\sqrt{x}\right)dx = \frac{2}{3}\sinh^{-1}\left(x^{3/2}\right) + C = \frac{2}{3}\ln\left(x^{3/2}+\sqrt{1+x^3}\right) + C$$

**93.** $$\int \frac{-1}{4x-x^2}\,dx = \int \frac{1}{(x-2)^2-4}\,dx = \frac{1}{4}\ln\left|\frac{(x-2)-2}{(x-2)+2}\right| = \frac{1}{4}\ln\left|\frac{x-4}{x}\right| + C$$

**94.** $$\int \frac{dx}{(x+2)\sqrt{x^2+4x+8}} = \int \frac{dx}{(x+2)\sqrt{(x+2)^2+4}} = -\frac{1}{2}\ln\left(\frac{2+\sqrt{(x+2)^2+4}}{|x+2|}\right) + C$$

**95.** $$\int \frac{1}{1-4x-2x^2}\,dx = \int \frac{1}{3-2(x+1)^2}\,dx = \frac{1}{\sqrt{2}}\int \frac{\sqrt{2}}{(\sqrt{3})^2-\left[\sqrt{2}(x+1)\right]^2}\,dx = \frac{1}{\sqrt{2}}\cdot\frac{1}{2\sqrt{3}}\ln\left|\frac{\sqrt{3}+\sqrt{2}(x+1)}{\sqrt{3}-\sqrt{2}(x+1)}\right| + C = \frac{1}{2\sqrt{6}}\ln\left|\frac{\sqrt{2}(x+1)+\sqrt{3}}{\sqrt{2}(x+1)-\sqrt{3}}\right| + C$$

**96.** $$\int \frac{1}{(x+1)\sqrt{2x^2+4x+8}}\,dx = \int \frac{1}{(x+1)\sqrt{2(x+1)^2+6}}\,dx$$

$$= \frac{1}{\sqrt{2}}\int \frac{1}{(x+1)\sqrt{(x+1)^2+(\sqrt{3})^2}}\,dx = -\frac{1}{\sqrt{6}}\ln\left(\frac{\sqrt{3}+\sqrt{(x+1)^2+3}}{x+1}\right) + C$$

**97.** $$\int_3^7 \frac{1}{\sqrt{x^2-4}}\,dx = \left[\ln\left(x+\sqrt{x^2-4}\right)\right]_3^7 = \ln\left(7+\sqrt{45}\right) - \ln\left(3+\sqrt{5}\right) = \ln\left(\frac{7+\sqrt{45}}{3+\sqrt{5}}\right) = \ln\left(\frac{\sqrt{5}+3}{2}\right)$$

**98.** $$\int_1^3 \frac{1}{x\sqrt{4+x^2}}\,dx = \left[-\frac{1}{2}\ln\left(\frac{2+\sqrt{4+x^2}}{|x|}\right)\right]_1^3$$

$$= -\frac{1}{2}\ln\left(\frac{2+\sqrt{13}}{3}\right) + \frac{1}{2}\ln\left(2+\sqrt{5}\right)$$

**99.** $$\int_{-1}^1 \frac{1}{16-9x^2}\,dx = \frac{1}{3}\int_{-1}^1 \frac{1}{4^2-(3x)^2}(3)\,dx$$

$$= \left[\frac{1}{3}\cdot\frac{1}{4}\cdot\frac{1}{2}\ln\left|\frac{4+3x}{4-3x}\right|\right]_{-1}^1$$

$$= \frac{1}{24}\left[\ln(7) - \ln\left(\frac{1}{7}\right)\right]$$

$$= \frac{1}{24}[\ln 7 - \ln 1 + \ln 7] = \frac{1}{12}\ln 7$$

**100.** $$\int_0^1 \frac{1}{\sqrt{25x^2+1}}\,dx = \frac{1}{5}\int_0^1 \frac{1}{\sqrt{(5x)^2+1}}(5)\,dx$$

$$= \left[\frac{1}{5}\ln\left(5x+\sqrt{25x^2+1}\right)\right]_0^1$$

$$= \frac{1}{5}\ln\left(5+\sqrt{26}\right)$$

**101.** Let $u = 4x - 1$, $du = 4\,dx$.

$$y = \int \frac{1}{\sqrt{80+8x-16x^2}}\,dx$$

$$= \frac{1}{4}\int \frac{4}{\sqrt{81-(4x-1)^2}}\,dx$$

$$= \frac{1}{4}\arcsin\left(\frac{4x-1}{9}\right) + C$$

**102.** Let $u = 2(x-1)$, $du = 2\,dx$.

$$y = \int \frac{1}{(x-1)\sqrt{-4x^2+8x-1}}\,dx$$

$$= \int \frac{2}{2(x-1)\sqrt{(\sqrt{3})^2-[2(x-1)]^2}}\,dx$$

$$= -\frac{1}{\sqrt{3}}\ln\left|\frac{\sqrt{3}+\sqrt{-4x^2+8x-1}}{2(x-1)}\right| + C$$

**103.** $$y = \int \frac{x^3-21x}{5+4x-x^2}\,dx = \int\left(-x-4+\frac{20}{5+4x-x^2}\right)dx$$

$$= \int(-x-4)\,dx + 20\int\frac{1}{3^2-(x-2)^2}\,dx$$

$$= -\frac{x^2}{2} - 4x + \frac{20}{6}\ln\left|\frac{3+(x-2)}{3-(x-2)}\right| + C$$

$$= -\frac{x^2}{2} - 4x + \frac{10}{3}\ln\left|\frac{1+x}{5-x}\right| + C$$

$$= -\frac{x^2}{2} - 4x - \frac{10}{3}\ln\left|\frac{5-x}{x+1}\right| + C$$

**104.** $$y = \int\frac{1-2x}{4x-x^2}\,dx = \int\frac{4-2x}{4x-x^2}\,dx + 3\int\frac{1}{(x-2)^2-4}\,dx$$

$$= \ln\left|4x-x^2\right| + \frac{3}{4}\ln\left|\frac{(x-2)-2}{(x-2)+2}\right| + C$$

$$= \ln\left|4x-x^2\right| + \frac{3}{4}\ln\left|\frac{x-4}{x}\right| + C$$

**105.** 
$$\begin{aligned} A &= 2\int_0^4 \operatorname{sech}\frac{x}{2}\,dx \\ &= 2\int_0^4 \frac{2}{e^{x/2}+e^{-x/2}}\,dx \\ &= 4\int_0^4 \frac{e^{x/2}}{\left(e^{x/2}\right)^2+1}\,dx \\ &= \left[8\arctan\left(e^{x/2}\right)\right]_0^4 \\ &= 8\arctan\left(e^2\right) - 2\pi \approx 5.207 \end{aligned}$$

**106.** 
$$\begin{aligned} A &= \int_0^2 \tanh 2x\,dx = \int_0^2 \frac{e^{2x}-e^{-2x}}{e^{2x}+e^{-2x}}\,dx \\ &= \frac{1}{2}\int_0^2 \frac{1}{e^{2x}+e^{-2x}}(2)\left(e^{2x}-e^{-2x}\right)dx \\ &= \left[\frac{1}{2}\ln\left(e^{2x}+e^{-2x}\right)\right]_0^2 = \frac{1}{2}\ln\left(e^4+e^{-4}\right) - \frac{1}{2}\ln 2 \\ &= \ln\sqrt{\frac{e^4+e^{-4}}{2}} \approx 1.654 \end{aligned}$$

**107.** 
$$\begin{aligned} A &= \int_0^2 \frac{5x}{\sqrt{x^4+1}}\,dx \\ &= \frac{5}{2}\int_0^2 \frac{2x}{\sqrt{\left(x^2\right)^2+1}}\,dx \\ &= \left[\frac{5}{2}\ln\left(x^2+\sqrt{x^4+1}\right)\right]_0^2 \\ &= \frac{5}{2}\ln\left(4+\sqrt{17}\right) \approx 5.237 \end{aligned}$$

**108.** 
$$\begin{aligned} A &= \int_3^5 \frac{6}{\sqrt{x^2-4}}\,dx \\ &= \left[6\ln\left(x+\sqrt{x^2-4}\right)\right]_3^5 \\ &= 6\ln\left(5+\sqrt{21}\right) - 6\ln\left(3+\sqrt{5}\right) \\ &= 6\ln\left(\frac{5+\sqrt{21}}{3+\sqrt{5}}\right) \approx 3.626 \end{aligned}$$

**109.** (a) 
$$\begin{aligned} \int_0^{\sqrt{3}} \frac{dx}{\sqrt{x^2+1}} &= \ln\left(x+\sqrt{x^2+1}\right)\Big]_0^{\sqrt{3}} \\ &= \ln\left(\sqrt{3}+2\right) \approx 1.317 \end{aligned}$$

(b) 
$$\begin{aligned} \int_0^{\sqrt{3}} \frac{dx}{\sqrt{x^2+1}} &= \left[\sinh^{-1}x\right]_0^{\sqrt{3}} \\ &= \sinh^{-1}\left(\sqrt{3}\right) \approx 1.317 \end{aligned}$$

**110.** (a) 
$$\begin{aligned} \int_{-1/2}^{1/2} \frac{dx}{1-x^2} &= \int_{-1/2}^{1/2}\left[\frac{1/2}{1+x} + \frac{1/2}{1-x}\right]dx \\ &= \left[\frac{1}{2}\ln|1+x| - \frac{1}{2}\ln|1-x|\right]_{-1/2}^{1/2} \\ &= \frac{1}{2}\left[\ln\frac{3}{2} - \ln\frac{1}{2} - \ln\frac{1}{2} + \ln\frac{3}{2}\right] \\ &= \ln\frac{3}{2} - \ln\frac{1}{2} = \ln 3 \end{aligned}$$

(b) 
$$\begin{aligned} \int_{-1/2}^{1/2} \frac{dx}{1-x^2} &= \left[\tanh^{-1}x\right]_{-1/2}^{1/2} \\ &= \frac{\ln 3}{2} - \left(-\frac{\ln 3}{2}\right) = \ln 3 \end{aligned}$$

**111.** 
$$\int \frac{3k}{16}\,dt = \int \frac{1}{x^2-12x+32}\,dx$$

$$\frac{3kt}{16} = \int \frac{1}{(x-6)^2-4}\,dx = \frac{1}{2(2)}\ln\left|\frac{(x-6)-2}{(x-6)+2}\right| + C = \frac{1}{4}\ln\left|\frac{x-8}{x-4}\right| + C$$

When $x = 0$:

$$t = 0$$

$$C = -\frac{1}{4}\ln(2)$$

When $x = 1$:

$$t = 10$$

$$\frac{30k}{16} = \frac{1}{4}\ln\left|\frac{-7}{-3}\right| - \frac{1}{4}\ln(2) = \frac{1}{4}\ln\left(\frac{7}{6}\right)$$

$$k = \frac{2}{15}\ln\left(\frac{7}{6}\right)$$

When $t = 20$:

$$\begin{aligned} \left(\frac{3}{16}\right)\left(\frac{2}{15}\right)\ln\left(\frac{7}{6}\right)(20) &= \frac{1}{4}\ln\frac{x-8}{2x-8} \\ \ln\left(\frac{7}{6}\right)^2 &= \ln\frac{x-8}{2x-8} \\ \frac{49}{36} &= \frac{x-8}{2x-8} \\ 62x &= 104 \\ x &= \frac{104}{62} = \frac{52}{31} \approx 1.677\text{ kg} \end{aligned}$$

**112.** (a) $v(t) = -32t$

(b) $s(t) = \int v(t)\,dt = \int(-32t)\,dt = -16t^2 + C$

$s(0) = -16(0)^2 + C = 400 \Rightarrow C = 400$

$s(t) = -16t^2 + 400$

(c) $\dfrac{dv}{dt} = -32 + kv^2$

$\displaystyle\int \frac{dv}{kv^2 - 32} = \int dt$

$\displaystyle\int \frac{dv}{32 - kv^2} = -\int dt$

Let $u = \sqrt{k}\,v$, then $du = \sqrt{k}\,dv$.

$$\frac{1}{\sqrt{k}} \cdot \frac{1}{2\sqrt{32}} \ln\left|\frac{\sqrt{32} + \sqrt{k}\,v}{\sqrt{32} - \sqrt{k}\,v}\right| = -t + C$$

Because $v(0) = 0$, $C = 0$.

$$\ln\left|\frac{\sqrt{32} + \sqrt{k}\,v}{\sqrt{32} - \sqrt{k}\,v}\right| = -2\sqrt{32k}\,t$$

$$\frac{\sqrt{32} + \sqrt{k}\,v}{\sqrt{32} - \sqrt{k}\,v} = e^{-2\sqrt{32k}\,t}$$

$$\sqrt{32} + \sqrt{k}\,v = e^{-2\sqrt{32k}\,t}\left(\sqrt{32} - \sqrt{k}\,v\right)$$

$$v\left(\sqrt{k} + \sqrt{k}\,e^{-2\sqrt{32k}\,t}\right) = \sqrt{32}\left(e^{-2\sqrt{32k}\,t} - 1\right)$$

$$v = \frac{\sqrt{32}\left(e^{-2\sqrt{32k}\,t} - 1\right)}{\sqrt{k}\left(e^{-2\sqrt{32k}\,t} + 1\right)} \cdot \frac{e^{\sqrt{32k}\,t}}{e^{\sqrt{32k}\,t}} = \frac{\sqrt{32}}{\sqrt{k}}\left[\frac{-\left(e^{\sqrt{32k}\,t} - e^{-\sqrt{32k}\,t}\right)}{e^{\sqrt{32k}\,t} + e^{-\sqrt{32k}\,t}}\right] = -\frac{\sqrt{32}}{\sqrt{k}}\tanh\left(\sqrt{32k}\,t\right)$$

(d) $\displaystyle\lim_{t\to\infty}\left[-\frac{\sqrt{32}}{\sqrt{k}}\tanh\left(\sqrt{32k}\,t\right)\right] = -\frac{\sqrt{32}}{\sqrt{k}}$

The velocity is bounded by $-\sqrt{32}/\sqrt{k}$.

(e) Because $\int \tanh(ct)\,dt = (1/c)\ln\cosh(ct)$ (which can be verified by differentiation), then

$$s(t) = \int -\frac{\sqrt{32}}{\sqrt{k}}\tanh\left(\sqrt{32k}\,t\right)dt = -\frac{\sqrt{32}}{\sqrt{k}}\frac{1}{\sqrt{32k}}\ln\left[\cosh\left(\sqrt{32k}\,t\right)\right] + C = -\frac{1}{k}\ln\left[\cosh\left(\sqrt{32k}\,t\right)\right] + C.$$

When $t = 0$,

$s(0) = C = 400 \Rightarrow 400 - (1/k)\ln\left[\cosh\left(\sqrt{32k}\,t\right)\right]$.

When $k = 0.01$:

$s_2(t) = 400 - 100\ln\left(\cosh\sqrt{0.32}\,t\right)$

$s_1(t) = -16t^2 + 400$

$s_1(t) = 0$ when $t = 5$ seconds

$s_2(t) = 0$ when $t \approx 8.3$ seconds

When air resistance is not neglected, it takes approximately 3.3 more seconds to reach the ground.

(f) As $k$ increases, the time required for the object to reach the ground increases.

**113.** $y = a \operatorname{sech}^{-1} \dfrac{x}{a} - \sqrt{a^2 - x^2}, \quad a > 0$

$$\frac{dy}{dx} = \frac{-1}{(x/a)\sqrt{1 - (x^2/a^2)}} + \frac{x}{\sqrt{a^2 - x^2}} = \frac{-a^2}{x\sqrt{a^2 - x^2}} + \frac{x}{\sqrt{a^2 - x^2}} = \frac{x^2 - a^2}{x\sqrt{a^2 - x^2}} = \frac{-\sqrt{a^2 - x^2}}{x}$$

**114.** Equation of tangent line through $P = (x_0, y_0)$: $y - a \operatorname{sech}^{-1} \dfrac{x_0}{a} + \sqrt{a^2 - x_0^2} = -\dfrac{\sqrt{a^2 - x_0^2}}{x_0}(x - x_0)$

When $x = 0$, $y = a \operatorname{sech}^{-1} \dfrac{x_0}{a} - \sqrt{a^2 - x_0^2} + \sqrt{a^2 - x_0^2} = a \operatorname{sech}^{-1} \dfrac{x_0}{a}$.

So, $Q$ is the point $\left[0, a \operatorname{sech}^{-1}(x_0/a)\right]$.

Distance from $P$ to $Q$: $d = \sqrt{x_0^2 + \left(-\sqrt{a^2 - x_0^2}\right)^2} = a$

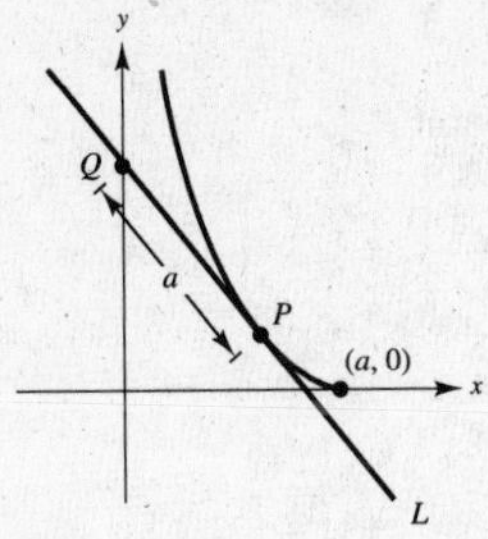


**115.** Let $\quad u = \tanh^{-1} x, \; -1 < x < 1$

$$\tanh u = x.$$

$$\frac{\sinh u}{\cosh u} = \frac{e^u - e^{-u}}{e^u + e^{-u}} = x$$

$$e^u - e^{-u} = xe^u + xe^{-u}$$

$$e^{2u} - 1 = xe^{2u} + x$$

$$e^{2u}(1 - x) = 1 + x$$

$$e^{2u} = \frac{1 + x}{1 - x}$$

$$2u = \ln\left(\frac{1 + x}{1 - x}\right)$$

$$u = \frac{1}{2}\ln\left(\frac{1 + x}{1 - x}\right), \; -1 < x < 1$$

**116.** Let $u = \sinh^{-1} t$. Then

$$\sinh u = \frac{e^u - e^{-u}}{2} = t$$

$$e^u - e^{-u} = 2t$$

$$e^{2u} - 2te^u - 1 = 0$$

$$e^u = \frac{2t \pm \sqrt{4t^2 + 4}}{2}$$

$$= t \pm \sqrt{t^2 + 1}$$

$$= t + \sqrt{t^2 + 1} \; (\text{because } e^u > 0)$$

$$u = \ln\left(t + \sqrt{t^2 + 1}\right)$$

**117.** Let $y = \arcsin(\tanh x)$. Then,

$\sin y = \tanh x = \dfrac{e^x - e^{-x}}{e^x + e^{-x}}$ and

$\tan y = \dfrac{e^x - e^{-x}}{2} = \sinh x.$

So, $y = \arctan(\sinh x)$. Therefore,

$\arctan(\sinh x) = \arcsin(\tanh x)$.

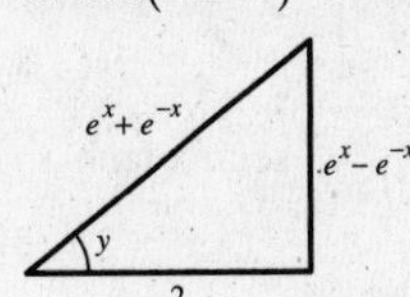

**118.** $\int_{-b}^{b} e^{xt}\,dt = \left[\frac{e^{xt}}{x}\right]_{-b}^{b}$

$$= \frac{e^{xb}}{x} - \frac{e^{-xb}}{x}$$

$$= \frac{2}{x}\left[\frac{e^{xb} - e^{-xb}}{2}\right]$$

$$= \frac{2}{x}\sinh(xb)$$

**119.** $y = \text{sech}^{-1}\, x$

$$\text{sech}\, y = x$$

$$-(\text{sech}\, y)(\tanh y)y' = 1$$

$$y' = \frac{-1}{(\text{sech}\, y)(\tanh y)}$$

$$= \frac{-1}{(\text{sech}\, y)\sqrt{1 - \text{sech}^2 y}}$$

$$= \frac{-1}{x\sqrt{1 - x^2}}$$

**120.** $y = \cosh^{-1} x$

$$\cosh y = x$$

$$(\sinh y)(y') = 1$$

$$y' = \frac{1}{\sinh y} = \frac{1}{\sqrt{\cosh^2 y - 1}} = \frac{1}{\sqrt{x^2 - 1}}$$

**121.** $y = \sinh^{-1} x$

$$\sinh y = x$$

$$(\cosh y)y' = 1$$

$$y' = \frac{1}{\cosh y} = \frac{1}{\sqrt{\sinh^2 y + 1}} = \frac{1}{\sqrt{x^2 + 1}}$$

**122.** $y = \cosh x = \frac{e^x + e^{-x}}{2}$

$$y' = \frac{e^x - e^{-x}}{2} = \sinh x$$

**123.** $y = \coth x = \frac{\cosh x}{\sinh x}$

$$y' = \frac{\sinh^2 x - \cosh^2 x}{\sinh^2 x} = \frac{-1}{\sinh^2 x} = -\text{csch}^2\, x$$

**124.** $y = \text{sech}\, x = \frac{2}{e^x + e^{-x}}$

$$y' = -2\left(e^x + e^{-x}\right)^{-2}\left(e^x - e^{-x}\right)$$

$$= \left(\frac{-2}{e^x + e^{-x}}\right)\left(\frac{e^x - e^{-x}}{e^x + e^{-x}}\right) = -\text{sech}\, x \tanh x$$

**125.** $y = c\cosh\frac{x}{c}$

Let $P(x_1, y_1)$ be a point on the catenary.

$$y' = \sinh\frac{x}{c}$$

The slope at $P$ is $\sinh(x_1/c)$. The equation of line $L$ is

$$y - c = \frac{-1}{\sinh(x_1/c)}(x - 0).$$

When $y = 0$, $c = \frac{x}{\sinh(x_1/c)} \Rightarrow x = c\sinh\left(\frac{x_1}{c}\right)$. The length of $L$ is

$$\sqrt{c^2\sinh^2\left(\frac{x_1}{c}\right) + c^2} = c \cdot \cosh\frac{x_1}{c} = y_1,$$

the ordinate $y_1$ of the point $P$.

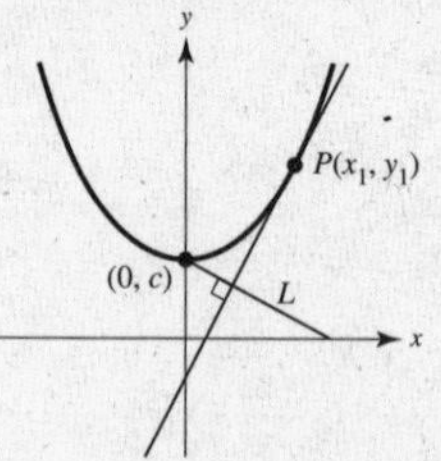


**126.** There is no such common normal. To see this, assume there is a common normal.

$y = \cosh x \Rightarrow y' = \sinh x$

Normal line at $(a, \cosh a)$ is

$$y - \cosh a = \frac{-1}{\sinh a}(x - a).$$

Similarly,

$$y - \sinh c = \frac{-1}{\cosh c}(x - c)$$

is normal at $(c, \sinh c)$. Also,

$$\frac{-1}{\sinh a} = \frac{-1}{\cosh c} \Rightarrow \cosh c = \sinh a.$$

The slope between the points is $\frac{\sinh c - \cosh a}{c - a}$.

Therefore, $-\frac{a - c}{\cosh a - \sinh c} = \cosh c = \sinh a.$

$\cosh c > 0 \Rightarrow a > 0$

$\sinh x < \cosh x$ for all

$x \Rightarrow \sinh c < \cosh c = \sinh a < \cosh a$. So, $c < a$. But,

$$-\frac{a - c}{\cosh a - \sinh c} < 0, \text{ a contradiction.}$$

# Review Exercises for Chapter 5

1.

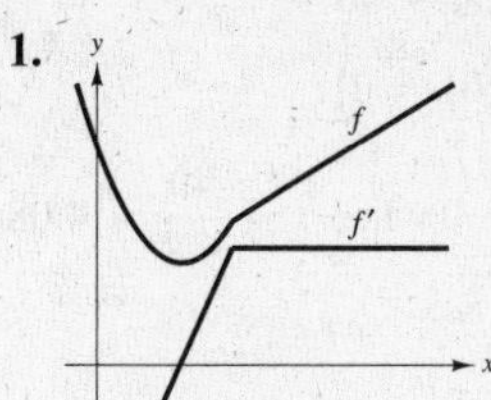


2.

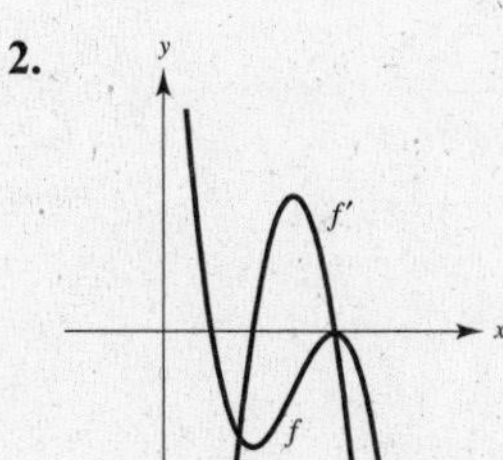


3. $\int(4x^2 + x + 3)\,dx = \frac{4}{3}x^3 + \frac{1}{2}x^2 + 3x + C$

4. $\int \frac{2}{\sqrt[3]{3x}}\,dx = \frac{2}{\sqrt[3]{3}}\int x^{-1/3}\,dx = \frac{2}{\sqrt[3]{3}}\frac{x^{2/3}}{(2/3)} + C$

$= \frac{3}{\sqrt[3]{3}}x^{2/3} + C$

$= (3x)^{2/3} + C$

5. $\int \frac{x^4 + 8}{x^3}\,dx = \int(x + 8x^{-3})\,dx = \frac{1}{2}x^2 - \frac{4}{x^2} + C$

6. $\int \frac{x^4 - 4x^2 + 1}{x^2}\,dx = \int(x^2 - 4 + x^{-2})\,dx$

$= \frac{1}{3}x^3 - 4x - \frac{1}{x} + C$

7. $\int(2x - 9\sin x)\,dx = x^2 + 9\cos x + C$

8. $\int(5\cos x - 2\sec^2 x)\,dx = 5\sin x - 2\tan x + C$

9. $\int(5 - e^x)\,dx = 5x - e^x + C$

10. $\int(t + e^t)\,dt = \frac{t^2}{2} + e^t + C$

11. $\int \frac{5}{x}\,dx = 5\ln|x| + C$

12. $\int \frac{10}{x}\,dx = 10\ln|x| + C$

13. $f'(x) = -6x,\ (-1, 1)$

$f(x) = \int -6x\,dx = -3x^2 + C$

When $x = 1$:

$f(1) = -3(1)^2 + C = -2$

$C = 1$

$f(x) = 1 - 3x^2$

14. $f''(x) = 2e^x,\ (0, 1)$

$f'(x) = \int 2e^x\,dx = 2e^x + C_1$

Because the slope of the tangent line at $(0, 1)$ is 3,

$f'(0) = 2 + C_1 = 3 \Rightarrow C_1 = 1$

$f'(x) = 2e^x + 1$

$f(x) = \int(2e^x + 1)\,dx = 2e^x + x + C_2$

$f(0) = 1 = 2 + C_2 \Rightarrow C_2 = -1$

$f(x) = 2e^x + x - 1$

15. $a(t) = a$

$v(t) = \int a\,dt = at + C_1$

$v(0) = 0 + C_1 = 0$ when $C_1 = 0$.

$v(t) = at$

$s(t) = \int at\,dt = \frac{a}{2}t^2 + C_2$

$s(0) = 0 + C_2 = 0$ when $C_2 = 0$.

$s(t) = \frac{a}{2}t^2$

$s(30) = \frac{a}{2}(30)^2 = 3600$ or

$a = \frac{2(3600)}{(30)^2} = 8\text{ ft/sec}^2.$

$v(30) = 8(30) = 240\text{ ft/sec}$

**16.** 45 mi/h = 66 ft/sec

30 mi/h = 44 ft/sec

$a(t) = -a$

$v(t) = -at + 66$ because $v(0) = 66$ ft/sec.

$s(t) = -\frac{a}{2}t^2 + 66t$ because $s(0) = 0$.

Solving the system

$v(t) = -at + 66 = 44$

$s(t) = -\frac{a}{2}t^2 + 66t = 264$

you obtain $t = 24/5$ and $a = 55/12$. Now solve $-(55/12)t + 66 = 0$ and get $t = 72/5$. So,

$$s\left(\frac{72}{5}\right) = -\frac{55/12}{2}\left(\frac{72}{5}\right)^2 + 66\left(\frac{72}{5}\right) \approx 475.2 \text{ ft.}$$

Stopping distance from 30 mi/h to rest is

$475.2 - 264 = 211.2$ ft.

**17.** $a(t) = -32$

$v(t) = -32t + 96$

$s(t) = -16t^2 + 96t$

(a) $v(t) = -32t + 96 = 0$ when $t = 3$ sec.

(b) $s(3) = -144 + 288 = 144$ ft

(c) $v(t) = -32t + 96 = \frac{96}{2}$ when $t = \frac{3}{2}$ sec.

(d) $s\left(\frac{3}{2}\right) = -16\left(\frac{9}{4}\right) + 96\left(\frac{3}{2}\right) = 108$ ft

**18.** $a(t) = -9.8 \text{ m/sec}^2$

$v(t) = -9.8t + v_0 = -9.8t + 40$

$s(t) = -4.9t^2 + 40t, \ (s(0) = 0)$

(a) $v(t) = -9.8t + 40 = 0$ when $t = \frac{40}{9.8} \approx 4.08$ sec.

(b) $s(4.08) \approx 81.63$ m

(c) $v(t) = -9.8t + 40 = 20$ when

$t = \frac{20}{9.8} \approx 2.04$ sec.

(d) $s(2.04) \approx 61.2$ m

**19.** (a) $\sum_{i=1}^{10}(2i - 1)$

(b) $\sum_{i=1}^{n} i^3$

(c) $\sum_{i=1}^{10}(4i + 2)$

**20.** $x_1 = 2, x_2 = -1, x_3 = 5, x_4 = 3, x_5 = 7$

(a) $\frac{1}{5}\sum_{i=1}^{5} x_i = \frac{1}{5}(2 - 1 + 5 + 3 + 7) = \frac{16}{5}$

(b) $\sum_{i=1}^{5}\frac{1}{x_i} = \frac{1}{2} - 1 + \frac{1}{5} + \frac{1}{3} + \frac{1}{7} = \frac{37}{210}$

(c) $\sum_{i=1}^{5}(2x_i - x_i^2) = \left[2(2) - (2)^2\right] + \left[2(-1) - (-1)^2\right] + \left[2(5) - (5)^2\right] + \left[2(3) - (3)^2\right] + \left[2(7) - (7)^2\right] = -56$

(d) $\sum_{i=2}^{5}(x_i - x_{i-1}) = (-1 - 2) + \left[5 - (-1)\right] + (3 - 5) + (7 - 3) = 5$

**21.** $y = \frac{10}{x^2 + 1}, \ \Delta x = \frac{1}{2}, \ n = 4$

$$S(n) = S(4) = \frac{1}{2}\left[\frac{10}{1} + \frac{10}{(1/2)^2 + 1} + \frac{10}{(1)^2 + 1} + \frac{10}{(3/2)^2 + 1}\right] \approx 13.0385$$

$$s(n) = s(4) = \frac{1}{2}\left[\frac{10}{(1/2)^2 + 1} + \frac{10}{1 + 1} + \frac{10}{(3/2)^2 + 1} + \frac{10}{2^2 + 1}\right] \approx 9.0385$$

$9.0385 <$ Area of Region $< 13.0385$

**22.** $y = 2^x,\ \Delta x = 1,\ n = 3$

$S(3) = 1\left[2^1 + 2^2 + 2^3\right] = 14$

$s(3) = 1\left[2^0 + 2^1 + 2^2\right] = 7$

$7 < \text{Area of region} < 14$

**23.** $y = 8 - 2x,\ \Delta x = \dfrac{3}{n}$, right endpoints

$$\begin{aligned}\text{Area} &= \lim_{n\to\infty}\sum_{i=1}^{n} f(ci)\Delta x\\ &= \lim_{n\to\infty}\sum_{i=1}^{n}\left(8 - 2\left(\frac{3i}{n}\right)\right)\frac{3}{n}\\ &= \lim_{n\to\infty}\frac{3}{n}\sum_{i=1}^{n}\left(8 - \frac{6i}{n}\right)\\ &= \lim_{n\to\infty}\frac{3}{n}\left[8n - \frac{6}{n}\frac{n(n+1)}{2}\right]\\ &= \lim_{n\to\infty}\left[24 - 9\frac{n+1}{n}\right] = 24 - 9 = 15\end{aligned}$$

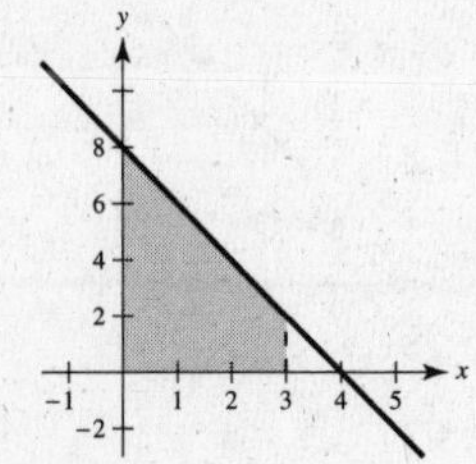

**24.** $y = x^2 + 3,\ \Delta x = \dfrac{2}{n}$, right endpoints

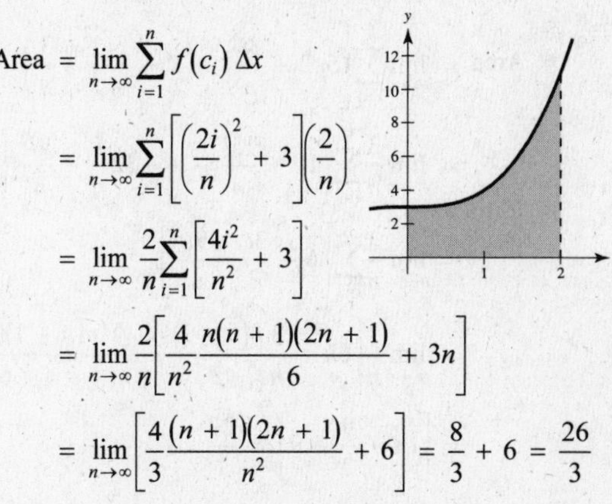

$$\begin{aligned}\text{Area} &= \lim_{n\to\infty}\sum_{i=1}^{n} f(c_i)\,\Delta x\\ &= \lim_{n\to\infty}\sum_{i=1}^{n}\left[\left(\frac{2i}{n}\right)^2 + 3\right]\left(\frac{2}{n}\right)\\ &= \lim_{n\to\infty}\frac{2}{n}\sum_{i=1}^{n}\left[\frac{4i^2}{n^2} + 3\right]\\ &= \lim_{n\to\infty}\frac{2}{n}\left[\frac{4}{n^2}\frac{n(n+1)(2n+1)}{6} + 3n\right]\\ &= \lim_{n\to\infty}\left[\frac{4}{3}\frac{(n+1)(2n+1)}{n^2} + 6\right] = \frac{8}{3} + 6 = \frac{26}{3}\end{aligned}$$

**25.** $y = 5 - x^2,\ \Delta x = \dfrac{3}{n}$

$$\begin{aligned}\text{Area} &= \lim_{n\to\infty}\sum_{i=1}^{n} f(c_i)\Delta x\\ &= \lim_{n\to\infty}\sum_{i=1}^{n}\left[5 - \left(-2 + \frac{3i}{n}\right)^2\right]\left(\frac{3}{n}\right)\\ &= \lim_{n\to\infty}\frac{3}{n}\sum_{i=1}^{n}\left[1 + \frac{12i}{n} - \frac{9i^2}{n^2}\right]\\ &= \lim_{n\to\infty}\frac{3}{n}\left[n + \frac{12}{n}\frac{n(n+1)}{2} - \frac{9}{n^2}\frac{n(n+1)(2n+1)}{6}\right]\\ &= \lim_{n\to\infty}\left[3 + 18\frac{n+1}{n} - \frac{9}{2}\frac{(n+1)(2n+1)}{n^2}\right]\\ &= 3 + 18 - 9 = 12\end{aligned}$$

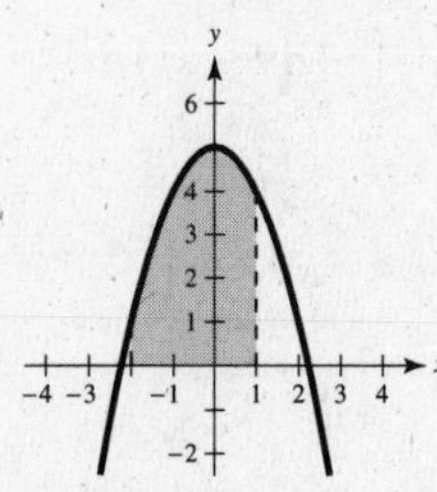

**26.** $y = \dfrac{1}{4}x^3,\ \Delta x = \dfrac{2}{n}$

$$\begin{aligned}\text{Area} &= \lim_{n\to\infty}\sum_{i=1}^{n} f(c_i)\Delta x\\ &= \lim_{n\to\infty}\sum_{i=1}^{n}\frac{1}{4}\left(2 + \frac{2i}{n}\right)^3\left(\frac{2}{n}\right)\\ &= \lim_{n\to\infty}\frac{1}{2n}\sum_{i=1}^{n}\left[8 + \frac{24i}{n} + \frac{24i^2}{n^2} + \frac{8i^3}{n^3}\right]\\ &= \lim_{n\to\infty}\frac{4}{n}\sum_{i=1}^{n}\left[1 + \frac{3i}{n} + \frac{3i^2}{n^2} + \frac{i^3}{n^3}\right]\\ &= \lim_{n\to\infty}\frac{4}{n}\left[n + \frac{3}{n}\frac{n(n+1)}{2} + \frac{3}{n^2}\frac{n(n+1)(2n+1)}{6} + \frac{1}{n^3}\frac{n^2(n+1)^2}{4}\right] = 4 + 6 + 4 + 1 = 15\end{aligned}$$

**27.** $x = 5y - y^2,\ 2 \le y \le 5,\ \Delta y = \dfrac{3}{n}$

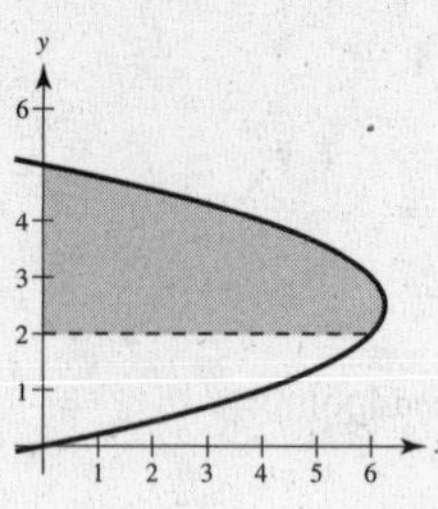


$$\begin{aligned}\text{Area} &= \lim_{n\to\infty}\sum_{i=1}^{n}\left[5\left(2 + \frac{3i}{n}\right) - \left(2 + \frac{3i}{n}\right)^2\right]\left(\frac{3}{n}\right)\\ &= \lim_{n\to\infty}\frac{3}{n}\sum_{i=1}^{n}\left[10 + \frac{15i}{n} - 4 - 12\frac{i}{n} - \frac{9i^2}{n^2}\right]\\ &= \lim_{n\to\infty}\frac{3}{n}\sum_{i=1}^{n}\left[6 + \frac{3i}{n} - \frac{9i^2}{n^2}\right]\\ &= \lim_{n\to\infty}\frac{3}{n}\left[6n + \frac{3}{n}\frac{n(n+1)}{2} - \frac{9}{n^2}\frac{n(n+1)(2n+1)}{6}\right]\\ &= \left[18 + \frac{9}{2} - 9\right] = \frac{27}{2}\end{aligned}$$

**28.** (a) $S = m\left(\dfrac{b}{4}\right)\left(\dfrac{b}{4}\right) + m\left(\dfrac{2b}{4}\right)\left(\dfrac{b}{4}\right) + m\left(\dfrac{3b}{4}\right)\left(\dfrac{b}{4}\right) + m\left(\dfrac{4b}{4}\right)\left(\dfrac{b}{4}\right) = \dfrac{mb^2}{16}(1 + 2 + 3 + 4) = \dfrac{5mb^2}{8}$

$s = m(0)\left(\dfrac{b}{4}\right) + m\left(\dfrac{b}{4}\right)\left(\dfrac{b}{4}\right) + m\left(\dfrac{2b}{4}\right)\left(\dfrac{b}{4}\right) + m\left(\dfrac{3b}{4}\right)\left(\dfrac{b}{4}\right) = \dfrac{mb^2}{16}(1 + 2 + 3) = \dfrac{3mb^2}{8}$

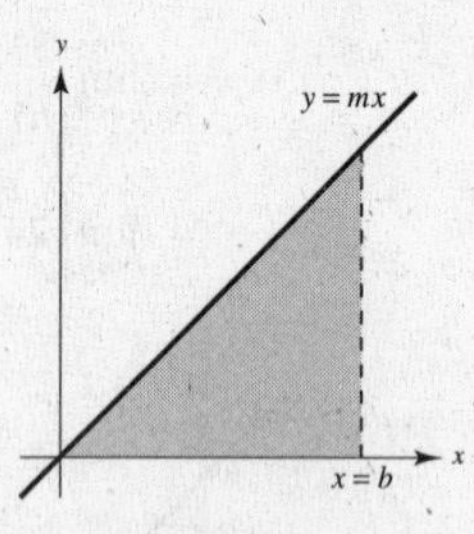


(b) $S(n) = \displaystyle\sum_{i=1}^{n} f\left(\frac{bi}{n}\right)\left(\frac{b}{n}\right) = \sum_{i=1}^{n}\left(\frac{mbi}{n}\right)\left(\frac{b}{n}\right) = m\left(\frac{b}{n}\right)^2\sum_{i=1}^{n} i = \frac{mb^2}{n^2}\left(\frac{n(n+1)}{2}\right) = \frac{mb^2(n+1)}{2n}$

$s(n) = \displaystyle\sum_{i=0}^{n-1} f\left(\frac{bi}{n}\right)\left(\frac{b}{n}\right) = \sum_{i=0}^{n-1} m\left(\frac{bi}{n}\right)\left(\frac{b}{n}\right) = m\left(\frac{b}{n}\right)^2\sum_{i=0}^{n-1} i = \frac{mb^2}{n^2}\left(\frac{(n-1)n}{2}\right) = \frac{mb^2(n-1)}{2n}$

(c) $\text{Area} = \displaystyle\lim_{n\to\infty}\frac{mb^2(n+1)}{2n} = \lim_{n\to\infty}\frac{mb^2(n-1)}{2n} = \frac{1}{2}mb^2 = \frac{1}{2}(b)(mb) = \frac{1}{2}(\text{base})(\text{height})$

**29.** $\displaystyle\lim_{\|\Delta\|\to 0}\sum_{i=1}^{n}(2c_i - 3)\Delta x_i = \int_4^6 (2x - 3)\,dx$

**30.** $\displaystyle\lim_{\|\Delta\|\to 0}\sum_{i=1}^{n} 3c_i\left(9 - c_i^2\right)\Delta x_i = \int_1^3 3x\left(9 - x^2\right)dx$

**31.**

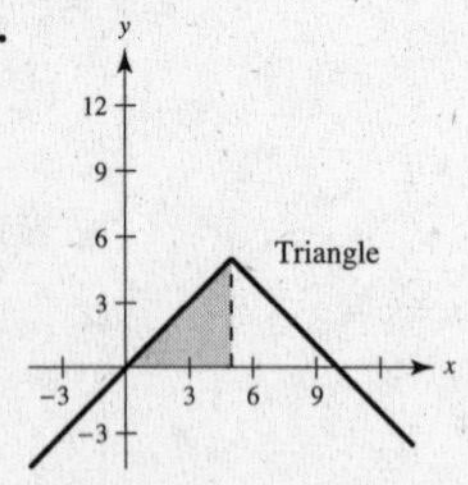


$\displaystyle\int_0^5 (5 - |x - 5|)\,dx = \tfrac{1}{2}(5)(5) = \tfrac{25}{2}$

(triangle)

**32.**

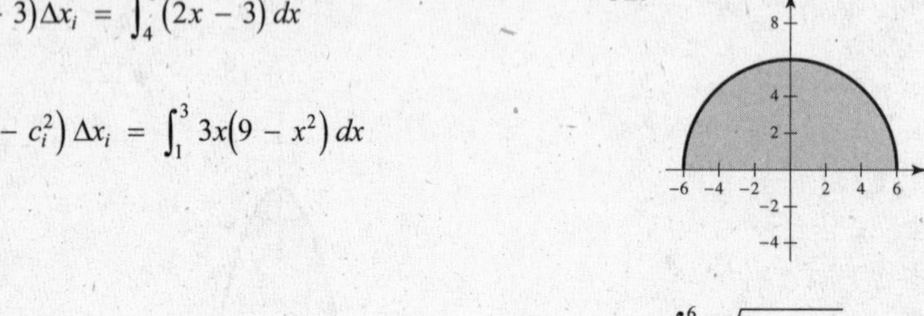


$\displaystyle\int_{-6}^{6}\sqrt{36 - x^2}\,dx = \tfrac{1}{2}\pi(6)^2 = 18\pi$

(semicircle)

**33.** (a) $\displaystyle\int_4^8 [f(x) + g(x)]\,dx = \int_4^8 f(x)\,dx + \int_4^8 g(x)\,dx = 12 + 5 = 17$

(b) $\displaystyle\int_4^8 [f(x) - g(x)]\,dx = \int_4^8 f(x)\,dx - \int_4^8 g(x)\,dx = 12 - 5 = 7$

(c) $\displaystyle\int_4^8 [2f(x) - 3g(x)]\,dx = 2\int_4^8 f(x)\,dx - 3\int_4^8 g(x)\,dx = 2(12) - 3(5) = 9$

(d) $\displaystyle\int_4^8 7\,f(x)\,dx = 7\int_4^8 f(x)\,dx = 7(12) = 84$

**34.** (a) $\int_0^6 f(x)\,dx = \int_0^3 f(x)\,dx + \int_3^6 f(x)\,dx = 4 + (-1) = 3$

(b) $\int_6^3 f(x)\,dx = -\int_3^6 f(x)\,dx = -(-1) = 1$

(c) $\int_4^4 f(x)\,dx = 0$

(d) $\int_3^6 -10\,f(x)\,dx = -10\int_3^6 f(x)\,dx = -10(-1) = 10$

**35.** $\int_1^8 \left(\sqrt[3]{x} + 1\right) dx = \left[\dfrac{3}{4}x^{4/3} + x\right]_1^8 = \left[\dfrac{3}{4}(16) + 8\right] - \left[\dfrac{3}{4} + 1\right] = \dfrac{73}{4}$, (c)

**36.** $\int_1^3 \dfrac{12}{x^3}\,dx = \left[\dfrac{12x^{-2}}{-2}\right]_1^3 = \left[\dfrac{-6}{x^2}\right]_1^3 = \dfrac{-6}{9} + 6 = \dfrac{16}{3}$, (d)

**37.** $\int_0^8 (3 + x)\,dx = \left[3x + \dfrac{x^2}{2}\right]_0^8 = 24 + \dfrac{64}{2} = 56$

**38.** $\int_{-3}^3 \left(t^2 + 1\right) dt = \left[\dfrac{t^3}{3} + t\right]_{-3}^3 = (9 + 3) - (-9 - 3) = 24$

**39.** $\int_{-1}^1 \left(4t^3 - 2t\right) dt = \left[t^4 - t^2\right]_{-1}^1 = 0$

**40.** $\int_{-2}^{-1} \left(x^4 + 3x^2 - 4\right) dx = \left[\dfrac{x^5}{5} + x^3 - 4x\right]_{-2}^{-1} = \left(-\dfrac{1}{5} - 1 + 4\right) - \left(-\dfrac{32}{5} - 8 + 8\right) = \dfrac{46}{5}$

**41.** $\int_4^9 x\sqrt{x}\,dx = \int_4^9 x^{3/2}\,dx = \left[\dfrac{2}{5}x^{5/2}\right]_4^9 = \dfrac{2}{5}\left[\left(\sqrt{9}\right)^5 - \left(\sqrt{4}\right)^5\right] = \dfrac{2}{5}(243 - 32) = \dfrac{422}{5}$

**42.** $\int_1^2 \left(\dfrac{1}{x^2} - \dfrac{1}{x^3}\right) dx = \int_1^2 \left(x^{-2} - x^{-3}\right) dx = \left[-\dfrac{1}{x} + \dfrac{1}{2x^2}\right]_1^2 = \left(-\dfrac{1}{2} + \dfrac{1}{8}\right) - \left(-1 + \dfrac{1}{2}\right) = \dfrac{1}{8}$

**43.** $\int_0^{3\pi/4} \sin\theta\,d\theta = \left[-\cos\theta\right]_0^{3\pi/4} = -\left(-\dfrac{\sqrt{2}}{2}\right) + 1 = 1 + \dfrac{\sqrt{2}}{2} = \dfrac{\sqrt{2} + 2}{2}$

**44.** $\int_{-\pi/4}^{\pi/4} \sec^2 t\,dt = \left[\tan t\right]_{-\pi/4}^{\pi/4} = 1 - (-1) = 2$

**45.** $\int_0^2 \left(x + e^x\right) dx = \left[\dfrac{x^2}{2} + e^x\right]_0^2 = 2 + e^2 - 1 = 1 + e^2$

**46.** $\int_1^6 \dfrac{3}{x}\,dx = 3\ln|x|\Big]_1^6 = 3\ln 6$

**47.** $\int_2^4 (3x - 4)\,dx = \left[\dfrac{3x^2}{2} - 4x\right]_2^4$

$= (24 - 16) - (6 - 8) = 10$

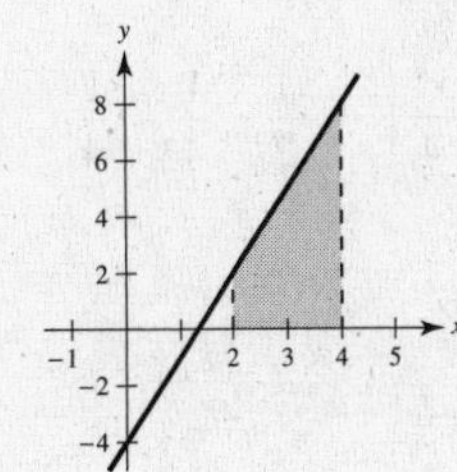

**48.** $\int_0^6 (8 - x)\,dx = \left[8x - \frac{x^2}{2}\right]_0^6 = 48 - 18 = 30$

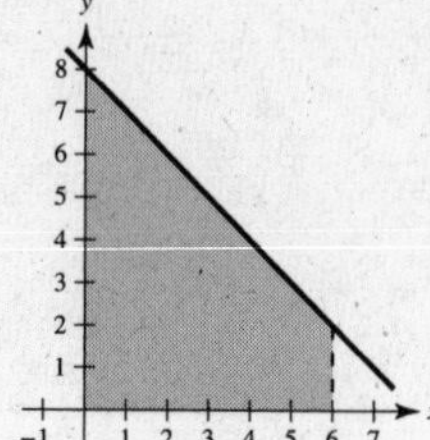

**49.** $\int_3^4 (x^2 - 9)\,dx = \left[\frac{x^3}{3} - 9x\right]_3^4$

$$= \left(\frac{64}{3} - 36\right) - (9 - 27)$$

$$= \frac{64}{3} - \frac{54}{3} = \frac{10}{3}$$

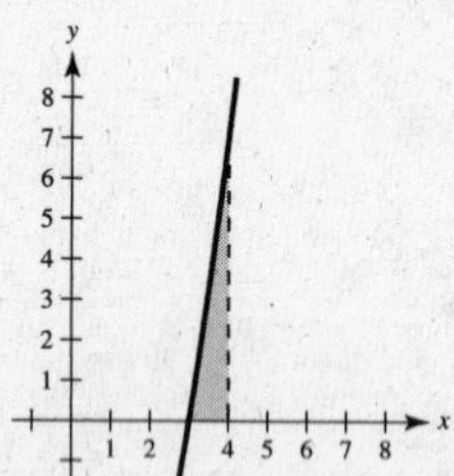

**50.** $\int_{-2}^3 (-x^2 + x + 6)\,dx = \left[-\frac{x^3}{3} + \frac{x^2}{2} + 6x\right]_{-2}^3$

$$= \left(-9 + \frac{9}{2} + 18\right) - \left(\frac{8}{3} + 2 - 12\right)$$

$$= \frac{125}{6}$$

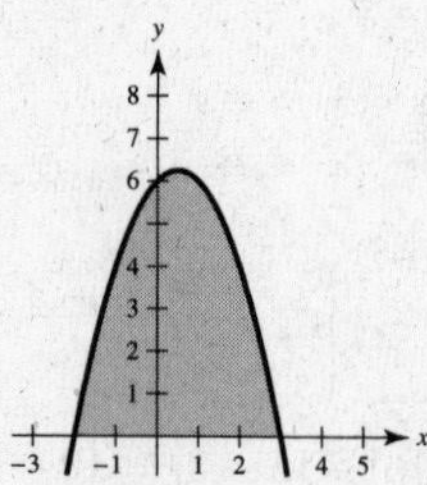

**51.** $\int_0^1 (x - x^3)\,dx = \left[\frac{x^2}{2} - \frac{x^4}{4}\right]_0^1 = \frac{1}{2} - \frac{1}{4} = \frac{1}{4}$

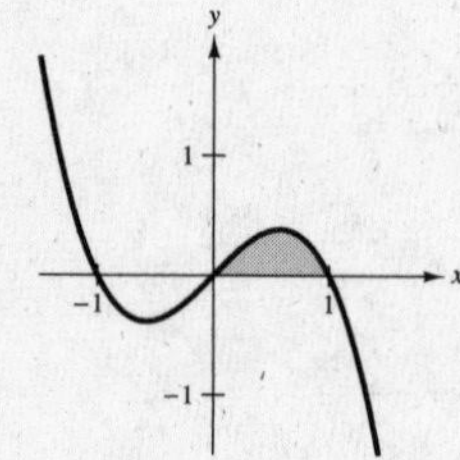

**52.** $\int_0^1 \sqrt{x}(1 - x)\,dx = \left(x^{1/2} - x^{3/2}\right)dx$

$$= \left[\tfrac{2}{3}x^{3/2} - \tfrac{2}{5}x^{5/2}\right]_0^1$$

$$= \tfrac{2}{3} - \tfrac{2}{5} = \tfrac{4}{15}$$

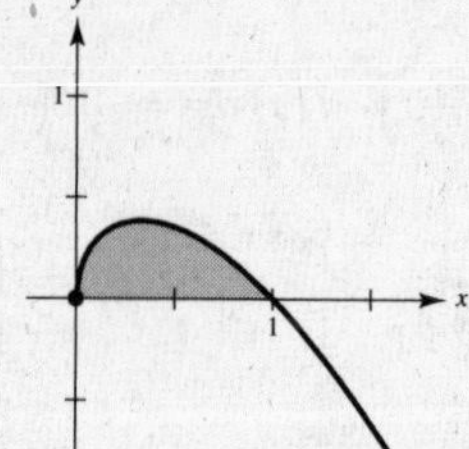

**53.** Area $= \int_1^9 \frac{4}{\sqrt{x}}\,dx = \left[\frac{4x^{1/2}}{(1/2)}\right]_1^9 = 8(3 - 1) = 16$

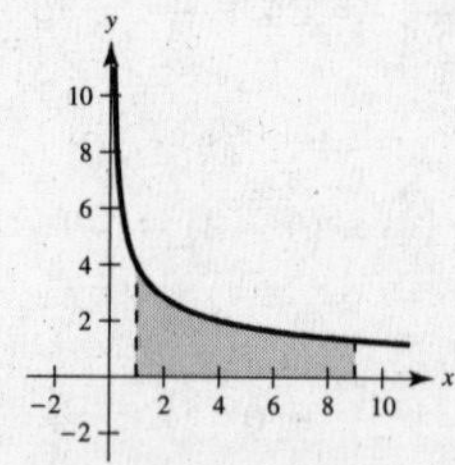

**54.** Area $= \int_0^{\pi/3} \sec^2 x\,dx$

$$= \left[\tan x\right]_0^{\pi/3} = \sqrt{3}$$

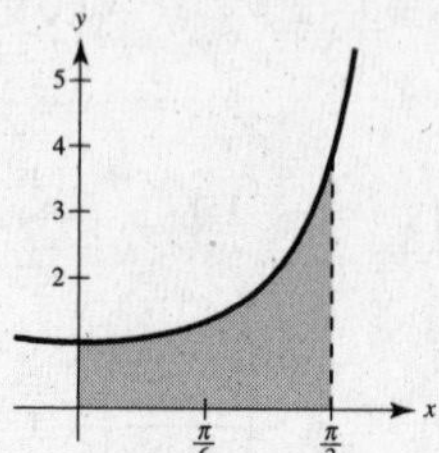

**55.** $y = \frac{2}{x}$

Area $= \int_1^2 \frac{2}{x}\,dx = \left[2 \ln x\right]_1^3 = 2 \ln 3 - 2 \ln 1 = \ln 9$

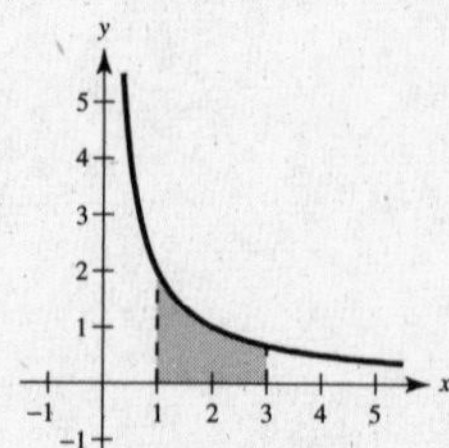

**56.** Area $= \int_0^2 \left(1 - e^x\right) dx = \left[x + e^x\right]_0^2$

$= 2 + e^2 - 1 = 1 + e^2 \approx 8.3891$

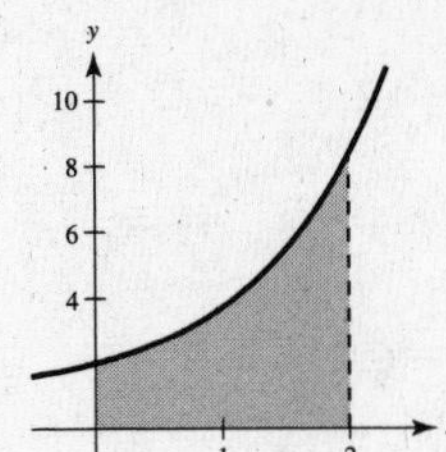

**57.** Average value: $\dfrac{1}{9-4}\int_4^9 \dfrac{1}{\sqrt{x}}\, dx = \left[\dfrac{1}{5}2\sqrt{x}\right]_4^9$

$= \dfrac{2}{5}(3 - 2) = \dfrac{2}{5}$

$\dfrac{2}{5} = \dfrac{1}{\sqrt{x}}$

$\sqrt{x} = \dfrac{5}{2}$

$x = \dfrac{25}{4}$

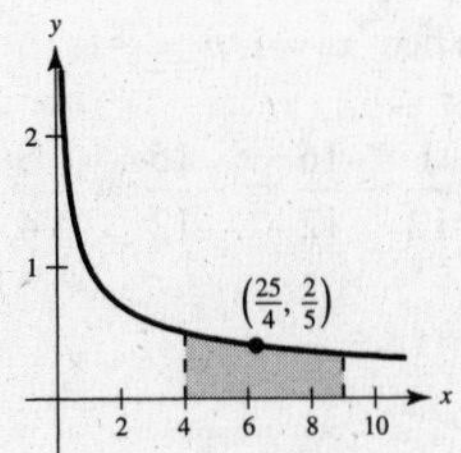

**58.** Average value: $\dfrac{1}{2-0}\int_0^2 x^3\, dx = \left[\dfrac{x^4}{8}\right]_0^2 = 2$

$x^3 = 2$

$x = \sqrt[3]{2}$

**59.** $F'(x) = x^2\sqrt{1 + x^3}$

**60.** $F'(x) = \dfrac{1}{x^2}$

**61.** $F'(x) = x^2 + 3x + 2$

**62.** $F'(x) = \csc^2 x$

**63.** $\int\left(x^2 - 3\right)^3 dx = \int\left(27 - 27x^2 + 9x^4 - x^6\right) dx$

$= 27x - 9x^3 + \dfrac{9}{5}x^5 - \dfrac{x^7}{7} + C$

**64.** $\int\left(x + \dfrac{1}{x}\right)^2 dx = \int\left(x^2 + 2 + x^{-2}\right) dx$

$= \dfrac{x^3}{3} + 2x - \dfrac{1}{x} + C$

**65.** $u = x^3 + 3,\ du = 3x^2\, dx$

$\int \dfrac{x^2}{\sqrt{x^3 + 3}}\, dx = \int\left(x^3 + 3\right)^{-1/2} x^2\, dx$

$= \dfrac{1}{3}\int\left(x^3 + 3\right)^{-1/2} 3x^2\, dx$

$= \dfrac{2}{3}\left(x^3 + 3\right)^{1/2} + C$

**66.** $u = 2x^3 + 5,\ du = 6x^2\, dx$

$\int 3x^2\sqrt{2x^3 - 5}\, dx = \frac{1}{2}\int\left(2x^3 - 5\right)^{1/2}\left(6x^2\right) dx$

$= \frac{1}{3}\left(2x^3 - 5\right)^{3/2} + C$

**67.** $u = 1 - 3x^2,\ du = -6x\, dx$

$\int x\left(1 - 3x^2\right)^4 dx = -\frac{1}{6}\int\left(1 - 3x^2\right)^4(-6x\, dx)$

$= -\frac{1}{30}\left(1 - 3x^2\right)^5 + C$

$= \frac{1}{30}\left(3x^2 - 1\right)^5 + C$

**68.** $u = x^2 + 8x - 7,\ du = (2x + 8)\, dx$

$\int \dfrac{x + 4}{\left(x^2 + 8x - 7\right)^2}\, dx = \dfrac{1}{2}\int\left(x^2 + 8x - 7\right)^{-2}(2x + 8)\, dx$

$= -\dfrac{1}{2}\left(x^2 + 8x - 7\right)^{-1} + C$

$= -\dfrac{1}{2\left(x^2 + 8x - 7\right)} + C$

**69.** $\int \sin^3 x \cos x\, dx = \frac{1}{4}\sin^4 x + C$

**70.** $\int x \sin 3x^2\, dx = \frac{1}{6}\int\left(\sin 3x^2\right)(6x)\, dx = -\frac{1}{6}\cos 3x^2 + C$

**71.** $\int \dfrac{\cos\theta}{\sqrt{1 - \sin\theta}}\, d\theta = -\int(1 - \sin\theta)^{-1/2}(-\cos\theta)\, d\theta$

$= -2(1 - \sin\theta)^{1/2} + C$

$= -2\sqrt{1 - \sin\theta} + C$

**72.** $\int \frac{\sin x}{\sqrt{\cos x}}\,dx = -\int (\cos x)^{-1/2}(-\sin x)\,dx = -2(\cos x)^{1/2} + C = -2\sqrt{\cos x} + C$

**73.** $\int \tan^n \sec^2 x\,dx = \frac{\tan^{n+1} x}{n+1} + C,\ n \neq -1$

**74.** $\int \sec 2x \tan 2x\,dx = \frac{1}{2}\int (\sec 2x \tan 2x)(2)\,dx = \frac{1}{2}\sec 2x + C$

**75.** $\int (1 + \sec \pi x)^2 \sec \pi x \tan \pi x\,dx = \frac{1}{\pi}\int (1 + \sec \pi x)^2(\pi \sec \pi x \tan \pi x)\,dx = \frac{1}{3\pi}(1 + \sec \pi x)^3 + C$

**76.** $\int \cot^4 \alpha \csc^2 \alpha\,d\alpha = -\int (\cot \alpha)^4(-\csc^2 \alpha)\,d\alpha = -\frac{1}{5}\cot^5 \alpha + C$

**77.** $\int xe^{-3x^2}\,dx = -\frac{1}{6}\int e^{-3x^2}(-6x)\,dx = -\frac{1}{6}e^{-3x^2} + C$

**78.** $\int \frac{e^{1/x}}{x^2}\,dx = -\int e^{1/x}\left(-\frac{1}{x^2}\right)dx = -e^{1/x} + C$

**79.** $\int (x + 1)5^{(x+1)^2}\,dx = \frac{1}{2}\int 5^{(x+1)^2}\,2(x + 1)\,dx$

$= \frac{1}{2\ln 5}5^{(x+1)^2} + C$

**80.** $\int \frac{1}{t^2}2^{-1/t}\,dt = \int 2^{-1/t}(t^{-2})\,dt = \frac{1}{\ln 2}2^{-1/t} + C$

**81.** $\int_{-2}^{1} x(x^2 - 6)\,dx = \int_{-2}^{1}(x^3 - 6x)\,dx = \left[\frac{x^4}{4} - 3x^2\right]_{-2}^{1}$

$= \left(\frac{1}{4} - 3\right) - (4 - 12) = \frac{21}{4}$

**82.** $\int_0^1 x^2(x^3 - 2)^3\,dx$

$u = x^3 - 2,\ du = 3x^2\,dx,\ x^2\,dx = \frac{1}{3}\,du$

When $x = 0, u = -2$. When $x = 1, u = -1$.

$\int_{-2}^{-1} u^3\frac{1}{3}\,du = \frac{u^4}{12}\Big]_{-2}^{-1} = \frac{1}{12} - \frac{16}{12} = -\frac{15}{12} = -\frac{5}{4}$

**83.** $\int_0^3 \frac{1}{\sqrt{1 + x}}\,dx = \int_0^3 (1 + x)^{-1/2}\,dx = \left[2(1 + x)^{1/2}\right]_0^3 = 4 - 2 = 2$

**84.** $\int_3^6 \frac{x}{3\sqrt{x^2 - 8}}\,dx = \frac{1}{6}\int_3^6 (x^2 - 8)^{-1/2}(2x)\,dx = \left[\frac{1}{3}(x^2 - 8)^{1/2}\right]_3^6 = \frac{1}{3}(2\sqrt{7} - 1)$

**85.** $u = 1 - y,\ y = 1 - u,\ dy = -du$

When $y = 0, u = 1$. When $y = 1, u = 0$.

$2\pi\int_0^1 (y + 1)\sqrt{1 - y}\,dy = 2\pi\int_1^0 -[(1 - u) + 1]\sqrt{u}\,du = 2\pi\int_1^0 (u^{3/2} - 2u^{1/2})\,du = 2\pi\left[\frac{2}{5}u^{5/2} - \frac{4}{3}u^{3/2}\right]_1^0 = \frac{28\pi}{15}$

**86.** $u = x + 1,\ x = u - 1,\ dx = du$

When $x = -1, u = 0$. When $x = 0, u = 1$.

$2\pi\int_{-1}^0 x^2\sqrt{x + 1}\,dx = 2\pi\int_0^1 (u - 1)^2\sqrt{u}\,du = 2\pi\int_0^1 (u^{5/2} - 2u^{3/2} + u^{1/2})\,du = 2\pi\left[\frac{2}{7}u^{7/2} - \frac{4}{5}u^{5/2} + \frac{2}{3}u^{3/2}\right]_0^1 = \frac{32\pi}{105}$

**87.** $\int_0^\pi \cos\left(\frac{x}{2}\right)dx = 2\int_0^\pi \cos\left(\frac{x}{2}\right)\frac{1}{2}\,dx = \left[2\sin\left(\frac{x}{2}\right)\right]_0^\pi = 2$

**88.** $\int_{-\pi/4}^{\pi/4} \sin 2x\,dx = 0$ because $\sin 2x$ is an odd function.

**89.** (a) $\int_0^{12} \left[2.880 + 2.125 \sin(0.578t + 0.745)\right] dt = \left[2.880t - \frac{2.125}{0.578}\cos(0.578t + 0.745)\right]_0^{12} \approx 36.63$ in.

(b) $\frac{1}{2}\int_8^{10} R(t)\, dt \approx 2.22$ in.

**90.** $\int_0^2 1.75 \sin \frac{\pi t}{2}\, dt = -\frac{2}{\pi}\left[1.75 \cos \frac{\pi t}{2}\right]_0^2 = -\frac{2}{\pi}(1.75)(-1 - 1) = \frac{7}{\pi} \approx 2.2282$ liters

**91.** Trapezoidal Rule $(n = 4)$: $\int_2^3 \frac{2}{1 + x^2}\, dx$

$$\approx \frac{1}{8}\left[\frac{2}{1 + 2^2} + 2\left(\frac{2}{1 + (9/4)^2}\right) + 2\left(\frac{2}{1 + (5/2)^2}\right) + 2\left(\frac{2}{1 + (11/4)^2}\right) + \frac{2}{1 + 3^2}\right] \approx 0.285$$

Simpson's Rule $(n = 4)$: $\int_2^3 \frac{2}{1 + x^2}\, dx$

$$\approx \frac{1}{12}\left[\frac{2}{1 + 2^2} + 4\left(\frac{2}{1 + (9/4)^2}\right) + 2\left(\frac{2}{1 + (5/2)^2}\right) + 4\left(\frac{2}{1 + (11/4)^2}\right) + \frac{2}{1 + 3^2}\right] \approx 0.284$$

Graphing utility: 0.284

**92.** Trapezoidal Rule $(n = 4)$: $\int_0^1 \frac{x^{3/2}}{3 - x^2}\, dx \approx \frac{1}{8}\left[0 + \frac{2(1/4)^{3/2}}{3 - (1/4)^2} + \frac{2(1/2)^{3/2}}{3 - (1/2)^2} + \frac{2(3/4)^{3/2}}{3 - (3/4)^2} + \frac{1}{2}\right] \approx 0.172$

Simpson's Rule $(n = 4)$: $\int_0^1 \frac{x^{3/2}}{3 - x^2}\, dx \approx \frac{1}{12}\left[0 + \frac{4(1/4)^{3/2}}{3 - (1/4)^2} + \frac{2(1/2)^{3/2}}{3 - (1/2)^2} + \frac{4(3/4)^{3/2}}{3 - (3/4)^2} + \frac{1}{2}\right] \approx 0.166$

Graphing utility: 0.166

**93.** Trapezoidal Rule $(n = 4)$:

$$\int_0^{\pi/2} \sqrt{x} \cos x\, dx \approx \frac{\pi}{16}\left[0 + 2\sqrt{\frac{\pi}{8}} \cos \frac{\pi}{8} + 2\sqrt{\frac{\pi}{4}} \cos \frac{\pi}{4} + 2\sqrt{\frac{3\pi}{8}} \cos \frac{3\pi}{8} + \sqrt{\frac{\pi}{2}} \cos \frac{\pi}{2}\right] \approx 0.637$$

Simpson's Rule $(n = 4)$:

$$\int_0^{\pi/2} \sqrt{x} \cos x\, dx \approx \frac{\pi}{24}\left[0 + 4\sqrt{\frac{\pi}{8}} \cos \frac{\pi}{8} + 2\sqrt{\frac{\pi}{4}} \cos \frac{\pi}{4} + 4\sqrt{\frac{3\pi}{8}} \cos \frac{3\pi}{8} + \sqrt{\frac{\pi}{2}} \cos \frac{\pi}{2}\right] \approx 0.685$$

Graphing Utility: 0.704

**94.** Trapezoidal Rule $(n = 4)$:

$$\int_0^{\pi} \sqrt{1 + \sin^2 x}\, dx \approx \frac{\pi}{8}\left[1 + 2\sqrt{1 + \sin^2\left(\frac{\pi}{4}\right)} + 2\sqrt{1 + \sin^2\left(\frac{\pi}{2}\right)} + 2\sqrt{1 + \sin^2\left(\frac{3\pi}{4}\right)} + \sqrt{1 + \sin^2(\pi)}\right] \approx 3.820$$

Simpson's Rule $(n = 4)$:

$$\int_0^{\pi} \sqrt{1 + \sin^2 x}\, dx \approx \frac{\pi}{12}\left[1 + 4\sqrt{1 + \sin^2\left(\frac{\pi}{4}\right)} + 2\sqrt{1 + \sin^2\left(\frac{\pi}{8}\right)} + 4\sqrt{1 + \sin^2\left(\frac{3\pi}{4}\right)} + \sqrt{1 + \sin^2(\pi)}\right] \approx 3.820$$

Graphing utility: 3.820

**95.** Trapezoidal Rule $(n = 4)$: $\int_{-1}^1 e^{-x^2}\, dx \approx \frac{1}{4}\left[e^{-1} + 2e^{-1/4} + 2 + 2e^{-1/4} + e^{-1}\right] \approx 1.463$

Simpson's Rule $(n = 4)$: $\int_{-1}^1 e^{-x^2}\, dx \approx \frac{1}{6}\left[e^{-1} + 4e^{-1/4} + 2 + 4e^{-1/4} + e^{-1}\right] \approx 1.494$

Graphing utility: 1.494

**96.** (a) $R < I < T < L$

(b) $S(4) = \frac{4-0}{3(4)}\left[f(0) + 4f(1) + 2f(2) + 4f(3) + f(4)\right] \approx \frac{1}{3}\left[4 + 4(2) + 2(1) + 4\left(\frac{1}{2}\right) + \frac{1}{4}\right] \approx 5.417$

**97.** $u = 7x - 2,\ du = 7\,dx$

$$\int \frac{1}{7x-2}\,dx = \frac{1}{7}\int \frac{1}{7x-2}(7)\,dx = \frac{1}{7}\ln|7x-2| + C$$

**98.** $u = x^2 - 1,\ du = 2x\,dx$

$$\int \frac{x}{x^2-1}\,dx = \frac{1}{2}\int \frac{2x}{x^2-1}\,dx = \frac{1}{2}\ln|x^2-1| + C$$

**99.** $\int \frac{\sin x}{1+\cos x}\,dx = -\int \frac{-\sin x}{1+\cos x}\,dx = -\ln|1+\cos x| + C$

**100.** $u = \ln x,\ du = \frac{1}{x}\,dx$

$$\int \frac{\ln\sqrt{x}}{x}\,dx = \frac{1}{2}\int(\ln x)\left(\frac{1}{x}\right)dx = \frac{1}{4}(\ln x)^2 + C$$

**101.** 
$$\int_1^4 \frac{2x+1}{2x}\,dx = \int_1^4\left(1 + \frac{1}{2x}\right)dx = \left[x + \frac{1}{2}\ln|x|\right]_1^4 = 4 + \frac{1}{2}\ln 4 - 1 = 3 + \ln 2$$

**102.** $\int_1^e \frac{\ln x}{x}\,dx = \int_1^e (\ln x)^1\left(\frac{1}{x}\right)dx = \left[\frac{1}{2}(\ln x)^2\right]_1^e = \frac{1}{2}$

**103.** $\int_0^{\pi/3} \sec\theta\,d\theta = \left[\ln|\sec\theta + \tan\theta|\right]_0^{\pi/3} = \ln\left(2 + \sqrt{3}\right)$

**104.** 
$$\int_0^{\pi/4}\tan\left(\frac{\pi}{4} - x\right)dx = \left[\ln\left|\cos\left(\frac{\pi}{4} - x\right)\right|\right]_0^{\pi/4} = 0 - \ln\left(\frac{1}{\sqrt{2}}\right) = \frac{1}{2}\ln 2$$

**105.** Let $u = e^{2x} + e^{-2x},\ du = \left(2e^{2x} - e^{-2x}\right)dx.$

$$\int \frac{e^{2x} - e^{-2x}}{e^{2x} + e^{-2x}}\,dx = \frac{1}{2}\int \frac{2e^{2x} - 2e^{-2x}}{e^{2x} + e^{-2x}}\,dx = \frac{1}{2}\ln\left(e^{2x} + e^{-2x}\right) + C$$

**106.** $\int \frac{e^{2x}}{e^{2x}+1}\,dx = \frac{1}{2}\ln\left(e^{2x} + 1\right) + C$

**107.** Let $u = e^{2x},\ du = 2e^{2x}\,dx.$

$$\int \frac{1}{e^{2x} + e^{-2x}}\,dx = \int \frac{e^{2x}}{1 + e^{4x}}\,dx = \frac{1}{2}\int \frac{1}{1 + \left(e^{2x}\right)^2}\left(2e^{2x}\right)dx = \frac{1}{2}\arctan\left(e^{2x}\right) + C$$

**108.** Let $u = 5x,\ du = 5\,dx.$

$$\int \frac{1}{3 + 25x^2}\,dx = \frac{1}{5}\int \frac{1}{\left(\sqrt{3}\right)^2 + (5x)^2}(5)\,dx = \frac{1}{5\sqrt{3}}\arctan\frac{5x}{\sqrt{3}} + C$$

**109.** Let $u = x^2,\ du = 2x\,dx.$

$$\int \frac{x}{\sqrt{1 - x^4}}\,dx = \frac{1}{2}\int \frac{1}{\sqrt{1 - \left(x^2\right)^2}}(2x)\,dx = \frac{1}{2}\arcsin x^2 + C$$

**110.** $\int \frac{1}{16 + x^2}\,dx = \frac{1}{4}\arctan\frac{x}{4} + C$

**111.** Let $u = 16 + x^2,\ du = 2x\,dx.$

$$\int \frac{x}{16 + x^2}\,dx = \frac{1}{2}\int \frac{1}{16 + x^2}(2x)\,dx = \frac{1}{2}\ln(16 + x)^2 + C$$

**112.** $\int \frac{4 - x}{4 - x^2}\,dx = 4\int \frac{1}{\sqrt{4 - x^2}}\,dx + \frac{1}{2}\int\left(4 - x^2\right)^{-1/2}(-2x)\,dx = 4\arcsin\frac{x}{2} + \sqrt{4 - x^2} + C$

**113.** Let $u = \arctan\left(\frac{x}{2}\right)$, $du = \frac{2}{4 + x^2}\,dx$.

$$\int \frac{\arctan(x/2)}{4 + x^2}\,dx = \frac{1}{2}\int\left(\arctan\frac{x}{2}\right)\left(\frac{2}{4 + x^2}\right)dx = \frac{1}{4}\left(\arctan\frac{x}{2}\right)^2 + C$$

**114.** Let $u = \arcsin(2x)$, $du = \frac{2}{\sqrt{1 - 4x^2}}\,dx$

$$\int \frac{\arcsin 2x}{\sqrt{1 - 4x^2}}\,dx = \frac{1}{2}\frac{\left[\arcsin(2x)\right]^2}{2} + C = \frac{(\arcsin 2x)^2}{4} + C$$

**115.** $\int \frac{dy}{\sqrt{A^2 - y^2}} = \int \sqrt{\frac{k}{m}}\,dt$

$$\arcsin\left(\frac{y}{A}\right) = \sqrt{\frac{k}{m}}t + C$$

Because $y = 0$ when $t = 0$, you have $C = 0$. So,

$$\sin\left(\sqrt{\frac{k}{m}}t\right) = \frac{y}{A}$$

$$y = A\sin\left(\sqrt{\frac{k}{m}}t\right).$$

**116.**

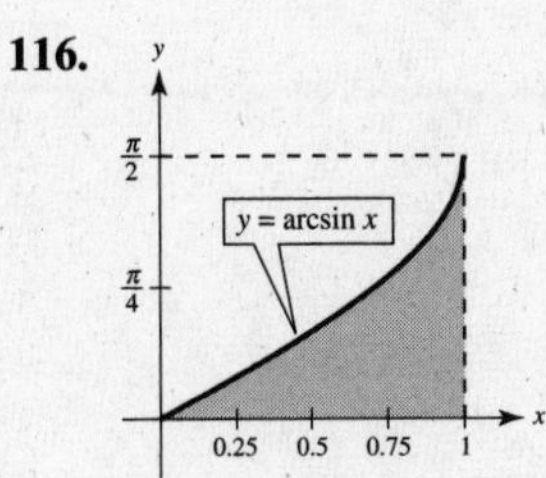


Because the area of region A is $1\left(\int_0^{\pi/2} \sin y\,dy\right)$, the shaded area is $\int_0^1 \arcsin x\,dx = \frac{\pi}{2} - 1 \approx 0.571$.

**117.** $y = 2x - \cosh\sqrt{x}$

$$y' = 2 - \frac{1}{2\sqrt{x}}\left(\sinh\sqrt{x}\right) = 2 - \frac{\sinh\sqrt{x}}{2\sqrt{x}}$$

**118.** $y = x\tanh^{-1} 2x$

$$y' = x\left(\frac{2}{1 - 4x^2}\right) + \tanh^{-1}2x = \frac{2x}{1 - 4x^2} + \tanh^{-1} 2x$$

**119.** Let $u = x^2$, $du = 2x\,dx$.

$$\int \frac{x}{\sqrt{x^4 - 1}}\,dx = \frac{1}{2}\int \frac{1}{\sqrt{\left(x^2\right)^2 - 1}}(2x)\,dx$$

$$= \frac{1}{2}\ln\left(x^2 + \sqrt{x^4 - 1}\right) + C$$

**120.** Let $u = x^3$, $du = 3x^2\,dx$.

$$\int x^2\left(\operatorname{sech} x^3\right)^2 dx = \frac{1}{3}\int\left(\operatorname{sech} x^3\right)^2\left(3x^2\right)dx$$

$$= \frac{1}{3}\tanh x^3 + C$$

# Problem Solving for Chapter 5

**1.** (a) $L(1) = \int_1^1 \frac{1}{t}\,dt = 0$

(b) $L'(x) = \frac{1}{x}$ by the Second Fundamental Theorem of Calculus.

$L'(1) = 1$

(c) $L(x) = 1 = \int_1^x \frac{1}{t}\,dt$ for $x \approx 2.718$

$$\int_1^{2.718} \frac{1}{t}\,dt = 0.999896$$

(**Note:** The exact value of $x$ is $e$, the base of the natural logarithm function.)

(d) First show that $\int_1^{x_1} \frac{1}{t}\,dt = \int_{1/x_1}^{1} \frac{1}{t}\,dt.$

To see this, let $u = \frac{t}{x_1}$ and $du = \frac{1}{x_1}\,dt.$

Then $\int_1^{x_1} \frac{1}{t}\,dt = \int_{1/x_1}^{1} \frac{1}{ux_1}(x_1\,du) = \int_{1/x_1}^{1} \frac{1}{u}\,du = \int_{1/x_1}^{1} \frac{1}{t}\,dt.$

$$\begin{aligned}\text{Now, } L(x_1 x_2) &= \int_1^{x_1 x_2} \frac{1}{t}\,dt = \int_{1/x_1}^{x_2} \frac{1}{u}\,du \quad \left(\text{using } u = \frac{t}{x_1}\right)\\ &= \int_{1/x_1}^{1} \frac{1}{u}\,du + \int_1^{x_2} \frac{1}{u}\,du\\ &= \int_1^{x_1} \frac{1}{u}\,du + \int_1^{x_2} \frac{1}{u}\,du\\ &= L(x_1) + L(x_2).\end{aligned}$$

**2.** (a) $F(x) = \int_2^x \sin t^2\,dt$

| $x$ | 0 | 1.0 | 1.5 | 1.9 | 2.0 | 2.1 | 2.5 | 3.0 | 4.0 | 5.0 |
|---|---|---|---|---|---|---|---|---|---|---|
| $F(x)$ | −0.8048 | −0.4945 | −0.0265 | 0.0611 | 0 | −0.0867 | −0.3743 | −0.0312 | −0.0576 | −0.2769 |

(b) $G(x) = \frac{1}{x-2}\int_2^x \sin t^2\,dt$

| $x$ | 1.9 | 1.95 | 1.99 | 2.01 | 2.1 |
|---|---|---|---|---|---|
| $G(x)$ | −0.6106 | −0.6873 | −0.7436 | −0.7697 | −0.8671 |

$\lim_{x\to 2} G(x) \approx -0.75$

(c) $F'(2) = \lim_{x\to 2} \frac{F(x) - F(2)}{x - 2} = \lim_{x\to 2} \frac{1}{x-2}\int_2^x \sin t^2\,dt = \lim_{x\to 2} G(x)$

Because $F'(x) = \sin x^2$, $F'(2) = \sin 4 = \lim_{x\to 2} G(x)$. (**Note:** $\sin 4 \approx -0.7568$)

**3.** $S(x) = \int_0^x \sin\left(\frac{\pi t^2}{2}\right)dt$

(a)

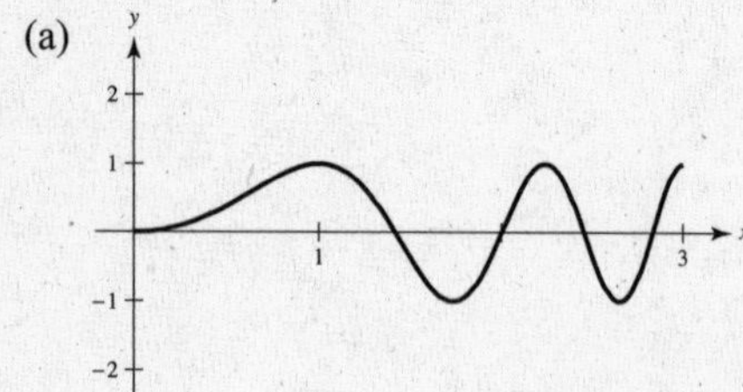


(b)

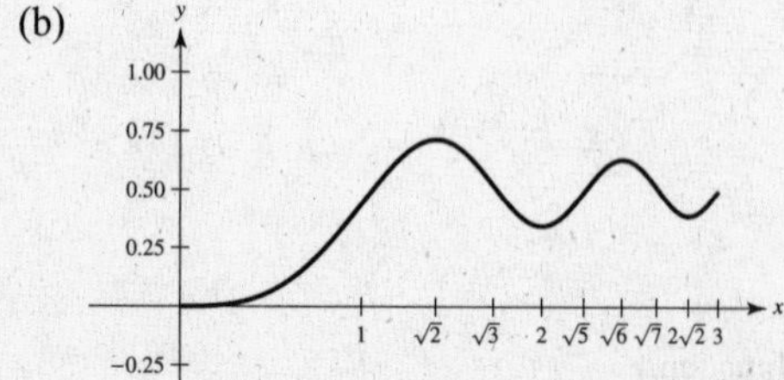


The zeros of $y = \sin\frac{\pi x^2}{2}$ correspond to the relative extrema of $S(x)$.

(c) $S'(x) = \sin\dfrac{\pi x^2}{2} = 0 \Rightarrow \dfrac{\pi x^2}{2} = n\pi \Rightarrow x^2 = 2n \Rightarrow x = \sqrt{2n}$, $n$ integer

Relative maxima at $x = \sqrt{2} \approx 1.4142$ and $x = \sqrt{6} \approx 2.4495$

Relative minima at $x = 2$ and $x = 2\sqrt{2} \approx 2.8284$

(d) $S''(x) = \cos\left(\dfrac{\pi x^2}{2}\right)(\pi x) = 0 \Rightarrow \dfrac{\pi x^2}{2} = \dfrac{\pi}{2} + n\pi \Rightarrow x^2 = 1 + 2n \Rightarrow x = \sqrt{1 + 2n}$, $n$ integer

Points of inflection at $x = 1, \sqrt{3}, \sqrt{5}$, and $\sqrt{7}$.

**4.** Let $d$ be the distance traversed and $a$ be the uniform acceleration. You can assume that $v(0) = 0$ and $s(0) = 0$. Then

$$a(t) = a$$

$$v(t) = at$$

$$s(t) = \frac{1}{2}at^2.$$

$$s(t) = d \text{ when } t = \sqrt{\frac{2d}{a}}.$$

The highest speed is $v = a\sqrt{\dfrac{2d}{a}} = \sqrt{2ad}$.

The lowest speed is $v = 0$.

The mean speed is $\dfrac{1}{2}\left(\sqrt{2ad} + 0\right) = \sqrt{\dfrac{ad}{2}}$.

The time necessary to traverse the distance $d$ at the mean speed is $t = \dfrac{d}{\sqrt{ad/2}} = \sqrt{\dfrac{2d}{a}}$

which is the same as the time calculated above.

**5.** (a)

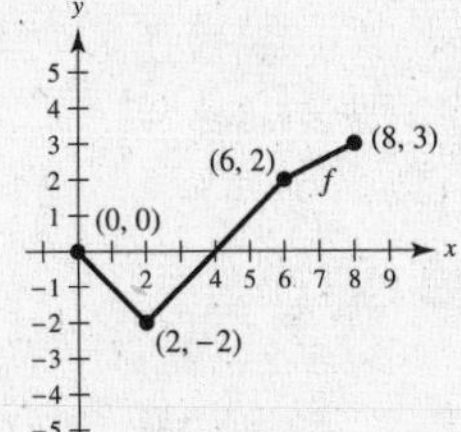


(b)

| $x$ | 0 | 1 | 2 | 3 | 4 | 5 | 6 | 7 | 8 |
|---|---|---|---|---|---|---|---|---|---|
| $F(x)$ | 0 | $-\frac{1}{2}$ | $-2$ | $-\frac{7}{2}$ | $-4$ | $-\frac{7}{2}$ | $-2$ | $\frac{1}{4}$ | 3 |

(c) $f(x) = \begin{cases} -x, & 0 \le x < 2 \\ x - 4, & 2 \le x < 6 \\ \frac{1}{2}x - 1, & 6 \le x \le 8 \end{cases}$

$$F(x) = \int_0^x f(t)\,dt = \begin{cases} (-x^2/2), & 0 \le x < 2 \\ (x^2/2) - 4x + 4, & 2 \le x < 6 \\ (1/4)x^2 - x - 5, & 6 \le x \le 8 \end{cases}$$

$F'(x) = f(x)$. $F$ is decreasing on $(0, 4)$ and increasing on $(4, 8)$. Therefore, the minimum is $-4$ at $x = 4$, and the maximum is 3 at $x = 8$.

(d) $F''(x) = f'(x) = \begin{cases} -1, & 0 < x < 2 \\ 1, & 2 < x < 6 \\ \frac{1}{2}, & 6 < x < 8 \end{cases}$

$x = 2$ is a point of inflection, whereas $x = 6$ is not.

**6.** (a)

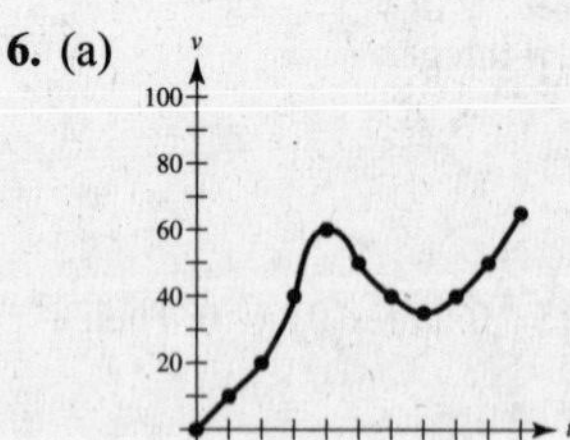

(b) $v$ is increasing (positive acceleration) on (0, 0.4) and (0.7, 1.0).

(c) Average acceleration $= \dfrac{v(0.4) - v(0)}{0.4 - 0} = \dfrac{60 - 0}{0.4} = 150 \text{ mi/h}^2$

(d) This integral is the total distance traveled in miles,

$$\int_0^1 v(t)\,dt \approx \tfrac{1}{10}\left[0 + 2(20) + 2(60) + 2(40) + 2(40) + 65\right] = \tfrac{385}{10} = 38.5 \text{ miles}$$

(e) One approximation is

$$a(0.8) \approx \frac{v(0.9) - v(0.8)}{0.9 - 0.8} = \frac{50 - 40}{0.1} = 100 \text{ mi/h}^2$$

(other answers possible)

**7.** (a) $\displaystyle\int_{-1}^1 \cos x\,dx \approx \cos\left(-\frac{1}{\sqrt{3}}\right) + \cos\left(\frac{1}{\sqrt{3}}\right) = 2\cos\left(\frac{1}{\sqrt{3}}\right) \approx 1.6758$

$$\int_{-1}^1 \cos x\,dx = \sin x\Big]_{-1}^1 = 2\sin(1) \approx 1.6829$$

Error: $|1.6829 - 1.6758| = 0.0071$

(b) $\displaystyle\int_{-1}^1 \frac{1}{1 + x^2}\,dx \approx \frac{1}{1 + (1/3)} + \frac{1}{1 + (1/3)} = \frac{3}{2}$

(**Note:** exact answer is $\pi/2 \approx 1.5708$)

(c) Let $p(x) = ax^3 + bx^2 + cx + d$.

$$\int_{-1}^1 p(x)\,dx = \left[\frac{ax^4}{4} + \frac{bx^3}{3} + \frac{cx^2}{2} + dx\right]_{-1}^1 = \frac{2b}{3} + 2d$$

$$p\left(-\frac{1}{\sqrt{3}}\right) + p\left(\frac{1}{\sqrt{3}}\right) = \left(\frac{b}{3} + d\right) + \left(\frac{b}{3} + d\right) = \frac{2b}{3} + 2d$$

**8.** $\displaystyle\int_0^x f(t)(x - t)\,dt = \int_0^x xf(t)\,dt - \int_0^x tf(t)\,dt = x\int_0^x f(t)\,dt - \int_0^x tf(t)\,dt$

So, $\displaystyle\frac{d}{dx}\int_0^x f(t)(x - t)\,dt = xf(x) + \int_0^x f(t)\,dt - xf(x) = \int_0^x f(t)\,dt$

Differentiating the other integral,

$$\frac{d}{dx}\int_0^x\left(\int_0^t f(v)\,dv\right)dt = \int_0^x f(v)\,dv.$$

So, the two original integrals have equal derivatives,

$$\int_0^x f(t)(x - t)\,dt = \int_0^x\left(\int_0^t f(v)\,dv\right)dt + C.$$

Letting $x = 0$, you see that $C = 0$.

**9.** Consider $F(x) = \left[f(x)\right]^2 \Rightarrow F'(x) = 2f(x)f'(x)$. So,

$$\begin{aligned}\int_a^b f(x)\,f'(x)\,dx &= \int_a^b \tfrac{1}{2}F'(x)\,dx\\ &= \left[\tfrac{1}{2}F(x)\right]_a^b\\ &= \tfrac{1}{2}\left[F(b) - F(a)\right]\\ &= \tfrac{1}{2}\left[f(b)^2 - f(a)^2\right].\end{aligned}$$

**10.** Consider $\int_0^1 \sqrt{x}\,dx = \frac{2}{3}x^{3/2}\Big]_0^1 = \frac{2}{3}$. The corresponding Riemann Sum using right-hand endpoints is

$$S(n) = \frac{1}{n}\left[\sqrt{\frac{1}{n}} + \sqrt{\frac{2}{n}} + \cdots + \sqrt{\frac{n}{n}}\right] = \frac{1}{n^{3/2}}\left[\sqrt{1} + \sqrt{2} + \cdots + \sqrt{n}\right].\text{ So, } \lim_{n\to\infty}\frac{\sqrt{1} + \sqrt{2} + \cdots + \sqrt{n}}{n^{3/2}} = \frac{2}{3}.$$

**11.** Consider $\int_0^1 x^5\,dx = \frac{x^6}{6}\Big]_0^1 = \frac{1}{6}$.

The corresponding Riemann Sum using right endpoints is

$$S(n) = \frac{1}{n}\left[\left(\frac{1}{n}\right)^5 + \left(\frac{2}{n}\right)^5 + \cdots + \left(\frac{n}{n}\right)^5\right] = \frac{1}{n^6}\left[1^5 + 2^5 + \cdots + n^5\right].\text{ So, } \lim_{n\to\infty}S(n) = \lim_{n\to\infty}\frac{1^5 + 2^5 + \cdots + n^5}{n^6} = \frac{1}{6}.$$

**12.** (a)

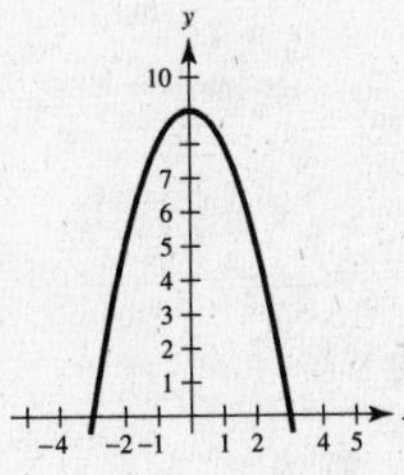


$$\text{Area} = \int_{-3}^{3}\left(9 - x^2\right)dx = 2\int_0^3\left(9 - x^2\right)dx = 2\left[9x - \frac{x^3}{3}\right]_0^3 = 2[27 - 9] = 36$$

(b) Base $= 6$, height $= 9$, Area $= \frac{2}{3}bh = \frac{2}{3}(6)(9) = 36$

(c) Let the parabola be given by $y = b^2 - a^2x^2, a, b > 0$.

$$\begin{aligned}\text{Area} &= 2\int_0^{b/a}\left(b^2 - a^2x^2\right)dx\\ &= 2\left[b^2x - a^2\frac{x^3}{3}\right]_0^{b/a}\\ &= 2\left[b^2\left(\frac{b}{a}\right) - \frac{a^2}{3}\left(\frac{b}{a}\right)^3\right]\\ &= 2\left[\frac{b^3}{a} - \frac{b^3}{3a}\right] = \frac{4b^3}{3a}\end{aligned}$$

Base $= \dfrac{2b}{a}$, height $= b^2$

Archimedes' Formula: Area $= \dfrac{2}{3}\left(\dfrac{2b}{a}\right)\left(b^2\right) = \dfrac{4b^3}{3a}$

**13.** By Theorem 5.8, $0 < f(x) \le M \Rightarrow \int_a^b f(x)\,dx \le \int_a^b M\,dx = M(b-a)$.

Similarly, $m \le f(x) \Rightarrow m(b-a) = \int_a^b m\,dx \le \int_a^b f(x)\,dx.$

So, $m(b-a) \le \int_a^b f(x)\,dx \le M(b-a)$. On the interval [0, 1], $1 \le \sqrt{1+x^4} \le \sqrt{2}$ and $b - a = 1$.

So, $1 \le \int_0^1 \sqrt{1+x^4}\,dx \le \sqrt{2}$. $\left(\textbf{Note: } \int_0^1 \sqrt{1+x^4}\,dx \approx 1.0894\right)$

**14.** (a) $(1+i)^3 = 1 + 3i + 3i^2 + i^3 \Rightarrow (1+i)^3 - i^3 = 3i^2 + 3i + 1$

(b)
$$3i^2 + 3i + 1 = (i+1)^3 - i^3$$
$$\sum_{i=1}^{n}(3i^2 + 3i + 1) = \sum_{i=1}^{n}\left[(i+1)^3 - i^3\right]$$
$$= (2^3 - 1^3) + (3^3 - 2^3) + \cdots + \left[\left((n+1)^3 - n^3\right)\right] = (n+1)^3 - 1$$

So, $(n+1)^3 = \sum_{i=1}^{n}(3i^2 + 3i + 1) + 1.$

(c)
$$(n+1)^3 - 1 = \sum_{i=1}^{n}(3i^2 + 3i + 1) = \sum_{i=1}^{n} 3i^2 + \frac{3(n)(n+1)}{2} + n$$
$$\Rightarrow \sum_{i=1}^{n} 3i^2 = n^3 + 3n^2 + 3n - \frac{3n(n+1)}{2} - n$$
$$= \frac{2n^3 + 6n^2 + 6n - 3n^2 - 3n - 2n}{2}$$
$$= \frac{2n^3 + 3n^2 + n}{2}$$
$$= \frac{n(n+1)(2n+1)}{2}$$
$$\Rightarrow \sum_{i=1}^{n} i^2 = \frac{n(n+1)(2n+1)}{6}$$

**15.** Because $-|f(x)| \le f(x) \le |f(x)|$, $-\int_a^b |f(x)|\,dx \le \int_a^b f(x)\,dx \le \int_a^b |f(x)|\,dx \Rightarrow \left|\int_a^b f(x)\,dx\right| \le \int_a^b |f(x)|\,dx.$

**16.** (a) $y = f(x) = \arcsin x$

$\sin y = x$

$$\text{Area } A = \int_{\pi/6}^{\pi/4} \sin y \cdot dy = \left[-\cos y\right]_{\pi/6}^{\pi/4} = -\frac{\sqrt{2}}{2} + \frac{\sqrt{3}}{2} = \frac{\sqrt{3} - \sqrt{2}}{2} \approx 0.1589$$

$$\text{Area } B = \left(\frac{1}{2}\right)\left(\frac{\pi}{6}\right) = \frac{\pi}{12} \approx 0.2618$$

(b)
$$\int_{1/2}^{\sqrt{2}/2} \arcsin x\,dx = \text{Area}(C) = \left(\frac{\pi}{4}\right)\left(\frac{\sqrt{2}}{2}\right) - A - B$$
$$= \frac{\pi\sqrt{2}}{8} - \frac{\sqrt{3} - \sqrt{2}}{2} - \frac{\pi}{12} = \pi\left(\frac{\sqrt{2}}{8} - \frac{1}{12}\right) + \frac{\sqrt{2} - \sqrt{3}}{2} \approx 0.1346$$

(c) Area $A = \int_0^{\ln 3} e^y\,dy$

$$= \left[e^y\right]_0^{\ln 3} = 3 - 1 = 2$$

Area $B = \int_1^3 \ln x\,dx = 3(\ln 3) - A = 3\ln 3 - 2 = \ln 27 - 2 \approx 1.2958$

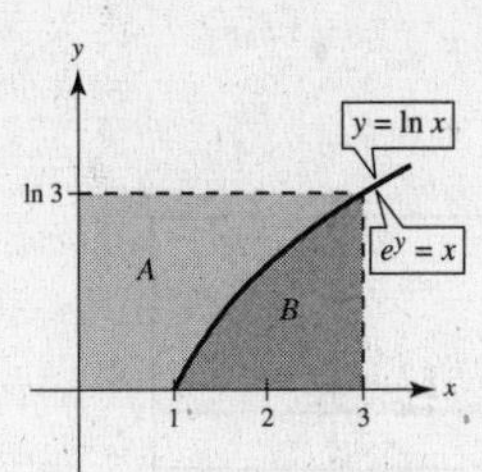


(d) $\tan y = x$

Area $A = \int_{\pi/4}^{\pi/3} \tan y\,dy$

$$= \left[-\ln\left|\cos y\right|\right]_{\pi/4}^{\pi/3}$$

$$= -\ln\frac{1}{2} + \ln\frac{\sqrt{2}}{2} = \ln\sqrt{2} = \frac{1}{2}\ln 2$$

Area $C = \int_1^{\sqrt{3}} \arctan x\,dx = \left(\frac{\pi}{3}\right)\left(\sqrt{3}\right) - \frac{1}{2}\ln 2 - \left(\frac{\pi}{4}\right)(1)$

$$= \frac{\pi}{12}\left(4\sqrt{3} - 3\right) - \frac{1}{2}\ln 2 \approx 0.6818$$

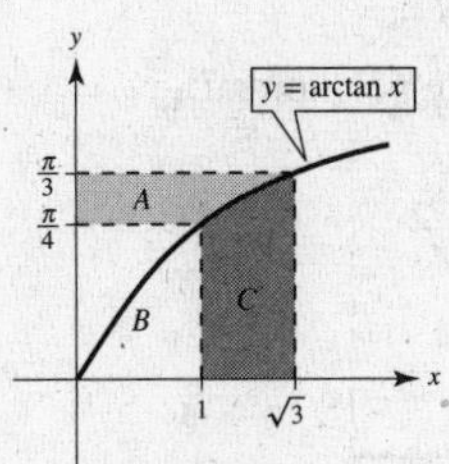


**17.** Let $u = 1 + \sqrt{x}$, $\sqrt{x} = u - 1$, $x = u^2 - 2u + 1$, $dx = (2u - 2)\,du$.

$$\text{Area} = \int_1^4 \frac{1}{\sqrt{x} + x}\,dx = \int_2^3 \frac{2u - 2}{(u - 1) + (u^2 - 2u + 1)}\,du$$

$$= \int_2^3 \frac{2(u - 1)}{u^2 - u}\,du$$

$$= \int_2^3 \frac{2}{u}\,du = \left[2\ln|u|\right]_2^3$$

$$= 2\ln 3 - 2\ln 2 = 2\ln\left(\frac{3}{2}\right)$$

$$\approx 0.8109$$

**18.** Let $u = \tan x$, $du = \sec^2 x\,dx$.

$$\text{Area} = \int_0^{\pi/4} \frac{1}{\sin^2 x + 4\cos^2 x}\,dx = \int_0^{\pi/4} \frac{\sec^2 x}{\tan^2 x + 4}\,dx$$

$$= \int_0^1 \frac{du}{u^2 + 4}$$

$$= \left[\frac{1}{2}\arctan\left(\frac{u}{2}\right)\right]_0^1$$

$$= \frac{1}{2}\arctan\left(\frac{1}{2}\right)$$

**19.** (a) (i) $y = e^x$

$y_1 = 1 + x$

(ii) $y = e^x$

$y_2 = 1 + x + \left(\dfrac{x^2}{2}\right)$

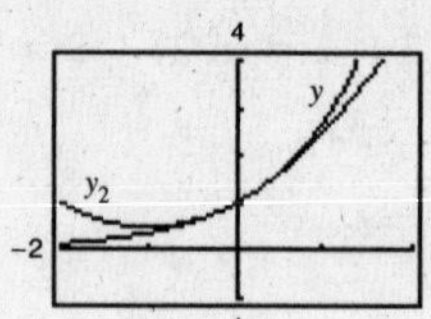


(iii) $y = e^x$

$y_3 = 1 + x + \dfrac{x^2}{2} + \dfrac{x^3}{6}$

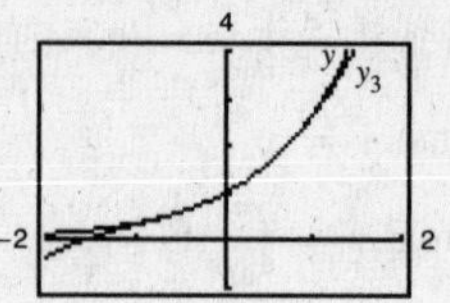


(b) $n^{\text{th}}$ term is $x^n/n!$ in polynomial: $y_4 = 1 + x + \dfrac{x^2}{2!} + \dfrac{x^3}{3!} + \dfrac{x^4}{4!}$

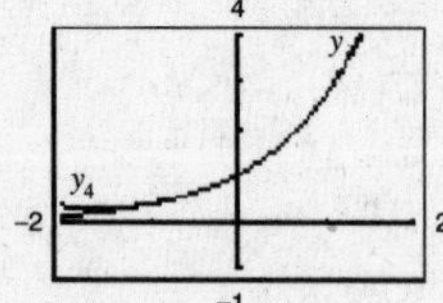


(c) Conjecture: $e^x = 1 + x + \dfrac{x^2}{2!} + \dfrac{x^3}{3!} + \cdots = \displaystyle\sum_{n=0}^{\infty} \frac{x^n}{n!}$

**20.** Let $A = \displaystyle\int_0^b \frac{f(x)}{f(x) + f(b - x)}\, dx.$

Let $u = b - x$, $du = -dx$.

$$\begin{aligned} A &= \int_b^0 \frac{f(b-u)}{f(b-u) + f(u)}(-du) \\ &= \int_0^b \frac{f(b-u)}{f(b-u) + f(u)}\, du \\ &= \int_0^b \frac{f(b-x)}{f(b-x) + f(u)}\, dx \end{aligned}$$

Then,

$$\begin{aligned} 2A &= \int_0^b \frac{f(x)}{f(x) + f(b-x)}\, dx + \int_0^b \frac{f(b-x)}{f(b-x) + f(x)}\, dx \\ &= \int_0^b 1\, dx = b. \end{aligned}$$

So, $A = \dfrac{b}{2}$.

$b = 1 \Rightarrow \displaystyle\int_0^1 \frac{\sin x}{\sin(1-x) + \sin x}\, dx = \frac{1}{2}$

# CHAPTER 6
# Differential Equations

# CHAPTER 6
# Differential Equations

## Section 6.1 Slope Fields and Euler's Method

**1.** Differential equation: $y' = 4y$

Solution: $y = Ce^{4x}$

Check: $y' = 4Ce^{4x} = 4y$

**2.** Differential Equation: $3y' + 5y = -e^{-2x}$

Solution: $y = e^{-2x}$

$y' = -2e^{-2x}$

Check: $3\left(-2e^{-2x}\right) + 5\left(e^{-2x}\right) = -e^{-2x}$

**3.** Differential equation: $y' = \dfrac{2xy}{x^2 - y^2}$

Solution: $x^2 + y^2 = Cy$

Check: $2x + 2yy' = Cy'$

$$y' = \frac{-2x}{(2y - C)}$$

$$y' = \frac{-2xy}{2y^2 - Cy}$$

$$= \frac{-2xy}{2y^2 - \left(x^2 + y^2\right)}$$

$$= \frac{-2xy}{y^2 - x^2}$$

$$= \frac{2xy}{x^2 - y^2}$$

**4.** Differential Equation: $\dfrac{dy}{dx} = \dfrac{xy}{y^2 - 1}$

Solution: $y^2 - 2 \ln y = x^2$

Check: $2yy' - \dfrac{2}{y}y' = 2x$

$$\left(y - \frac{1}{y}\right)y' = x$$

$$y' = \frac{x}{y - \frac{1}{y}}$$

$$y' = \frac{xy}{y^2 - 1}$$

**5.** Differential Equation: $y'' + y = 0$

Solution: $y = C_1 \sin x - C_2 \cos x$

$y' = C_1 \cos x + C_2 \sin x$

$y'' = -C_1 \sin x + C_2 \cos x$

Check: $y'' + y = \left(-C_1 \sin x + C_2 \cos x\right) + \left(C_1 \sin x - C_2 \cos x\right) = 0$

**6.** Differential equation: $y'' + 2y' + 2y = 0$

Solution: $y = C_1e^{-x} \cos x + C_2e^{-x} \sin x$

Check:

$$y' = -(C_1 + C_2)e^{-x} \sin x + (-C_1 + C_2)e^{-x} \cos x$$

$$y'' = 2C_1e^{-x} \sin x - 2C_2e^{-x} \cos x$$

$$y'' + 2y' + 2y = 2C_1e^{-x} \sin x - 2C_2e^{-x} \cos x +$$

$$2\left(-(C_1 + C_2)e^{-x} \sin x + (-C_1 + C_2)e^{-x} \cos x\right) + 2\left(C_1e^{-x} \cos x + C_2e^{-x} \sin x\right)$$

$$= (2C_1 - 2C_1 - 2C_2 + 2C_2)e^{-x} \sin x + (-2C_2 - 2C_1 + 2C_2 + 2C_1)e^{-x} \cos x = 0$$

**7.** Differential Equation: $y'' + y = \tan x$

Solution: $y = -\cos x \ln|\sec x + \tan x|$

$$y' = (-\cos x)\frac{1}{\sec x + \tan x}(\sec x \cdot \tan x + \sec^2 x) + \sin x \ln|\sec x + \tan x|$$

$$= \frac{(-\cos x)}{\sec x + \tan x}(\sec x)(\tan x + \sec x) + \sin x \ln|\sec x + \tan x|$$

$$= -1 + \sin x \ln|\sec x + \tan x|$$

$$y'' = (\sin x)\frac{1}{\sec x + \tan x}(\sec x \cdot \tan x + \sec^2 x) + \cos x \ln|\sec x + \tan x|$$

$$= (\sin x)(\sec x) + \cos x \ln|\sec x + \tan x|$$

Check: $y'' + y = (\sin x)(\sec x) + \cos x \ln|\sec x + \tan x| - \cos x \ln|\sec x + \tan x| = \tan x.$

**8.** Differential Equation: $y'' + 4y' = 2e^x$

Solution: $y = \frac{2}{5}(e^{-4x} + e^x)$

$$y' = \frac{2}{5}(-4e^{-4x} + e^x) = -\frac{8}{5}e^{-4x} + \frac{2}{5}e^x$$

$$y'' = \frac{32}{5}e^{-4x} + \frac{2}{5}e^x$$

Check: $y'' + 4y' = \left(\frac{32}{5}e^{-4x} + \frac{2}{5}e^x\right) + 4\left(-\frac{8}{5}e^{-4x} + \frac{2}{5}e^x\right) = \left(\frac{2}{5} + \frac{8}{5}\right)e^x = 2e^x$

**9.** $y = \sin x \cos x - \cos^2 x$

$$y' = -\sin^2 x + \cos^2 x + 2\cos x \sin x$$

$$= -1 + 2\cos^2 x + \sin 2x$$

Differential Equation:

$$2y + y' = 2(\sin x \cos x - \cos^2 x) + (-1 + 2\cos^2 x + \sin 2x)$$

$$= 2\sin x \cos x - 1 + \sin 2x$$

$$= 2\sin 2x - 1$$

Initial condition $\left(\frac{\pi}{4}, 0\right)$:

$$\sin\frac{\pi}{4}\cos\frac{\pi}{4} - \cos^2\frac{\pi}{4} = \frac{\sqrt{2}}{2}\cdot\frac{\sqrt{2}}{2} - \left(\frac{\sqrt{2}}{2}\right)^2 = 0$$

**10.** $y = \frac{1}{2}x^2 - 2\cos x - 3$

$$y' = x + 2\sin x$$

Differential equation: $y' = x + 2\sin x$

Initial condition $(0, -5)$: $0 - 2\cos 0 - 3 = -5$

**11.** $y = 4e^{-6x^2}$

$$y' = 4e^{-6x^2}(-12x) = -48xe^{-6x^2}$$

Differential equation:

$$y' = -12xy = -12x\left(4e^{-6x^2}\right) = -48xe^{-6x^2}$$

Initial condition $(0, 4)$: $4e^0 = 4$

**12.** $y = e^{-\cos x}$

$$y' = e^{-\cos x}(\sin x) = \sin x \cdot e^{-\cos x}$$

Differential Equation:

$$y' = \sin x \cdot e^{-\cos x} = \sin x(y) = y\sin x$$

Initial condition $\left(\frac{\pi}{2}, 1\right)$: $e^{-\cos(\pi/2)} = e^0 = 1$

**In Exercises 13–20, the differential equation is $y^{(4)} - 16y = 0$.**

**13.**
$$y = 3\cos x$$
$$y^{(4)} = 3\cos x$$
$$y^{(4)} - 16y = -45\cos x \neq 0$$
No

**14.**
$$y = 2\sin x$$
$$y^{(4)} = 2\sin x$$
$$y^{(4)} - 16y = 2\sin x - 16(2\sin x) \neq 0$$
No

**15.**
$$y = 3\cos 2x$$
$$y^{(4)} = 48\cos 2x$$
$$y^{(4)} - 16y = 48\cos 2x - 48\cos 2x = 0$$
Yes

**16.**
$$y = 3\sin 2x$$
$$y^{(4)} = 48\sin 2x$$
$$y^{(4)} - 16y = 48\sin 2x - 16(3\sin 2x) = 0$$
Yes

**17.**
$$y = e^{-2x}$$
$$y^{(4)} = 16e^{-2x}$$
$$y^{(4)} - 16y = 16e^{-2x} - 16e^{-2x} = 0$$
Yes

**18.**
$$y = 5\ln x$$
$$y^{(4)} = -\frac{30}{x^4}$$
$$y^{(4)} - 16y = -\frac{30}{x^4} - 80\ln x \neq 0$$
No

**19.**
$$y = C_1e^{2x} + C_2e^{-2x} + C_3\sin 2x + C_4\cos 2x$$
$$y^{(4)} = 16C_1e^{2x} + 16C_2e^{-2x} + 16C_3\sin 2x + 16C_4\cos 2x$$
$$y^{(4)} - 16y = 0$$
Yes

**20.**
$$y = 3e^{2x} - 4\sin 2x$$
$$y^{(4)} = 48e^{2x} - 64\sin 2x$$
$$y^{(4)} - 16y = (48e^{2x} - 64\sin 2x) - 16(3e^{2x} - 4\sin 2x) = 0$$
Yes

**In Exercises 21–28, the differential equation is $xy' - 2y = x^3e^x$.**

**21.** $y = x^2,\ y' = 2x$
$$xy' - 2y = x(2x) - 2(x^2) = 0 \neq x^3e^x$$
No

**22.** $y = x^3,\ y' = 3x^2$
$$xy' - 2y = x(3x^2) - 2x^3 = x^3 \neq x^3e^x$$
No

**23.** $y = x^2e^x,\ y' = x^2e^x + 2xe^x = e^x(x^2 + 2x)$
$$xy' - 2y = x(e^x(x^2 + 2x)) - 2(x^2e^x) = x^3e^x$$
Yes

**24.** $y = x^2(2 + e^x),\ y' = x^2(e^x) + 2x(2 + e^x)$
$$xy' - 2y = x\left[x^2e^x + 2xe^x + 4x\right] - 2\left[x^2e^x + 2x^2\right]$$
$$= x^3e^x$$
Yes

**25.** $y = \sin x,\ y' = \cos x$
$$xy' - 2y = x(\cos x) - 2(\sin x) \neq x^3e^x$$
No

**26.** $y = \cos x,\ y' = -\sin x$
$$xy' - 2y = x(-\sin x) - 2\cos x \neq x^3e^x$$
No

**27.** $y = \ln x,\ y' = \frac{1}{x}$
$$xy' - 2y = x\left(\frac{1}{x}\right) - 2\ln x \neq x^3e^x$$
No

**28.** $y = x^2e^x - 5x^2,\ y' = x^2e^x + 2xe^x - 10x$
$$xy' - 2y = x\left[x^2e^x + 2xe^x - 10x\right] - 2\left[x^2e^x - 5x^2\right]$$
$$= x^3e^x$$
Yes

**29.** $y = Ce^{-x/2}$ passes through $(0, 3)$.

$3 = Ce^0 = C \Rightarrow C = 3$

Particular solution: $y = 3e^{-x/2}$

**30.** $y(x^2 + y) = C$ passes through $(0, 2)$.

$2(0 + 2) = C \Rightarrow C = 4$

Particular solution: $y(x^2 + y) = 4$

**31.** $y^2 = Cx^3$ passes through $(4, 4)$.

$16 = C(64) \Rightarrow C = \frac{1}{4}$

Particular solution: $y^2 = \frac{1}{4}x^3$ or $4y^2 = x^3$

**32.** $2x^2 - y^2 = C$ passes through $(3, 4)$.

$2(9) - 16 = C \Rightarrow C = 2$

Particular solution: $2x^2 - y^2 = 2$

**33.** Differential equation: $4yy' - x = 0$

General solution: $4y^2 - x^2 = C$

Particular solutions: $C = 0$, Two intersecting lines

$C = \pm 1$, $C = \pm 4$, Hyperbolas

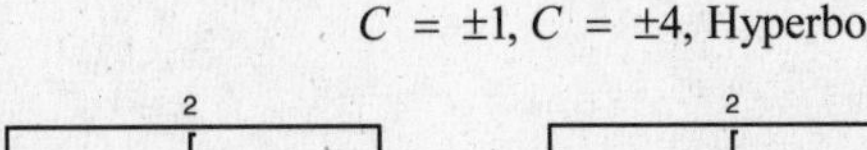

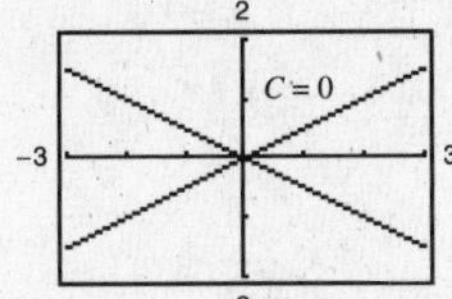


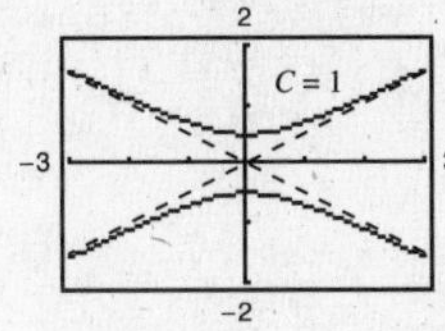


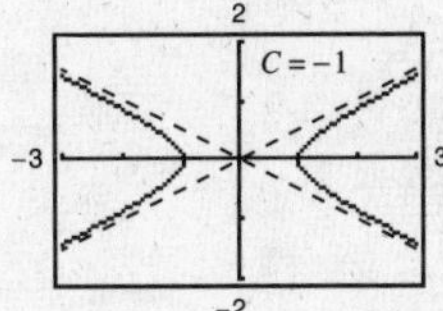


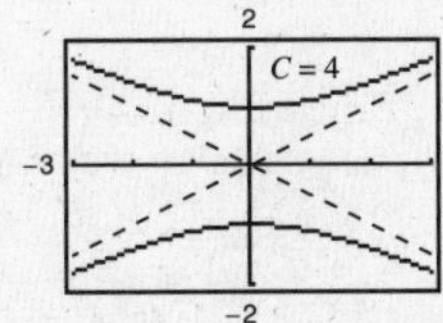


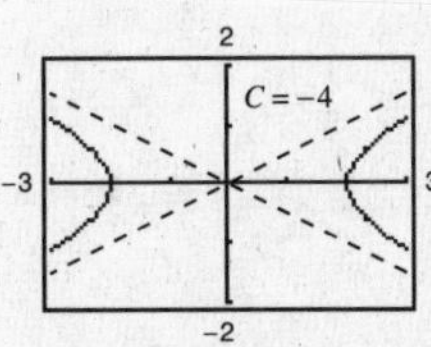


**34.** Differential equation: $yy' + x = 0$

General solution: $x^2 + y^2 = C$

Particular solutions: $C = 0$, Point

$C = 1$, $C = 4$, Circles

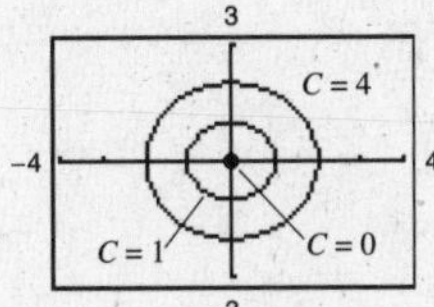


**35.** Differential equation: $y' + 2y = 0$

General solution: $y = Ce^{-2x}$

$y' + 2y = C(-2)e^{-2x} + 2(Ce^{-2x}) = 0$

Initial condition $(0, 3)$: $3 = Ce^0 = C$

Particular solution: $y = 3e^{-2x}$

**36.** Differential equation: $3x + 2yy' = 0$

General solution: $3x^2 + 2y^2 = C$

$6x + 4yy' = 0$

$2(3x + 2yy') = 0$

$3x + 2yy' = 0$

Initial condition $(1, 3)$:

$3(1)^2 + 2(3)^2 = 3 + 18 = 21 = C$

Particular solution: $3x^2 + 2y^2 = 21$

**37.** Differential equation: $y'' + 9y = 0$

General solution: $y = C_1 \sin 3x + C_2 \cos 3x$

$$y' = 3C_1 \cos 3x - 3C_2 \sin 3x,$$
$$y'' = -9C_1 \sin 3x - 9C_2 \cos 3x$$
$$y'' + 9y = (-9C_1 \sin 3x - 9C_2 \cos 3x) + 9(C_1 \sin 3x + C_2 \cos 3x) = 0$$

Initial conditions $\left(\frac{\pi}{6}, 2\right)$ and $y' = 1$ when $x = \frac{\pi}{6}$:

$$2 = C_1 \sin\left(\frac{\pi}{2}\right) + C_2 \cos\left(\frac{\pi}{2}\right) \Rightarrow C_1 = 2$$
$$y' = 3C_1 \cos 3x - 3C_2 \sin 3x$$
$$1 = 3C_1 \cos\left(\frac{\pi}{2}\right) - 3C_2 \sin\left(\frac{\pi}{2}\right) = -3C_2 \Rightarrow C_2 = -\frac{1}{3}$$

Particular solution: $y = 2 \sin 3x - \frac{1}{3} \cos 3x$

**38.** Differential equation: $xy'' + y' = 0$

General solution: $y = C_1 + C_2 \ln x$

$$y' = C_2\left(\frac{1}{x}\right), y'' = -C_2\left(\frac{1}{x^2}\right)$$
$$xy'' + y' = x\left(-C_2\frac{1}{x^2}\right) + C_2\frac{1}{x} = 0$$

Initial conditions $(2, 0)$ and $y' = \frac{1}{2}$ when $x = 2$:

$$0 = C_1 + C_2 \ln 2$$
$$y' = \frac{C_2}{x}$$
$$\frac{1}{2} = \frac{C_2}{2} \Rightarrow C_2 = 1, C_1 = -\ln 2$$

Particular solution: $y = -\ln 2 + \ln x = \ln \frac{x}{2}$

**39.** Differential equation: $x^2y'' - 3xy' + 3y = 0$

General solution: $y = C_1x + C_2x^3$

$$y' = C_1 + 3C_2x^2, y'' = 6C_2x$$
$$x^2y'' - 3xy' + 3y = x^2(6C_2x) - 3x(C_1 + 3C_2x^2) + 3(C_1x + C_2x^3) = 0$$

Initial conditions $(2, 0)$ and $y' = 4$ when $x = 2$:

$$0 = 2C_1 + 8C_2$$
$$y' = C_1 + 3C_2x^2$$
$$4 = C_1 + 12C_2$$
$$\left.\begin{aligned} C_1 + 4C_2 &= 0 \\ C_1 + 12C_2 &= 4 \end{aligned}\right\} C_2 = \tfrac{1}{2}, C_1 = -2$$

Particular solution: $y = -2x + \frac{1}{2}x^3$

**40.** Differential equation: $9y'' - 12y' + 4y = 0$

General solution: $y = e^{2x/3}(C_1 + C_2x)$

$$y' = \tfrac{2}{3}e^{2x/3}(C_1 + C_2x) + C_2e^{2x/3} = e^{2x/3}\left(\tfrac{2}{3}C_1 + C_2 + \tfrac{2}{3}C_2x\right)$$

$$y'' = \tfrac{2}{3}e^{2x/3}\left(\tfrac{2}{3}C_1 + C_2 + \tfrac{2}{3}C_2x\right) + e^{2x/3}\tfrac{2}{3}C_2 = \tfrac{2}{3}e^{2x/3}\left(\tfrac{2}{3}C_1 + 2C_2 + \tfrac{2}{3}C_2x\right)$$

$$9y'' - 12y' + 4y = 9\left(\tfrac{2}{3}e^{2x/3}\right)\left(\tfrac{2}{3}C_1 + 2C_2 + \tfrac{2}{3}C_2x\right) - 12\left(e^{2x/3}\right)\left(\tfrac{2}{3}C_1 + C_2 + \tfrac{2}{3}C_2x\right) + 4\left(e^{2x/3}\right)(C_1 + C_2x) = 0$$

Initial conditions $(0, 4)$ and $(3, 0)$:

$$0 = e^2(C_1 + 3C_2)$$

$$4 = (1)(C_1 + 0) \Rightarrow C_1 = 4$$

$$0 = e^2(4 + 3C_2) \Rightarrow C_2 = -\tfrac{4}{3}$$

Particular solution: $y = e^{2x/3}\left(4 - \tfrac{4}{3}x\right)$

**41.** $\dfrac{dy}{dx} = 6x^2$

$$y = \int 6x^2\,dx = 2x^3 + C$$

**42.** $\dfrac{dy}{dx} = 2x^3 - 3x$

$$y = \int (2x^3 - 3x)\,dx = \frac{x^4}{2} - \frac{3}{2}x^2 + C$$

**43.** $\dfrac{dy}{dx} = \dfrac{x}{1 + x^2}$

$$y = \int \frac{x}{1 + x^2}\,dx = \frac{1}{2}\ln(1 + x^2) + C$$

$(u = 1 + x^2,\ du = 2x\,dx)$

**44.** $\dfrac{dy}{dx} = \dfrac{e^x}{4 + e^x}$

$$y = \int \frac{e^x}{4 + e^x}\,dx = \ln(4 + e^x) + C$$

**45.** $\dfrac{dy}{dx} = \dfrac{x - 2}{x} = 1 - \dfrac{2}{x}$

$$y = \int\left(1 - \frac{2}{x}\right)dx$$

$$= x - 2\ln|x| + C = x - \ln x^2 + C$$

**46.** $\dfrac{dy}{dx} = x\cos x^2$

$$y = \int x\cos(x^2)\,dx = \frac{1}{2}\sin(x^2) + C$$

$(u = x^2,\ du = 2x\,dx)$

**47.** $\dfrac{dy}{dx} = \sin 2x$

$$y = \int \sin 2x\,dx = -\frac{1}{2}\cos 2x + C$$

$(u = 2x,\ du = 2\,dx)$

**48.** $\dfrac{dy}{dx} = \tan^2 x = \sec^2 x - 1$

$$y = \int(\sec^2 x - 1)\,dx = \tan x - x + C$$

**49.** $\dfrac{dy}{dx} = x\sqrt{x - 6}$

Let $u = \sqrt{x - 6}$, then $x = u^2 + 6$ and $dx = 2u\,du$.

$$\begin{aligned} y = \int x\sqrt{x - 6}\,dx &= \int (u^2 + 6)(u)(2u)\,du \\ &= 2\int(u^4 + 6u^2)\,du \\ &= 2\left(\frac{u^5}{5} + 2u^3\right) + C \\ &= \frac{2}{5}(x - 6)^{5/2} + 4(x - 6)^{3/2} + C \\ &= \frac{2}{5}(x - 6)^{3/2}(x - 6 + 10) + C \\ &= \frac{2}{5}(x - 6)^{3/2}(x + 4) + C \end{aligned}$$

**50.** $\dfrac{dy}{dx} = 2x\sqrt{3 - x}$

Let $u = \sqrt{3 - x}$, then $x = 3 - u^2$ and $dx = -2u\,du$

$$\begin{aligned} y &= \int 2x\sqrt{3 - x}\,dx = \int 2(3 - u^2)u(-2u\,du) \\ &= \int (4u^4 - 12u^2)du \\ &= \frac{4u^5}{5} - 4u^3 + C \\ &= \frac{4}{5}(3 - x)^{5/2} - 4(3 - x)^{3/2} + C \\ &= \frac{4}{5}(3 - x)^{3/2}(3 - x - 5) + C \\ &= -\frac{4}{5}(3 - x)^{3/2}(x + 2) + C \end{aligned}$$

**51.** $\dfrac{dy}{dx} = xe^{x^2}$

$$y = \int xe^{x^2}\,dx = \frac{1}{2}e^{x^2} + C$$

$(u = x^2, du = 2x\,dx)$

**52.** $\dfrac{dy}{dx} = 5e^{-x/2}$

$$y = \int 5e^{-x/2}\,dx = 5(-2)\int e^{-x/2}\left(-\frac{1}{2}\right)dx = -10e^{-x/2} + C$$

**53.**

| $x$ | $-4$ | $-2$ | $0$ | $2$ | $4$ | $8$ |
|---|---|---|---|---|---|---|
| $y$ | $2$ | $0$ | $4$ | $4$ | $6$ | $8$ |
| $dy/dx$ | $-4$ | Undef. | $0$ | $1$ | $\frac{4}{3}$ | $2$ |

**54.**

| $x$ | $-4$ | $-2$ | $0$ | $2$ | $4$ | $8$ |
|---|---|---|---|---|---|---|
| $y$ | $2$ | $0$ | $4$ | $4$ | $6$ | $8$ |
| $dy/dx$ | $6$ | $2$ | $4$ | $2$ | $2$ | $0$ |

**55.**

| $x$ | $-4$ | $-2$ | $0$ | $2$ | $4$ | $8$ |
|---|---|---|---|---|---|---|
| $y$ | $2$ | $0$ | $4$ | $4$ | $6$ | $8$ |
| $dy/dx$ | $-2\sqrt{2}$ | $-2$ | $0$ | $0$ | $-2\sqrt{2}$ | $-8$ |

**56.**

| $x$ | $-4$ | $-2$ | $0$ | $2$ | $4$ | $8$ |
|---|---|---|---|---|---|---|
| $y$ | $2$ | $0$ | $4$ | $4$ | $6$ | $8$ |
| $dy/dx$ | $\sqrt{3}$ | $0$ | $-\sqrt{3}$ | $-\sqrt{3}$ | $0$ | $\sqrt{3}$ |

**57.** $\dfrac{dy}{dx} = \sin 2x$

For $x = 0$, $\dfrac{dy}{dx} = 0$. Matches (b).

**58.** $\dfrac{dy}{dx} = \dfrac{1}{2}\cos x$

For $x = 0$, $\dfrac{dy}{dx} = \dfrac{1}{2}$. Matches (c).

**59.** $\dfrac{dy}{dx} = e^{-2x}$

As $x \to \infty$, $\dfrac{dy}{dx} \to 0$. Matches (d).

**60.** $\dfrac{dy}{dx} = \dfrac{1}{x}$

For $x = 0$, $\dfrac{dy}{dx}$ is undefined (vertical tangent). Matches (a).

**61.** (a), (b)

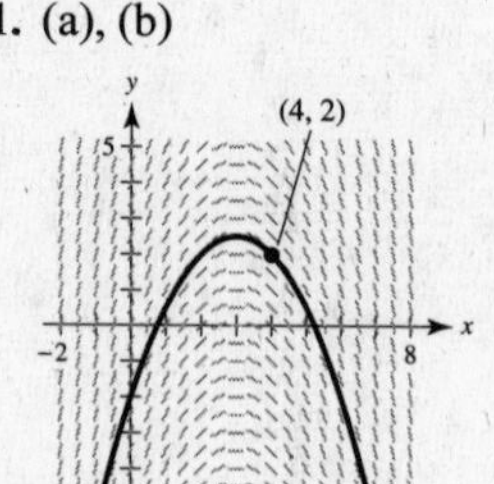


(c) As $x \to \infty$, $y \to -\infty$.

As $x \to -\infty$, $y \to -\infty$.

**62.** (a), (b)

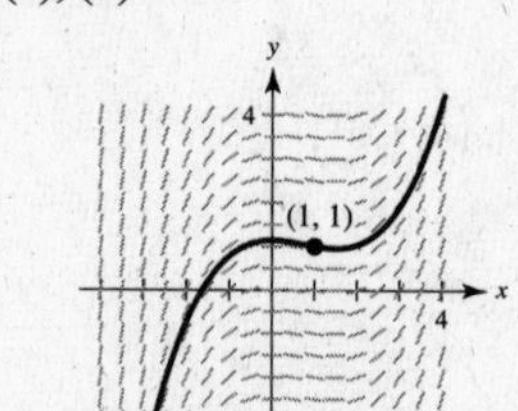


(c) As $x \to \infty$, $y \to \infty$.

As $x \to -\infty$, $y \to -\infty$.

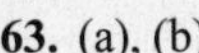

**63.** (a), (b)

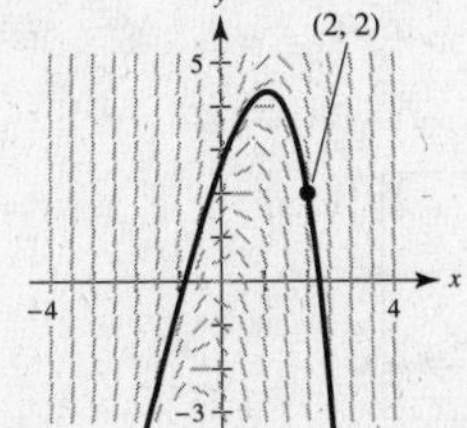


(c) As $x \to \infty$, $y \to -\infty$.

As $x \to -\infty$, $y \to -\infty$.

**64.** (a), (b)

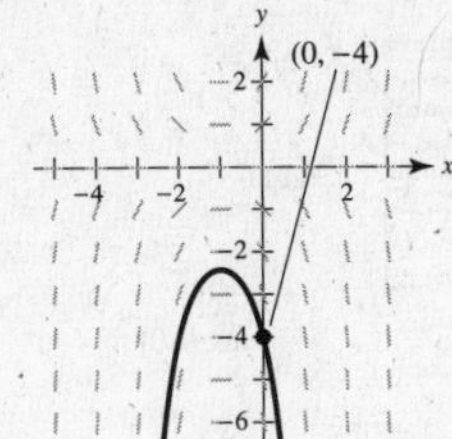


(c) As $x \to \infty$, $y \to -\infty$.

As $x \to -\infty$, $y \to -\infty$.

**65.** (a) $y' = \dfrac{1}{x}, (1, 0)$

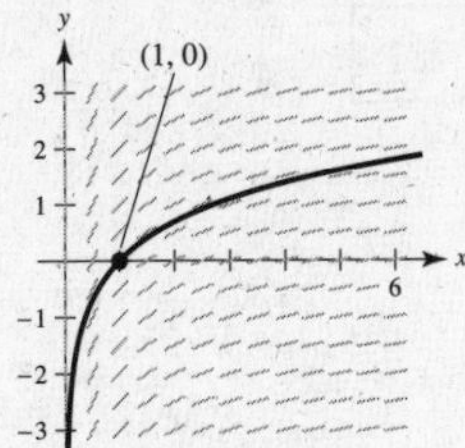


As $x \to \infty$, $y \to \infty$.

[Note: The solution is $y = \ln x$.]

(b) $y' = \dfrac{1}{x}, (2, -1)$

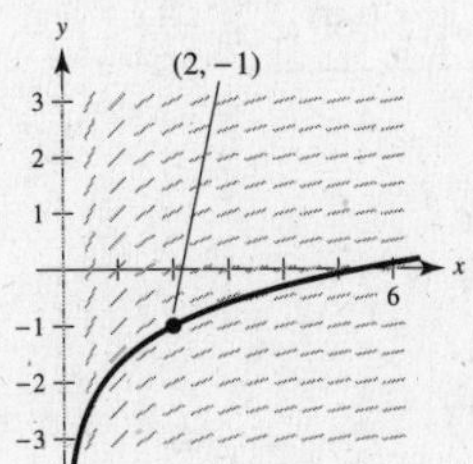


As $x \to \infty$, $y \to \infty$.

**66.** (a) $y' = \dfrac{1}{y}, (0, 1)$

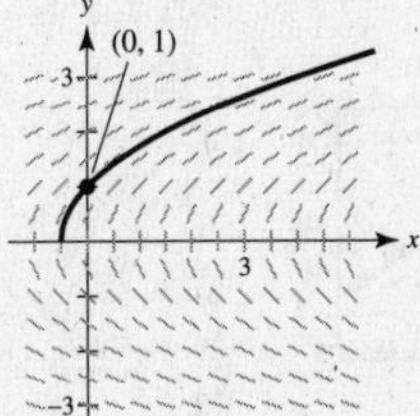


As $x \to \infty$, $y \to \infty$.

(b) $y' = \dfrac{1}{y}, (1, 1)$

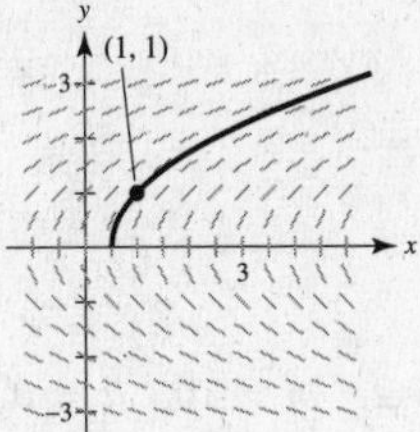


As $x \to \infty$, $y \to \infty$.

**67.** $\dfrac{dy}{dx} = 0.25y,\ y(0) = 4$

(a), (b)

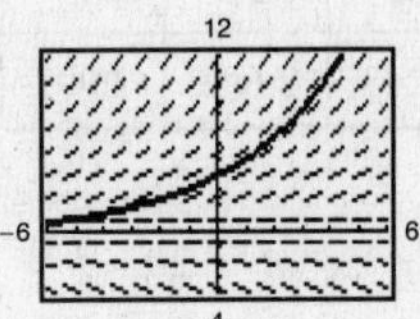


**68.** $\dfrac{dy}{dx} = 4 - y,\ y(0) = 6$

(a), (b)

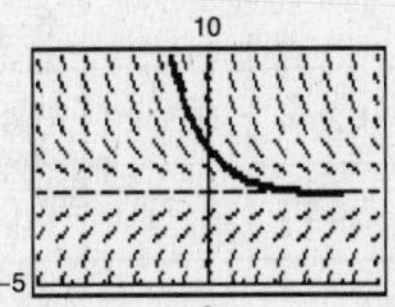


**69.** $\dfrac{dy}{dx} = 0.02y(10 - y),\ y(0) = 2$

(a), (b)

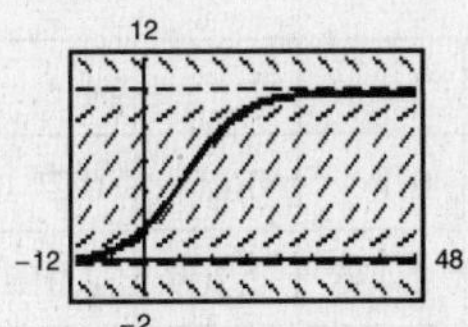

**70.** $\dfrac{dy}{dx} = 0.2x(2 - y),\ y(0) = 9$

(a), (b)

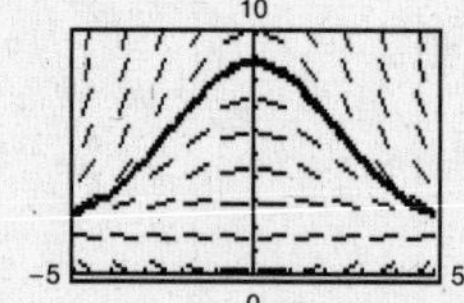


**71.** $\dfrac{dy}{dx} = 0.4y(3 - x),\ y(0) = 1$

(a), (b)

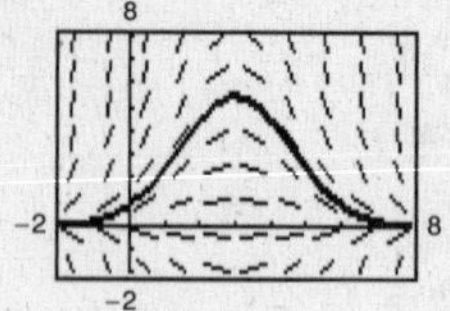


**72.** $\dfrac{dy}{dx} = \dfrac{1}{2}e^{-x/8} \sin \dfrac{\pi y}{4},\ y(0) = 2$

(a), (b)

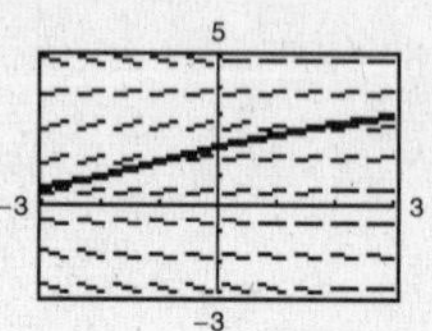


**73.** $y' = x + y, \quad y(0) = 2, \quad n = 10, \quad h = 0.1$

$y_1 = y_0 + hF(x_0, y_0) = 2 + (0.1)(0 + 2) = 2.2$

$y_2 = y_1 + hF(x_1, y_1) = 2.2 + (0.1)(0.1 + 2.2) = 2.43$, etc.

| $n$ | 0 | 1 | 2 | 3 | 4 | 5 | 6 | 7 | 8 | 9 | 10 |
|---|---|---|---|---|---|---|---|---|---|---|---|
| $x_n$ | 0 | 0.1 | 0.2 | 0.3 | 0.4 | 0.5 | 0.6 | 0.7 | 0.8 | 0.9 | 1.0 |
| $y_n$ | 2 | 2.2 | 2.43 | 2.693 | 2.992 | 3.332 | 3.715 | 4.146 | 4.631 | 5.174 | 5.781 |

**74.** $y' = x + y, \quad y(0) = 2, \quad n = 20, \quad h = 0.05$

$y_1 = y_0 + hF(x_0, y_0) = 2 + (0.05)(0 + 2) = 2.1$

$y_2 = y_1 + hF(x_1, y_1) = 2.1 + (0.05)(0.05 + 2.1) = 2.2075$, etc.

The table shows the values for $n = 0, 2, 4, \ldots, 20$.

| $n$ | 0 | 2 | 4 | 6 | 8 | 10 | 12 | 14 | 16 | 18 | 20 |
|---|---|---|---|---|---|---|---|---|---|---|---|
| $x_n$ | 0 | 0.1 | 0.2 | 0.3 | 0.4 | 0.5 | 0.6 | 0.7 | 0.8 | 0.9 | 1.0 |
| $y_n$ | 2 | 2.208 | 2.447 | 2.720 | 3.032 | 3.387 | 3.788 | 4.240 | 4.749 | 5.320 | 5.960 |

**75.** $y' = 3x - 2y, \quad y(0) = 3, \quad n = 10, \quad h = 0.05$

$y_1 = y_0 + hF(x_0, y_0) = 3 + (0.05)(3(0) - 2(3)) = 2.7$

$y_2 = y_1 + hF(x_1, y_1) = 2.7 + (0.05)(3(0.05) + 2(2.7)) = 2.4375$, etc.

| $n$ | 0 | 1 | 2 | 3 | 4 | 5 | 6 | 7 | 8 | 9 | 10 |
|---|---|---|---|---|---|---|---|---|---|---|---|
| $x_n$ | 0 | 0.05 | 0.1 | 0.15 | 0.2 | 0.25 | 0.3 | 0.35 | 0.4 | 0.45 | 0.5 |
| $y_n$ | 3 | 2.7 | 2.438 | 2.209 | 2.010 | 1.839 | 1.693 | 1.569 | 1.464 | 1.378 | 1.308 |

**76.** $y' = 0.5x(3 - y), \quad y(0) = 1, \quad n = 5, \quad h = 0.4$

$y_1 = y_0 + hF(x_0, y_0) = 1 + (0.4)(0.5(0)(3 - 1)) = 1$

$y_2 = y_1 + hF(x_1, y_1) = 1 + (0.4)(0.5(0.4)(3 - 1)) = 1.16$, etc.

| $n$ | 0 | 1 | 2 | 3 | 4 | 5 |
|---|---|---|---|---|---|---|
| $x_n$ | 0 | 0.4 | 0.8 | 1.2 | 1.6 | 2.0 |
| $y_n$ | 1 | 1 | 1.16 | 1.454 | 1.825 | 2.201 |

**77.** $y' = e^{xy}, \quad y(0) = 1, \quad n = 10, \quad h = 0.1$

$y_1 = y_0 + hF(x_0, y_0) = 1 + (0.1)e^{0(1)} = 1.1$

$y_2 = y_1 + hF(x_1, y_1) = 1.1 + (0.1)e^{(0.1)(1.1)} \approx 1.2116$, etc.

| $n$ | 0 | 1 | 2 | 3 | 4 | 5 | 6 | 7 | 8 | 9 | 10 |
|---|---|---|---|---|---|---|---|---|---|---|---|
| $x_n$ | 0 | 0.1 | 0.2 | 0.3 | 0.4 | 0.5 | 0.6 | 0.7 | 0.8 | 0.9 | 1.0 |
| $y_n$ | 1 | 1.1 | 1.212 | 1.339 | 1.488 | 1.670 | 1.900 | 2.213 | 2.684 | 3.540 | 5.958 |

**78.** $y' = \cos x + \sin y, y(0) = 5, n = 10, h = 0.1$

$y_1 = y_0 + hF(x_0, y_0) = 5 + (0.1)(\cos 0 + \sin 5) \approx 5.0041$

$y_2 = y_1 + hF(x_1, y_1) = 5.0041 + (0.1)(\cos(0.1) + \sin(5.0041)) \approx 5.0078$, etc.

| $n$ | 0 | 1 | 2 | 3 | 4 | 5 | 6 | 7 | 8 | 9 | 10 |
|---|---|---|---|---|---|---|---|---|---|---|---|
| $x_n$ | 0 | 0.1 | 0.2 | 0.3 | 0.4 | 0.5 | 0.6 | 0.7 | 0.8 | 0.9 | 1.0 |
| $y_n$ | 5 | 5.004 | 5.008 | 5.010 | 5.010 | 5.007 | 4.999 | 4.985 | 4.965 | 4.938 | 4.903 |

**79.** $\dfrac{dy}{dx} = y, y = 3e^x, (0, 3)$

| $x$ | 0 | 0.2 | 0.4 | 0.6 | 0.8 | 1 |
|---|---|---|---|---|---|---|
| $y(x)$ (exact) | 3 | 3.6642 | 4.4755 | 5.4664 | 6.6766 | 8.1548 |
| $y(x)$ $(h = 0.2)$ | 3 | 3.6000 | 4.3200 | 5.1840 | 6.2208 | 7.4650 |
| $y(x)$ $(h = 0.1)$ | 3 | 3.6300 | 4.3923 | 5.3147 | 6.4308 | 7.7812 |

**80.** $\dfrac{dy}{dx} = \dfrac{2x}{y}, y = \sqrt{2x^2 + 4}, \quad (0, 2)$

| $x$ | 0 | 0.2 | 0.4 | 0.6 | 0.8 | 1 |
|---|---|---|---|---|---|---|
| $y(x)$ (exact) | 2 | 2.0199 | 2.0785 | 2.1726 | 2.2978 | 2.4495 |
| $y(x)$ $(h = 0.2)$ | 2 | 2.0000 | 2.0400 | 2.1184 | 2.2317 | 2.3751 |
| $y(x)$ $(h = 0.1)$ | 2 | 2.0100 | 2.0595 | 2.1460 | 2.2655 | 2.4131 |

**81.** $\frac{dy}{dx} = y + \cos x,\ y = \frac{1}{2}(\sin x - \cos x + e^x),\quad (0, 0)$

| $x$ | 0 | 0.2 | 0.4 | 0.6 | 0.8 | 1 |
|---|---|---|---|---|---|---|
| $y(x)$ (exact) | 0 | 0.2200 | 0.4801 | 0.7807 | 1.1231 | 1.5097 |
| $y(x)\ (h = 0.2)$ | 0 | 0.2000 | 0.4360 | 0.7074 | 1.0140 | 1.3561 |
| $y(x)\ (h = 0.1)$ | 0 | 0.2095 | 0.4568 | 0.7418 | 1.0649 | 1.4273 |

**82.** As $h$ increases (from 0.1 to 0.2), the error increases.

**83.** $\frac{dy}{dt} = -\frac{1}{2}(y - 72),\quad (0, 140),\ h = 0.1$

(a)

| $t$ | 0 | 1 | 2 | 3 |
|---|---|---|---|---|
| Euler | 140 | 112.7 | 96.4 | 86.6 |

(b) $y = 72 + 68e^{-t/2}$ exact

| $t$ | 0 | 1 | 2 | 3 |
|---|---|---|---|---|
| Exact | 140 | 113.24 | 97.016 | 87.173 |

(c) $\frac{dy}{dt} = -\frac{1}{2}(y - 72),\quad (0, 140),\ h = 0.05$

| $t$ | 0 | 1 | 2 | 3 |
|---|---|---|---|---|
| Euler | 140 | 112.98 | 96.7 | 86.9 |

The approximations are better using $h = 0.05$.

**84.** When $x = 0$, $y' = 0$, so (d) is not possible.

When $x, y > 0$, $y' < 0$ (decreasing function) so (c) is the equation.

**85.** The general solution is a family of curves that satisfies the differential equation. A particular solution is one member of the family that satisfies given conditions.

**86.** A slope field for the differential equation $y' = F(x, y)$ consists of small line segments at various points $(x, y)$ in the plane. The line segment equals the slope $y' = F(x, y)$ of the solution $y$ at the point $(x, y)$.

**87.** Consider $y' = F(x, y)$, $y(x_0) = y_0$. Begin with a point $(x_0, y_0)$ that satisfies the initial condition, $y(x_0) = y_0$. Then, using a step size of $h$, find the point $(x_1, y_1) = (x_0 + h, y_0 + hF(x_0, y_0))$. Continue generating the sequence of points $(x_{n+1}, y_{n+1}) = (x_n + h, y_n + hF(x_n, y_n))$.

**88.** $y = Ce^{kx}$

$\frac{dy}{dx} = Cke^{kx}$

Because $dy/dx = 0.07y$, you have $Cke^{kx} = 0.07Ce^{kx}$.

So, $k = 0.07$.

$C$ cannot be determined.

**89.** False. $y = x^3$ is a solution to $xy' - 3y = 0$, but $y = x^3 + 1$ is not a solution.

**90.** True

**91.** True

**92.** False. The slope field could represent many different differential equations, such as $y' = 2x + 4y$.

**93.** $\frac{dy}{dx} = -2y, y(0) = 4, y = 4e^{-2x}$

(a)

| $x$ | 0 | 0.2 | 0.4 | 0.6 | 0.8 | 1 |
|---|---|---|---|---|---|---|
| $y$ | 4 | 2.6813 | 1.7973 | 1.2048 | 0.8076 | 0.5413 |
| $y_1$ | 4 | 2.5600 | 1.6384 | 1.0486 | 0.6711 | 0.4295 |
| $y_2$ | 4 | 2.4000 | 1.4400 | 0.8640 | 0.5184 | 0.3110 |
| $e_1$ | 0 | 0.1213 | 0.1589 | 0.1562 | 0.1365 | 0.1118 |
| $e_2$ | 0 | 0.2813 | 0.3573 | 0.3408 | 0.2892 | 0.2303 |
| $r$ | | 0.4312 | 0.4447 | 0.4583 | 0.4720 | 0.4855 |

(b) If $h$ is halved, then the error is approximately halved $(r \approx 0.5)$.

(c) When $h = 0.05$, the errors will again be approximately halved.

**94.** $\frac{dy}{dx} = x - y, y(0) = 1, y = x - 1 + 2e^{-x}$

(a)

| $x$ | 0 | 0.2 | 0.4 | 0.6 | 0.8 | 1 |
|---|---|---|---|---|---|---|
| $y$ | 1 | 0.8375 | 0.7406 | 0.6976 | 0.6987 | 0.7358 |
| $y_1$ | 1 | 0.8200 | 0.7122 | 0.6629 | 0.6609 | 0.6974 |
| $y_2$ | 1 | 0.8000 | 0.6800 | 0.6240 | 0.6192 | 0.6554 |
| $e_1$ | 0 | 0.0175 | 0.0284 | 0.0347 | 0.0378 | 0.0384 |
| $e_2$ | 0 | 0.0375 | 0.0606 | 0.0736 | 0.0795 | 0.0804 |
| $r$ | | 0.47 | 0.47 | 0.47 | 0.48 | 0.48 |

(b) If $h$ is halved, then the error is halved $(r \approx 0.5)$.

(c) When $h = 0.05$, the error will again be approximately halved.

**95.** (a) $L\frac{dI}{dt} + RI = E(t)$

$4\frac{dI}{dt} + 12I = 24$

$\frac{dI}{dt} = \frac{1}{4}(24 - 12I) = 6 - 3I$

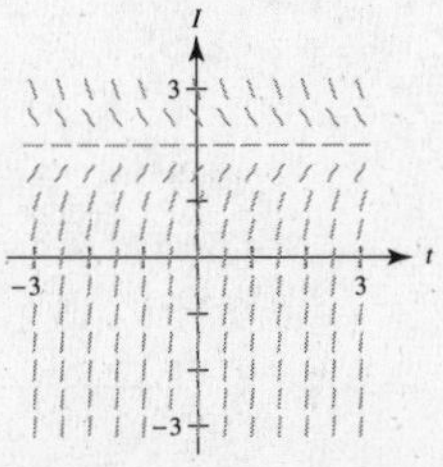

(b) As $t \to \infty$, $I \to 2$. That is, $\lim_{t\to\infty} I(t) = 2$. In fact, $I = 2$ is a solution to the differential equation.

**96.**

$$\begin{aligned} y &= e^{kt} \\ y' &= ke^{kt} \\ y'' &= k^2e^{kt} \\ y'' - 16y &= 0 \\ k^2e^{kt} - 16e^{kt} &= 0 \\ k^2 - 16 &= 0 \qquad (\text{because } e^{kt} \neq 0) \\ k &= \pm 4 \end{aligned}$$

**97.** $y = A \sin \omega t$

$y' = A\omega \cos \omega t$

$y'' = -A\omega^2 \sin \omega t$

$y'' + 16y = 0$

$-A\omega^2 \sin \omega t + 16A \sin \omega t = 0$

$A \sin \omega t\left[16 - \omega^2\right] = 0$

If $A \neq 0$, then $\omega = \pm 4$.

**98.** $f(x) + f''(x) = -xg(x)f'(x), \qquad g(x) \geq 0$

$$2f(x)f'(x) + 2f'(x)f''(x) = -2xg(x)\left[f'(x)\right]^2$$

$$\frac{d}{dx}\left[f(x)^2 + f'(x)^2\right] = -2x\, g(x)\left[f'(x)\right]^2$$

For $x < 0, -2x\, g(x)\left[f'(x)\right]^2 \geq 0$.

For $x > 0, -2x\, g(x)\left[f'(x)\right]^2 \leq 0$.

So, $f(x)^2 + f'(x)^2$ is increasing for $x < 0$ and decreasing for $x > 0$.

$f(x)^2 + f'(x)^2$ has a maximum at $x = 0$. So, it is bounded by its value at $x = 0$, $f(0)^2 + f'(0)^2$. So, $f$ (and $f'$) is bounded.

**99.** Let the vertical line $x = k$ cut the graph of the solution $y = f(x)$ at $(k, t)$. The tangent line at $(k, t)$ is

$$y - t = f'(k)(x - k)$$

Because $y' + p(x)y = q(x)$, you have

$$y - t = \left[q(k) - p(k)t\right](x - k)$$

For any value of $t$, this line passes through the point $\left(k + \frac{1}{p(k)}, \frac{q(k)}{p(k)}\right)$.

To see this, note that

$$\frac{q(k)}{p(k)} - t \stackrel{?}{=} \left[q(k) - p(k)t\right]\left(k + \frac{1}{p(k)} - k\right)$$

$$\stackrel{?}{=} q(k)k - p(k)tk + \frac{q(k)}{p(k)} - t - kq(k) + p(k)kt = \frac{q(k)}{p(k)} - t.$$

## Section 6.2 Differential Equations: Growth and Decay

**1.** $\dfrac{dy}{dx} = x + 3$

$$y = \int (x + 3)\, dx = \frac{x^2}{2} + 3x + C$$

**2.** $\dfrac{dy}{dx} = 6 - x$

$$y = \int (6 - x)\, dx = 6x - \frac{x^2}{2} + C$$

**3.** $\dfrac{dy}{dx} = y + 3$

$$\frac{dy}{y + 3} = dx$$

$$\int \frac{1}{y + 3}\, dy = \int dx$$

$$\ln|y + 3| = x + C_1$$

$$y + 3 = e^{x + C_1} = Ce^x$$

$$y = Ce^x - 3$$

**4.** $\dfrac{dy}{dx} = 6 - y$

$$\frac{dy}{6 - y} = dx$$

$$\int \frac{-1}{6 - y}\, dy = \int -dx$$

$$\ln|6 - y|dy = -x + C_1$$

$$6 - y = e^{-x + C_1} = Ce^{-x}$$

$$y = 6 - Ce^{-x}$$

**5.** $y' = \dfrac{5x}{y}$

$$yy' = 5x$$

$$\int yy'\, dx = \int 5x\, dx$$

$$\int y\, dy = \int 5x\, dx$$

$$\frac{1}{2}y^2 = \frac{5}{2}x^2 + C_1$$

$$y^2 - 5x^2 = C$$

**6.**
$$y' = \frac{\sqrt{x}}{7y}$$
$$7yy' = \sqrt{x}$$
$$\int 7yy'\,dx = \int \sqrt{x}\,dx$$
$$\frac{7y^2}{2} = \frac{2}{3}x^{3/2} + C_1$$
$$21y^2 - 4x^{3/2} = C$$

**7.**
$$y' = \sqrt{x}y$$
$$\frac{y'}{y} = \sqrt{x}$$
$$\int \frac{y'}{y}\,dx = \int \sqrt{x}\,dx$$
$$\int \frac{dy}{y} = \int \sqrt{x}\,dx$$
$$\ln|y| = \frac{2}{3}x^{3/2} + C_1$$
$$y = e^{(2/3)x^{3/2} + C_1}$$
$$= e^{C_1}e^{(2/3)x^{3/2}}$$
$$= Ce^{(2x^{3/2})/3}$$

**8.**
$$y' = x(1 + y)$$
$$\frac{y'}{1 + y} = x$$
$$\int \frac{y'}{1 + y}\,dx = \int x\,dx$$
$$\int \frac{dy}{1 + y} = \int x\,dx$$
$$\ln(1 + y) = \frac{x^2}{2} + C_1$$
$$1 + y = e^{(x^2/2) + C_1}$$
$$y = e^{C_1}e^{x^2/2} - 1$$
$$= Ce^{x^2/2} - 1$$

**9.** $(1 + x^2)y' - 2xy = 0$
$$y' = \frac{2xy}{1 + x^2}$$
$$\frac{y'}{y} = \frac{2x}{1 + x^2}$$
$$\int \frac{y'}{y}\,dx = \int \frac{2x}{1 + x^2}\,dx$$
$$\int \frac{dy}{y} = \int \frac{2x}{1 + x^2}\,dx$$
$$\ln|y| = \ln(1 + x^2) + C_1$$
$$\ln|y| = \ln(1 + x^2) + \ln C$$
$$\ln|y| = \ln\left[C(1 + x^2)\right]$$
$$y = C(1 + x^2)$$

**10.**
$$xy + y' = 100x$$
$$y' = 100x + xy = x(100 - y)$$
$$\frac{y'}{100 - y} = x$$
$$\int \frac{y'}{100 - y}\,dx = \int x\,dx$$
$$\int \frac{1}{100 - y}\,dy = \int x\,dx$$
$$-\ln(100 - y) = \frac{x^2}{2} + C_1$$
$$\ln(100 - y) = -\frac{x^2}{2} - C_1$$
$$100 - y = e^{-(x^2/2) - C_1}$$
$$-y = e^{-C_1}e^{-x^2/2} - 100$$
$$y = 100 - Ce^{-x^2/2}$$

**11.**
$$\frac{dQ}{dt} = \frac{k}{t^2}$$
$$\int \frac{dQ}{dt}\,dt = \int \frac{k}{t^2}\,dt$$
$$\int dQ = -\frac{k}{t} + C$$
$$Q = -\frac{k}{t} + C$$

**12.**
$$\frac{dP}{dt} = k(25 - t)$$
$$\int \frac{dP}{dt}\,dt = \int k(25 - t)\,dt$$
$$\int dP = -\frac{k}{2}(25 - t)^2 + C$$
$$P = -\frac{k}{2}(25 - t)^2 + C$$

**13.** $$\frac{dN}{ds} = k(500 - s)$$

$$\int \frac{dN}{ds}\,ds = \int k(500 - s)\,ds$$

$$\int dN = -\frac{k}{2}(500 - s)^2 + C$$

$$N = -\frac{k}{2}(500 - s)^2 + C$$

**14.** $$\frac{dy}{dx} = kx(L - y)$$

$$\frac{1}{L - y}\frac{dy}{dx} = kx$$

$$\int \frac{1}{L - y}\frac{dy}{dx}\,dx = \int kx\,dx$$

$$\int \frac{1}{L - y}\,dy = \frac{kx^2}{2} + C_1$$

$$-\ln(L - y) = \frac{kx^2}{2} + C_1$$

$$L - y = e^{-(kx^2/2) - C_1}$$

$$-y = -L + e^{-C_1}e^{-kx^2/2}$$

$$y = L - Ce^{-kx^2/2}$$

**15.** (a)

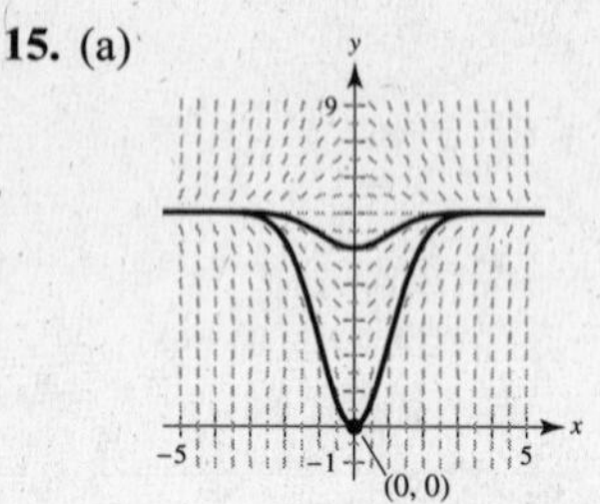


(b) $$\frac{dy}{dx} = x(6 - y), \quad (0, 0)$$

$$\frac{dy}{y - 6} = -x\,dx$$

$$\ln|y - 6| = -\frac{x^2}{2} + C$$

$$y - 6 = e^{-x^2/2 + C} = C_1e^{-x^2/2}$$

$$y = 6 + C_1e^{-x^2/2}$$

$$(0, 0):\ 0 = 6 + C_1 \Rightarrow C_1 = -6$$

$$y = 6 - 6e^{-x^2/2}$$

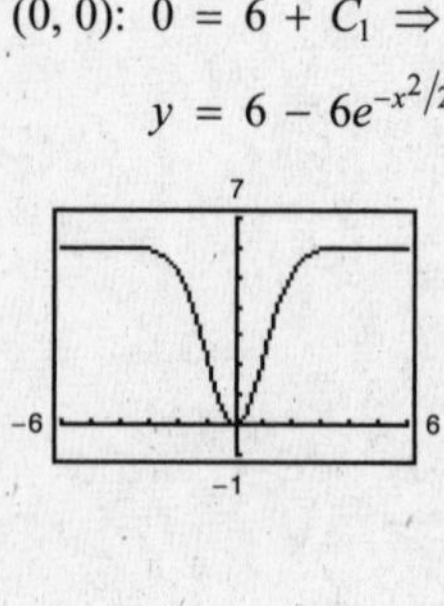


**16.** (a)

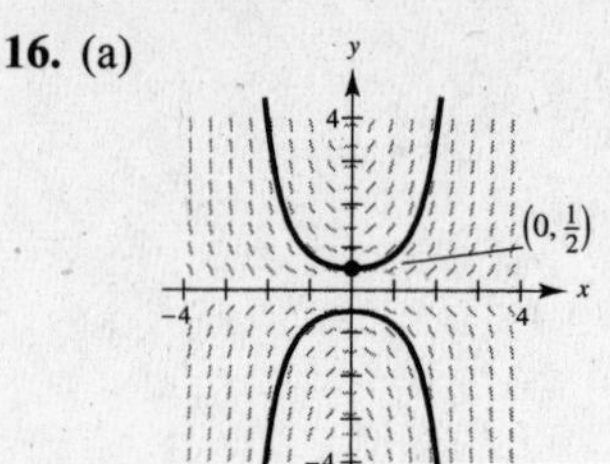


(b) $$\frac{dy}{dx} = xy, \quad \left(0, \frac{1}{2}\right)$$

$$\frac{dy}{y} = x\,dx$$

$$\ln|y| = \frac{x^2}{2} + C$$

$$y = e^{x^2/2 + C} = C_1e^{x^2/2}$$

$$\left(0, \frac{1}{2}\right):\ \frac{1}{2} = C_1e^0 \Rightarrow C_1 = \frac{1}{2}$$

$$y = \frac{1}{2}e^{x^2/2}$$

**17.** $$\frac{dy}{dt} = \frac{1}{2}t, \quad (0, 10)$$

$$\int dy = \int \frac{1}{2}t\,dt$$

$$y = \frac{1}{4}t^2 + C$$

$$10 = \frac{1}{4}(0)^2 + C \Rightarrow C = 10$$

$$y = \frac{1}{4}t^2 + 10$$

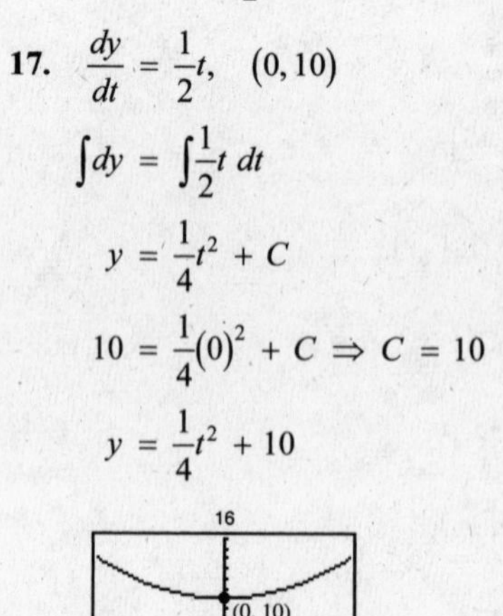


**18.** $$\frac{dy}{dt} = -\frac{3}{4}\sqrt{t}, \quad (0, 10)$$

$$\int dy = \int -\frac{3}{4}\sqrt{t}\,dt$$

$$y = -\frac{1}{2}t^{3/2} + C$$

$$10 = -\frac{1}{2}(0)^{3/2} + C \Rightarrow C = 10$$

$$y = -\frac{1}{2}t^{3/2} + 10$$

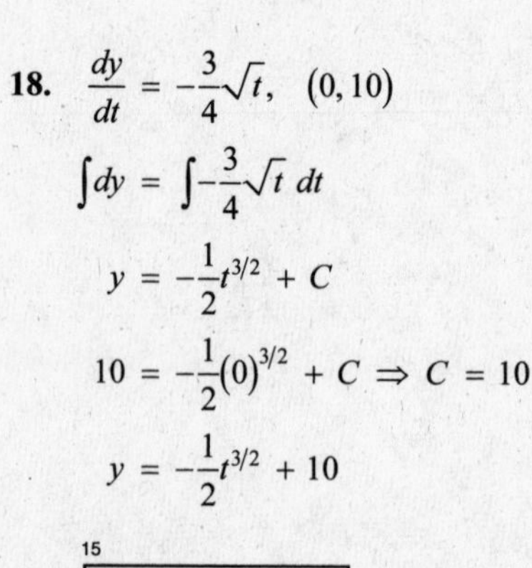

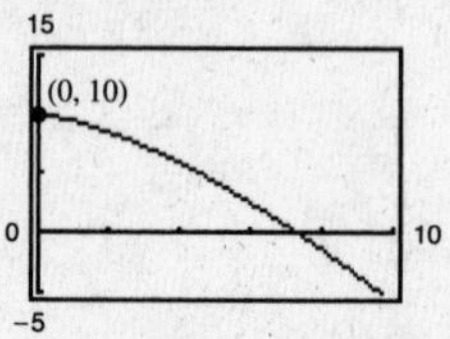

**19.** $\dfrac{dy}{dt} = -\dfrac{1}{2}y, \quad (0, 10)$

$$\int \frac{dy}{y} = \int -\frac{1}{2}\,dt$$

$$\ln|y| = -\frac{1}{2}t + C_1$$

$$y = e^{-(t/2)+C_1} = e^{C_1}e^{-t/2} = Ce^{-t/2}$$

$$10 = Ce^0 \Rightarrow C = 10$$

$$y = 10e^{-t/2}$$

16

(0, 10)

−1 10

−1

**20.** $\dfrac{dy}{dt} = \dfrac{3}{4}y, \quad (0, 10)$

$$\int \frac{dy}{y} = \int \frac{3}{4}\,dt$$

$$\ln y = \frac{3}{4}t + C_1$$

$$y = e^{(3/4)t + C_1}$$

$$= e^{C_1}e^{(3/4)t} = Ce^{3t/4}$$

$$10 = Ce^0 \Rightarrow C = 10$$

$$y = 10e^{3t/4}$$

40

(0, 10)

−5 5

−5

**21.** $\dfrac{dy}{dx} = ky$

$y = Ce^{kx}$ (Theorem 6.1)

$(0, 6)$: $6 = Ce^{k(0)} = C$

$(4, 15)$: $15 = 6e^{k(4)} \Rightarrow k = \dfrac{1}{4}\ln\left(\dfrac{5}{2}\right)$

$$y = 6e^{[(1/4)\ln(5/2)]x} \approx 6e^{0.2291x}$$

When $x = 8$,

$$y = 6e^{(1/4)\ln(5/2)(8)} = 6e^{\ln(5/2)^2} = 6\left(\frac{25}{4}\right) = \frac{75}{2}.$$

**22.** $\dfrac{dN}{dt} = kN$

$N = Ce^{kt}$ (Theorem 6.1)

$(0, 250)$: $C = 250$

$(1, 400)$: $400 = 250e^k \Rightarrow k = \ln\dfrac{400}{250} = \ln\dfrac{8}{5}$

$$N = 250e^{\ln(8/5)t} \approx 250e^{0.4700t}$$

When $t = 4$, $N = 250e^{4\ln(8/5)} = 250e^{\ln(8/5)^4}$

$$= 250\left(\frac{8}{5}\right)^4 = \frac{8192}{5}.$$

**23.** $\dfrac{dV}{dt} = kV$

$V = Ce^{kt}$ (Theorem 6.1)

$(0, 20{,}000)$: $C = 20{,}000$

$(4, 12{,}500)$: $12{,}500 = 20{,}000e^{4k} \Rightarrow k = \dfrac{1}{4}\ln\left(\dfrac{5}{8}\right)$

$$V = 20{,}000e^{[(1/4)\ln(5/8)]t} \approx 20{,}000e^{-0.1175t}$$

When $t = 6$, $V = 20{,}000e^{(1/4)\ln(5/8)(6)} = 20{,}000e^{\ln(5/8)^{3/2}}$

$$= 20{,}000\left(\frac{5}{8}\right)^{3/2} \approx 9882.118.$$

**24.** $\dfrac{dP}{dt} = kP$

$P = Ce^{kt}$ (Theorem 6.1)

$(0, 5000)$: $C = 5000$

$(1, 4750)$: $4750 = 5000e^k \Rightarrow k = \ln\left(\dfrac{19}{20}\right)$

$$P = 5000e^{\ln(19/20)t} \approx 5000e^{-0.0513t}$$

When $t = 5$, $P = 5000e^{\ln(19/20)(5)}$

$$= 5000\left(\frac{19}{20}\right)^5 \approx 3868.905.$$

**25.** $y = Ce^{kt}, \quad \left(0, \dfrac{1}{2}\right), (5, 5)$

$$C = \frac{1}{2}$$

$$y = \frac{1}{2}e^{kt}$$

$$5 = \frac{1}{2}e^{5k}$$

$$k = \frac{\ln 10}{5}$$

$$y = \frac{1}{2}e^{[(\ln 10)/5]t} = \frac{1}{2}\left(10^{t/5}\right) \text{ or } y \approx \frac{1}{2}e^{0.4605t}$$

**26.** $y = Ce^{kt}, \quad (0, 4), \left(5, \frac{1}{2}\right)$

$C = 4$

$y = 4e^{kt}$

$\frac{1}{2} = 4e^{5k}$

$k = \frac{\ln(1/8)}{5} \approx -0.4159$

$y = 4e^{-0.4159t}$

**27.** $y = Ce^{kt}, \quad (1, 5), (5, 2)$

$5 = Ce^{k} \Rightarrow 10 = 2Ce^{k}$

$2 = Ce^{5k} \Rightarrow 10 = 5Ce^{k}$

$2Ce^{k} = 5Ce^{5k}$

$2e^{k} = 5e^{5k}$

$\frac{2}{5} = e^{4k}$

$k = \frac{1}{4}\ln\left(\frac{2}{5}\right) = \ln\left(\frac{2}{5}\right)^{1/4}$

$C = 5e^{-k} = 5e^{(-1/4)\ln(2/5)} = 5\left(\frac{2}{5}\right)^{-1/4} = 5\left(\frac{5}{2}\right)^{1/4}$

$y = 5\left(\frac{5}{2}\right)^{1/4} e^{[(1/4)\ln(2/5)]t} \approx 6.2872\,e^{-0.2291t}$

**28.** $y = Ce^{kt}, \quad \left(3, \frac{1}{2}\right), (4, 5)$

$\frac{1}{2} = Ce^{3k} \Rightarrow 1 = 2Ce^{3k}$

$5 = Ce^{4k} \Rightarrow 1 = \frac{1}{5}Ce^{4k}$

$2Ce^{3k} = \frac{1}{5}Ce^{4k}$

$10e^{3k} = e^{4k}$

$10 = e^{k}$

$k = \ln 10 \approx 2.3026$

$y = Ce^{2.3026t}$

$5 = Ce^{2.3026(4)}$

$C \approx 0.0005$

$y = 0.0005e^{2.3026t}$

**29.** In the model $y = Ce^{kt}$, $C$ represents the initial value of $y$ (when $t = 0$). $k$ is the proportionality constant.

**30.** $y' = \frac{dy}{dt} = ky$

**31.** $\frac{dy}{dx} = \frac{1}{2}xy$

$\frac{dy}{dx} > 0$ when $xy > 0$. Quadrants I and III.

**32.** $\frac{dy}{dx} = \frac{1}{2}x^2y$

$\frac{dy}{dx} > 0$ when $y > 0$. Quadrants I and II.

**33.** Because the initial quantity is 20 grams,

$y = 20e^{kt}$.

Because the half-life is 1599 years,

$10 = 20e^{k(1599)}$

$k = \frac{1}{1599}\ln\left(\frac{1}{2}\right)$.

So, $y = 20e^{[\ln(1/2)/1599]t}$.

When $t = 1000$, $y = 20e^{[\ln(1/2)/1599](1000)} \approx 12.96$ g.

When $t = 10{,}000$, $y \approx 0.26$ g.

**34.** Because the half-life is 1599 years,

$\frac{1}{2} = 1e^{k(1599)}$

$k = \frac{1}{1599}\ln\left(\frac{1}{2}\right)$.

Because there are 1.5 grams after 1000 years,

$1.5 = Ce^{[\ln(1/2)/1599](1000)}$

$C \approx 2.314$.

So, the initial quantity is approximately 2.314 g.

When $t = 10{,}000$, $y = 2.314e^{[\ln(1/2)/1599](10{,}000)}$

$\approx 0.03$ g.

**35.** Because the half-life is 1599 years,

$\frac{1}{2} = 1e^{k(1599)}$

$k = \frac{1}{1599}\ln\left(\frac{1}{2}\right)$.

Because there is 0.1 gram after 10,000 years,

$0.1 = Ce^{[\ln(1/2)/1599](10{,}000)}$

$C \approx 7.63$.

So, the initial quantity is approximately 7.63 g.

When $t = 1000$, $y = 7.63e^{[\ln(1/2)/1599](1000)}$

$\approx 4.95$ g.

**36.** Because the half-life is 5715 years,

$\frac{1}{2} = 1e^{k(5715)}$

$k = \frac{1}{5715}\ln\left(\frac{1}{2}\right).$

Because there are 3 grams after 10,000 years,

$3 = Ce^{[\ln(1/2)/5715](10{,}000)}$

$C \approx 10.089.$

So, the initial quantity is approximately 10.09 g.

When $t = 1000$, $y = 10.09e^{[\ln(1/2)/5715](1000)}$

$\approx 8.94$ g.

**37.** Because the initial quantity is 5 grams, $C = 5$.

Because the half-life is 5715 years,

$2.5 = 5e^{k(5715)}$

$k = \frac{1}{5715}\ln\left(\frac{1}{2}\right).$

When $t = 1000$ years, $y = 5e^{[\ln(1/2)/5715](1000)} \approx 4.43$ g.

When $t = 10{,}000$ years, $y = 5e^{[\ln(1/2)/5715](10{,}000)}$

$\approx 1.49$ g.

**38.** Because the half-life is 5715 years,

$\frac{1}{2} = 1e^{k(5715)}$

$k = \frac{1}{5715}\ln\left(\frac{1}{2}\right).$

Because there are 1.6 grams when $t = 1000$ years,

$1.6 = Ce^{[\ln(1/2)/5715](1000)}$

$C \approx 1.806.$

So, the initial quantity is approximately 1.806 g.

When $t = 10{,}000$, $y = 1.806e^{[\ln(1/2)/5715](10{,}000)}$

$\approx 0.54$ g.

**39.** Because the half-life is 24,100 years,

$\frac{1}{2} = 1e^{k(24{,}100)}$

$k = \frac{1}{24{,}100}\ln\left(\frac{1}{2}\right).$

Because there are 2.1 grams after 1000 years,

$2.1 = Ce^{[\ln(1/2)/24{,}100](1000)}$

$C \approx 2.161.$

So, the initial quantity is approximately 2.161 g.

When $t = 10{,}000$, $y = 2.161e^{[\ln(1/2)/24{,}100](10{,}000)}$

$\approx 1.62$ g.

**40.** Because the half-life is 24,100 years,

$\frac{1}{2} = 1e^{k(24{,}100)}$

$k = \frac{1}{24{,}100}\ln\left(\frac{1}{2}\right).$

Because there is 0.4 gram after 10,000 years,

$0.4 = Ce^{[\ln(1/2)/24{,}100](10{,}000)}$

$C \approx 0.533.$

So, the initial quantity is approximately 0.533 g.

When $t = 1000$, $y = 0.533e^{[\ln(1/2)/24{,}100](1000)}$

$\approx 0.52$ g.

**41.** $y = Ce^{kt}$

$\frac{1}{2}C = Ce^{k(1599)}$

$k = \frac{1}{1599}\ln\left(\frac{1}{2}\right)$

When $t = 100$, $y = Ce^{[\ln(1/2)/1599](100)}$

$\approx 0.9576C$

So, 95.76% remains after 100 years.

**42.** $y = Ce^{kt}$

$\frac{1}{2}C = Ce^{k(5715)}$

$k = \frac{1}{5715}\ln\left(\frac{1}{2}\right)$

$0.15C = Ce^{[\ln(1/2)/5715]t}$

$\ln(0.15) = \frac{\ln\left(\frac{1}{2}\right)t}{5715}$

$t \approx 15{,}641.8$ years

**43.** Because $A = 4000e^{0.06t}$, the time to double is given by

$8000 = 4000e^{0.06t}$

$2 = e^{0.06t}$

$\ln 2 = 0.06t$

$t = \frac{\ln 2}{0.06} \approx 11.55$ years.

Amount after 10 years: $A = 4000e^{(0.06)(10)} \approx \$7288.48$

**44.** Because $A = 18{,}000e^{0.055t}$, the time to double is given by

$36{,}000 = 18{,}000e^{0.055t}$

$2 = e^{0.055t}$

$\ln 2 = 0.055t$

$t = \frac{\ln 2}{0.055} \approx 12.6$ years.

Amount after 10 years:

$A = 18{,}000e^{(0.055)(10)} \approx \$31{,}198.55$

**45.** Because $A = 750e^{rt}$ and $A = 1500$ when $t = 7.75$, you have the following.

$$1500 = 750e^{7.75r}$$

$$r = \frac{\ln 2}{7.75} \approx 0.0894 = 8.94\%$$

Amount after 10 years: $A = 750e^{0.0894(10)} \approx \$1833.67$

**46.** Because $A = 12{,}500e^{rt}$ and $A = 25{,}000$ when $t = 5$, you have the following.

$$25{,}000 = 12{,}500e^{5r}$$

$$r = \frac{\ln 2}{5} \approx 0.1386 = 13.86\%$$

Amount after 10 years:
$A = 12{,}500e^{[(\ln 2)/5](10)} = \$50{,}000$

**47.** Because $A = 500e^{rt}$ and $A = 1292.85$ when $t = 10$, you have the following.

$$1292.85 = 500e^{10r}$$

$$r = \frac{\ln(1292.85/500)}{10} \approx 0.0950 = 9.50\%$$

The time to double is given by

$$1000 = 500e^{0.0950t}$$

$$t = \frac{\ln 2}{0.095} \approx 7.30 \text{ years.}$$

**48.** Because $A = 2000e^{rt}$ and $A = 5436.56$ when $t = 10$, you have the following.

$$5436.56 = 2000e^{10r}$$

$$r = \frac{\ln(5436.56/2000)}{10} \approx 0.10 = 10\%$$

The time to double is given by

$$4000 = 2000e^{0.10t}$$

$$t = \frac{\ln 2}{0.10} \approx 6.93 \text{ years.}$$

**49.** $1{,}000{,}000 = P\left(1 + \frac{0.075}{12}\right)^{(12)(20)}$

$$P = 1{,}000{,}000\left(1 + \frac{0.075}{12}\right)^{-240}$$

$$\approx \$224{,}174.18$$

**50.** $1{,}000{,}000 = P\left(1 + \frac{0.06}{12}\right)^{(12)(40)}$

$$P = 1{,}000{,}000(1.005)^{-480} \approx \$91{,}262.08$$

**51.** $1{,}000{,}000 = P\left(1 + \frac{0.08}{12}\right)^{(12)(35)}$

$$P = 1{,}000{,}000\left(1 + \frac{0.08}{12}\right)^{-420}$$

$$= \$61{,}377.75$$

**52.** $1{,}000{,}000 = P\left(1 + \frac{0.09}{12}\right)^{(12)(25)}$

$$P = 1{,}000{,}000\left(1 + \frac{0.09}{12}\right)^{-300}$$

$$\approx \$106{,}287.83$$

**53.** (a) $2000 = 1000(1 + 0.07)^t$

$$2 = 1.07^t$$

$$\ln 2 = t \ln 1.07$$

$$t = \frac{\ln 2}{\ln 1.07} \approx 10.24 \text{ years}$$

(b) $2000 = 1000\left(1 + \frac{0.07}{12}\right)^{12t}$

$$2 = \left(1 + \frac{0.007}{12}\right)^{12t}$$

$$\ln 2 = 12t \ln\left(1 + \frac{0.07}{12}\right)$$

$$t = \frac{\ln 2}{12 \ln\left(1 + (0.07/12)\right)} \approx 9.93 \text{ years}$$

(c) $2000 = 1000\left(1 + \frac{0.07}{365}\right)^{365t}$

$$2 = \left(1 + \frac{0.07}{365}\right)^{365t}$$

$$\ln 2 = 365t \ln\left(1 + \frac{0.07}{365}\right)$$

$$t = \frac{\ln 2}{365 \ln\left(1 + (0.07/365)\right)} \approx 9.90 \text{ years}$$

(d) $2000 = 1000e^{(0.07)t}$

$$2 = e^{0.07t}$$

$$\ln 2 = 0.07t$$

$$t = \frac{\ln 2}{0.07} \approx 9.90 \text{ years}$$

**54.** (a) $2000 = 1000(1 + 0.6)^t$

$2 = 1.06^t$

$\ln 2 = t \ln 1.06$

$t = \dfrac{\ln 2}{\ln 1.06} \approx 11.90$ years

(b) $2000 = 1000\left(1 + \dfrac{0.06}{12}\right)^{12t}$

$2 = \left(1 + \dfrac{0.06}{12}\right)^{12t}$

$\ln 2 = 12t \ln\left(1 + \dfrac{0.06}{12}\right)$

$t = \dfrac{1}{12}\dfrac{\ln 2}{\ln\left(1 + \dfrac{0.06}{12}\right)} \approx 11.58$ years

(c) $2000 = 1000\left(1 + \dfrac{0.06}{365}\right)^{365t}$

$2 = \left(1 + \dfrac{0.06}{365}\right)^{365t}$

$\ln 2 = 365t \ln\left(1 + \dfrac{0.06}{365}\right)$

$t = \dfrac{1}{365}\dfrac{\ln 2}{\ln\left(1 + \dfrac{0.06}{365}\right)} \approx 11.55$ years

(d) $2000 = 1000e^{0.06t}$

$2 = e^{0.06t}$

$\ln 2 = 0.06t$

$t = \dfrac{\ln 2}{0.06} \approx 11.55$ years

**55.** (a) $2000 = 1000(1 + 0.085)^t$

$2 = 1.085^t$

$\ln 2 = t \ln 1.085$

$t = \dfrac{\ln 2}{\ln 1.085} \approx 8.50$ years

(b) $2000 = 1000\left(1 + \dfrac{0.085}{12}\right)^{12t}$

$2 = \left(1 + \dfrac{0.085}{12}\right)^{12t}$

$\ln 2 = 12t \ln\left(1 + \dfrac{0.085}{12}\right)$

$t = \dfrac{1}{12}\dfrac{\ln 2}{\ln\left(1 + \dfrac{0.085}{12}\right)} \approx 8.18$ years

(c) $2000 = 1000\left(1 + \dfrac{0.085}{365}\right)^{365t}$

$2 = \left(1 + \dfrac{0.085}{365}\right)^{365t}$

$\ln 2 = 365t \ln\left(1 + \dfrac{0.085}{365}\right)$

$t = \dfrac{1}{365}\dfrac{\ln 2}{\ln\left(1 + \dfrac{0.085}{365}\right)} \approx 8.16$ years

(d) $2000 = 1000e^{0.085t}$

$2 = e^{0.085t}$

$\ln 2 = 0.085t$

$t = \dfrac{\ln 2}{0.085} \approx 8.15$ years

**56.** (a) $2000 = 1000(1 + 0.055)^t$

$2 = 1.055^t$

$\ln 2 = t \ln 1.055$

$t = \dfrac{\ln 2}{\ln 1.055} \approx 12.95$ years

(b) $2000 = 1000\left(1 + \dfrac{0.055}{12}\right)^{12t}$

$2 = \left(1 + \dfrac{0.055}{12}\right)^{12t}$

$\ln 2 = 12t \ln\left(1 + \dfrac{0.055}{12}\right)$

$t = \dfrac{1}{12}\dfrac{\ln 2}{\ln\left(1 + \dfrac{0.055}{12}\right)} \approx 12.63$ years

(c) $2000 = 1000\left(1 + \dfrac{0.055}{365}\right)^{365t}$

$2 = \left(1 + \dfrac{0.055}{365}\right)^{365t}$

$\ln 2 = 365t \ln\left(1 + \dfrac{0.055}{365}\right)$

$t = \dfrac{1}{365}\dfrac{\ln 2}{\ln\left(1 + \dfrac{0.055}{365}\right)} \approx 12.60$ years

(d) $2000 = 1000e^{0.055t}$

$2 = e^{0.055t}$

$\ln 2 = 0.055t$

$t = \dfrac{\ln 2}{0.055} \approx 12.60$ years

**57.** (a) $P = Ce^{kt} = Ce^{-0.006t}$

$P(7) = 2.3 = Ce^{-0.006(7)} \Rightarrow C \approx 2.40$

$P = 2.40e^{-0.006t}$

(b) For $t = 15$, $P = 2.40e^{-0.006(15)} \approx 2.19$ million.

(c) Because $k < 0$, the population is decreasing.

**58.** (a) $P = Ce^{kt} = Ce^{0.017t}$

$P(7) = 80.3 = Ce^{0.017(7)} \Rightarrow C \approx 71.29$

$P = 71.29e^{0.017t}$

(b) For $t = 15$, $P = 71.29e^{0.017(15)} \approx 92.0$ million.

(c) Because $k > 0$, the population is increasing.

**59.** (a) $P = Ce^{kt} = Ce^{0.024t}$

$P(7) = 6.7 = Ce^{0.024(7)} \Rightarrow C \approx 5.66$

$P = 5.66e^{0.024t}$

(b) For $t = 15$, $P = 5.66e^{0.024(15)} \approx 8.11$ million.

(c) Because $k > 0$, the population is increasing.

**60.** (a) $P = Ce^{kt} = Ce^{-0.003t}$

$P(7) = 10.0 = Ce^{-0.003(7)} \Rightarrow C \approx 10.21$

$P = 10.21e^{-0.003t}$

(b) For $t = 15$, $P = 10.21e^{-0.003(15)} \approx 9.76$ million.

(c) Because $k < 0$, the population is decreasing.

**61.** (a) $P = Ce^{kt} = Ce^{0.036t}$

$P(7) = 30.3 = Ce^{0.036(7)} \Rightarrow C \approx 23.55$

$P = 23.55e^{0.036t}$

(b) For $t = 15$, $P = 23.55e^{0.036(15)} \approx 40.41$ million.

(c) Because $k > 0$, the population is increasing.

**62.** (a) Because the population increases by a constant each month, the rate of change from month to month will always be the same. So, the slope is constant, and the model is linear.

(b) Although the percentage increase is constant each month, the rate of growth is not constant. The rate of change of $y$ is given by

$$\frac{dy}{dt} = ry$$

which is an exponential model.

**63.** (a) $N = 100.1596(1.2455)^t$

(b) $N = 400$ when $t = 6.3$ hours (graphing utility)

Analytically,

$$400 = 100.1596(1.2455)^t$$

$$1.2455^t = \frac{400}{100.1596} = 3.9936$$

$$t \ln 1.2455 = \ln 3.9936$$

$$t = \frac{\ln 3.9936}{\ln 1.2455} \approx 6.3 \text{ hours.}$$

**64.** (a) Let $y = Ce^{kt}$.

At time 2: $125 = Ce^{k(2)} \Rightarrow C = 125e^{-2k}$

At time 4:

$$350 = Ce^{k(4)} \Rightarrow 350 = \left(125e^{-2k}\right)\left(e^{4k}\right)$$

$$\tfrac{14}{5} = e^{2k}$$

$$2k = \ln \tfrac{14}{5}$$

$$k = \tfrac{1}{2} \ln \tfrac{14}{5} \approx 0.5148$$

$$C = 125e^{-2k}$$

$$= 125e^{-2(1/2)\ln(14/5)}$$

$$= 125\left(\tfrac{5}{14}\right) = \tfrac{625}{14} \approx 44.64$$

Approximately 45 bacteria at time 0.

(b) $y = \frac{625}{14}e^{(1/2)\ln(14/5)t} \approx 44.64e^{0.5148t}$

(c) When $t = 8$,

$$y = \tfrac{625}{14}e^{(1/2)\ln(14/5)8} = \tfrac{625}{14}\left(\tfrac{14}{5}\right)^4 = 2744.$$

(d) $25{,}000 = \frac{625}{14}e^{(1/2)\ln(14/5)t} \Rightarrow t \approx 12.29$ hours

**65.** (a) $19 = 30\left(1 - e^{20k}\right)$

$$30e^{20k} = 11$$

$$k = \frac{\ln(11/30)}{20} \approx -0.0502$$

$$N \approx 30\left(1 - e^{-0.0502t}\right)$$

(b) $25 = 30\left(1 - e^{-0.0502t}\right)$

$$e^{-0.0502t} = \frac{1}{6}$$

$$t = \frac{-\ln 6}{-0.0502} \approx 36 \text{ days}$$

**66.** (a) $20 = 30\left(1 - e^{30k}\right)$

$30e^{30k} = 10$

$k = \dfrac{\ln(1/3)}{30} = \dfrac{-\ln 3}{30} \approx -0.0366$

$N \approx 30\left(1 - e^{-0.0366t}\right)$

(b) $25 = 30\left(1 - e^{-0.0366t}\right)$

$e^{-0.0366t} = \dfrac{1}{6}$

$t = \dfrac{-\ln 6}{-0.0366} \approx 49 \text{ days}$

**67.** (a) $P_1 = Ce^{kt} = 181e^{kt}$

$205 = 181e^{10k} \Rightarrow k = \dfrac{1}{10}\ln\left(\dfrac{205}{181}\right) \approx 0.01245$

$P_1 \approx 181e^{0.01245t} \approx 181(1.01253)^t$

(b) Using a graphing utility, $P_2 \approx 182.3248(1.01091)^t$.

(c)

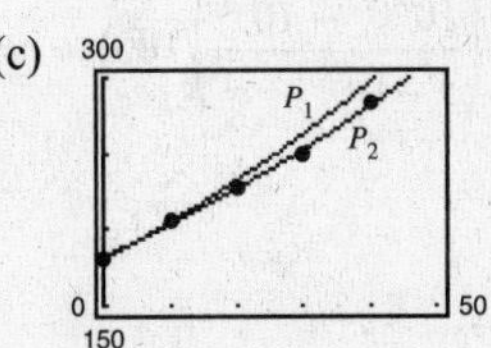


The model $P_2$ fits the data better.

(d) Using the model $P_2$,

$320 = 182.3248(1.01091)^t$

$\dfrac{320}{182.3248} = (1.01091)^t$

$t = \dfrac{\ln(320/182.3248)}{\ln(1.01091)}$

$\approx 51.8$ years, or 2011.

**68.** (a) $R = 1654.2353(1.0590)^t = 1654.2353\,e^{0.0573t}$

$I = 0.01942t^4 - 1.3690t^3 + 21.970t^2 - 93.66t + 435.6$

(b)

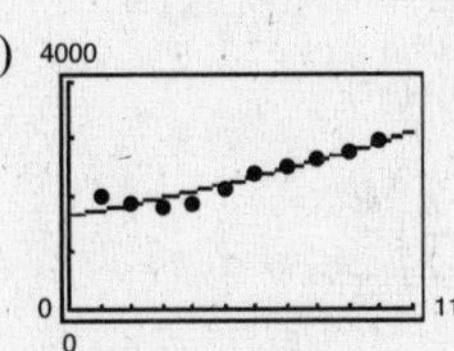


According to the model, $R'(t) \approx 94.79e^{0.0573t}$.

(c)

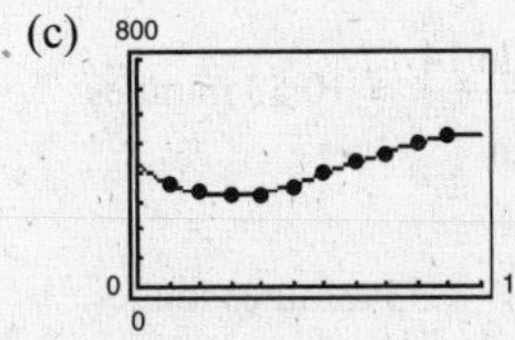


(d) $P(t) = \dfrac{I}{R}$

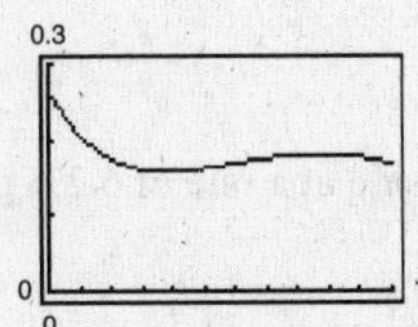


**69.** $\beta(I) = 10\log_{10}\dfrac{I}{I_0},\ I_0 = 10^{-16}$

(a) $\beta\left(10^{-14}\right) = 10\log_{10}\dfrac{10^{-14}}{10^{-16}} = 20 \text{ decibels}$

(b) $\beta\left(10^{-9}\right) = 10\log_{10}\dfrac{10^{-9}}{10^{-16}} = 70 \text{ decibels}$

(c) $\beta\left(10^{-6.5}\right) = 10\log_{10}\dfrac{10^{-6.5}}{10^{-16}} = 95 \text{ decibels}$

(d) $\beta\left(10^{-4}\right) = 10\log_{10}\dfrac{10^{-4}}{10^{-16}} = 120 \text{ decibels}$

**70.** $93 = 10\log_{10}\frac{I}{10^{-16}} = 10(\log_{10} I + 16)$

$-6.7 = \log_{10} I \Rightarrow I = 10^{-6.7}$

$80 = 10\log_{10}\frac{I}{10^{-16}} = 10(\log_{10} I + 16)$

$-8 = \log_{10} I \Rightarrow I = 10^{-8}$

Percentage decrease: $\left(\frac{10^{-6.7} - 10^{-8}}{10^{-6.7}}\right)(100) \approx 95\%$

**71.** $A(t) = V(t)e^{-0.10t}$

$= 100{,}000e^{0.8\sqrt{t}}e^{-0.10t}$

$= 100{,}000e^{0.8\sqrt{t}-0.10t}$

$\frac{dA}{dt} = 100{,}000\left(\frac{0.4}{\sqrt{t}} - 0.10\right)e^{0.8\sqrt{t}-0.10t}$

$= 0$ when $t = 16$.

The timber should be harvested in the year 2024, $(2008 + 16)$. **Note:** You could also use a graphing utility to graph $A(t)$ and find the maximum of $A(t)$. Use the viewing rectangle $0 \le x \le 30$ and $0 \le y \le 600{,}000$.

**72.** $R = \frac{\ln I - \ln I_0}{\ln 10} = \frac{\ln I - 0}{\ln 10}, I = e^{R\ln 10} = 10^R$

(a) $8.3 = \frac{\ln I - \ln I_0}{\ln 10}$

$I = 10^{8.3} \approx 199{,}526{,}231.5$

(b) $2R = \frac{\ln I - \ln I_0}{\ln 10}$

$I = e^{2R\ln 10} = e^{2R\ln 10} = \left(e^{R\ln 10}\right)^2 = \left(10^R\right)^2$

Increases by a factor of $e^{2R\ln 10}$ or $10^R$.

(c) $R = \frac{\ln I - \ln I_0}{\ln 10}$

$\frac{dR}{dI} = \frac{1}{I\ln(10)}$

**73.** Because $\frac{dy}{dt} = k(y - 80)$

$\int \frac{1}{y - 80}\,dy = \int k\,dt$

$\ln(y - 80) = kt + C.$

When $t = 0$, $y = 1500$. So, $C = \ln 1420$.

When $t = 1$, $y = 1120$. So,

$k(1) + \ln 1420 = \ln(1120 - 80)$

$k = \ln 1040 - \ln 1420 = \ln\frac{104}{142}.$

So, $y = 1420e^{[\ln(104/142)]t} + 80.$

When $t = 5$, $y \approx 379.2$°F.

**74.** $\frac{dy}{dt} = k(y - 20)$

$y = 20 + Ce^{kt}$ (See Example 6)

$160 = 20 + Ce^{k(0)} \Rightarrow C = 140$

$60 = 20 + 140e^{k(5)}$

$\frac{2}{7} = e^{5k}$

$k = \frac{1}{5}\ln\left(\frac{2}{7}\right) \approx -0.25055$

$30 = 20 + 140e^{(1/5)\ln(2/7)t}$

$\frac{1}{14} = e^{\ln(2/7)t/5} = \left(\frac{2}{7}\right)^{t/5}$

$\ln\frac{1}{14} = \frac{t}{5}\ln\frac{2}{7}$

$t = \frac{5\ln\frac{1}{14}}{\ln\frac{2}{7}} = \frac{5\ln 14}{\ln\frac{7}{2}} \approx 10.53$ minutes

It will take $10.53 - 5 = 5.53$ minutes longer.

**75.** False. If $y = Ce^{kt}$, $y' = Cke^{kt} \ne$ constant.

**76.** True

**77.** False. The prices are rising at a rate of 6.2% per year.

**78.** True

## Section 6.3 Differential Equations: Separation of Variables

**1.** $\dfrac{dy}{dx} = \dfrac{x}{y}$

$\int y\,dy = \int x\,dx$

$\dfrac{y^2}{2} = \dfrac{x^2}{2} + C_1$

$y^2 - x^2 = C$

**2.** $\dfrac{dy}{dx} = \dfrac{3x^2}{y^2}$

$\int y^2\,dy = \int 3x^2\,dx$

$\dfrac{y^3}{3} = x^3 + C_1$

$y^3 - 3x^3 = C$

**3.** $x^2 + 5y\dfrac{dy}{dx} = 0$

$5y\dfrac{dy}{dx} = -x^2$

$\int 5y\,dy = \int -x^2\,dx$

$\dfrac{5y^2}{2} = -\dfrac{x^3}{3} + C_1$

$15y^2 + 2x^3 = C$

**4.** $\dfrac{dy}{dx} = \dfrac{x^2 - 3}{6y^2}$

$\int 6y^2\,dy = \int (x^2 - 3)\,dx$

$2y^3 = \dfrac{x^3}{3} - 3x + C_1$

$6y^3 - x^3 + 9x = C$

**5.** $\dfrac{dr}{ds} = 0.75\,r$

$\int \dfrac{dr}{r} = \int 0.75\,ds$

$\ln|r| = 0.75\,s + C_1$

$r = e^{0.75s + C_1}$

$r = Ce^{0.75s}$

**6.** $\dfrac{dr}{ds} = 0.75\,s$

$\int dr = \int 0.75\,s\,ds$

$r = 0.75\dfrac{s^2}{2} + C$

$r = 0.375\,s^2 + C$

**7.** $(2 + x)y' = 3y$

$\int \dfrac{dy}{y} = \int \dfrac{3}{2 + x}\,dx$

$\ln|y| = 3\ln|2 + x| + \ln C = \ln\left|C(2 + x)^3\right|$

$y = C(x + 2)^3$

**8.** $xy' = y$

$\int \dfrac{dy}{y} = \int \dfrac{dx}{x}$

$\ln y = \ln x + \ln C = \ln Cx$

$y = Cx$

**9.** $yy' = 4\sin x$

$y\dfrac{dy}{dx} = 4\sin x$

$\int y\,dy = \int 4\sin x\,dx$

$\dfrac{y^2}{2} = -4\cos x + C_1$

$y^2 = C - 8\cos x$

**10.** $yy' = -8\cos(\pi x)$

$y\dfrac{dy}{dx} = -8\cos(\pi x)$

$\int y\,dy = \int -8\cos(\pi x)\,dx$

$\dfrac{y^2}{2} = -\dfrac{8\sin(\pi x)}{\pi} + C$

$y^2 = -\dfrac{16}{\pi}\sin(\pi x) + C$

**11.** $\sqrt{1 - 4x^2}\,y' = x$

$dy = \dfrac{x}{\sqrt{1 - 4x^2}}\,dx$

$\int dy = \int \dfrac{x}{\sqrt{1 - 4x^2}}\,dx$

$= -\dfrac{1}{8}\int (1 - 4x^2)^{-1/2}(-8x\,dx)$

$y = -\dfrac{1}{4}\sqrt{1 - 4x^2} + C$

**12.** $\sqrt{x^2 - 16}\,y' = 11x$

$\dfrac{dy}{dx} = \dfrac{11x}{\sqrt{x^2 - 16}}$

$\int dy = \int \dfrac{11x}{\sqrt{x^2 - 16}}\,dx$

$y = 11\sqrt{x^2 - 16} + C$

**13.** $y \ln x - xy' = 0$

$$\int \frac{dy}{y} = \int \frac{\ln x}{x}\,dx \quad \left(u = \ln x,\ du = \frac{dx}{x}\right)$$

$$\ln|y| = \frac{1}{2}(\ln x)^2 + C_1$$

$$y = e^{(1/2)(\ln x)^2 + C_1} = Ce^{(\ln x)^2/2}$$

**14.** $12yy' - 7e^x = 0$

$$12y\frac{dy}{dx} = 7e^x$$

$$\int 12y\,dy = \int 7e^x\,dx$$

$$6y^2 = 7e^x + C$$

**15.** $yy' - 2e^x = 0$

$$y\frac{dy}{dx} = 2e^x$$

$$\int y\,dy = \int 2e^x\,dx$$

$$\frac{y^2}{2} = 2e^x + C$$

Initial condition $(0, 3)$: $\frac{9}{2} = 2 + C \Rightarrow C = \frac{5}{2}$

Particular solution: $\frac{y^2}{2} = 2e^x + \frac{5}{2}$

$$y^2 = 4e^x + 5$$

**16.** $\sqrt{x} + \sqrt{y}y' = 0$

$$\int y^{1/2}dy = -\int x^{1/2}\,dx$$

$$\frac{2}{3}y^{3/2} = -\frac{2}{3}x^{3/2} + C_1$$

$$y^{3/2} + x^{3/2} = C$$

Initial condition $(1, 9)$:

$$(9)^{3/2} + (1)^{3/2} = 27 + 1 = 28 = C$$

Particular solution: $y^{3/2} + x^{3/2} = 28$

**17.** $y(x + 1) + y' = 0$

$$\int \frac{dy}{y} = -\int (x + 1)\,dx$$

$$\ln|y| = -\frac{(x + 1)^2}{2} + C_1$$

$$y = Ce^{-(x+1)^2/2}$$

Initial condition $(-2, 1)$: $1 = Ce^{-1/2}, C = e^{1/2}$

Particular solution: $y = e^{\left[1-(x+1)^2\right]/2} = e^{-\left(x^2+2x\right)/2}$

**18.** $2xy' - \ln x^2 = 0$

$$2x\frac{dy}{dx} = 2\ln x$$

$$\int dy = \int \frac{\ln x}{x}\,dx$$

$$y = \frac{(\ln x)^2}{2} + C$$

Initial condition $(1, 2)$: $2 = C$

Particular solution: $y = \frac{1}{2}(\ln x)^2 + 2$

**19.** $y(1 + x^2)y' = x(1 + y^2)$

$$\frac{y}{1 + y^2}\,dy = \frac{x}{1 + x^2}\,dx$$

$$\frac{1}{2}\ln(1 + y^2) = \frac{1}{2}\ln(1 + x^2) + C_1$$

$$\ln(1 + y^2) = \ln(1 + x^2) + \ln C = \ln\left[C(1 + x^2)\right]$$

$$1 + y^2 = C(1 + x^2)$$

Initial condition $(0, \sqrt{3})$: $1 + 3 = C \Rightarrow C = 4$

Particular solution: $1 + y^2 = 4(1 + x^2)$

$$y^2 = 3 + 4x^2$$

**20.** $y\sqrt{1 - x^2}\frac{dy}{dx} = x\sqrt{1 - y^2}$

$$\int (1 - y^2)^{-1/2}y\,dy = \int (1 - x^2)^{-1/2}x\,dx$$

$$-(1 - y^2)^{1/2} = -(1 - x^2)^{1/2} + C$$

Initial condition $(0, 1)$: $0 = -1 + C \Rightarrow C = 1$

Particular solution: $\sqrt{1 - y^2} = \sqrt{1 - x^2} - 1$

**21.** $\frac{du}{dv} = uv\sin v^2$

$$\int \frac{du}{u} = \int v\sin v^2\,dv$$

$$\ln|u| = -\frac{1}{2}\cos v^2 + C_1$$

$$u = Ce^{-(\cos v^2)/2}$$

Initial condition: $u(0) = 1$: $C = \frac{1}{e^{-1/2}} = e^{1/2}$

Particular solution: $u = e^{(1 - \cos v^2)/2}$

**22.** $\dfrac{dr}{ds} = e^{r-2s}$

$$\int e^{-r}\,dr = \int e^{-2s}\,ds$$

$$-e^{-r} = -\frac{1}{2}e^{-2s} + C$$

Initial condition:

$r(0) = 0: -1 = -\dfrac{1}{2} + C \Rightarrow C = -\dfrac{1}{2}$

Particular solution:

$$-e^{-r} = -\frac{1}{2}e^{-2s} - \frac{1}{2}$$

$$e^{-r} = \frac{1}{2}e^{-2s} + \frac{1}{2}$$

$$-r = \ln\left(\frac{1}{2}e^{-2s} + \frac{1}{2}\right) = \ln\left(\frac{1 + e^{-2s}}{2}\right)$$

$$r = \ln\left(\frac{2}{1 + e^{-2s}}\right)$$

**23.** $dP - kP\,dt = 0$

$$\int\frac{dP}{P} = k\int dt$$

$$\ln|P| = kt + C_1$$

$$P = Ce^{kt}$$

Initial condition: $P(0) = P_0, P_0 = Ce^0 = C$

Particular solution: $P = P_0e^{kt}$

**24.** $dT + k(T - 70)\,dt = 0$

$$\int\frac{dT}{T - 70} = -k\int dt$$

$$\ln(T - 70) = -kt + C_1$$

$$T - 70 = Ce^{-kt}$$

Initial condition:

$T(0) = 140: 140 - 70 = 70 = Ce^0 = C$

Particular solution: $T - 70 = 70e^{-kt}$

$$T = 70(1 + e^{-kt})$$

**25.** $y' = \dfrac{dy}{dx} = \dfrac{x}{4y}$

$$\int 4y\,dy = \int x\,dx$$

$$2y^2 = \frac{x^2}{2} + C$$

Initial condition $(0, 2)$: $2(2^2) = 0 + C \Rightarrow C = 8$

Particular solution: $2y^2 = \dfrac{x^2}{2} + 8$

$$4y^2 - x^2 = 16$$

**26.** $\dfrac{dy}{dx} = -\dfrac{9x}{16y}$

$$\int 16y\,dy = -\int 9x\,dx$$

$$8y^2 = -\frac{9}{2}x^2 + C$$

Initial condition $(1, 1)$: $8 = -\dfrac{9}{2} + C, C = \dfrac{25}{2}$

Particular solution: $8y^2 = -\dfrac{9}{2}x^2 + \dfrac{25}{2}$

$$16y^2 + 9x^2 = 25$$

**27.** $y' = \dfrac{dy}{dx} = \dfrac{y}{2x}$

$$\int\frac{2}{y}\,dy = \int\frac{1}{x}\,dx$$

$$2\ln|y| = \ln|x| + C_1 = \ln|x| + \ln C$$

$$y^2 = Cx$$

Initial condition $(9, 1)$: $1 = 9C \Rightarrow C = \dfrac{1}{9}$

Particular solution: $y^2 = \dfrac{1}{9}x$

$$9y^2 - x = 0$$

$$y = \frac{1}{3}\sqrt{x}$$

**28.** $\dfrac{dy}{dx} = \dfrac{2y}{3x}$

$$\int\frac{3}{y}\,dy = \int\frac{2}{x}\,dx$$

$$\ln y^3 = \ln x^2 + \ln C$$

$$y^3 = Cx^2$$

Initial condition $(8, 2)$: $2^3 = C(8^2), C = \dfrac{1}{8}$

Particular solution: $8y^3 = x^2$

$$y = \frac{1}{2}x^{2/3}$$

**29.** $m = \dfrac{dy}{dx} = \dfrac{0 - y}{(x + 2) - x} = -\dfrac{y}{2}$

$$\int\frac{dy}{y} = \int -\frac{1}{2}\,dx$$

$$\ln|y| = -\frac{1}{2}x + C_1$$

$$y = Ce^{-x/2}$$

**30.** $m = \dfrac{dy}{dx} = \dfrac{y-0}{x-0} = \dfrac{y}{x}$

$$\int \frac{dy}{y} = \int \frac{dx}{x}$$

$$\ln y = \ln x + C_1 = \ln x + \ln C = \ln Cx$$

$$y = Cx$$

**31.** $f(x, y) = x^3 - 4xy^2 + y^3$

$$f(tx, ty) = t^3x^3 - 4txt^2y^2 + t^3y^3 = t^3(x^3 - 4xy^2 + y^3)$$

Homogeneous of degree 3

**32.** $f(x, y) = x^3 + 3x^2y^2 - 2y^2$

$$f(tx, ty) = t^3x^3 + 3t^4x^2y^2 - 2t^2y^2$$

Not homogeneous

**33.** $f(x, y) = \dfrac{x^2y^2}{\sqrt{x^2+y^2}}$

$$f(tx, ty) = \frac{t^4x^2y^2}{\sqrt{t^2x^2+t^2y^2}} = t^3\frac{x^2y^2}{\sqrt{x^2+y^2}}$$

Homogeneous of degree 3

**34.** $f(x, y) = \dfrac{xy}{\sqrt{x^2+y^2}}$

$$f(tx, ty) = \frac{tx\,ty}{\sqrt{t^2x^2+t^2y^2}} = \frac{t^2xy}{t\sqrt{x^2+y^2}} = t\frac{xy}{\sqrt{x^2+y^2}}$$

Homogeneous of degree 1

**35.** $f(x, y) = 2\ln xy$

$$f(tx, ty) = 2\ln[txty] = 2\ln[t^2xy] = 2(\ln t^2 + \ln xy)$$

Not homogeneous

**36.** $f(x, y) = \tan(x + y)$

$$f(tx, ty) = \tan(tx + ty) = \tan[t(x + y)]$$

Not homogeneous

**37.** $f(x, y) = 2\ln\dfrac{x}{y}$

$$f(tx, ty) = 2\ln\frac{tx}{ty} = 2\ln\frac{x}{y}$$

Homogeneous of degree 0

**38.** $f(x, y) = \tan\dfrac{y}{x}$

$$f(tx, ty) = \tan\frac{ty}{tx} = \tan\frac{y}{x}$$

Homogeneous of degree 0

**39.** $y' = \dfrac{x+y}{2x},\ y = vx$

$$v + x\frac{dv}{dx} = \frac{x+vx}{2x}$$

$$x\frac{dv}{dx} = \frac{1+v}{2} - v = \frac{1-v}{2}$$

$$2\int\frac{dv}{1-v} = \int\frac{dx}{x}$$

$$-\ln(1-v)^2 = \ln|x| + \ln C = \ln|Cx|$$

$$\frac{1}{(1-v)^2} = |Cx|$$

$$\frac{1}{[1-(y/x)]^2} = |Cx|$$

$$\frac{x^2}{(x-y)^2} = |Cx|$$

$$|x| = C(x-y)^2$$

**40.** $y' = \dfrac{(x^3+y^3)}{xy^2}$

$$xy^2dy = (x^3 + y^3)\,dx$$

$$y = vx,\quad dy = x\,dv + v\,dx$$

$$x(vx)^2(x\,dv + v\,dx) = (x^3 + (vx)^3)\,dx$$

$$x^4v^2\,dv + x^3v^3\,dx = x^3\,dx + v^3x^3\,dx$$

$$xv^2\,dv = dx$$

$$\int v^2\,dv = \int\frac{1}{x}\,dx$$

$$\frac{v^3}{3} = \ln|x| + C$$

$$\left(\frac{y}{x}\right)^3 = 3\ln|x| + C$$

$$y^3 = 3x^3\ln|x| + Cx^3$$

**41.**

$$y' = \frac{x - y}{x + y}, \quad y = vx$$

$$v + x\frac{dv}{dx} = \frac{x - xv}{x + xv}$$

$$v\,dx + x\,dv = \frac{1 - v}{1 + v}\,dx$$

$$x\,dv = \left(\frac{1 - v}{1 + v} - v\right)dx = \frac{1 - 2v - v^2}{1 + v}\,dx$$

$$\int \frac{v + 1}{v^2 + 2v - 1}\,dv = -\int \frac{dx}{x}$$

$$\frac{1}{2}\ln\left|v^2 + 2v - 1\right| = -\ln|x| + \ln C_1 = \ln\left|\frac{C_1}{x}\right|$$

$$\left|v^2 + 2v - 1\right| = \frac{C}{x^2}$$

$$\left|\frac{y^2}{x^2} + 2\frac{y}{x} - 1\right| = \frac{C}{x^2}$$

$$\left|y^2 + 2xy - x^2\right| = C$$

**42.**

$$y' = \frac{x^2 + y^2}{2xy}, \quad y = vx$$

$$v + x\frac{dv}{dx} = \frac{x^2 + v^2x^2}{2x^2v}$$

$$2v\,dx + 2x\,dv = \frac{1 + v^2}{v}\,dx$$

$$\int \frac{2v}{v^2 - 1}\,dv = -\int \frac{dx}{x}$$

$$\ln\left(v^2 - 1\right) = -\ln x + \ln C = \ln\frac{C}{x}$$

$$v^2 - 1 = \frac{C}{x}$$

$$\frac{y^2}{x^2} - 1 = \frac{C}{x}$$

$$y^2 - x^2 = Cx$$

**43.**

$$y' = \frac{xy}{x^2 - y^2}, \quad y = vx$$

$$v + x\frac{dv}{dx} = \frac{x^2v}{x^2 - x^2v^2}$$

$$v\,dx + x\,dv = \frac{v}{1 - v^2}\,dx$$

$$x\,dv = \left(\frac{v}{1 - v^2} - v\right)dx = \left(\frac{v^3}{1 - v^2}\right)dx$$

$$\int \frac{1 - v^2}{v^3}\,dv = \int \frac{dx}{x}$$

$$-\frac{1}{2v^2} - \ln|v| = \ln|x| + \ln C_1 = \ln|C_1x|$$

$$\frac{-1}{2v^2} = \ln|C_1xv|$$

$$\frac{-x^2}{2y^2} = \ln|C_1y|$$

$$y = Ce^{-x^2/2y^2}$$

**44.**

$$y' = \frac{2x + 3y}{x}, \quad y = vx$$

$$v + x\frac{dv}{dx} = \frac{2x + 3vx}{x} = 2 + 3v$$

$$x\frac{dv}{dx} = 2 + 2v$$

$$\int \frac{dv}{1 + v} = 2\int \frac{dx}{x}$$

$$\ln|1 + v| = \ln x^2 + \ln C = \ln x^2C$$

$$1 + v = x^2C$$

$$1 + \frac{y}{x} = x^2C$$

$$\frac{y}{x} = x^2C - 1$$

$$y = Cx^3 - x$$

**45.** $x\,dy - \left(2xe^{-y/x} + y\right)dx = 0, \quad y = vx$

$$x(v\,dx + x\,dv) - \left(2xe^{-v} + vx\right)dx = 0$$

$$\int e^v\,dv = \int \frac{2}{x}\,dx$$

$$e^v = \ln C_1x^2$$

$$e^{y/x} = \ln C_1 + \ln x^2$$

$$e^{y/x} = C + \ln x^2$$

Initial condition $(1, 0)$: $1 = C$

Particular solution: $e^{y/x} = 1 + \ln x^2$

**46.** $-y^2\,dx + x(x + y)\,dy = 0, \quad y = vx$

$$-x^2v^2\,dx + \left(x^2 + x^2v\right)(v\,dx + x\,dv) = 0$$

$$\int \frac{1 + v}{v}\,dv = -\int \frac{dx}{x}$$

$$v + \ln v = -\ln x + \ln C_1 = \ln \frac{C_1}{x}$$

$$v = \ln \frac{C_1}{xv}$$

$$\frac{C_1}{vx} = e^v$$

$$\frac{C_1}{y} = e^{y/x}$$

$$y = Ce^{-y/x}$$

Initial condition $(1, 1)$: $1 = Ce^{-1} \Rightarrow C = e$

Particular solution: $y = e^{1-y/x}$

**47.** $\left(x\sec\frac{y}{x} + y\right)dx - x\,dy = 0, \quad y = vx$

$$(x\sec v + xv)\,dx - x(v\,dx + x\,dv) = 0$$

$$(\sec v + v)\,dx = v\,dx + x\,dv$$

$$\int \cos v\,dv = \int \frac{dx}{x}$$

$$\sin v = \ln x + \ln C_1$$

$$x = Ce^{\sin v}$$

$$= Ce^{\sin(y/x)}$$

Initial condition $(1, 0)$: $1 = Ce^0 = C$

Particular solution: $x = e^{\sin(y/x)}$

**48.** $\left(2x^2 + y^2\right)dx + xy\,dy = 0$

Let $y = vx$, $dy = x\,dv + v\,dx$.

$$\left(2x^2 + v^2x^2\right)dx + x(vx)(x\,dv + v\,dx) = 0$$

$$\left(2x^2 + 2x^2v^2\right)dx + x^3v\,dv = 0$$

$$\left(2 + 2v^2\right)dx = -xv\,dv$$

$$\int -\frac{2}{x}\,dx = \int \frac{v}{1 + v^2}\,dv$$

$$-2\ln x = \frac{1}{2}\ln\left(1 + v^2\right) + C_1$$

$$\ln x^{-2} = \ln\left(1 + v^2\right)^{1/2} + \ln C$$

$$x^{-2} = C\left(1 + v^2\right)^{1/2}$$

$$\frac{1}{x^2} = C\left(1 + \frac{y^2}{x^2}\right)^{1/2} = \frac{C}{x}\left(x^2 + y^2\right)^{1/2}$$

$$\frac{1}{x} = C\left(x^2 + y^2\right)^{1/2}$$

Initial condition $(1, 0)$: $1 = C(1 + 0) \Rightarrow C = 1$

Particular solution: $\dfrac{1}{x} = \sqrt{x^2 + y^2}$

$$1 = x\sqrt{x^2 + y^2}$$

**49.** $\dfrac{dy}{dx} = x$

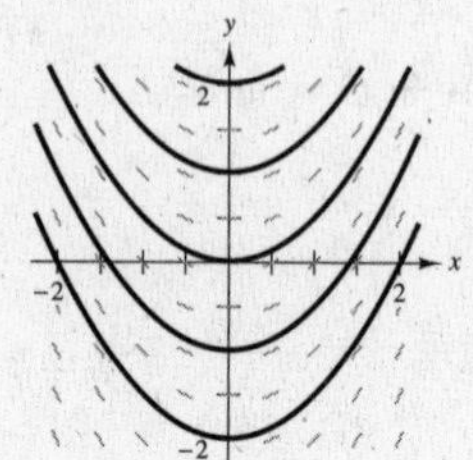


$$y = \int x\,dx = \frac{1}{2}x^2 + C$$

**50.** $\dfrac{dy}{dx} = -\dfrac{x}{y}$

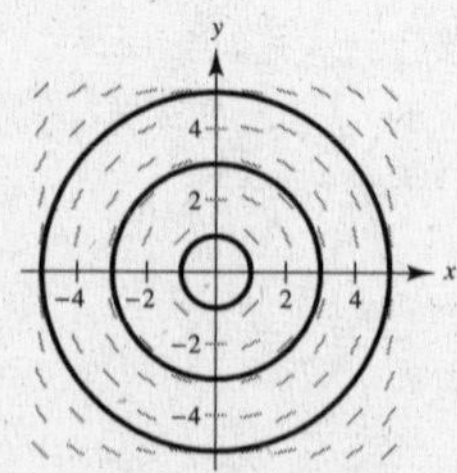


$$y\,dy = -x\,dx$$

$$\frac{y^2}{2} = -\frac{x^2}{2} + C_1$$

$$y^2 + x^2 = C$$

**51.** $\dfrac{dy}{dx} = 4 - y$

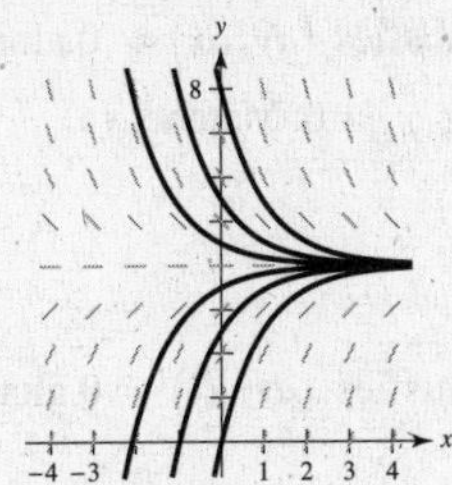

$$\int \frac{dy}{4-y} = \int dx$$

$$\ln|4 - y| = -x + C_1$$

$$4 - y = e^{-x+C_1}$$

$$y = 4 + Ce^{-x}$$

**52.** $\dfrac{dy}{dx} = 0.25x(4 - y)$

$$\frac{dy}{4-y} = 0.25x\,dx$$

$$\int \frac{dy}{y-4} = \int -0.25x\,dx = -\frac{1}{4}\int x\,dx$$

$$\ln|y - 4| = -\frac{1}{8}x^2 + C_1$$

$$y - 4 = e^{C_1 - (1/8)x^2} = Ce^{-(1/8)x^2}$$

$$y = 4 + Ce^{-(1/8)x^2}$$

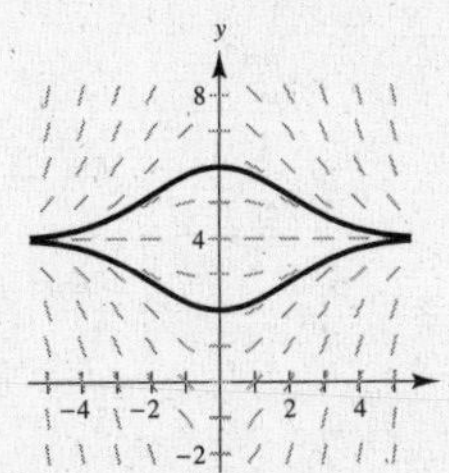

**53.** (a) Euler's Method gives $y \approx 0.1602$ when $x = 1$.

(b) $\dfrac{dy}{dx} = -6xy$

$$\int \frac{dy}{y} = \int -6x$$

$$\ln|y| = -3x^2 + C_1$$

$$y = Ce^{-3x^2}$$

$$y(0) = 5 \Rightarrow C = 5$$

$$y = 5e^{-3x^2}$$

(c) At $x = 1$, $y = 5e^{-3(1)} \approx 0.2489$.

Error: $0.2489 - 0.1602 \approx 0.0887$

**54.** (a) Euler's Method gives $y \approx 0.2622$ when $x = 1$.

(b) $\dfrac{dy}{dx} = -6xy^2$

$$\int \frac{dy}{y^2} = \int -6x\,dx$$

$$-\frac{1}{y} = -3x^2 + C_1$$

$$y = \frac{1}{3x^2 + C}$$

$$3 = \frac{1}{C} \Rightarrow C = \frac{1}{3}$$

$$y = \frac{1}{3x^2 + \frac{1}{3}} = \frac{3}{9x^2 + 1}$$

(c) At $x = 1$, $y = \dfrac{3}{9(1) + 1} = \dfrac{3}{10} = 0.3$.

Error: $0.3 - 0.2622 = 0.0378$

**55.** (a) Euler's Method gives $y \approx 3.0318$ when $x = 2$.

(b) $\dfrac{dy}{dx} = \dfrac{2x + 12}{3y^2 - 4}$

$$\int (3y^2 - 4)\,dy = \int (2x + 12)\,dx$$

$$y^3 - 4y = x^2 + 12x + C$$

$$y(1) = 2: 2^3 - 4(2) = 1 + 12 + C \Rightarrow C = -13$$

$$y^3 - 4y = x^2 + 12x - 13$$

(c) At $x = 2$,

$$y^3 - 4y = 2^2 + 12(2) - 13 = 15$$

$$y^3 - 4y - 15 = 0$$

$$(y - 3)(y^2 + 3y + 5) = 0 \Rightarrow y = 3.$$

Error: $3.0318 - 3 = 0.0318$

**56.** (a) Euler's Method gives $y \approx 1.7270$ when $x = 1.5$.

(b) $\dfrac{dy}{dx} = 2x(1 + y^2)$

$$\int \frac{dy}{1 + y^2} = \int 2x\,dx$$

$$\arctan y = x^2 + C$$

$$\arctan(0) = 1^2 + C \Rightarrow C = -1$$

$$\arctan(y) = x^2 - 1$$

$$y = \tan(x^2 - 1)$$

(c) At $x = 1.5$, $y = \tan(1.5^2 - 1) \approx 3.0096$.

Error: $1.7270 - 3.0096 = -1.2826$

**57.** $\dfrac{dy}{dt} = ky, \quad y = Ce^{kt}$

Initial amount: $y(0) = y_0 = C$

Half-life: $\dfrac{y_0}{2} = y_0 e^{k(1599)}$

$$k = \frac{1}{1599}\ln\left(\frac{1}{2}\right)$$

$$y = Ce^{[\ln(1/2)/1599]t}$$

When $t = 50$, $y = 0.9786C$ or 97.86%.

**58.** $\dfrac{dy}{dt} = ky, \quad y = Ce^{kt}$

Initial conditions: $y(0) = 40,\ y(1) = 35$

$$40 = Ce^0 = C$$

$$35 = 40e^k$$

$$k = \ln\frac{7}{8}$$

Particular solution: $y = 40e^{t\ln(7/8)}$

When 75% has been changed:

$$10 = 40e^{t\ln(7/8)}$$

$$\frac{1}{4} = e^{t\ln(7/8)}$$

$$t = \frac{\ln(1/4)}{\ln(7/8)} \approx 10.38 \text{ hours}$$

**59.** (a) $\dfrac{dy}{dx} = k(y - 4)$

(b) The direction field satisfies $(dy/dx) = 0$ along $y = 4$; but not along $y = 0$. Matches (a).

**60.** (a) $\dfrac{dy}{dx} = k(x - 4)$

(b) The direction field satisfies $(dy/dx) = 0$ along $x = 4$. Matches (b).

**61.** (a) $\dfrac{dy}{dx} = ky(y - 4)$

(b) The direction field satisfies $(dy/dx) = 0$ along $y = 0$ and $y = 4$. Matches (c).

**62.** (a) $\dfrac{dy}{dx} = ky^2$

(b) The direction field satisfies $(dy/dx) = 0$ along $y = 0$, and grows more positive as $y$ increases. Matches (d).

**63.** (a)
$$\frac{dw}{dt} = k(1200 - w)$$

$$\int \frac{dw}{1200 - w} = \int k\,dt$$

$$\ln|1200 - w| = -kt + C_1$$

$$1200 - w = e^{-kt + C_1} = Ce^{-kt}$$

$$w = 1200 - Ce^{-kt}$$

$$w(0) = 60 = 1200 - C \Rightarrow C = 1200 - 60 = 1140$$

$$w = 1200 - 1140e^{-kt}$$

(b)

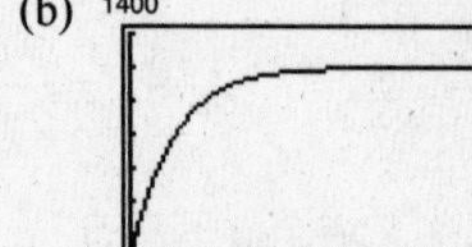


$k = 0.8$

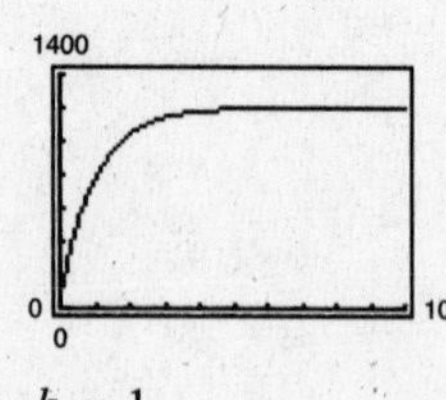


$k = 0.9$

1400
0
10
0

$k = 1$

(c) $k = 0.8$: $t = 1.31$ years

$k = 0.9$: $t = 1.16$ years

$k = 1.0$: $t = 1.05$ years

(d) Maximum weight: 1200 pounds

$$\lim_{x \to \infty} w = 1200$$

**64.** From Exercise 63:

$$w = 1200 - Ce^{-kt},\ k = 1$$
$$w = 1200 - Ce^{-t}$$
$$w(0) = w_0 = 1200 - C \Rightarrow C = 1200 - w_0$$
$$w = 1200 - (1200 - w_0)e^{-t}$$

**65.** Given family (circles): $x^2 + y^2 = C$

$$2x + 2yy' = 0$$
$$y' = -\frac{x}{y}$$

Orthogonal trajectory (lines): $y' = \dfrac{y}{x}$

$$\int \frac{dy}{y} = \int \frac{dx}{x}$$
$$\ln|y| = \ln|x| + \ln K$$
$$y = Kx$$

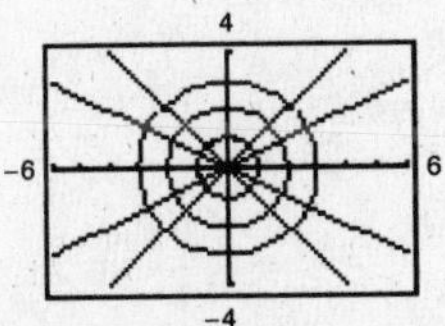


**66.** Given family (hyperbolas): $x^2 - 2y^2 = C$

$$2x - 4yy' = 0$$
$$y' = \frac{x}{2y}$$

Orthogonal trajectory (curves): $y' = -\dfrac{2y}{x}$

$$\int \frac{dy}{y} = -\int \frac{2}{x}\,dx$$
$$\ln y = -2\ln x + \ln K$$
$$y = Kx^{-2} = \frac{K}{x^2}$$

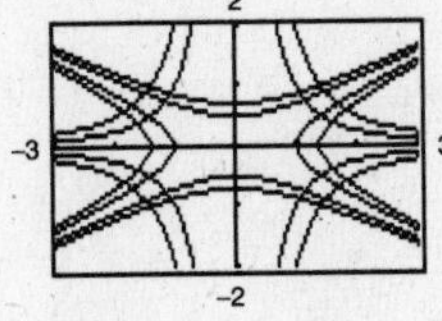


**67.** Given family (parabolas): $x^2 = Cy$

$$2x = Cy'$$
$$y' = \frac{2x}{C} = \frac{2x}{x^2/y} = \frac{2y}{x}$$

Orthogonal trajectory (ellipses): $y' = -\dfrac{x}{2y}$

$$2\int y\,dy = -\int x\,dx$$
$$y^2 = -\frac{x^2}{2} + K_1$$
$$x^2 + 2y^2 = K$$

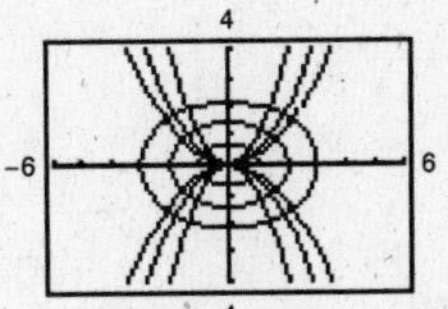


**68.** Given family (parabolas): $y^2 = 2Cx$

$$2yy' = 2C$$
$$y' = \frac{C}{y} = \frac{y^2}{2x}\left(\frac{1}{y}\right) = \frac{y}{2x}$$

Orthogonal trajectory (ellipses): $y' = -\dfrac{2x}{y}$

$$\int y\,dy = -\int 2x\,dx$$
$$\frac{y^2}{2} = -x^2 + K_1$$
$$2x^2 + y^2 = K$$

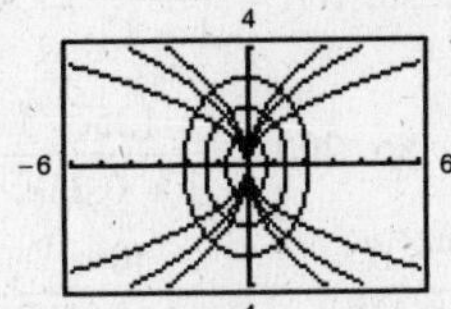


**69.** Given family (curves): $y^2 = Cx^3$

$$2yy' = 3Cx^2$$
$$y' = \frac{3Cx^2}{2y}$$
$$= \frac{3x^2}{2y}\left(\frac{y^2}{x^3}\right) = \frac{3y}{2x}$$

Orthogonal trajectory (ellipses): $y' = -\dfrac{2x}{3y}$

$$3\int y\,dy = -2\int x\,dx$$
$$\frac{3y^2}{2} = -x^2 + K_1$$
$$3y^2 + 2x^2 = K$$

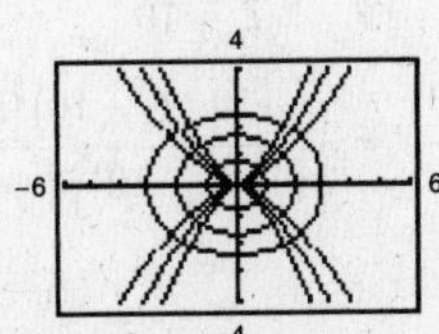

**70.** Given family (exponential functions): $y = Ce^x$

$$y' = Ce^x = y$$

Orthogonal trajectory (parabolas): $y' = -\dfrac{1}{y}$

$$\int y\,dy = -\int dx$$

$$\frac{y^2}{2} = -x + K_1$$

$$y^2 = -2x + K$$

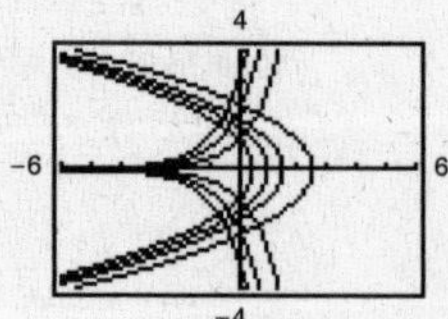

**71.**

$$\frac{dN}{dt} = kN(500 - N)$$

$$\int \frac{dN}{N(500 - N)} = \int k\,dt$$

$$\frac{1}{500}\int\left[\frac{1}{N} + \frac{1}{500 - N}\right]dN = \int k\,dt$$

$$\ln|N| - \ln|500 - N| = 500(kt + C_1)$$

$$\frac{N}{500 - N} = e^{500kt + C_2} = Ce^{500kt}$$

$$N = \frac{500Ce^{500kt}}{1 + Ce^{500kt}}$$

When $t = 0$, $N = 100$. So, $100 = \dfrac{500C}{1 + C} \Rightarrow C = 0.25$. Therefore, $N = \dfrac{125e^{500kt}}{1 + 0.25e^{500kt}}$.

When $t = 4$, $N = 200$. So, $200 = \dfrac{125e^{2000k}}{1 + 0.25e^{2000k}} \Rightarrow k = \dfrac{\ln(8/3)}{2000} \approx 0.00049$.

Therefore, $N = \dfrac{125e^{0.2452t}}{1 + 0.25e^{0.2452t}} = \dfrac{500}{1 + 4e^{-0.2452t}}$.

**72.** The differential equation is given by the following.

$$\frac{dS}{dt} = kS(L - S)$$

$$\int \frac{dS}{S(L - S)} = \int k\,dt$$

$$\frac{1}{L}\left[\ln|S| - \ln|L - S|\right] = kt + C_1$$

$$\frac{S}{L - S} = Ce^{Lkt}$$

$$S = \frac{CLe^{Lkt}}{1 + Ce^{Lkt}} = \frac{CL}{C + e^{-Lkt}}$$

When $t = 0$, $S = 10$. So, $C = \dfrac{10}{L - 10}$.

Therefore, $S = \dfrac{CL}{C + e^{-Lkt}} = \dfrac{[10/(L - 10)]L}{[10/(L - 10)] + e^{-Lkt}} = \dfrac{10L}{10 + (L - 10)e^{-Lkt}}$.

**73.** The general solution is $y = -\dfrac{1}{kt + C}$.

Because $y = 45$ when $t = 0$, it follows that

$45 = -\dfrac{1}{C}$ and $C = -\dfrac{1}{45}$.

Therefore, $y = -\dfrac{1}{kt - (1/45)} = \dfrac{45}{1 - 45kt}$.

Because $y = 4$ when $t = 2$, you have

$4 = \dfrac{45}{1 - 45k(2)} \Rightarrow k = -\dfrac{41}{360}$.

So, $y = \dfrac{45}{1 + (41/8)t} = \dfrac{360}{8 + 41t}$.

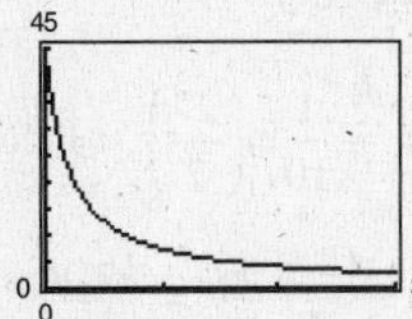


**74.** The general solution is $y = -1/(kt + C)$.

Because $y = 75$ when $t = 0$, you have $C = -1/75$.

So, $y = -\dfrac{1}{kt - (1/75)} = \dfrac{75}{1 - 75kt}$.

Because $y = 12$ when $t = 1$, you have

$12 = \dfrac{75}{1 - 75k} \Rightarrow k = -\dfrac{7}{100}$.

So, you have $y = \dfrac{75}{1 + 5.25t} = \dfrac{300}{4 + 21t}$.

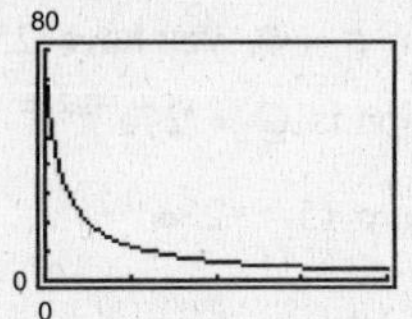


**75.** Because $y = 100$ when $t = 0$, it follows that $100 = 500e^{-C}$, which implies that $C = \ln 5$. So, you have $y = 500e^{(-\ln 5)e^{-kt}}$. Because $y = 150$ when $t = 2$, it follows that

$$150 = 500e^{(-\ln 5)e^{-2k}}$$

$$e^{-2k} = \frac{\ln 0.3}{\ln 0.2}$$

$$k = -\frac{1}{2}\ln\frac{\ln 0.3}{\ln 0.2} \approx 0.1452.$$

So, $y$ is given by $y = 500e^{-1.6904e^{-0.1451t}}$.

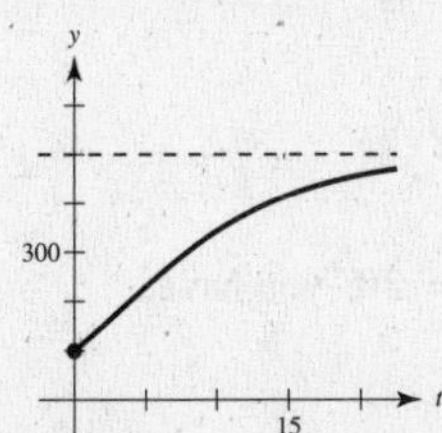


**76.** The general solution is $y = 5000e^{-Ce^{-kt}}$. Because $y = 500$ when $t = 0$, it follows that $500 = 5000e^{-C}$ which implies that $C = -\ln\frac{1}{10} = \ln 10$. So, you have $y = 5000e^{(-\ln 10)e^{-kt}}$. Because $y = 625$ when $t = 1$, it follows that

$$625 = 5000e^{(-\ln 10)e^{-k}}$$

$$e^{-k} = \frac{\ln(1/8)}{\ln(1/10)}$$

$$k = -\ln\left(\frac{\ln(1/8)}{\ln(1/10)}\right) \approx 0.1019.$$

So, you have $y = 5000e^{(-2.3026)e^{(-0.1019)t}}$.

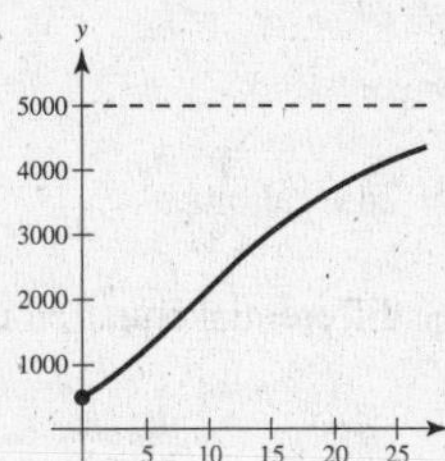


**77.** From Example 11, the general solution is $y = 60e^{-Ce^{-kt}}$.

Because $y = 8$ when $t = 0$,

$$8 = 60e^{-C} \Rightarrow C = \ln\frac{15}{2} \approx 2.0149.$$

Because $y = 15$ when $t = 3$,

$$15 = 60e^{-2.0149e^{-3k}}$$

$$\frac{1}{4} = e^{-2.0149e^{-3k}}$$

$$\ln\frac{1}{4} = -2.0149e^{-3k}$$

$$k = -\frac{1}{3}\ln\left(\frac{\ln(1/4)}{-2.0149}\right) \approx 0.1246.$$

So, $y = 60e^{-2.0149e^{-0.1246t}}$.

When $t = 10$, $y \approx 34$ beavers.

**78.** From Example 11, the general solution is

$$y = 400e^{-Ce^{-kt}}.$$

Because $y = 30$ when $t = 0$,

$$30 = 400e^{-C} \Rightarrow C = \ln\left(\frac{40}{3}\right) \approx 2.5903.$$

Because $y = 90$ when $t = 1$,

$$90 = 400e^{-2.5903e^{-k}}$$

$$\frac{9}{40} = e^{-2.5903e^{-k}}$$

$$\ln\left(\frac{9}{40}\right) = -2.5903e^{-k}$$

$$k = -\ln\left(\frac{\ln(9/40)}{-2.5903}\right) \approx 0.5519.$$

So, $y = 400e^{-2.5903e^{-0.5519t}}$.

Finally, when $t = 3$, $y \approx 244$ rabbits.

**79.** Following Example 12, the differential equation is

$$\frac{dy}{dt} = ky(1 - y)(2 - y)$$

and its general solution is

$$\frac{y(2 - y)}{(1 - y)^2} = Ce^{2kt}.$$

$$y = \frac{1}{2} \text{ when } t = 0 \Rightarrow \frac{(1/2)(3/2)}{(1/2)^2} = C \Rightarrow C = 3$$

$$y = 0.75 = \frac{3}{4} \text{ when}$$

$$t = 4 \Rightarrow \frac{(3/4)(5/4)}{(1/4)^2} = 15 = 3e^{2k(4)}$$

$$\Rightarrow 5 = e^{8k}$$

$$\Rightarrow k = \frac{1}{8}\ln 5 \approx 0.2012.$$

So, the particular solution is $\dfrac{y(2 - y)}{(1 - y)^2} = 3e^{0.4024t}$.

Using a symbolic algebra utility or graphing utility, you find that when $t = 10$,

$$\frac{y(2 - y)}{(1 - y)^2} = 3e^{0.4024(10)}$$

and $y \approx 0.92$, or 92%.

**80.** Following Example 12, the differential equation is

$$\frac{dy}{dt} = ky(1 - y)(2 - y)$$

and its general solution is

$$\frac{y(2 - y)}{(1 - y)^2} = Ce^{2kt}.$$

$$y = 0.4 \text{ when } t = 0 \Rightarrow \frac{(0.4)(1.6)}{(0.6)^2} = \frac{16}{9} = C$$

$$y = 0.8 \text{ when } t = 5 \Rightarrow \frac{(0.8)(1.2)}{(0.2)^2} = 24 = \frac{16}{9}e^{2k(5)}$$

$$\Rightarrow \frac{27}{2} = e^{10k}$$

$$\Rightarrow k = \frac{1}{10}\ln\left(\frac{27}{2}\right) \approx 0.2603$$

So, the particular solution is $\dfrac{y(2 - y)}{(1 - y)^2} = \dfrac{16}{9}e^{0.5205t}$.

Using a symbolic algebra utility or graphing utility, you find that when $t = 8$, $y \approx 0.91$, or 91%.

**81.** (a) $\dfrac{dQ}{dt} = -\dfrac{Q}{20}$

$$\int\frac{dQ}{Q} = \int -\frac{1}{20}\,dt$$

$$\ln|Q| = -\frac{1}{20}t + C_1$$

$$Q = e^{-(1/20)t + C_1} = Ce^{-(1/20)t}$$

Because $Q = 25$ when $t = 0$, you have $25 = C$.

So, the particular solution is $Q = 25e^{-(1/20)t}$.

(b) When $Q = 15$, you have $15 = 25e^{-(1/20)t}$.

$$\frac{3}{5} = e^{-(1/20)t}$$

$$\ln\left(\frac{3}{5}\right) = -\frac{1}{20}t$$

$$-20\ln\left(\frac{3}{5}\right) = t$$

$t \approx 10.217$ minutes

**82.** Because $Q' + \frac{1}{20}Q = \frac{5}{2}$ is a first-order linear differential equation with $P(x) = \frac{1}{20}$ and $R(x) = \frac{5}{2}$, you have the integrating factor $u(t) = e^{\int(1/20)dt} = e^{(1/20)t}$, and the general solution is

$$Q = e^{-0.05t}\int\frac{5}{2}e^{0.05t}\,dt = e^{-0.05t}\left(50e^{0.05t} + C\right) = 50 + Ce^{-0.05t}.$$

Because $Q = 0$ when $t = 0$, you have $C = -50$ and $Q = 50\left(1 - e^{-0.05t}\right)$. Finally, when $t = 30$, you have $Q \approx 38.843$ lb/gal.

**83.** (a) $\dfrac{dy}{dt} = ky$

$$\int \frac{dy}{y} = \int k\,dt$$

$$\ln y = kt + C_1$$

$$y = e^{kt+C_1} = Ce^{kt}$$

(b) $y(0) = 20 \Rightarrow C = 20$

$$y(1) = 16 = 20e^k \Rightarrow k = \ln\frac{16}{20} = \ln\left(\frac{4}{5}\right)$$

$$y = 20e^{t\ln(4/5)}$$

When 75% has changed:

$$5 = 20e^{t\ln(4/5)}$$

$$\frac{1}{4} = e^{t\ln(4/5)}$$

$$t = \frac{\ln(1/4)}{\ln(4/5)} \approx 6.2 \text{ hours}$$

**84.** $\dfrac{ds}{dh} = \dfrac{k}{h}$

$$\int ds = \int \frac{k}{h}\,dh$$

$$s = k\ln h + C_1 = k\ln Ch$$

Because $s = 25$ when $h = 2$ and $s = 12$ when $h = 6$, it follows that $25 = k\ln(2C)$ and $12 = k\ln(6C)$, which implies

$$C = \frac{1}{2}e^{-(25/13)\ln 3} \approx 0.0605$$

and

$$k = \frac{25}{\ln(2C)} = \frac{-13}{\ln 3} \approx -11.8331.$$

Therefore, $s$ is given by the following.

$$\begin{aligned} s &= -\frac{13}{\ln 3}\ln\left[\frac{h}{2}e^{-(25/13)\ln 3}\right] \\ &= -\frac{13}{\ln 3}\left[\ln\frac{h}{2} - \frac{25}{13}\ln 3\right] \\ &= -\frac{1}{\ln 3}\left[13\ln\frac{h}{2} - 25\ln 3\right] \\ &= 25 - \frac{13\ln(h/2)}{\ln 3},\quad 2 \le h \le 15 \end{aligned}$$

**85.** The general solution is $y = Ce^{kt}$. Because $y = 0.60C$ when $t = 1$, you have

$$0.60C = Ce^k \Rightarrow k = \ln 0.60 \approx -0.5108.$$

So, $y = Ce^{-0.5108t}$. When $y = 0.20C$, you have

$$0.20C = Ce^{-0.5108t}$$

$$\ln 0.20 = -0.5108t$$

$$t \approx 3.15 \text{ hours.}$$

**86.** $\displaystyle\int\left(\frac{1}{y}\frac{dy}{dt}\right)dt = \int\left(\frac{1}{x}\frac{dx}{dt}\right)dt$

$$\int \frac{1}{y}\,dy = \int \frac{1}{x}\,dx$$

$$\ln|y| = \ln|x| + C_1 = \ln|Cx|$$

$$y = Cx$$

**87.** $\displaystyle\int \frac{1}{kP + N}\,dP = \int dt$

$$\frac{1}{k}\ln|kP + N| = t + C_1$$

$$kP + N = C_2e^{kt}$$

$$P = Ce^{kt} - \frac{N}{k}$$

**88.** $\dfrac{dy}{dx} = -0.2y$

$$y = Ce^{-0.2x}$$

$$y(0) = 29.92 \Rightarrow C = 29.92 \Rightarrow y = 29.92e^{-0.2x}$$

(a) 8364 feet $\approx$ 1.5841 miles

$y(1.5841) \approx 21.80$ inches

(b) 23,320 feet $\approx$ 3.8485 miles

$y(3.8485) \approx 13.86$ inches

**89.** $$\frac{dA}{dt} = rA + P$$

$$\frac{dA}{rA + P} = dt$$

$$\int \frac{dA}{rA + P} = \int dt$$

$$\frac{1}{r}\ln(rA + P) = t + C_1$$

$$\ln(rA + P) = rt + C_2$$

$$rA + P = e^{rt + C_2}$$

$$A = \frac{C_3e^{rt} - P}{r}$$

$$A = Ce^{rt} - \frac{P}{r}$$

When $t = 0$: $A = 0$

$$0 = C - \frac{P}{r} \Rightarrow C = \frac{P}{r}$$

$$A = \frac{P}{r}\left(e^{rt} - 1\right)$$

**90.** (a) $A = \frac{P}{r}\left(e^{rt} - 1\right)$

$$A = \frac{275{,}000}{0.06}\left(e^{0.08(10)} - 1\right) \approx \$4{,}212{,}796.94$$

(b) $A = \frac{550{,}000}{0.05}\left(e^{0.059(25)} - 1\right) \approx \$31{,}424{,}909.75$

**91.** From Exercise 89,

$$A = \frac{P}{r}\left(e^{rt} - 1\right).$$

Because $A = 260{,}000{,}000$ when $t = 8$ and $r = 0.0725$, you have

$$P = \frac{Ar}{e^{rt} - 1}$$

$$= \frac{(260{,}000{,}000)(0.0725)}{e^{(0.0725)(8)} - 1}$$

$$\approx \$23{,}981{,}015.77.$$

**92.** $$1{,}000{,}000 = \frac{125{,}000}{0.08}\left(e^{0.08t} - 1\right)$$

$$1.64 = e^{0.08t}$$

$$t = \frac{\ln(1.64)}{0.08} \approx 6.18 \text{ years}$$

**93.** $$\frac{dy}{dt} = 0.02y\ln\left(\frac{5000}{y}\right)$$

(a)

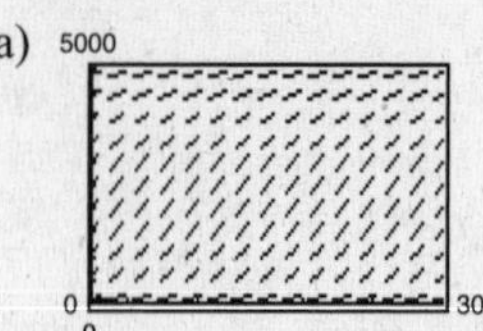


(b) As $t \to \infty$, $y \to L = 5000$.

(c) Using a computer algebra system or separation of variables, the general solution is

$$y = 5000e^{-Ce^{-kt}} = 5000e^{-Ce^{-0.02t}}.$$

Using the initial condition $y(0) = 500$, you obtain

$$500 = 5000e^{-C} \Rightarrow C = \ln 10 \approx 2.3026.$$

So, $y = 5000e^{-2.3026e^{-0.02t}}$.

(d)

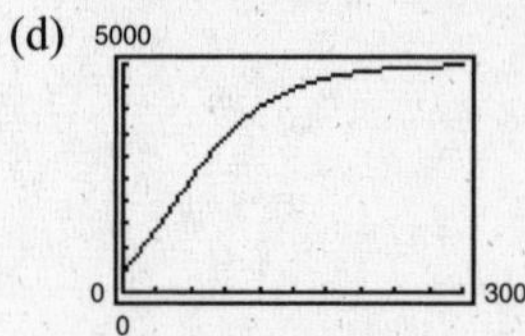


The graph is concave upward on $(0, 41.7)$ and concave downward on $(41.7, \infty)$.

**94.** $$\frac{dy}{dt} = 0.05y\ln\left(\frac{1000}{y}\right)$$

(a)

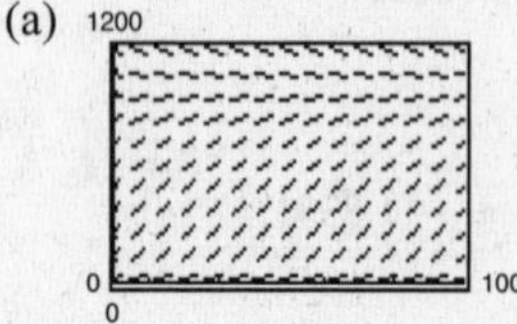


(b) As $t \to \infty$, $y \to L = 1000$.

(c) Using a computer algebra system or separation of variables, the general solution is

$$y = 1000e^{-Ce^{-kt}} = 1000e^{-Ce^{-0.05t}}.$$

Using the initial condition $y(0) = 100$, you obtain

$$100 = 1000e^{-C} \Rightarrow C = \ln 10 \approx 2.3026.$$

So, $y = 1000e^{-2.3026e^{-0.05t}}$.

(d)

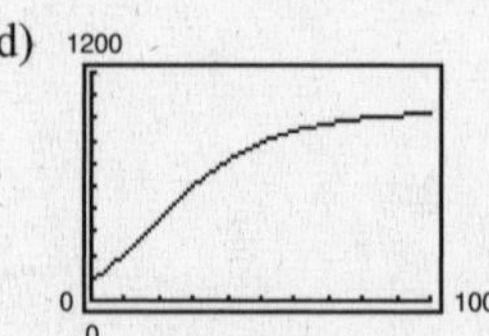


The graph is concave upward on $(0, 16.7)$ and concave downward on $(16.7, \infty)$.

**95.** A differential equation can be solved by separation of variables if it can be written in the form

$$M(x) + N(y)\frac{dy}{dx} = 0.$$

To solve a separable equation, rewrite as,

$$M(x)\,dx = -N(y)\,dy$$

and integrate both sides.

**96.** $M(x, y)\,dx + N(x, y)\,dy = 0$, where $M$ and $N$ are homogeneous functions of the same degree. See Example 5a.

**97.** Two families of curves are mutually orthogonal if each curve in the first family intersects each curve in the second family at right angles.

**98.** (a) $y(1 + x)\,dx + x\,dy = 0$

$$x\,dy = -y(1 + x)\,dx$$

$$\frac{1}{y}\,dy = -\frac{(1 + x)}{x}\,dx$$

Separable

(b) $y' = \dfrac{dy}{dx} = y^{1/2}$

$$\frac{dy}{y^{1/2}} = dx$$

Separable

(c) $\dfrac{dy}{dx} + xy = 5$

Not separable

(d) $\dfrac{dy}{dx} = x - xy - y + 1$

$$= x(1 - y) + (1 - y)$$

$$= (x + 1)(1 - y)$$

$$\frac{dy}{1 - y} = (x + 1)\,dx$$

Separable

**99.** False. $\dfrac{dy}{dx} = \dfrac{x}{y}$ is separable, but $y = 0$ is not a solution.

**100.** True

$$\frac{dy}{dx} = (x - 2)(y + 1)$$

**101.** False

$$f(tx, ty) = t^2x^2 - 4xyt^2 + 6t^2y^2 + 1$$
$$\neq t^2 f(x, y)$$

**102.** True

$$x^2 + y^2 = 2Cy \qquad x^2 + y^2 = 2Kx$$

$$\frac{dy}{dx} = \frac{x}{C - y} \qquad \frac{dy}{dx} = \frac{K - x}{y}$$

$$\frac{x}{C - y}\cdot\frac{K - x}{y} = \frac{Kx - x^2}{Cy - y^2}$$
$$= \frac{2Kx - 2x^2}{2Cy - 2y^2}$$
$$= \frac{x^2 + y^2 - 2x^2}{x^2 + y^2 - 2y^2}$$
$$= \frac{y^2 - x^2}{x^2 - y^2}$$
$$= -1$$

**103.** $fg' + gf' = f'g'$ Product Rule

$$(f - f')g' + gf' = 0$$

$$g' + \frac{f'}{f - f'}g = 0$$

Need $f - f' = e^{x^2} - 2xe^{x^2} = (1 - 2x)e^{x^2} \neq 0$, so avoid $x = \dfrac{1}{2}$.

$$\frac{g'}{g} = \frac{f'}{f' - f} = \frac{2xe^{x^2}}{(2x - 1)e^{x^2}} = 1 + \frac{1}{2x - 1}$$

$$\ln|g(x)| = x + \frac{1}{2}\ln|2x - 1| + C_1$$

$$g(x) = Ce^x|2x - 1|^{1/2}$$

So there exists $g$ and interval $(a, b)$, as long as $\dfrac{1}{2} \notin (a, b)$.

## Section 6.4 The Logistic Equation

**1.** $y = \dfrac{12}{1 + e^{-x}}$

Because $y(0) = 6$, it matches (c) or (d).

Because (d) approaches its horizontal asymptote slower than (c), it matches (d).

**2.** $y = \dfrac{12}{1 + 3e^{-x}}$

Because $y(0) = \dfrac{12}{4} = 3$, it matches (a).

**3.** $y = \dfrac{12}{1 + \frac{1}{2}e^{-x}}$

Because $y(0) = \dfrac{12}{\left(\frac{3}{2}\right)} = 8$, it matches (b).

**4.** $y = \dfrac{12}{1 + e^{-2x}}$

Because $y(0) = 6$, it matches (c) or (d).

Because $y$ approaches $L = 12$ faster for (c), it matches (c).

**5.** $y = \dfrac{8}{1 + e^{-2t}} = 8\left(1 + e^{-2t}\right)^{-1}$; $L = 8, k = 2, b = 1$

$$\frac{dy}{dt} = -8\left(1 + e^{-2t}\right)^{-2}\left(-2e^{-2t}\right)$$

$$= \frac{8}{\left(1 + e^{-2t}\right)} \cdot \frac{2e^{-2t}}{\left(1 + e^{-2t}\right)}$$

$$= 2y\left(\frac{e^{-2t}}{1 + e^{-2t}}\right)$$

$$= 2y\left(1 - \frac{8}{8\left(1 + e^{-2t}\right)}\right)$$

$$= 2y\left(1 - \frac{y}{8}\right)$$

$$y(0) = \frac{8}{1 + e^{0}} = 4$$

**6.** $y = \dfrac{10}{1 + 3e^{-4t}} = 10\left(1 + 3e^{-4t}\right)^{-1}$;

$L = 10, k = 4, b = 3$

$$\frac{dy}{dt} = -10\left(1 + 3e^{-4t}\right)^{-2}\left(-12e^{-4t}\right)$$

$$= \frac{10}{1 + 3e^{-4t}} \cdot \frac{12e^{-4t}}{\left(1 + 3e^{-4t}\right)}$$

$$= 4y \cdot \left(\frac{3e^{-4t}}{1 + 3e^{-4t}}\right)$$

$$= 4y\left(1 - \frac{1}{1 + 3e^{-4t}}\right)$$

$$= 4y\left(1 - \frac{10}{10\left(1 + 3e^{-4t}\right)}\right)$$

$$= 4y\left(1 - \frac{y}{10}\right)$$

$$y(0) = \frac{10}{1 + 3e^{0}} = \frac{10}{4} = \frac{5}{2}$$

**7.** $y = 12\left(1 + 6e^{-t}\right)^{-1}$; $L = 12, k = 1, b = 6$

$$y' = -12\left(1 + 6e^{-t}\right)^{-2}\left(-6e^{-t}\right)$$

$$= \left(\frac{12}{1 + 6e^{-t}}\right)\left(\frac{6e^{-t}}{1 + 6e^{-t}}\right)$$

$$= y\left(1 - \frac{1}{1 + 6e^{-t}}\right)$$

$$= y\left(1 - \frac{12}{12\left(1 + 6e^{-t}\right)}\right)$$

$$= y\left(1 - \frac{y}{12}\right)$$

$$y(0) = \frac{12}{1 + 6} = \frac{12}{7}$$

**8.** $y = 14\left(1 + 5e^{-3t}\right)^{-1}$; $L = 14, k = 3, b = 5$

$$y' = -14\left(1 + 5e^{-3t}\right)^{-2}\left(-15e^{-3t}\right)$$

$$= 3\left(\frac{14}{1 + 5e^{-3t}}\right)\left(\frac{5e^{-3t}}{1 + 5e^{-3t}}\right)$$

$$= 3y\left(1 - \frac{1}{1 + 5e^{-3t}}\right)$$

$$= 3y\left(1 - \frac{14}{14\left(1 + 5e^{-3t}\right)}\right)$$

$$= 3y\left(1 - \frac{y}{14}\right)$$

$$y(0) = \frac{14}{1 + 5} = \frac{7}{3}$$

**9.** $P(t) = \dfrac{2100}{1 + 29e^{-0.75t}}$

(a) $k = 0.75$

(b) $L = 2100$

(c) $P(0) = \dfrac{2100}{1 + 29} = 70$

(d)
$$1050 = \frac{2100}{1 + 29e^{-0.75t}}$$
$$1 + 29e^{-0.75t} = 2$$
$$e^{-0.75t} = \frac{1}{29}$$
$$-0.75t = \ln\left(\frac{1}{29}\right) = -\ln 29$$
$$t = \frac{\ln 29}{0.75} \approx 4.4897 \text{ years}$$

(e) $\dfrac{dP}{dt} = 0.75P\left(1 - \dfrac{P}{2100}\right)$

**10.** $P(t) = \dfrac{5000}{1 + 39e^{-0.2t}}$

(a) $k = 0.2$

(b) $L = 5000$

(c) $P(0) = \dfrac{5000}{1 + 39} = 125$

(d)
$$\begin{aligned} 2500 &= \frac{5000}{1 + 39e^{-0.2t}} \\ 1 + 39e^{-0.2t} &= 2 \\ e^{-0.2t} &= \frac{1}{39} \\ -0.2t &= \ln\left(\frac{1}{39}\right) = -\ln 39 \\ t &= \frac{\ln 39}{0.2} \approx 18.3178 \text{ years} \end{aligned}$$

(e) $\dfrac{dP}{dt} = 0.2P\left(1 - \dfrac{P}{5000}\right)$

**11.** $P(t) = \dfrac{6000}{1 + 4999e^{-0.8t}}$

(a) $k = 0.8$

(b) $L = 6000$

(c) $P(0) = \dfrac{6000}{1 + 4999} = \dfrac{6}{5}$

(d)
$$\begin{aligned} 3000 &= \frac{6000}{1 + 4999e^{-0.8t}} \\ 1 + 4999e^{-0.8t} &= 2 \\ e^{-0.8t} &= \frac{1}{4999} \\ -0.8t &= \ln\left(\frac{1}{4999}\right) = -\ln 4999 \\ t &= \frac{\ln 4999}{0.8} \approx 10.65 \text{ years} \end{aligned}$$

(e) $\dfrac{dP}{dt} = 0.8P\left(1 - \dfrac{P}{6000}\right)$

**12.** $P(t) = \dfrac{1000}{1 + 8e^{-0.2t}}$

(a) $k = 0.2$

(b) $L = 1000$

(c) $P(0) = \dfrac{1000}{1 + 8} = \dfrac{1000}{9}$

(d)
$$\begin{aligned} 500 &= \frac{1000}{1 + 8e^{-0.2t}} \\ 1 + 8e^{-0.2t} &= 2 \\ e^{-0.2t} &= \frac{1}{8} \\ -0.2t &= \ln\left(\frac{1}{8}\right) = -\ln 8 \\ t &= \frac{\ln 8}{0.2} \approx 10.40 \text{ years} \end{aligned}$$

(e) $\dfrac{dP}{dt} = 0.2P\left(1 - \dfrac{P}{1000}\right)$

**13.** $\dfrac{dP}{dt} = 3P\left(1 - \dfrac{P}{100}\right)$

(a) $k = 3$

(b) $L = 100$

(c)

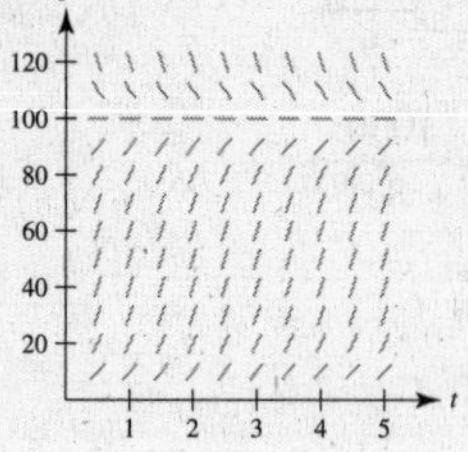

(d) $\dfrac{d^2P}{dt^2} = 3P'\left(1 - \dfrac{P}{100}\right) + 3P\left(\dfrac{-P'}{100}\right)$

$$= 3\left[3P\left(1 - \frac{P}{100}\right)\right]\left(1 - \frac{P}{100}\right) - \frac{3P}{100}\left[3P\left(1 - \frac{P}{100}\right)\right] = 9P\left(1 - \frac{P}{100}\right)\left(1 - \frac{P}{100} - \frac{P}{100}\right) = 9P\left(1 - \frac{P}{100}\right)\left(1 - \frac{2P}{100}\right)$$

$\dfrac{d^2P}{dt^2} = 0$ for $P = 50$, and by the first Derivative Test, this is a maximum. $\left(\text{Note: } P = 50 = \dfrac{L}{2} = \dfrac{100}{2}\right)$

**14.** $\dfrac{dP}{dt} = 0.5P\left(1 - \dfrac{P}{250}\right)$

(a) $k = 0.5$

(b) $L = 250$

(c)

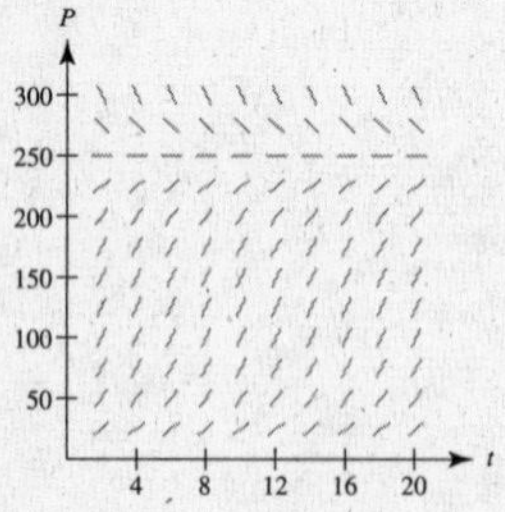

(d) $\dfrac{dP}{dt}$ is a maximum for $P = \dfrac{250}{2} = 125$ (see Exercise 13).

**15.** $\dfrac{dP}{dt} = 0.1P - 0.0004P^2 = 0.1P(1 - 0.004P) = 0.1P\left(1 - \dfrac{P}{250}\right)$

(a) $k = 0.1 = \dfrac{1}{10}$

(b) $L = 250$

(c)

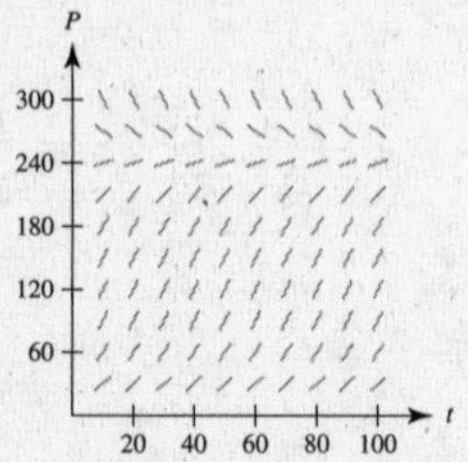

(d) $P = \dfrac{250}{2} = 125$ (Same argument as in Exercise 13)

**16.** $\frac{dP}{dt} = 0.4P - 0.00025P^2 = 0.4P\left(1 - \frac{P}{1600}\right)$

(a) $k = 0.4$

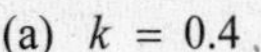

(b) $L = 1600$

(c)

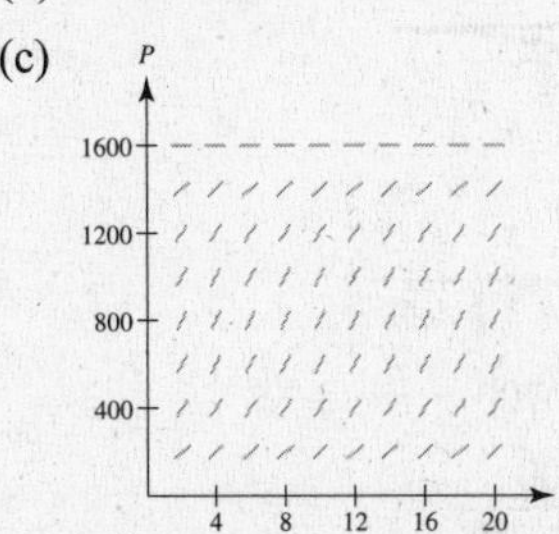


(d) $\frac{dP}{dt}$ is a maximum for $P = \frac{1600}{2} = 800$ (see Exercise 13).

**17.** $\frac{dy}{dt} = y\left(1 - \frac{y}{36}\right), \quad y(0) = 4$

$k = 1, L = 36$

$y = \frac{L}{1 + be^{-kt}} = \frac{36}{1 + be^{-t}}$

$(0, 4)$: $4 = \frac{36}{1 + b} \Rightarrow b = 8$

Solution: $y = \frac{36}{1 + 8e^{-t}}$

$y(5) = \frac{36}{1 + 8e^{-5}} \approx 34.16$

$y(100) = \frac{36}{1 + 8e^{-100}} \approx 36.00$

**18.** $\frac{dy}{dt} = 2.8y\left(1 - \frac{y}{10}\right), \quad y(0) = 7$

$k = 2.8, L = 10$

$y = \frac{L}{1 + be^{-kt}} = \frac{10}{1 + be^{-2.8t}}$

$(0, 7)$: $7 = \frac{10}{1 + b} \Rightarrow 1 + b = \frac{10}{7} \Rightarrow b = \frac{3}{7}$

Solution: $y = \frac{10}{1 + \left(\frac{3}{7}\right)e^{-2.8t}}$

$y(5) = \frac{10}{1 + \left(\frac{3}{7}\right)e^{-2.8(5)}} \approx 10.00$

$y(100) = \frac{10}{1 + \left(\frac{3}{7}\right)e^{-2.8(100)}} \approx 10.00$

**19.** $\frac{dy}{dt} = \frac{4y}{5} - \frac{y^2}{150} = \frac{4}{5}y\left(1 - \frac{y}{120}\right), \quad y(0) = 8$

$k = \frac{4}{5} = 0.8, L = 120$

$y = \frac{L}{1 + be^{-kt}} = \frac{120}{1 + be^{-0.8t}}$

$y(0) = 8: 8 = \frac{120}{1 + b} \Rightarrow b = 14$

Solution: $y = \frac{120}{1 + 14e^{-0.8t}}$

$y(5) = \frac{120}{1 + 14e^{-0.8(5)}} \approx 95.51$

$y(100) = \frac{120}{1 + 14e^{-0.8(100)}} \approx 120.0$

**20.** $\frac{dy}{dt} = \frac{3y}{20} - \frac{y^2}{1600} = \frac{3}{20}y\left(1 - \frac{y}{240}\right); \quad y(0) = 15$

$k = \frac{3}{20}, L = 240$

$y = \frac{L}{1 + be^{-kt}} = \frac{240}{1 + be^{(-3/20)t}}$

$y(0) = 15: 15 = \frac{240}{1 + b} \Rightarrow b = 15$

Solution: $y = \frac{240}{1 + 15e^{(-3/20)t}}$

$y(5) = \frac{240}{1 + 15e^{(-3/20)(5)}} \approx 29.68$

$y(100) = \frac{240}{1 + 15e^{(-3/20)(100)}} \approx 240.0$

**21.** $L = 250$ and $y(0) = 350$

Matches (c).

**22.** $L = 100$ and $y(0) = 100$

Matches (d).

**23.** $L = 250$ and $y(0) = 50$

Matches (b).

**24.** $L = 100$ and $y(0) = 50$

Matches (a).

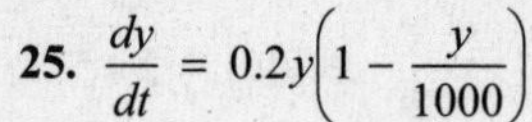

**25.** $\dfrac{dy}{dt} = 0.2y\left(1 - \dfrac{y}{1000}\right)$

(a)

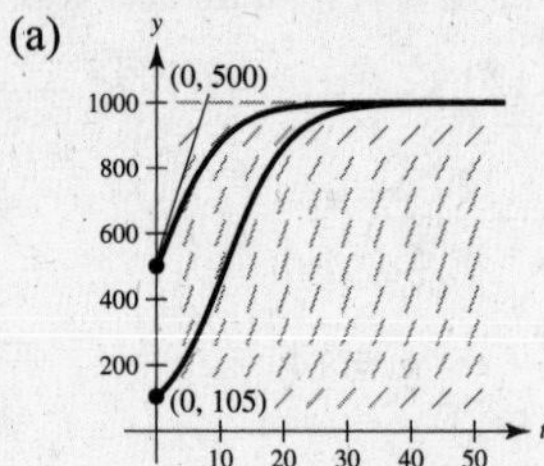


(b) $k = 0.2, L = 1000$

$$y = \frac{1000}{1 + be^{-0.2t}}$$

$$y(0) = 105 = \frac{1000}{1 + b}$$

$$1 + b = \frac{1000}{105} = \frac{200}{21}$$

$$b = \frac{179}{21} \approx 8.524$$

$$y = \frac{1000}{1 + (179/21)e^{-0.2t}}$$

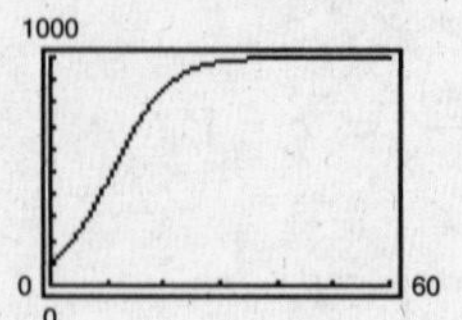


**26.** $\dfrac{dy}{dt} = 0.9y\left(1 - \dfrac{y}{200}\right)$

(a)

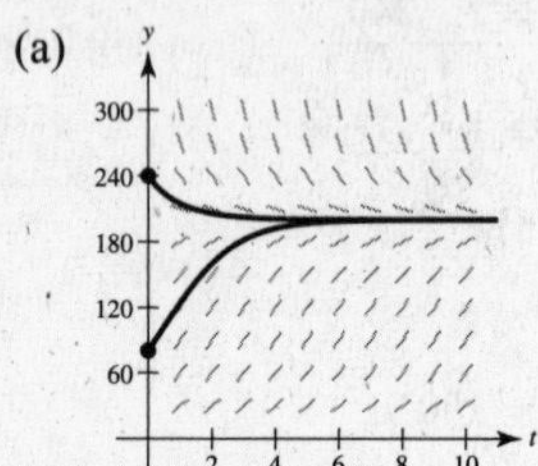


(b) $k = 0.9, L = 200$

$$y = \frac{200}{1 + be^{-0.9t}}$$

$$y(0) = 240 = \frac{200}{1 + b}$$

$$1 + b = \frac{200}{240} = \frac{5}{6}$$

$$b = -\frac{1}{6}$$

$$y = \frac{200}{1 - (1/6)e^{-0.9t}}$$

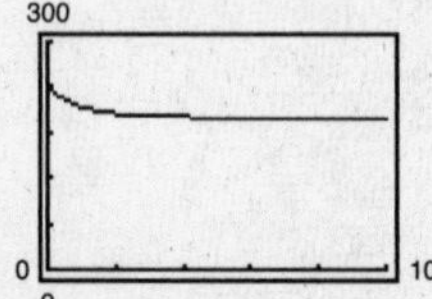


**27.** $\dfrac{dy}{dt} = 0.6y\left(1 - \dfrac{y}{700}\right)$

(a)

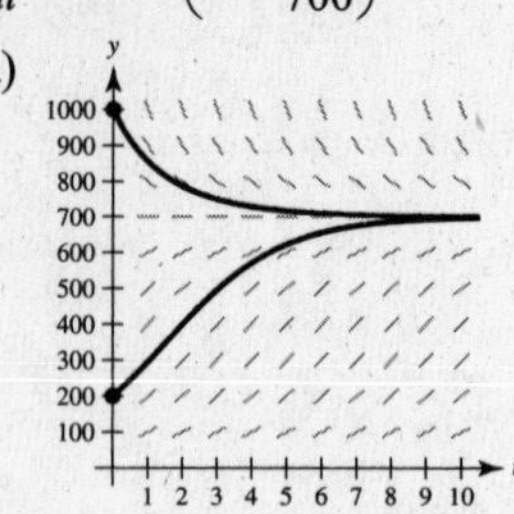


(b) $k = 0.6, L = 700$

$$y = \frac{700}{1 + be^{-0.6t}}$$

$$y(0) = 1000 = \frac{700}{1 + b}$$

$$1 + b = \frac{700}{1000} = \frac{7}{10}$$

$$b = -\frac{3}{10} = -0.3$$

$$y = \frac{700}{1 - 0.3e^{-0.6t}}$$

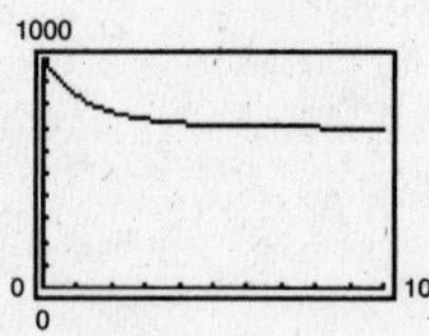


**28.** $\dfrac{dy}{dt} = 0.4y\left(1 - \dfrac{y}{500}\right)$

(a)

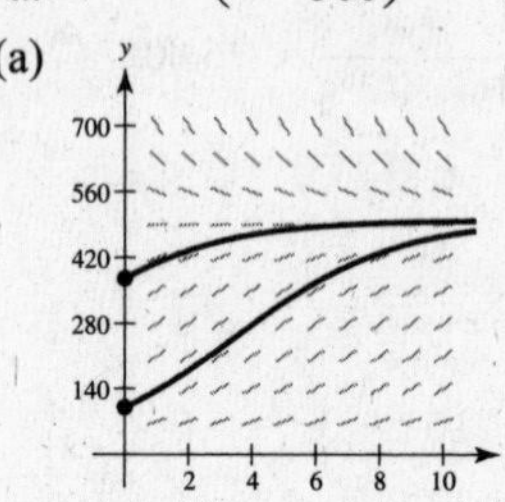


(b) $k = 0.4, L = 500$

$$y = \frac{500}{1 + be^{-0.4t}}$$

$$y(0) = 375 = \frac{500}{1 + b}$$

$$1 + b = \frac{500}{375} = \frac{4}{3}$$

$$b = \frac{1}{3}$$

$$y = \frac{500}{1 + (1/3)e^{-0.4t}}$$

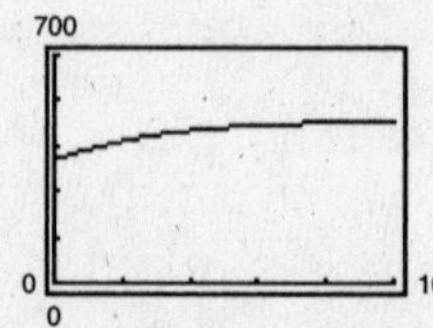

**29.** $L$ represents the value that $y$ approaches as $t$ approaches infinity. $L$ is the carrying capacity.

**30.** No, it is not possible to determine $b$. However, $L = 2500$ and $k = 0.75$. You need an initial condition to determine $b$.

**31.** Yes, the logistic differential equation is separable. See Example 1.

**32.** Answers will vary. *Sample answer*: There might be limits on available food or space.

**33.** (a) $P = \dfrac{L}{1 + be^{-kt}}, L = 200, P(0) = 25$

$$25 = \frac{200}{1 + b} \Rightarrow b = 7$$

$$39 = \frac{200}{1 + 7e^{-k(2)}}$$

$$1 + 7e^{-2k} = \frac{200}{39}$$

$$e^{-2k} = \frac{23}{39}$$

$$k = -\frac{1}{2}\ln\left(\frac{23}{39}\right) = \frac{1}{2}\ln\left(\frac{39}{23}\right) \approx 0.2640$$

$$P = \frac{200}{1 + 7e^{-0.2640t}}$$

(b) For $t = 5$, $P \approx 70$ panthers.

(c)
$$100 = \frac{200}{1 + 7e^{-0.264t}}$$

$$1 + 7e^{-0.264t} = 2$$

$$-0.264t = \ln\left(\frac{1}{7}\right)$$

$$t \approx 7.37 \text{ years}$$

(d)
$$\frac{dP}{dt} = kP\left(1 - \frac{P}{L}\right)$$

$$= 0.264P\left(1 - \frac{P}{200}\right), \quad P(0) = 25$$

Using Euler's Method, $P \approx 65.6$ when $t = 5$.

(e) $P$ is increasing most rapidly where $P = 200/2 = 100$, corresponds to $t \approx 7.37$ years.

**34.** (a) $y = \dfrac{L}{1 + be^{-kt}}$, $L = 20$, $y(0) = 1$, $y(2) = 4$

$$1 = \frac{20}{1+b} \Rightarrow b = 19$$

$$4 = \frac{20}{1 + 19e^{-2k}}$$

$$1 + 19e^{-2k} = 5$$

$$19e^{-2k} = 4$$

$$k = -\frac{1}{2}\ln\left(\frac{4}{19}\right) = \frac{1}{2}\ln\left(\frac{19}{4}\right) \approx 0.7791$$

$$y = \frac{20}{1 + 19e^{-0.7791t}}$$

(b) For $t = 5$, $y \approx 14.43$ grams.

(c) $$18 = \frac{20}{1 + 19e^{-0.7791t}}$$

$$1 + 19e^{-0.7791t} = \frac{20}{18} = \frac{10}{9}$$

$$19e^{-0.7791t} = \frac{1}{9}$$

$$e^{-0.7791t} = \frac{1}{171}$$

$$t = -\frac{1}{0.7791}\ln\left(\frac{1}{171}\right) \approx 6.60 \text{ hours}$$

(d) $\dfrac{dy}{dt} = ky\left(1 - \dfrac{y}{L}\right) = \dfrac{1}{2}\ln\left(\dfrac{19}{4}\right)y\left(1 - \dfrac{y}{20}\right)$

| $t$ | 0 | 1 | 2 | 3 | 4 | 5 |
|---|---|---|---|---|---|---|
| Exact | 1 | 2.06 | 4.00 | 7.05 | 10.86 | 14.43 |
| Euler | 1 | 1.74 | 2.98 | 4.95 | 7.86 | 11.57 |

(e) The weight is increasing most rapidly when $y = L/2 = 20/2 = 10$, corresponding to $t \approx 3.78$ hours.

**35.** False. If $y > L$, then $dy/dt < 0$ and the population decreases.

**36.** True. If $0 < y < L$, then $dy/dt > 0$ and the population increases.

**37.** $\dfrac{dy}{dt} = ky\left(1 - \dfrac{y}{L}\right)$, $y(0) < L$

$$\frac{d^2y}{dt^2} = ky'\left(1 - \frac{y}{L}\right) + ky\left(-\frac{y'}{L}\right) = k^2y\left(1 - \frac{y}{L}\right)^2 + ky\left[\frac{-ky\left(1 - \frac{y}{L}\right)}{L}\right] = k^2\left(1 - \frac{y}{L}\right)y\left[\left(1 - \frac{y}{L}\right) - \frac{y}{L}\right] = k^2\left(1 - \frac{y}{L}\right)y\left(1 - \frac{2y}{L}\right)$$

So, $\dfrac{d^2y}{dt^2} = 0$ when $1 - \dfrac{2y}{L} = 0 \Rightarrow y = \dfrac{L}{2}$.

By the First Derivative Test, this is a maximum.

**38.** $y = \dfrac{1}{1 + be^{-kt}}$

$$y' = \frac{-1}{\left(1 + be^{-kt}\right)^2}\left(-bke^{-kt}\right)$$

$$= \frac{k}{\left(1 + be^{-kt}\right)} \cdot \frac{be^{-kt}}{\left(1 + be^{-kt}\right)}$$

$$= \frac{k}{\left(1 + be^{-kt}\right)} \cdot \frac{1 + be^{-kt} - 1}{\left(1 + be^{-kt}\right)}$$

$$= \frac{k}{\left(1 + be^{-kt}\right)} \cdot \left(1 - \frac{1}{1 + be^{-kt}}\right)$$

$$= ky(1 - y)$$

## Section 6.5 First-Order Linear Differential Equations

**1.** $xy' + y = xe^x$

$$y' + \frac{1}{x}y = e^x$$

Linear

**2.** $2xy - y'\ln x = y$

$$(\ln x)y' + (1 - 2x)y = 0$$

$$y' + \frac{(1 - 2x)}{\ln x}y = 0$$

Linear

**3.** $y' - y\sin x = xy^2$

Not linear, because of the $xy^2$-term.

**4.** $\dfrac{2 - y'}{y} = 5x$

$$2 - y' = 5xy$$

$$y' + 5xy = 2$$

Linear

**5.** $\dfrac{dy}{dx} + \left(\dfrac{1}{x}\right)y = 6x + 2$

Integrating factor: $e^{\int (1/x)\,dx} = e^{\ln x} = x$

$$xy = \int x(6x + 2)\,dx = 2x^3 + x^2 + C$$

$$y = 2x^2 + x + \frac{C}{x}$$

**6.** $\dfrac{dy}{dx} + \dfrac{2}{x}y = 3x - 5$

Integrating factor: $e^{\int 2/x\,dx} = e^{\ln x^2} = x^2$

$$x^2y = \int x^2(3x - 5)\,dx = \frac{3}{4}x^4 + \frac{5x^3}{3} + C$$

$$y = \frac{3}{4}x^2 + \frac{5}{3}x + \frac{C}{x^2}$$

**7.** $y' - y = 16$

Integrating factor: $e^{\int -1\,dx} = e^{-x}$

$$e^{-x}y' - e^{-x}y = 16e^{-x}$$

$$ye^{-x} = \int 16e^{-x}\,dx = -16e^{-x} + C$$

$$y = -16 + Ce^x$$

**8.** $y' + 2xy = 10x$

Integrating factor: $e^{\int 2x\,dx} = e^{x^2}$

$$ye^{x^2} = \int 10xe^{x^2}\,dx = 5e^{x^2} + C$$

$$y = 5 + Ce^{-x^2}$$

**9.** $(y + 1)\cos x\,dx = dy$

$$y' = (y + 1)\cos x = y\cos x + \cos x$$

$$y' - (\cos x)y = \cos x$$

Integrating factor: $e^{\int -\cos x\,dx} = e^{-\sin x}$

$$y'e^{-\sin x} - (\cos x)e^{-\sin x}y = (\cos x)e^{-\sin x}$$

$$ye^{-\sin x} = \int (\cos x)e^{-\sin x}\,dx$$

$$= -e^{-\sin x} + C$$

$$y = -1 + Ce^{\sin x}$$

**10.** $\left[(y-1)\sin x\right]dx - dy = 0$

$$y' - (\sin x)y = -\sin x$$

Integrating factor: $e^{\int -\sin x\,dx} = e^{\cos x}$

$$ye^{\cos x} = \int -\sin x e^{\cos x}\,dx = e^{\cos x} + C$$

$$y = 1 + Ce^{-\cos x}$$

**11.** $(x-1)y' + y = x^2 - 1$

$$y' + \left(\frac{1}{x-1}\right)y = x + 1$$

Integrating factor: $e^{\int[1/(x-1)]\,dx} = e^{\ln|x-1|} = x - 1$

$$y(x-1) = \int(x^2-1)\,dx = \frac{1}{3}x^3 - x + C_1$$

$$y = \frac{x^3 - 3x + C}{3(x-1)}$$

**12.** $y' + 3y = e^{3x}$

Integrating factor: $e^{\int 3\,dx} = e^{3x}$

$$ye^{3x} = \int e^{3x}e^{3x}dx = \int e^{6x}dx = \frac{1}{6}e^{6x} + C$$

$$y = \frac{1}{6}e^{3x} + Ce^{-3x}$$

**13.** $y' - 3x^2y = e^{x^3}$

Integrating factor: $e^{-\int 3x^2\,dx} = e^{-x^3}$

$$ye^{-x^3} = \int e^{x^3}e^{-x^3}\,dx = \int dx = x + C$$

$$y = (x + C)e^{x^3}$$

**14.** $y' + y\tan x = \sec x$

Integrating factor: $e^{\int \tan x\,dx} = e^{-\ln|\cos x|} = \sec x$

$$y\sec x = \int \sec^2 x\,dx = \tan x + C$$

$$y = \sin x + C\cdot\cos x$$

**15.** (a) Answers will vary.

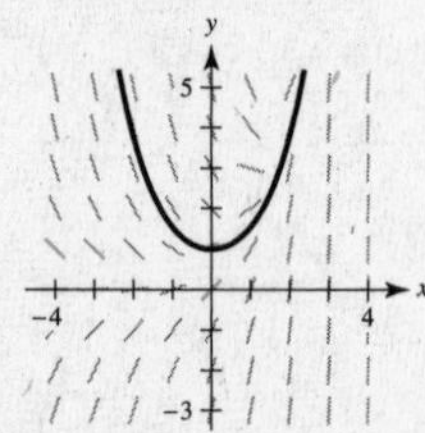

(b) $\dfrac{dy}{dx} = e^x - y$

$\dfrac{dy}{dx} + y = e^x$  Integrating factor: $e^{\int dx} = e^x$

$$e^xy' + e^xy = e^{2x}$$

$$(ye^x) = \int e^{2x}dx$$

$$ye^x = \frac{1}{2}e^{2x} + C$$

$$y(0) = 1 \Rightarrow 1 = \frac{1}{2} + C \Rightarrow C = \frac{1}{2}$$

$$ye^x = \frac{1}{2}e^{2x} + \frac{1}{2}$$

$$y = \frac{1}{2}e^x + \frac{1}{2}e^{-x} = \frac{1}{2}(e^x + e^{-x})$$

(c)

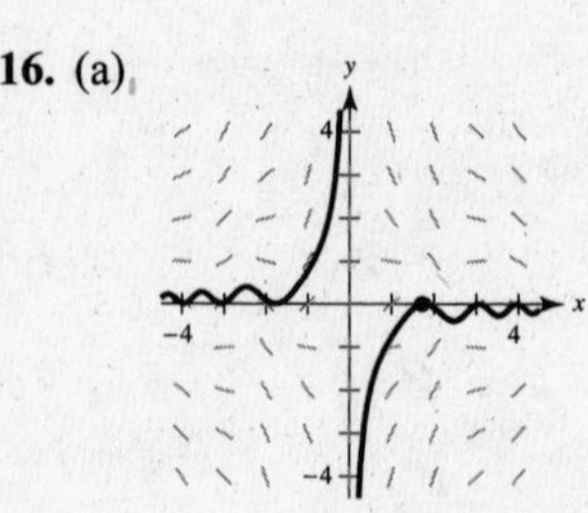

**16.** (a)

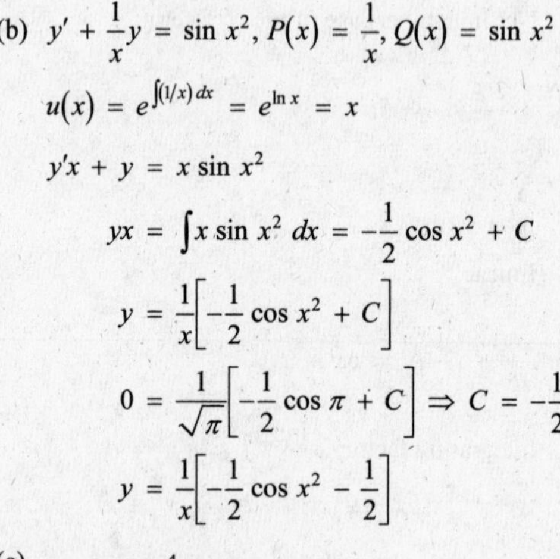

(b) $y' + \dfrac{1}{x}y = \sin x^2$, $P(x) = \dfrac{1}{x}$, $Q(x) = \sin x^2$

$$u(x) = e^{\int(1/x)\,dx} = e^{\ln x} = x$$

$$y'x + y = x\sin x^2$$

$$yx = \int x\sin x^2\,dx = -\frac{1}{2}\cos x^2 + C$$

$$y = \frac{1}{x}\left[-\frac{1}{2}\cos x^2 + C\right]$$

$$0 = \frac{1}{\sqrt{\pi}}\left[-\frac{1}{2}\cos\pi + C\right] \Rightarrow C = -\frac{1}{2}$$

$$y = \frac{1}{x}\left[-\frac{1}{2}\cos x^2 - \frac{1}{2}\right]$$

(c)

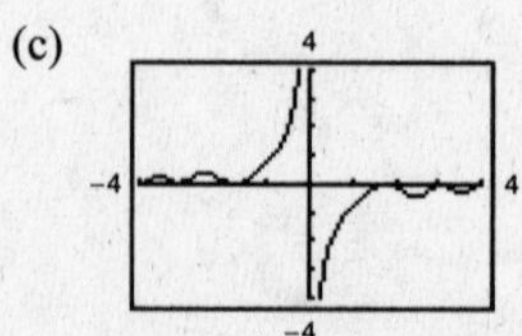

**17.** $y' \cos^2 x + y - 1 = 0$

$$y' + (\sec^2 x)y = \sec^2 x$$

Integrating factor: $e^{\int \sec^2 x\, dx} = e^{\tan x}$

$$ye^{\tan x} = \int \sec^2 x e^{\tan x}\, dx = e^{\tan x} + C$$

$$y = 1 + Ce^{-\tan x}$$

Initial condition: $y(0) = 5, C = 4$

Particular solution: $y = 1 + 4e^{-\tan x}$

**18.** $x^3 y' + 2y = e^{1/x^2}$

$$y' + \left(\frac{2}{x^3}\right)y = \frac{1}{x^3}e^{1/x^2}$$

Integrating factor: $e^{\int (2/x^3)\, dx} = e^{-(1/x^2)}$

$$ye^{-1/x^2} = \int \frac{1}{x^3}\, dx = -\frac{1}{2x^2} + C_1$$

$$y = e^{1/x^2}\left(\frac{Cx^2 - 1}{2x^2}\right)$$

Initial condition: $y(1) = e, C = 3$

Particular solution: $y = e^{1/x^2}\left(\frac{3x^2 - 1}{2x^2}\right)$

**19.** $y' + y \tan x = \sec x + \cos x$

Integrating factor: $e^{\int \tan x\, dx} = e^{\ln|\sec x|} = \sec x$

$$y \sec x = \int \sec x(\sec x + \cos x)\, dx = \tan x + x + C$$

$$y = \sin x + x \cos x + C \cos x$$

Initial condition: $y(0) = 1, 1 = C$

Particular solution: $y = \sin x + (x + 1) \cos x$

**20.** $y' + y \sec x = \sec x$

Integrating factor:

$$e^{\int \sec x\, dx} = e^{\ln|\sec x + \tan x|} = \sec x + \tan x$$

$$y(\sec x + \tan x) = \int (\sec x + \tan x) \sec x\, dx$$

$$= \sec x + \tan x + C$$

$$y = 1 + \frac{C}{\sec x + \tan x}$$

Initial condition: $y(0) = 4, 4 = 1 + \frac{C}{1 + 0}, C = 3$

Particular solution:

$$y = 1 + \frac{3}{\sec x + \tan x} = 1 + \frac{3 \cos x}{1 + \sin x}$$

**21.** $y' + \left(\frac{1}{x}\right)y = 0$

Integrating factor: $e^{\int (1/x)\, dx} = e^{\ln|x|} = x$

Separation of variables:

$$\frac{dy}{dx} = -\frac{y}{x}$$

$$\int \frac{1}{y}\, dy = \int -\frac{1}{x}\, dx$$

$$\ln y = -\ln x + \ln C$$

$$\ln xy = \ln C$$

$$xy = C$$

Initial condition: $y(2) = 2, C = 4$

Particular solution: $xy = 4$

**22.** $y' + (2x - 1)y = 0$

Integrating factor: $e^{\int (2x-1)\, dx} = e^{x^2 - x}$

$$ye^{x^2 - x} = C$$

$$y = Ce^{x - x^2}$$

Separation of variables:

$$\int \frac{1}{y}\, dy = \int (1 - 2x)\, dx$$

$$\ln y + \ln C_1 = x - x^2$$

$$yC_1 = e^{x - x^2}$$

$$y = Ce^{x - x^2}$$

Initial condition: $y(1) = 2, 2 = C$

Particular solution: $y = 2e^{x - x^2}$

**23.** $x\, dy = (x + y + 2)\, dx$

$$\frac{dy}{dx} = \frac{x + y + 2}{x} = \frac{y}{x} + 1 + \frac{2}{x}$$

$$\frac{dy}{dx} - \frac{1}{x}y = 1 + \frac{2}{x}$$

Integrating factor: $e^{\int -(1/x)\, dx} = e^{\ln x^{-1}} = \frac{1}{x}$

$$y = x\int \left(1 + \frac{2}{x}\right)\frac{1}{x}\, dx = x\int \left(\frac{1}{x} + \frac{2}{x^2}\right) dx$$

$$= x\left[\ln|x| - \frac{2}{x} + C\right]$$

$$= -2 + x \ln|x| + Cx$$

Initial condition: $y(1) = 10 = -2 + C \Rightarrow C = 12$

Particular solution: $y = -2 + x \ln|x| + 12x$

**24.** $2xy' - y = x^3 - x$

$$\frac{dy}{dx} - \frac{1}{2x}y = \frac{x^2}{2} - \frac{1}{2}$$

Integrating factor: $e^{\int -(1/2x)\,dx} = e^{\ln x^{-1/2}} = \dfrac{1}{x^{1/2}}$

$$y = x^{1/2}\int\left(\frac{x^2}{2} - \frac{1}{2}\right)\frac{1}{x^{1/2}}\,dx = x^{1/2}\int\left(\frac{x^{3/2}}{2} - \frac{x^{-1/2}}{2}\right)dx$$

$$= x^{1/2}\left[\frac{x^{5/2}}{5} - x^{1/2} + C\right]$$

$$= \frac{x^3}{5} - x + C\sqrt{x}$$

Initial condition:

$$y(4) = 2 = \frac{64}{5} - 4 + 2C \Rightarrow C = -\frac{17}{5}$$

Particular solution: $y = \dfrac{x^3}{5} - x - \dfrac{17}{5}\sqrt{x}$

**25.** $y' + 3x^2y = x^2y^3$

$n = 3, Q = x^2, P = 3x^2$

$$y^{-2}e^{\int(-2)3x^2\,dx} = \int(-2)x^2e^{\int(-2)3x^2\,dx}\,dx$$

$$y^{-2}e^{-2x^3} = -\int 2x^2e^{-2x^3}\,dx$$

$$y^{-2}e^{-2x^3} = \frac{1}{3}e^{-2x^3} + C$$

$$y^{-2} = \frac{1}{3} + Ce^{2x^3}$$

$$\frac{1}{y^2} = Ce^{2x^3} + \frac{1}{3}$$

**26.** $y' + xy = xy^{-1}$

$n = -1, Q = x, P = x, e^{\int 2x\,dx} = e^{x^2}$

$$y^2e^{x^2} = \int 2xe^{x^2}\,dx = e^{x^2} + C$$

$$y^2 = 1 + Ce^{-x^2}$$

**27.** $y' + \left(\dfrac{1}{x}\right)y = xy^2$

$n = 2, Q = x, P = x^{-1}$

$$e^{\int-(1/x)\,dx} = e^{-\ln|x|} = x^{-1}$$

$$y^{-1}x^{-1} = \int -x(x^{-1})\,dx = -x + C$$

$$\frac{1}{y} = -x^2 + Cx$$

$$y = \frac{1}{Cx - x^2}$$

**28.** $y' + \left(\dfrac{1}{x}\right)y = x\sqrt{y}$

$n = \dfrac{1}{2}, Q = x, P = x^{-1}$

$$e^{\int(1/2)(1/x)\,dx} = e^{(1/2)\ln x} = \sqrt{x}$$

$$y^{1/2}x^{1/2} = \int\frac{1}{2}x^{1/2}(x)\,dx$$

$$= \frac{1}{5}x^{5/2} + C_1 = \frac{x^{5/2} + C}{5}$$

$$y = \frac{\left(x^{5/2} + C\right)^2}{25x}$$

**29.** $xy' + y = xy^3$

$$y' + \frac{1}{x}y = y^3$$

$n = 3, Q = 1, P = \dfrac{1}{x}$

$$e^{\int\frac{-2}{x}\,dx} = e^{-2\ln x} = x^{-2}$$

$$y^{-2}x^{-2} = \int -2x^{-2}\,dx + C = 2x^{-1} + C$$

$$y^{-2} = 2x + Cx^2$$

$$y^2 = \frac{1}{2x + Cx^2} \quad\text{or}\quad \frac{1}{y^2} = 2x + Cx^2$$

**30.** $y' - y = y^3$

$n = 3, P = -1, Q = 1, \quad e^{\int-2(-1)\,dx} = e^{2x}$

$$y^{-2}e^{2x} = \int(-2)e^{2x}\,dx = -e^{2x} + C$$

$$y^{-2} = -1 + Ce^{-2x}$$

$$y^2 = \frac{1}{-1 + Ce^{-2x}}$$

**31.** $y' - y = e^x\sqrt[3]{y}, n = \frac{1}{3}, Q = e^x, P = -1$

$$e^{\int-(2/3)\,dx} = e^{-(2/3)x}$$

$$y^{2/3}e^{-(2/3)x} = \int\tfrac{2}{3}e^xe^{-(2/3)x}\,dx = \int\tfrac{2}{3}e^{(1/3)x}\,dx$$

$$y^{2/3}e^{-(2/3)x} = 2e^{(1/3)x} + C$$

$$y^{2/3} = 2e^x + Ce^{2x/3}$$

**32.** $yy' - 2y^2 = e^x$

$$y' - 2y = e^xy^{-1}$$

$n = -1, Q = e^x, P = -2$

$$e^{\int 2(-2)\,dx} = e^{-4x}$$

$$y^2e^{-4x} = \int 2e^{-4x}e^x\,dx = -\tfrac{2}{3}e^{-3x} + C$$

$$y^2 = -\tfrac{2}{3}e^x + Ce^{4x}$$

**33.** (a)

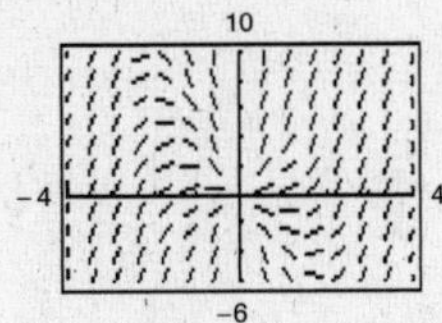

(b) $\frac{dy}{dx} - \frac{1}{x}y = x^2$

Integrating factor: $e^{\int -1/x\,dx} = e^{-\ln x} = \frac{1}{x}$

$$\frac{1}{x}y' - \frac{1}{x^2}y = x$$

$$\left(\frac{1}{x}y\right) = \int x\,dx = \frac{x^2}{2} + C$$

$$y = \frac{x^3}{2} + Cx$$

$(-2, 4)$: $4 = \frac{-8}{2} - 2C \Rightarrow C = -4 \Rightarrow y = \frac{x^3}{2} - 4x = \frac{1}{2}x\left(x^2 - 8\right)$

$(2, 8)$: $8 = \frac{8}{2} + 2C \Rightarrow C = 2 \Rightarrow y = \frac{x^3}{2} + 2x = \frac{1}{2}x\left(x^2 + 4\right)$

(c)

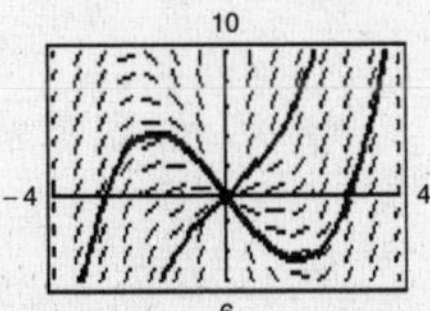

**34.** (a)

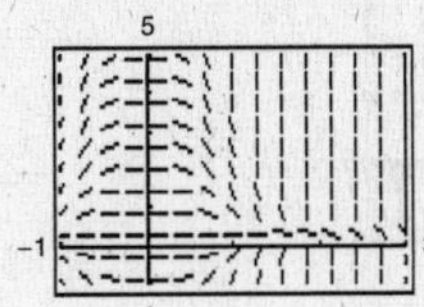

(b) $y' + 4x^3y = x^3$

Integrating factor: $e^{\int 4x^3\,dx} = e^{x^4}$

$$y'e^{x^4} + 4x^3ye^{x^4} = x^3e^{x^4}$$

$$ye^{x^4} = \int x^3e^{x^4}\,dx = \tfrac{1}{4}e^{x^4} + C$$

$$y = \tfrac{1}{4} + Ce^{-x^4}$$

$\left(0, \frac{7}{2}\right)$: $\frac{7}{2} = \frac{1}{4} + C \Rightarrow C = \frac{13}{4} \Rightarrow y = \frac{1}{4} + \frac{13}{4}e^{-x^4}$

$\left(0, -\frac{1}{2}\right)$: $-\frac{1}{2} = \frac{1}{4} + C \Rightarrow C = -\frac{3}{4} \Rightarrow y = \frac{1}{4} - \frac{3}{4}e^{-x^4}$

(c)

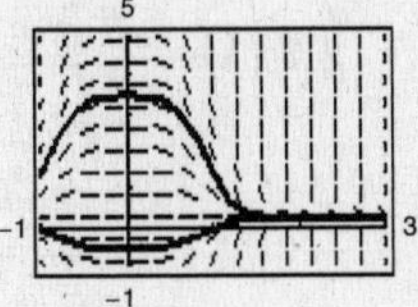

**35.** (a)

(b) $y' + (\cot x)y = 2$

Integrating factor: $e^{\int \cot x\, dx} = e^{\ln|\sin x|} = \sin x$

$y'\sin x + (\cos x)y = 2\sin x$

$$y\sin x = \int 2\sin x\, dx = -2\cos x + C$$

$$y = -2\cot x + C\csc x$$

$(1, 1)$: $1 = -2\cot 1 + C\csc 1 \Rightarrow C = \dfrac{1 + 2\cot 1}{\csc 1} = \sin 1 + 2\cos 1$

$$y = -2\cot x + (\sin 1 + 2\cos 1)\csc x$$

$(3, -1)$: $-1 = -2\cot 3 + C\csc 3 \Rightarrow C = \dfrac{2\cot 3 - 1}{\csc 3} = 2\cos 3 - \sin 3$

$$y = -2\cot x + (2\cos 3 - \sin 3)\csc x$$

(c)

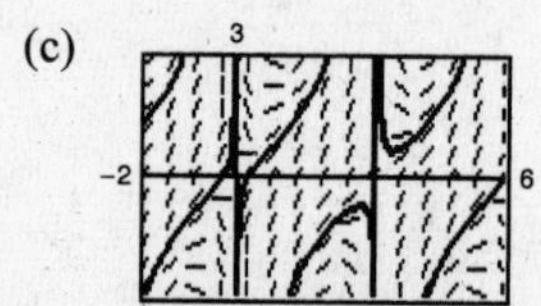

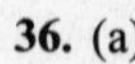

**36.** (a)

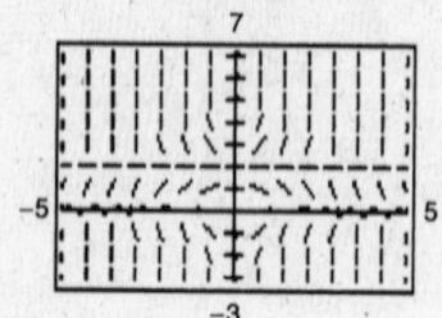

(b) $y' + 2xy = xy^2$

Bernoulli equation, $n = 2$ letting

$z = y^{1-2} = y^{-1}$, you obtain $e^{\int -2x\, dx} = e^{-x^2}$ and

$\int(-1)xe^{-x^2}\, dx = \dfrac{1}{2}e^{-x^2}$. The solution is:

$$y^{-1}e^{-x^2} = \frac{1}{2}e^{-x^2} + C$$

$$\frac{1}{y} = \frac{1}{2} + Ce^{x^2} = \frac{1 + 2Ce^{x^2}}{2}$$

$$y = \frac{2}{1 + 2Ce^{x^2}}$$

$(0, 3)$: $3 = \dfrac{2}{1 + 2C} \Rightarrow 1 + 2C = \dfrac{2}{3} \Rightarrow C = -\dfrac{1}{6}$

$$y = \frac{2}{1 - \left(e^{x^2}/3\right)} = \frac{6}{3 - e^{x^2}}$$

$(0, 1)$: $1 = \dfrac{2}{1 + 2C} \Rightarrow 1 + 2C = 2 \Rightarrow C = \dfrac{1}{2}$

$$y = \frac{2}{1 + e^{x^2}}$$

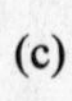

(c)

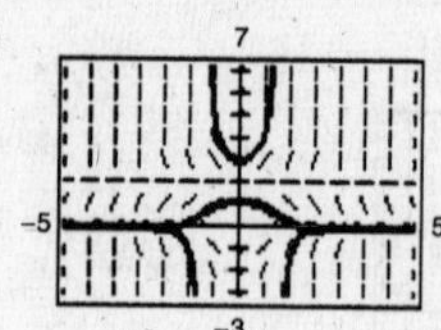

**37.** (a) $\dfrac{dQ}{dt} = q - kQ$, $q$ constant

(b) $Q' + kQ = q$

Let $P(t) = k$, $Q(t) = q$, then the integrating factor is $u(t) = e^{kt}$.

$$Q = e^{-kt}\int qe^{kt}\, dt = e^{-kt}\left(\frac{q}{k}e^{kt} + C\right) = \frac{q}{k} + Ce^{-kt}$$

When $t = 0$: $Q = Q_0$

$$Q_0 = \frac{q}{k} + C \Rightarrow C = Q_0 - \frac{q}{k}$$

$$Q = \frac{q}{k} + \left(Q_0 - \frac{q}{k}\right)e^{-kt}$$

(c) $\displaystyle\lim_{t\to\infty} Q = \frac{q}{k}$

**38.** (a) $\dfrac{dN}{dt} = k(75 - N)$

(b) $N' + kN = 75k$

Integrating factor: $e^{\int k\,dt} = e^{kt}$

$N'e^{kt} + kNe^{kt} = 75\,ke^{kt}$

$\left(Ne^{kt}\right)' = 75\,ke^{kt}$

$Ne^{kt} = \int 75\,ke^{kt} = 75\,e^{kt} + C$

$N = 75 + Ce^{-kt}$

(c) For $t = 1$, $N = 20$:

$20 = 75 + Ce^{-k} \Rightarrow -55 = Ce^{-k}$

For $t = 20$, $N = 35$:

$35 = 75 + Ce^{-20k} \Rightarrow -40 = Ce^{-20k}$

$\dfrac{55}{40} = \dfrac{Ce^{-k}}{Ce^{-20k}} \Rightarrow e^{19k} = \dfrac{11}{8} \Rightarrow k = \dfrac{1}{19}\ln\left(\dfrac{11}{8}\right)$

$\approx 0.0168$

$Ce^{-k} = -55$

$C = -55e^{k} \approx -55.9296$

$N = 75 - 55.9296\,e^{-0.0168t}$

**39.** Let $Q$ be the number of pounds of concentrate in the solution at any time $t$. Because the number of gallons of solution in the tank at any time $t$ is $v_0 + (r_1 - r_2)t$ and because the tank loses $r_2$ gallons of solution per minute, it must lose concentrate at the rate

$$\left[\frac{Q}{v_0 + (r_1 - r_2)t}\right]r_2.$$

The solution gains concentrate at the rate $r_1q_1$. Therefore, the net rate of change is

$$\frac{dQ}{dt} = q_1r_1 - \left[\frac{Q}{v_0 + (r_1 - r_2)t}\right]r_2$$

or

$$\frac{dQ}{dt} + \frac{r_2Q}{v_0 + (r_1 - r_2)t} = q_1r_1.$$

**40.** From Exercise 39, and using $r_1 = r_2 = r$,

$$\frac{dQ}{dt} + \frac{rQ}{v_0} = q_1r.$$

**41.** (a) $Q' + \dfrac{r^2Q}{v_0 + (r_1 - r_2)t} = q_1r_1$

$Q(0) = q_0,\ q_0 = 25,\ q_1 = 0,\ v_0 = 200,$

$r_1 = 10,\ r_2 = 10,\ Q' + \dfrac{1}{20}Q = 0$

$\int \dfrac{1}{Q}\,dQ = \int -\dfrac{1}{20}\,dt$

$\ln Q = -\dfrac{1}{20}t + \ln C_1$

$Q = Ce^{-(1/20)t}$

Initial condition: $Q(0) = 25,\ C = 25$

Particular solution: $Q = 25e^{-(1/20)t}$

(b) $15 = 25e^{-(1/20)t}$

$\ln\left(\dfrac{3}{5}\right) = -\dfrac{1}{20}t$

$t = -20\ln\left(\dfrac{3}{5}\right) \approx 10.2$ min

(c) $\lim\limits_{t\to\infty} 25e^{-(1/20)t} = 0$

**42.** (a) $Q' + \dfrac{r^2Q}{v_0 + (r_1 - r_2)t} = q_1r_1$

$Q(0) = q_0 = 25,\ q_1 = 0.04,\ v_0 = 200,$

$r_1 = 10,\ r_2 = 10,\ Q' + \dfrac{1}{20}Q = 0.4$

Integrating factor: $e^{(1/20)t}$

$Qe^{(-1/20)t} = \int 0.4e^{(1/20)t}\,dt = 8e^{(1/20)t} + C$

$Q = 8 + Ce^{(-1/20)t}$

$Q = (0) = 25 = 8 + C \Rightarrow C = 17$

$Q = 8 + 17e^{(-1/20)t}$

(b) $15 = 8 + 17e^{(-1/20)t}$

$7 = 17e^{(-1/20)t}$

$\ln\left(\dfrac{7}{17}\right) = -\dfrac{1}{20}t \Rightarrow t = -20\ln\left(\dfrac{7}{17}\right) \approx 17.75$ min

(c) $\lim\limits_{t\to\infty} Q(t) = 8$ lb

**43.** (a) The volume of the solution in the tank is given by $v_0 + (r_1 - r_2)t$.

Therefore, $100 + (5 - 3)t = 200$ or $t = 50$ minutes.

(b) $Q' + \dfrac{r_2 Q}{v_0 + (r_1 - r_2)t} = q_1 r_1$

$Q(0) = q_0, q_0 = 0, q_1 = 0.5, v_0 = 100, r_1 = 5,$

$r_2 = 3, Q' + \dfrac{3}{100 + 2t}Q = 2.5$

Integrating factor: $e^{\int[3/(100+2t)]\,dt} = (50 + t)^{3/2}$

$$Q(50 + t)^{3/2} = \int 2.5(50 + t)^{3/2}\,dt = (50 + t)^{5/2} + C$$

$$Q = (50 + t) + C(50 + t)^{-3/2}$$

Initial condition:

$Q(0) = 0, 0 = 50 + C(50^{-3/2}), C = -50^{5/2}$

Particular solution:

$$Q = (50 + t) - 50^{-5/2}(50 + t)^{-3/2}$$

$$Q(50) = 100 - 50^{5/2}(100)^{-3/2}$$

$$= 100 - \frac{25}{\sqrt{2}} \approx 82.32 \text{ lb}$$

**44.** (a) The volume of the solution is given by $v_0 + (r_1 - r_2)t = 100 + (5 - 3)t = 200 \Rightarrow t = 50$ minutes.

(b) $Q' + \dfrac{r_2 Q}{v_0 + (r_1 - r_2)t} = q_1 r_1$

$Q(0) = q_0 = 0, q_1 = 1, v_0 = 100, r_1 = 5, r_2 = 3$

$Q' + \dfrac{3Q}{100 + 2t} = 5$

Integrating factor is $(50 + t)^{3/2}$, as in Exercise 43.

$$Q(50 + t)^{3/2} = \int 5(50 + t)^{3/2}\,dt = 2(50 + t)^{5/2} + C$$

$$Q = 2(50 + t) + C(50 + t)^{-3/2}$$

$Q(0) = 0$:

$0 = 100 + C(50)^{-3/2} \Rightarrow C = -100(50)^{3/2} = -2(50)^{5/2}$

$Q = 2(50 + t) - 2(50)^{5/2}(50 + t)^{-3/2}$

When $t = 50$, $Q = 200 - 2(50)^{5/2}(100)^{-3/2} = 200 - \dfrac{50}{\sqrt{2}} \approx 164.64$ lb (double the answer to Exercise 43b)

**45.** From Example 6,

$$\frac{dv}{dt} + \frac{kv}{m} = g$$

$$v = \frac{mg}{k}\left(1 - e^{-kt/m}\right), \quad \text{Solution}$$

$$g = -32,\ mg = -8,\ v(5) = -101,\ m = \frac{-8}{g} = \frac{1}{4}$$

implies that $-101 = \frac{-8}{k}\left(1 - e^{-5k/(1/4)}\right)$.

Using a graphing utility, $k \approx 0.050165$, and $v = -159.47\left(1 - e^{-0.2007t}\right)$.

As $t \to \infty$, $v \to -159.47$ ft/sec. The graph of $v$ is shown below.

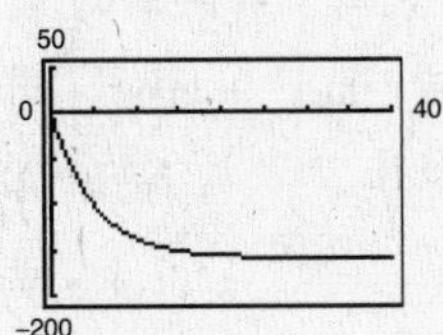


**46.** 
$$\begin{aligned} s(t) &= \int v(t)\,dt \\ &= \int -159.47\left(1 - e^{-0.2007t}\right)dt \\ &= -159.47t - 794.57e^{-0.2007t} + C \end{aligned}$$

$$s(0) = 5000 = -794.57 + C \Rightarrow C = 5794.57$$

$$s(t) = -159.47t - 794.57e^{-0.2007t} + 5794.57$$

The graph of $s(t)$ is shown below.

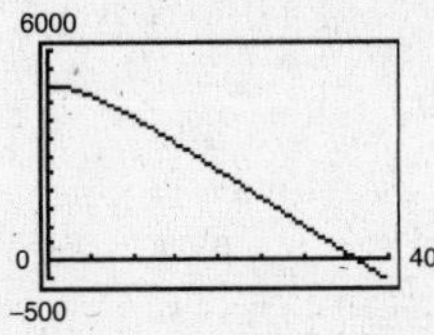


$s(t) = 0$ when $t \approx 36.33$ sec.

**47.** $L\frac{dI}{dt} + RI = E_0,\ I' + \frac{R}{L}I = \frac{E_0}{L}$

Integrating factor: $e^{\int(R/L)\,dt} = e^{Rt/L}$

$$I\,e^{Rt/L} = \int \frac{E_0}{L}e^{Rt/L}\,dt = \frac{E_0}{R}e^{Rt/L} + C$$

$$I = \frac{E_0}{R} + Ce^{-Rt/L}$$

**48.** $I(0) = 0$, $E_0 = 120$ volts, $R = 600$ ohms, $L = 4$ henrys

$$I = \frac{E_0}{R} + Ce^{-Rt/L}$$

$$0 = \frac{120}{600} + C \Rightarrow C = -\frac{1}{5}$$

$$I = \frac{1}{5} - \frac{1}{5}e^{-150t}$$

$$\lim_{t\to\infty} I = \frac{1}{5} \text{ amp}$$

$$\begin{aligned} (0.90)\frac{1}{5} &= 0.18 = \frac{1}{5}\left(1 - e^{-150t}\right) \\ 0.9 &= 1 - e^{-150t} \\ e^{-150t} &= 0.1 \\ -150t &= \ln(0.1) \\ t &= \frac{\ln(0.1)}{-150} \approx 0.0154 \text{ sec} \end{aligned}$$

**49.** The term "first-order" refers to the fact that the derivative is order one, and not a higher order derivative.

**50.** $\frac{dy}{dx} + P(x)y = Q(x)$ Standard form

$u(x) = e^{\int P(x)\,dx}$ Integrating factor

**51.** $y' + P(x)y = Q(x)y^n$ Standard form

Let $z = y^{1-n}$ $(n \neq 0, 1)$. Multiplying by $(1 - n)y^{-n}$ produces

$$(1 - n)y^{-n}y' + (1 - n)P(x)y^{1-n} = (1 - n)Q(x)$$

$$z' + (1 - n)P(x)z = (1 - n)Q(x).\ \text{Linear}$$

**52.** $y' + P(x)y = Q(x)$

Integrating factor: $u = e^{\int P(x)\,dx}$

$$\begin{aligned} y'u + P(x)yu &= Q(x)u \\ (uy)' &= Q(x)u \end{aligned}$$

so $u'(x) = P(x)u$

Answer (a)

**53.** $y' - 2x = 0$

$$\int dy = \int 2x\,dx$$

$$y = x^2 + C$$

Matches c.

**54.** $y' - 2y = 0$

$$\int \frac{dy}{y} = \int 2\,dx$$

$$\ln y = 2x + C_1$$

$$y = Ce^{2x}$$

Matches d.

**55.** $y' - 2xy = 0$

$$\int \frac{dy}{y} = \int 2x\,dx$$

$$\ln y = x^2 + C_1$$

$$y = Ce^{x^2}$$

Matches a.

**56.** $y' - 2xy = x$

$$\int \frac{dy}{2y + 1} = \int x\,dx$$

$$\frac{1}{2}\ln(2y + 1) = \frac{1}{2}x^2 + C_1$$

$$2y + 1 = C_2e^{x^2}$$

$$y = -\frac{1}{2} + Ce^{x^2}$$

Matches b.

**57.** $e^{2x+y}\,dx - e^{x-y}\,dy = 0$

Separation of variables:

$$e^{2x}e^{y}\,dx = e^{x}e^{-y}\,dy$$

$$\int e^{x}\,dx = \int e^{-2y}\,dy$$

$$e^{x} = -\tfrac{1}{2}e^{-2y} + C_1$$

$$2e^{x} + e^{-2y} = C$$

**58.** $\dfrac{dy}{dx} = \dfrac{x - 3}{y(y + 4)}$

Separation of variables:

$$\int (y^2 + 4y)\,dy = \int (x - 3)\,dx$$

$$\frac{y^3}{3} + 2y^2 = \frac{x^2}{2} - 3x + C_1$$

$$2y^3 + 12y^2 = 3x^2 - 18x + C$$

**59.** $(y\cos x - \cos x)\,dx + dy = 0$

Separation of variables:

$$\int \cos x\,dx = \int \frac{-1}{y - 1}\,dy$$

$$\sin x = -\ln(y - 1) + \ln C$$

$$\ln(y - 1) = -\sin x + \ln C$$

$$y = Ce^{-\sin x} + 1$$

**60.** $y' = 2x\sqrt{1 - y^2}$

Separation of variables:

$$\int \frac{1}{\sqrt{1 - y^2}}\,dy = \int 2x\,dx$$

$$\arcsin y = x^2 + C$$

$$y = \sin(x^2 + C)$$

**61.** $(3y^2 + 4xy)\,dx + (2xy + x^2)\,dy = 0$

Homogeneous: $y = vx$, $dy = v\,dx + x\,dv$

$$(3v^2x^2 + 4vx^2)\,dx + (2vx^2 + x^2)(v\,dx + x\,dv) = 0$$

$$\int \frac{5}{x}\,dx + \int \left(\frac{2v + 1}{v^2 + v}\right)dv = 0$$

$$\ln x^5 + \ln\left|v^2 + v\right| = \ln C$$

$$x^5(v^2 + v) = C$$

$$x^3y^2 + x^4y = C$$

**62.** $(x + y)\,dx - x\,dy = 0$

Linear: $y' - \dfrac{1}{x}y = 1$

Integrating factor: $e^{\int -(1/x)\,dx} = e^{\ln\left|x^{-1}\right|} = \dfrac{1}{x}$

$$y\frac{1}{x} = \int \frac{1}{x}\,dx = \ln|x| + C$$

$$y = x(\ln|x| + C)$$

**63.** $(2y - e^x)\,dx + x\,dy = 0$

Linear: $y' + \left(\dfrac{2}{x}\right)y = \dfrac{1}{x}e^x$

Integrating factor: $e^{\int (2/x)\,dx} = e^{\ln x^2} = x^2$

$$yx^2 = \int x^2\frac{1}{x}e^x\,dx = e^x(x - 1) + C$$

$$y = \frac{e^x}{x^2}(x - 1) + \frac{C}{x^2}$$

**64.** $(y^2 + xy)\,dx - x^2\,dy = 0$

Homogeneous: $y = vx$, $dy = v\,dx + x\,dv$

$$(v^2x^2 + vx^2)\,dx - x^2(v\,dx + x\,dv) = 0$$

$$v^2\,dx - x\,dv = 0$$

$$\int \frac{1}{x}\,dx = \int \frac{1}{v^2}\,dv$$

$$\ln x = -\frac{1}{v} + C$$

$$y = \frac{x}{C - \ln|x|}$$

**65.** $(x^2y^4 - 1)\,dx + x^3y^3\,dy = 0$

$$y' + \left(\frac{1}{x}\right)y = x^{-3}y^{-3}$$

Bernoulli: $n = -3, Q = x^{-3}, P = x^{-1}$,

$$e^{\int (4/x)\,dx} = e^{\ln x^4} = x^4$$

$$y^4x^4 = \int 4(x^{-3})(x^4)\,dx = 2x^2 + C$$

$$x^4y^4 - 2x^2 = C$$

**66.** $y\,dx + (3x + 4y)\,dy = 0$

Homogeneous: $x = vy,\ dx = v\,dy + y\,dv$

$$y(v\,dy + y\,dv) + (3vy + 4y)\,dy = 0$$

$$\int \frac{1}{v+1}\,dv = \int -\frac{4}{y}\,dy$$

$$\ln|v + 1| = -\ln y^4 + \ln C$$

$$y^4(v + 1) = C$$

$$y^3(x + y) = C$$

**67.** $3(y - 4x^2)\,dx = -x\,dy$

$$x\frac{dy}{dx} = -3y + 12x^2$$

$$y' + \frac{3}{x}y = 12x$$

Integrating factor: $e^{\int (3/x)\,dx} = e^{3\ln x} = x^3$

$$y'x^3 + \frac{3}{x}x^3y = 12x(x^3) = 12x^4$$

$$yx^3 = \int 12x^4\,dx = \frac{12}{5}x^5 + C$$

$$y = \frac{12}{5}x^2 + \frac{C}{x^3}$$

**68.** $x\,dx + (y + e^y)(x^2 + 1)\,dy = 0$

Separation of variables:

$$\int \frac{x}{x^2 + 1}\,dx = \int -(y + e^y)\,dy$$

$$\frac{1}{2}\ln(x^2 + 1) = -\frac{1}{2}y^2 - e^y + C_1$$

$$\ln(x^2 + 1) + y^2 + 2e^y = C$$

**69.** False. The equation contains $\sqrt{y}$.

**70.** True. $y' + (x - e^x)y = 0$ is linear.

## Section 6.6 Predator-Prey Differential Equations

**1.** $\dfrac{dx}{dt} = ax - bxy = 0.9x - 0.05xy$

$$\frac{dy}{dt} = -my + nxy = -0.6y + 0.008xy$$

$$\frac{dx}{dt} = \frac{dy}{dt} = 0 \Rightarrow 0.9x - 0.05xy = x(0.9 - 0.05y) = 0$$

$$-0.6y + 0.008xy = y(-0.6 + 0.008x) = 0$$

If $x = 0$, then $y = 0$.

If $y = \dfrac{0.9}{0.05} = \dfrac{90}{5} = 18$, then $x = \dfrac{0.6}{0.008} = \dfrac{600}{8} = 75$.

Solutions: $(0, 0)$ and $(75, 18)$

**2.** $\dfrac{dx}{dt} = ax - bxy = 0.75x - 0.006xy$

$\dfrac{dy}{dt} = -my + nxy = -0.9y + 0.003xy$

$$\frac{dx}{dt} = \frac{dy}{dt} = 0 \Rightarrow 0.75x - 0.006xy = x(0.75 - 0.06y) = 0$$

$$-0.9y + 0.003xy = y(-0.9 + 0.003x) = 0$$

If $x = 0$, then $y = 0$.

If $y = \dfrac{0.75}{0.006} = \dfrac{750}{6} = 125$, then $x = \dfrac{0.9}{0.003} = \dfrac{900}{3} = 300$.

Solutions: $(0, 0)$ and $(300, 125)$

**3.** $\dfrac{dx}{dt} = ax - bxy = 0.5x - 0.01xy$

$\dfrac{dy}{dt} = -my + nxy = -0.49y + 0.007xy$

$$\frac{dx}{dt} = \frac{dy}{dt} = 0 \Rightarrow 0.5x - 0.01xy = x(0.5 - 0.01y) = 0$$

$$-0.49y + 0.007xy = y(-0.49 + 0.007x) = 0$$

If $x = 0$, then $y = 0$.

If $y = \dfrac{0.5}{0.01} = \dfrac{50}{1} = 50$, then $x = \dfrac{0.49}{0.007} = \dfrac{490}{7} = 70$.

Solutions: $(0, 0)$ and $(70, 50)$

**4.** $\dfrac{dx}{dt} = ax - bxy = 1.2x - 0.04xy$

$\dfrac{dy}{dt} = -my + nxy = -1.2y + 0.02xy$

$$\frac{dx}{dt} = \frac{dy}{dt} = 0 \Rightarrow 1.2x - 0.04xy = x(1.2 - 0.04y) = 0$$

$$-1.2y + 0.02xy = y(-1.2 + 0.02x) = 0$$

If $x = 0$, then $y = 0$.

If $y = \dfrac{1.2}{0.04} = \dfrac{120}{4} = 30$, then $x = \dfrac{1.2}{0.02} = \dfrac{120}{2} = 60$.

Solutions: $(0, 0)$ and $(60, 30)$

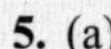
**5.** (a)

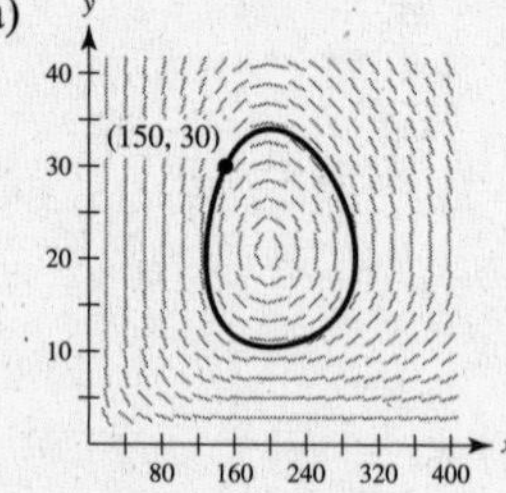

(b)

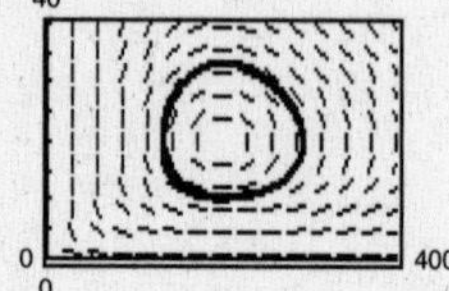


**6.** (a)

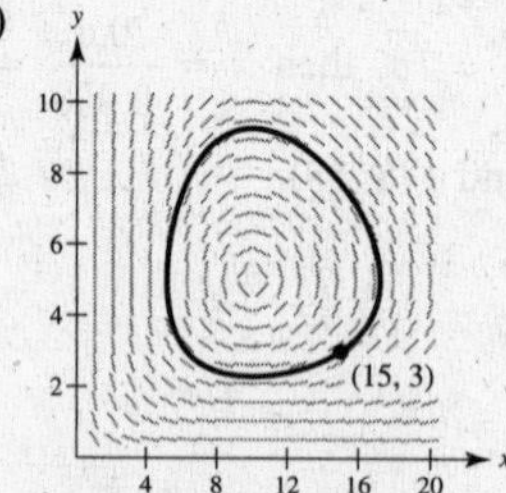

(b)

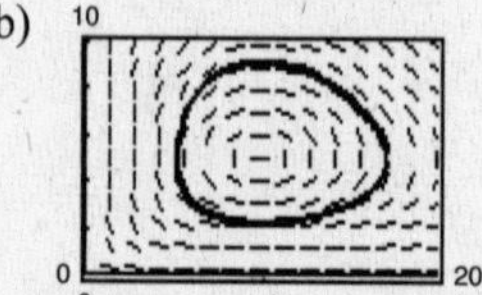

**7.** (a) The initial conditions are $x(0) = 40$ and $y(0) = 20$.

(b)

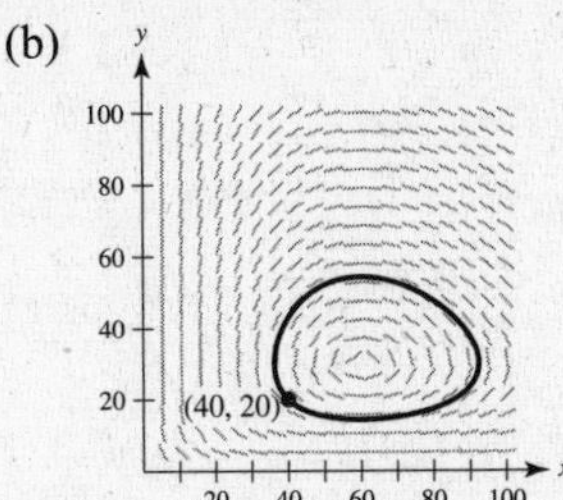


**8.** (a) The initial conditions are $x(0) = 60$ and $y(0) = 10$.

(b)

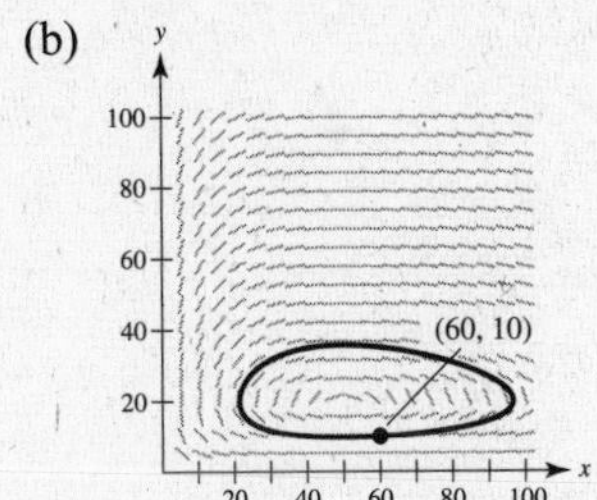


**9.** Critical points are $(x, y) = (0,0)$ and

$$(x, y) = \left(\frac{m}{n}, \frac{a}{b}\right) = \left(\frac{0.3}{0.006}, \frac{0.8}{0.04}\right) = (50, 20).$$

**10.**

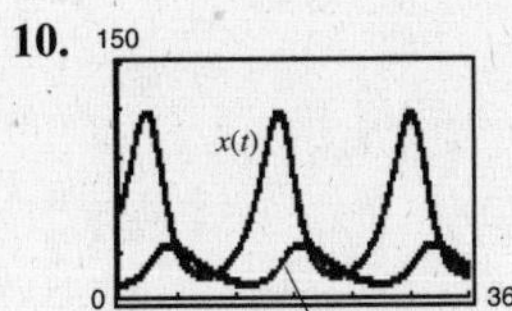


**11.**

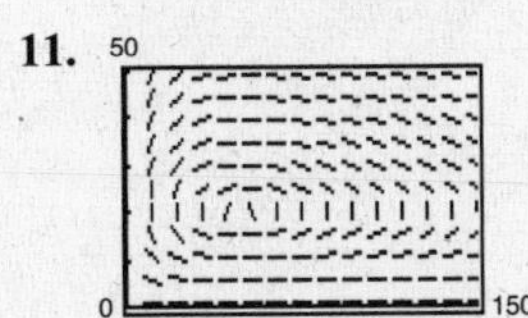


**12.**

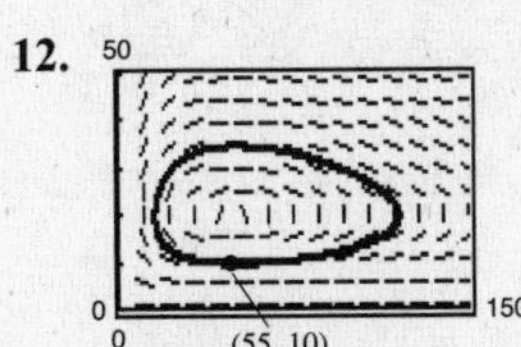


**13.** Critical points are $(x, y) = (0,0)$ and

$$(x, y) = \left(\frac{m}{n}, \frac{a}{b}\right)$$

$$= \left(\frac{0.4}{0.00004}, \frac{0.1}{0.00008}\right)$$

$$= (10{,}000, 1250).$$

**14.**

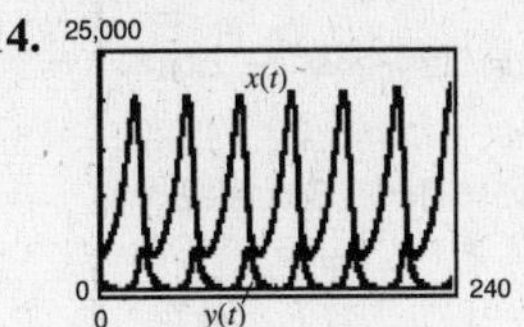


**15.**

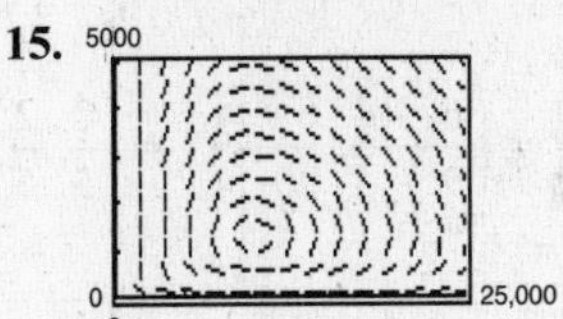


**16.**

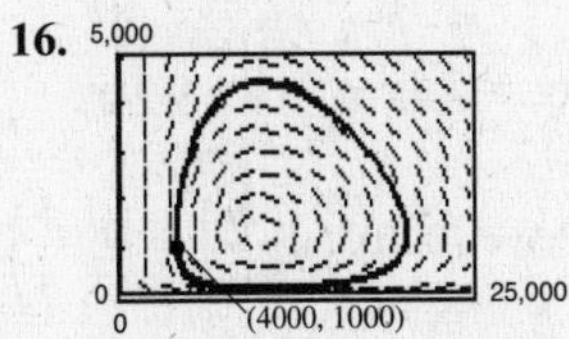


**17.** Using $x(0) = 50$ and $y(0) = 20$, you obtain the constant solutions $x = 50$ and $y = 20$.

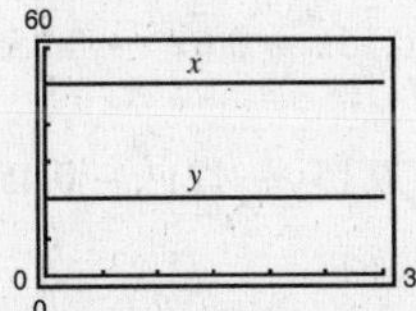


The slope field is the same, but the solution curve reduces to a single point at $(50, 20)$.

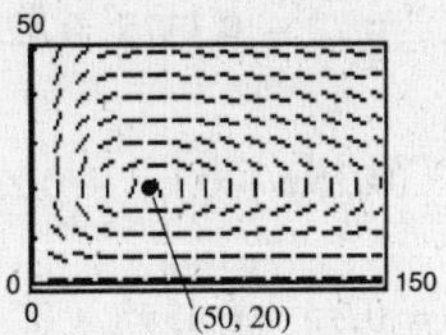


**18.** Using $x(0) = 10{,}000$ and $y(0) = 1250$, you obtain the constant solutions $x = 10{,}000$ and $y = 1250$.

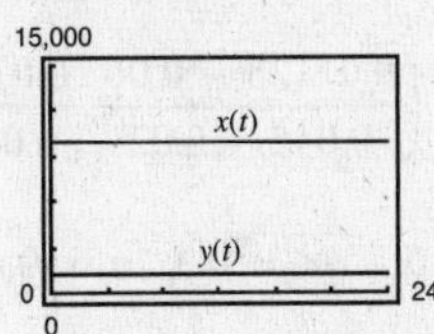


The slope field is the same, but the solution curve reduces to a single point at $(10{,}000, 1250)$.

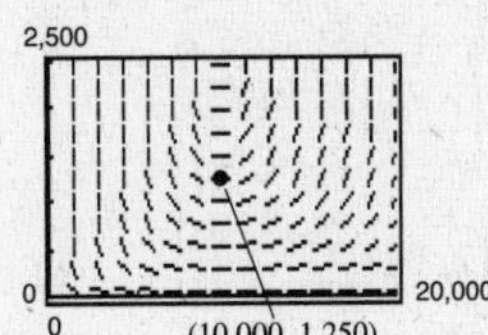

**19.** $\dfrac{dx}{dt} = ax - bx^2 - cxy = 2x - 3x^2 - 2xy$

$\dfrac{dy}{dt} = my - ny^2 - pxy = 2y - 3y^2 - 2xy$

From Example 5, you have $(0, 0)$, $\left(0, \dfrac{m}{n}\right) = \left(0, \dfrac{2}{3}\right)$, $\left(\dfrac{a}{b}, 0\right) = \left(\dfrac{2}{3}, 0\right)$ and

$$\left(\frac{an - mc}{bn - cp}, \frac{bm - ap}{bn - cp}\right) = \left(\frac{6 - 4}{9 - 4}, \frac{6 - 4}{9 - 4}\right) = \left(\frac{2}{5}, \frac{2}{5}\right).$$

**20.** $\dfrac{dx}{dt} = ax - bx^2 - cxy = x - 0.5x^2 - 0.5xy$

$\dfrac{dy}{dt} = my - ny^2 - pxy = 2.5y - 2y^2 - 0.5xy$

From Example 5, you have $(0, 0)$, $\left(0, \dfrac{m}{n}\right) = \left(0, \dfrac{5}{4}\right)$, $\left(\dfrac{a}{b}, 0\right) = (2, 0)$ and

$$\left(\frac{an - mc}{bn - cp}, \frac{bm - ap}{bn - cp}\right) = \left(\frac{2 - 5/4}{1 - 1/4}, \frac{5/4 - 1/2}{1 - 1/4}\right) = (1, 1).$$

**21.** $\dfrac{dx}{dt} = ax - bx^2 - cxy = 0.15x - 0.6x^2 - 0.75xy$

$\dfrac{dy}{dt} = my - ny^2 - pxy = 0.15y - 12y^2 - 0.45xy$

From Example 5, you have $(0, 0)$, $\left(0, \dfrac{m}{n}\right) = \left(0, \dfrac{1}{8}\right)$, $\left(\dfrac{a}{b}, 0\right) = \left(\dfrac{1}{4}, 0\right)$ and

$$\left(\frac{an - mc}{bn - cp}, \frac{bm - ap}{bn - cp}\right) = \left(\frac{0.18 - 0.1125}{0.72 - 0.3375}, \frac{0.09 - 0.0675}{0.72 - 0.3375}\right) = \left(\frac{3}{17}, \frac{1}{17}\right) \approx (0.1765, 0.0588).$$

**22.** $\dfrac{dx}{dt} = ax - bx^2 - cxy = 0.025x - 0.1x^2 - 0.2xy$

$\dfrac{dy}{dt} = my - ny^2 - pxy = 0.3y - 0.45y^2 - 0.1xy$

From Example 5, you have $(0, 0)$, $\left(0, \dfrac{m}{n}\right) = \left(0, \dfrac{2}{3}\right)$, $\left(\dfrac{a}{b}, 0\right) = \left(\dfrac{1}{4}, 0\right)$ and

$$\left(\frac{an - mc}{bn - cp}, \frac{bm - ap}{bn - cp}\right) = \left(\frac{0.01125 - 0.06}{0.045 - 0.02}, \frac{0.03 - 0.0025}{0.045 - 0.02}\right) = (-1.95, 1.1) = \left(-\frac{39}{20}, \frac{11}{10}\right).$$

**23.** $a = 0.8$, $b = 0.4$, $c = 0.1$, $m = 0.3$, $n = 0.6$, $p = 0.1$

Four critical points:

$(0, 0)$

$\left(0, \dfrac{m}{n}\right) = \left(0, \dfrac{0.3}{0.6}\right) = \left(0, \dfrac{1}{2}\right)$

$\left(\dfrac{a}{b}, 0\right) = \left(\dfrac{0.8}{0.4}, 0\right) = (2, 0)$

$\left(\dfrac{an - mc}{bn - cp}, \dfrac{bm - ap}{bn - cp}\right) = \left(\dfrac{0.45}{0.23}, \dfrac{0.04}{0.23}\right) = \left(\dfrac{45}{23}, \dfrac{4}{23}\right)$

**24.**

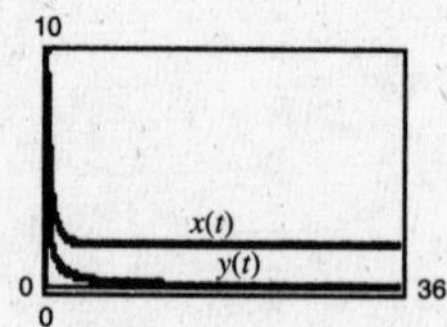


Both species survive.

**25.** $a = 0.8,\ b = 0.4,\ c = 1,\ m = 0.3,\ n = 0.6,\ p = 1$

Four critical points:

$(0, 0)$

$\left(0, \frac{m}{n}\right) = \left(0, \frac{0.3}{0.6}\right) = \left(0, \frac{1}{2}\right)$

$\left(\frac{a}{b}, 0\right) = \left(\frac{0.8}{0.4}, 0\right) = (2, 0)$

$$\left(\frac{an - mc}{bn - cp}, \frac{bm - ap}{bn - cp}\right) = \left(\frac{0.18}{-0.76}, \frac{-0.68}{-0.76}\right) = \left(-\frac{9}{38}, \frac{17}{19}\right)$$

**26.**

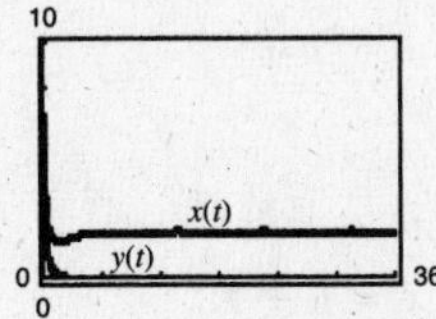


One species (the trout) becomes extinct.

**27.** Assuming the initial conditions are the critical points $\left(x(0), y(0)\right) = \left(\frac{45}{23}, \frac{4}{23}\right)$ you obtain constant solutions.

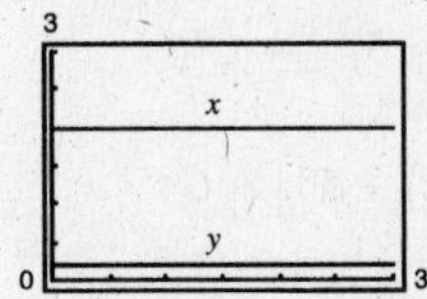


**28.** Assuming the initial conditions are the critical points $\left(x(0), y(0)\right) = \left(0, \frac{1}{2}\right)$ you obtain constant solutions.

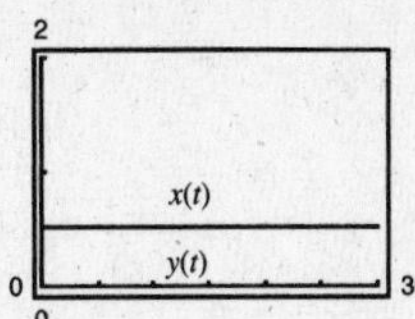


**29.** Yes, they are separable. See bottom of page 437.

**30.** Solve the equations

$$\frac{dx}{dt} = ax - bxy = 0$$

$$\frac{dy}{dt} = -my + nxy = 0$$

to obtain critical points

$(0, 0)$ and $\left(\frac{m}{n}, \frac{a}{b}\right)$.

The solutions will be constant for these initial conditions.

**31.** As in Exercise 30, using any of the four critical points as initial conditions will yield constant solutions.

**32.**

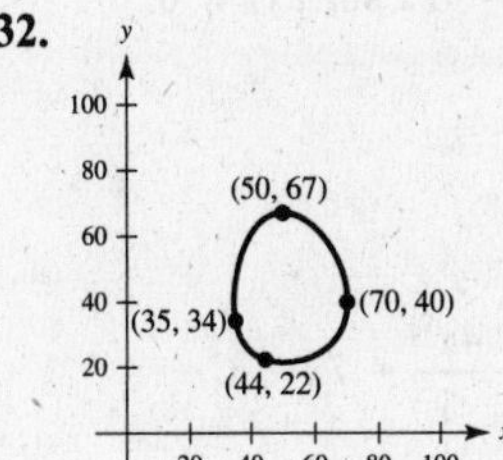


**33.** (a) If $y = 0$, then $\frac{dx}{dt} = ax\left(1 - \frac{x}{L}\right)$, which is a logistic equation.

(b) $\frac{dx}{dt} = 0.4x\left(1 - \frac{x}{100}\right) - 0.01xy$

$\frac{dy}{dt} = -0.3y + 0.005xy$

$(0, 0)$ is a critical point. If $y = 0$, then $x = 100$ and $(100, 0)$ is a critical point. If $x,\ y \neq 0$, then

$0.4\left(1 - \frac{x}{100}\right) = 0.01y$

$-0.3 + 0.05x = 0.$

So, $x = \frac{0.3}{0.005} = 60$ and $0.4\left(1 - \frac{60}{100}\right) = 0.01y \Rightarrow y = 16.$

The third critical point is $(60, 16)$.

(c)

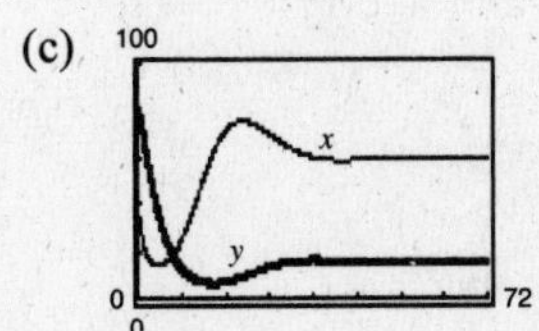

(d)

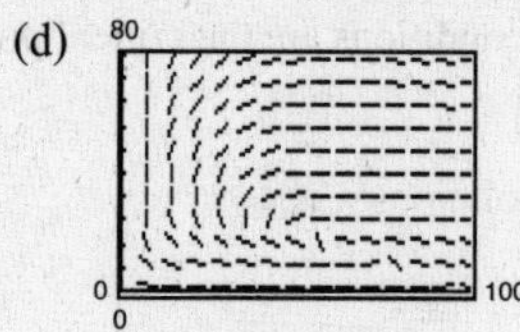

(e)

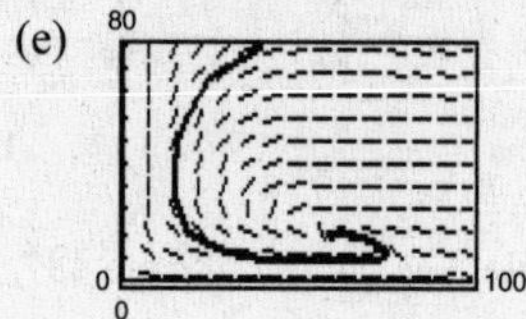

## Review Exercises for Chapter 6

**1.** $y = x^3, y' = 3x^2$

$2xy' + 4y = 2x(3x^2) + 4(x^3) = 10x^3$

Yes, it is a solution.

**2.** $y = 2\sin 2x$

$y' = 4\cos 2x$

$y'' = -8\sin 2x$

$y''' = -16\cos 2x$

$y''' - 8y = -16\cos 2x - 8(2\sin 2x) \neq 0$

Not a solution

**3.** $\dfrac{dy}{dx} = 4x^2 + 7$

$y = \int(4x^2 + 7)\,dx = \dfrac{4x^3}{3} + 7x + C$

**4.** $\dfrac{dy}{dx} = 3x^3 - 8x$

$y = \int(3x^3 - 8x)\,dx = \dfrac{3}{4}x^4 - 4x^2 + C$

**5.** $\dfrac{dy}{dx} = \cos 2x$

$y = \int \cos 2x\,dx = \dfrac{1}{2}\sin 2x + C$

**6.** $\dfrac{dy}{dx} = 2\sin x$

$y = \int 2\sin x\,dx = -2\cos x + C$

**7.** $\dfrac{dy}{dx} = x\sqrt{x - 5}$

$y = \int x\sqrt{x - 5}\,dx$

Let $u = x - 5$, $du = dx$, $x = u + 5$:

$$y = \int(u + 5)\sqrt{u}\,du$$
$$= \int\left(u^{3/2} + 5u^{1/2}\right)du$$
$$= \frac{2}{5}u^{5/2} + \frac{10}{3}u^{3/2} + C$$
$$= \frac{2}{5}(x - 5)^{5/2} + \frac{10}{3}(x - 5)^{3/2} + C$$
$$= \frac{1}{15}(x - 5)^{3/2}\left[6(x - 5) + 50\right] + C$$
$$= \frac{1}{15}(x - 5)^{3/2}(6x + 20) + C$$

**8.** $\dfrac{dy}{dx} = 2x\sqrt{x - 7}$

$y = \int 2x\sqrt{x - 7}\,dx$

Let $u = x - 7$, $du = dx$, $x = u + 7$:

$$y = \int 2(u + 7)u^{1/2}\,du$$
$$= \frac{4}{5}u^{5/2} + \frac{28}{3}u^{3/2} + C$$
$$= \frac{4}{5}(x - 7)^{5/2} + \frac{28}{3}(x - 7)^{3/2} + C$$
$$= \frac{4}{15}(x - 7)^{3/2}(3x + 14) + C$$

**9.** $\dfrac{dy}{dx} = e^{2-x}$

$y = \int e^{2-x}\,dx = -e^{2-x} + C$

**10.** $\dfrac{dy}{dx} = 3e^{-x/3}$

$y = \int 3e^{-x/3}\,dx = -9e^{-x/3} + C$

**11.** $\dfrac{dy}{dx} = 2x - y$

| $x$ | $-4$ | $-2$ | 0 | 2 | 4 | 8 |
|---|---|---|---|---|---|---|
| $y$ | 2 | 0 | 4 | 4 | 6 | 8 |
| $dy/dx$ | $-10$ | $-4$ | $-4$ | 0 | 2 | 8 |

**12.** $\dfrac{dy}{dx} = x \sin\left(\dfrac{\pi y}{4}\right)$

| $x$ | $-4$ | $-2$ | 0 | 2 | 4 | 8 |
|---|---|---|---|---|---|---|
| $y$ | 2 | 0 | 4 | 4 | 6 | 8 |
| $dy/dx$ | $-4$ | 0 | 0 | 0 | $-4$ | 0 |

**13.** $y' = 3 - x, \quad (2, 1)$

(a) and (b)

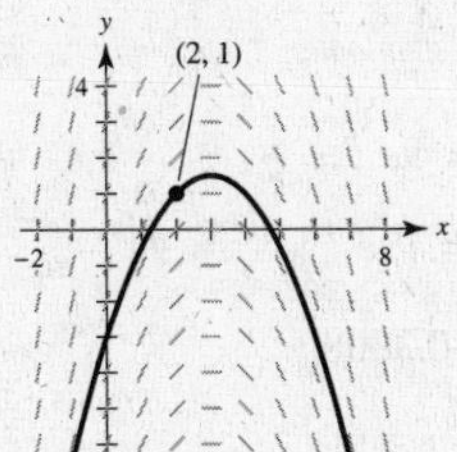

**14.** $y' = 2x^2 - x, \quad (0, 2)$

(a) and (b)

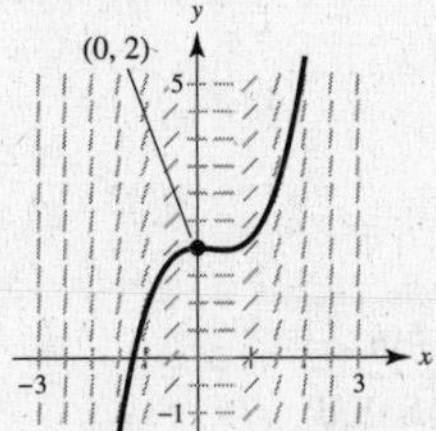

**15.** $y' = \frac{1}{4}x^2 - \frac{1}{3}x, \quad (0, 3)$

(a) and (b)

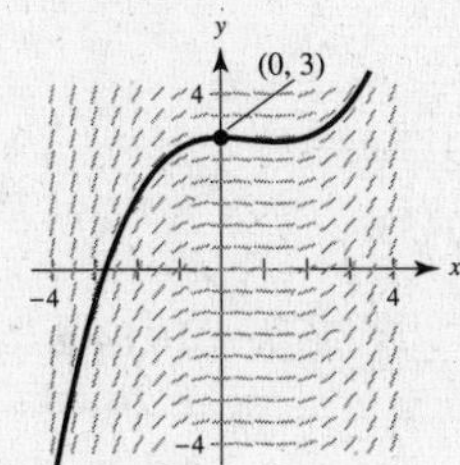

**16.** $y' = y + 4x, \quad (-1, 1)$

(a) and (b)

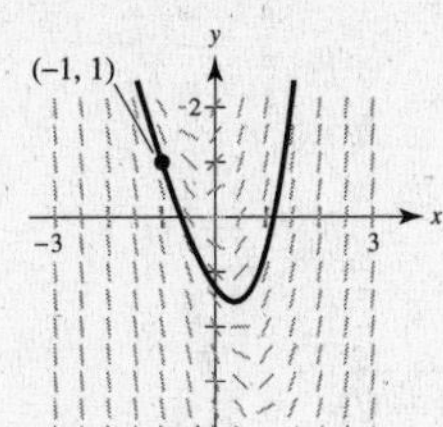

**17.** $y' = \dfrac{xy}{x^2 + 4}, \quad (0, 1)$

(a) and (b)

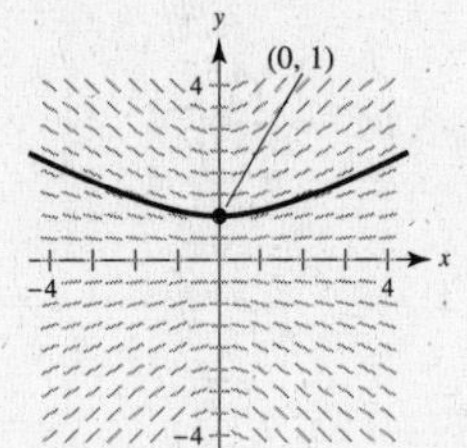

**18.** $y' = \dfrac{y}{x^2 + 1}, \quad (0, -2)$

(a) and (b)

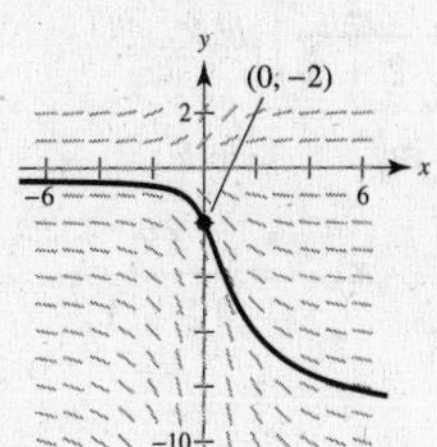

**19.** $\dfrac{dy}{dx} = 8 - x$

$$y = \int (8 - x)\, dx = 8x - \frac{x^2}{2} + C$$

**20.**

$$\frac{dy}{dx} = y + 8$$

$$\int \frac{dy}{y + 8} = \int dx$$

$$\ln|y + 8| = x + C_1$$

$$|y + 8| = e^{x + C_1} = Ce^x$$

$$y = -8 + Ce^x$$

**21.** $$\frac{dy}{dx} = (3+y)^2$$
$$\int (3+y)^{-2}\,dy = \int dx$$
$$-(3+y)^{-1} = x + C$$
$$3 + y = \frac{-1}{x+C}$$
$$y = -3 - \frac{1}{x+C}$$

**22.** $$\frac{dy}{dx} = 10\sqrt{y}$$
$$\int y^{-1/2}\,dy = \int 10\,dx$$
$$2y^{1/2} = 10x + C_1$$
$$y^{1/2} = 5x + C \qquad \left(C = \frac{C_1}{2}\right)$$
$$y = (5x + C)^2$$

**23.** $(2+x)y' - xy = 0$
$$(2+x)\frac{dy}{dx} = xy$$
$$\int \frac{1}{y}\,dy = \int \frac{x}{2+x}\,dx$$
$$\int \frac{1}{y}\,dy = \int \left(1 - \frac{2}{2+x}\right)dx$$
$$\ln|y| = x - 2\ln|2+x| + C_1$$
$$y = Ce^x(2+x)^{-2} = \frac{Ce^x}{(2+x)^2}$$

**24.** $xy' - (x+1)y = 0$
$$x\frac{dy}{dx} = (x+1)y$$
$$\int \frac{dy}{y} = \int \frac{x+1}{x}\,dx$$
$$\ln|y| = x + \ln|x| + C_1$$
$$y = Cxe^x$$

**25.** $y = Ce^{kt}$
$$\left(0, \tfrac{3}{4}\right): \tfrac{3}{4} = C$$
$$(5, 5): 5 = \tfrac{3}{4}e^{k(5)}$$
$$\tfrac{20}{3} = e^{5k}$$
$$k = \tfrac{1}{5}\ln\left(\tfrac{20}{3}\right)$$
$$y = \tfrac{3}{4}e^{[\ln(20/3)/5]t} \approx \tfrac{3}{4}e^{0.379t}$$

**26.** $y = Ce^{kt}$
$$\left(2, \tfrac{3}{2}\right): \tfrac{3}{2} = Ce^{2k} \Rightarrow C = \tfrac{3}{2}e^{-2k}$$
$$(4, 5): 5 = Ce^{4k} = \left(\tfrac{3}{2}e^{-2k}\right)e^{4k} = \tfrac{3}{2}e^{2k}$$
$$\tfrac{10}{3} = e^{2k} \Rightarrow k = \tfrac{1}{2}\ln\left(\tfrac{10}{3}\right)$$
So, $C = \tfrac{3}{2}e^{-2(1/2)\ln(10/3)} = \tfrac{3}{2}\left(\tfrac{3}{10}\right) = \tfrac{9}{20}$.

Finally, $y = \tfrac{9}{20}e^{(1/2)\ln(10/3)t}$.

**27.** $y = Ce^{kt}$
$$(0, 5): C = 5$$
$$\left(5, \frac{1}{6}\right): \frac{1}{6} = 5e^{5k}$$
$$k = \frac{1}{5}\ln\left(\frac{1}{30}\right) = \frac{-\ln 30}{5}$$
$$y = 5e^{[-t\ln 30]/5} \approx 5e^{-0.680t}$$

**28.** $y = Ce^{kt}$
$$(1, 9): 9 = Ce^{k} \Rightarrow C = 9e^{-k}$$
$$(6, 2): 2 = Ce^{6k} \Rightarrow 2 = \left(9e^{-k}\right)e^{6k} = 9e^{5k}$$
$$k = \tfrac{1}{5}\ln\left(\tfrac{2}{9}\right) \approx -0.3008$$
So, $C = 9e^{(-1/5)\ln(2/9)} = 9\left(\tfrac{2}{9}\right)^{-1/5} \approx 12.15864$.

Finally, $y \approx 12.1586e^{-0.3008t}$.

**29.** $\dfrac{dP}{dh} = kp, \quad P(0) = 30$
$$P(h) = 30e^{kh}$$
$$P(18{,}000) = 30e^{18{,}000k} = 15$$
$$k = \frac{\ln(1/2)}{18{,}000} = \frac{-\ln 2}{18{,}000}$$
$$P(h) = 30e^{-(h\ln 2)/18{,}000}$$
$$P(35{,}000) = 30e^{-(35{,}000\ln 2)/18{,}000} \approx 7.79 \text{ inches}$$

**30.** $y = Ce^{kt} = 15e^{kt}$
$$7.5 = 15e^{k(1599)}$$
$$k = \tfrac{1}{1599}\ln\left(\tfrac{1}{2}\right) \approx -0.000433$$
When $t = 750$, $y = 15e^{-0.000433(750)} \approx 10.84$ g.

**31.** $S = Ce^{k/t}$

(a) $S = 5$ when $t = 1$

$$5 = Ce^k$$

$$\lim_{t\to\infty} Ce^{k/t} = C = 30$$

$$5 = 30e^k$$

$$k = \ln\frac{1}{6} \approx -1.7918$$

$$S = 30e^{-1.7918/t}$$

(b) When $t = 5$, $S \approx 20.9646$ which is 20,965 units.

(c)

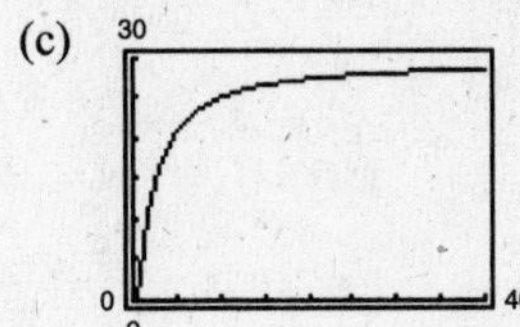


**32.** $S = 25(1 - e^{kt})$

(a) $4 = 25(1 - e^{k(1)}) \Rightarrow 1 - e^k = \frac{4}{25} \Rightarrow e^k = \frac{21}{25}$

$$\Rightarrow k = \ln\left(\frac{21}{25}\right) \approx -0.1744$$

$$S = 25(1 - e^{-0.1744t})$$

(b) 25,000 units $\left(\lim_{t\to\infty} S = 25\right)$

(c) When $t = 5$, $S \approx 14.545$ which is 14,545 units.

(d)

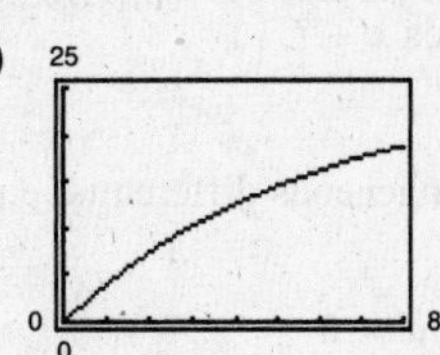


**33.** $P = Ce^{0.0185t}$

$$2C = Ce^{0.0185t}$$

$$2 = e^{0.0185t}$$

$$\ln 2 = 0.0185t$$

$$t = \frac{\ln 2}{0.0185} \approx 37.5 \text{ years}$$

**34.** (a) $\dfrac{dy}{ds} = -0.012y,\ s > 50$

$$\frac{-1}{0.012}\int\frac{dy}{y} = \int ds$$

$$\frac{-1}{0.012}\ln y = s + C_1$$

$$y = Ce^{-0.012s}$$

When $s = 50$, $y = 28 = Ce^{-0.012(50)} \Rightarrow C = 28e^{0.6}$

$y = 28e^{0.6-0.012s}$, $s > 50$.

(b)

| Speed ($s$) | 50 | 55 | 60 | 65 | 70 |
|---|---|---|---|---|---|
| Miles per Gallon ($y$) | 28 | 26.4 | 24.8 | 23.4 | 22.0 |

**35.** $\dfrac{dy}{dx} = \dfrac{x^5 + 7}{x} = x^4 + \dfrac{7}{x}$

$$y = \int\left(x^4 + \frac{7}{x}\right)dx = \frac{x^5}{5} + 7\ln|x| + C$$

**36.** $\dfrac{dy}{dx} = \dfrac{e^{-2x}}{1 + e^{-2x}}$

$$\int dy = \int\frac{e^{-2x}}{1 + e^{-2x}}\,dx = -\frac{1}{2}\int\frac{-2e^{-2x}}{1 + e^{-2x}}\,dx$$

$$y = -\frac{1}{2}\ln(1 + e^{-2x}) + C$$

**37.** $y' - 16xy = 0$

$$\frac{dy}{dx} = 16xy$$

$$\int\frac{1}{y}\,dy = \int 16x\,dx$$

$$\ln|y| = 8x^2 + C_1$$

$$y = e^{8x^2 + C_1}$$

$$y = Ce^{8x^2}$$

**38.** $y' - e^y \sin x = 0$

$$\frac{dy}{dx} = e^y \sin x$$

$$\int e^{-y}\,dy = \int \sin x\,dx$$

$$-e^{-y} = -\cos x + C_1$$

$$e^y = \frac{1}{\cos x + C} \qquad (C = -C_1)$$

$$y = \ln\left|\frac{1}{\cos x + C}\right| = -\ln\left|\cos x + C\right|$$

**39.** $\dfrac{dy}{dx} = \dfrac{x^2 + y^2}{2xy}$ (homogeneous differential equation)

$$\left(x^2 + y^2\right)dx - 2xy\,dy = 0$$

Let $y = vx$, $dy = x\,dv + v\,dx$.

$$\left(x^2 + v^2x^2\right)dx - 2x(vx)(x\,dv + v\,dx) = 0$$

$$\left(x^2 + v^2x^2 - 2x^2v^2\right)dx - 2x^3v\,dv = 0$$

$$\left(x^2 - x^2v^2\right)dx = 2x^3v\,dv$$

$$\left(1 - v^2\right)dx = 2xv\,dv$$

$$\int\frac{dx}{x} = \int\frac{2v}{1 - v^2}\,dv$$

$$\ln|x| = -\ln\left|1 - v^2\right| + C_1 = -\ln\left|1 - v^2\right| + \ln C$$

$$x = \frac{C}{1 - v^2} = \frac{C}{1 - (y/x)^2} = \frac{Cx^2}{x^2 - y^2}$$

$$1 = \frac{Cx}{x^2 - y^2} \quad \text{or} \quad C_1 = \frac{x}{x^2 - y^2}$$

**40.** $\dfrac{dy}{dx} = \dfrac{3(x + y)}{x}$ (homogeneous differential equation)

$$3(x + y)\,dx - x\,dy = 0$$

Let $y = vx$, $dy = x\,dv + v\,dx$.

$$3(x + vx)\,dx - x(x\,dv + v\,dx) = 0$$

$$(3x + 2vx)\,dx - x^2\,dv = 0$$

$$(3 + 2v)\,dx = x\,dv$$

$$\int\frac{1}{x}\,dx = \int\frac{1}{3 + 2v}\,dv$$

$$\ln|x| = \frac{1}{2}\ln|3 + 2v| + C_1 = \ln(3 + 2v)^{1/2} + \ln C_2$$

$$x = C_2(3 + 2v)^{1/2}$$

$$x^2 = C(3 + 2v) = C\left(3 + 2\left(\frac{y}{x}\right)\right)$$

$$x^3 = C(3x + 2y) = 3Cx + 2Cy$$

$$y = \frac{x^3 - 3Cx}{2C}$$

**41.** $y = C_1x + C_2x^3$

$y' = C_1 + 3C_2x^2$

$y'' = 6C_2x$

$$x^2y'' - 3xy' + 3y = x^2(6C_2x) - 3x(C_1 + 3C_2x^2) + 3(C_1x + C_2x^3)$$
$$= 6C_2x^3 - 3C_1x - 9C_2x^3 + 3C_1x + 3C_2x^3 = 0$$

$x = 2, y = 0$: $0 = 2C_1 + 8C_2 \Rightarrow C_1 = -4C_2$

$x = 2, y' = 4$: $4 = C_1 + 12C_2$

$$4 = (-4C_2) + 12C_2 = 8C_2 \Rightarrow C_2 = \tfrac{1}{2}, C_1 = -2$$

$y = -2x + \frac{1}{2}x^3$

**42.** $\dfrac{dv}{dt} = kv - 9.8$

(a) $\displaystyle\int \frac{dv}{kv - 9.8} = \int dt$

$$\frac{1}{k}\ln|kv - 9.8| = t + C_1$$
$$\ln|kv - 9.8| = kt + C_2$$
$$kv - 9.8 = e^{kt + C_2} = C_3e^{kt}$$
$$v = \frac{1}{k}\left[9.8 + C_3e^{kt}\right]$$

At $t = 0$, $v_0 = \dfrac{1}{k}(9.8 + C_3) \Rightarrow C_3 = kv_0 - 9.8$

$$v = \frac{1}{k}\left[9.8 + (kv_0 - 9.8)e^{kt}\right].$$

Note that $k < 0$ because the object is moving downward.

(b) $\displaystyle\lim_{t\to\infty} v(t) = \frac{9.8}{k}$

(c) $\displaystyle s(t) = \int \frac{1}{k}\left[9.8 + (kv_0 - 9.8)e^{kt}\right] dt = \frac{1}{k}\left[9.8t + \frac{1}{k}(kv_0 - 9.8)e^{kt}\right] + C = \frac{9.8t}{k} + \frac{1}{k^2}(kv_0 - 9.8)e^{kt} + C$

$$s(0) = \frac{1}{k^2}(kv_0 - 9.8) + C \Rightarrow C = s_0 - \frac{1}{k^2}(kv_0 - 9.8)$$

$$s(t) = \frac{9.8t}{k} + \frac{1}{k^2}(kv_0 - 9.8)e^{kt} + s_0 - \frac{1}{k^2}(kv_0 - 9.8) = \frac{9.8t}{k} + \frac{1}{k^2}(kv_0 - 9.8)(e^{kt} - 1) + s_0$$

**43.** $\dfrac{dy}{dx} = -\dfrac{4x}{y}$

$$\int y\,dy = \int -4x\,dx$$
$$\frac{y^2}{2} = -2x^2 + C_1$$

$4x^2 + y^2 = C$ ellipses

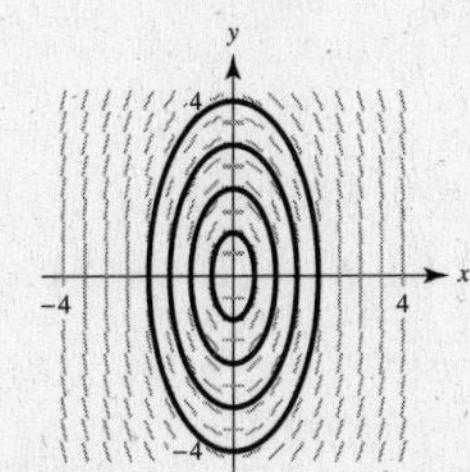


**44.** $\dfrac{dy}{dx} = 3 - 2y$

$$\int \frac{dy}{2y - 3} = \int -dx$$
$$\frac{1}{2}\ln|2y - 3| = -x + C_1$$
$$\ln|2y - 3| = -2x + 2C_1$$
$$|2y - 3| = C_2e^{-2x}$$
$$2y = 3 + C_2e^{-2x}$$
$$y = \frac{3}{2} + Ce^{-2x}$$

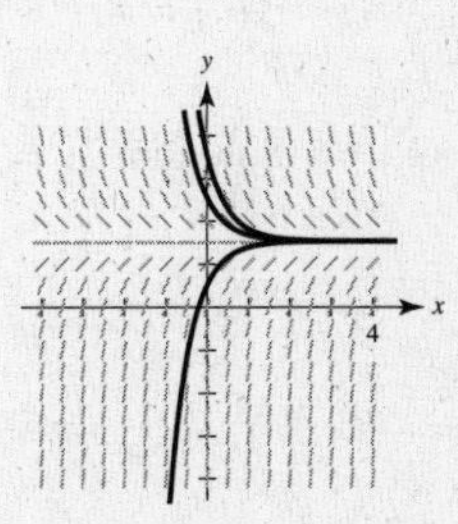

**45.** $P(t) = \dfrac{5250}{1 + 34e^{-0.55t}}$

(a) $k = 0.55$

(b) $L = 5250$

(c) $P(0) = \dfrac{5250}{1 + 34} = 150$

(d) $$\begin{aligned} 2625 &= \frac{5250}{1 + 34e^{-0.55t}} \\ 1 + 34e^{-0.55t} &= 2 \\ e^{-0.55t} &= \frac{1}{34} \\ t &= -\frac{1}{0.55}\ln\left(\frac{1}{34}\right) \approx 6.41 \text{ yr} \end{aligned}$$

(e) $\dfrac{dP}{dt} = 0.55P\left(1 - \dfrac{P}{5250}\right)$

**46.** $P(t) = \dfrac{4800}{1 + 14e^{-0.15t}}$

(a) $k = 0.15$

(b) $L = 4800$

(c) $P(0) = \dfrac{4800}{1 + 14} = 320$

(d) $$\begin{aligned} 2400 &= \frac{4800}{1 + 14e^{-0.15t}} \\ 14e^{-0.15t} &= 1 \\ t &= -\frac{1}{0.15}\ln\left(\frac{1}{14}\right) \approx 17.59 \text{ yr} \end{aligned}$$

(e) $\dfrac{dP}{dt} = 0.15P\left(1 - \dfrac{P}{4800}\right)$

**47.** $\dfrac{dy}{dt} = y\left(1 - \dfrac{y}{80}\right), \quad (0, 8)$

$k = 1, L = 80$

$$y = \frac{L}{1 + be^{-kt}} = \frac{80}{1 + be^{-t}}$$

$y(0) = 8: \quad 8 = \dfrac{80}{1 + b} \Rightarrow b = 9$

Solution: $y = \dfrac{80}{1 + 9e^{-t}}$

**48.** $\dfrac{dy}{dt} = 1.76y\left(1 - \dfrac{y}{8}\right), \quad (0, 3)$

$k = 1.76, L = 8$

$$y = \frac{L}{1 + be^{-kt}} = \frac{8}{1 + be^{-1.76t}}$$

$y(0) = 3: \quad 3 = \dfrac{8}{1 + b} \Rightarrow b = \dfrac{5}{3}$

Solution: $y = \dfrac{8}{1 + \left(\frac{5}{3}\right)e^{-1.76t}}$

**49.** (a) $L = 20{,}400,\ y(0) = 1200,\ y(1) = 2000$

$$\begin{aligned} y &= \frac{20{,}400}{1 + be^{-kt}} \\ y(0) = 1200 &= \frac{20{,}400}{1 + b} \Rightarrow b = 16 \\ y(1) = 2000 &= \frac{20{,}400}{1 + 16e^{-k}} \\ 16e^{-k} &= \frac{46}{5} \\ k &= -\ln\frac{23}{40} = \ln\frac{40}{23} \approx 0.553 \\ y &= \frac{20{,}400}{1 + 16e^{-0.553t}} \end{aligned}$$

(b) $y(8) \approx 17{,}118$ trout

(c) $10{,}000 = \dfrac{20{,}400}{1 + 16e^{-0.553t}} \Rightarrow t \approx 4.94$ yr

**50.** $\dfrac{dy}{dt} = 0.553y\left(1 - \dfrac{y}{20{,}400}\right), \quad y(0) = 1200$

Use Euler's method with $h = 1$.

| $t$ | 0 | 2 | 4 | 6 | 8 |
|---|---|---|---|---|---|
| Exact | 1200 | 3241 | 7414 | 12,915 | 17,117 |
| Euler | 1200 | 2743 | 5853 | 10,869 | 16,170 |

Euler's method gives $y(8) \approx 16{,}170$ trout.

**51.** $$\begin{aligned} \frac{dS}{dt} &= k(L - S) \\ \int \frac{dS}{L - S} &= \int k\,dt \\ -\ln|L - S| &= kt + C_1 \\ L - S &= e^{-kt - C_1} \\ S &= L + Ce^{-kt} \end{aligned}$$

Because $S = 0$ when $t = 0$, you have

$0 = L + C \Rightarrow C = -L$. So, $S = L(1 - e^{-kt})$.

**52.** The general solution is $S = L(1 - e^{-kt})$.

(a) Because $L = 100$ and $S = 25$ when $t = 2$, you have the following.

$$25 = 100(1 - e^{-2k})$$
$$\frac{1}{4} = 1 - e^{-2k}$$
$$e^{-2k} = \frac{3}{4}$$
$$-2k = \ln\frac{3}{4}$$
$$k = -\frac{1}{2}\ln\frac{3}{4} \approx 0.1438$$

So, the particular solution is $S = 100(1 - e^{-0.1438t})$.

(b) Because $L = 500$ and $S = 50$ when $t = 1$, you have the following.

$$50 = 500(1 - e^{-k})$$
$$\frac{1}{10} = 1 - e^{-k}$$
$$e^{-k} = \frac{9}{10}$$
$$-k = \ln\frac{9}{10}$$
$$k = -\ln\frac{9}{10} = \ln\frac{10}{9} \approx 0.1054$$

So, the particular solution is $S = 500(1 - e^{-0.1054t})$.

**53.** The differential equation is given by the following.

$$\frac{dP}{dn} = kP(L - P)$$
$$\int \frac{1}{P(L - P)}\,dP = \int k\,dn$$
$$\frac{1}{L}\left[\ln|P| - \ln|L - P|\right] = kn + C_1$$
$$\frac{P}{L - P} = Ce^{Lkn}$$
$$P = \frac{CLe^{Lkn}}{1 + Ce^{Lkn}} = \frac{CL}{e^{-Lkn} + C}$$

**54.** The general solution is $P = \dfrac{CL}{C + e^{-Lkn}}$.

(a) Because $L = 1$ and $P = 0.50$ when $n = 0$, and $P = 0.85$ when $n = 4$, you have the following.

$$0.50 = \frac{C}{C + 1} \Rightarrow C = 1$$
$$0.85 = \frac{1}{1 + e^{-4k}} \Rightarrow k = -\frac{1}{4}\ln\frac{3}{17} \approx 0.4337$$

Therefore, $P = \dfrac{1}{1 + e^{-0.4337n}}$.

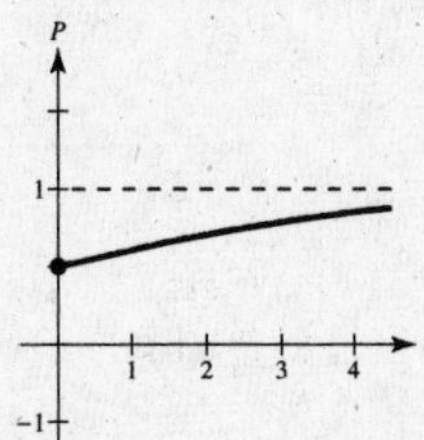

(b) Because $L = 0.80$ and $P = 0.25$ when $n = 0$, and $P = 0.60$ when $n = 10$, you have the following.

$$0.25 = \frac{0.80C}{C + 1} \Rightarrow C = \frac{5}{11}$$
$$0.60 = \frac{(5/11)(0.80)}{(5/11) + e^{-8k}} \Rightarrow k = -\frac{1}{8}\ln\frac{5}{33} \approx 0.2359$$

Therefore, $P = \dfrac{4}{5 + 11e^{-0.1887n}}$.

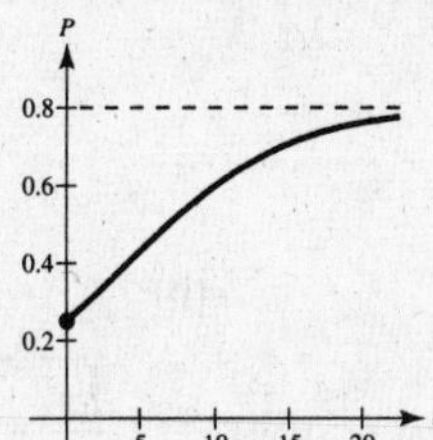

**55.** (a)

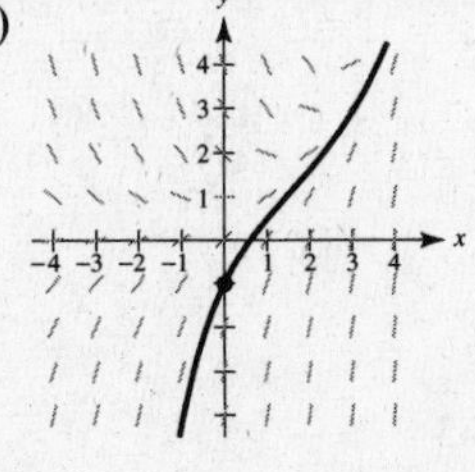

(b)

$$y' = e^{x/2} - y$$
$$y' + y = e^{x/2}, \quad \text{Integrating factor: } e^{\int dx} = e^x$$
$$ye^x = \int e^{x/2}e^x\,dx = \int e^{(3/2)x}\,dx$$
$$= \frac{2}{3}e^{(3/2)x} + C$$
$$y = \frac{2}{3}e^{x/2} + Ce^{-x}$$
$$y(0) = -1 = \frac{2}{3} + C \Rightarrow C = -\frac{5}{3}$$
$$y = \frac{2}{3}e^{x/2} - \frac{5}{3}e^{-x} = \frac{1}{3}\left[2e^{x/2} - 5e^{-x}\right]$$

(c)

**56.** (a)

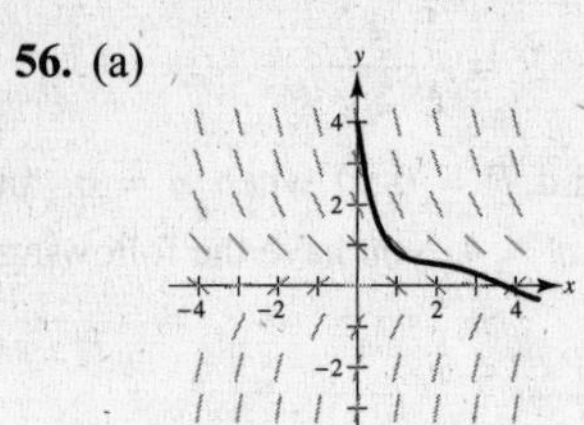

(b)

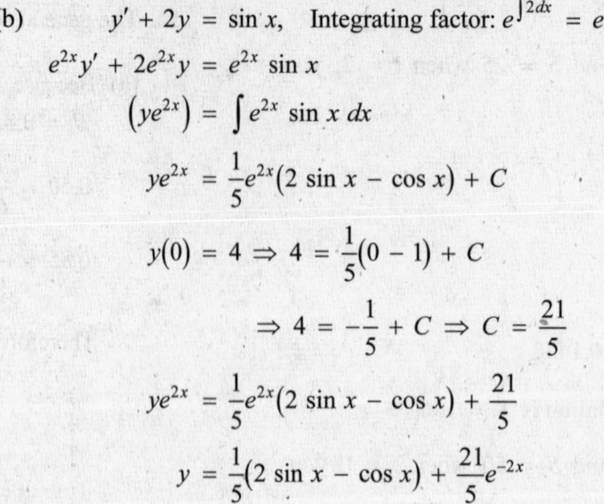

$$y' + 2y = \sin x, \quad \text{Integrating factor: } e^{\int 2\,dx} = e^{2x}$$

$$e^{2x}y' + 2e^{2x}y = e^{2x}\sin x$$

$$\left(ye^{2x}\right)' = \int e^{2x}\sin x\,dx$$

$$ye^{2x} = \frac{1}{5}e^{2x}(2\sin x - \cos x) + C$$

$$y(0) = 4 \Rightarrow 4 = \frac{1}{5}(0 - 1) + C$$

$$\Rightarrow 4 = -\frac{1}{5} + C \Rightarrow C = \frac{21}{5}$$

$$ye^{2x} = \frac{1}{5}e^{2x}(2\sin x - \cos x) + \frac{21}{5}$$

$$y = \frac{1}{5}(2\sin x - \cos x) + \frac{21}{5}e^{-2x}$$

(c)

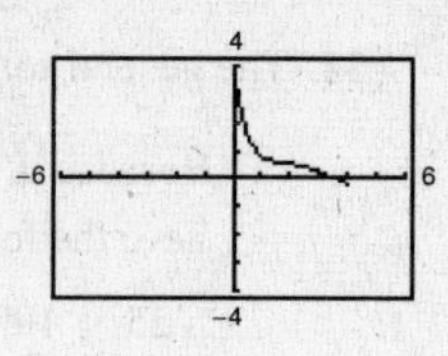


**57.** (a)

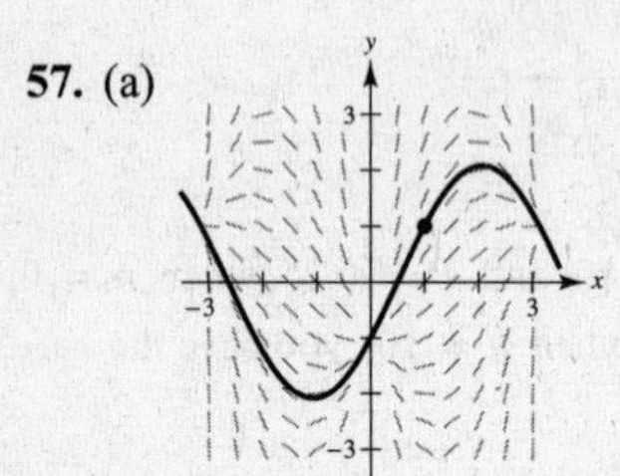

(b)

$$\frac{dy}{dx} = \csc x + y\cot x$$

$$\frac{dy}{dx} - (\cot x)y = \csc x$$

$$\text{Integrating factor: } e^{\int -\cot x\,dx} = e^{-\ln|\sin x|} = \csc x$$

$$\csc x \cdot y' - \csc x\cot x \cdot y = \csc^2 x$$

$$(y\csc x)' = \csc^2 x$$

$$y\csc x = \int \csc^2 x\,dx = -\cot x + C$$

$$y = -\cos x + C\sin x$$

$$y(1) = 1 \Rightarrow 1 = -\cos 1 + C\sin 1$$

$$\Rightarrow C = \frac{1 + \cos 1}{\sin 1} \approx 1.8305$$

$$y = -\cos x + 1.8305\sin x$$

(c)

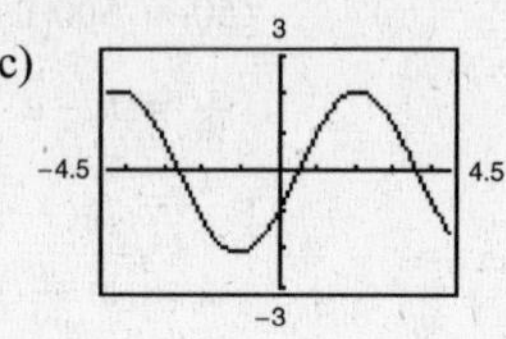


**58.** (a)

(b)

$$\frac{dy}{dx} = \csc x - y\cot x$$

$$\frac{dy}{dx} + (\cot x)y = \csc x$$

$$\text{Integrating factor: } e^{\int \cot x\,dx} = e^{\ln|\sin x|} = \sin x$$

$$\sin x\,y' + \cos x\,y = 1$$

$$(y\sin x)' = 1$$

$$y\sin x = x + C$$

$$y(1) = 2 \Rightarrow 2\sin 1 = 1 + C$$

$$\Rightarrow C = 2\sin 1 - 1 \approx 0.683$$

$$y = x\csc x + C\csc x$$

$$y = x\csc x + 0.683\csc x$$

(c)

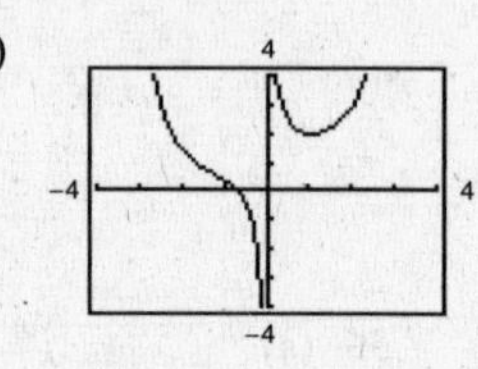

**59.** $y' - y = 10$

$P(x) = -1, Q(x) = 10$

$u(x) = e^{\int -dx} = e^{-x}$

$$y = \frac{1}{e^{-x}}\int 10e^{-x}\,dx$$
$$= e^{x}\left(-10e^{-x} + C\right)$$
$$= -10 + Ce^{x}$$

**60.** $e^{x}y' + 4e^{x}y = 1$

$y' + 4y = e^{-x}$

$P(x) = 4, Q(x) = e^{-x}$

$u(x) = e^{\int 4\,dx} = e^{4x}$

$$y = \frac{1}{e^{4x}}\int e^{-x}e^{4x}\,dx = e^{-4x}\left(\frac{1}{3}e^{3x} + C\right) = \frac{1}{3}e^{-x} + Ce^{-4x}$$

**61.** $4y' = e^{x/y} + y$

$y' - \frac{1}{4}y = \frac{1}{4}e^{x/4}$

$P(x) = -\frac{1}{4}, Q(x) = \frac{1}{4}e^{x/4}$

$u(x) = e^{\int -(1/4)\,dx} = e^{-(1/4)x}$

$$y = \frac{1}{e^{-(1/4)x}}\int \frac{1}{4}e^{x/4}e^{-(1/4)x}\,dx$$
$$= e^{(1/4)x}\left(\frac{1}{4}x + C\right)$$
$$= \frac{1}{4}xe^{x/4} + Ce^{x/4}$$

**62.** $\frac{dy}{dx} - \frac{5y}{x^2} = \frac{1}{x^2}$

$P(x) = -\frac{5}{x^2}, Q(x) = \frac{1}{x^2}$

$u(x) = e^{\int -(5/x^2)\,dx} = e^{5/x}$

$$y = \frac{1}{e^{5/x}}\int \frac{1}{x^2}e^{5/x}\,dx = \frac{1}{e^{5/x}}\left(-\frac{1}{5}e^{5/x} + C\right) = -\frac{1}{5} + Ce^{-5/x}$$

**63.** $(x - 2)y' + y = 1$

$\frac{dy}{dx} + \frac{1}{x - 2}y = \frac{1}{x - 2}$

$P(x) = \frac{1}{x - 2}, Q(x) = \frac{1}{x - 2}$

$u(x) = e^{\int (1/(x-2))\,dx} = e^{\ln|x-2|} = x - 2$

$$y = \frac{1}{x - 2}\int\left(\frac{1}{x - 2}\right)(x - 2)\,dx = \frac{1}{x - 2}(x + C)$$

**64.** $(x + 3)y' + 2y = 2(x + 3)^2$

$\frac{dy}{dx} + \frac{2}{x + 3}y = 2(x + 3)$

$P(x) = \frac{2}{x + 3}, Q(x) = 2(x + 3)$

$u(x) = e^{\int (2/(x+3))\,dx} = e^{2\ln(x+3)} = (x + 3)^2$

$$y = \frac{1}{(x + 3)^2}\int 2(x + 3)(x + 3)^2\,dx$$
$$= \frac{1}{(x + 3)^2}\left[\frac{(x + 3)^4}{2} + C\right]$$
$$= \frac{(x + 3)^2}{2} + \frac{C}{(x + 3)^2}$$

**65.** $(3y + \sin 2x)\,dx - dy = 0$

$y' - 3y = \sin 2x$

Integrating factor: $e^{\int -3\,dx} = e^{-3x}$

$$ye^{-3x} = \int e^{-3x}\sin 2x\,dx$$
$$= \tfrac{1}{13}e^{-3x}(-3\sin 2x - 2\cos 2x) + C$$
$$y = -\tfrac{1}{13}(3\sin 2x + 2\cos 2x) + Ce^{3x}$$

**66.** $dy = \left(y\tan x + 2e^{x}\right)dx$

$\frac{dy}{dx} - (\tan x)y = 2e^{x}$

Integrating factor: $e^{-\int \tan x\,dx} = e^{\ln|\cos x|} = \cos x$

$$y\cos x = \int 2e^{x}\cos x\,dx = e^{x}(\cos x + \sin x) + C$$
$$y = e^{x}(1 + \tan x) + C\sec x$$

**67.** $y' + 5y = e^{5x}$

Integrating factor: $e^{\int 5\,dx} = e^{5x}$

$$ye^{5x} = \int e^{10x}\,dx = \tfrac{1}{10}e^{10x} + C$$
$$y = \tfrac{1}{10}e^{5x} + Ce^{-5x}$$

**68.** $y' - \left(\frac{a}{x}\right)y = bx^3$

Integrating factor: $e^{-\int (a/x)\,dx} = e^{-a\ln x} = x^{-a}$

$$yx^{-a} = \int bx^3\left(x^{-a}\right)dx = \frac{b}{4 - a}x^{4-a} + C$$
$$y = \frac{bx^4}{4 - a} + Cx^{a}$$

**69.** $y' + y = xy^2$ Bernoulli equation

$n = 2$, let $z = y^{1-2} = y^{-1}$, $z' = -y^{-2}y'$.

$$\left(-y^{-2}\right)y' + \left(-y^{-2}\right)y = -x$$

$$z' - z = -x \quad \text{Linear equation}$$

$$u(x) = e^{\int -dx} = e^{-x}$$

$$z = \frac{1}{e^{-x}}\int -xe^{-x}\,dx = e^{x}\left[xe^{-x} + e^{-x} + C\right]$$

$$y^{-1} = x + 1 + Ce^{x}$$

$$y = \frac{1}{x + 1 + Ce^{x}}$$

**70.** $y' + 2xy = xy^2$ Bernoulli equation

$n = 2$, let $z = y^{1-2} = y^{-1}$, $z' = -y^{-2}y'$.

$$\left(-y^{-2}\right)y' + 2xy\left(-y^{-2}\right) = -x$$

$$z' - 2xz = -x \quad \text{Linear equation}$$

$$u(x) = e^{\int -2x\,dx} = e^{-x^2}$$

$$z = \frac{1}{e^{-x^2}}\int(-x)e^{-x^2}\,dx = e^{x^2}\left(\frac{1}{2}e^{-x^2} + C\right)$$

$$\frac{1}{y} = \frac{1}{2} + Ce^{x^2}$$

$$y = \frac{1}{\frac{1}{2} + Ce^{x^2}} = \frac{2}{1 + C_1e^{x^2}}$$

**71.** $y' + \frac{1}{x}y = \frac{y^3}{x^2}$ Bernoulli equation

$n = 3$, let $z = y^{1-3} = y^{-2}$, $z' = -2y^{-3}y'$.

$$\left(-2y^{-3}\right)y' + \frac{1}{x}y\left(-2y^{-3}\right) = -\frac{2}{x^2}$$

$$z' - \frac{2}{x}z = -\frac{2}{x^2} \quad \text{Linear equation}$$

$$u(x) = e^{\int -(2/x)\,dx} = e^{-2\ln x} = x^{-2}$$

$$z = \frac{1}{x^{-2}}\int -\frac{2}{x^2}\left(x^{-2}\right)dx = x^2\left(\frac{2x^{-3}}{3} + C\right)$$

$$\frac{1}{y^2} = \frac{2}{3x} + Cx^2$$

**72.** $xy' + y = xy^2$

$y' + \frac{1}{x}y = y^2$ Bernoulli Equation

$n = 2$, let $z = y^{1-2} = y^{-1}$, $z' = -y^{-2}y'$.

$$-y^{-2}y' + \frac{1}{x}y\left(-y^{-2}\right) = y^2\left(-y^{-2}\right)$$

$$z' - \frac{1}{x}z = -1 \quad \text{Linear equation}$$

$$u(x) = e^{\int -(1/x)\,dx} = \frac{1}{x}$$

$$z = x\int -\frac{1}{x}\,dx = -x\left[\ln|x| + C\right]$$

$$\frac{1}{y} = -x\ln x + Cx$$

$$y = \frac{1}{Cx - x\ln x}$$

**73.** Answers will vary. *Sample answer*: $\left(x^2 + 3y^2\right)dx - 2xy\,dy = 0$

Solution: Let $y = vx$, $dy = x\,dv + v\,dx$.

$$\left(x^2 + 3v^2x^2\right)dx - 2x(vx)(x\,dv + v\,dx) = 0$$

$$\left(x^2 + v^2x^2\right)dx - 2x^3v\,dv = 0$$

$$\left(1 + v^2\right)dx = 2\,xv\,dv$$

$$\int\frac{dx}{x} = \int\frac{2v}{1 + v^2}\,dv$$

$$\ln|x| = \ln\left|1 + v^2\right| + C_1$$

$$x = C\left(1 + v^2\right) = C\left(1 + \frac{y^2}{x^2}\right)$$

$$x^3 = C\left(x^2 + y^2\right)$$

**74.** Answers will vary. *Sample answer*: $y' = y\left(1 - \dfrac{y}{40}\right)$

Solution: $k = 1, L = 40$

$$y = \frac{L}{1 + be^{-kt}} = \frac{40}{1 + be^{-t}}$$

**75.** Answers will vary.

*Sample answer*: $x^3y' + 2x^2y = 1$

$$y' + \frac{2}{x}y = \frac{1}{x^3}$$

$$u(x) = e^{\int(2/x)\,dx} = x^2$$

$$y = \frac{1}{x^2}\int\frac{1}{x^3}(x^2)\,dx = \frac{1}{x^2}\big[\ln|x| + C\big]$$

**76.** Answers will vary. *Sample answer*: $y' + xy = xy^{-1}$

Solution: $n = -1, Q = x, P = x, e^{\int 2x\,dx} = e^{x^2}$

$$y^2e^{x^2} = \int 2xe^{x^2}\,dx = e^{x^2} + C$$

$$y^2 = 1 + Ce^{-x^2}$$

**77.** $\dfrac{dA}{dt} - rA = -P$

For this linear differential equation, you have $P(t) = -r$ and $Q(t) = -P$. Therefore, the integrating factor is $u(x) = e^{\int -r\,dt} = e^{-rt}$ and the solution is

$$A = e^{rt}\int -Pe^{-rt}\,dt = e^{rt}\left(\frac{P}{r}e^{-rt} + C\right) = \frac{P}{r} + Ce^{rt}.$$

Because $A = A_0$ when $t = 0$, you have $C = A_0 - (P/r)$ which implies that

$$A = \frac{P}{r} + \left(A_0 - \frac{P}{r}\right)e^{rt}.$$

**78.** $A_0 = 500{,}000, \quad r = 0.10$

(a) $P = 40{,}000$

$$A = \frac{40{,}000}{0.10} + \left(500{,}000 - \frac{40{,}000}{0.10}\right)e^{0.10t} = 100{,}000\left(4 + e^{0.10t}\right)$$

The balance continues to increase.

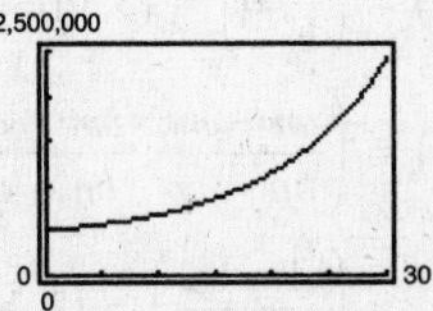

(b) $P = 50{,}000$

$$A = \frac{50{,}000}{0.10} + \left(500{,}000 - \frac{50{,}000}{0.10}\right)e^{0.10t} = 500{,}000$$

The balance remains at \$500,000.

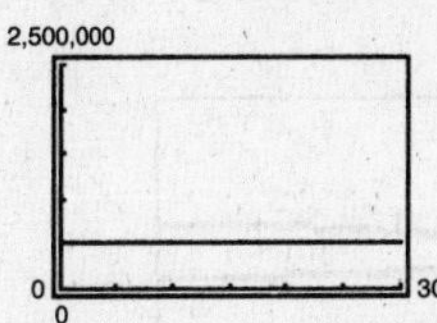


(c) $P = 60{,}000$

$$A = \frac{60{,}000}{0.10} + \left(500{,}000 - \frac{60{,}000}{0.10}\right)e^{0.10t} = 100{,}000\left(6 - e^{0.10t}\right)$$

The balance decreases and is depleted in $t = (\ln 6)/0.10 \approx 17.9$ years.

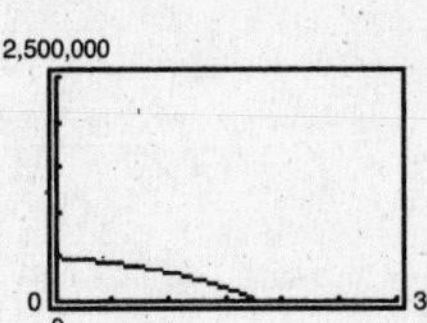


**79.** $$A = \frac{200{,}000}{0.14} + \left(1{,}000{,}000 - \frac{200{,}000}{0.14}\right)e^{0.14t}$$

$$0 = 200{,}000\left[\frac{50}{7} + \left(5 - \frac{50}{7}\right)e^{0.14t}\right]$$

$$e^{0.14t} = \frac{10}{3}$$

$$t = \frac{\ln(10/3)}{0.14} \approx 8.6 \text{ years}$$

**80.** (a) $\dfrac{dx}{dt} = ax - bxy = 0.3x - 0.02xy$

$\dfrac{dy}{dt} = -my + nxy = -0.4y + 0.01xy$

(b) $x' = y' = 0$ when $(x, y) = (0, 0)$ and

$$(x, y) = \left(\frac{m}{n}, \frac{a}{b}\right) = \left(\frac{0.4}{0.01}, \frac{0.3}{0.02}\right) = (40, 14).$$

(c)

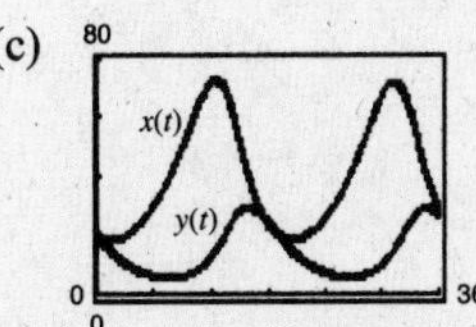

**81.** (a) $\frac{dx}{dt} = ax - bxy = 0.4x - 0.04xy$

$\frac{dy}{dt} = -my + nxy = -0.6y + 0.02xy$

(b) $x' = y' = 0$ when $(x, y) = (0, 0)$ and

$$(x, y) = \left(\frac{m}{n}, \frac{a}{b}\right) = \left(\frac{0.6}{0.02}, \frac{0.4}{0.04}\right) = (30, 10).$$

(c)

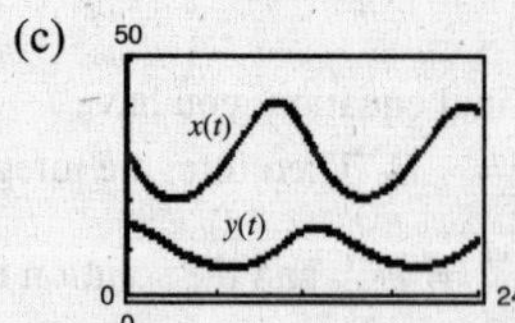


**82.** (a) $\frac{dx}{dt} = ax - bx^2 - cxy = 3x - x^2 - xy$

$\frac{dy}{dt} = my - ny^2 - pxy = 2y - y^2 - 0.5xy$

(b) $x' = y' = 0$ when $(x, y) = (0, 0)$,

$$(x, y) = \left(0, \frac{m}{n}\right) = (0, 2),$$

$$(x, y) = \left(\frac{a}{b}, 0\right) = (3, 0),$$

$$(x, y) = \left(\frac{an - mc}{bn - cp}, \frac{bm - ap}{bn - cp}\right)$$

$$= \left(\frac{1}{1/2}, \frac{1/2}{1/2}\right) = (2, 1).$$

(c)

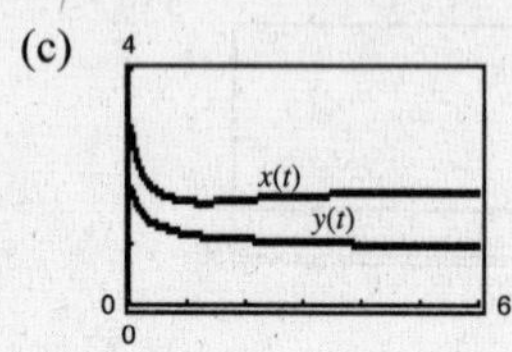


**83.** (a) $\frac{dx}{dt} = ax - bx^2 - cxy = 15x - 2x^2 - 4xy$

$\frac{dy}{dt} = my - ny^2 - pxy = 17y - 2y^2 - 4xy$

(b) $x' = y' = 0$ when $(x, y) = (0, 0)$,

$$(x, y) = \left(0, \frac{m}{n}\right) = \left(0, \frac{17}{2}\right),$$

$$(x, y) = \left(\frac{a}{b}, 0\right) = \left(\frac{15}{2}, 0\right),$$

$$(x, y) = \left(\frac{an - mc}{bn - cp}, \frac{bm - ap}{bn - cp}\right)$$

$$= \left(\frac{-38}{-12}, \frac{-26}{-12}\right) = \left(\frac{19}{6}, \frac{13}{6}\right).$$

(c)

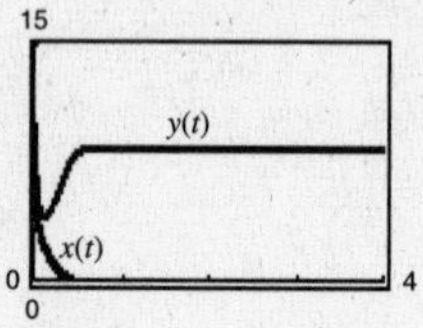

One species, $x$, becomes extinct.

# Problem Solving for Chapter 6

**1.** (a)
$$\frac{dy}{dt} = y^{1.01}$$
$$\int y^{-1.01}\,dy = \int dt$$
$$\frac{y^{-0.01}}{-0.01} = t + C_1$$
$$\frac{1}{y^{0.01}} = -0.01t + C$$
$$y^{0.01} = \frac{1}{C - 0.01t}$$
$$y = \frac{1}{(C - 0.01t)^{100}}$$
$$y(0) = 1\colon 1 = \frac{1}{C^{100}} \Rightarrow C = 1$$

So, $y = \dfrac{1}{(1 - 0.01t)^{100}}$.

For $T = 100$, $\lim\limits_{t\to T^-} y = \infty$.

(b)
$$\int y^{-(1+\varepsilon)}\,dy = \int k\,dt$$
$$\frac{y^{-\varepsilon}}{-\varepsilon} = kt + C_1$$
$$y^{-\varepsilon} = -\varepsilon kt + C$$
$$y = \frac{1}{(C - \varepsilon kt)^{1/\varepsilon}}$$
$$y(0) = y_0 = \frac{1}{C^{1/\varepsilon}} \Rightarrow C^{1/\varepsilon} = \frac{1}{y_0} \Rightarrow C = \left(\frac{1}{y_0}\right)^{\varepsilon}$$

So, $y = \dfrac{1}{\left(\dfrac{1}{y_0^{\varepsilon}} - \varepsilon kt\right)^{1/\varepsilon}}$.

For $t \to \dfrac{1}{y_0^{\varepsilon}\varepsilon k}$, $y \to \infty$.

**2.** Because $\dfrac{dy}{dt} = k(y - 20)$,
$$\int \frac{1}{y - 20}\,dy = \int k\,dt$$
$$\ln|y - 20| = kt + C$$
$$y = Ce^{kt} + 20.$$

When $t = 0$, $y = 72$. So, $C = 52$.

When $t = 1$, $y = 48$. So, $48 = 52e^{k} + 20$,

$e^{k} = \dfrac{28}{52} = \dfrac{7}{13}$, and $k = \ln\dfrac{7}{13}$.

So, $y = 52e^{[\ln(7/13)]t} + 20$.

When $t = 5$, $y = 52e^{5\ln(7/13)} + 20 \approx 22.35°\text{F}$.

**3.** (a) $\dfrac{dS}{dt} = k_1 S(L - S)$

$S = \dfrac{L}{1 + Ce^{-kt}}$ is a solution because
$$\frac{dS}{dt} = -L\left(1 + Ce^{-kt}\right)^{-2}\left(-Cke^{-kt}\right)$$
$$= \frac{LC\,ke^{-kt}}{\left(1 + Ce^{-kt}\right)^2}$$
$$= \left(\frac{k}{L}\right)\frac{L}{1 + Ce^{-kt}} \cdot \frac{C\,Le^{-kt}}{1 + Ce^{-kt}}$$
$$= \left(\frac{k}{L}\right)\frac{L}{1 + Ce^{-kt}} \cdot \left(L - \frac{L}{1 + Ce^{-kt}}\right)$$
$$= k_1 S(L - S), \text{ where } k_1 = \frac{k}{L}.$$

$L = 100$. Also, $S = 10$ when $t = 0 \Rightarrow C = 9$.

And, $S = 20$ when $t = 1 \Rightarrow k = -\ln\dfrac{4}{9}$.

Particular Solution: $S = \dfrac{100}{1 + 9e^{\ln(4/9)t}} = \dfrac{100}{1 + 9e^{-0.8109t}}$

(b)
$$\frac{dS}{dt} = k_1 S(100 - S)$$
$$\frac{d^2S}{dt^2} = k_1\left[S\left(-\frac{dS}{dt}\right) + (100 - S)\frac{dS}{dt}\right]$$
$$= k_1(100 - 2S)\frac{dS}{dt}$$
$$= 0 \text{ when } S = 50 \text{ or } \frac{dS}{dt} = 0.$$

Choosing $S = 50$, you have:
$$50 = \frac{100}{1 + 9e^{\ln(4/9)t}}$$
$$2 = 1 + 9e^{\ln(4/9)t}$$
$$\frac{\ln(1/9)}{\ln(4/9)} = t$$
$$t \approx 2.7 \text{ months}$$

(This is the point of inflection.)

(c)

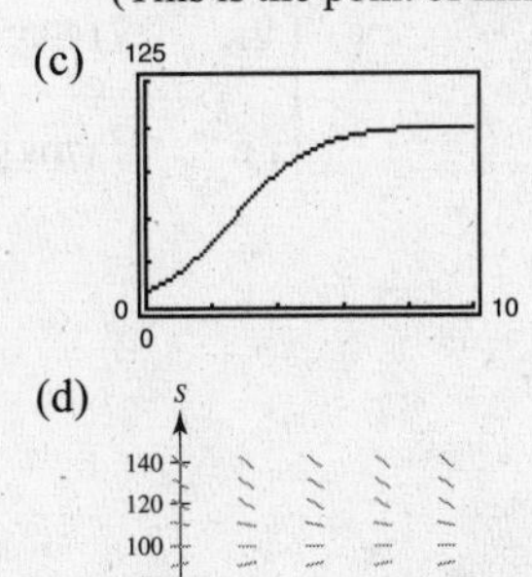


(d)

(e) Sales will decrease toward the line $S = L$.

**4.** (a) $y' = x - y, y(0) = 1, h = 0.1$

Using the modified Euler Method, you obtain:

| $x$ | $y$ |
|---|---|
| 0 | 1.0 |
| 0.1 | 0.91 |
| 0.2 | 0.83805 |
| $\vdots$ | $\vdots$ |
| 1.0 | 0.73708 |

(b) 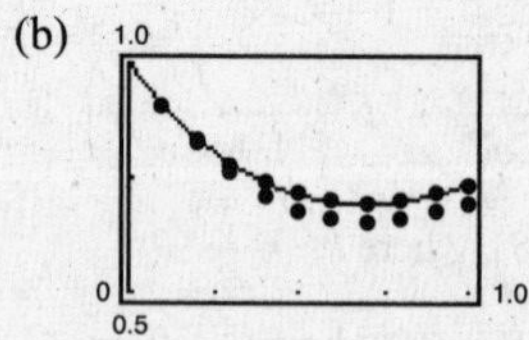


The modified Euler Method is more accurate.

```
[                   ]
[.1    .9           ]
[                   ]
[.2    .82          ]
[                   ]
[.3    .758         ]
[                   ]
[.4    .7122        ]
[                   ]
[.5    .68098       ]
[                   ]
[.6    .662882      ]
[                   ]
[.7    .6565938     ]
[                   ]
[.8    .66093442    ]
[                   ]
[.9    .674840978   ]
[                   ]
[1.0   .6973568802  ]
```

```
[x              y   ]
[                   ]
[0              1   ]
[                   ]
[.1   .9100000000   ]
[                   ]
[.2   .8380500000   ]
[                   ]
[.3   .7824352500   ]
[                   ]
[.4   .7416039013   ]
[                   ]
[.5   .7141515307   ]
[                   ]
[.6   .6988071353   ]
[                   ]
[.7   .6944204575   ]
[                   ]
[.8   .6999505140   ]
[                   ]
[.9   .7144552152   ]
[                   ]
[1.0  .7370819698   ]
```

**5.** Let $u = \frac{1}{2}k\left(t - \frac{\ln b}{k}\right)$.

$$1 + \tanh u = 1 + \frac{e^4 - e^{-u}}{e^u + e^{-u}} = \frac{2}{1 + e^{-2u}}$$

$$e^{-2u} = e^{-k(t-(\ln b/k))} = e^{\ln b}e^{-kt} = be^{-kt}$$

Finally,

$$\frac{1}{2}L\left[1 + \tanh\left(\frac{1}{2}k\left(t - \frac{\ln b}{k}\right)\right)\right] = \frac{L}{2}[1 + \tanh u]$$

$$= \frac{L}{2}\frac{2}{1 + be^{-kt}}$$

$$= \frac{L}{1 + be^{-kt}}.$$

Notice the graph of the logistics function is just a shift of the graph of the hyperbolic tangent. (See section 5.9.)

**6.** $\left[f(x)g(x)\right]' \stackrel{?}{=} f'(x)g'(x)$

(a) Let $g(x) = x, g'(x) = 1$, then

$$\left[f(x)x\right]' = f'(x)$$

$$f'(x)x + f(x) = f'(x)$$

$$\frac{df}{dx}(x - 1) = -f(x)$$

$$\int\frac{df}{f} = \int\frac{dx}{1 - x}$$

$$\ln\left|f(x)\right| = -\ln\left|1 - x\right|$$

$$f(x) = \frac{1}{1 - x}.$$

(b)

$$(fg)' = f'g'$$

$$f'g + fg' = f'g'$$

$$f'(g - g') = -fg'$$

$$\frac{f'}{f} = \frac{g'}{g' - g}$$

$$\ln\left|f\right| = \int\frac{g'}{g' - g}\,dx$$

$$f = e^{\int\frac{g'}{g'-g}dx}$$

(c) If $g(x) = e^x$, then $g'(x) - g(x) = e^x - e^x = 0$.

So, no $f$ can exist.

**7.** $k = \left(\frac{1}{12}\right)^2 \pi$

$g = 32$

$x^2 + (y-6)^2 = 36$ Equation of tank

$$x^2 = 36 - (y-6)^2 = 12y - y^2$$

Area of cross section: $A(h) = (12h - h^2)\pi$

$$A(h)\frac{dh}{dt} = -k\sqrt{2gh}$$

$$(12h - h^2)\pi\frac{dh}{dt} = -\frac{1}{144}\pi\sqrt{64h}$$

$$(12h - h^2)\frac{dh}{dt} = -\frac{1}{18}h^{1/2}$$

$$\int(18h^{3/2} - 216h^{1/2})\,dh = \int dt$$

$$\frac{36}{5}h^{5/2} - 144h^{3/2} = t + C$$

$$\frac{h^{3/2}}{5}(36h - 720) = t + C$$

When $h = 6, t = 0$ and $C = \frac{6^{3/2}}{5}(-504) \approx -1481.45.$

The tank is completely drained when

$h = 0 \Rightarrow t = 1481.45 \text{ sec} \approx 24 \text{ min, } 41 \text{ sec.}$

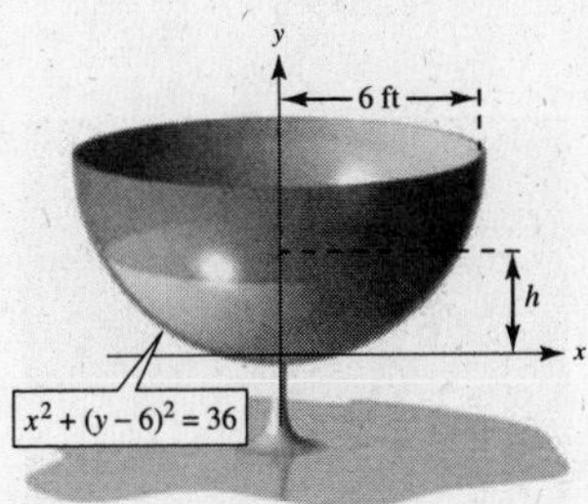


**8.** (a) $A(h)\frac{dh}{dt} = -k\sqrt{2gh}$

$$\pi r^2\frac{dh}{dt} = -k\sqrt{64h}$$

$$h^{-1/2}\,dh = \frac{-8k}{\pi r^2}\,dt = -C\,dt, \quad C = \frac{8k}{\pi r^2}$$

$$2\sqrt{h} = -Ct + C_1$$

$$2\sqrt{18} = C_1 \quad (\text{at } t = 0, h = 18)$$

So, $2\sqrt{h} = -Ct + 6\sqrt{2}.$

At $t = 30(60) = 1800, h = 12$:

$$2\sqrt{12} = -1800\,C + 6\sqrt{2}$$

$$\frac{6\sqrt{2} - 4\sqrt{3}}{1800} = C \approx 0.000865$$

So, $2\sqrt{h} = -0.000865t + 6\sqrt{2}.$

$$h = 0 \Rightarrow t = \frac{6\sqrt{2}}{0.000865}$$

$$\approx 9809.1 \text{ seconds } (2 \text{ h}, 43 \text{ min}, 29 \text{ sec})$$

(b) $t = 3600 \text{ sec} \Rightarrow 2\sqrt{h} = -0.000865(3600) + 6\sqrt{2}$

$$\Rightarrow h \approx 7.21 \text{ ft}$$

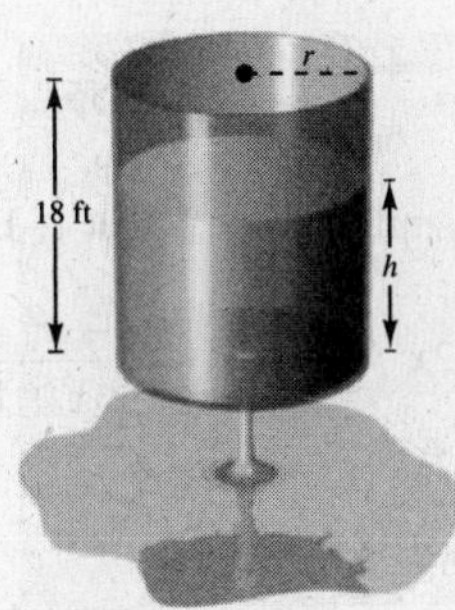


**9.** $A(h)\frac{dh}{dt} = -k\sqrt{2gh}$

$$\pi 64\frac{dh}{dt} = \frac{-\pi}{36}8\sqrt{h}$$

$$\int h^{-1/2}\,dh = \int\frac{-1}{288}\,dt$$

$$2\sqrt{h} = \frac{-t}{288} + C$$

$$h = 20: 2\sqrt{20} = C = 4\sqrt{5}$$

$$2\sqrt{h} = \frac{-t}{288} + 4\sqrt{5}$$

$$h = 0 \Rightarrow t = 4\sqrt{5}(288)$$

$$\approx 2575.95 \text{ sec} \approx 42 \text{ min, } 56 \text{ sec}$$

**10.** Let the radio receiver be located at $(x_0, 0)$. The tangent line to $y = x - x^2$ joins $(-1, 1)$ and $(x_0, 0)$.

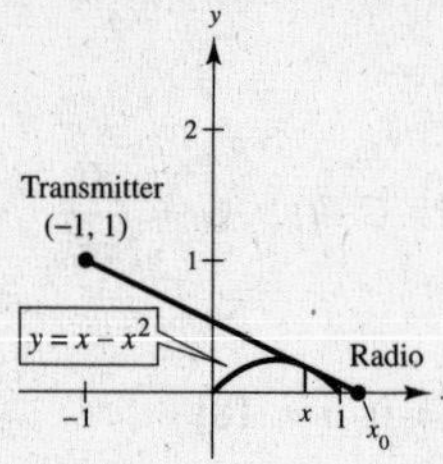


(a) If $(x, y)$ is the point of tangency on $y = x - x^2$, then

$$1 - 2x = \frac{y - 1}{x + 1} = \frac{x - x^2 - 1}{x + 1}$$

$$x - 2x^2 + 1 - 2x = x - x^2 - 1$$

$$x^2 + 2x - 2 = 0$$

$$x = \left(\frac{-2 \pm \sqrt{4 + 8}}{2}\right) = -1 + \sqrt{3}$$

$$y = x - x^2 = 3\sqrt{3} - 5.$$

Then $\dfrac{1 - 0}{-1 - x_0} = \dfrac{1 - 3\sqrt{3} + 5}{-1 + 1 - \sqrt{3}} = \dfrac{6 - 3\sqrt{3}}{-\sqrt{3}}$

$$\sqrt{3} = (1 + x_0)\left(6 - 3\sqrt{3}\right) = 6 - 3\sqrt{3} + x_0\left(6 - 3\sqrt{3}\right)$$

$$x_0 = \frac{4\sqrt{3} - 6}{6 - 3\sqrt{3}} \approx 1.155.$$

(b) Now let the transmitter be located at $(-1, h)$.

$$1 - 2x = \frac{y - h}{x + 1} = \frac{x - x^2 - h}{x + 1}$$

$$x - 2x^2 + 1 - 2x = x - x^2 - h$$

$$x^2 + 2x - h - 1 = 0$$

$$x = \frac{\left(-2 \pm \sqrt{4 + 4(h + 1)}\right)}{2} = -1 + \sqrt{2 + h}$$

$$y = x - x^2 = 3\sqrt{2 + h} - h - 4$$

Then, $\dfrac{h - 0}{-1 - x_0} = \dfrac{h - \left(3\sqrt{2 + h} - h - 4\right)}{-1 - \left(-1 + \sqrt{2 + h}\right)} = \dfrac{2h + 4 - 3\sqrt{2 + h}}{-\sqrt{2 + h}}$

$$\frac{x_0 + 1}{h} = \frac{\sqrt{2 + h}}{2h + 4 - 3\sqrt{2 + h}}$$

$$x_0 = \frac{h\sqrt{2 + h}}{2h + 4 - 3\sqrt{2 + h}} - 1.$$

(c)

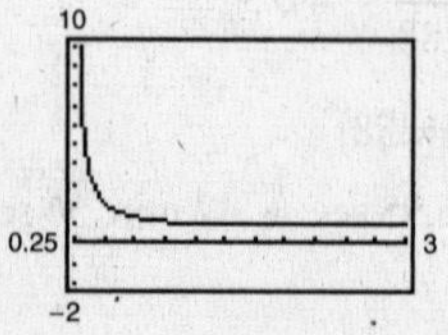

There is a vertical asymptote at $h = \frac{1}{4}$, which is the height of the mountain.

**11.** $\dfrac{ds}{dt} = 3.5 - 0.019s$

(a) $\displaystyle\int \frac{-ds}{3.5 - 0.019s} = -\int dt$

$$\frac{1}{0.019}\ln|3.5 - 0.019s| = -t + C_1$$

$$\ln|3.5 - 0.019s| = -0.019t + C_2$$

$$3.5 - 0.019s = C_3e^{-0.019t}$$

$$0.019s = 3.5 - C_3e^{-0.019t}$$

$$s = 184.21 - Ce^{-0.019t}$$

(b)

(c) As $t \to \infty$, $Ce^{-0.019t} \to 0$, and $s \to 184.21$.

**12.** (a) $\displaystyle\int \frac{dC}{C} = \int -\frac{R}{V}\,dt$

$$\ln|C| = -\frac{R}{V}t + K_1$$

$$C = Ke^{-Rt/V}$$

Because $C = C_0$ when $t = 0$, it follows that $K = C_0$ and the function is $C = C_0e^{-Rt/V}$.

(b) Finally, as $t \to \infty$, you have

$$\lim_{t\to\infty} C = \lim_{t\to\infty} C_0e^{-Rt/V} = 0.$$

**13.** From Exercise 12, you have $C = C_0e^{-Rt/V}$.

(a) For $V = 2$, $R = 0.5$, and $C_0 = 0.6$, you have $C = 0.6e^{-0.25t}$.

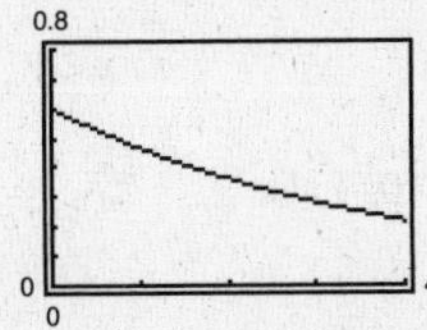


(b) For $V = 2$, $R = 1.5$, and $C_0 = 0.6$, you have $C = 0.6e^{-0.75t}$.

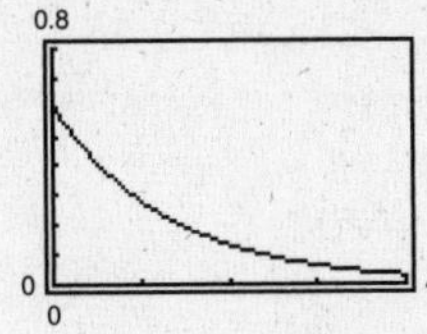


**14.** (a) $\displaystyle\int \frac{1}{Q - RC}\,dC = \int \frac{1}{V}\,dt$

$$-\frac{1}{R}\ln|Q - RC| = \frac{t}{V} + K_1$$

$$Q - RC = e^{-R[(t/V)+K_1]}$$

$$C = \frac{1}{R}\left(Q - e^{-R[(t/V)+K_1]}\right) = \frac{1}{R}\left(Q - Ke^{-Rt/V}\right)$$

Because $C = 0$ when $t = 0$, it follows that $K = Q$ and you have $C = \dfrac{Q}{R}\left(1 - e^{-Rt/V}\right)$.

(b) As $t \to \infty$, the limit of $C$ is $Q/R$.

# Appendix C.1

1. $0.7 = \frac{7}{10}$

   Rational

2. $-3678 = \dfrac{-3678}{1}$

   Rational

3. $\dfrac{3\pi}{2}$

   Irrational (because $\pi$ is irrational)

4. $3\sqrt{2} - 1$

   Irrational (because $\sqrt{2}$ is irrational)

5. $4.345\overline{1451}$

   Rational

6. $\frac{22}{7}$

   Rational

7. $\sqrt[3]{64} = 4$

   Rational

8. $0.8177\overline{8177}$

   Rational

9. $4\frac{5}{8} = \frac{37}{8}$

   Rational

10. $\left(\sqrt{2}\right)^3 = 2\sqrt{2}$

    Irrational

11. Let $x = 0.36\overline{36}$.

    $$\begin{aligned} 100x &= 36.36\overline{36} \\ -x &= -0.36\overline{36} \\ \hline 99x &= 36 \end{aligned}$$

    $x = \frac{36}{99} = \frac{4}{11}$

12. Let $x = 0.318\overline{18}$.

    $$\begin{aligned} 1000x &= 318.18\overline{18} \\ -10x &= -3.18\overline{18} \\ \hline 990x &= 315 \end{aligned}$$

    $x = \frac{315}{990} = \frac{7}{22}$

13. Let $x = 0.297\overline{297}$.

    $$\begin{aligned} 1000x &= 0.297\overline{297} \\ -x &= -297.297\overline{297} \\ \hline 999x &= 297 \end{aligned}$$

    $x = \frac{297}{999} = \frac{11}{37}$

14. Let $x = 0.9900\overline{9900}$.

    $$\begin{aligned} 10{,}000x &= 9900.9900\overline{9900} \\ -x &= -0.9900\overline{9900} \\ \hline 9999x &= 9900 \end{aligned}$$

    $x = \frac{9900}{9999} = \frac{100}{101}$

15. Given $a < b$:

    (a) $a + 2 < b + 2$; True

    (b) $5b < 5a$; False

    (c) $5 - a > 5 - b$; True

    (d) $\dfrac{1}{a} < \dfrac{1}{b}$; False

    (e) $(a - b)(b - a) > 0$; False

    (f) $a^2 < b^2$; False

16.

| Interval Notation | Set Notation | Graph |
|---|---|---|
| $[-2, 0)$ | $\{x: -2 \le x < 0\}$ | 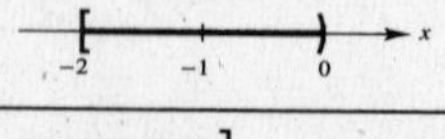 |
| $(-\infty, -4]$ | $\{x: x \le -4\}$ | 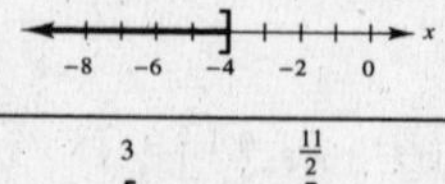 |
| $\left[3, \frac{11}{2}\right]$ | $\left\{x: 3 \le x \le \frac{11}{2}\right\}$ | 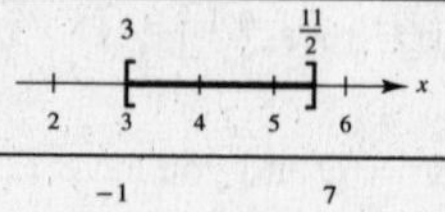 |
| $(-1, 7)$ | $\{x: -1 < x < 7\}$ | 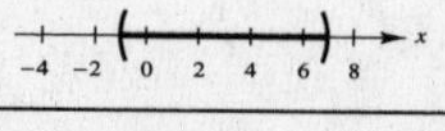 |

**17.** $x$ is greater than $-3$ and less than 3.

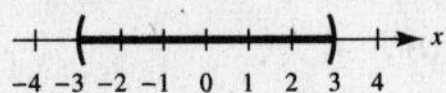

The interval is bounded.

**18.** $x$ is greater than, or equal to, 4.

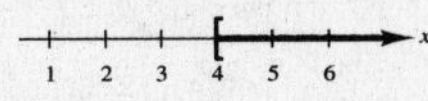

The interval is unbounded.

**19.** $x$ is less than, or equal to, 5.

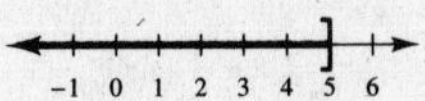

The interval is unbounded.

**20.** $x$ is greater than or equal to 0, and less than 8.

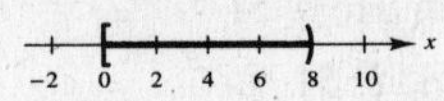

The interval is bounded.

**21.** $y \geq 4, [4, \infty)$

**22.** $q \geq 0, [0, \infty)$

**23.** $0.03 < r \leq 0.07, (0.03, 0.07]$

**24.** $T > 90°, (90°, \infty)$

**25.** $2x - 1 \geq 0$

$2x \geq 1$

$x \geq \frac{1}{2}$

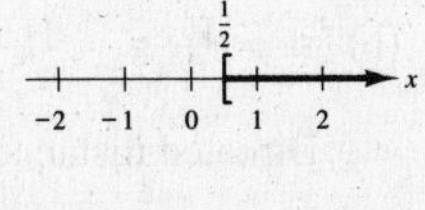

**26.** $3x + 1 \geq 2x + 2$

$3x \geq 2x + 1$

$x \geq 1$

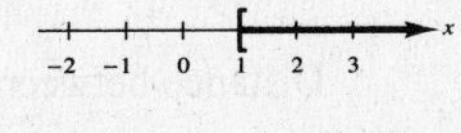

**27.** $-4 < 2x - 3 < 4$

$-1 < 2x < 7$

$-\frac{1}{2} < x < \frac{7}{2}$

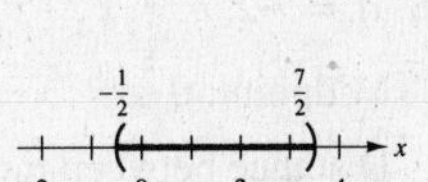

**28.** $0 \leq x + 3 < 5$

$-3 \leq x < 2$

**29.** $\frac{x}{2} + \frac{x}{3} > 5$

$3x + 2x > 30$

$5x > 30$

$x > 6$

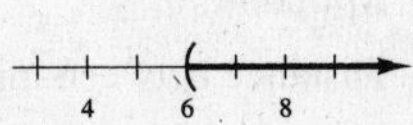

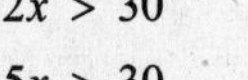

**30.** $x > \frac{1}{x}$

$x - \frac{1}{x} > 0$

$\frac{x^2 - 1}{x} > 0$

$\frac{(1 + x)(x - 1)}{x} > 0$

Test intervals: $(-\infty, -1), (-1, 0), (0, 1), (1, \infty)$

Solution: $-1 < x < 0$ or $x > 1$

**31.** $|x| < 1 \Rightarrow -1 < x < 1$

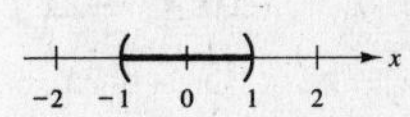

**32.** $\frac{x}{2} - \frac{x}{3} > 5$

$3x - 2x > 30$

$x > 30$

**33.** $\left|\frac{x - 3}{2}\right| \geq 5$

$x - 3 \geq 10$ or $x - 3 \leq -10$

$x \geq 13$ $\quad x \leq -7$

**34.** $\left|\frac{x}{2}\right| > 3 \Rightarrow x > 6$ or $x < -6$

**35.** $|x - a| < b$

$-b < x - a < b$

$a - b < x < a + b$

**36.** $|x + 2| < 5$

$-5 < x + 2 < 5$

$-7 < x < 3$

**37.** $|2x + 1| < 5$

$-5 < 2x + 1 < 5$

$-6 < 2x < 4$

$-3 < x < 2$

**38.** $|3x + 1| \geq 4$

$3x + 1 \geq 4$ or $3x + 1 \leq -4$

$3x \geq 3$ $\quad 3x \leq -5$

$x \geq 1$ $\quad x \leq -\frac{5}{3}$

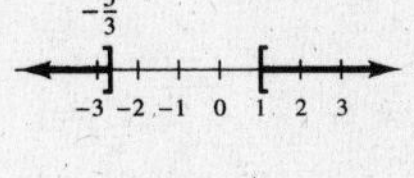

**39.** $\left|1 - \frac{2x}{3}\right| < 1$

$$-1 < 1 - \frac{2x}{3} < 1$$

$$-2 < -\frac{2x}{3} < 0$$

$$3 > x > 0$$

**40.** $|9 - 2x| < 1$

$$-1 < 9 - 2x < 1$$

$$-10 < -2x < -8$$

$$5 > x > 4$$

**41.** $x^2 \le 3 - 2x$

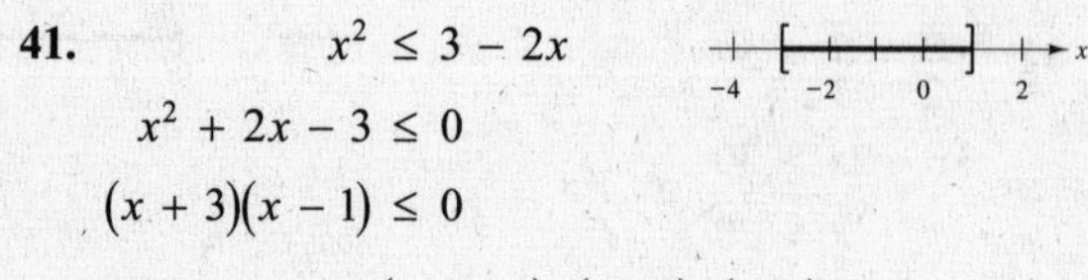

$$x^2 + 2x - 3 \le 0$$

$$(x + 3)(x - 1) \le 0$$

Test intervals: $(-\infty, -3), (-3, 1), (1, \infty)$

Solution: $-3 \le x \le 1$

**42.** $x^4 - x \le 0$

$$x(x^3 - 1) \le 0$$

$$x = 0$$

$$x = 1$$

Test intervals: $(-\infty, 0), (0, 1), (1, \infty)$

Solution: $0 \le x \le 1$

**43.** $x^2 + x - 1 \le 5$

$$x^2 + x - 6 \le 0$$

$$(x + 3)(x - 2) \le 0$$

$$x = -3$$

$$x = 2$$

Test intervals: $(-\infty, -3), (-3, 2), (2, \infty)$

Solution: $-3 \le x \le 2$

**44.** $2x^2 + 1 < 9x - 3$

$$2x^2 - 9x + 4 < 0$$

$$(2x - 1)(x - 4) < 0$$

$$x = \tfrac{1}{2}$$

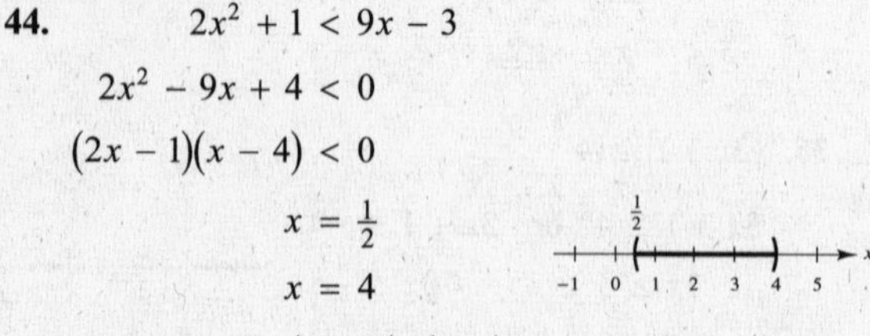

$$x = 4$$

Test intervals: $\left(-\infty, \frac{1}{2}\right), \left(\frac{1}{2}, 4\right), (4, \infty)$

Solution: $\frac{1}{2} < x < 4$

**45.** $a = -1, b = 3$

Directed distance from $a$ to $b$: 4

Directed distance from $b$ to $a$: $-4$

Distance between $a$ and $b$: 4

**46.** $a = -\frac{5}{2}, b = \frac{13}{4}$

Directed distance from $a$ to $b$: $\frac{23}{4}$

Directed distance from $b$ to $a$: $-\frac{23}{4}$

Distance between $a$ and $b$: $\frac{23}{4}$

**47.** (a) $a = 126, b = 75$

Directed distance from $a$ to $b$: $-51$

Directed distance from $b$ to $a$: 51

Distance between $a$ and $b$: 51

(b) $a = -126, b = -75$

Directed distance from $a$ to $b$: 51

Directed distance from $b$ to $a$: $-51$

Distance between $a$ and $b$: 51

**48.** (a) $a = 9.34, b = -5.65$

Directed distance from $a$ to $b$: $-14.99$

Directed distance from $b$ to $a$: 14.99

Distance between $a$ and $b$: 14.99

(b) $a = \frac{16}{5}, b = \frac{112}{75}$

Directed distance from $a$ to $b$: $-\frac{128}{75}$

Directed distance from $b$ to $a$: $\frac{128}{75}$

Distance between $a$ and $b$: $\frac{128}{75}$

**49.** $a = -2, b = 2$

Midpoint: 0

Distance between midpoint and each endpoint: 2

$$|x - 0| \le 2$$

$$|x| \le 2$$

**50.** $a = -3, b = 3$

Midpoint: 0

Distance between midpoint and each endpoint: 3

$$|x - 0| \ge 3$$

$$|x| \ge 3$$

**51.** $a = 0, b = 4$

Midpoint: 2

Distance between midpoint and each endpoint: 2

$$|x - 2| > 2$$

**52.** $a = 20, b = 24$

Midpoint: 22

Distance between midpoint and each endpoint: 2

$|x - 22| \geq 2$

**53.** (a) All numbers that are at most 10 units from 12

$|x - 12| \leq 10$

(b) All numbers that are at least 10 units from 12

$|x - 12| \geq 10$

**54.** (a) $y$ is at most 2 units from $a$: $|y - a| \leq 2$

(b) $y$ is less than $\delta$ units from $c$: $|y - c| < \delta$

**55.** $a = -1, b = 3$

Midpoint: $\dfrac{-1 + 3}{2} = 1$

**56.** $a = -5, b = -\dfrac{3}{2}$

Midpoint: $\dfrac{-5 + (-3/2)}{2} = -\dfrac{13}{4}$

**57.** (a) $[7, 21]$

Midpoint: 14

(b) $[8.6, 11.4]$

Midpoint: 10

**58.** (a) $[-6.85, 9.35]$

Midpoint: 1.25

(b) $[-4.6, -1.3]$

Midpoint: $-2.95$

**59.** $R = 115.95x, C = 95x + 750, R > C$

$$115.95x > 95x + 750$$
$$20.95x > 750$$
$$x > 35.7995$$
$$x \geq 36 \text{ units}$$

**60.** $C = 0.32m + 2300, C < 10{,}000$

$$0.32m + 2300 < 10{,}000$$
$$0.32m < 7700$$
$$m < 24{,}062.5 \text{ miles}$$

**61.** $\left|\dfrac{x - 50}{5}\right| \geq 1.645$

$$\frac{x - 50}{5} \leq -1.645 \quad \text{or} \quad \frac{x - 50}{5} \geq 1.645$$
$$x - 50 \leq -8.225 \qquad x - 50 \geq 8.225$$
$$x \leq 41.775 \qquad x \geq 58.225$$
$$x \leq 41 \qquad x \geq 59$$

**62.** $|p - 2{,}250{,}000| < 125{,}000$

$$-125{,}000 < p - 2{,}250{,}000 < 125{,}000$$
$$2{,}125{,}000 < p < 2{,}375{,}000$$

High = 2,375,000 barrels

Low = 2,125,000 barrels

**63.** (a) $\pi \approx 3.1415926535$

$\frac{355}{113} \approx 3.141592920$

$\frac{355}{113} > \pi$

(b) $\pi \approx 3.1415926535$

$\frac{22}{7} \approx 3.142857143$

$\frac{22}{7} > \pi$

**64.** (a) $\frac{224}{151} \approx 1.483443709$

$\frac{144}{97} \approx 1.484536082$

$\frac{144}{97} > \frac{224}{151}$

(b) $\frac{73}{81} \approx 0.901234568$

$\frac{6427}{7132} \approx 0.901149748$

$\frac{73}{81} > \frac{6427}{7132}$

**65.** Speed of light: $2.998 \times 10^8$ meters per second

Distance traveled in one year = rate × time

$$d = (2.998 \times 10^8) \times (365 \times 24 \times 60 \times 60)$$

days × hours × minutes × seconds

$$= (2.998 \times 10^8) \times (3.1536 \times 10^7) \approx 9.45 \times 10^{15}$$

This is best estimated by (b).

**66.** The significant digits of a number are the digits of the number beginning with the first nonzero digit to the left of the decimal point (or the first digit to the right of the decimal point if there isn't a nonzero digit to the left of the decimal point) and ending with the last digit to the right. The following examples all have three significant digits.

100, 307, 0.123, 0.012, 0.001, 1.23, 12.3, 0.120, 0.300

**67.** False; 2 is a nonzero integer and the reciprocal of 2 is $\frac{1}{2}$.

**68.** True; if $x(x \neq 0)$ is rational, then $x = p/q$ where $p$ and $q$ are nonzero integers. The reciprocal of $x$ is $1/x = q/p$ which is also the ratio of two integers.

**69.** True

**70.** False; $|0| = 0$ which is not positive.

**71.** True; if $x < 0$, then $|x| = -x = \sqrt{x^2}$.

**72.** True; because $a$ and $b$ are **distinct**, $a \neq b$ and one of the numbers must be larger than the other one.

**73.** If $a \geq 0$ and $b \geq 0$, then $|ab| = ab = |a||b|$.

If $a < 0$ and $b < 0$, then $|ab| = ab = (-a)(-b) = |a||b|$.

If $a \geq 0$ and $b < 0$, then $|ab| = -ab = a(-b) = |a||b|$.

If $a < 0$ and $b \geq 0$, then $|ab| = -ab = (-a)b = |a||b|$.

**74.** $|a - b| = |(-1)(b - a)| = |-1||b - a| = (1)|b - a| = |b - a|$

**75.** $\left|\frac{a}{b}\right| = \left|a\left(\frac{1}{b}\right)\right| = |a|\left|\frac{1}{b}\right| = |a| \cdot \frac{1}{|b|} = \frac{|a|}{|b|}, \ b \neq 0$

**76.** If $a \geq 0$, then $|a| = a = \sqrt{a^2}$.

If $a < 0$, then $|a| = -a = \sqrt{(-a)^2} = \sqrt{a^2}$.

**77.** $n = 1$, $\quad |a| = |a|$

$n = 2$, $\quad |a^2| = |a \cdot a| = |a||a| = |a|^2$

$n = 3$, $\quad |a^3| = |a^2 \cdot a| = |a^2||a| = |a|^2|a| = |a|^3$

$\vdots$

$|a^n| = |a^{n-1}a| = |a^{n-1}||a| = |a|^{n-1}|a| = |a|^n$

**78.** If $a \geq 0$, then $a = |a|$. So, $-|a| \leq a \leq |a|$.

If $a < 0$, then $a = -|a|$. So, $-|a| \leq a \leq |a|$.

**79.** $|a| \leq k \Leftrightarrow \sqrt{a^2} \leq k \Leftrightarrow a^2 \leq k^2 \Leftrightarrow a^2 - k^2 \leq 0 \Leftrightarrow (a + k)(a - k) \leq 0 \Leftrightarrow -k \leq a \leq k, \ k > 0$

**80.** $k \leq |a| \Leftrightarrow k \leq \sqrt{a^2} \Leftrightarrow k^2 \leq a^2 \Leftrightarrow 0 \leq a^2 - k^2 \Leftrightarrow 0 \leq (a + k)(a - k) \Leftrightarrow k \leq a$ or $a \leq -k, \ k > 0$

**81.** $\left.\begin{array}{l}|7-12| = |-5| = 5\\ |7| - |12| = 7 - 12 = -5\end{array}\right\} |7 - 12| > |7| - |12|$

$\left.\begin{array}{l}|12-7| = |5| = 5\\ |12| - |7| = 12 - 7 = 5\end{array}\right\} |12 - 7| = |12| - |7|$

You know that $|a||b| \geq ab$. So, $-2|a||b| \leq -2ab$. Because $a^2 = |a|^2$ and $b^2 = |b|^2$, you have

$$\begin{aligned}|a|^2 + |b|^2 - 2|a||b| &\leq a^2 + b^2 - 2ab\\ 0 \leq \left(|a| - |b|\right)^2 &\leq (a - b)^2\\ \sqrt{\left(|a| - |b|\right)^2} &\leq \sqrt{(a - b)^2}\\ \big||a| - |b|\big| &\leq |a - b|.\end{aligned}$$

Because $|a| - |b| \leq \big||a| - |b|\big|$, you have $|a| - |b| \leq |a - b|$. So, $|a - b| \geq |a| - |b|$.

**82.** $$\begin{aligned}\frac{1}{2}\left(a + b + |a - b|\right) &= \frac{1}{2}(a + b) + \frac{1}{2}|a - b|\\ &= \frac{a + b}{2} + \frac{1}{2}|a - b|\\ &= \text{Midpoint} + \frac{1}{2}\text{ the distance between } a \text{ and } b\\ &= \max(a, b)\end{aligned}$$

$$\begin{aligned}\min(a, b) &= \text{Midpoint} - \frac{1}{2}\text{ the distance between } a \text{ and } b\\ &= \frac{a + b}{2} - \frac{1}{2}|a - b|\\ &= \frac{1}{2}\left(a + b - |a - b|\right)\end{aligned}$$

# Appendix C.2

**1.** (a)

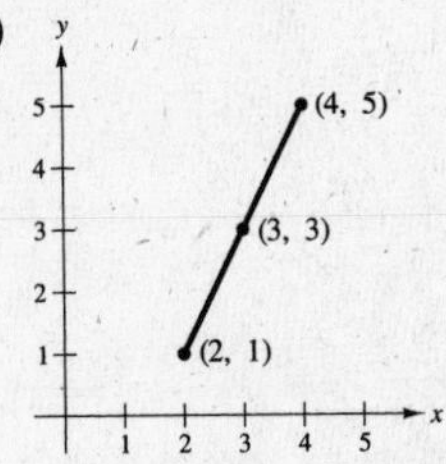


(b) $d = \sqrt{(4 - 2)^2 + (5 - 1)^2}$
$= \sqrt{4 + 16} = \sqrt{20} = 2\sqrt{5}$

(c) Midpoint: $\left(\frac{4 + 2}{2}, \frac{5 + 1}{2}\right) = (3, 3)$

**2.** (a)

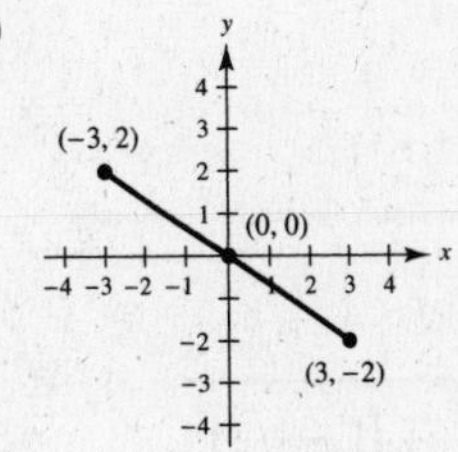


(b) $d = \sqrt{(3 + 3)^2 + (-2 - 2)^2}$
$= \sqrt{36 + 16} = \sqrt{52} = 2\sqrt{13}$

(c) Midpoint: $\left(\frac{-3 + 3}{2}, \frac{2 + (-2)}{2}\right) = (0, 0)$

**3.** (a)

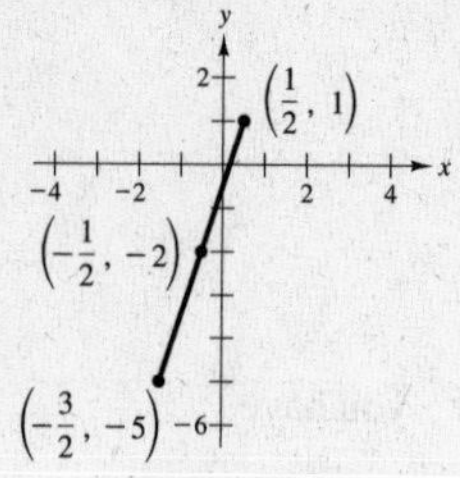


(b) $d = \sqrt{\left(\frac{1}{2} + \frac{3}{2}\right)^2 + (1 + 5)^2}$

$= \sqrt{4 + 36} = \sqrt{40} = 2\sqrt{10}$

(c) Midpoint: $\left(\frac{(-3/2) + (1/2)}{2}, \frac{-5 + 1}{2}\right) = \left(-\frac{1}{2}, -2\right)$

**4.** (a)

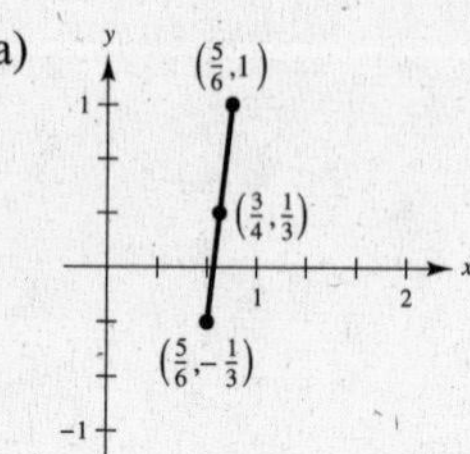


(b) $d = \sqrt{\left(\frac{5}{6} - \frac{4}{6}\right)^2 + \left(\frac{3}{3} + \frac{1}{3}\right)^2}$

$= \sqrt{\frac{1}{36} + \frac{64}{36}} = \frac{\sqrt{65}}{6}$

(c) Midpoint: $\left(\frac{(2/3) + (5/6)}{2}, \frac{(-1/3) + 1}{2}\right) = \left(\frac{3}{4}, \frac{1}{3}\right)$

**5.** (a)

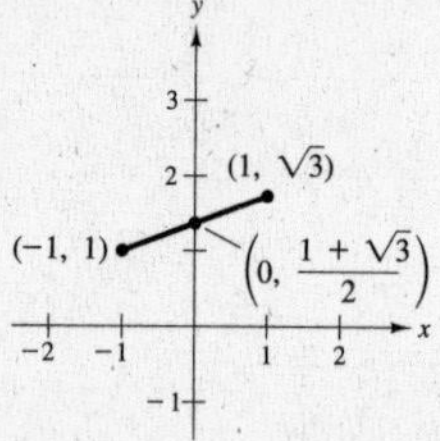


(b) $d = \sqrt{(-1 - 1)^2 + \left(1 - \sqrt{3}\right)^2}$

$= \sqrt{4 + 1 - 2\sqrt{3} + 3} = \sqrt{8 - 2\sqrt{3}}$

(c) Midpoint: $\left(\frac{-1 + 1}{2}, \frac{1 + \sqrt{3}}{2}\right) = \left(0, \frac{1 + \sqrt{3}}{2}\right)$

**6.** (a)

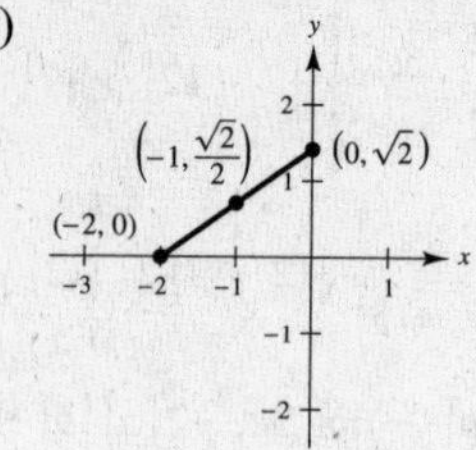


(b) $d = \sqrt{(-2 + 0)^2 + \left(0 - \sqrt{2}\right)^2}$

$= \sqrt{4 + 2} = \sqrt{6}$

(c) Midpoint: $\left(\frac{-2 + 0}{2}, \frac{0 + \sqrt{2}}{2}\right) = \left(-1, \frac{\sqrt{2}}{2}\right)$

**7.** $x = -2 \Rightarrow$ quadrants II, III

$y > 0 \Rightarrow$ quadrants I, II

Therefore, quadrant II

**8.** $y < -2 \Rightarrow$ quadrant III or IV

**9.** $xy > 0 \Rightarrow$ quadrants I or III

**10.** $(x, -y)$ in quadrant II $\Rightarrow$ $(x, y)$ in quadrant III

**11.** $d_1 = \sqrt{9 + 36} = \sqrt{45}$

$d_2 = \sqrt{4 + 1} = \sqrt{5}$

$d_3 = \sqrt{25 + 25} = \sqrt{50}$

$(d_1)^2 + (d_2)^2 = (d_3)^2$

Right triangle

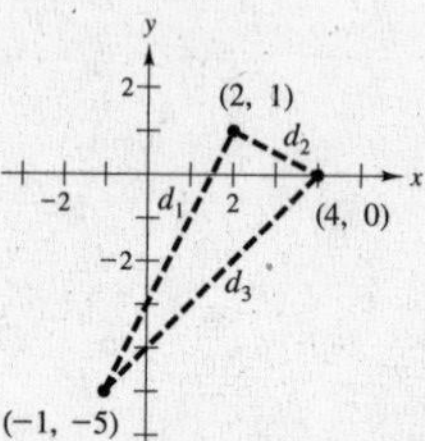


**12.** $d_1 = \sqrt{9 + 49} = \sqrt{58}$

$d_2 = \sqrt{25 + 4} = \sqrt{29}$

$d_3 = \sqrt{4 + 25} = \sqrt{29}$

$d_2 = d_3$

Isosceles triangle

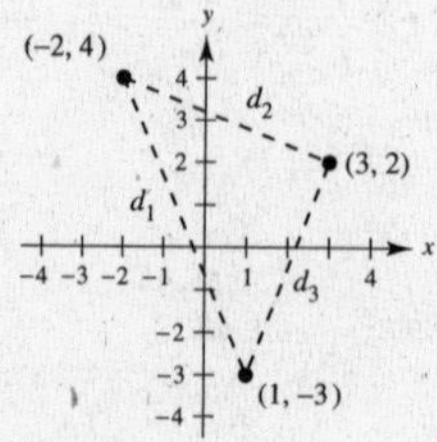

**13.** $d_1 = d_2 = d_3 = d_4 = \sqrt{5}$

Rhombus

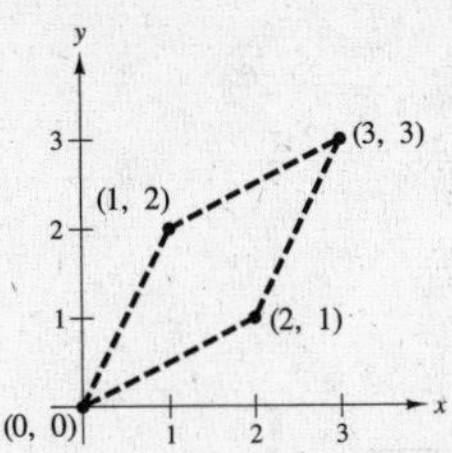


**14.** $d_1 = \sqrt{9 + 36} = \sqrt{45} = d_3$

$d_2 = \sqrt{1 + 9} = \sqrt{10} = d_4$

Parallelogram

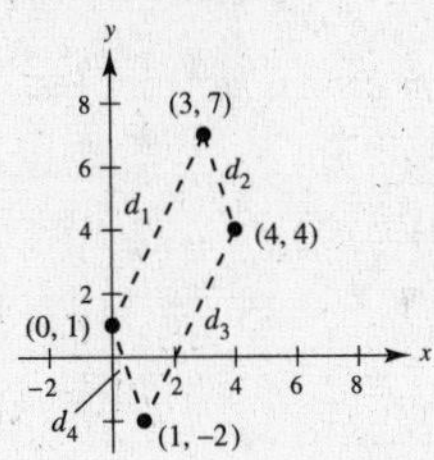


**15.**

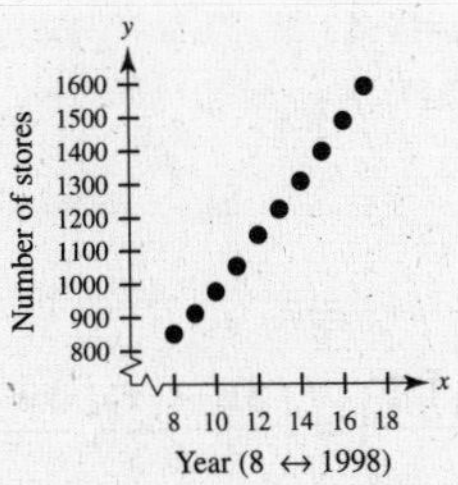


**16.**

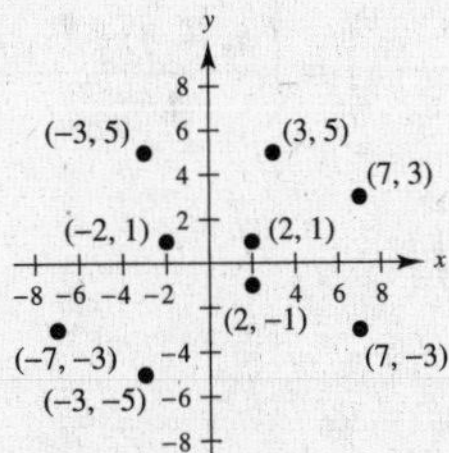


The new point $(-x, y)$ is located in a position symmetrical about the $y$-axis. Similarly, changing $(x, y)$ to $(x, -y)$ moves the point to a position symmetrical about the $x$-axis.

**17.** $d_1 = \sqrt{4 + 16} = \sqrt{20} = 2\sqrt{5}$

$d_2 = \sqrt{1 + 4} = \sqrt{5}$

$d_3 = \sqrt{9 + 36} = 3\sqrt{5}$

$d_1 + d_2 = d_3$

Collinear

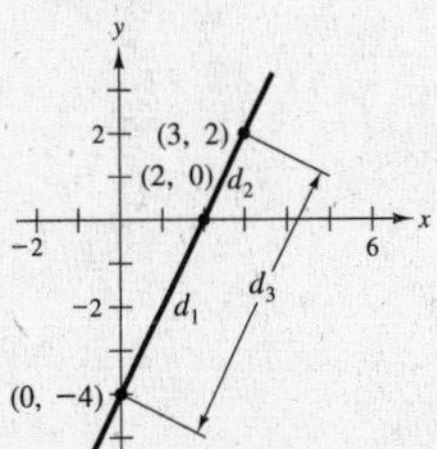


**18.** $d_1 = \sqrt{49 + 100} = \sqrt{149} \approx 12.2066$

$d_2 = \sqrt{25 + 49} = \sqrt{74} \approx 8.6023$

$d_3 = \sqrt{144 + 289} = \sqrt{433} \approx 20.8087$

$d_1 + d_2 \neq d_3$

Not collinear

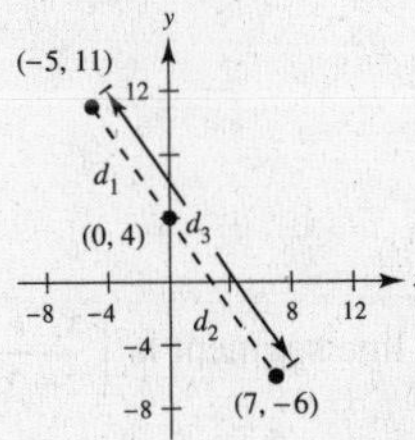


**19.** $d_1 = \sqrt{1 + 1} = \sqrt{2}$

$d_2 = \sqrt{9 + 4} = \sqrt{13}$

$d_3 = \sqrt{16 + 9} = 5$

$d_1 + d_2 \neq d_3$

Not collinear

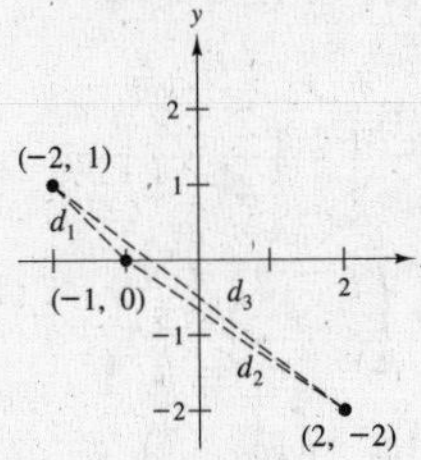

**20.** $d_1 = \sqrt{16 + 4} = \sqrt{20} = 2\sqrt{5}$

$d_2 = \sqrt{4 + 4} = \sqrt{8} = 2\sqrt{2}$

$d_3 = \sqrt{36 + 16} = \sqrt{52} = 2\sqrt{13}$

$d_1 + d_2 \neq d_3$

Not collinear

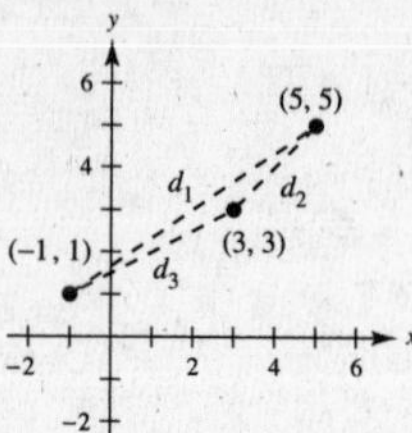


**21.** $5 = \sqrt{(x - 0)^2 + (-4 - 0)^2}$

$5 = \sqrt{x^2 + 16}$

$25 = x^2 + 16$

$9 = x^2$

$x = \pm 3$

**22.** $5 = \sqrt{(x - 2)^2 + (2 + 1)^2}$

$5 = \sqrt{(x - 2)^2 + 9}$

$25 = (x - 2)^2 + 9$

$16 = (x - 2)^2$

$\pm 4 = x - 2$

$x = 2 \pm 4 = -2, 6$

**23.** $8 = \sqrt{(3 - 0)^2 + (y - 0)^2}$

$8 = \sqrt{9 + y^2}$

$64 = 9 + y^2$

$55 = y^2$

$y = \pm\sqrt{55}$

**24.** $8 = \sqrt{(5 - 5)^2 + (y - 1)^2}$

$8 = \sqrt{(y - 1)^2}$

$8 = |y - 1|$

$y - 1 = 8$ or $y - 1 = -8$

$y = 9$ $\quad$ $y = -7$

**25.** The midpoint of the given line segment is $\left(\frac{x_1 + x_2}{2}, \frac{y_1 + y_2}{2}\right)$.

The midpoint between $(x_1, y_1)$ and $\left(\frac{x_1 + x_2}{2}, \frac{y_1 + y_2}{2}\right)$ is $\left(\frac{x_1 + (x_1 + x_2)/2}{2}, \frac{y_1 + (y_1 + y_2)/2}{2}\right) = \left(\frac{3x_1 + x_2}{4}, \frac{3y_1 + y_2}{4}\right)$.

The midpoint between $\left(\frac{x_1 + x_2}{2}, \frac{y_1 + y_2}{2}\right)$ and $(x_2, y_2)$ is $\left(\frac{(x_1 + x_2)/2 + x_2}{2}, \frac{(y_1 + y_2)/2 + y_2}{2}\right) = \left(\frac{x_1 + 3x_2}{4}, \frac{y_1 + 3y_2}{4}\right)$.

Thus, the three points are $\left(\frac{3x_1 + x_2}{4}, \frac{3y_1 + y_2}{4}\right), \left(\frac{x_1 + x_2}{2}, \frac{y_1 + y_2}{2}\right), \left(\frac{x_1 + 3x_2}{4}, \frac{y_1 + 3y_2}{4}\right)$.

**26.** (a) $\left(\frac{3(1) + 4}{4}, \frac{3(-2) + (-1)}{4}\right) = \left(\frac{7}{4}, -\frac{7}{4}\right)$

$\left(\frac{1 + 4}{2}, \frac{-2 + (-1)}{2}\right) = \left(\frac{5}{2}, -\frac{3}{2}\right)$

$\left(\frac{1 + 3(4)}{4}, \frac{-2 + 3(-1)}{4}\right) = \left(\frac{13}{4}, -\frac{5}{4}\right)$

(b) $\left(\frac{3(-2) + 0}{4}, \frac{3(-3) + 0}{4}\right) = \left(-\frac{3}{2}, -\frac{9}{4}\right)$

$\left(\frac{-2 + 0}{2}, \frac{-3 + 0}{2}\right) = \left(-1, -\frac{3}{2}\right)$

$\left(\frac{-2 + 3(0)}{4}, \frac{-3 + 3(0)}{4}\right) = \left(-\frac{1}{2}, -\frac{3}{4}\right)$

**27.** Center: $(0, 0)$

Radius: 1

Matches graph (c)

**28.** Center: $(1, 3)$

Radius: 2

Matches graph (b)

**29.** Center: $(1, 0)$

Radius: 0

Matches graph (a)

**30.** Center: $\left(-\frac{1}{2}, \frac{3}{4}\right)$

Radius: $\frac{1}{2}$

Matches graph (d)

**31.** $(x - 0)^2 + (y - 0)^2 = (3)^2$

$x^2 + y^2 - 9 = 0$

**32.** $(x - 0)^2 + (y - 0)^2 = (5)^2$

$x^2 + y^2 - 25 = 0$

**33.** $(x - 2)^2 + (y + 1)^2 = (4)^2$

$x^2 + y^2 - 4x + 2y - 11 = 0$

**34.** $(x + 4)^2 + (y - 3)^2 = \left(\frac{5}{8}\right)^2$

$64(x + 4)^2 + 64(y - 3)^2 = 25$

$64x^2 + 64y^2 + 512x - 384y + 1575 = 0$

**35.** Radius $= \sqrt{(-1 - 0)^2 + (2 - 0)^2} = \sqrt{5}$

$(x + 1)^2 + (y - 2)^2 = 5$

$x^2 + 2x + 1 + y^2 - 4y + 4 = 5$

$x^2 + y^2 + 2x - 4y = 0$

**36.** Radius $= \sqrt{[3 - (-1)]^2 + (-2 - 1)^2} = 5$

$(x - 3)^2 + (y + 2)^2 = 25$

$x^2 - 6x + 9 + y^2 + 4y + 4 = 25$

$x^2 + y^2 - 6x + 4y - 12 = 0$

**37.** Center $=$ Midpoint $= (3, 2)$

Radius $= \sqrt{10}$

$(x - 3)^2 + (y - 2)^2 = \left(\sqrt{10}\right)^2$

$x^2 - 6x + 9 + y^2 - 4y + 4 = 10$

$x^2 + y^2 - 6x - 4y + 3 = 0$

**38.** Center $=$ Midpoint $= (0, 0)$

Radius $= \sqrt{2}$

$(x - 0)^2 + (y - 0)^2 = \left(\sqrt{2}\right)^2$

$x^2 + y^2 - 2 = 0$

**39.** Place the center of Earth at the origin. Then you have

$x^2 + y^2 = (22{,}000 + 4000)^2$

$x^2 + y^2 = 26{,}000^2.$

**40.** Let $d$ be the diameter of the water pipe and $z$ be the distance between the water pipe and the corner of the wall. If you let $y$ equal the hypotenuse of the triangle whose one vertex is located at the center of the air duct, then $y = z + d + (D/2)$. The hypotenuse of the triangle whose one vertex is located at the center of the water pipe is $z + (d/2)$. Using the Pythagorean Theorem, you can find $z$ as follows.

$$\left(z + \frac{d}{2}\right)^2 = \left(\frac{d}{2}\right)^2 + \left(\frac{d}{2}\right)^2$$

$$\left(z + \frac{d}{2}\right)^2 = \frac{d^2}{2}$$

$$z + \frac{d}{2} = \frac{d}{\sqrt{2}}$$

$$z = \frac{d}{\sqrt{2}} - \frac{d}{2}$$

Now solve for $d$, using the fact that these are similar triangles.

$$\frac{\frac{d}{2}}{z + \frac{d}{2}} = \frac{\frac{D}{2}}{y}$$

$$\frac{\frac{d}{2}}{\frac{d}{\sqrt{2}} - \frac{d}{2} + \frac{d}{2}} = \frac{\frac{D}{2}}{z + d + \frac{D}{2}}$$

$$\frac{\frac{d}{2}}{\frac{d}{\sqrt{2}}} = \frac{\frac{D}{2}}{\frac{d}{\sqrt{2}} - \frac{d}{2} + d + \frac{D}{2}}$$

$$\frac{d}{2}\left(\frac{d}{\sqrt{2}} + \frac{d}{2} + \frac{D}{2}\right) = \frac{d}{\sqrt{2}} \cdot \frac{D}{2}$$

$$d\left(\frac{1}{\sqrt{2}} + \frac{1}{2}\right) + \frac{D}{2} = \frac{D}{\sqrt{2}}$$

$$d\left(\frac{2 + \sqrt{2}}{2\sqrt{2}}\right) = \frac{D}{\sqrt{2}} - \frac{D}{2}$$

$$d\left(\frac{2 + \sqrt{2}}{2\sqrt{2}}\right) = D\left(\frac{2 - \sqrt{2}}{2\sqrt{2}}\right)$$

$$d = D\left(\frac{2 - \sqrt{2}}{2 + \sqrt{2}}\right)$$

The diameter of the largest water pipe which can be run in the right angle corner behind the air duct is

$$D\left(\frac{2 - \sqrt{2}}{2 + \sqrt{2}}\right).$$

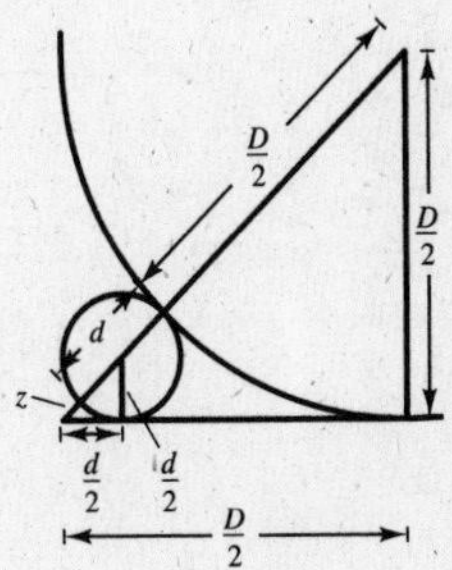

**41.** $x^2 + y^2 - 2x + 6y + 6 = 0$

$$(x^2 - 2x + 1) + (y^2 + 6y + 9) = -6 + 1 + 9$$

$$(x - 1)^2 + (y + 3)^2 = 4$$

Center: $(1, -3)$

Radius: 2

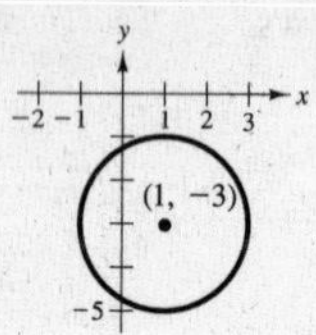


**42.** $x^2 + y^2 - 2x + 6y - 15 = 0$

$$(x^2 - 2x + 1) + (y^2 + 6y + 9) = 15 + 1 + 9$$

$$(x - 1)^2 + (y + 3)^2 = 25$$

Center: $(1, -3)$

Radius: 5

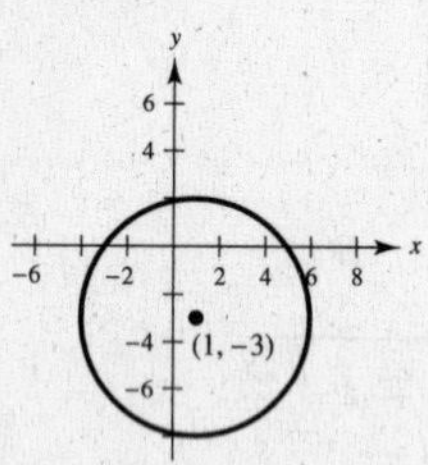


**43.** $x^2 + y^2 - 2x + 6y + 10 = 0$

$$(x^2 - 2x + 1) + (y^2 + 6y + 9) = -10 + 1 + 9$$

$$(x - 1)^2 + (y + 3)^2 = 0$$

Only a point $(1, -3)$

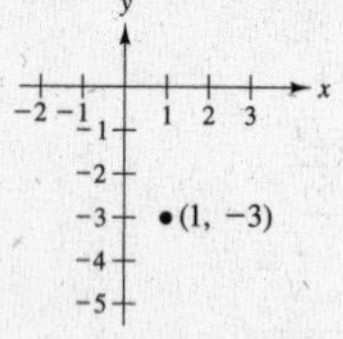


**44.** $3x^2 + 3y^2 - 6y - 1 = 0$

$$3x^2 + 3(y^2 - 2y + 1) = 1 + 3$$

$$x^2 + (y - 1)^2 = \frac{4}{3}$$

Center: $(0, 1)$

Radius: $\dfrac{2\sqrt{3}}{3}$

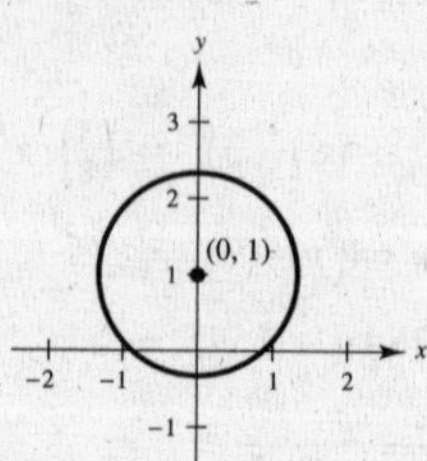


**45.** $2x^2 + 2y^2 - 2x - 2y - 3 = 0$

$$2\left(x^2 - x + \tfrac{1}{4}\right) + 2\left(y^2 - y + \tfrac{1}{4}\right) = 3 + \tfrac{1}{2} + \tfrac{1}{2}$$

$$\left(x - \tfrac{1}{2}\right)^2 + \left(y - \tfrac{1}{2}\right)^2 = 2$$

Center: $\left(\frac{1}{2}, \frac{1}{2}\right)$

Radius: $\sqrt{2}$

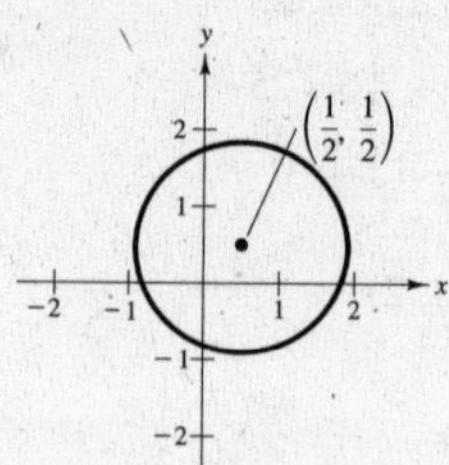


**46.** $4x^2 + 4y^2 - 4x + 2y - 1 = 0$

$$4\left(x^2 - x + \frac{1}{4}\right) + 4\left(y^2 + \frac{y}{2} + \frac{1}{16}\right) = 1 + 1 + \frac{1}{4}$$

$$4\left(x - \frac{1}{2}\right)^2 + 4\left(y + \frac{1}{4}\right)^2 = \frac{9}{4}$$

$$\left(x - \frac{1}{2}\right)^2 + \left(y + \frac{1}{4}\right)^2 = \frac{9}{16}$$

Center: $\left(\dfrac{1}{2}, -\dfrac{1}{4}\right)$

Radius: $\dfrac{3}{4}$

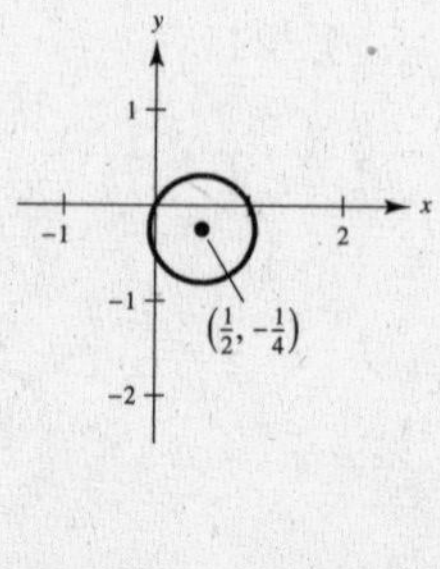

**47.**

$$16x^2 + 16y^2 + 16x + 40y - 7 = 0$$

$$16\left(x^2 + x + \frac{1}{4}\right) + 16\left(y^2 + \frac{5y}{2} + \frac{25}{16}\right) = 7 + 4 + 25$$

$$16\left(x + \frac{1}{2}\right)^2 + 16\left(y + \frac{5}{4}\right)^2 = 36$$

$$\left(x + \frac{1}{2}\right)^2 + \left(y + \frac{5}{4}\right)^2 = \frac{9}{4}$$

Center: $\left(-\frac{1}{2}, -\frac{5}{4}\right)$

Radius: $\frac{3}{2}$

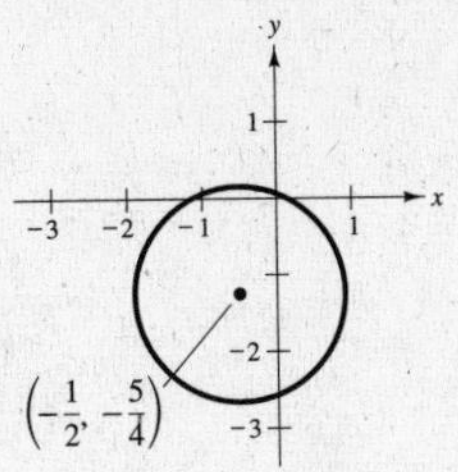


**48.**

$$x^2 + y^2 - 4x + 2y + 3 = 0$$

$$\left(x^2 - 4x + 4\right) + \left(y^2 + 2y + 1\right) = -3 + 4 + 1$$

$$(x - 2)^2 + (y + 1)^2 = 2$$

Center: $(2, -1)$

Radius: $\sqrt{2}$

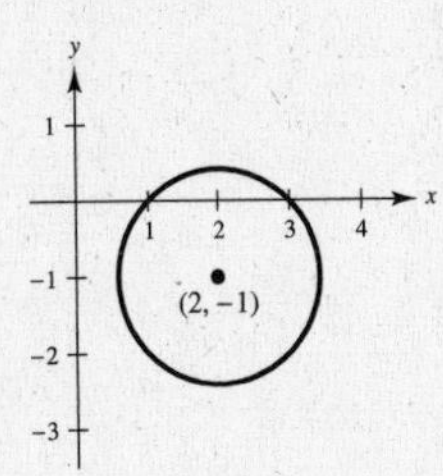


**49.**

$$4x^2 + 4y^2 - 4x + 24y - 63 = 0$$

$$x^2 + y^2 - x + 6y = \frac{63}{4}$$

$$\left(x^2 - x + \frac{1}{4}\right) + \left(y^2 + 6y + 9\right) = \frac{63}{4} + \frac{1}{4} + 9$$

$$\left(x - \frac{1}{2}\right)^2 + (y + 3)^2 = 25$$

$$(y + 3)^2 = 25 - \left(x - \frac{1}{2}\right)^2$$

$$y + 3 = \pm\sqrt{25 - \left(x - \frac{1}{2}\right)^2}$$

$$y = -3 \pm \sqrt{25 - \left(x - \frac{1}{2}\right)^2}$$

$$= \frac{-6 \pm \sqrt{99 + 4x - 4x^2}}{2}$$

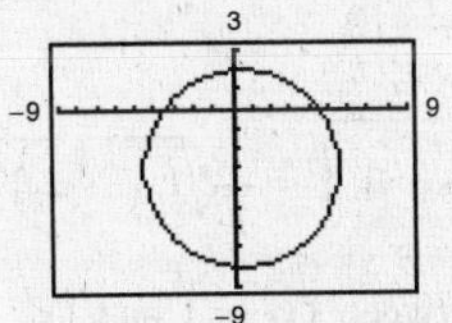


**50.**

$$x^2 + y^2 - 8x - 6y - 11 = 0$$

$$\left(x^2 - 8x + 16\right) + \left(y^2 - 6y + 9\right) = 11 + 16 + 9$$

$$(x - 4)^2 + (y - 3)^2 = 36$$

$$(y - 3)^2 = 36 - (x - 4)^2$$

$$y - 3 = \pm\sqrt{36 - (x - 4)^2}$$

$$y = 3 \pm \sqrt{20 + 8x - x^2}$$

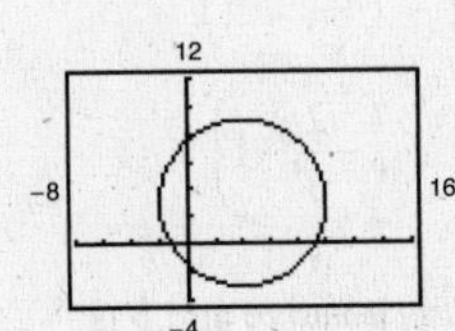

**51.**
$$x^2 + y^2 - 4x + 2y + 1 \le 0$$
$$(x^2 - 4x + 4) + (y^2 + 2y + 1) \le -1 + 4 + 1$$
$$(x - 2)^2 + (y + 1)^2 \le 4$$

Center: $(2, -1)$

Radius: 2

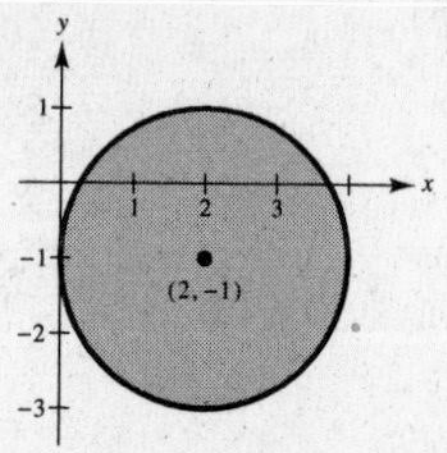

**52.** $(x - 1)^2 + \left(y - \frac{1}{2}\right)^2 > 1$

Center: $\left(1, \frac{1}{2}\right)$

Radius: 1

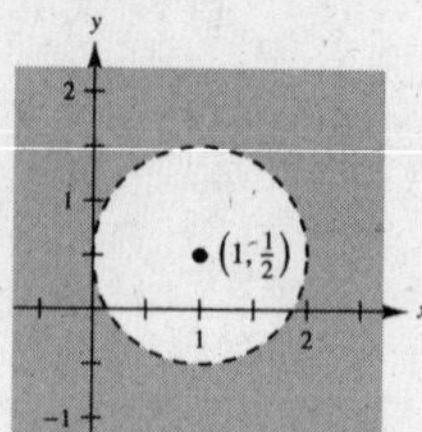

**53.** The distance between $(x_1, y_1)$ and $\left(\frac{2x_1 + x_2}{3}, \frac{2y_1 + y_2}{3}\right)$ is

$$d = \sqrt{\left(x_1 - \frac{2x_1 + x_2}{3}\right)^2 + \left(y_1 - \frac{2y_1 + y_2}{3}\right)^2}$$
$$= \sqrt{\left(\frac{x_1 - x_2}{3}\right)^2 + \left(\frac{y_1 - y_2}{3}\right)^2}$$
$$= \sqrt{\frac{1}{9}\left[(x_1 - x_2)^2 + (y_1 - y_2)^2\right]} = \frac{1}{3}\sqrt{(x_1 - x_2)^2 + (y_1 - y_2)^2}$$

which is $\frac{1}{3}$ of the distance between $(x_1, y_1)$ and $(x_2, y_2)$.

$$\left(\frac{\left(\frac{2x_1 + x_2}{3}\right) + x_2}{2}, \frac{\left(\frac{2y_1 + y_2}{3}\right) + y_2}{2}\right) = \left(\frac{x_1 + 2x_2}{3}, \frac{y_1 + 2y_2}{3}\right)$$

is the second point of the trisection.

**54.** (a) $\left(\frac{2(1) + 4}{3}, \frac{2(-2) + 1}{3}\right) = (2, -1)$

$\left(\frac{1 + 2(4)}{3}, \frac{-2 + 2(1)}{3}\right) = (3, 0)$

(b) $\left(\frac{2(-2) + 0}{3}, \frac{2(-3) + 0}{3}\right) = \left(-\frac{4}{3}, -2\right)$

$\left(\frac{-2 + 2(0)}{3}, \frac{-3 + 2(0)}{3}\right) = \left(-\frac{2}{3}, -1\right)$

**55.** True; if $ab < 0$ then either $a$ is positive and $b$ is negative (Quadrant IV) or $a$ is negative and $b$ is positive (Quadrant II).

**56.** False

$$d = \sqrt{\left[(a + b) - (a - b)\right]^2 + (a - a)^2}$$
$$= \sqrt{(2b)^2 + 0^2} = \sqrt{4b^2} = 2|b|$$

**57.** True

**58.** True; if $ab = 0$ then $a = 0$ ($y$-axis) or $b = 0$ ($x$-axis).

**59.** Let one vertex be at $(0, 0)$ and another at $(a, 0)$.

Midpoint of $(0, 0)$ and $(d, e)$ is $\left(\dfrac{d}{2}, \dfrac{e}{2}\right)$.

Midpoint of $(b, c)$ and $(a, 0)$ is $\left(\dfrac{a+b}{2}, \dfrac{c}{2}\right)$.

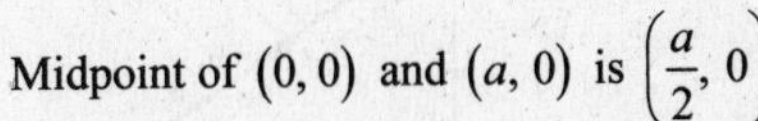

Midpoint of $(0, 0)$ and $(a, 0)$ is $\left(\dfrac{a}{2}, 0\right)$.

Midpoint of $(b, c)$ and $(d, e)$ is $\left(\dfrac{b+d}{2}, \dfrac{c+e}{2}\right)$.

Midpoint of line segment joining $\left(\dfrac{d}{2}, \dfrac{e}{2}\right)$ and $\left(\dfrac{a+b}{2}, \dfrac{c}{2}\right)$ is $\left(\dfrac{a+b+d}{4}, \dfrac{c+e}{4}\right)$.

Midpoint of line segment joining $\left(\dfrac{a}{2}, 0\right)$ and $\left(\dfrac{b+d}{2}, \dfrac{c+e}{2}\right)$ is $\left(\dfrac{a+b+d}{4}, \dfrac{c+e}{4}\right)$.

Therefore the line segments intersect at their midpoints.

**60.** Let the circle of radius $r$ be centered at the origin. Let $(a, b)$ and $(r, 0)$ be the endpoints of the chord. The midpoint $M$ of the chord is $((a+r)/2, b/2)$. We will show that OM is perpendicular to MR by verifying that $d_1^2 + d_2^2 = d_3^2$.

$$d_1^2 = \left(\frac{a+r}{2} - 0\right)^2 + \left(\frac{b}{2} - 0\right)^2 = \left(\frac{a+r}{2}\right)^2 + \left(\frac{b}{2}\right)^2$$

$$d_2^2 = \left(\frac{a+r}{2} - r\right)^2 + \left(\frac{b}{2} - 0\right)^2 = \left(\frac{a-r}{2}\right)^2 + \left(\frac{b}{2}\right)^2$$

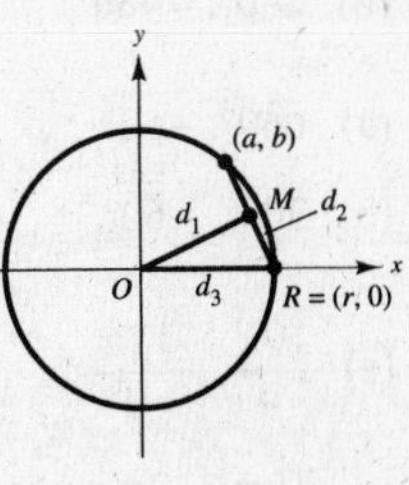


$$\begin{aligned} d_1^2 + d_2^2 &= \left(\frac{a^2 + 2ar + r^2}{4} + \frac{b^2}{4}\right) + \left(\frac{a^2 - 2ar + r^2}{4} + \frac{b^2}{4}\right) \\ &= \frac{a^2}{2} + \frac{r^2}{2} + \frac{b^2}{2} \\ &= \frac{1}{2}(a^2 + b^2) + \frac{1}{2}r^2 \\ &= \frac{1}{2}r^2 + \frac{1}{2}r^2 = r^2 = d_3^2 \end{aligned}$$

**61.** Let $(a, b)$ be a point on the semicircle of radius $r$, centered at the origin. We will show that the angle at $(a, b)$ is a right angle by verifying that $d_1^2 + d_2^2 = d_3^2$.

$$\begin{aligned} d_1^2 &= (a+r)^2 + (b-0)^2 \\ d_2^2 &= (a-r)^2 + (b-0)^2 \\ d_1^2 + d_2^2 &= (a^2 + 2ar + r^2 + b^2) + (a^2 - 2ar + r^2 + b^2) \\ &= 2a^2 + 2b^2 + 2r^2 \\ &= 2(a^2 + b^2) + 2r^2 \\ &= 2r^2 + 2r^2 \\ &= 4r^2 = (2r)^2 = d_3^2 \end{aligned}$$

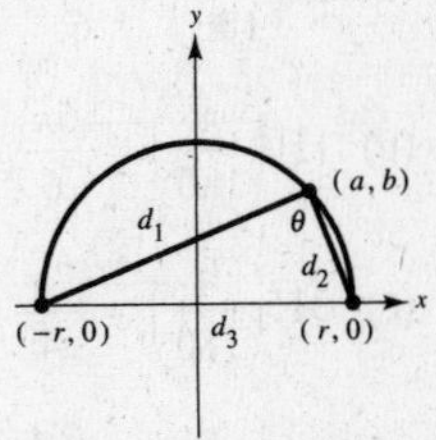

**62.** To show that $\left(\frac{x_1 + x_2}{2}, \frac{y_1 + y_2}{2}\right)$ is the midpoint of the line segment joining $(x_1, y_1)$ and $(x_2, y_2)$, we must show that $d_1 = d_2$ and $d_1 + d_2 = d_3$ (see graph).

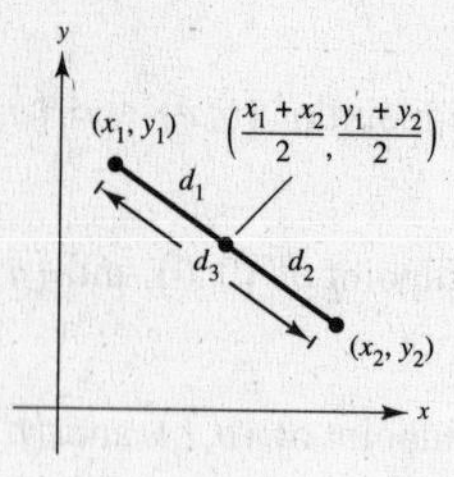


$$d_1 = \sqrt{\left(\frac{x_1 + x_2}{2} - x_1\right)^2 + \left(\frac{y_1 + y_2}{2} - y_1\right)^2}$$

$$= \sqrt{\left(\frac{x_2 - x_1}{2}\right)^2 + \left(\frac{y_2 - y_1}{2}\right)^2} = \frac{1}{2}\sqrt{(x_2 - x_1)^2 + (y_2 - y_1)^2}$$

$$d_2 = \sqrt{\left(x_2 - \frac{x_1 + x_2}{2}\right)^2 + \left(y_2 - \frac{y_1 - y_2}{2}\right)^2}$$

$$= \sqrt{\left(\frac{x_2 - x_1}{2}\right)^2 + \left(\frac{y_2 - y_1}{2}\right)^2} = \frac{1}{2}\sqrt{(x_2 - x_1)^2 + (y_2 - y_1)^2}$$

$$d_3 = \sqrt{(x_2 - x_1)^2 + (y_2 - y_1)^2}$$

Therefore, $d_1 = d_2$ and $d_1 + d_2 = d_3$.

# Appendix C.3

**1.** (a) 396°, −324°

(b) 240°, −480°

**2.** (a) 660°, −60°

(b) 300°, −60°

**3.** (a) $\frac{19\pi}{9}, -\frac{17\pi}{9}$

(b) $\frac{10\pi}{3}, -\frac{2\pi}{3}$

**4.** (a) $\frac{7\pi}{4}, -\frac{\pi}{4}$

(b) $\frac{26\pi}{9}, -\frac{10\pi}{9}$

**5.** (a) $30\left(\frac{\pi}{180}\right) = \frac{\pi}{6} \approx 0.524$

(b) $150\left(\frac{\pi}{180}\right) = \frac{5\pi}{6} \approx 2.618$

(c) $315\left(\frac{\pi}{180}\right) = \frac{7\pi}{4} \approx 5.498$

(d) $120\left(\frac{\pi}{180}\right) = \frac{2\pi}{3} \approx 2.094$

**6.** (a) $-20\left(\frac{\pi}{180}\right) = -\frac{\pi}{9} \approx -0.349$

(b) $-240\left(\frac{\pi}{180}\right) = -\frac{4\pi}{3} \approx -4.189$

(c) $-270\left(\frac{\pi}{180}\right) = -\frac{3\pi}{2} \approx -4.712$

(d) $144\left(\frac{\pi}{180}\right) = -\frac{4\pi}{5} \approx 2.513$

**7.** (a) $\frac{3\pi}{2}\left(\frac{180}{\pi}\right) = 270°$

(b) $\frac{7\pi}{6}\left(\frac{180}{\pi}\right) = 210°$

(c) $-\frac{7\pi}{12}\left(\frac{180}{\pi}\right) = -105°$

(d) $-2.637\left(\frac{180}{\pi}\right) \approx -151.1°$

**8.** (a) $\frac{7\pi}{3}\left(\frac{180}{\pi}\right) = 420°$

(b) $-\frac{11\pi}{30}\left(\frac{180}{\pi}\right) = -66°$

(c) $\frac{11\pi}{6}\left(\frac{180}{\pi}\right) = 330°$

(d) $0.438\left(\frac{180}{\pi}\right) \approx 25.1°$

9.

| $r$ | 8 ft | 15 in. | 85 cm | 24 in. | $\dfrac{12{,}963}{\pi}$ mi |
|---|---|---|---|---|---|
| $s$ | 12 ft | 24 in. | $63.75\pi$ cm | 96 in. | 8642 mi |
| $\theta$ | 1.5 | 1.6 | $\dfrac{3\pi}{4}$ | 4 | $\dfrac{2\pi}{3}$ |

**10.** (a) $50 \text{ mi/h} = \dfrac{50(5280)}{60} = 4400 \text{ ft/min}$

Circumference of tire: $C = 2.5\pi$ feet

Revolutions per minute: $\dfrac{4400}{2.5\pi} \approx 560.2$

(b) $\theta = \dfrac{4400}{2.5\pi}(2\pi) = 3520$ radians

Angular speed: $\dfrac{\theta}{t} = \dfrac{3520 \text{ radians}}{1 \text{ minute}} = 3520 \text{ rad/min}$

**11.** (a) $x = 3, y = 4, r = 5$

$\sin\theta = \frac{4}{5}$ $\quad\csc\theta = \frac{5}{4}$

$\cos\theta = \frac{3}{5}$ $\quad\sec\theta = \frac{5}{3}$

$\tan\theta = \frac{4}{3}$ $\quad\cot\theta = \frac{3}{4}$

(b) $x = -12, y = -5, r = 13$

$\sin\theta = -\frac{5}{13}$ $\quad\csc\theta = -\frac{13}{5}$

$\cos\theta = -\frac{12}{13}$ $\quad\sec\theta = -\frac{13}{12}$

$\tan\theta = \frac{5}{12}$ $\quad\cot\theta = \frac{12}{5}$

**12.** (a) $x = 8, y = -15, r = 17$

$\sin\theta = -\dfrac{15}{17}$ $\quad\csc\theta = -\dfrac{17}{15}$

$\cos\theta = \dfrac{8}{17}$ $\quad\sec\theta = \dfrac{17}{8}$

$\tan\theta = -\dfrac{15}{8}$ $\quad\cot\theta = -\dfrac{8}{15}$

(b) $x = 1, y = -1, r = \sqrt{2}$

$\sin\theta = -\dfrac{\sqrt{2}}{2}$ $\quad\csc\theta = -\sqrt{2}$

$\cos\theta = \dfrac{\sqrt{2}}{2}$ $\quad\sec\theta = \sqrt{2}$

$\tan\theta = -1$ $\quad\cot\theta = -1$

**13.** (a) $\sin\theta < 0 \Rightarrow \theta$ is in Quadrant III or IV.

$\cos\theta < 0 \Rightarrow \theta$ is in Quadrant II or III.

$\sin\theta < 0$ **and** $\cos\theta < 0 \Rightarrow \theta$ is in Quadrant III.

(b) $\sec\theta > 0 \Rightarrow \theta$ is in Quadrant I or IV.

$\cot\theta < 0 \Rightarrow \theta$ is in Quadrant II or IV.

$\sec\theta > 0$ **and** $\cot\theta < 0 \Rightarrow \theta$ is in Quadrant IV.

**14.** (a) $\sin\theta > 0 \Rightarrow \theta$ is in Quadrant I or II.

$\cos\theta < 0 \Rightarrow \theta$ is in Quadrant II or III.

$\sin\theta > 0$ **and** $\cos\theta < 0 \Rightarrow \theta$ is in Quadrant II.

(b) $\csc\theta < 0 \Rightarrow \theta$ is in Quadrant III or IV.

$\tan\theta > 0 \Rightarrow \theta$ is in Quadrant I or III.

$\csc\theta < 0$ **and** $\tan\theta > 0 \Rightarrow \theta$ is in Quadrant III.

**15.** $x^2 + 1^2 = 2^2 \Rightarrow x = \sqrt{3}$

$\cos\theta = \dfrac{x}{2} = \dfrac{\sqrt{3}}{2}$

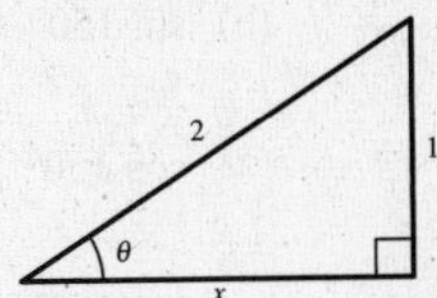


**16.** $x^2 + 1^2 = 3^2 \Rightarrow x = \sqrt{8} = 2\sqrt{2}$

$\tan\theta = \dfrac{1}{x} = \dfrac{1}{2\sqrt{2}} = \dfrac{\sqrt{2}}{4}$

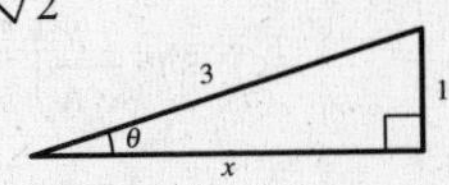


**17.** $4^2 + y^2 = 5^2 \Rightarrow y = 3$

$\cot\theta = \dfrac{4}{y} = \dfrac{4}{3}$

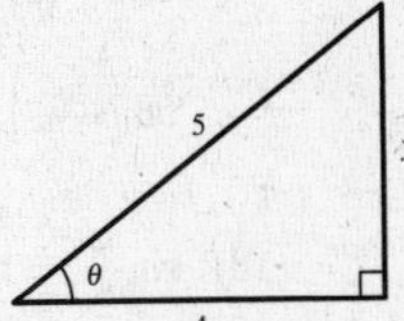


**18.** $5^2 + y^2 = 13^2 \Rightarrow y = 12$

$\csc\theta = \dfrac{13}{y} = \dfrac{13}{12}$

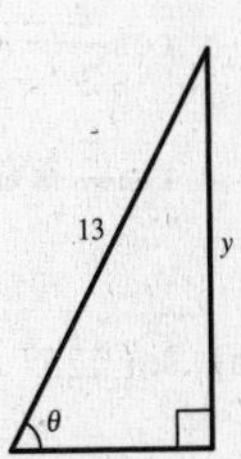


**19.** (a) $\sin 60° = \dfrac{\sqrt{3}}{2}$

$\cos 60° = \dfrac{1}{2}$

$\tan 60° = \sqrt{3}$

(b) $\sin 120° = \sin 60° = \dfrac{\sqrt{3}}{2}$

$\cos 120° = -\cos 60° = -\dfrac{1}{2}$

$\tan 120° = -\tan 60° = -\sqrt{3}$

(c) $\sin\dfrac{\pi}{4} = \dfrac{\sqrt{2}}{2}$

$\cos\dfrac{\pi}{4} = \dfrac{\sqrt{2}}{2}$

$\tan\dfrac{\pi}{4} = 1$

(d) $\sin\dfrac{5\pi}{4} - \sin\dfrac{\pi}{4} = -\dfrac{\sqrt{2}}{2}$

$\cos\dfrac{5\pi}{4} = \cos\dfrac{\pi}{4} = -\dfrac{\sqrt{2}}{2}$

$\tan\dfrac{5\pi}{4} = \tan\dfrac{\pi}{4} = 1$

**20.** (a) $\sin(-30°) = -\sin 30° = -\dfrac{1}{2}$

$\cos(-30°) = \cos 30° = \dfrac{\sqrt{3}}{2}$

$\tan(-30°) = -\tan 30° = -\dfrac{\sqrt{3}}{3}$

(b) $\sin 150° = \sin 30° = \dfrac{1}{2}$

$\cos 150° = -\cos 30° = -\dfrac{\sqrt{3}}{2}$

$\tan 150° = -\tan 30° = -\dfrac{\sqrt{3}}{3}$

(c) $\sin\left(-\dfrac{\pi}{6}\right) = -\sin\dfrac{\pi}{6} = -\dfrac{1}{2}$

$\cos\left(-\dfrac{\pi}{6}\right) = \cos\dfrac{\pi}{6} = \dfrac{\sqrt{3}}{2}$

$\tan\left(-\dfrac{\pi}{6}\right) = -\tan\dfrac{\pi}{6} = -\dfrac{\sqrt{3}}{3}$

(d) $\sin\dfrac{\pi}{2} = 1$

$\cos\dfrac{\pi}{2} = 0$

$\tan\dfrac{\pi}{2}$ is undefined.

**21.** (a) $\sin 225° = -\sin 45° = -\dfrac{\sqrt{2}}{2}$

$\cos 225° = -\cos 45° = -\dfrac{\sqrt{2}}{2}$

$\tan 225° = \tan 45° = 1$

(b) $\sin(-225°) = \sin 45° = \dfrac{\sqrt{2}}{2}$

$\cos(-225°) = -\cos 45° = -\dfrac{\sqrt{2}}{2}$

$\tan(-225°) = -\tan 45° = -1$

(c) $\sin\dfrac{5\pi}{3} = -\sin\dfrac{\pi}{3} = -\dfrac{\sqrt{3}}{2}$

$\cos\dfrac{5\pi}{3} = \cos\dfrac{\pi}{3} = \dfrac{1}{2}$

$\tan\dfrac{5\pi}{3} = -\tan\dfrac{\pi}{3} = -\sqrt{3}$

(d) $\sin\dfrac{11\pi}{6} = -\sin\dfrac{\pi}{6} = -\dfrac{1}{2}$

$\cos\dfrac{11\pi}{6} = \cos\dfrac{\pi}{6} = \dfrac{\sqrt{3}}{2}$

$\tan\dfrac{11\pi}{6} = -\tan\dfrac{\pi}{6} = -\dfrac{\sqrt{3}}{3}$

**22.** (a) $\sin 750° = \sin 30° = \dfrac{1}{2}$

$\cos 750° = \cos 30° = \dfrac{\sqrt{3}}{2}$

$\tan 750° = \tan 30° = \dfrac{\sqrt{3}}{3}$

(b) $\sin 510° = \sin 30° = \dfrac{1}{2}$

$\cos 510° = -\cos 30° = -\dfrac{\sqrt{3}}{2}$

$\tan 510° = -\tan 30° = -\dfrac{\sqrt{3}}{3}$

(c) $\sin\dfrac{10\pi}{3} = -\sin\dfrac{\pi}{3} = -\dfrac{\sqrt{3}}{2}$

$\cos\dfrac{10\pi}{3} = -\cos\dfrac{\pi}{3} = -\dfrac{1}{2}$

$\tan\dfrac{10\pi}{3} = \tan\dfrac{\pi}{3} = \sqrt{3}$

(d) $\sin\dfrac{17\pi}{3} = -\sin\dfrac{\pi}{3} = -\dfrac{\sqrt{3}}{2}$

$\cos\dfrac{17\pi}{3} = \cos\dfrac{\pi}{3} = \dfrac{1}{2}$

$\tan\dfrac{17\pi}{3} = -\tan\dfrac{\pi}{3} = \sqrt{3}$

**23.** (a) $\sin 10° \approx 0.1736$

(b) $\csc 10° \approx 5.759$

**24.** (a) $\sec 225° \approx -1.414$

(b) $\sec 135° \approx -1.414$

**25.** (a) $\tan\dfrac{\pi}{9} \approx 0.3640$

(b) $\tan\dfrac{10\pi}{9} \approx 0.3640$

**26.** (a) $\cot 1.35 \approx 0.2245$

(b) $\tan 1.35 \approx 4.455$

**27.** (a) $\cos\theta = \dfrac{\sqrt{2}}{2}$

$\theta = \dfrac{\pi}{4}, \dfrac{7\pi}{4}$

(b) $\cos\theta = -\dfrac{\sqrt{2}}{2}$

$\theta = \dfrac{3\pi}{4}, \dfrac{5\pi}{4}$

**28.** (a) $\sec\theta = 2$

$$\theta = \frac{\pi}{3}, \frac{5\pi}{3}$$

(b) $\sec\theta = -2$

$$\theta = \frac{2\pi}{3}, \frac{4\pi}{3}$$

**29.** (a) $\tan\theta = 1$

$$\theta = \frac{\pi}{4}, \frac{5\pi}{4}$$

(b) $\cot\theta = -\sqrt{3}$

$$\theta = \frac{5\pi}{6}, \frac{11\pi}{6}$$

**30.** (a) $\sin\theta = \frac{\sqrt{3}}{2}$

$$\theta = \frac{\pi}{3}, \frac{2\pi}{3}$$

(b) $\sin\theta = -\frac{\sqrt{3}}{2}$

$$\theta = \frac{4\pi}{3}, \frac{5\pi}{3}$$

**31.** $2\sin^2\theta = 1$

$$\sin\theta = \pm\frac{\sqrt{2}}{2}$$

$$\theta = \frac{\pi}{4}, \frac{3\pi}{4}, \frac{5\pi}{4}, \frac{7\pi}{4}$$

**32.** $\tan^2\theta = 3$

$$\tan\theta = \pm\sqrt{3}$$

$$\theta = \frac{\pi}{3}, \frac{2\pi}{3}, \frac{4\pi}{3}, \frac{5\pi}{3}$$

**33.** $\tan^2\theta = \tan\theta = 0$

$$\tan\theta(\tan\theta - 1) = 0$$

$\tan\theta = 0$ $\quad$ $\tan\theta = 1$

$\theta = 0, \pi$ $\quad$ $\theta = \frac{\pi}{4}, \frac{5\pi}{4}$

**34.** $2\cos^2\theta - \cos\theta - 1 = 0$

$$(2\cos\theta + 1)(\cos\theta - 1) = 0$$

$\cos\theta = -\frac{1}{2}$ $\quad$ $\cos\theta = 1$

$\theta = \frac{2\pi}{3}, \frac{4\pi}{3}$ $\quad$ $\theta = 0$

**35.** $\sec\theta\csc\theta - 2\csc\theta = 0$

$$\csc\theta(\sec\theta - 2) = 0$$

$(\csc\theta \neq 0$ for any value of $\theta)$

$$\sec\theta = 2$$

$$\theta = \frac{\pi}{3}, \frac{5\pi}{3}$$

**36.** $\sin\theta = \cos\theta$

$$\tan\theta = 1$$

$$\theta = \frac{\pi}{4}, \frac{5\pi}{4}$$

**37.** $\cos^2\theta + \sin\theta = 1$

$$1 - \sin^2\theta + \sin\theta = 1$$

$$\sin^2\theta - \sin\theta = 0$$

$$\sin\theta(\sin\theta - 1) = 0$$

$\sin\theta = 0$ $\quad$ $\sin\theta = 1$

$\theta = 0, \pi$ $\quad$ $\theta = \frac{\pi}{2}$

**38.** $\cos\left(\frac{\theta}{2}\right) - \cos\theta = 1$

$$\cos\left(\frac{\theta}{2}\right) = \cos\theta + 1$$

$$\sqrt{\left(\frac{1}{2}\right)(1 + \cos\theta)} = \cos\theta + 1$$

$$\left(\frac{1}{2}\right)(1 + \cos\theta) = \cos^2\theta + 2\cos\theta + 1$$

$$0 = \cos^2\theta + \left(\frac{3}{2}\right)\cos\theta + \left(\frac{1}{2}\right)$$

$$0 = \left(\frac{1}{2}\right)(2\cos^2\theta + 3\cos\theta + 1)$$

$$0 = \left(\frac{1}{2}\right)(2\cos\theta + 1)(\cos\theta + 1)$$

$\cos\theta = -\frac{1}{2}$ $\quad$ $\cos\theta = -1$

$\theta = \frac{2\pi}{3}$ $\quad$ $\theta = \pi$

$(0 = 4\pi/3$ is extraneous)

**39.** $(275 \text{ ft/sec})(60 \text{ sec}) = 16{,}500$ feet

$$\sin 18° = \frac{a}{16{,}500}$$

$$a = 16{,}500 \sin 18° \approx 5099 \text{ feet}$$

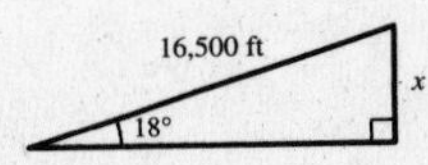

**40.** $\tan 3.5° = \dfrac{h}{13 + x}$ and $\tan 9° = \dfrac{h}{x}$

$$(13 + x)\tan 3.5° = h \qquad x \tan 9° = h$$

$$13 \tan 3.5° + x \tan 3.5° = x \tan 9°$$

$$13 \tan 3.5° = x(\tan 9° - \tan 3.5°)$$

$$\frac{13 \tan 3.5°}{\tan 9° - \tan 3.5°} = x$$

$$h = x \tan 9° = \frac{13 \tan 3.5° \tan 9°}{\tan 9° - \tan 3.5°} \approx 1.295 \text{ miles or } 6839.307 \text{ feet}$$

**41.** (a) Period: $\pi$

Amplitude: 2

(b) Period: 2

Amplitude: $\frac{1}{2}$

**42.** (a) Period: $4\pi$

Amplitude: $\frac{3}{2}$

(b) Period: $6\pi$

Amplitude: 2

**43.** Period: $\frac{1}{2}$

Amplitude: 3

**44.** Period: 20

Amplitude: $\frac{2}{3}$

**45.** Period: $\dfrac{\pi}{2}$

**46.** Period: $\frac{1}{2}$

**47.** Period: $\dfrac{2\pi}{5}$

**48.** Period: $\dfrac{\pi}{2}$

**49.** (a) $f(x) = c \sin x$; changing $c$ changes the amplitude.

When $c = -2$: $f(x) = -2 \sin x$.

When $c = -1$: $f(x) = -\sin x$.

When $c = 1$: $f(x) = \sin x$.

When $c = 2$: $f(x) = 2 \sin x$.

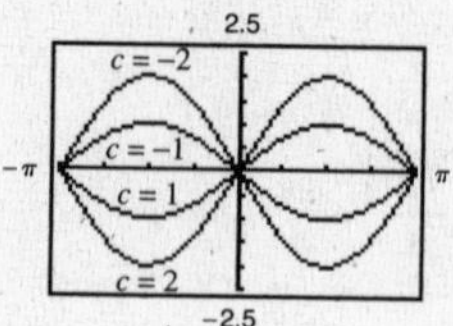


(b) $f(x) = \cos(cx)$; changing $c$ changes the period.

When $c = -2$: $f(x) = \cos(-2x) = \cos 2x$.

When $c = -1$: $f(x) = \cos(-x) = \cos x$.

When $c = 1$: $f(x) = \cos x$.

When $c = 2$: $f(x) = \cos 2x$.

(c) $f(x) = \cos(\pi x - c)$; changing $c$ causes a horizontal shift.

When $c = -2$: $f(x) = \cos(\pi x + 2)$.

When $c = -1$: $f(x) = \cos(\pi x + 1)$.

When $c = 1$: $f(x) = \cos(\pi x - 1)$.

When $c = 2$: $f(x) = \cos(\pi x - 2)$.

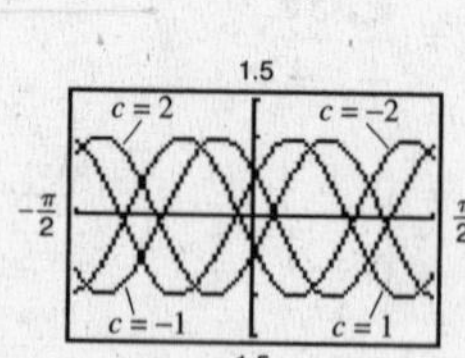

**50.** (a) $f(x) = \sin x + c$; changing $c$ causes a vertical shift.

When $c = -2$: $f(x) = \sin x - 2$.

When $c = -1$: $f(x) = \sin x - 1$.

When $c = 1$: $f(x) = \sin x + 1$.

When $c = 2$: $f(x) = \sin x + 2$.

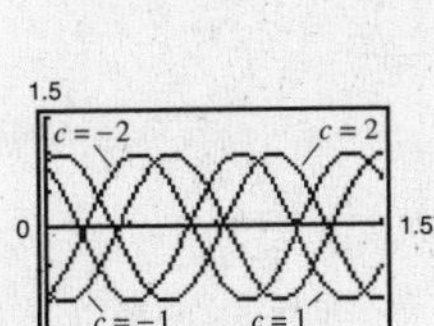


(b) $f(x) = -\sin(2\pi x - c)$; changing $c$ causes a horizontal shift.

When $c = -2$: $f(x) = -\sin(2\pi x + 2)$.

When $c = -1$: $f(x) = \sin(2\pi x + 1)$.

When $c = 1$: $f(x) = \sin(2\pi x - 1)$.

When $c = 2$: $f(x) = -\sin(2\pi x - 2)$.

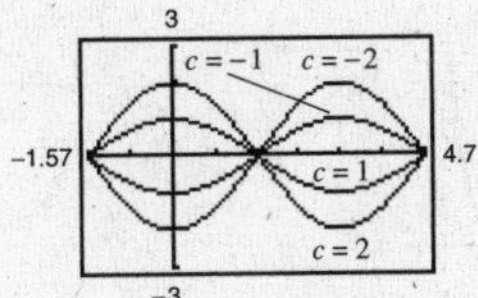


(c) $f(x) = c \cos x$; changing $c$ changes the amplitude.

When $c = -2$: $f(x) = -2 \cos x$.

When $c = -1$: $f(x) = -\cos x$.

When $c = 1$: $f(x) = \cos x$.

When $c = 2$: $f(x) = 2 \cos x$.

3

-1.57 4.71

c = -1 c = -2

c = 1

c = 2

-3

**51.** $y = \sin \dfrac{x}{2}$

Period: $4\pi$

Amplitude: 1

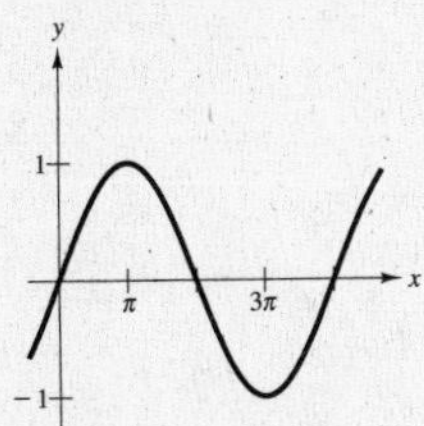

**52.** $y = 2 \cos 2x$

Period: $\pi$

Amplitude: 2

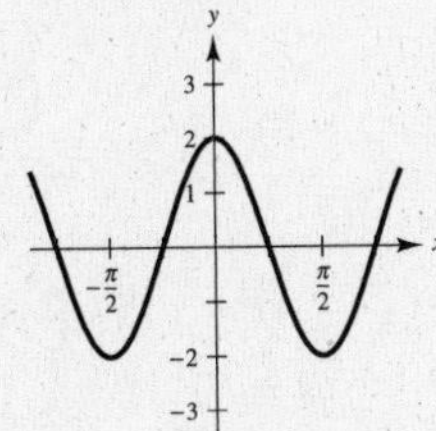

**53.** $y = -\sin \dfrac{2\pi x}{3}$

Period: 3

Amplitude: 1

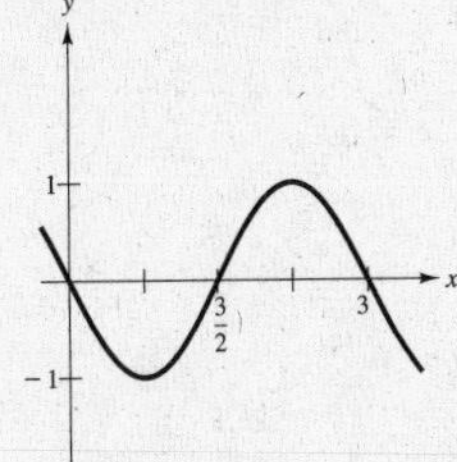

**54.** $y = 2 \tan x$

Period: $\pi$

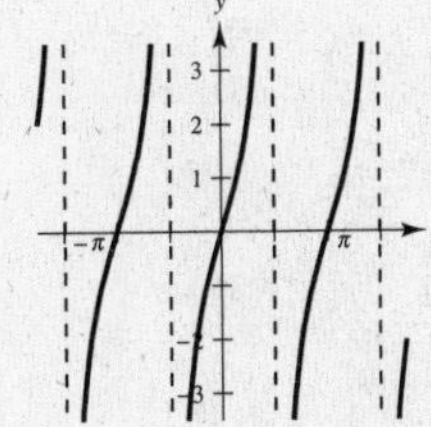

**55.** $y = \csc\frac{x}{2}$

Period: $4\pi$

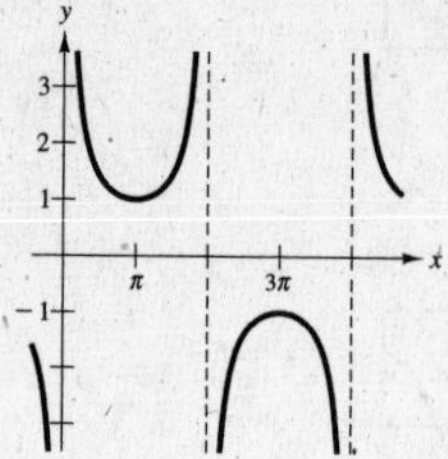

**56.** $y = \tan 2x$

Period: $\frac{\pi}{2}$

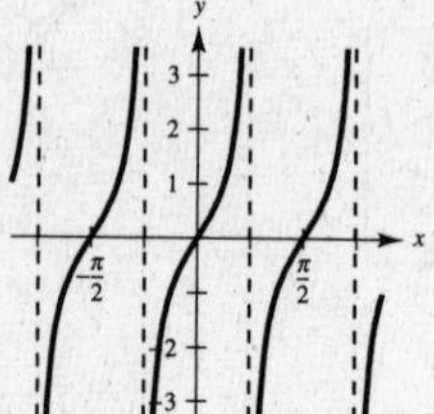

**57.** $y = 2 \sec 2x$

Period: $\pi$

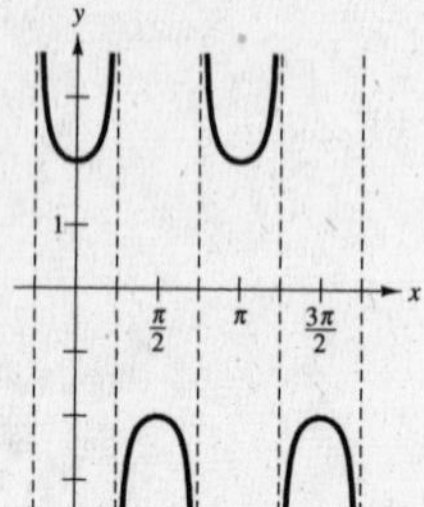

**58.** $y = \csc 2\pi x$

Period: 1

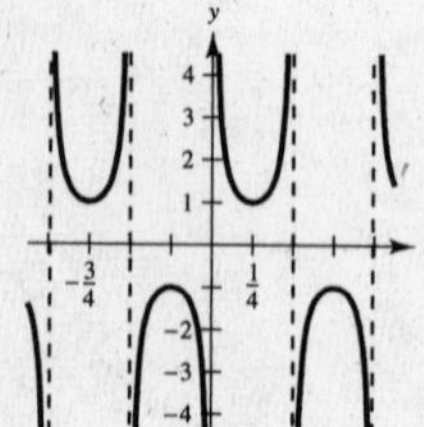

**59.** $y = \sin(x + \pi)$

Period: $2\pi$

Amplitude: 1

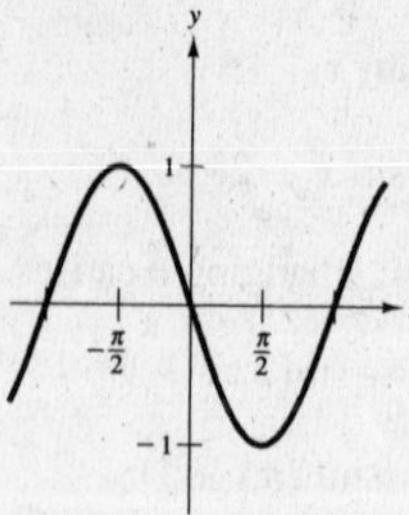

**60.** $y = \cos\left(x - \frac{\pi}{3}\right)$

Period: $2\pi$

Amplitude: 1

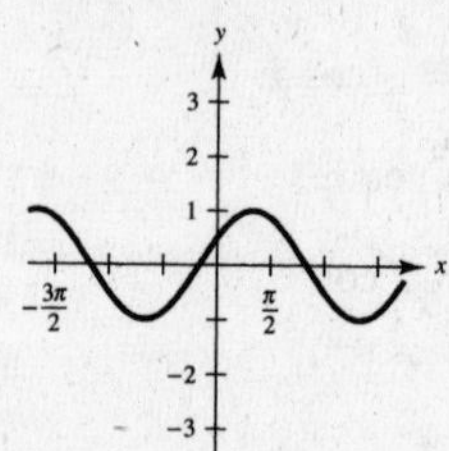

**61.** $y = 1 + \cos\left(x - \frac{\pi}{2}\right)$

Period: $2\pi$

Amplitude: 1

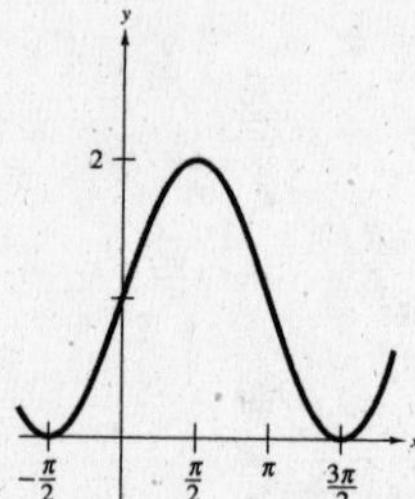

**62.** $y = 1 + \sin\left(x + \frac{\pi}{2}\right)$

Period: $2\pi$

Amplitude: 1

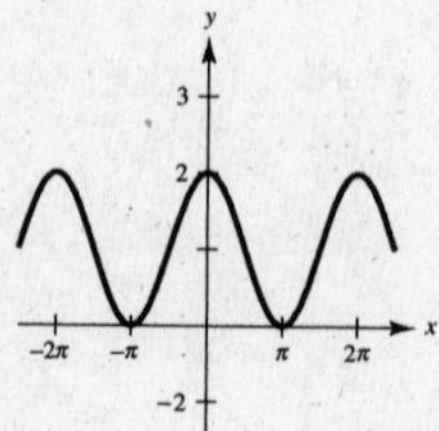

**63.** $y = a\cos(bx - c)$

From the graph, we see that the amplitude is 3, the period is $4\pi$, and the horizontal shift is $\pi$. Thus,

$$a = 3$$

$$\frac{2\pi}{b} = 4\pi \Rightarrow b = \frac{1}{2}$$

$$\frac{c}{d} = \pi \Rightarrow c = \frac{\pi}{2}.$$

Therefore, $y = 3\cos[(1/2)x - (\pi/2)]$.

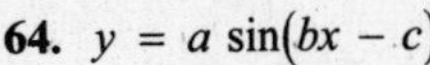

**64.** $y = a\sin(bx - c)$

From the graph, we see that the amplitude is $\frac{1}{2}$, the period is $\pi$, and the horizontal shift is 0. Also, the graph is reflected about the $x$-axis. Thus,

$$a = -\frac{1}{2}$$

$$\frac{2\pi}{b} = \pi \Rightarrow b = 2$$

$$\frac{c}{b} = 0 \Rightarrow c = 0.$$

Therefore, $y = -\frac{1}{2}\sin 2x$.

**65.** $f(x) = \sin x$

$g(x) = |\sin x|$

$h(x) = \sin|x|$

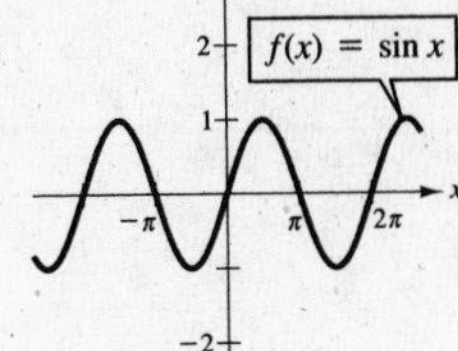


g(x) = |sin x|

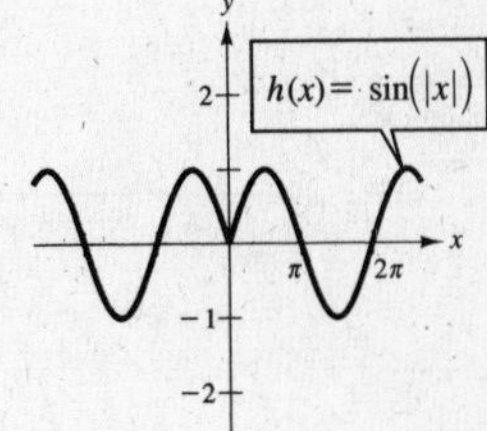


The graph of $|f(x)|$ will reflect any parts of the graph of $f(x)$ below the $x$-axis about the $y$-axis.

The graph of $f(|x|)$ will reflect the part of the graph of $f(x)$ to the right of the $y$-axis about the $y$-axis.

**66.** If $h = 51 + 50\sin\left(8\pi t - \frac{\pi}{2}\right)$, then $h = 1$ when $t = 0$.

**67.** $S = 58.3 + 32.5\cos\frac{\pi t}{6}$

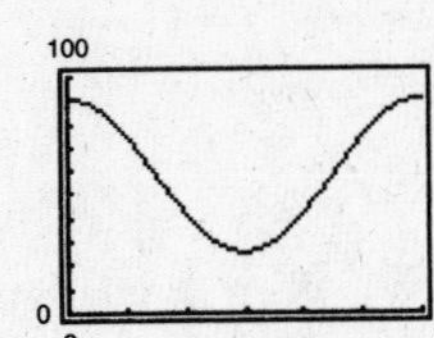

Sales exceed 75,000 during the months of January, November, and December.

**68.** (a) $5.35 - 2 = 3.35$

$5.35 + 2 = 7.35$

(b) $5.35 - 2(3) = -0.65$

(c) $13.35 = 5.35 + 2(4)$

$-4.65 = 5.35 - 2(5)$

True; because $f$ and $g$ have periods of 2 and intersect at $x = 5.35$, $f(13.35) = g(-4.65)$.

**69.** $f(x) = \frac{4}{\pi}\left(\sin\pi x + \frac{1}{3}\sin 3\pi x\right)$

$g(x) = \frac{4}{\pi}\left(\sin\pi x + \frac{1}{3}\sin 3\pi x + \frac{1}{5}\sin 5\pi x\right)$

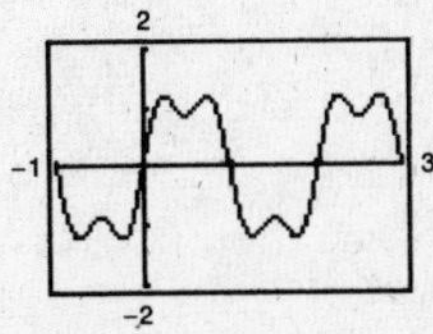

Pattern: $f(x) = \frac{4}{\pi}\left(\sin\pi x + \frac{1}{3}\sin 3\pi x + \frac{1}{5}\sin 5\pi x + \cdots + \frac{1}{2n-1}\sin(2n-1)\pi x\right)$, $n = 1, 2, 3\ldots$

**70.** $f(x) = \frac{1}{2} - \frac{4}{\pi^2}\left(\cos\pi x + \frac{1}{9}\cos 3\pi x\right)$

$g(x) = \frac{1}{2} - \frac{4}{\pi^2}\left(\cos\pi x + \frac{1}{9}\cos 3\pi x + \frac{1}{25}\cos 5\pi x\right)$

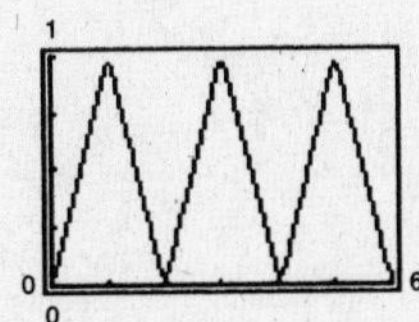

Pattern: $f(x) = \frac{1}{2} - \frac{4}{\pi^2}\left(\cos\pi x + \frac{1}{9}\cos 3\pi x + \frac{1}{25}\cos 5\pi x + \cdots + \frac{1}{(2n-1)^2}\cos(2n-1)\pi x\right)$, $n = 1, 2, 3\ldots$